The Art of
Public Speaking

ELEVENTH EDITION

Stephen E. Lucas
University of Wisconsin–Madison

Louisiana State University

Mc
Graw
Hill
Education

2 3 4 5 6 7 8 9 0 BKM BKM 17 16 15 14

ISBN-13: 978-1-259-39046-3
ISBN-10: 1-259-39046-2

Learning Solutions Consultant: Courtney Jones
Project Manager: Catherine Bethke
Cover Designer: Irene Morris

About the Author

Stephen E. Lucas is Professor of Communication Arts and Evjue-Bascom Professor in the Humanities at the University of Wisconsin–Madison. He received his bachelor's degree from the University of California, Santa Barbara, and his master's and doctorate degrees from Penn State University.

Professor Lucas has been recognized for his work as both a scholar and a teacher. His first book, *Portents of Rebellion: Rhetoric and Revolution in Philadelphia, 1765–1776*, received the Golden Anniversary Award of the National Communication Association and was nominated for a Pulitzer Prize. His major articles include "The Schism in Rhetorical Scholarship" (1981), "The Renaissance of American Public Address: Text and Context in Rhetorical Criticism" (1988), "The Stylistic Artistry of the Declaration of Independence" (1990), and "The Rhetorical Ancestry of the Declaration of Independence" (1998), for which he received the Golden Anniversary Monograph Award of the National Communication Association. His most recent book is *Words of a Century: The Top 100 American Speeches, 1900–1999* (2009).

Professor Lucas has received a number of teaching awards, including the Chancellor's Award for Excellence in Teaching at the University of Wisconsin and the National Communication Association's Donald Ecroyd Award for Outstanding Teaching in Higher Education. His lecture course on "The Rhetoric of Campaigns and Revolutions" is among the most popular on campus and has twice been selected for statewide broadcast in its entirety by Wisconsin Public Radio. Professor Lucas is featured in the Educational Video Group's program on the history of American public address, and he has appeared on the History Channel's documentary on the Declaration of Independence.

Professor Lucas has directed the introductory public speaking course at the University of Wisconsin–Madison since 1973. Over the years he has been responsible for numerous teaching innovations and has supervised the training of hundreds of graduate assistants. In addition to participating in public speaking workshops and colloquia at schools throughout the United States, he has served as a judge for the major national English-language public speaking competitions in China, has lectured at numerous Chinese universities, and has conducted workshops for Chinese instructors on teaching public speaking. *The Art of Public Speaking* has been published in China both in translation and in English editions.

Stephen Lucas and his wife, Patty, live in Madison, Wisconsin, and have two sons, Jeff and Ryan. His interests include travel, sports, art, and photography.

Contents in Brief

Contents

Chapter 3 Listening 47

Chapter 4 Giving Your First Speech 63

PART TWO SPEECH PREPARATION: GETTING STARTED

Chapter 5 Selecting a Topic and a Purpose 77

Chapter 6 Analyzing the Audience 97

Chapter 7 Gathering Materials 119

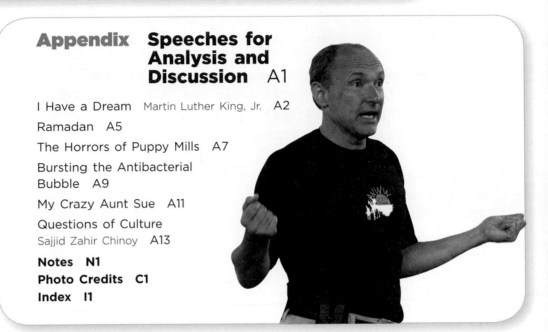

Appendix Speeches for Analysis and Discussion   A1

SPEECHES

SPEECHES BY GENRE

INTRODUCTORY SPEECHES

Self-Introduction

Introducing a Classmate

INFORMATIVE SPEECHES

A Note from the Author

*T*he Art of Public Speaking will pass its 30th anniversary in the course of this edition. When I wrote the first edition, I could not have imagined the extraordinary response the book would receive. I am deeply appreciative of the students and teachers who have made it the leading work on its subject at colleges and universities across the United States and around the world.

In preparing this edition, I have retained what readers have identified as the main strengths of the book. *The Art of Public Speaking* is informed by classical and contemporary theories of rhetoric, but it does not present theory for its own sake. Keeping a steady eye on the practical skills of public speaking, it offers full coverage of all major aspects of speech preparation and presentation.

It also follows David Hume's advice that one "who would teach eloquence must do it chiefly by examples." Whenever possible, I have tried to *show* the principles of public speaking in action in addition to describing them. Thus you will find in the book a large number of narratives, speech excerpts, and full sample speeches that illustrate the principles of effective public speaking.

Because the immediate task facing students is to present speeches in the classroom, I rely heavily on examples that relate directly to students' classroom needs and experiences. The speech classroom, however, is a training ground where students develop skills that will serve them throughout life. Therefore, I also include a large number of illustrations drawn from the kinds of speaking experiences students will face after they graduate from college.

Because speeches are performative acts, students need to be able to view speakers in action as well as read their words on the printed page. *The Art of Public Speaking* has an extensive video program that is available both on DVD and on *Connect Public Speaking,* the book's innovative online learning platform. The video program includes 27 full student speeches, plus more than 60 speech excerpts. Nine of the full speeches and more than 25 of the excerpts are new to this edition.

*Connec*t also provides a wide range of teaching and learning resources in addition to the speech videos. These resources include hands-on study tools, critical-thinking exercises, speech analysis questions, worksheets, assessment forms, and more. Taken together, the book and *Connect* provide an interactive public speaking program that meets the needs of students and teachers alike.

The Art of Public Speaking has changed over the years in response to changes in technology, student demographics, and instructional needs. But it has never lost sight of the fact that the most important part of speaking is thinking. The ability to think critically is vital to a world in which personality and image too often substitute for thought and substance. While helping students become capable, responsible speakers, *The Art of Public Speaking* also seeks to help them become capable, responsible thinkers.

Preface

FEATURES OF THE ELEVENTH EDITION

The eleventh edition of *The Art of Public Speaking* builds on its predecessors with expanded coverage in key areas that students find most challenging—plunging into the first speech, avoiding fallacies, using supporting materials properly, citing sources orally, developing and presenting visual aids, and taking public speaking from classroom to career.

These content revisions are combined with a thorough revision of *Connect Public Speaking,* the pathbreaking online learning platform for *The Art of Public Speaking* at www.mcgraw-hillconnect.com. The book, *Connect,* and the other resources available with *The Art of Public Speaking* are all designed to work hand in hand. They provide an integrated teaching and learning system that is without parallel among public speaking textbooks.

Helping students make the leap from principles to performance

THE ART OF PUBLIC SPEAKING CONNECTS STUDENTS TO THE PRACTICE OF PUBLIC SPEAKING.

Clear, consistent coverage and a friendly, authoritative voice that speaks personally to students and gives them the principles they need to create and deliver dynamic public speeches.

Print and video examples show the principles of public speaking in action rather than just describing them.   NEW

NEW ■ Every chapter of *The Art of Public Speaking* has been thoroughly revised to present relevant, easy-to-grasp real-world models that speak to the newest generation of students.

NEW ■ Student speeches on DVD and on *Connect* provide models of major speech genres. There are a total of 27 full student speeches (9 new to this edition), including 5 "Needs Improvement" versions. There are also more than 60 videos (27 new to this edition) that illustrate specific skills and concepts from the book. Icons in the margins of the main text direct readers to the appropriate videos.

■ Written and narrated by Stephen E. Lucas, *Introductions, Conclusions, and Visual Aids* utilizes the principles of visual learning

to reinforce key concepts from the book. Part One of this 30-minute DVD uses excerpts from a wide range of student speeches to illustrate the principles of effective introductions and conclusions. Part Two contains examples of speakers using a variety of visual aids and presentation media.

NEW **LearnSmart, *Connect's* adaptive diagnostic study tool, helps students absorb and internalize key ideas from the text.** LearnSmart adapts to individual students and, based on their responses, identifies strengths and weaknesses in their grasp of course content. By tracking student responses, instructors can use class time to focus on subjects that students find most challenging.

Helping students apply principles discussed in the text to the creation of their own speeches

THE ART OF PUBLIC SPEAKING CONNECTS STUDENTS TO CONFIDENCE IN PUBLIC SPEAKING.

NEW **Improved coverage of persuasive speaking.** Chapter 16, "Speaking to Persuade," includes many new examples, including a new full speech with commentary. Chapter 17, "Methods of Persuasion," has a revised discussion of reasoning, plus expanded coverage of fallacies and a new sample speech with commentary.

A full chapter on "Giving Your First Speech" (Chapter 4). This chapter gives students the support they need to present their first speeches at the start of the term—long before most of the principles of public speaking have been covered in class. Two new sample speeches with commentary provide models of introductory presentations.   **NEW**

More on supporting ideas and source citation. In response to requests from instructors, Chapter 8 provides expanded coverage of how to use supporting materials and how to cite sources orally. Chapter 7 takes account of new developments in online research and provides criteria for assessing information gleaned from the Internet.   **NEW**

Revised chapter on visual aids (Chapter 14). Among other changes, the popular PowerPoint appendix has been integrated into the main chapter, providing more streamlined and up-to-date coverage of visual aids.   **NEW**

Interactive assignments and activities in *Connect* take online pedagogy to a new level. The latest version of *Connect* offers a wide range of assignable and assessable online activities. These include exercises for critical thinking, speech videos with questions for analysis, scrambled outline exercises, chapter study questions, key-term diagnostics, and speech checklists and worksheets.   **NEW**

Strong connection between public speaking principles and real-world application. "Using Public Speaking in Your Career" activities place students in realistic, professional scenarios and help them make the leap from classroom to career.   **NEW**

Comprehensive chapter-ending pedagogy builds critical thinking skills. Each chapter contains review questions and exercises for critical thinking. The exercises require students to work with—and to think about—skills and concepts covered in the chapter. They are vital to the integrated teaching and learning system that has helped make *The Art of Public Speaking* so successful.

Student Workbook. This popular supplement contains exercises, check-lists, worksheets, evaluation forms, and other materials designed to help students master the principles of effective speechmaking presented in the text.

Helping novices gain practice time and become effective public speakers

THE ART OF PUBLIC SPEAKING CONNECTS STUDENTS TO SUCCESS IN PUBLIC SPEAKING.

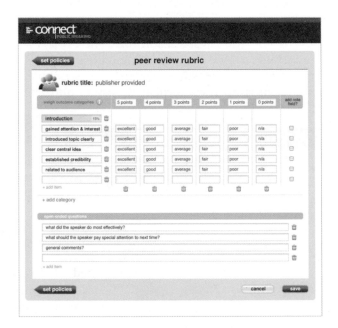

NEW   **Speech Capture.** This cutting-edge tool lets instructors evaluate speeches live, using a fully customizable rubric. Instructors can also upload speech videos on behalf of students, as well as create and manage peer review assignments. Students can upload their own videos for self-review and/or peer review.

NEW   **Outline Tool, with enhanced user interface.** The Outline Tool guides students systematically through the process of organizing and outlining their speeches. Instructors can customize parts of the outliner, and also turn it off if they don't want their students to use it.

NEW   **Topic Helper, as well as access to EasyBib and Survey Monkey online tools.** The Topic Helper helps students select a topic for speech assignments. EasyBib is a Web-based tool that automates the formatting of citations and bibliographies. Survey Monkey, also a Web-based tool, helps students create and manage audience-analysis questionnaires.

RESOURCES FOR INSTRUCTORS

The Art of Public Speaking has an exceptional set of instructional resources that provide a fully integrated, comprehensive teaching and learning program for instructors of all experience levels.

Easier online course management through *Connect*-Blackboard CMS integration. McGraw-Hill's partnership with Blackboard allows for full integration of McGraw-Hill content and digital tools into Blackboard, featuring single sign-on capability for students and faculty.

NEW

Annotated Instructor's Edition. The *Annotated Instructor's Edition* provides a wealth of teaching aids for each chapter in the book. It is also cross-referenced with *Connect,* the *Instructor's Manual,* the Instructor's Resource CD-ROM, and other supplements that accompany *The Art of Public Speaking.*

Instructor's Manual. This comprehensive guide to teaching from *The Art of Public Speaking* contains suggested course outlines and speaking assignments; chapter outlines; supplementary exercises and classroom activities; feedback for all exercises and activities; and 45 additional speeches for discussion and analysis.

Test Bank. The *Test Bank* furnishes 2,600 examination questions based on *The Art of Public Speaking.*

The *Instructor's Manual,* Test Bank, and PowerPoint slides are available on *Connect,* the Online Learning Center, and the Instructor's Resource CD-ROM.

PowerPoint Slides with Video Clips. Fully revised for this edition, more than 400 PowerPoint slides include text, photographs, illustrations, and video clips, and can be customized by instructors for lecture or discussion.

Online Learning Center. The *Art of Public Speaking* Online Learning Center, located at www.mhhe.com/lucas11e, enables teachers to download the full roster of teaching resources:

- *Instructor's Manual*
- *Test Bank* (Microsoft Word files, as well as computerized EZTest versions)
- PowerPoint slides
- *Teaching Public Speaking*
- *Teaching Public Speaking Online,* fully revised for the eleventh edition by Jennifer Cochrane of Indiana University and Purdue University at Indianapolis
- *Handbook for Teachers of Non-Native Speakers of English*

Instructor's Resource CD-ROM. The *Instructor's Manual, Test Bank,* Power-Point slides, and other items in the Online Learning Center are also available on this CD-ROM.

ACKNOWLEDGMENTS

"'Tis the good reader," said Ralph Waldo Emerson, "that makes the good book." I have been fortunate to have very good readers indeed, and I would like to thank the reviewers, symposium and focus-group participants, and contributors whose names appear on pages xxiii–xxv for their expertise and helpful comments and suggestions.

In addition, I would like to express my gratitude both to the students at the University of Wisconsin whose speeches provided the material for many of the examples in the book and to members of the Communication Arts 100 teaching staff who helped me by collecting sample speeches and by offering feedback on the tenth edition. I am especially grateful to Sarah Jedd, assistant director of Communication Arts 100, for her splendid work in that capacity and for her many contributions to the book.

Thanks go as well to Margaret Procario for her work on the *Instructor's Manual* and the *Test Bank;* to Jennifer Cochrane for her supplement on using *The Art of Public Speaking* in an online course; and to Ashley Hinck, who helped with the research for this edition. Above all, I am indebted to Paul Stob, who worked with me on the book and supplements throughout the preparation of this edition. His contributions were indispensable.

I also owe thanks to *The Art of Public Speaking* team at McGraw-Hill. David Patterson, Susan Gouijnstook, Mikola De Roo, Suzie Flores, and Jamie Daron joined the book this edition, and they have continued its tradition of excellence. Now in her fourth edition as marketing manager, Leslie Oberhuber continues to prove why she is one of the best in the business. Mike Ryan, Steve Debow, and Ed Stanford all provided executive support and direction.

In this day and age, publishing a textbook involves much more than the book itself. Working with the editorial team, Janet Byrne Smith and Adam Dweck skillfully managed the new version of *Connect.* Other members of the *Connect* team included Vicki Splaine, Debabrata Acharya, Pravarna Besa, Manish Gupta, Irina Reznick, Sanjay Shinde, Sujoy Banerjee, John Brady, Priscila Depano, Nidhi Kumari, and Suzy Cho. Meghan Campbell coordinated the addition of LearnSmart to the online resources.

As production editor for the book, Carey Eisner handled a thousand details with skill and aplomb. Preston Thomas oversaw the creation of a new design and cover. Natalia Peschiera coordinated the photo program, and Jennifer Blankenship located a wealth of images on a tight schedule. Vicki Malinee helped steer the supplements through production.

As always, my biggest debt is to my wife, Patty, whose love and support have sustained me through the years.

Stephen E. Lucas
Madison, Wisconsin

REVIEWERS, SYMPOSIUM AND FOCUS-GROUP PARTICIPANTS, AND CONTRIBUTORS

Main-Text Reviewers

Bob Alexander, *Bossier Parish Community College*

Barbara Armentrout, *Central Piedmont Community College*

Richard Armstrong, *Wichita State University*

Gretchen Arthur, *International Academy of Technology and Design*

Leonard Assante, *Volunteer State Community College*

Jennifer Becker, *University of Missouri–Columbia*

Kimberly Berry, *Ozarks Technical Community College*

Patrick Breslin, *Santa Fe Community College*

Christa Brown, *Minnesota State University–Mankato*

Ferald J. Bryan, *Northern Illinois University*

Jack Byer, *Bucks County Community College*

Richard Capp, *Hill College*

Nick Carty, *Dalton State University*

Mary Carver, *University of Central Oklahoma*

Crystal Church, *Cisco Junior College*

Jennifer Cochrane, *Indiana University–Purdue University, Indianapolis*

Shirley Lerch Crum, *Coastal Carolina Community College*

Karen Dwyer, *University of Nebraska–Omaha*

Tracy Fairless, *University of Central Oklahoma*

Rick Falvo, *College of Lake County*

Bryan Fisher, *Francis Marion University*

Bonnie Gabel, *McHenry County College*

Paul Gaustad, *Georgia Perimeter College*

Kevin Gillen, *Indiana University*

Donna Gotch, *California State University, San Bernardino*

Catherine Gragg, *San Jacinto College*

JoAnna Grant, *California State University, San Bernardino*

Neva Kay Gronert, *Arapahoe Community College*

Omar Guevara, *Weber State University*

Karen Hamburg, *Camden Community College*

Tina M. Harris, *University of Georgia*

Daria Heinemann, *Keiser University*

Marcia Hotchkiss, *Tennessee State University*

Delwyn Jones, *Moraine Valley Community College*

Susan Kilgard, *Anne Arundel Community College*

Amy King, *Central Piedmont Community College*

Patricia King, *McHenry County College*

Linda Kurz, *University of Missouri–Kansas City*

Jerri Lynn Kyle, *Missouri State University*

Kathleen LeBesco, *Marymount Manhattan College*

Mark Lewis, *Riverside Community College*

Sujanet Mason, *Luzerne County Community College*

Peg McCree, *Middle Tennessee State University*

Nicki L. Michalski, *Lamar University*

Marjorie Keeshan Nadler, *Miami University*

Ronn Norfleet, *Kentucky Community and Technical College System–Jefferson Community and Technical College*

Kekeli Nuviadenu, *Bethune-Cookman College*

Holly Payne, *Western Kentucky University*

Theodore Petersen, *Helmick Johnson Community College*

Jeff Peterson, *Washington State University–Pullman*

James (Tim) Pierce, *Northern Illinois University*

Jean R. Powers, *Holmes Community College*

Barry Poyner, *Truman State University*

William Price, *Georgia Perimeter College*

James E. Putz, *University of Wisconsin–La Crosse*

Jennifer Reem, *Nova Southeastern University*

Belinda Russell, *Northeast Mississippi Community College*

Diane Ryan, *Tidewater Community College*

Rhona Rye, *California State Polytechnic University, Pomona*

Cara Schollenberger, *Bucks County Community College*

Jay Self, *Truman State University*

Michael J. Shannon, *Moraine Valley Community College*

Gale Sharpe, *San Jacinto College*

Richard Sisson, *Georgia Perimeter College*

Amy R. Slagell, *Iowa State University*

Katherine Taylor, *University of Louisville*

Cindu Thomas-George, *College of Lake County*

Joseph Valenzano, *University of Nevada, Las Vegas*

Jill Voran, *Anne Arundel Community College*

Linda J. White, *Central Piedmont Community College*

Theresa White, *Faulkner State Community College*

Alan Winson, *John Jay College of Criminal Justice*

Carleen Yokotake, *Leeward Community College*

Symposia and Regional Focus-Group Participants

Donna Acerra, *Northampton Community College*

Krista Appelquist, *Moraine Valley Community College*

Vera Barkus, *Kennedy-King College*

Barbara Baron, *Brookdale Community College*

Mardia Bishop, *University of Illinois–Champaign*

Audrey Bourne, *North Idaho College*

Karen Braselton, *Vincennes University*

Melissa Broeckelman-Post, *California State University– Los Angeles*

Cynthia Brown El, *Macomb Community College, Center Campus*

Kristin Bruss, *University of Kansas–Lawrence*

Bobette Bushnell, *Oregon State University*

Pamela Cannamore, *Kennedy-King College*

Helen Chester, *Milwaukee Area Technical College– Milwaukee*

Jennifer Cochrane, *Indiana University–Purdue University, Indianapolis*

Jennifer Del Quadro, *Northampton Community College*

Amber Erickson, *University of Cincinnati*

Kris Galyen, *University of Cincinnati*

Joan Geller, *Johnson & Wales University*

Ava Good, *San Jacinto College*

JoAnna Grant, *California State University, San Bernardino*

Delwyn Jones, *Moraine Valley Community College*

Amy King, *Central Piedmont Community College*

Bryan Kirby, *Ivy Technical Community College, Indiana*

Steven Lebeau, *Indiana University–Purdue University, Indianapolis*

Cindy Leonard, *Bluegrass Community and Technical College, Main Campus*

Tobi Mackler, *Montgomery County Community College*

Molly Mayer, *University of Cincinnati*

James McCoy, *College of Southern Nevada–Henderson*

Peg McCree, *Middle Tennessee State University*
Libby McGlone, *Columbus State Community College*
Delois Medhin, *Milwaukee Area Technical College–Milwaukee*
Stanley Moore, *Henry Ford Community College*
Marjorie Keeshan Nadler, *Miami University*
John Nash, *Moraine Valley Community College*
Ronn Norfleet, *Kentucky Community and Technical College System–Jefferson Community and Technical College*
Edward Panetta, *University of Georgia*
Alexander Papp, *Cuyahoga Community College*
Tim Pierce, *Northern Illinois University*
Sunnye Pruden, *Lone Star College, CyFair*
Jeff Przybylo, *William Rainey Harper College*
Shawn Queeney, *Bucks County Community College*
David Schneider, *Saginaw Valley State University*
Mike Shannon, *Moraine Valley Community College*
Amy R. Slagell, *Iowa State University*
Karen Slawter, *Northern Kentucky University*
Rick Soller, *College of Lake County*
Cindu Thomas-George, *College of Lake County*
Patrice Whitten, *William Rainey Harper College*
Julie Williams, *San Jacinto College*
Josie Wood, *Chemeketa Community College*
Henry Young, *Cuyahoga Community College*

Connect Board of Advisors

Sam Arenivar, *MiraCosta College*
Katherine Castle, *University of Nebraska–Lincoln*
Jennifer Cochrane, *Indiana University–Purdue University, Indianapolis*
Rich Jones, *Eastern Illinois University*
Bryan Kirby, *Ivy Technical Community College, Indiana*
Christine Lemesianou, *Montclair State University*
Maria Luskay, *Pace University*
Jeff Przybylo, *William Rainey Harper College*
Mike Shannon, *Moraine Valley Community College*
Julie Williams, *San Jacinto College*

LearnSmart Contributors

Mary Carver, *University of Central Oklahoma*
Jennifer Cochrane, *Indiana University–Purdue University, Indianapolis*
Ava Good, *San Jacinto College*
Amy King, *Central Piedmont Community College*
Marjorie Keeshan Nadler, *Miami University, Lead Subject Matter Expert*

Connect and LearnSmart Reviewers

Brent Adrian, *Central Community College–Grand Island campus*
Richard N. Armstrong, *Wichita State University*
Frank Barnhart, *Columbus State Community College*
Kimberly Berry, *Ozarks Technical Community College*
Annette Bever, *Vernon College*
Justin Braxton-Brown, *Hopkinsville Community College*
Melissa Broeckelman-Post, *California State University–Los Angeles*
Drew Butler, *Middle Tennessee State University*
Nick Carty, *Dalton State*
Leslie Collins, *Modesto Junior College*
Paige Davis, *Lone Star College, CyFair*
Denise Elmer, *Southeast Community College–Beatrice*

Pam Glasnapp, *University of Central Missouri*
JoAnna Grant, *California State University, San Bernardino*
Stacy B. Gresell, *Lone Star College, CyFair*
Jill Hall, *Jefferson Community and Technical College, Downtown*
Daria Heinemann, *Keiser University*
Richard Jones, *Eastern Illinois University*
Patti Keeling, *Chabot College*
Tressa Kelly, *University of West Florida*
Darren Linvill, *Clemson University*
Natonya Listach, *Middle Tennessee State University*
Jodie Mandel, *College of Southern Nevada–Henderson*
James McCoy, *College of Southern Nevada–Henderson*
Peg McCree, *Middle Tennessee State University*
Libby McGlone, *Columbus State Community College*
Terri Metzger, *California State University, San Bernardino*
John Nash, *Moraine Valley Community College*
Maria Parnell, *Brevard Community College–Melbourne*
Jean Perry, *Glendale Community College*
Tim Pierce, *Northern Illinois University*
William Price, *Georgia Perimeter College*
Greg Rickert, *Bluegrass Community and Technical College*
Thomas Sabetta, *University of Kentucky*
Jay Self, *Truman State University*
Michael Shannon, *Moraine Valley Community College*
Susan Silcott, *Ohio University Lancaster*
Richard (Kim) Sisson, *Georgia Perimeter College*
Katherine Taylor, *University of Louisville*
Alice Veksler, *University of Connecticut–Storrs*
Ann Marie Whyte, *Penn State University–Harrisburg*
Julie Williams, *San Jacinto College*

Design Reviewers

Barbara Baron, *Brookdale Community College*
Elizabeth Jill Coker, *Itawamba Community College–Tupelo*
Ferald J. Bryan, *Northern Illinois University*
Jack Byer, *Bucks County Community College*
Terri Helmick, *Johnson County Community College*
Steven King, *Ivy Technical Community College, Indiana*
Elizabeth Rumschlag, *Baker College, Auburn Hills*
David Simon, *Northern Illinois University*
Katherine Taylor, *University of Louisville*
Kristi Whitehill, *Ivy Technical Community College, Indiana*

Public-Speaking Survey Participants

Bob Alexander, *Bossier Parish Community College*
Barbara Armentrout, *Central Piedmont Community College*
Richard N. Armstrong, *Brevard Community College–Titusville*
Barbara Baron, *Brookdale Community College*
Kimberly Berry, *Ozarks Technical Community College*
Laura Berry, *Pearl River Community College*
Molly Brown, *Clinton Community College*
Ferald J. Bryan, *Northern Illinois University*
Jack Byer, *Bucks County Community College*
Rebecca Carlton, *Indiana University Southeast*
Mary Carver, *University of Central Oklahoma*
Helen Chester, *Milwaukee Area Technical College*

Cerbrina Chou, *Chemeketa Community College*
Melissa Click, *University of Missouri–Columbia*
Ron Compton, *Triton College*
Audrey Deterding, *Indiana University Southeast*
Kelly Driskell, *Trinity Valley Community College*
James Duncan, *Anderson University*
Karen Dwyer, *University of Nebraska, Omaha*
Rick Falvo, *College of Lake County*
Tori Forncrook, *Georgia Perimeter College*
Rebecca J. Franco, *Indiana University Southeast*
Meredith Frank, *La Salle University*
Bonnie Gabel, *McHenry County College*
Jodi Gaete, *Suffolk County Community College*
Colleen Garside, *Weber State University*
Paul Gaustad, *Georgia Perimeter College*
Jeffrey Gentry, *Rogers State University*
Pamela M. Glasnapp, *University of Central Missouri*
Robert Glenn, III, *Kentucky Community and Technical College System–Owensboro Community and Technical College*
Ava Good, *San Jacinto College*
Thomas Green, *Faulkner State Community College*
Neva Kay Gronert, *Arapahoe Community College*
William F. Harlow, *University of Texas–Permian Basin*
Kate Harris, *Loyola University–Chicago; Roosevelt University*
Tina Harris, *University of Georgia*
Terri Helmick, *Johnson County Community College*
Marcia Hotchkiss, *Tennessee State University*
Dr. David Johnson, *University of Maryland Eastern Shore*
Brenda Jones, *Franklin University*
Kate Kane, *Northeastern Illinois University*
Amy King, *Central Piedmont Community College*
Patricia King, *McHenry County College*
Sandy King, *Anne Arundel Community College*
Vijay Krishna, *College of the Canyons*
Linda Kurz, *University of Missouri–Kansas City*
Abby Lackey, *Jackson State Community College*
Victoria Leonard, *Cape Fear Community College*
Sujanet Mason, *Luzerne County Community College*
Wolfgang Mcaninch-Runzi, *University of Texas–Permian Basin*
Alison McCrowell Lietzenmayer, *Old Dominion University*

Nicki Michalski, *Lamar University–Beaumont*
Diane Miller, *Finlandia University; Michigan Technological University*
Holly Miller, *University of Nebraska–Omaha*
Stanley Moore, *Henry Ford Community College*
David Moss, *Mt. San Jacinto College–Menifee*
Heidi Murphy, *Central New Mexico Community College*
Ulysses Newkirk, *Kentucky Community and Technical College System–Owensboro Community and Technical College*
Ronn Norfleet, *Kentucky Community and Technical College System*
Dr. Lisa M. Orick-Martinez, *Central New Mexico Community College*
Maria Parnell, *Brevard Community College–Melbourne*
Jeff Przybylo, *William Rainey Harper College*
Jason Andrew Ramsey, *Indiana University Southeast*
Pamela J. Reid, *Copiah-Lincoln Community College*
Cynthia Robinson-Moore, *University of Nebraska–Omaha*
Rhona Rye, *California State Polytechnic University, Pomona*
Thomas J. Sabetta, *Cape Fear Community College*
Jay Self, *Truman State University*
Alisa Shubb, *University of California, Davis*
James Spurrier, *Vincennes University*
Katherine Taylor, *University of Louisville*
Lisa Turowski, *Towson University*
Alice Veksler, *University of Connecticut–Storrs*
Tom Vickers, *Embry Riddle Aero University–Daytona Beach*
Janice M. Vierk, *Metropolitan Community College–Omaha*
Myra H. Walters, *Edison State College*
Stephanie Webster, *University of Florida, Gainesville*
Linda J. White, *Central Piedmont Community College*
Theresa White, *Faulkner State Community College*
Cicely Wilson, *Victory University (formerly Crichton College)*
Alan Winson, *John Jay College of Criminal Justice*
Josie Wood, *Chemeketa Community College*
Tina Zagara, *Georgia Perimeter College*

The Art of
Public Speaking

Speaking in Public

Growing up in a tough neighborhood in the South Bronx, Geoffrey Canada had no intention of becoming a public speaker. A good student, he went to college at Bowdoin and then to graduate school at Harvard, where he earned a master's degree in education. After teaching in New Hampshire and Boston, he returned to New York City, where in 1990 he founded the Harlem Children's Zone.

Called "one of the biggest social experiments of our time" by the *New York Times Magazine,* the Harlem Children's Zone seeks not just to educate children, but to develop a community system that addresses issues such as health care, violence, substance abuse, and job training. Over the years, Canada has raised more than $100 million for the project, and he has helped change the lives of thousands of kids and families.

How has Canada achieved all this? Partly through his education, his commitment to children, and his seemingly limitless energy. But just as important is his ability to communicate with people through public speaking, which has been a primary vehicle for spreading his message. He has been described as a "charismatic, passionate, eloquent" speaker who leaves his audiences "awed."

If you had asked Geoffrey Canada early in his life, "Do you see yourself as a major public speaker?" he probably would have laughed at the idea. Yet today he gives more than 100 presentations a year. Along the way, he has spoken at the White House, has lectured at Harvard and Princeton, and has addressed the Aspen Institute and the Google International Zeitgeist. He has also appeared on *60 Minutes* and is featured in the film *Waiting for Superman*.

The Power of Public Speaking

connect

View John F. Kennedy, Martin Luther King, Ronald Reagan, Barbara Jordan, and other speakers in the online Media Library for this chapter (Video 1.1)

Throughout history people have used public speaking as a vital means of communication. What the Greek leader Pericles said more than 2,500 years ago is still true today: "One who forms a judgment on any point but cannot explain" it clearly "might as well never have thought at all on the subject."[1] Public speaking, as its name implies, is a way of making your ideas public—of sharing them with other people and of influencing other people.

During modern times, many women and men around the globe have spread their ideas and influence through public speaking. In the United States, the list includes Franklin Roosevelt, Billy Graham, Cesar Chavez, Barbara Jordan, Ronald Reagan, Martin Luther King, Hillary Clinton, and Barack Obama. In other countries, we see the power of public speaking employed by such people as former British Prime Minister Margaret Thatcher, South African leader Nelson Mandela, Burmese democracy champion Aung San Suu Kyi, and Kenyan environmentalist and Nobel Prize winner Wangari Maathai.

As you read these names, you may think to yourself, "That's fine. Good for them. But what does that have to do with me? I don't plan to be a president or a preacher or a crusader for any cause." Nevertheless, the need for public speaking will almost certainly touch you sometime in your life—maybe tomorrow, maybe not for five years. Can you imagine yourself in any of these situations?

You are one of seven management trainees in a large corporation. One of you will get the lower-management job that has just opened. There is to be a large staff meeting at which each of the trainees will discuss the project he or she has been developing. One by one your colleagues make their presentations. They have no experience in public speaking and are intimidated by the higher-ranking managers present. Their speeches are stumbling and awkward. You, however, call upon all the skills you learned in your public speaking course. You deliver an informative talk that is clear, well reasoned, and articulate. You get the job.

One of your children has a learning disability. You hear that your local school board has decided, for budget reasons, to eliminate the special teacher who has been helping your child. At an open meeting of the school board, you stand up and deliver a thoughtful, compelling speech on the necessity for keeping the special teacher. The school board changes its mind.

You are the assistant manager in a branch office of a national company. Your immediate superior, the branch manager, is about to retire, and there will be a retirement dinner. All the executives from the home office will attend. As his close working associate, you are asked to give a farewell toast at the party. You prepare and deliver a speech that is both witty and touching—a perfect tribute to your boss. After the speech, everyone applauds enthusiastically, and a few people have tears in their eyes. The following week you are named branch manager.

Fantasies? Not really. Any of these situations could occur. In a recent survey of more than 300 business leaders, the ability to communicate effectively—including public speaking—was ranked first among the skills of college graduates sought by employers. In another survey, the American Management Association asked 2,000 managers and executives to rank the skills most essential in today's workplace. What was at the top of their list? Communication skills.[2]

The importance of such skills is true across the board—for accountants and architects, teachers and technicians, scientists and stockbrokers. Even in highly specialized fields such as civil and mechanical engineering, employers consistently rank the ability to communicate above technical knowledge when deciding whom to hire and whom to promote.

Businesses are also asking people to give more speeches in the early stages of their careers, and many young professionals are using public speaking as a way to stand out in today's highly competitive job market.[3] In fact, the ability to speak effectively is so prized that college graduates are increasingly being asked to give a presentation as part of their job interview.

Nor has the growth of the Internet and other new technologies reduced the need for public speaking. In this age of e-mail and Twitter, businesses are concerned that college graduates are losing the ability to talk in a professional way. As career expert Lindsey Pollak states, "It's so rare to find somebody who has that combination of really good technical skills and really good verbal communication skills. You will be head and shoulders above your colleagues if you can combine those two."[4]

The same is true in community life. Public speaking is a vital means of civic engagement. It is a way to express your ideas and to have an impact on issues that matter in society. As a form of empowerment, it can—and often does—make a difference in things people care about very much. The key phrase here is "make a difference." This is what most of us want to do in life—to make a difference, to change the world in some small way. Public speaking offers you an opportunity to make a difference in something you care about very much.

The Tradition of Public Speaking

Given the importance of public speaking, it's not surprising that it has been taught and studied around the globe for thousands of years. Almost all cultures have an equivalent of the English word "orator" to designate someone with special skills in public speaking. The oldest known handbook on effective speech was written on papyrus in Egypt some 4,500 years ago. Eloquence was highly prized in ancient India, Africa, and China, as well as among the Aztecs and other pre-European cultures of North and South America.[5]

In classical Greece and Rome, public speaking played a central role in education and civic life. It was also studied extensively. Aristotle's *Rhetoric,* composed during the third century B.C., is still considered the most important work on its subject, and many of its principles are followed by speakers (and writers) today. The great Roman leader Cicero used his speeches to defend liberty and wrote several works about oratory in general.

Over the centuries, many other notable thinkers have dealt with issues of rhetoric, speech, and language—including the Roman educator Quintilian, the Christian preacher St. Augustine, the medieval writer Christine de Pizan, the British philosopher Francis Bacon, and the American critic Kenneth Burke. In recent years, communication researchers have provided an increasingly scientific basis for understanding the methods and strategies of effective speech.

Your immediate objective is to apply those methods and strategies in your classroom speeches. What you learn, however, will be applicable long after you leave college. The principles of public speaking are derived from a long tradition and have been confirmed by a substantial body of research. The more you know about those principles, the more effective you will be in your own speeches—and the more effective you will be in listening to the speeches of other people.

Similarities Between Public Speaking and Conversation

How much time do you spend each day talking to other people? The average adult spends about 30 percent of her or his waking hours in conversation. By the time you read this book, you will have spent much of your life perfecting the art of conversation. You may not realize it, but you already employ a wide range of skills when talking to people. These skills include the following:

1. *Organizing your thoughts logically.* Suppose you were giving someone directions to get to your house. You wouldn't do it this way:

When you turn off the highway, you'll see a big diner on the left. But before that, stay on the highway to Exit 67. Usually a couple of the neighbors' dogs are in the street, so go slow after you turn at the blinking light. Coming from your house you get on the highway through Maple Street. If you pass the taco stand, you've gone too far. The house is blue.

Instead, you would take your listener systematically, step by step, from his or her house to your house. You would organize your message.

2. *Tailoring your message to your audience.* You are a geology major. Two people ask you how pearls are formed. One is your roommate; the other is your nine-year-old niece. You answer as follows:

To your roommate: "When any irritant, say a grain of sand, gets inside the oyster's shell, the oyster automatically secretes a substance called nacre, which is principally calcium carbonate and is the same material that lines the oyster's shell. The nacre accumulates in layers around the irritant core to form the pearl."

To your niece: "Imagine you're an oyster on the ocean floor. A grain of sand gets inside your shell and makes you uncomfortable. So you decide to cover it up. You cover it with a material called mother-of-pearl. The covering builds up around the grain of sand to make a pearl."

Many skills used in conversation also apply in public speaking. As you learn to speak more effectively, you may also learn to communicate more effectively in other situations.

3. *Telling a story for maximum impact.* Suppose you are telling a friend about a funny incident at last week's football game. You don't begin with the punch line ("Keisha fell out of the stands right onto the field. Here's how it started. . . ."). Instead, you carefully build up your story, adjusting your words and tone of voice to get the best effect.

4. *Adapting to listener feedback.* Whenever you talk with someone, you are aware of that person's verbal, facial, and physical reactions. For example:

You are explaining an interesting point that came up in biology class. Your listener begins to look confused, puts up a hand as though to stop you, and says "Huh?" You go back and explain more clearly.

A friend has asked you to listen while she practices a speech. At the end you tell her, "There's just one part I really don't like—that quotation from the attorney general." Your friend looks very hurt and says, "That was my favorite part!" So you say, "But if you just worked the quotation in a little differently, it would be wonderful."

Each day, in casual conversation, you do all these things many times without thinking about them. You already possess these communication skills. And these are among the most important skills you will need for public speaking.

To illustrate, let's return briefly to one of the hypothetical situations at the beginning of this chapter. When addressing the school board about the need for a special teacher:

- You *organize* your ideas to present them in the most persuasive manner. You steadily build up a compelling case about how the teacher benefits the school.
- You *tailor your message* to your audience. This is no time to launch an impassioned defense of special education in the United States. You must show how the issue is important to the people in that very room—to their children and to the school.

- You *tell your story* for maximum impact. Perhaps you relate an anecdote to demonstrate how much your child has improved. You also have statistics to show how many other children have been helped.
- You *adapt to listener feedback.* When you mention the cost of the special teacher, you notice sour looks on the faces of the school board members. So you patiently explain how small that cost is in relation to the overall school budget.

In many ways, then, public speaking requires the same skills used in ordinary conversation. Most people who communicate well in daily talk can learn to communicate just as well in public speaking. By the same token, training in public speaking can make you a more adept communicator in a variety of situations, such as conversations, classroom discussions, business meetings, and interviews.

Differences Between Public Speaking and Conversation

Despite their similarities, public speaking and everyday conversation are not identical. Imagine that you are telling a story to a friend. Then imagine yourself telling the story to a group of seven or eight friends. Now imagine telling the same story to 20 or 30 people. As the size of your audience grows, you will find yourself adapting to three major differences between conversation and public speaking:

1. *Public speaking is more highly structured.* It usually imposes strict time limitations on the speaker. In most cases, the situation does not allow listeners to interrupt with questions or commentary. The speaker must accomplish her or his purpose in the speech itself. In preparing the speech, the speaker must anticipate questions that might arise in the minds of listeners and answer them. Consequently, public speaking demands much more detailed planning and preparation than ordinary conversation.

2. *Public speaking requires more formal language.* Slang, jargon, and bad grammar have little place in public speeches. As committed as he is to improving the quality of education in urban schools, when Geoffrey Canada speaks to a legislative committee, he doesn't say, "We've got to get every damn incompetent teacher out of the classroom!" Listeners usually react negatively to speakers who do not elevate and polish their language when addressing an audience. A speech should be "special."

3. *Public speaking requires a different method of delivery.* When conversing informally, most people talk quietly, interject stock phrases such as "like" and "you know," adopt a casual posture, and use what are called vocalized pauses ("uh," "er," "um"). Effective public speakers, however, adjust their voices to be heard clearly throughout the audience. They assume a more erect posture. They avoid distracting mannerisms and verbal habits.

With study and practice, you will be able to master these differences and expand your conversational skills into speechmaking. Your speech class will provide the opportunity for this study and practice.

Developing Confidence: Your Speech Class

One of the major concerns of students in any speech class is stage fright. We may as well face the issue squarely. Many people who converse easily in all kinds of everyday situations become frightened at the idea of standing up before a group to make a speech.

If you are worried about stage fright, you may feel better knowing that you are not alone. A 2001 Gallup Poll asked Americans to list their greatest fears. Forty percent identified speaking before a group as their top fear, exceeded only by the 51 percent who said they were afraid of snakes. A 2005 survey produced similar results, with 42 percent of respondents being terrified by the prospect of speaking in public. In comparison, only 28 percent said they were afraid of dying.[6]

in a different study, researchers concentrated on social situations and, again, asked their subjects to list their greatest fears. More than 9,000 people were interviewed. Here is the ranking of their answers:[7]

stage fright

Anxiety over the prospect of giving a speech in front of an audience.

Greatest Fear

Public speaking

Speaking up in a meeting or class

Meeting new people

Talking to people in authority

Important examination or interview

Going to parties

Talking with strangers

Again, speechmaking is at the top in provoking anxiety.

NERVOUSNESS IS NORMAL

If you feel nervous about giving a speech, you are in very good company. Some of the greatest public speakers in history have suffered from stage fright, including Abraham Lincoln, Margaret Sanger, and Winston Churchill. The famous Roman orator Cicero said, "I turn pale at the outset of a speech and quake in every limb and in my soul."[8]

Oprah Winfrey, Conan O'Brien, and Jay Leno all report being anxious about speaking in public. Early in his career, Leonardo DiCaprio was so nervous about giving an acceptance speech that he hoped he would not win the Academy Award for which he had been nominated. Eighty-one percent of business executives say public speaking is the most nerve-wracking experience they face.[9] What comedian Jerry Seinfeld said in jest sometimes seems literally true: "Given a choice, at a funeral most of us would rather be the one in the coffin than the one giving the eulogy."

Actually, most people tend to be anxious before doing something important in public. Actors are nervous before a play, politicians are nervous before a campaign speech, athletes are nervous before a big game. The ones who succeed have learned to use their nervousness to their advantage. Listen to tennis star Rafael Nadal speaking after his 2010 Wimbledon title match against Tomas Berdych. "I was a little bit more nervous than usual," he admitted. "But if you are not nervous in the finals of Wimbledon, you are not human!" Putting his butterflies to good use, Nadal beat Berdych in straight sets to claim his second Wimbledon championship.

Much the same thing happens in speechmaking. Most experienced speakers have stage fright before taking the floor, but their nervousness is a healthy sign that they are getting "psyched up" for a good effort. Novelist and lecturer I. A. R. Wylie once said: "After many years of practice I am, I suppose, really a 'practiced speaker.' But I rarely rise to my feet without a throat constricted with terror and a furiously thumping heart. When, for some reason, I *am* cool and self-assured, the speech is always a failure."

In other words, it is perfectly normal—even desirable—to be nervous at the start of a speech. Your body is responding as it would to any stressful situation—by producing extra *adrenaline.*

This sudden shot of adrenaline is what makes your heart race, your hands shake, your knees knock, and your skin perspire. Every public speaker experiences all these reactions to some extent. The question is: How can you control your nervousness and make it work for you rather than against you?

adrenaline

A hormone released into the bloodstream in response to physical or mental stress.

DEALING WITH NERVOUSNESS

Rather than trying to eliminate every trace of stage fright, you should aim at transforming it from a negative force into what one expert calls *positive nervousness*—"a zesty, enthusiastic, lively feeling with a slight edge to it. . . . It's still nervousness, but it feels different. You're no longer victimized by it; instead, you're vitalized by it. You're in control of it."[10]

Don't think of yourself as having stage fright. Instead, think of it as "stage excitement" or "stage enthusiasm."[11] It can help you get focused and energized in the same way that it helps athletes, musicians, and others get primed for a game or a concert. Actress Jane Lynch, talking about her gig hosting *Saturday Night Live*, said that she got through it with "that perfect cocktail of nervousness and excitement." Think of that cocktail as a normal part of giving a successful speech.

Here are six time-tested ways you can turn your nervousness from a negative force into a positive one.

positive nervousness

Controlled nervousness that helps energize a speaker for her or his presentation.

Acquire Speaking Experience

You have already taken the first step. You are enrolled in a public speaking course, where you will learn about speechmaking and gain speaking experience. Think back to your first day at kindergarten, your first date, your first day at a new job. You were probably nervous in each situation because you were facing something new and unknown. Once you became accustomed to the situation, it was no longer threatening. So it is with public speaking. For most students, the biggest part of stage fright is fear of the unknown. The more you learn about public speaking and the more speeches you give, the less threatening speechmaking will become.

Of course, the road to confidence will sometimes be bumpy. Learning to give a speech is not much different from learning any other skill—it proceeds by trial and error. The purpose of your speech class is to shorten the process, to minimize the errors, to give you a nonthreatening arena—a sort of laboratory—in which to undertake the "trial."

The need for public speaking arises in many situations. Here Dr. John Holcomb updates the media on the condition of U.S. Representative Gabrielle Giffords after she was shot at a meeting in Tucson, Arizona.

Your teacher recognizes that you are a novice and is trained to give the kind of guidance you need to get started. In your fellow students you have a highly sympathetic audience who will provide valuable feedback to help you improve your speaking skills. As the class goes on, your fears about public speaking will gradually recede until they are replaced by only a healthy nervousness before you rise to speak.[12]

Prepare, Prepare, Prepare

Another key to gaining confidence is to pick speech topics you truly care about—and then to prepare your speeches so thoroughly that you cannot help but be successful. Here's how one student combined enthusiasm for his topic with thorough preparation to score a triumph in speech class:

Jesse Young was concerned about taking a speech class. Not having any experience as a public speaker, he got butterflies in his stomach just thinking about talking in front of an audience. But when the time came for Jesse's first speech, he was determined to make it a success.

Jesse chose Habitat for Humanity as the topic for his speech. He had been a volunteer for three years, and he believed deeply in the organization and its mission. The purpose of his speech was to explain the origins, philosophy, and activities of Habitat for Humanity.

As Jesse spoke, it became clear that he was enthusiastic about his subject and genuinely wanted his classmates to share his enthusiasm. Because he was intent on communicating with his audience, he forgot to be nervous. He spoke clearly, fluently, and dynamically. Soon the entire class was engrossed in his speech.

Afterward, Jesse admitted that he had surprised even himself. "It was amazing," he said. "Once I passed the first minute or so, all I thought about were those people out there listening. I could tell that I was really getting through to them."

How much time should you devote to preparing your speeches? A standard rule of thumb is that each minute of speaking time requires one to two hours of preparation time—perhaps more, depending on the amount of research needed for the speech. This may seem like a lot of time, but the rewards are well worth it. One professional speech consultant estimates that proper preparation can reduce stage fright by up to 75 percent.[13]

If you follow the techniques suggested by your teacher and in the rest of this book, you will stand up for every speech fully prepared. Imagine that the day for your first speech has arrived. You have studied your audience and selected a topic you know will interest them. You have researched the speech thoroughly and practiced it several times until it feels absolutely comfortable. You have even tried it out before two or three trusted friends. How can you help but be confident of success?

Think Positively

Confidence is mostly the well-known power of positive thinking. If you think you can do it, you usually can. On the other hand, if you predict disaster and doom, that is almost always what you will get. This is especially true when it comes to public speaking. Speakers who think negatively about themselves and the speech experience are much more likely to be overcome by stage fright than are speakers who think positively. Here are some ways you can transform negative thoughts into positive ones as you work on your speeches:

Negative Thought	Positive Thought
I wish I didn't have to give this speech.	This speech is a chance for me to share my ideas and gain experience as a speaker.
I'm not a great public speaker.	No one's perfect, but I'm getting better with each speech I give.
I'm always nervous when I give a speech.	Everyone's nervous. If other people can handle it, I can too.
No one will be interested in what I have to say.	I have a good topic and I'm fully prepared. Of course they'll be interested.

Many psychologists believe that the ratio of positive to negative thoughts in regard to stressful activities such as speechmaking should be at least five to one. That is, for each negative thought, you should counter with a minimum of five positive ones. Doing so will not make your nerves go away completely, but it will help keep them under control so you can concentrate on communicating your ideas rather than on brooding about your fears and anxieties.

Use the Power of Visualization

Visualization is closely related to positive thinking. It is used by athletes, musicians, actors, speakers, and others to enhance their performance in stressful situations. How does it work? Listen to long-distance runner Vicki Huber:

> Right before a big race, I'll picture myself running, and I will try and put all of the other competitors in the race into my mind. Then I will try and imagine

every possible situation I might find myself in . . . behind someone, being boxed in, pushed, shoved or cajoled, different positions on the track, laps to go, and, of course, the final stretch. And I always picture myself winning the race, no matter what happens during the event.

Of course, Huber doesn't win every race she runs, but research has shown that the kind of mental imaging she describes can significantly increase athletic performance.[14] It has also shown that visualization can help speakers control their stage fright.[15]

The key to visualization is creating a vivid mental blueprint in which you see yourself succeeding in your speech. Picture yourself in your classroom rising to speak. See yourself at the lectern, poised and self-assured, making eye contact with your audience and delivering your introduction in a firm, clear voice. Feel your confidence growing as your listeners get more and more caught up in what you are saying. Imagine your sense of achievement as you conclude the speech knowing you have done your very best.

As you create these images in your mind's eye, be realistic but stay focused on the positive aspects of your speech. Don't allow negative images to eclipse the positive ones. Acknowledge your nervousness, but picture yourself overcoming it to give a vibrant, articulate presentation. If one part of the speech always seems to give you trouble, visualize yourself getting through it without any hitches. And be specific. The more lucid your mental pictures, the more successful you are likely to be.

As with your physical rehearsal of the speech, this kind of mental rehearsal should be repeated several times in the days before you speak. It doesn't guarantee that every speech will turn out exactly the way you envision it—and it certainly is no substitute for thorough preparation. But used in conjunction with the other methods of combating stage fright, it is a proven way to help control your nerves and to craft a successful presentation.

visualization

Mental imaging in which a speaker vividly pictures himself or herself giving a successful presentation.

Know That Most Nervousness Is Not Visible

Many novice speakers are worried about appearing nervous to the audience. It's hard to speak with poise and assurance if you think you look tense and insecure. One of the most valuable lessons you will learn as your speech class proceeds is that only a fraction of the turmoil you feel inside is visible on the outside. "Your nervous system may be giving you a thousand shocks," says one experienced speaker, "but the viewer can see only a few of them."[16]

Even though your palms are sweating and your heart is pounding, your listeners probably won't realize how tense you are—especially if you do your best to act cool and confident on the outside. Most of the time when students confess after a speech, "I was so nervous I thought I was going to die," their classmates are surprised. To them the speaker looked calm and assured.

Knowing this should make it easier for you to face your listeners with confidence. As one student stated after watching a videotape of her first classroom speech, "I was amazed at how calm I looked. I assumed everyone would be able to see how scared I was, but now that I know they can't, I won't be nearly so nervous in the future. It really helps to know that you look in control even though you may not feel that way."

Don't Expect Perfection

It may also help to know that there is no such thing as a perfect speech. At some point in every presentation, every speaker says or does something that

Like many well-known public figures, Conan O'Brien often experiences stage fright before a speech. Most speakers report that their nervousness drops significantly after the first 30 to 60 seconds of a presentation.

does not come across exactly as he or she had planned. Fortunately, such moments are usually not evident to the audience. Why? Because the audience does not know what the speaker *plans* to say. It hears only what the speaker *does* say. If you momentarily lose your place, reverse the order of a couple statements, or forget to pause at a certain spot, no one need be the wiser. When such moments occur, just proceed as if nothing happened.

Even if you do make an obvious mistake during a speech, that is no catastrophe. If you have ever listened to Martin Luther King's "I Have a Dream," you may recall that he stumbles twice during the speech. Most likely, however, you don't remember. Why? Because you were focusing on King's message, rather than on the fine points of his delivery.

One of the biggest reasons people are concerned about making a mistake in a speech is that they view speechmaking as a performance rather than an act of communication. They feel the audience is judging them against a scale of absolute perfection in which every misstated word or awkward gesture will count against them. But speech audiences are not like judges in a violin recital or an ice-skating contest. They are not looking for a virtuoso performance, but for a well-thought-out address that communicates the speaker's ideas clearly and directly. Sometimes an error or two can actually enhance a speaker's appeal by making her or him seem more human.[17]

As you work on your speeches, make sure you prepare thoroughly and do all you can to get your message across to your listeners. But don't panic about being perfect or about what will happen if you make a mistake. Once you free your mind of these burdens, you will find it much easier to approach your speeches with confidence and even with enthusiasm.

Besides stressing the six points just discussed, your teacher will probably give you several tips for dealing with nervousness in your first speeches. They may include:

- Be at your best physically and mentally. It's not a good idea to stay up until 3:00 A.M. partying with friends or cramming for an exam the night before your speech. A good night's sleep will serve you better.

- As you are waiting to speak, quietly tighten and relax your leg muscles, or squeeze your hands together and then release them. Such actions help reduce tension by providing an outlet for your extra adrenaline.

- Take a couple slow, deep breaths before you start to speak. When they are tense, most people take short, shallow breaths, which only reinforces their anxiety. Deep breathing breaks this cycle of tension and helps calm your nerves.

- Work especially hard on your introduction. Research has shown that a speaker's anxiety level begins to drop significantly after the first 30 to 60 seconds of a presentation.[18] Once you get through the introduction, you should find smoother sailing the rest of the way.

- Make eye contact with members of your audience. Remember that they are individual people, not a blur of faces. And they are your friends.

- Concentrate on communicating with your audience rather than on worrying about your stage fright. If you get caught up in your speech, your audience will too.

- Use visual aids. They create interest, draw attention away from you, and make you feel less self-conscious.

 **checklist**

Speaking with Confidence

YES	NO	
☐	☐	1. Am I enthusiastic about my speech topic?
☐	☐	2. Have I thoroughly developed the content of my speech?
☐	☐	3. Have I worked on the introduction so my speech will get off to a good start?
☐	☐	4. Have I worked on the conclusion so my speech will end on a strong note?
☐	☐	5. Have I rehearsed my speech orally until I am confident about its delivery?
☐	☐	6. Have I worked on turning negative thoughts about my speech into positive ones?
☐	☐	7. Do I realize that nervousness is normal, even among experienced speakers?
☐	☐	8. Do I understand that most nervousness is not visible to the audience?
☐	☐	9. Am I focused on communicating with my audience, rather than on worrying about my nerves?
☐	☐	10. Have I visualized myself speaking confidently and getting a positive response from the audience?

If you are like most students, you will find your speech class to be a very positive experience. As one student wrote on her course evaluation at the end of the class:

I was really dreading this class. The idea of giving all those speeches scared me half to death. But I'm glad now that I stuck with it. It's a small class, and I got to know a lot of the students. Besides, this is one class in which I got to express *my* ideas, instead of spending the whole time listening to the teacher talk. I even came to enjoy giving the speeches. I could tell at times that the audience was really with me, and that's a great feeling.

Over the years, thousands of students have developed confidence in their speechmaking abilities. As your confidence grows, you will be better able to stand before other people and tell them what you think and feel and know—and to make them think and feel and know those same things. The best part about confidence is that it nurtures itself. After you score your first triumph, you will be that much more confident the next time. And as you become a more confident public speaker, you will likely become more confident in other areas of your life as well.

Public Speaking and Critical Thinking

That guy at the party last night really owned me when we were talking about the economy. I know my information is right, and I'm sure his argument didn't make sense, but I can't put my finger on the problem.

I worked really hard on my term paper, but it's just not right. It doesn't seem to hang together, and I can't figure out what's wrong.

Political speeches are so one-sided. The candidates sound good, but they all talk in slogans and generalities. It's really hard to decide who has the best stands on the issues.

Have you ever found yourself in similar situations? If so, you may find help in your speech class. Besides building confidence, a course in public speaking can develop your skills as a critical thinker. Those skills can make the difference between the articulate debater and the pushover, the A student and the C student, the thoughtful voter and the coin tosser.

What is critical thinking? To some extent, it's a matter of logic—of being able to spot weaknesses in other people's arguments and to avoid them in your own. It also involves related skills such as distinguishing fact from opinion, judging the credibility of statements, and assessing the soundness of evidence. In the broadest sense, critical thinking is focused, organized thinking—the ability to see clearly the relationships among ideas.[19]

If you are wondering what this has to do with your public speaking class, the answer is quite a lot. As the class proceeds, you will probably spend a good deal of time organizing your speeches. While this may seem like a purely mechanical exercise, it is closely interwoven with critical thinking. If the structure of your speech is disjointed and confused, odds are that your thinking is also disjointed and confused. If, on the other hand, the structure is clear and cohesive, there is a good chance your thinking is too. Organizing a speech is not just a matter of arranging the ideas you already have. Rather, it is an important part of shaping the ideas themselves.

What is true of organization is true of many aspects of public speaking. The skills you learn in your speech class can help you become a more effective thinker in a number of ways. As you work on expressing your ideas in clear, accurate language, you will enhance your ability to think clearly and accurately. As you study the role of evidence and reasoning in speechmaking, you will see how they can be used in other forms of communication as well. As you learn to listen critically to speeches in class, you will be better able to assess the ideas of speakers (and writers) in a variety of situations.

To return to the examples at the beginning of this section:

The guy at the party last night—would well-honed critical thinking skills help you find the holes in his argument?

The term paper—would better organization and a clear outline help pull it together?

Political speeches—once you get past the slogans, are the candidates drawing valid conclusions from sound evidence?

If you take full advantage of your speech class, you will be able to enhance your skills as a critical thinker in many circumstances. This is one reason public speaking has been regarded as a vital part of education since the days of ancient Greece.

Using public speaking in your CAREER

It's been three years since you graduated from college. After gaining experience as an administrative assistant at a major office equipment manufacturer, you've just been promoted to marketing manager for office copiers. Though you have occasionally given brief reports to other members of your work team, you're now facing your first speech to a large audience. At your company's annual sales meeting, you will address the sales force about the company's new multifunction printer/copiers, and how to sell them to dealers such as Office Depot and OfficeMax.

You're pleased to have this opportunity and you know it shows the company's faith in your abilities. Yet the closer you get to the day of the speech, the harder it is to control the butterflies in your stomach. There will be 200 people in your audience, including all the sales managers and regional managers, in addition to the sales force. All eyes will be on you. It's important that you come across as confident and well informed, but you're afraid your stage fright will send the opposite message. What strategies will you use to control your nerves and make them work for you?

The Speech Communication Process

As you begin your first speeches, you may find it helpful to understand what goes on when one person talks to another. Regardless of the kind of speech communication involved, there are seven elements—speaker, message, channel, listener, feedback, interference, and situation. Here we focus on how these elements interact when a public speaker addresses an audience.

SPEAKER

speaker

The person who is presenting an oral message to a listener.

Speech communication begins with a speaker. If you pick up the telephone and call a friend, you are acting as a speaker. (Of course, you will also act as a listener when your friend is talking.) In public speaking, you will usually present your entire speech without interruption.

Your success as a speaker depends on *you*—on your personal credibility, your knowledge of the subject, your preparation of the speech, your manner of speaking, your sensitivity to the audience and the occasion. But successful speaking also requires enthusiasm.

You can't expect people to be interested in what you say unless you are interested yourself. If you are truly excited about your subject, your audience is almost sure to get excited along with you. You can learn all the techniques of effective speechmaking, but before they can be of much use, you must first have something to say—something that sparks your own enthusiasm.

MESSAGE

message

Whatever a speaker communicates to someone else.

The message is whatever a speaker communicates to someone else. If you are calling a friend, you might say, "I'll be a little late picking you up tonight." That is the message. But it may not be the only message. Perhaps there is a certain tone in your voice that suggests reluctance, hesitation. The underlying message might be "I really don't want to go to that party. You talked me into it, but I'm going to put it off as long as I can."

Your goal in public speaking is to have your *intended* message be the message that is *actually* communicated. Achieving this depends both on what you say (the verbal message) and on how you say it (the nonverbal message).

Getting the verbal message just right requires work. You must narrow your topic down to something you can discuss adequately in the time allowed for the speech. You must do research and choose supporting details to make your ideas clear and convincing. You must organize your ideas so listeners can follow them without getting lost. And you must express your message in words that are accurate, clear, vivid, and appropriate.

Besides the message you send with words, you send a message with your tone of voice, appearance, gestures, facial expression, and eye contact. Imagine that one of your classmates gets up to speak about student loans. Throughout her speech she slumps behind the lectern, takes long pauses to remember what she wants to say, stares at the ceiling, and fumbles with her visual aids.

Her intended message is "We must make more money available for student loans." But the message she actually communicates is "I haven't prepared very well for this speech." One of your jobs as a speaker is to make sure your nonverbal message does not distract from your verbal message.

The powers of critical thinking you develop in researching and organizing your speeches can be applied in many forms of communication, including meetings and group projects.

CHANNEL

The channel is the means by which a message is communicated. When you pick up the phone to call a friend, the telephone is the channel. Public speakers may use one or more of several channels, each of which will affect the message received by the audience.

Consider a speech to Congress by the President of the United States. The speech is carried to the nation by the channels of radio and television. For the radio audience the message is conveyed entirely by the President's voice. For the television audience the message is conveyed by both the President's voice and the televised image. The people in Congress have a more direct channel. They not only hear the President's voice as amplified through a microphone, but they also see him and the setting firsthand.

In a public speaking class, your channel is the most direct of all. Your classmates will see you and hear you without any electronic intervention.

channel

The means by which a message is communicated.

LISTENER

The listener is the person who receives the communicated message. Without a listener, there is no communication. When you talk to a friend on the phone, you have one listener. In public speaking you will have many listeners.

Everything a speaker says is filtered through a listener's *frame of reference*— the total of his or her knowledge, experience, goals, values, and attitudes. Because a speaker and a listener are different people, they can never have exactly the same frame of reference. And because a listener's frame of reference can never be exactly the same as a speaker's, the meaning of a message will never be exactly the same to a listener as to a speaker.

You can easily test the impact of different frames of reference. Ask each of your classmates to describe a chair. If you have 20 classmates, you'll probably get 20 different descriptions. One student might picture a large, overstuffed

listener

The person who receives the speaker's message.

frame of reference

The sum of a person's knowledge, experience, goals, values, and attitudes. No two people can have exactly the same frame of reference.

easy chair, another an elegant straight-backed chair, yet another an office chair, a fourth a rocking chair, and so on.

Even if two or more envision the same general type—say, a rocking chair—their mental images of the chair could still be different. One might be thinking of an early American rocker, another of a modern Scandinavian rocker—the possibilities are unlimited. And "chair" is a fairly simple concept. What about "patriotism" or "freedom"?

Because people have different frames of reference, a public speaker must take great care to adapt the message to the particular audience being addressed. To be an effective speaker, you must be *audience-centered.* You will quickly lose your listeners' attention if your presentation is either too basic or too sophisticated. You will also lose your audience if you do not relate to their experience, interests, knowledge, and values. When you make a speech that causes listeners to say "That is important to *me,*" you will almost always be successful.

FEEDBACK

feedback

The messages, usually nonverbal, sent from a listener to a speaker.

When the President addresses the nation on television, he is engaged in one-way communication. You can talk back to the television set, but the President won't hear you. Most situations, however, involve *two-way* communication. Your listeners don't simply absorb your message like human sponges. They send back messages of their own. These messages are called feedback.

In public speaking there is plenty of feedback to let you know how your message is being received. Do your listeners lean forward in their seats, as if paying close attention? Do they have quizzical looks on their faces? Do they shuffle their feet and gaze at the clock? The message sent by these reactions could be "I am fascinated," "I am bored," "I agree with you," "I don't agree with you," or any number of others. As a speaker, you need to be alert to these reactions and adjust your message accordingly.

Like any kind of communication, feedback is affected by one's frame of reference. How would you feel if, immediately after your speech, all your classmates started to rap their knuckles on the desks? Would you run out of the room in despair? Not if you were in a European university. In many parts of Europe, students rap their knuckles on their desks to show admiration for a classroom lecture. You must understand the feedback to be able to deal with it.

INTERFERENCE

interference

Anything that impedes the communication of a message. Interference can be external or internal to listeners.

Interference is anything that impedes the communication of a message. When you talk on the telephone, sometimes there is static, or wires get crossed so that two different conversations are going on at once. That is a kind of interference.

In public speaking there are two kinds of interference. One, like the static or crossed wires in a phone conversation, is *external* to the audience. Many classrooms are subject to this kind of interference—from traffic outside the building, the clatter of a radiator, students conversing in the hall, a room that is stifling hot or freezing cold. Any of these can distract listeners from what you are saying.

A second kind of interference is *internal* and comes from within your audience. Perhaps one of your listeners has a toothache. She may be so distracted by the pain that she doesn't pay attention to your speech. Another listener could be worrying about a test in the next class period. Yet another could be brooding about an argument with his girlfriend.

FIGURE 1.1

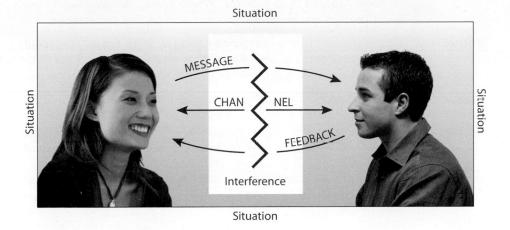

As a speaker, you must try to hold your listeners' attention despite these various kinds of interference. In the chapters that follow you will find many ways to do this.

SITUATION

The situation is the time and place in which speech communication occurs. Conversation always takes place in a certain situation. Sometimes the situation helps—as when you propose marriage over an intimate candlelight dinner. Other times it may hurt—as when you try to speak words of love in competition with a blaring stereo. When you have to talk with someone about a touchy issue, you usually wait until the situation is just right.

Public speakers must also be alert to the situation. Certain occasions—funerals, church services, graduation ceremonies—require certain kinds of speeches. Physical setting is also important. It makes a great deal of difference whether a speech is presented indoors or out, in a small classroom or in a gymnasium, to a densely packed crowd or to a handful of scattered souls. When you adjust to the situation of a public speech, you are only doing on a larger scale what you do every day in conversation.

(For a complete model of the speech communication process, see Figure 1.1 above.[20])

THE SPEECH COMMUNICATION PROCESS: EXAMPLE WITH COMMENTARY

The following example shows how the various components of the speech communication process interact:

Situation	It was 5:15 P.M., and the fall sales conference of OmniBrands, Inc., had been going on all day. A series of new-product presentations to buyers from the company's largest customers had taken much longer than expected.
Speaker	Alyson Kaufman was worried. As a marketing manager for fragrances, she was the last speaker of the day. When Alyson rose to address

situation

The time and place in which speech communication occurs.

the audience, she knew she faced a difficult situation. She had been allotted 45 minutes to introduce her products, and the meeting was scheduled to end in 15 minutes. What's more, holiday sales of her entire product line depended in large part on this presentation.

Channel

Interference

Alyson stepped to the microphone and began to speak. She could see members of the audience looking at their watches, and she knew they were eager to get to dinner after a long day of presentations.

Adapting to Interference

"Good afternoon," Alyson said, "thanks for your attention. I know everyone is ready for dinner—I certainly am. I was given 45 minutes for my presentation—okay, everybody groan—but with your kind cooperation, I'll do my best to finish in under half an hour. I think you'll find the time well worth your while, because the products I am going to tell you about will seriously boost your holiday sales." Alyson was relieved to see several people smiling as they settled back in their seats.

Message

Now that she had the audience's attention, Alyson presented each new product as briefly as she could. She streamlined her planned presentation to emphasize the features that would be most appealing to the buyers and the ones they would be most likely to remember. She ended by handing out samples of the products and promising to contact anyone who needed more information. She quickly added her e-mail address to her PowerPoint slides and was encouraged to see people writing it down.

Feedback

As promised, Alyson finished in under half an hour. "And that wraps it up!" she concluded. "Let's eat!" Later, the marketing director complimented Alyson on dealing so well with a tough situation. "You did a great job," the marketing director said. "Next year, we'll try to make all the presentations as concise and efficient as yours."

Public Speaking in a Multicultural World

CULTURAL DIVERSITY IN THE MODERN WORLD

The United States has always been a diverse society. By the middle of the 19th century, it contained so many people from so many lands that novelist Herman Melville exclaimed, "You cannot spill a drop of American blood without spilling the blood of the whole world."[21]

One can only imagine what Melville would say today! The United States is the most diverse society on earth. That diversity can be seen in cities and towns, schools and businesses, community groups, and houses of worship all across the land. Consider the following:

- There are 195 nations in the world, and every one of them has someone living in the United States.
- Nearly 50 percent of the people in Miami were born outside the United States.
- More than 55 million people in the United States speak a language other than English at home.

These kinds of developments are not limited to the United States. We live in an age of international multiculturalism. The Internet allows for instant communication around the world. CNN is broadcast to more than 1 billion people globally. Social media connect people across ancient boundaries. Despite political, social, and religious differences, all nations are becoming part of a vast global network. For example:

- There are 82,000 transnational corporations around the world, and they account for one-third of the world's economic output.
- McDonald's sells twice as many hamburgers and French fries abroad than it does in the United States; Nike makes 63 percent of its sales through exports.
- France has as many Muslims as practicing Catholics; radio CHIN in Toronto, Canada, broadcasts in 31 languages.

CULTURAL DIVERSITY AND PUBLIC SPEAKING

Speechmaking becomes more complex as cultural diversity increases. Part of the complexity stems from the differences in language from culture to culture. Nothing separates one culture from another more than language. Language and culture are so closely bound that "we communicate the way we do because we are raised in a particular culture and learn its language, rules, and norms."[22]

The meanings attached to gestures, facial expressions, and other nonverbal signals also vary from culture to culture. Even the gestures for such basic messages as "hello" and "goodbye" are culturally based. The North American "goodbye" wave is interpreted in many parts of Europe and South America as the motion for "no," while the Italian and Greek gesture for "goodbye" is the same as the U.S. signal for "come here."[23]

Public speaking is a vital mode of communication in most cultures around the world. Here journalist Roxana Saberi, who was imprisoned in Iran for more than 100 days, speaks at a forum on media freedom held in Doha, Qatar.

Many stories have been told about the fate of public speakers who fail to take into account cultural differences between themselves and their audiences. Consider the following scenario:[24]

> The sales manager of a U.S. electronics firm is in Brazil to negotiate a large purchase of computers by a South American corporation. After three days of negotiations, the sales manager holds a gala reception for all the major executives to build goodwill between the companies.
>
> As is the custom on such occasions, time is set aside during the reception for an exchange of toasts. When it is the sales manager's turn to speak, he praises the Brazilian firm for its many achievements and talks eloquently of his respect for its president and other executives. The words are perfect, and the sales manager can see his audience smiling in approval.
>
> And then—disaster. As the sales manager closes his speech, he raises his hand and flashes the classic U.S. "OK" sign to signal his pleasure at the progress of the negotiations. Instantly the festive mood is replaced with stony silence; smiles turn to icy stares. The sales manager has given his Brazilian audience a gesture with roughly the same meaning as an extended middle finger in the United States.
>
> The next day, the Brazilian firm announces that it will buy its computers from another company.

As this story illustrates, public speakers can ill afford to overlook their listeners' cultural values and customs. The methods of effective speech explained throughout this book will be helpful to you when addressing culturally diverse audiences. Here we need to stress the importance of avoiding the ethnocentrism that often blocks communication between speakers and listeners of different cultural backgrounds.

AVOIDING ETHNOCENTRISM

ethnocentrism

The belief that one's own group or culture is superior to all other groups or cultures.

Ethnocentrism is the belief that our own group or culture—whatever it may be—is superior to all other groups or cultures. Because of ethnocentrism, we identify with our group or culture and see its values, beliefs, and customs as "right" or "natural"—in comparison to the values, beliefs, and customs of other groups or cultures, which we tend to think of as "wrong" or "unnatural."[25]

Ethnocentrism is part of every culture, and it can play a positive role in creating group pride and loyalty. But it can also lead to prejudice and hostility toward different racial, ethnic, religious, or cultural groups. To be an effective public speaker in a multicultural world, you need to keep in mind that all people have their special beliefs and customs.

Avoiding ethnocentrism does not mean that you must agree with the values and practices of all groups and cultures. At times you might try to convince people of different cultures to change their traditional ways of doing things—as speakers from the United Nations seek to persuade farmers in Africa to adopt more productive methods of agriculture, or as delegates from the United States and China attempt to influence the other country's trade policies.

If such speakers are to be successful, however, they must show respect for the cultures of the people they address. They need to adapt their messages to the values and expectations of their listeners.

When you work on your speeches, be alert to how cultural factors might affect how listeners respond. As we shall see in Chapter 6, for classroom speeches you can use audience-analysis questionnaires to learn about the backgrounds and opinions of your classmates. For speeches outside the classroom, the person who invites you to speak can usually provide information about the audience.

Once you know about any cultural factors that might affect your listeners' response, try to put yourself in their place and to hear your message through their ears. If there is a language difference, avoid words or phrases that might cause misunderstanding. When researching the speech, keep an eye out for visual aids and other materials that will relate to a wide range of listeners. When delivering the speech, be alert to feedback that might indicate the audience is having trouble grasping your ideas.

It is also important to avoid ethnocentrism when listening to speeches. When you listen to a speaker from a different cultural background, be on guard against the temptation to judge the speaker on the basis of his or her appearance or manner of delivery. No matter what the cultural background of the speaker, you should listen to her or him as attentively as you would want your audience to listen to you.[26]

Summary

Public speaking has been a vital means of personal empowerment and civic engagement throughout history. The need for effective public speaking will almost certainly touch you sometime in your life. Your speech class will give you training in researching topics, organizing your ideas, and presenting yourself skillfully. This training is invaluable for every type of communication.

There are many similarities between public speaking and daily conversation, but public speaking is also different from conversation. First, it usually imposes strict time limitations and requires more detailed preparation than does ordinary conversation. Second, it requires more formal language. Listeners react negatively to speeches loaded with slang, jargon, and bad grammar. Third, public speaking demands a different method of delivery. Effective speakers adjust their voices to the larger audience and work at avoiding distracting physical mannerisms and verbal habits.

One of the major concerns of students in any speech class is stage fright. Your class will give you an opportunity to gain confidence and make your nervousness work for you rather than against you. You will take a big step toward overcoming stage fright if you think positively, prepare thoroughly, visualize yourself giving a successful speech, keep in mind that most nervousness is not visible to the audience, and think of your speech as communication rather than as a performance in which you must do everything perfectly.

A course in public speaking can also help develop your skills as a critical thinker. Critical thinking helps you organize your ideas, spot weaknesses in other people's reasoning, and avoid them in your own.

The speech communication process includes seven elements—speaker, message, channel, listener, feedback, interference, and situation. The speaker is the person who initiates a speech transaction. Whatever the speaker communicates is the message, which is sent by means of a particular channel. The listener receives the communicated message and provides feedback to the speaker. Interference is anything that impedes the communication of a message, and the situation is the time and place in which speech communication occurs. The interaction of these seven elements determines the outcome in any instance of speech communication.

Because of the diversity of modern life, many—perhaps most—of the audiences you address will include people of different cultural backgrounds. When you work on your speeches, be alert to how such factors might affect the responses of your listeners and adapt your message accordingly. Above all, avoid the ethnocentric belief that your own culture or group is superior to all others. Also keep in mind the importance of avoiding ethnocentrism when listening to speeches. Accord every speaker the same courtesy and attentiveness you would want from your listeners.

Key Terms

stage fright *(9)*

adrenaline *(10)*

positive nervousness *(10)*

visualization *(13)*

critical thinking *(16)*

speaker *(18)*

message *(18)*

channel *(19)*

listener *(19)*

frame of reference *(19)*

feedback *(20)*

interference *(20)*

situation *(21)*

ethnocentrism *(24)*

Review Questions

After reading this chapter, you should be able to answer the following questions:

1. In what ways is public speaking likely to make a difference in your life?
2. How is public speaking similar to everyday conversation?
3. How is public speaking different from everyday conversation?
4. Why is it normal—even desirable—to be nervous at the start of a speech?
5. How can you control your nervousness and make it work for you in your speeches?
6. What are the seven elements of the speech communication process? How do they interact to determine the success or failure of a speech?
7. What is ethnocentrism? Why do public speakers need to avoid ethnocentrism when addressing audiences with diverse cultural, racial, or ethnic backgrounds?

connect

For further review, go to the LearnSmart study module for this chapter.

Exercises for Critical Thinking

1. Think back on an important conversation you had recently in which you wanted to achieve a particular result. (*Examples:* asking your employer to change your work schedule; explaining to a friend how to change the oil and filter in a car; attempting to talk your spouse or partner into buying the computer you like rather than the one he or she prefers.) Work up a brief analysis of the conversation.

In your analysis, explain the following: (1) your purpose in the conversation and the message strategy you chose to achieve your purpose; (2) the communication channels used during the conversation and how they affected the outcome; (3) the interference—internal or external—you encountered during the conversation; (4) the steps you took to adjust to feedback; (5) the strategic changes you would make in preparing for and carrying out the conversation if you had it to do over again.

2. Divide a sheet of paper into two columns. Label one column "Characteristics of an Effective Public Speaker." Label the other column "Characteristics of an Ineffective Public Speaker." In the columns, list and briefly explain what you believe to be the five most important characteristics of effective and ineffective speakers. Be prepared to discuss your ideas in class.

3. On the basis of the lists you developed for Exercise 2, candidly evaluate your own strengths and weaknesses as a speaker. Identify the three primary aspects of speechmaking you most want to improve.

Ethics and Public Speaking

The Importance of Ethics

Guidelines for Ethical Speaking

Plagiarism

Guidelines for Ethical Listening

When the rumors started, Brian Pertzborn, chief financial officer for a prominent charity in the southwest United States, called a press conference. Dozens of reporters showed up. Brian looked directly into the cameras and said, "I assure you that no one at this charity has taken money away from the children and families we work so hard to serve. Embezzlement is illegal and a serious breach of trust. I would never let either happen."

Brian's presentation was highly convincing, and for a time it quieted the rumors. Unfortunately, his statements were false. Two months later, he was indicted by the federal government for stealing more than $2.5 million from the charity.

At the trial, it became clear that Brian was guilty as charged. It also came out that on the very day of his press conference, he had tried to cover his tracks by transferring some of the embezzled money to an overseas bank account.

When the judge sentenced Brian to a stiff prison sentence, she made it clear that she was influenced partly by Brian's lies at the press conference. Had he told the truth, his pleas for leniency might have been better received.

This is not a happy story, but it shows why public speaking needs to be guided by a strong sense of integrity. Brian Pertzborn was persuasive when speaking to the press, but he was unethical in lying to cover his illegal activities. As a result, he hurt people who relied on the charity, destroyed his reputation, and ended up with a long jail sentence. Perhaps if he had confessed before the cameras that day, he would have received a fine and a reprimand instead of the harshest sentence the judge could impose.

The goal of public speaking is to gain a desired response from listeners—but not at any cost. Speechmaking is a form of power and therefore carries with it heavy ethical responsibilities. As the Roman rhetorician Quintilian stated 2,000 years ago, the ideal of speechmaking is the good person speaking well. In this chapter, we explore that ideal by looking at the importance of ethics in public speaking, the ethical obligations of speakers and listeners, and the practical problem of plagiarism and how to avoid it.

The Importance of Ethics

ethics

The branch of philosophy that deals with issues of right and wrong in human affairs.

Ethics is the branch of philosophy that deals with issues of right and wrong in human affairs. Questions of ethics arise whenever we ask whether a course of action is moral or immoral, fair or unfair, just or unjust, honest or dishonest.

We face such questions daily in almost every part of our lives. The parent must decide how to deal with a child who has been sent home from school for unruly behavior. The researcher must decide whether to shade her data "just a bit" in order to gain credit for an important scientific breakthrough. The shopper must decide what to do with the $5 extra change mistakenly given by the clerk at the grocery store. The student must decide whether to say anything about a friend he has seen cheating on a final exam.

Questions of ethics also come into play whenever a public speaker faces an audience. In an ideal world, as the Greek philosopher Plato noted, all public speakers would be truthful and devoted to the good of society. Yet history tells us that the power of speech is often abused—sometimes with disastrous results. Adolf Hitler was unquestionably a persuasive speaker. His oratory galvanized the German people, but his aims were horrifying and his tactics despicable. He remains to this day the ultimate example of why the power of the spoken word needs to be guided by a strong sense of ethical integrity.

As a public speaker, you will face ethical issues at every stage of the speechmaking process—from the initial decision to speak through the final presentation of the message. And the answers will not always be easy. Consider the following example:

Felicia Robinson is running for school board in a large eastern city. Her opponent is conducting what Felicia regards as a highly unethical campaign. In addition to twisting the facts about school taxes, the opponent is pandering to racial prejudice by raising resentment against African Americans and recently arrived immigrants.

Five days before the election, Felicia, who is slightly behind in the polls, learns that the district attorney is preparing to indict her opponent for shady business practices. But the indictment will not be formally issued until after the election.

Nor can it be taken as evidence that her opponent is guilty—like all citizens, he has the right to be presumed innocent until proven otherwise.

Still, news of the indictment could be enough to throw the election Felicia's way, and her advisers urge her to make it an issue in her remaining campaign speeches. Should Felicia follow their advice?

There are creditable arguments to be made on both sides of the ethical dilemma faced by Felicia Robinson. She has tried to run an honest campaign, and she is troubled by the possibility of unfairly attacking her opponent—despite the fact that he has shown no such scruples himself. Yet she knows that the impending indictment may be her last chance to win the election, and she is convinced that a victory for her opponent will spell disaster for the city's school system. Torn between her commitment to fair play, her desire to be elected, and her concern for the good of the community, she faces the age-old ethical dilemma of whether the ends justify the means.

"So," you may be asking yourself, "what is the answer to Felicia Robinson's dilemma?" But in complex cases such as hers there are no cut-and-dried answers. As the leading book on communication ethics states, "We should formulate meaningful ethical guidelines, not inflexible rules."[1] Your ethical decisions will be guided by your values, your conscience, your sense of right and wrong.

But this does not mean such decisions are simply a matter of personal whim or fancy. Sound ethical decisions involve weighing a potential course of action against a set of ethical standards or guidelines. Just as there are guidelines for ethical behavior in other areas of life, so there are guidelines for ethical conduct in public speaking. These guidelines will not automatically solve every ethical quandary you face as a speaker, but knowing them will provide a reliable compass to help you find your way.

ethical decisions

Sound ethical decisions involve weighing a potential course of action against a set of ethical standards or guidelines.

Guidelines for Ethical Speaking

MAKE SURE YOUR GOALS ARE ETHICALLY SOUND

Not long ago, I spoke with a former student—we'll call her Melissa—who had turned down a job in the public relations department of the American Tobacco Institute. Why? Because the job would have required her to lobby on behalf of the cigarette industry. Melissa did not believe she could ethically promote a product that she saw as responsible for thousands of deaths and illnesses each year.

Given Melissa's view of the dangers of cigarette smoking, there can be no doubt that she made an ethically informed decision. On the other side of the coin, someone with a different view of cigarette smoking could make an ethically informed decision to *take* the job. The point of this example is not to judge the rightness or wrongness of Melissa's decision (or of cigarette smoking), but to illustrate how ethical considerations can affect a speaker's choice of goals.

Your first responsibility as a speaker is to ask whether your goals are ethically sound. During World War II, Hitler stirred the German people to condone war, invasion, and genocide. More recently, we have seen politicians who betray the public trust for personal gain, business leaders who defraud investors of millions of dollars, preachers who lead lavish lifestyles at the expense of their religious duties. There can be no doubt that these are not worthy goals.

But think back for a moment to the examples of speechmaking given in Chapter 1. What do the speakers hope to accomplish? Improve the quality of education. Report on a business project. Pay tribute to a fellow worker. Support Habitat for Humanity. Few people would question that these goals are ethically sound.

As with other ethical issues, there can be gray areas when it comes to assessing a speaker's goals—areas in which reasonable people with well-defined standards of right and wrong can legitimately disagree. But this is not a reason to avoid asking ethical questions. If you are to be a responsible public speaker, you cannot escape assessing the ethical soundness of your goals.

BE FULLY PREPARED FOR EACH SPEECH

"A speech," as Jenkin Lloyd Jones states, "is a solemn responsibility." You have an obligation—to yourself and to your listeners—to prepare fully every time you stand in front of an audience. The obligation to yourself is obvious: The better you prepare, the better your speech will be. But the obligation to your listeners is no less important. Think of it this way: The person who makes a bad 30-minute speech to an audience of 200 people wastes only a half hour of her or his own time. But that same speaker wastes 100 hours of the audience's time—more than four full days. This, Jones exclaimed, "should be a hanging offense!"

At this stage of your speaking career, of course, you will probably not be facing many audiences of 200 people. And you will probably not be giving many speeches in which the audience has come for the sole purpose of listening to you. But neither the size nor the composition of your audience changes your ethical responsibility to be fully prepared. Your speech classmates are as worthy of your best effort as if you were addressing a jury or a business meeting, a union conference or a church congregation, the local Rotary club or even the United States Senate.

Being prepared for a speech involves everything from analyzing your audience to creating visual aids, organizing your ideas to rehearsing your delivery. Most crucial from an ethical standpoint, though, is being fully informed about your subject. Why is this so important? Consider the following story:

Victoria Nuñez, a student at a large state university, gave a classroom speech on suicide prevention. Victoria had learned about the topic from her mother, a volunteer on a suicide-prevention hotline, but she also consulted her psychology textbook, read several magazine articles on the warning signs of suicide, and interviewed a crisis-intervention counselor at the campus health service.

In addition to her research, Victoria gave a lot of thought to planning and delivering her speech. She created a handout for the class listing signs that a person might attempt suicide and providing contact information for local mental-health resources. On the day of her speech, Victoria was thoroughly prepared—and she gave an excellent presentation.

Only a few days later, one of Victoria's classmates, Paul Nichols, had a conversation with his roommate that raised a warning flag about whether the roommate might be depressed and in danger of suicide. Based on the information in Victoria's speech, Paul spoke to his roommate, got him to talk about his worries, and convinced him to seek counseling. Paul might have saved his roommate's life, thanks to Victoria's speech.

Among current public speakers, United Nations Secretary General Ban Ki-moon is well regarded for his ethically sound goals and public speaking skills.

This is an especially dramatic case, but it demonstrates how your speeches can have a genuine impact on your listeners. As a speaker, you have an ethical responsibility to consider that impact and to make sure you prepare fully so as not to communicate erroneous information or misleading advice. If Victoria had not done such a thorough job researching her speech, she might have given her classmates faulty information—information that might have had tragic results.

No matter what the topic, no matter who the audience, you need to explore your speech topic as thoroughly as possible. Investigate the whole story; learn about all sides of an issue; seek out competing viewpoints; get the facts right. Not only will you give a better speech, you will also fulfill one of your major ethical obligations.

BE HONEST IN WHAT YOU SAY

Nothing is more important to ethical speechmaking than honesty. Public speaking rests on the unspoken assumption that "words can be trusted and people will be truthful."[2] Without this assumption, there is no basis for communication, no reason for one person to believe anything that another person says.

Does this mean *every* speaker must *always* tell "the truth, the whole truth, and nothing but the truth"? We can all think of situations in which this is impossible (because we do not know the whole truth) or inadvisable (because it would be tactless or imprudent). Consider a parent who tells his two-year-old daughter that her screeching violin solo is "beautiful." Or a speaker who tells a falsehood in circumstances when disclosing the truth might touch off mob violence. Few people would find these actions unethical.[3]

In contrast, think back to the case of Brian Pertzborn at the start of this chapter. Brian knew he had embezzled money from the charity. Yet he denied that he had done so, even as he was profiting at the expense of people who depended on the charity's services. There is no way to excuse Brian's behavior.

Such blatant contempt for the truth is one kind of dishonesty in public speaking. But more subtle forms of dishonesty are just as unethical. They include juggling statistics, quoting out of context, misrepresenting sources, painting tentative findings as firm conclusions, citing unusual cases as typical examples, and substituting innuendo and half-truths for evidence and proof. All of these violate the speaker's duty to be accurate and fair in presenting information.

While on the subject of honesty in speechmaking, we should also note that ethically responsible speakers do not present other people's words as their own. They do not plagiarize their speeches. This subject is so important that we devote a separate section to it later in this chapter.

AVOID NAME-CALLING AND OTHER FORMS OF ABUSIVE LANGUAGE

"Sticks and stones can break my bones, but words can never hurt me." This popular children's chant could not be more wrong. Words may not literally break people's bones, but they can leave psychological scars as surely as sticks and stones can leave physical scars. As one writer explains, "Our identities, who and what we are, how others see us, are greatly affected by the names we are called and the words with which we are labeled."[4] This is why almost all communication ethicists warn public speakers to avoid name-calling and other forms of abusive language.

Name-Calling and Personal Dignity

Name-calling is the use of language to defame, demean, or degrade individuals or groups. When applied to various groups in America, it includes such epithets as "fag," "kike," "nigger," "honkey," "wop," "jap," "chink," and "spic." Such terms have been used to debase people because of their sexual orientation, religious beliefs, or ethnic background. These words dehumanize the groups they are directed against and imply that they do not deserve to be treated with dignity and respect.

In Chapter 12, we will look at ways you can avoid biased language in your speeches. For now, the point to remember is that, contrary to what some people claim, avoiding racist, sexist, and other kinds of abusive language is not simply a matter of political correctness. Such language is ethically suspect because it devalues and stereotypes the people in question.

Such language is also a destructive social force. When used repeatedly and systematically over time, it helps reinforce attitudes that encourage prejudice, hate crimes, and civil rights violations.[5] The issue is not one of politics, but of respecting the dignity of the diverse groups in contemporary society.

Name-Calling and Free Speech

Name-calling and abusive language also pose ethical problems in public speaking when they are used to silence opposing voices. A democratic society depends upon the free and open expression of ideas. In the United States, all citizens have the right to join in the never-ending dialogue of democracy. As a public speaker, you have an ethical obligation to help preserve that right by avoiding tactics such as name-calling that inherently impugn the accuracy or respectability of public statements made by groups or individuals who voice opinions different from yours.

This obligation is the same regardless of whether you are black or white, Christian or Muslim, male or female, gay or straight, liberal or conservative. A pro-union public employee who castigates everyone opposed to her ideas as an "enemy of the middle class" is on as thin ice ethically as a politician who labels all his adversaries "tax-and-spend liberals."

Like other ethical questions in public speaking, name-calling raises some thorny issues. Although name-calling can be hazardous to free speech, it is still protected under the free-speech clause of the Bill of Rights. This is why the American Civil Liberties Union, a major defender of constitutional rights, has opposed broadly worded codes against abusive speech on college campuses. To date, such codes have not survived legal challenges, and many schools are developing more sharply focused regulations that they hope will stand up in court.[6]

But whatever the legal outcome may be, it will not alter the ethical responsibility of public speakers—on or off campus—to avoid name-calling and other kinds of abusive language. Legality and ethics, though related, are not identical. There is nothing illegal about falsifying statistics in a speech, but there is no doubt that it is unethical. The same is true of name-calling. It may not be illegal to cast racial, sexual, or religious slurs at people in a speech, but it is still unethical. Not only does it demean the dignity of the groups or individuals being attacked, but it undermines the right of all groups in the United States to be fairly heard.

PUT ETHICAL PRINCIPLES INTO PRACTICE

It is easy to pay lip service to the importance of ethics. It is much harder to act ethically. Yet that is just what a responsible public speaker must do. As one popular book on ethics states, "Being ethical means behaving ethically *all the time*—not only when it's convenient."[7]

Questions of ethics arise whenever a speaker faces an audience. Here former soldier Melissa Stockwell, who was injured in the line of duty, talks at the annual Paralympic Military Sports Camp.

As you work on your speeches, you will ask yourself such questions as "Is my choice of topic suitable for the audience?" "Are my supporting materials clear and convincing?" "How can I phrase my ideas to give them more punch?" These are *strategic* questions. As you answer them, you will try to make your speech as informative, as persuasive, or as entertaining as possible.

But you will also face moments of *ethical* decision—similar, perhaps, to those faced by Brian Pertzborn, Felicia Robinson, and other speakers in this chapter. When those moments arrive, don't simply brush them aside and go on your way. Keep in mind the guidelines for ethical speechmaking we have discussed and do your best to follow them through thick and thin. Make sure you can answer yes to all the questions on the Checklist for Ethical Public Speaking below.[8]

✔ checklist

Ethical Public Speaking

YES	NO	
☐	☐	1. Have I examined my goals to make sure they are ethically sound?
		a. Can I defend my goals on ethical grounds if they are questioned or challenged?
		b. Would I want other people to know my true motives in presenting this speech?
☐	☐	2. Have I fulfilled my ethical obligation to prepare fully for the speech?
		a. Have I done a thorough job of studying and researching the topic?
		b. Have I prepared diligently so as not to communicate erroneous or misleading information to my listeners?
☐	☐	3. Is the speech free of plagiarism?
		a. Can I vouch that the speech represents my own work, my own thinking, my own language?
		b. Do I cite the sources of all quotations and paraphrases?
☐	☐	4. Am I honest in what I say in the speech?
		a. Is the speech free of any false or deliberately deceptive statements?
		b. Does the speech present statistics, testimony, and other kinds of evidence fairly and accurately?
		c. Does the speech contain valid reasoning?
		d. If the speech includes visual aids, do they present facts honestly and reliably?
☐	☐	5. Do I use the power of language ethically?
		a. Do I avoid name-calling and other forms of abusive language?
		b. Does my language show respect for the right of free speech and expression?
☐	☐	6. All in all, have I made a conscious effort to put ethical principles into practice in preparing my speech?

Plagiarism

"Plagiarism" comes from *plagiarius,* the Latin word for kidnapper. To plagiarize means to present another person's language or ideas as your own—to give the impression you have written or thought something yourself when you have actually taken it from someone else.[9] We often think of plagiarism as an ethical issue in the classroom, but it can have repercussions in other situations:

Joanne Calabro was in her second year as school superintendent in the northern New Jersey town of Fort Lee. In the spring, she spoke at a ceremony for students being inducted into the National Honor Society. It was a brief speech—only six minutes—but the repercussions would last much, much longer.

One of the students at the ceremony recognized some of Calabro's passages and decided to check them online. He discovered that she had lifted the entire speech from a sample induction address posted on About.com. Further evidence came from a videotape of Calabro delivering the speech.

When confronted with the facts, Calabro admitted to an error in judgment but insisted she had done nothing illegal. In fact, the speech on About.com was protected by copyright law, and Calabro might have been liable to legal action had the Web firm been so inclined. What she could not escape were the ethical consequences. Facing severe criticism within the school district and from the press, she had little choice but to resign her post as superintendent.[10]

As this story shows, plagiarism is a serious matter. If you are caught plagiarizing a speech in class, the punishment can range from a failing grade to expulsion from school. If you are caught plagiarizing outside the classroom, you stand to forfeit your good name, to damage your career, or, if you are sued, to lose a large amount of money. It is worth your while, then, to make sure you know what plagiarism is and how to avoid it.

GLOBAL PLAGIARISM

Global plagiarism is stealing your speech entirely from another source and passing it off as your own. The most blatant—and unforgivable—kind of plagiarism, it is grossly unethical.

Global plagiarism in a college classroom usually occurs because a student puts off the assignment until the last minute. Then, in an act of desperation, the student downloads a speech from the Internet or gets one written by a friend and delivers it as his or her own.

The best way to avoid this, of course, is not to leave your speech until the last minute. Most teachers explain speech assignments far enough in advance that you should have no trouble getting an early start. By starting early, you will give yourself plenty of time to prepare a first-rate speech—a speech of your own.

If, for some reason, you fail to get your speech ready on time, do not succumb to the lure of plagiarism. Whatever penalty you suffer from being late will pale in comparison with the consequences if you are caught plagiarizing.

PATCHWORK PLAGIARISM

patchwork plagiarism

Stealing ideas or language from two or three sources and passing them off as one's own.

Unlike global plagiarism, in which a speaker pirates an entire speech from a single source, patchwork plagiarism occurs when a speaker pilfers from two or three sources. Here's an example:

Daniel Fine chose "Recent Discoveries About Dinosaurs" as the topic for his informative speech. In his research, Daniel found three especially helpful sources. The first was a printed guide to a recent museum exhibition about new dinosaur discoveries in North and South America. The second was Wikipedia, and the third was Montana State University's Web site about its dinosaur research program.

Unfortunately, instead of using these materials creatively to write a speech in his own words, Daniel lifted long passages from the museum guide, Wikipedia, and the university Web site and patched them together with a few transitions. When he was finished, he had a speech that was composed almost entirely of other people's words.

When Daniel's teacher read his speech outline, it did not sound authentic to her. So she plugged several phrases from the outline into Google. In less than a minute, she had found both the Wikipedia article and the Montana State University Web site. Soon after, she found an online version of the museum guide. Daniel was caught red-handed.

This story illustrates an important point about plagiarism. Daniel did not take his speech from a single source. He even did a little research. But copying from a few sources is no less plagiarism than is copying from a single source. When you give a speech, you declare that it is your work—the product of your thinking, your beliefs, your language. Daniel's speech did not contain any of these. Instead, it was cut and pasted wholly from other people's words.

"But," you may be thinking, "not many students are experts on their speech topics. Why should they be expected to come up with new ideas that even the experts haven't thought of?"

The answer is they aren't. The key is not whether you have something absolutely original to say, but whether you do enough research and thinking to come up with your own slant on the topic.

As with global plagiarism, one key to averting patchwork plagiarism is to start working on your speech as soon as possible. The longer you work on it, the more apt you are to come up with your own approach. It is also vital to consult a large number of sources in your research. If you have only two or three sources, you are far more likely to fall into the trap of patchwork plagiarism than if you consult a wide range of research materials.

INCREMENTAL PLAGIARISM

incremental plagiarism

Failing to give credit for particular parts of a speech that are borrowed from other people.

In global plagiarism and patchwork plagiarism, the entire speech is cribbed more or less verbatim from a single source or a few sources. But plagiarism can exist even when the speech as a whole is not pirated. This is called incremental plagiarism. It occurs when the speaker fails to give credit for particular parts—increments—of the speech that are borrowed from other people. The most important of these increments are quotations and paraphrases.

Speakers who begin work on their speeches early and consult a wide range of sources are less likely to fall into the trap of plagiarism than are speakers who procrastinate and rely on a limited number of sources.

Quotations

Whenever you quote someone directly, you must attribute the words to that person. Suppose you are giving a speech on Malcolm X, the famous African-American leader of the 1960s. While doing your research, you run across the following passage from Bruce Perry's acclaimed biography, *Malcolm: The Life of the Man Who Changed Black America:*

> Malcolm X fathered no legislation. He engineered no stunning Supreme Court victories or political campaigns. He scored no major electoral triumphs. Yet because of the way he articulated his followers' grievances and anger, the impact he had upon the body politic was enormous.[11]

This is a fine quotation that summarizes the nature and importance of Malcolm's impact on American politics. It would make a strong addition to your speech—as long as you acknowledge Perry as the author. The way to avoid plagiarism in this instance is to introduce Perry's statement by saying something like:

> In *Malcolm: The Life of the Man Who Changed Black America*, historian Bruce Perry says the following about Malcolm's impact on American politics: . . .

Or,

> According to historian Bruce Perry in his book *Malcolm: The Life of the Man Who Changed Black America*, . . .

Now you have clearly identified Perry and given him credit for his words rather than presenting them as your own.

Paraphrases

paraphrase

To restate or summarize an author's ideas in one's own words.

When you paraphrase an author, you restate or summarize her or his ideas in your own words. Suppose, once again, that your topic is Malcolm X. But this time you decide to paraphrase the statement from Bruce Perry's biography rather than quoting it. You might say:

> Malcolm X was not a politician. He did not pass any laws, or win any Supreme Court victories, or get elected to any office. But he stated the grievances and anger of his followers so powerfully that the whole nation took notice.

Even though you do not quote Perry directly, you still appropriate the structure of his ideas and a fair amount of his language. Thus you still need to give him credit—just as if you were repeating his words verbatim.

It is especially important in this case to acknowledge Perry because you are borrowing his opinion—his judgment—about Malcolm X. If you simply recount basic facts about Malcolm's life—he was born in Omaha, Nebraska, converted to the Nation of Islam while in prison, traveled to Mecca toward the end of his life, was assassinated in February 1965—you do not have to report the source of your information. These facts are well known and can be found in any standard reference work.

On the other hand, there is still considerable debate about Malcolm's views of other African-American leaders, the circumstances surrounding his death, and what he might have done had he lived. If you were to cite Perry's views on any of these matters—regardless of whether you quoted or paraphrased—you would need to acknowledge him as your source.

As more than one speaker (and writer) has discovered, it is possible to commit incremental plagiarism quite by accident. This is less offensive than deliberate plagiarism, but it is plagiarism nonetheless. There are two ways to guard against incremental plagiarism. The first is to be careful when taking research notes to distinguish among direct quotations, paraphrased material, and your own comments. (See Chapter 7 for a full discussion of research methods.) The second way to avoid incremental plagiarism is to err on the side of caution. In other words, when in doubt, cite your source.

PLAGIARISM AND THE INTERNET

When it comes to plagiarism, no subject poses more confusion—or more temptation—than the Internet. Because it's so easy to copy information from the Web, many people are not aware of the need to cite sources when they use Internet materials in their speeches. If you don't cite Internet sources, you are just as guilty of plagiarism as if you take information from print sources without proper citation.

One way to avoid patchwork plagiarism or incremental plagiarism when working with the Internet is to take careful research notes. Make sure you keep a record of the following: (1) the title of the Internet document, (2) the author or organization responsible for the document, (3) the date on which the document was last updated, (4) the date on which you accessed the site. You will need all this information for your speech bibliography.

You will also need to identify your Internet sources when you present the speech. It's not enough to say "As I found on the Web" or "According to the Internet." You need to specify the author and the Web site. In Chapter 8,

Having graduated with a degree in public administration and hoping to pursue a career in politics, you have been fortunate to receive a staff position with one of the leading senators in your state legislature. Since your arrival two months ago, you have answered phones, ordered lunch, made copies, stapled mailings, and stuffed envelopes. Finally you have been asked to look over a speech the senator will deliver at your alma mater. Surely, you think, this will be the first of many important assignments once your value is recognized.

After reading the speech, however, your enthusiasm is dampened. You agree wholeheartedly with its support of a bill to fund scholarships for low-income students, but you're dismayed by its attack on opponents of the bill as "elitist bigots who would deny a college education to those who need it most." You haven't been asked to comment on the ethics of the speech, and you certainly don't want to jeopardize your position on the senator's staff. At the same time, you think his use of name-calling may actually arouse sympathy for the opposition.

The senator would like your comments in two hours. What will you tell him?

we'll look more closely at how to cite Internet documents. For now, keep in mind that providing such citations is one of your ethical responsibilities as a public speaker.

Another problem with regard to the Internet is the large number of Web sites that sell entire speeches or papers. In addition to being highly unethical, using material from one of these sites is extremely risky. The same technology that makes it easy to plagiarize from the Web makes it easy for teachers to locate material that has been plagiarized and the exact source from which it has been taken.

You should also know that almost all the speeches (and papers) offered for sale on the Web are of very low quality. If you are ever tempted to purchase one, keep in mind there is a good chance you will waste your money and get caught in the process. Here, as in other aspects of life, honesty is the best policy.

Guidelines for Ethical Listening

So far in this chapter we have focused on the ethical duties of public speakers. But speechmaking is not a one-way street. Listeners also have ethical obligations. They are (1) to listen courteously and attentively; (2) to avoid prejudging the speaker; and (3) to maintain the free and open expression of ideas. Let us look at each.

BE COURTEOUS AND ATTENTIVE

Imagine that you are giving your first classroom speech. You have put a great deal of time into writing the speech, and you have practiced your delivery until you are confident you can do well—especially once you get over the initial rush of stage fright.

You have worked hard on your introduction, and your speech gets off to a fine start. Most of your classmates are paying close attention, but some are not. One appears to be doing homework for another class. Another keeps sneaking glances at his cell phone. Two or three are gazing out the window, and one is leaning back in his chair with his eyes shut!

You try to block them out of your mind—especially since the rest of the class seems interested in what you are saying—but the longer you speak, the more concerned you become. "What am I doing wrong?" you wonder to yourself. "How can I get these people to pay attention?" The more you think about this, the more your confidence and concentration waver.

When you momentarily lose your place halfway through the speech, you start to panic. Your nerves, which you have held in check so far, take the upper hand. Your major thought now becomes "How can I get this over as fast as possible?" Flustered and distracted, you rush through the rest of your speech and sit down.

Just as public speakers have an ethical obligation to prepare fully for each speech, so listeners have a responsibility to be courteous and attentive during the speech. This responsibility—which is a matter of civility in any circumstance—is especially important in speech class. You and your classmates are in a learning situation in which you need to support one another.

When you listen to speeches in class, give your fellow students the same courtesy and attention you want from them. Come to class prepared to listen to—and to learn from—your classmates' speeches. As you listen, be conscious of the feedback you are sending the speaker. Sit up in your chair rather than slouching; maintain eye contact with the speaker; show support and encouragement in your facial expressions. Keep in mind the power you have as a listener over the speaker's confidence and composure, and exercise that power with a strong sense of ethical responsibility.

AVOID PREJUDGING THE SPEAKER

We have all heard that you can't judge a book by its cover. The same is true of speeches. You can't judge a speech by the name, race, lifestyle, appearance, or reputation of the speaker. As the National Communication Association states in its Credo for Ethical Communication, listeners should "strive to understand and respect" speakers "before evaluating and responding to their messages."[12]

This does not mean you must agree with every speaker you hear. Your aim is to listen carefully to the speaker's ideas, to assess the evidence and reasoning offered in support of those ideas, and to reach an intelligent judgment about the speech. In Chapter 3, we will discuss specific steps you can take to improve your listening skills. For now, it is enough to know that if you prejudge a speaker—either positively or negatively—you will fail in one of your ethical responsibilities as a listener.

MAINTAIN THE FREE AND OPEN EXPRESSION OF IDEAS

As we saw earlier in this chapter, a democratic society depends on the free and open expression of ideas. The right of free expression is so important that it is protected by the First Amendment to the U.S. Constitution, which declares, in part, that "Congress shall make no law . . . abridging the freedom

It is vital for a democratic society to maintain the free and open expression of ideas. Here Rabbi Greg Marx addresses an assembly in Philadelphia devoted to promoting religious tolerance.

of speech." Just as public speakers need to avoid name-calling and other tactics that can undermine free speech, so listeners have an obligation to maintain the right of speakers to be heard.

As with other ethical issues, the extent of this obligation is open to debate. Disputes over the meaning and scope of the First Amendment arise almost daily in connection with issues such as terrorism, pornography, and hate speech. The question underlying such disputes is whether *all* speakers have a right to be heard.

There are some kinds of speech that are not protected under the First Amendment—including defamatory falsehoods that destroy a person's reputation, threats against the life of the President, and inciting an audience to illegal action in circumstances where the audience is likely to carry out the action. Otherwise, the Supreme Court has held—and most experts in communication ethics have agreed—that public speakers have an almost unlimited right of free expression.

In contrast to this view, it has been argued that some ideas are so dangerous, so misguided, or so offensive that society has a duty to suppress them. But who is to determine which ideas are too dangerous, misguided, or offensive to be uttered? Who is to decide which speakers are to be heard and which are to be silenced?

No matter how well intentioned they may be, efforts to "protect" society by restricting free speech usually end up repressing minority viewpoints and unpopular opinions. In U.S. history, such efforts were used to keep women off the public platform until the 1840s, to muzzle labor organizers during the 1890s, and to impede civil rights leaders in the 1960s. Imagine what American society might be like if these speakers had been silenced!

It is important to keep in mind that ensuring a person's freedom to express her or his ideas does not imply agreement with those ideas. You can disagree entirely with the message but still support the speaker's right to express it. As the National Communication Association states in its Credo for Ethical Communication, "freedom of expression, diversity of perspective, and tolerance of dissent" are vital to "the informed decision making fundamental to a civil society."[13]

Summary

Because public speaking is a form of power, it carries with it heavy ethical responsibilities. Today, as for the past 2,000 years, the good person speaking well remains the ideal of commendable speechmaking.

There are five basic guidelines for ethical public speaking. The first is to make sure your goals are ethically sound—that they are consistent with the welfare of society and your audience. The second is to be fully prepared for each speech. The third is to be honest in what you say. The fourth is to avoid name-calling and other forms of abusive language. The final guideline is to put ethical principles into practice at all times.

Of all the ethical lapses a speaker can commit, few are more serious than plagiarism. Global plagiarism is lifting a speech entirely from a single source. Patchwork plagiarism involves stitching a speech together by copying from a few sources. Incremental plagiarism occurs when a speaker fails to give credit for specific quotations and paraphrases that are borrowed from other people.

In addition to your ethical responsibilities as a speaker, you have ethical obligations as a listener. The first is to listen courteously and attentively. The second is to avoid prejudging the speaker. The third is to support the free and open expression of ideas. In all these ways, your speech class will offer a good testing ground for questions of ethical responsibility.

Key Terms

ethics *(30)*

ethical decisions *(31)*

name-calling *(34)*

Bill of Rights *(35)*

plagiarism *(37)*

global plagiarism *(37)*

patchwork plagiarism *(38)*

incremental plagiarism *(38)*

paraphrase *(40)*

Review Questions

After reading this chapter, you should be able to answer the following questions:

connect

For further review, go to the LearnSmart study module for this chapter.

1. What is ethics? Why is a strong sense of ethical responsibility vital for public speakers?

2. What are the five guidelines for ethical speechmaking discussed in this chapter?

3. What is the difference between global plagiarism and patchwork plagiarism? What are the best ways to avoid these two kinds of plagiarism?

4. What is incremental plagiarism? How can you steer clear of it when dealing with quotations and paraphrases?

5. What are the three guidelines for ethical listening discussed in this chapter?

Exercises for Critical Thinking

1. Look back at the story of Felicia Robinson on pages 30–31. Evaluate her dilemma in light of the guidelines for ethical speechmaking presented in this chapter. Explain what you believe would be the most ethical course of action in her case.

2. The issue of insulting and abusive speech—especially slurs directed against people on the basis of race, religion, gender, or sexual orientation—is extremely controversial. Do you believe society should punish such speech with criminal penalties? To what degree are colleges and universities justified in trying to discipline students who engage in such speech? Do you feel it is proper to place any boundaries on free expression in order to prohibit insulting and abusive speech? Why or why not? Be prepared to explain your ideas in class.

3. All of the following situations could arise in your speech class. Identify the ethical issues in each and explain what, as a responsible speaker or listener, your course of action would be.

   a. You are speaking on the topic of prison reform. In your research, you run across two public opinion polls. One of them, an independent survey by the Gallup Organization, shows that a majority of people in your state oppose your position. The other poll, suspect in its methods and conducted by a partisan organization, says a majority of people in your state support your position. Which poll do you cite in your speech? If you cite the second poll, do you point out its shortcomings?

   b. When listening to an informative speech by one of your classmates, you realize that much of it is plagiarized from a Web site you visited a couple weeks earlier. What do you do? Do you say something when your instructor asks for comments about the speech? Do you mention your concern to the instructor after class? Do you talk with the speaker? Do you remain silent?

   c. While researching your persuasive speech, you find a quotation from an article by a highly respected expert that will nail down one of your most important points. But as you read the rest of the article, you realize that the author does not in fact support the policy you are advocating. Do you still include the quotation in your speech?

3

Listening

I t had been a long day at the office. By the time Jason Whitehawk pulled his late-model car into the driveway at home, he was exhausted. As he trudged into the house, he routinely asked his wife, "How did things go with you at work today?"

"Oh, pretty well," she replied, "except for the terrorist attack in the morning and the outbreak of bubonic plague in the afternoon."

Jason nodded his head as he made his way to the sofa. "That's nice," he said. "At least someone had a good day."

This story illustrates what one research study after another has revealed—most people are shockingly poor listeners. We fake paying attention. We can look right at someone, appear interested in what that person says, even nod our head or smile at the appropriate moments—all without really listening.

Not listening doesn't mean we don't hear. *Hearing* is a physiological process, involving the vibration of sound waves on our eardrums and the firing of electrochemical impulses from the inner ear to the central auditory system of the brain. But *listening* involves paying close attention to, and making sense of, what we hear. Even when we think we are listening carefully, we usually grasp only 50 percent of what we hear. After 24 hours we can remember only 10 percent of the original message.[1] It's little wonder that listening has been called a lost art.[2]

Listening Is Important

Although most people listen poorly, there are exceptions. Top-flight business executives, successful politicians, brilliant teachers—nearly all are excellent listeners.[3] So much of what they do depends on absorbing information that is given verbally—and absorbing it quickly and accurately. If you had an interview with the president of a major corporation, you might be shocked (and flattered) to see how closely that person listened to your words.

In our communication-oriented age, listening is more important than ever. According to one study, more than 60 percent of errors made in business come from poor listening.[4] Replacing poor listening with good listening improves efficiency, sales, customer satisfaction, and employee morale. This is why, in most companies, effective listeners hold higher positions and are promoted more often than ineffective listeners. When business managers are asked to rank-order the communication skills most crucial to their jobs, they usually rank listening number one.[5]

Even if you don't plan to be a corporate executive, the art of listening can be helpful in almost every part of your life. This is not surprising when you realize that people spend more time listening than in any other communicative activity—more than reading, more than writing, more even than speaking.

Think for a moment about your own life as a college student. Most class time in U.S. colleges and universities is spent listening to discussions and lectures. A number of studies have shown a strong correlation between listening and academic success. Students with the highest grades are usually those with the strongest listening skills. The reverse is also true—students with the lowest grades are usually those with the weakest listening skills.[6]

There is plenty of reason, then, to take listening seriously. Employers and employees, parents and children, wives and husbands, doctors and patients, students and teachers—all depend on the apparently simple skill of listening. Regardless of your profession or walk of life, you never escape the need for a well-trained ear.

Listening is also important to you as a speaker. It is probably the way you get most of your ideas and information—from television, radio, conversation, and lectures. If you do not listen well, you will not understand what you hear and may pass along your misunderstanding to others.

Besides, in class—as in life—you will listen to many more speeches than you give. It is only fair to pay close attention to your classmates' speeches; after all, you want them to listen carefully to *your* speeches. An excellent way to improve your own speeches is to listen attentively to the speeches of other people. Over and over, teachers find that the best speakers are usually the best listeners.

A side benefit of your speech class is that it offers an ideal opportunity to work on the art of listening. During the 95 percent of the time when you are not speaking, you have nothing else to do but listen and learn. You can sit there like a stone—or you can use the time profitably to master a skill that will serve you in a thousand ways.

Listening and Critical Thinking

One of the ways listening can serve you is by enhancing your skills as a critical thinker. We can identify four kinds of listening:[7]

- *Appreciative listening*—listening for pleasure or enjoyment, as when we listen to music, to a comedy routine, or to an entertaining speech.
- *Empathic listening*—listening to provide emotional support for the speaker, as when a psychiatrist listens to a patient or when we lend a sympathetic ear to a friend in distress.
- *Comprehensive listening*—listening to understand the message of a speaker, as when we attend a classroom lecture or listen to directions for finding a friend's house.
- *Critical listening*—listening to evaluate a message for purposes of accepting or rejecting it, as when we listen to the sales pitch of a car salesperson or the campaign speech of a political candidate.

Although all four kinds of listening are important, this chapter deals primarily with comprehensive listening and critical listening. They are the kinds of listening you will use most often when listening to speeches in class, when taking lecture notes in other courses, when communicating at work, and when responding to the barrage of commercials, political messages, and other persuasive appeals you face every day. They are also the kinds of listening that are most closely tied to critical thinking.

As we saw in Chapter 1, critical thinking involves a number of skills. Some of those skills—summarizing information, recalling facts, distinguishing main points from minor points—are central to comprehensive listening. Other skills of critical thinking—separating fact from opinion, spotting weaknesses in reasoning, judging the soundness of evidence—are especially important in critical listening.

When you engage in comprehensive listening or critical listening, you must use your mind as well as your ears. When your mind is not actively involved, you may be hearing, but you are not *listening*. In fact, listening and critical thinking are so closely allied that training in listening is also training in how to think.

At the end of this chapter, we'll discuss steps you can take to improve your skills in comprehensive and critical listening. If you follow these steps, you may also become a better critical thinker.

appreciative listening

Listening for pleasure or enjoyment.

empathic listening

Listening to provide emotional support for a speaker.

comprehensive listening

Listening to understand the message of a speaker.

critical listening

Listening to evaluate a message for purposes of accepting or rejecting it.

Four Causes of Poor Listening

NOT CONCENTRATING

The brain is incredibly efficient. Although we talk at a rate of 120 to 150 words a minute, the brain can process 400 to 800 words a minute.[8] This would seem to make listening very easy, but actually it has the opposite effect. Because we can process a speaker's words and still have plenty of spare "brain time," we are tempted to interrupt our listening by thinking about other things. Here's what happens:

> Elena Kim works in the public communications department of a large insurance company. She attends regular staff meetings with the communications director. The meetings provide necessary information, but sometimes they seem to drag on forever.
>
> This morning the director is talking about the company's new executive vice president, who has just moved to headquarters from a regional firm in Florida. "Mr. Fernandez has never worked in a company this size, but his experience in Florida . . ."
>
> "Florida," Elena dreams. "Sun, endless beaches, and the club scene in South Beach. Maybe I can snatch a few days' vacation in January. . . ."
>
> Sternly, Elena pulls her attention back to the meeting. The communications director is now discussing the company's latest plan for public-service announcements. Elena is not involved in the plan, and her attention wanders once more.
>
> That morning she had another argument with her roommate about cleaning the kitchen and taking out the garbage. Maybe it's time to decide if she can afford to live without a roommate. It sure would make for fewer hassles.
>
> ". . . an area Elena has researched extensively," the director is saying. Uh oh! *What* area does the director mean? Everyone looks at Elena, as she frantically tries to recall the last words said at the meeting.

It's not that Elena *meant* to lose track of the discussion. But there comes a point at which it's so easy to let your thoughts wander rather than to concentrate on what is being said. After all, concentrating is hard work. Louis Nizer, the famous trial lawyer, says, "So complete is this concentration that at the end of a court day in which I have only listened, I find myself wringing wet despite a calm and casual manner."[9]

Later in this chapter, we will look at some things you can do to concentrate better on what you hear.

LISTENING TOO HARD

Until now we have been talking about not paying close attention to what we hear. But sometimes we listen *too* hard. We turn into human sponges, soaking up a speaker's every word as if every word were equally important. We try to remember all the names, all the dates, all the places. In the process we often miss the speaker's main point. What is worse, we may end up confusing the facts as well.

> Shortly after graduating from college, Carlos Molina landed an excellent job as a Web developer. Knowing he had never been good at budgeting his money, he signed up for a financial planning workshop.

---

spare "brain time"

The difference between the rate at which most people talk (120 to 150 words a minute) and the rate at which the brain can process language (400 to 800 words a minute).

People spend more time listening than in any other communicative activity. One benefit of your speech class is that it can improve your listening skills in a variety of situations.

The first session was about retirement planning. Simone Fisher, who was conducting the workshop, explained that 7 in 10 Americans between the ages of 22 and 35 do not have a monthly budget or a savings plan. Carlos wrote down every number Simone mentioned.

"To have a retirement income equal to 75 percent of your current salary," Simone continued, "you will need to invest at least 6 percent of your present earnings. You also need to account for inflation over time. This afternoon, we will meet with each of you personally to calculate your individual savings needs. In the meantime, I want to stress that the most important thing is to start saving now."

Carlos zealously typed each statistic into his laptop. When Simone opened the floor for questions, Carlos raised his hand and said, "I have two questions. When should I start saving for retirement? And how do I figure out how to account for future inflation?"

This is a typical example of losing the speaker's point by concentrating on details. Carlos had fixed his mind on remembering all the statistics in Simone's presentation, but he blocked out the main message—that it is best to start saving now and that he would get help developing an individual plan.

Rather than trying to remember everything a speaker says, efficient listeners usually concentrate on main points and evidence. We'll discuss these things more thoroughly later in the chapter.

JUMPING TO CONCLUSIONS

Kiah Lee, a recent college graduate, took a job as an editorial assistant in the research department of a regional magazine. Shortly after Kiah arrived, the editor in charge of the research department left the magazine for another job. For the next two months, Kiah struggled to handle the work of the research department by herself. She often felt in over her head, but she knew this was a good opportunity to learn, and she hated to give up her new responsibilities.

One day Derek Perkins, the editor in chief of the magazine, comes into Kiah's office to talk. The following conversation takes place:

Derek: You've done a great job these last two months, Kiah. But you know we really need a new editor. So we've decided to make some changes.

Kiah: I'm not surprised. I know I've made my share of mistakes.

Derek: Everyone makes mistakes when they're starting out. And you've been carrying a lot of responsibility. That's why . . .

Kiah: I know I'm inexperienced, and this is an important department.

Derek: Yes, it is. And it's not an easy job. We really need an editor and an assistant to handle all the work. That's why I wanted to tell you . . .

Kiah: I understand. I knew all along that I was just filling in.

Derek: Kiah, you're not listening.

Kiah: Yes, I am. You're trying to be nice, but you're here to tell me that you've hired a new editor and I'll be going back to my old job.

Derek: No, that's not it at all. I think you've done a fine job under difficult circumstances. You've proved yourself, and I intend to make *you* the editor. But I think you'll need an assistant to help you.

Why is there so much confusion here? Clearly, Kiah is unsure about her future at the magazine. So when Derek starts to talk about making some changes, Kiah jumps to a conclusion and assumes the worst. The misunderstanding could have been avoided if, when Derek had said, "We've decided to make some changes," Kiah had asked, "What changes?"—and then *listened.*

This is one form of jumping to conclusions—putting words into a speaker's mouth. It is one reason why we sometimes communicate so poorly with people we are closest to. Because we're so sure we know what they mean, we don't listen to what they actually say.

Another way of jumping to conclusions is prematurely rejecting a speaker's ideas as boring or misguided. That would be a mistake. Let's say the announced topic is "Architecture and History." It sounds dull. So you tune out—and miss a fascinating discussion filled with human-interest stories about buildings and other structures from the ancient pyramids to the latest skyscrapers.

Nearly every speech has something to offer you—whether it be information, point of view, or technique. You are cheating yourself if you prejudge and choose not to listen.

FOCUSING ON DELIVERY AND PERSONAL APPEARANCE

Avid readers of American history, Greg and Marissa were thrilled when they saw a poster at their local bookstore advertising a lecture by the author of a new book on the Battle of Gettysburg. The book had received good reviews, and Greg and Marissa made plans to attend the lecture.

Arriving at the bookstore, they took their seats and listened while the speaker discussed his research and major findings. "That was great," Marissa exclaimed when they got back to the car. But Greg was scowling. "What's wrong?" Marissa asked.

"I know you're going to think this is stupid," Greg began. "The guy was a decent speaker, and he seemed to know his stuff. But did you see the sport coat he was wearing? It's so retro—and his tie was atrocious. No matter how I tried, I kept thinking that he hadn't gone shopping since the 1980s."

This story illustrates a common problem. Sometimes we judge people by the way they look or speak and don't listen to what they say. It's easy to become distracted by a speaker's accent, personal appearance, or vocal mannerisms and lose sight of the message. Focusing on a speaker's delivery or personal appearance is one of the major sources of interference in the speech communication process, and it is something we always need to guard against.

How to Become a Better Listener

TAKE LISTENING SERIOUSLY

The first step toward becoming a better listener is to accord listening the seriousness it deserves. Good listeners are not born that way. They have *worked* at learning how to listen effectively. Good listening does not go hand in hand with intelligence, education, or social standing. Like any other skill, it comes from practice and self-discipline. Check your current skills as a listener by completing the Listening Self-Evaluation Worksheet on page 54.[10] Once you have identified your shortcomings as a listener, make a serious effort to overcome them.

BE AN ACTIVE LISTENER

So many aspects of modern life encourage us to listen passively. We listen to our iPods while studying. Parents listen to their children while fixing dinner. Television reporters listen to a politician's speech while walking around the auditorium looking for their next interview.

This type of passive listening is a habit—but so is active listening. Active listeners give their undivided attention to the speaker in a genuine effort to understand his or her point of view. In conversation, they do not interrupt the speaker or finish his or her sentences. When listening to a speech, they do not allow themselves to be distracted by internal or external interference, and they do not prejudge the speaker. They take listening seriously and do the best they can to stay focused on the speaker and his or her message.

There are a number of steps you can take to improve your skills of active listening. They include resisting distractions, not allowing yourself to be diverted by a speaker's appearance or delivery, suspending judgment until you have heard the speaker out, focusing your listening, and developing note-taking skills. We'll discuss each of these in turn.

active listening

Giving undivided attention to a speaker in a genuine effort to understand the speaker's point of view.

LISTENING SELF-EVALUATION

How often do you indulge in the following bad listening habits? Check yourself carefully in each one.

HABIT	FREQUENCY					SCORE
	Almost Always	Usually	Sometimes	Seldom	Almost Never	
1. Giving in to mental distractions	_____	_____	_____	_____	_____	_____
2. Giving in to physical distractions	_____	_____	_____	_____	_____	_____
3. Trying to recall everything a speaker says	_____	_____	_____	_____	_____	_____
4. Rejecting a topic as uninteresting before hearing the speaker	_____	_____	_____	_____	_____	_____
5. Faking paying attention	_____	_____	_____	_____	_____	_____
6. Jumping to conclusions about a speaker's meaning	_____	_____	_____	_____	_____	_____
7. Deciding a speaker is wrong before hearing everything she or he has to say	_____	_____	_____	_____	_____	_____
8. Judging a speaker on personal appearance	_____	_____	_____	_____	_____	_____
9. Not paying attention to a speaker's evidence	_____	_____	_____	_____	_____	_____
10. Focusing on delivery rather than on what the speaker says	_____	_____	_____	_____	_____	_____
					TOTAL	_____

How to score:
For every "almost always" checked, give yourself a score of   2
For every "usually" checked, give yourself a score of   4
For every "sometimes" checked, give yourself a score of   6
For every "seldom" checked, give yourself a score of   8
For every "almost never" checked, give yourself a score of   10

Total score interpretation:

Below 70	You need lots of training in listening.
From 71–90	You listen well.
Above 90	You listen exceptionally well.

Effective listeners take their task seriously. If you approach listening as an active process, you will significantly sharpen your powers of concentration and comprehension.

RESIST DISTRACTIONS

In an ideal world, we could eliminate all physical and mental distractions. In the real world, however, we cannot. Because we think so much faster than a speaker can talk, it's easy to let our attention wander. Sometimes it's very easy—when the room is too hot, when construction machinery is operating right outside the window, when the speaker is tedious. But our attention can stray even in the best of circumstances—if for no other reason than a failure to stay alert and make ourselves concentrate.

Whenever you find this happening, make a conscious effort to pull your mind back to what the speaker is saying. Then force it to stay there. One way to do this is to think ahead of the speaker—try to anticipate what will come next. This is not the same as jumping to conclusions. When you jump to conclusions, you put words into the speaker's mouth and don't listen to what is said. In this case you *will* listen—and measure what the speaker says against what you had anticipated.

Another way to keep your mind on a speech is to review mentally what the speaker has already said and make sure you understand it. Yet another is to listen between the lines and assess what a speaker implies verbally or says nonverbally with body language. Suppose a speaker is introducing someone to an audience. The speaker says, "It gives me great pleasure to present to you my very dear friend, Ashley Hauser." But the speaker doesn't shake hands with Ashley. He doesn't even look at her—just turns his back and leaves the podium. Is Ashley really his "very dear friend"? Certainly not.

Attentive listeners can pick up all kinds of clues to a speaker's real message. At first you may find it difficult to listen so intently. If you work at it, however, your concentration is bound to improve.

DON'T BE DIVERTED BY APPEARANCE OR DELIVERY

If you had attended Abraham Lincoln's momentous Cooper Union speech of 1860, this is what you would have seen:

> The long, ungainly figure upon which hung clothes that, while new for this trip, were evidently the work of an unskilled tailor; the large feet and clumsy hands, of which, at the outset, at least, the orator seemed to be unduly conscious; the long, gaunt head, capped by a shock of hair that seemed not to have been thoroughly brushed out, made a picture which did not fit in with New York's conception of a finished statesman.[11]

But although he seemed awkward and uncultivated, Lincoln had a powerful message about the moral evils of slavery. Fortunately, the audience at Cooper Union did not let his appearance stand in the way of his words.

Similarly, you must be willing to set aside preconceived judgments based on a person's looks or manner of speech. Gandhi was an unimpressive-looking man who often spoke dressed in a simple white cotton cloth. Renowned physicist Stephen Hawking is severely disabled and can speak only with the aid of a voice synthesizer. Yet imagine how much poorer the world would be if no one listened to them. Even though it may tax your tolerance, patience, and concentration, don't let negative feelings about a speaker's appearance or delivery keep you from listening to the message.

On the other hand, try not to be misled if the speaker has an unusually attractive appearance. It's all too easy to assume that because someone is good-looking and has a polished delivery, he or she is speaking eloquently. Some of the most unscrupulous speakers in history have been handsome people with hypnotic delivery skills. Again, be sure you respond to the message, not to the package it comes in.

SUSPEND JUDGMENT

Unless we listen only to people who think exactly as we do, we are going to hear things with which we disagree. When this happens, our natural inclination is to argue mentally with the speaker or to dismiss everything she or he says. But neither response is fair, and in both cases we blot out any chance of learning or being persuaded.

Does this mean you must agree with everything you hear? Not at all. It means you should hear people out *before* reaching a final judgment. Try to understand their point of view. Listen to their ideas, examine their evidence, assess their reasoning. *Then* make up your mind. The aim of active listening is to set aside "one's own prejudices, frames of reference, and desires so as to experience as far as possible the speaker's world from the inside."[12] It has been said more than once that a closed mind is an empty mind.

FOCUS YOUR LISTENING

As we have seen, skilled listeners do not try to absorb a speaker's every word. Rather, they focus on specific things in a speech. Here are three suggestions to help you focus your listening.

Listen for Main Points

Most speeches contain from two to four main points. Here, for example, are the main points of a recent speech by Jack Hayes, director of the U.S. National Weather Service:[13]

1. The past 50 years have witnessed a number of pioneering innovations in meteorology.

2. Today, meteorologists can provide better weather warnings than at any time in history.

3. Future advances in meteorology will require visionary ideas and economic resources.

These three main points are the heart of Hayes's message. As with any speech, they are the most important things to listen for.

Unless a speaker is terribly scatterbrained, you should be able to detect his or her main points with little difficulty. Often a speaker will give some idea at the outset of the main points to be discussed in the speech. For example, at the end of his introduction, Hayes said he was going to reflect on "where we were, where we are, and . . . where we go from here." As the speech progressed, Hayes moved from point to point with signposts such as "Let's take a brief look at how far we've come" and "What's on the horizon for us?" After this, only the most inattentive of listeners could have missed his main points.

Listen for Evidence

Identifying a speaker's main points, however, is not enough. You must also listen for supporting evidence. By themselves, Hayes's main points are only assertions. You may be inclined to believe them just because they come from an important meteorologist. Yet a careful listener will be concerned about evidence no matter who is speaking. Had you been listening to Hayes's speech, you would have heard him support his claims with a mass of verifiable evidence. Here is an excerpt:

Over the past 20 years, advances in science and technology have enabled us to increase public preparation for flash floods from 10 minutes to an hour and 10 minutes, a seven-fold improvement.

We've improved accuracy in hurricane-track forecasting. In 1970, 48-hour track error was about 250 nautical miles. In 2009, it was less than 100 nautical miles. In fact, our current average error at 96 hours is better than our 48-hour forecast was in 1970, giving coastal residents and businesses two more days to prepare for the likes of a hurricane Katrina.

There are four basic questions to ask about a speaker's evidence:

Is it *accurate*?

Is it taken from *objective* sources?

Is it *relevant* to the speaker's claims?

Is it *sufficient* to support the speaker's point?

In Hayes's case, the answer to each question is yes. His figures about meteorological advances are well established in the public record and can be verified by independent sources. The figures are clearly relevant to Hayes's claim that improvements in meteorology are saving lives and money, and they are sufficient to support that claim. If Hayes's evidence were inaccurate, biased, irrelevant, or insufficient, you should be wary of accepting his claim.

We shall discuss these—and other—tests of evidence in detail in Chapters 8 and 17. For now, it's enough to know that you should be on guard against unfounded assertions and sweeping generalizations. Keep an eye out for the speaker's evidence and for its accuracy, objectivity, relevance, and sufficiency.

Listen for Technique

We said earlier that you should not let a speaker's delivery distract you from the message, and this is true. However, if you want to become an effective speaker, you should study the methods other people use to speak effectively.

Analyze the introduction: What methods does the speaker use to gain attention, to relate to the audience, to establish credibility and goodwill? Assess the organization of the speech: Is it clear and easy to follow? Can you pick out the speaker's main points? Can you follow when the speaker moves from one point to another?

Study the speaker's language: Is it accurate, clear, vivid, appropriate? Does the speaker adapt well to the audience and occasion? Finally, diagnose the speaker's delivery: Is it fluent, dynamic, convincing? Does it strengthen or weaken the impact of the speaker's ideas? How well does the speaker use eye contact, gestures, and visual aids?

As you listen, focus on the speaker's strengths and weaknesses. If the speaker is not effective, try to determine why. If he or she is effective, try to pick out techniques you can use in your own speeches. If you listen in this way, you will be surprised by how much you can learn about successful speaking.

DEVELOP NOTE-TAKING SKILLS

Speech students are often amazed at how easily their teacher can pick out a speaker's main points, evidence, and techniques. Of course, the teacher knows what to listen for and has had plenty of practice. But the next time you get an opportunity, watch your teacher during a speech. Chances are she or he will be listening with a laptop or pen and paper. When note taking is done properly, it is a surefire way to improve your concentration and keep track of a speaker's ideas.

The key words here are *when done properly*. Unfortunately, many people don't take notes effectively. Some try to take down everything a speaker says. They view the enterprise as a race that pits their note-taking speed against the speaker's rate of speech. As the speaker starts to talk, the note taker starts to write or type. But soon the speaker is winning the race. In a desperate effort to keep up, the note taker tries to go faster and faster. But even this is not enough. The speaker pulls so far ahead that the note taker can never catch up.[14]

Some people go to the opposite extreme. They arrive armed with pen, laptop, and the best of intentions. They know they can't write down everything, so they wait for the speaker to say something that grabs their attention.

Research confirms that listening carefully and taking effective notes are vital skills for success in college. They will also benefit you in countless situations throughout life.

Every once in a while the speaker rewards them with a joke, a dramatic story, or a startling fact. Then the note taker records a few words and leans back to await the next fascinating tidbit. By the end of the lecture, the note taker has a set of tidbits—and little or no record of the speaker's important ideas.

As these examples illustrate, most inefficient note takers suffer from one or both of two problems: They don't know *what* to listen for, and they don't know *how* to record what they do listen for.[15] The solution to the first problem is to focus on a speaker's main points and evidence. But once you know what to listen for, you still need a sound method of note taking.

Although there are a number of systems, most students find the *key-word outline* best for listening to classroom lectures and formal speeches. As its name suggests, this method briefly notes a speaker's main points and supporting evidence in rough outline form. Suppose a speaker says:

> Hospitals in the United States are facing a serious shortage of nurses. According to the American Hospital Association, the nurse shortage nationwide has reached an alarming total of 135,000. What's worse, a recent article in *Health Affairs* projects that the shortage will reach 260,000 by 2025. Hospitals in major cities such as New York, Los Angeles, and Miami have had to reduce services because of a lack of nurses.
>
> There are four major causes for this shortage of nurses. One cause is that there are not enough faculty members at nursing schools to train the number of nurses needed by hospitals. A second cause is that nurses can find employment at medical facilities other than hospitals. A third cause is that many nurses are reluctant to stay on the job because of poor working hours that include nights, holidays, and weekends. A fourth cause is that nurses are burdened with excessive paperwork.

key-word outline

An outline that briefly notes a speaker's main points and supporting evidence in rough outline form.

A key-word note taker would record something like this:

Serious nurse shortage
    Total of 135,000
    260,000 by 2025
    Reduced services at hospitals

Four major causes
    Low faculty at nursing schools
    Employment available beyond hospitals
    Poor working hours
    Excessive paperwork

Notice how brief the notes are. Yet they accurately summarize the speaker's ideas. They are also very clear. By separating main points from subpoints and evidence, the outline format shows the relationships among the speaker's ideas.

Perfecting this—or any other—system of note taking requires practice. But with a little effort you should see results soon. As you become a better note taker, you will become a better listener. There is also a good chance you will become a better student. Research confirms that students who take effective notes usually receive higher grades than those who do not.[16]

Summary

Most people are poor listeners. Even when we think we are listening carefully, we usually grasp only half of what we hear, and we retain even less. Improving your listening skills can be helpful in every part of your life, including speechmaking.

The most important cause of poor listening is giving in to distractions and letting our thoughts wander. Sometimes, however, we listen too hard. We try to remember every word a speaker says, and we lose the main message by concentrating on details. In other situations, we may jump to conclusions and prejudge a speaker without hearing out the message. Finally, we often judge people by their appearance or speaking manner instead of listening to what they say.

You can overcome these poor listening habits by taking several steps. First, take listening seriously and commit yourself to becoming a better listener. Second, work at being an active listener. Give your undivided attention to the speaker in a genuine effort to understand her or his ideas. Third, resist distractions. Make a conscious effort to keep your mind on what the speaker is saying. Fourth, try not to be diverted by appearance or delivery. Set aside preconceived judgments based on a person's looks or manner of speech.

Fifth, suspend judgment until you have heard the speaker's entire message. Sixth, focus your listening by paying attention to main points, to evidence, and to the speaker's techniques. Finally, develop your note-taking skills. When done properly, note taking is an excellent way to improve your concentration and to keep track of a speaker's ideas.

Key Terms

hearing *(48)*

listening *(48)*

appreciative listening *(49)*

empathic listening *(49)*

comprehensive listening *(49)*

critical listening *(49)*

spare "brain time" *(50)*

active listening *(53)*

key-word outline *(59)*

Review Questions

After reading this chapter, you should be able to answer the following questions:

1. What is the difference between hearing and listening?
2. How is listening connected with critical thinking?
3. Why is it important to develop strong listening skills?
4. What are the four main causes of poor listening?
5. What are seven ways to become a better listener?

connect

For further review, go to the LearnSmart study module for this chapter.

Exercises for Critical Thinking

1. Which of the four causes of poor listening discussed in this chapter do you consider the most important? Choose a specific case of poor listening in which you were involved. Explain what went wrong.
2. Using the Listening Self-Evaluation Worksheet on page 54, undertake a candid evaluation of your major strengths and weaknesses as a listener. Explain what steps you need to take to become a better listener.
3. Watch the lead story this week on *60 Minutes, Dateline,* or *20/20*. Using the key-word outline method of note taking, record the main ideas of the story.
4. Choose a lecture in one of your other classes. Analyze what the lecturer does most effectively. Identify three things the lecturer could do better to help students keep track of the lecture.

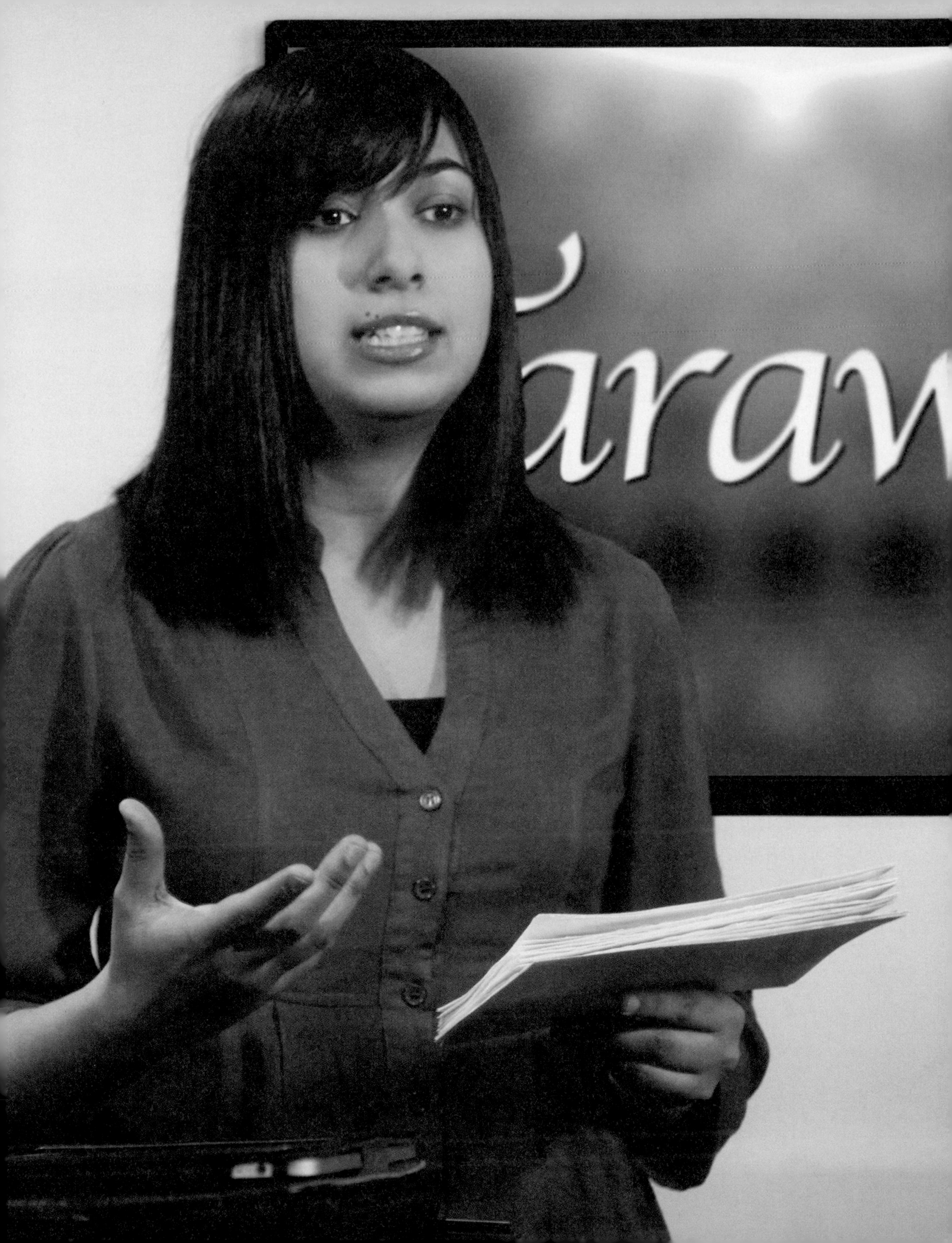

4

Giving Your First Speech

Preparing Your Speech

Delivering Your Speech

Sample Speeches with Commentary

You may be surprised to learn that one of the first assignments in your class is to give a speech. You say to yourself, "What am I going to do? I have barely started this course, yet I'm supposed to stand up in front of everyone and give a speech! I've only read a few pages in the textbook, and I don't know much about public speaking. Where do I begin?"

If these are your thoughts, you aren't alone. Most beginning speech students have a similar reaction. Fortunately, giving your first speech sounds a lot harder than it is. The purpose of this chapter is to help you get started on preparing and delivering your speech. Later chapters will expand on the subjects discussed here and will apply them to different kinds of speeches.

Preparing Your Speech

Usually a brief, simple presentation, the first assignment is often called an ice breaker speech because it is designed to "break the ice" by getting students up in front of the class as soon as possible. This is an important step because much of the anxiety associated with public speaking comes from lack of experience giving speeches. Once you have broken the ice by giving a speech, you will feel less anxious and will have taken the first step on the road to confidence.

DEVELOPING THE SPEECH

There are a number of possible assignments for the first speech. One is a speech of self-introduction that provides insight into the speaker's background, personality, beliefs, or goals. In other cases, students are asked to introduce a classmate, rather than themselves. Some instructors require yet a different kind of speech. Make sure you understand exactly what your instructor requires.

Focusing Your Topic

No matter what kind of introductory speech you are assigned, be sure to focus your presentation sharply so it conforms to the assigned time limit. One of the most common mistakes students make on their first speech is trying to cover too much.

It would be impossible, for example, to tell your audience everything about your life in a two- or three-minute speech. A better approach would be to focus on one or two events that have helped define who you are—competing in the state track meet, tutoring disadvantaged children, getting your first job, and the like. This allows you to make a few well-developed points about a clearly defined subject.

On the other hand, avoid the temptation to narrow the focus of your topic too much. Few listeners would be pleased to hear a two- or three-minute discussion of advanced trumpet-playing techniques. Such a speech would be too specialized for most classroom audiences.

Developing Your Topic

Once you have a topic for your speech, be creative in developing it. Think of ways to structure the speech so it will be interesting and meaningful to your audience. Look, for example, at the sample speeches with commentary at the end of this chapter. The first speaker explains aspects of his personality by referring to three of the apps on his cell phone. The second speaker uses the notion of a fork in the road when introducing one of her classmates. In both cases, the speakers found a creative way to frame their information.

Another possibility is to think of ways you can make your presentation mysterious or suspenseful. Suppose you are telling the audience about meeting a celebrity, visiting a famous place, or participating in a newsworthy event. Rather than identifying the celebrity at the outset, you might save his or her name for the end of your speech. As your story unfolds, tantalize your classmates with clues about your celebrity's gender, physical characteristics, special talents, and the like, but keep the name secret until the last moment.

Audiences are also interested in dangerous situations, adventure, and drama. If your task is to introduce a fellow student, find out if she or he has ever been in danger. Suppose your classmate was caught in a flood or spent

Your first speech provides a foundation for speeches you will give later. As you develop your skills, you will find yourself able to speak confidently and with strong eye contact in class and out.

a year in Africa with the Peace Corps. The details would make excellent material for a speech.

If you think about it, every person has faced risk, done the unusual, or triumphed over hardship. Try to find ways to include such fascinating experiences in your speech.

You can also make your speech interesting by using colorful, descriptive language. One speaker used this technique when introducing a fellow student, named Alexa, to the class. The speaker began by saying:

> The spotlight shines. The music blares. The crowd cheers. The colors, bright and vibrant, bleed together as Alexa and her partner sail around the dance floor. Her partner touches her hand and her waist, but only briefly. He then spins her away, and she glides across the floor in what seems like a single motion. Alexa has worked many weeks for this moment. Alexa, you see, is a championship ballroom dancer.

connect

View the introduction from "Gotta Dance" in the online Media Library for this chapter (Video 4.1).

The speaker could have said, "Alexa is a terrific ballroom dancer and finds it quite thrilling." Instead, the speaker painted a word picture so listeners could visualize the dance floor, the brilliant colors of the costumes, and the excitement of the competition as Alexa and her partner perform in perfect symmetry. Colorful and concrete illustrations like this are always more interesting than dull language and abstract generalizations.

You might wonder whether you should use humor to make your first speech entertaining. Audiences love witty remarks, jokes, and funny situations, but like anything else, humor is effective only when done well. It should flow naturally out of the speech content rather than being contrived. If you are not normally a funny person, you are better off giving a sincere, enthusiastic speech and leaving out the jokes. In no case should you include humor that involves obscenity, embarrasses individuals, or negatively stereotypes groups of people. The best kind of humor gently pokes fun at ourselves or at universal human foibles.

ORGANIZING THE SPEECH

Regardless of your topic, a speech usually has three main parts—an introduction, a body, and a conclusion. In Chapter 10, we will discuss each of these parts in detail. Here we focus on what you need to know about them as you prepare your introductory speech.

Introduction

introduction

The opening section of a speech.

Your first job in the introduction is to get the attention and interest of the audience. You can do this by posing a question, telling a story, making a startling statement, or opening with a quotation. The purpose of all these methods is to create a dramatic, colorful opening that will make your audience want to hear more.

For an example, look at the speech excerpt on Video 4.2 in the online Media Library for this chapter. The speaker's assignment was to present a narrative about a significant experience in his life. This is how he began:

connect

View the beginning of "The Secret" in the online Media Library for this chapter (Video 4.2).

> I never knew the secret until I took a year off from school, traveled halfway around the world, and lived for a year in Thailand. I was there to teach English, but the trip ended up being much more than a job. It was a voyage of discovery. I didn't know exactly what I would find, but I came home with a truly valuable secret.

After this introduction, the audience was eager to hear more about the speaker's secret.

In addition to gaining attention and interest, the introduction should orient your listeners toward the subject matter of your speech. In the longer speeches you will give later in the term, you will usually need to provide an explicit preview statement that identifies the main points to be discussed in the body of your speech. (For example, "Today I will inform you about the symptoms, causes, and treatment of sleep apnea.")

Because your introductory speech is so short, you may not need a detailed preview statement. But you still need to give your audience a clear sense of your topic and purpose. (Be sure to check with your instructor to see what kind of preview statement he or she prefers for the introductory speech.)

Body

body

The main section of a speech.

After getting the audience's attention and revealing your topic, you are ready to move into the body of your speech. In some speeches, the body seems to organize itself. If you are telling a story about a significant experience in your life, you will relate the events chronologically, in the order they occurred.

chronological order

A method of speech organization in which the main points follow a time pattern.

But not all speeches follow such a format. Suppose you have been asked to give a presentation introducing a classmate. You could organize the most important biographical facts about your subject in chronological order, but this might result in a dull, superficial speech: "Maria was born in Los Angeles in 1993, attended elementary school from 1998 to 2005, and graduated from high school in 2011."

topical order

A method of speech organization in which the main points divide the topic into logical and consistent subtopics.

A better way of structuring your remarks might be to discuss three of the most important aspects of Maria's life, such as hobbies, career goals, and family. This is called the topical method of organization, which subdivides the speech topic into its natural, logical, or conventional parts. Although there are many other ways to organize a speech, your first presentation will probably use either chronological or topical order.

Regardless of the method of organization you use, remember to limit the number of main points in the body of your speech. In a two-minute presentation, you won't have time to develop more than two or three main points.

Once you have selected those points, make sure each one focuses on a single aspect of the topic. For example, if your first point concerns your classmate's hometown, don't introduce irrelevant information about her job or favorite music. Save this material for a separate point, or cut it.

Try to make your main points stand out by introducing each with a transition statement. In a speech about a classmate, you might begin the first main point by saying:

Rico's family moved a great deal throughout his childhood.

When you reach the second point, you might introduce it like this:

Moving a lot led to Rico's outgoing nature and confidence in making friends. In fact, he has friends all around the world with whom he corresponds regularly over Facebook.

You have now let your audience know that the first main point is over and that you are starting the second one. The third main point might begin as follows:

Corresponding with people all over the world is more than just a hobby for Rico, since he is majoring in international relations.

Transitions such as these will help your audience keep track of your main points.

Conclusion

When you finish discussing your final point, you will be ready to move into your conclusion. You need to accomplish two tasks in this part of the speech: let the audience know you are about to finish and reinforce your central idea.

If possible, end on a dramatic, clever, or thought-provoking note. For example, when talking about his "secret" in the speech mentioned earlier, the student devoted the body of his presentation to explaining his experiences in Thailand and how they opened his eyes to the universality of human experience. Then, in his conclusion, he wrapped up by saying:

I needed to be in an entirely different culture to learn the secret—that despite differences in ancestry, language, history, and religion, human beings are pretty much the same wherever they might be. I thought I was going to meet people who were totally alien to me. Instead, I found that family, friendship, kindness, and community are as important on one side of the world as on the other.

The final lines end the speech on a strong note and underscore why the speaker's time in Thailand was so important.

Delivering Your Speech

Once you have selected a subject and organized the content into a clear structure, it is time to work on the delivery of your speech. Because this is your first speech of the term, no one expects you to give a perfectly polished

main points

The major points developed in the body of a speech.

transition

A word or phrase that indicates when a speaker has finished one thought and is moving on to another.

conclusion

The final section of a speech.

connect

View the ending of "The Secret" in the online Media Library for this chapter (Video 4.3).

When developing your first speech, plan what you want to say, organize the material clearly, practice thoroughly, and use the extemporaneous method of delivery. You may be surprised at how much you enjoy the experience.

presentation. Your aim is to do as well as possible while laying a foundation you can build upon in later speeches. With this is mind, we'll look briefly at the extemporaneous method of speech delivery, the importance of rehearsing your speech, and some of the major factors to consider when speech day arrives.

SPEAKING EXTEMPORANEOUSLY

You might be inclined, as are many beginning speakers, to write out your speech like an essay and read it word for word to your listeners. The other extreme is to prepare very little for the speech—to wing it by trusting to your wits and the inspiration of the moment. Neither approach is appropriate.

Most experts recommend speaking extemporaneously, which combines the careful preparation and structure of a manuscript presentation with the spontaneity and enthusiasm of an unrehearsed talk. Your aim in an extemporaneous speech is to plan your major points and supporting material without trying to memorize the precise language you will use on the day of the speech.

The extemporaneous method requires you to know the content of your speech quite well. In fact, when you use this method properly, you become so familiar with the substance of your talk that you need only a few brief notes to remind you of the points you intend to cover. The notes should consist of key words or phrases, rather than complete sentences and paragraphs. This way, when you are in front of the audience, you will tell them what you know about the topic in your own words.

Prepare your notes by writing or printing key terms and phrases on index cards or sheets of paper. Some instructors require students to use index cards because they are small and unobtrusive, don't rustle or flop over, and can be held in one hand, which allows the speaker to gesture more easily. Other teachers recommend sheets of paper because you can get more information on them and because it is easier to print out computer files on paper. If you are unsure what your instructor prefers, ask well before your speech is due.

Whether you use index cards or sheets of paper, your notes should be large enough to read clearly at arm's length. Many experienced speakers double- or triple-space their notes because this makes them easier to see at a glance. Write or print on only one side of the index card or paper, and use the fewest notes you can manage and still present the speech fluently and confidently.

You can see an example of extemporaneous delivery on Video 4.4 in the online Media Library for this chapter. The student is giving a speech of self-introduction using a personal object—in this case, a softball glove—to explain something important about herself. As you view the excerpt, notice that even though the speaker's points are well planned, she is not tied to a manuscript. When talking about her glove, she sets down her notes and points to things on the glove that reflect different aspects of her life. All the while, she speaks directly to her classmates and makes strong eye contact with them.

At first, it may seem very demanding to deliver a speech extemporaneously. In fact, though, you use the extemporaneous method in everyday conversation. Do you read from a manuscript when you tell your friends an amusing story? Of course not. You recall the essential details of your story and tell the tale to different friends, on different occasions, using somewhat different language each time. You feel relaxed and confident with your friends, so you just tell them what is on your mind in a conversational tone. Try to do the same thing in your speech.

connect

View an excerpt from "A Heart Worn on My Hand" in the online Media Library for this chapter (Video 4.4).

REHEARSING THE SPEECH

When you watch a truly effective extemporaneous speaker, the speech comes out so smoothly that it seems almost effortless. In fact, that smooth delivery is the result of a great deal of practice. As your speech course progresses, you will gain more experience and will become more comfortable delivering your speeches extemporaneously.

The first time you rehearse your introductory speech, however, you will probably struggle. Words may not come easily, and you may forget some things you planned to say. Don't become discouraged. Keep going and complete the speech as well as you can. Concentrate on gaining control of the ideas rather than on trying to learn the speech word for word. You will improve every time you practice.

For this approach to work, you must rehearse the speech out loud. Looking silently over your notes is not enough. Speaking the words aloud will help you master the content of your talk. Once you have a fairly good grasp of the speech, ask friends or family members to listen and to give constructive feedback. Don't be shy about asking. Most people love to give their opinion about something, and it's crucial that you rehearse with a live audience before presenting the speech in class.

As you practice, time your speech to make sure it is neither too long nor too short. Because of nerves, most people talk faster during their first speech than when they practice it. When you rehearse at home, make certain your speech runs slightly longer than the minimum time limit. That way, if your speaking rate increases when you get in front of your classmates, your speech won't end up being too short.

PRESENTING THE SPEECH

Delivering your first speech can be a nerve-wracking experience. As your class proceeds and you gain more experience, your confidence (and skill) will grow by leaps and bounds. We will take a detailed look at speech delivery in Chapter 13, but here are a few things to concentrate on in your first presentation.

Starting Your Speech

When it is your turn to speak, move to the front of the room and face the audience. Assume a relaxed but upright posture. Plant your feet a bit less than shoulder-width apart and allow your arms to hang loosely by your side. Arrange your notes before you start to speak. Then take a moment to look over your audience and to smile. This will help you establish rapport with your classmates from the start.

Gestures

gestures

Motions of a speaker's hands or arms during a speech.

Once you are into the speech, feel free to use your hands to gesture, but don't try to plan all your gestures ahead of time. If you don't normally use your hands expressively during informal conversation, you shouldn't feel compelled to gesture a lot during your speech. Whatever gestures you do use should flow naturally from your feelings.

Above all, don't let your gestures or bodily actions distract listeners from your message. Do your best to avoid nervous mannerisms such as twisting your hair, wringing your hands, shifting your weight from one foot to the other, rocking back and forth, or tapping your fingers on the lectern. No matter how nervous you feel, try to appear calm and relaxed.

Eye Contact

eye contact

Direct visual contact with the eyes of another person.

During your talk, look at your classmates as often as you can. One of the major reasons for speaking extemporaneously is to maintain eye contact with your audience. In your own experience, you know how much more impressive a speaker is when she or he looks at the audience while speaking.

If you have practiced the extemporaneous method of delivery and prepared your notes properly, you should be able to maintain eye contact with your audience most of the time. Be sure to look to the left and right of the room, as well as to the center, and avoid the temptation to speak exclusively to one or two sympathetic individuals.

If you are too nervous to look your classmates directly in the eye, try looking just to the side of each person, or just above his or her head. In this way, you will convey a sense of eye contact while easing your nerves.

Voice

Try to use your voice as expressively as you would in normal conversation. Concentrate on projecting to the back of the room and, despite your nerves, fight the temptation to race through your speech. If you make a conscious effort to speak up, slow down, and project clearly, you will be on the right track to an effective presentation.

Look, for example, at Video 4.5 in the online Media Library for this chapter, which presents excerpts from two ice breaker speeches. Neither speaker had taken a public speaking class before, yet both rose to the occasion by focusing on the basic elements of delivery we have just discussed. As you watch the video, notice how both—despite their nervousness—convey a sense of poise and confidence, establish strong eye contact with their classmates, and use the extemporaneous method of delivery. Work on doing the same in your first speech.

connect

View excerpts from "Rhymes with Orange" and "My Life from Toe to Head" in the online Media Library for this chapter (Video 4.5).

Dealing with Nerves

As we saw in Chapter 1, it's normal to be nervous before delivering a speech of any kind. By applying the tips presented in that chapter for managing stage fright, you can stand up for your speech primed for success.

If you have butterflies in your stomach while you wait to go to the lectern, sit quietly in your chair and take several slow, deep breaths. You can also help reduce your tension by tightening and relaxing your leg muscles, or by squeezing your hands together and then releasing them. Keep in mind that while you may be anxious about giving your speech, usually your nervousness will not be visible to your audience.

All the topics discussed in this chapter are developed in much more detail in the rest of this book. For now, keep your introductory assignment in perspective. Remember that neither your audience nor your instructor expects perfection. You are not a professional speaker, and this is the first speech of the class. Do your best on the assignment and have fun with it. Plan what you want to say, organize the material clearly, practice thoroughly, and use the extemporaneous method of delivery. You may be surprised by how much you enjoy giving your first speech.

Sample Speeches with Commentary

The following presentations were prepared by students in beginning speech classes at the University of Wisconsin. The first is a speech of self-introduction; the second is a speech introducing a classmate. As you read the speeches, notice how clearly they are organized and how creatively they are developed. You can watch the delivery of both speeches in the online Media Library for this chapter.

connect

View "There's an App for That" and "Fork in the Road" in the online Media Library for this chapter (Videos 4.6 and 4.7).

There's an App for That

The introduction captures attention and reveals the topic. By answering questions with the phrase "There's an app for that," the speaker provides a creative touch that runs through the entire speech. He ends the introduction by previewing the points he will discuss in the body.

A Portuguese dictionary? There's an app for that. How to cook so she's impressed? Yeah, there's an app for that. A game to play when class gets boring? There's an app for that, too. But is there an app for me, Michael Taylor? I'd like to think there are a few. Some of the things that make me who I am can be found by looking at the Photobucket, ESPN, and Pandora apps on my iPhone.

Each main point in the body is clearly stated and discussed. As you can see from the online video, the speaker communicates sincerely and with good eye contact. His wry sense of humor about his family adds a nice touch.

The first app you'd find would be Photobucket, which my little sister made me download. It holds the newest photos of life back home and allows my sister to share her photography talents with me. My family is warm and caring, and half the time they drive me nuts, but what is family for anyway? I know I can turn to them for anything, and I feel very lucky to have grown up in a family where there was always someone to support me.

As the speech proceeds, notice how the speaker uses his favorite apps to provide insight into his life, rather than to talk about the apps themselves.

Because I'm an athlete, I'd be lost without my ESPN Score-Center app. It gives me up-to-the-minute scores on any sport. I played football, baseball, and basketball in high school, and I would rather be on a team than compete by myself. Through sports, I have learned the importance of being part of something bigger than myself. I've also learned how to lose with dignity and how to win with class.

The speaker completes the body by explaining his love of music. Information about activities and hobbies is often included in a speech of self-introduction.

Finally, there's the Pandora app, which makes it super easy to explore new songs and groups. I've been involved with music ever since I started playing piano as a kid. Now I play jazz guitar, and I sing. While in high school, I performed with a couple of groups around the Twin Cities, and I really enjoyed it. As for here in Madison, I'm still looking for opportunities to showcase my talents.

The conclusion summarizes the speaker's main points. It then ties the entire speech together by returning to the question asked in the introduction and answering it with one last refrain of "There's an app for that."

So, through the Photobucket, ESPN, and Pandora apps I can answer my initial question: Is there really an app for Michael Taylor? Yeah, there's an app for that.

Fork in the Road

This paragraph is the speaker's introduction. The opening quotation gains attention, while the next sentence relates the quotation to the speaker's audience. Then the speaker identifies the central idea by noting that her classmate Bethany is facing her own fork in the road.

Inspirational speaker Liz Murray once said, a "fork in the road happens over a hundred times a day, and the choices you make will determine the shape of your life." At one point or another, we all come to that fork in the road, when we are forced to choose between two paths, not sure where either will lead. Our classmate Bethany is now at that point, forced to decide between her two passions: art and medicine.

The body of this speech contains two main points, each of which deals with a possible direction for Bethany's life. The first focuses on her passion for art. As is evident from the online video, the speaker presents her ideas extemporaneously. She has strong eye contact, excellent vocal variety, and a personable manner of delivery.

From an early age, Bethany has been passionate about art. She has been drawing since the age of three and has continued to improve her skills ever since. Over the years, she has won many awards for her drawings, including the Wisconsin Scholastic Art Award. Bethany draws people, places, and things that she sees on a daily basis in the world around her. Drawing allows her to relax and to escape from the stress of life. And now, because of her passion, she is considering making art her career.

The second main point deals with Bethany's passion for medicine. The story of J.C. explains why Bethany is so interested in medicine as a possible career. When well delivered, stories are an excellent way to make ideas concrete and to get listeners involved in a speech.

In addition to art, however, Bethany is also passionate about medicine. She dreams about one day doing medical mission work in Africa. She is motivated in part by her friend J.C., a Rwanda refugee whose leg was severely injured in an explosion about ten years ago. For eight years, J.C. lived with bomb-shell fragments in his lower leg. It was only two years ago, when he and his mother moved to the United States, that he was finally able to have surgery. Bethany's friendship with J.C. has inspired her to help those who lack sufficient medical care and to make her think that a career in medicine is right for her.

The speaker concludes by restating the central theme of her speech. Echoing language from the introduction gives the speech a strong sense of unity. The final words end on a positive note by stating that whichever path Bethany chooses, it will be "a road to success."

It can be said that Bethany has reached her fork in the road. She has a passion for drawing and a passion for medicine. Will she choose to follow her love for art and pursue a career as an artist? Or will she choose to follow her love for medical mission work and pursue a career as a doctor? It's hard to know right now, but either path Bethany chooses will surely be a road to success.

Summary

The purpose of this chapter is to help you get ready for your ice breaker speech. Later chapters will look more closely at all the aspects of speech preparation and delivery discussed here.

Once you know the exact assignment for your ice breaker speech, you can start working out your ideas. Focus on a limited number of main points and develop them creatively. Your speech will have three parts—introduction, body, and conclusion. Use transition statements to help the audience keep track of your points as the speech progresses.

Your teacher will probably ask you to deliver the speech extemporaneously. This means that the speech is carefully prepared in advance, but the exact language is chosen at the moment of delivery. To be successful, you will need to rehearse the speech multiple times to make sure you have full command of it.

When speech day comes, you will almost surely have butterflies in your stomach. Remember that nervousness is normal. Concentrate on communicating with your audience, rather than on worrying about your nerves. Try to appear calm and relaxed on the outside, no matter how you feel on the inside. Establish eye contact with the audience, use your voice expressively, and make sure your gestures and mannerisms do not distract from your message.

Key Terms

ice breaker speech *(64)*

introduction *(66)*

body *(66)*

chronological order *(66)*

topical order *(66)*

main points *(67)*

transition *(67)*

conclusion *(67)*

extemporaneous speech *(68)*

gestures *(70)*

eye contact *(70)*

Review Questions

connect

For further review, go to the LearnSmart study module for this chapter.

After reading this chapter, you should be able to answer the following questions:

1. What two major steps are discussed in this chapter for developing your introductory speech?

2. When organizing your introductory speech, you should divide it into what three sections?

3. What method of delivery does this chapter recommend for your introductory speech?

4. What steps should you take when rehearsing your first speech?

5. What five elements of speech delivery are discussed in this chapter with regard to presenting your first speech?

1. Examine the two sample speeches with commentary on pages 72–73. Choose one, and answer the following questions about it.

   a. How does the opening paragraph gain the attention of the audience, introduce the subject of the speech, and preview the main points to be discussed in the body?

   b. How clearly is the body of the speech organized? What does the speaker do to help listeners follow the progression of ideas?

   c. How does the speaker conclude? Does the conclusion reinforce the central theme of the speech?

2. Are there occasions outside the classroom on which you might give a speech of self-introduction? Identify such an occasion and explain how you might apply the principles of introductory speeches discussed in this chapter.

5

Selecting a Topic and a Purpose

Choosing a Topic

Determining the General Purpose

Determining the Specific Purpose

Phrasing the Central Idea

As you read through this book, you will find examples of hundreds of speeches that were delivered in classrooms, in the political arena, in community and business situations. Here is a very small sample of the topics they cover:

acupuncture	Native American casinos
breast cancer	obsessive-compulsive disorder
Cesar Chavez	phony pharmaceuticals
Everglades	Québec
free trade	Ramadan
Great Wall	school vouchers
Habitat for Humanity	Underground Railroad
identity theft	women's gymnastics
Jerusalem	x-rays
laser surgery	Yellowstone
Martin Luther King	zoos

Undoubtedly you noticed that the list runs from A to Z. This array of topics wasn't planned. It happened naturally in the course of presenting many different kinds of speeches. The list is given here to show you that there are literally endless possibilities for speech topics—from A to Z.

Choosing a Topic

topic

The subject of a speech.

The first step in speechmaking is choosing a topic. For speeches outside the classroom this is seldom a problem. Usually the speech topic is determined by the occasion, the audience, and the speaker's qualifications. When Bill Clinton lectures at a college campus, he often speaks about global citizenship. Christine Amanpour will discuss women and journalism. Stephen Colbert might share his views on current events. The same is true of ordinary citizens. The doctor is asked to inform high-school athletes and their parents about sports injuries, the head of a neighborhood coalition speaks about zoning regulations, the florist discusses how to grow thriving houseplants.

In a public speaking class, the situation is different. Students generally have great leeway in selecting topics. This would appear to be an advantage, since it allows you to talk about matters of personal interest. Yet there may be no facet of speech preparation that causes more gnashing of teeth than selecting a topic.

It is a constant source of amazement to teachers that students who regularly chat with their friends about almost any subject under the sun become mentally paralyzed when faced with the task of deciding what to talk about in their speech class. Fortunately, once you get over this initial paralysis, you should have little trouble choosing a good topic.

There are two broad categories of potential topics for your classroom speeches: (1) subjects you know a lot about and (2) subjects you want to know more about. Let's start with the first.

TOPICS YOU KNOW A LOT ABOUT

Most people speak best about subjects with which they are most familiar. When thinking about a topic, draw on your own knowledge and experience. Everyone knows things or has done things that can be used in a speech.

Think for a moment about unusual experiences you may have had or special expertise you may have acquired. One student, who grew up in Turkey, presented a fascinating speech about daily life in that country. Another used her knowledge as a jewelry store salesperson to prepare a speech on how to judge the value of cut diamonds. A third student, who had lived through a tornado, gave a gripping speech about that terrifying experience.

Too dramatic? Nothing in your life is as interesting? Yet another student, who described herself as "just a housewife who is returning to school to finish the education she started 20 years ago," delivered a witty speech on the adjustments she had to make in coming back to college—sitting in class with students young enough to be her children, balancing her academic work against her family commitments, and the satisfaction of completing the education she had begun years earlier.

When you look for a speech topic, keep in mind special expertise you may have or sports, hobbies, travel, and other personal experiences that would make for an interesting presentation.

Here are a few more examples of speech topics based largely on the students' personal knowledge and experience:

Interning at a Crime Lab

The Basics of Backpacking

Performing with the Native American Dance Troupe

How to Have a Successful Job Interview

TOPICS YOU WANT TO KNOW MORE ABOUT

On the other hand, you may decide to make your speech a learning experience for yourself as well as for your audience. You may choose a subject about which you already have some knowledge or expertise but not enough to prepare a speech without doing additional research. You may even select a topic that you want to explore for the first time. Say, for example, you've always been interested in Stonehenge but never knew much about it. This would be a perfect opportunity to research a fascinating subject and turn it into a fascinating speech.

Or suppose you run across a subject in one of your other classes that catches your fancy. Why not investigate it further for your speech class? One student used this approach to develop a speech on the subject of neuromarketing, which uses recent advancements in neuroscience to study the way people respond to products and promotions. After hearing about the subject in her marketing class, the student researched the topic further. In the process, she learned that neuromarketing is currently being used by some of the biggest corporations in the world. Using what she learned in her research, she put together a captivating speech that kept everyone's attention from beginning to end.

connect

View an excerpt from "Neuromarketing: Whispers of the Brain" in the online Media Library for this chapter (Video 5.1).

Still another possibility—especially for persuasive speeches—is to think of subjects about which you hold strong opinions and beliefs. They may include national or international concerns such as gun control or climate change. Or perhaps you are closely involved in a local issue such as a school board election or a proposal to build a new student center. Not all such topics must be "political." They can deal with anything from graduation requirements to helping people with physical disabilities, from dormitory regulations to building a church recreation center.

BRAINSTORMING FOR TOPICS

After all this, you may still be thinking, "I *don't* care about neuromarketing. I've *never* been to Turkey. I'm *not* active in politics. WHAT am I going to talk about?" If you are having trouble selecting a topic, there are a number of brainstorming procedures you can follow to get started.

Personal Inventory

First, make a quick inventory of your experiences, interests, hobbies, skills, beliefs, and so forth. Jot down anything that comes to mind, no matter how silly or irrelevant it may seem. From this list may come a general subject area out of which you can fashion a specific topic. This method has worked for many students.

Clustering

If the first method doesn't work, try a technique called clustering. Take a sheet of paper and divide it into nine columns as follows: People, Places, Things, Events, Processes, Concepts, Natural Phenomena, Problems, and Plans and Policies. Then list in each column the first four or five items that come to mind. The result might look like this:

People	Places	Things
Barack Obama	Afghanistan	iPad
Hillary Clinton	Grand Canyon	Twitter
Sarah Palin	the moon	3-D TV
Lady Gaga	my hometown	movies

Events	Processes
graduation	learning CPR
Passover	cooking Indian food
Chinese New Year	avoiding credit-card debt
Cinco de Mayo	writing a job resumé

Concepts	Natural Phenomena
conservatism	asteroids
medical ethics	lightning
free-speech theories	tornadoes
Buddhism	earthquakes

brainstorming

A method of generating ideas for speech topics by free association of words and ideas.

Problems	Plans and Policies
national debt	offshore drilling
terrorism	charter schools
election fraud	domestic partner benefits
campus crime	immigration reform

Very likely, several items on your lists will strike you as potential topics. If not, take the items you find most intriguing and compose sublists for each. Try to free-associate. Write down a word or idea. What does that trigger in your mind? Whatever it is, write that down next, and keep going until you have four or five ideas on your list. For example, working from the lists printed above, one student composed sublists for movies, campus crime, and lightning:

connect

For an additional resource on speech topics, check the Topic Helper under the Library tab in Connect.

Movies	Campus Crime	Lightning
Academy Awards	police	thunder
prizes	fingerprints	noise
lotteries	hands	traffic
gambling	gloves	air pollution

Can you follow her trail of association? In the first column, movies made her think of the Academy Awards. The Academy Awards are prizes. Prizes reminded her of lotteries. Lotteries are a form of gambling. Suddenly, this student remembered an article she had read on the problem of gambling addiction in America. The idea clicked in her mind. After considerable research, she developed an excellent speech titled "Gambling Addiction: Why You Can't Beat the Odds."

That's a far cry from movies! If you started out free-associating from movies, you would doubtless end up somewhere completely different. This is what clustering is all about.

Internet Search

By clustering, most people come up with a topic rather quickly. But if you are still stymied, try an Internet search. Browse through a subject-based Web site, an online encyclopedia, or some other reference portal until you come across what might be a good topic. As an experiment, one student scanned the *Merriam-Webster Online Dictionary,* limiting herself to the letter *m*. Within 10 minutes, she had come up with these potential topics:

magic	minimum wage	Medal of Honor	middle ear
Madrid	moon	martial arts	muscular dystrophy
monarchy	meteorite	maple syrup	Mardi Gras
marriage	Marine Corps	mushroom	Mafia

Whatever the means you use for selecting a topic, *start early.* Pay attention to interesting subjects in conversation, on television and the Internet, in newspapers and magazines. Jot down ideas for topics as they occur to you.

Having an inventory of possible topics to choose from is much better than having to rack your brain for one at the last minute. If you get an early start on choosing a topic, you will have plenty of time to pick just the right one and prepare a first-rate speech.

Determining the General Purpose

general purpose

The broad goal of a speech.

Along with choosing a topic, you need to determine the general purpose of your speech. Usually it will fall into one of two overlapping categories—to inform or to persuade.

When your general purpose is to inform, you act as a teacher or lecturer. Your goal is to convey information clearly, accurately, and interestingly. If you describe how to lift weights, narrate the major events of the latest Middle East crisis, or report on your sorority's financial position, you are speaking to inform. Your aim is to enhance the knowledge and understanding of your listeners—to give them information they did not have before.

When your general purpose is to persuade, you act as an advocate or a partisan. You go beyond giving information to espousing a cause. You want to *change* or *structure* the attitudes or actions of your audience. If you try to convince your listeners that they should start a regular program of weight lifting, that the United States should modify its policy in the Middle East, or that your sorority should start a fund-raising drive to balance its budget, then you are speaking to persuade. In doing so, you cannot help but give information, but your primary goal is to win over your listeners to your point of view—to get them to believe something or do something as a result of your speech.

In speech classes, the general purpose is usually specified as part of the speech assignment. For speeches outside the classroom, however, you have to make sure of your general purpose yourself. Usually this is easy to do. Are you going to explain, report, or demonstrate something? Then your general purpose is to inform. Are you going to sell, advocate, or defend something? Then your general purpose is to persuade. But no matter what the situation, you must be certain of exactly what you hope to achieve by speaking.

Determining the Specific Purpose

specific purpose

A single infinitive phrase that states precisely what a speaker hopes to accomplish in his or her speech.

Once you have chosen a topic and a general purpose, you must narrow your choices to determine the specific purpose of your speech. The specific purpose should focus on one aspect of a topic. You should be able to state your specific purpose in a single infinitive phrase (to inform my audience about . . . ; to persuade my audience to . . .) that indicates *precisely* what you hope to accomplish with your speech.

For example, Duane Winfield, a student at a large state university, decided to give his first classroom speech on a topic from his personal experience. For the past two years, he had volunteered his time to perform music for patients in mental hospitals, nursing homes, and residences for disabled adults. He had seen how enthusiastically the patients responded to music, even when they remained unmoved by other kinds of stimuli. Duane's experience had given him a better understanding of the benefits of music therapy, and he wanted to share this understanding with his classmates. This gave him a topic and a general purpose, which he stated like this:

Topic: Music therapy

General Purpose: To inform

So far, so good. But what aspect of his topic would Duane discuss? The kinds of facilities in which he had worked? His specific role as a performer? The evidence that music therapy can improve patients' mental health? The needs of patients with different kinds of illnesses? He had to choose something interesting that he could cover in a six-minute speech. Finally, he settled on describing his most memorable experiences with patients to show how music therapy affected them. He stated his specific purpose this way:

Specific Purpose: To inform my audience about the benefits of music therapy for people with psychological or cognitive disabilities.

This turned out to be an excellent choice, and Duane's speech was among the best in the class.

Notice how clear the specific purpose statement is. Notice also how it relates the topic directly to the audience. That is, it states not only what the *speaker* wants to *say* but also what the speaker wants the *audience* to *know* as a result of the speech. This is very important, for it helps keep the audience at the center of your attention as you prepare your speech.

Using public speaking in your CAREER

Your communication degree has helped you land a job as spokesperson for the mayor of a medium-sized city on the West Coast. A year after starting the job, you are selected to organize an information campaign explaining the benefits of a new youth center proposed by the mayor.

To launch this campaign, you've decided to hold a news briefing at the end of the week. To open the briefing, you will present a short set of comments on the mayor's initiative. You decide to focus on four benefits of the youth center: (1) It will offer a range of activities—from sports to the arts—in a safe environment; (2) It will provide social networks for youths from all walks of life; (3) It will operate most hours of the day and night; (4) It will be free and open to everyone.

Following the format used in this chapter, state the general purpose, specific purpose, central idea, and main points of your comments.

Look what happens when the specific purpose statement does not include the audience.

Specific Purpose: To explain the benefits of music therapy for people with psychological or cognitive disabilities.

Explain to whom? To musicians? To medical students? To social workers? Those would be three different speeches. The musicians would want to know about the kinds of music Duane played. The medical students would want to hear about research on the benefits of music therapy. The social workers would want to learn how to implement a music program. Communicating effectively with each group would require preparing a different speech.

When the audience slips out of the specific purpose, it may slip out of the speaker's consciousness. You may begin to think that your task is the general one of preparing "an informative speech," when in fact your task is the specific one of informing a particular group of people. As we shall see in the next chapter, it is almost impossible to prepare a good speech without keeping constantly in mind the *people* for whom it is intended.

TIPS FOR FORMULATING THE SPECIFIC PURPOSE STATEMENT

Formulating a specific purpose is the most important early step in developing a successful speech. When writing your purpose statement, follow the general principles outlined on the following pages.

Write the Purpose Statement as a Full Infinitive Phrase, Not as a Fragment

Ineffective: 3-D technology.

More Effective: To inform my audience about the three major kinds of current 3-D technology.

The ineffective statement is adequate as an announcement of the speech topic, but it is not thought out fully enough to indicate the specific purpose.

Express Your Purpose as a Statement, Not as a Question

Ineffective: What is Día de los Muertos?

More Effective: To inform my audience about the history of Mexico's Día de los Muertos celebration.

The question might arouse the curiosity of an audience, but it is not effective as a specific purpose statement. It gives no indication about what direction the speech will take or what the speaker hopes to accomplish.

Avoid Figurative Language in Your Purpose Statement

Ineffective: To persuade my audience that the campus policy on student parking really stinks.

Choosing a topic is the first step in speech preparation. One way to come up with a good topic is to think about issues on which you hold strong opinions and beliefs.

More Effective: To persuade my audience that the campus policy on student parking should be revised to provide more spaces for students before 5 p.m.

Although the ineffective statement indicates something of the speaker's viewpoint, it does not state concisely what he or she hopes to achieve. Figurative language can reinforce ideas within a speech, but it is too ambiguous for a specific purpose statement.

Limit Your Purpose Statement to One Distinct Idea

Ineffective: To persuade my audience to become literacy tutors and to donate time to the Special Olympics.

This purpose statement expresses two unrelated ideas, either of which could be the subject of a speech. The easiest remedy is to select one or the other as a focus for your presentation.

More Effective: To persuade my audience to become literacy tutors.

Or:

More Effective: To persuade my audience to donate time to the Special Olympics.

Does this mean that you can never use the word "and" in your specific purpose statement? Not at all. Suppose your specific purpose is "To inform my audience about the causes and effects of epilepsy." In this case, "and" is appropriate because it connects two related parts of a unified topic. What you need to avoid is not simply the word "and," but a specific purpose statement that contains two unrelated ideas, either of which could be developed into a speech in its own right.

Make Sure Your Specific Purpose Is Not Too Vague or General

Ineffective: To persuade my audience that something should be done about unsafe school buses.

More Effective: To persuade my audience that the federal government should impose stronger safety standards for school buses in the United States.

The ineffective purpose statement falls into one of the most common traps— it is too broad and ill-defined. It gives no clues about what the speaker believes should be done about school buses. The more effective purpose statement is sharp and concise. It reveals clearly what the speaker plans to discuss.

The more precise your specific purpose, the easier it will be to prepare your speech. Consider this topic and specific purpose:

Topic: Hot-air balloons.

Specific Purpose: To inform my audience about hot-air balloons.

With such a hazy purpose, you have no systematic way of limiting your research or of deciding what to include in the speech and what to exclude. The origins of hot-air balloons, how they work, their current popularity—all could be equally relevant to a speech designed "to inform my audience about hot-air balloons."

In contrast, look at this topic and specific purpose:

Topic: Hot-air balloons.

Specific Purpose: To inform my audience about the scientific uses of hot-air balloons.

Now it is easy to decide what is germane and what is not. The origins of hot-air balloons, how they work, their popularity for recreation—all are interesting, but none is essential to the specific purpose of explaining "the scientific uses of hot-air balloons." Thus you need not worry about researching these matters or about explaining them in your speech. You can spend your preparation time efficiently.

QUESTIONS TO ASK ABOUT YOUR SPECIFIC PURPOSE

Sometimes you will arrive at your specific purpose almost immediately after choosing your topic. At other times you may do quite a bit of research before deciding on a specific purpose. Much will depend on how familiar you are with the topic, as well as on any special demands imposed by the assignment, the audience, or the occasion. But whenever you settle on your specific purpose, ask yourself the following questions about it.

Does My Purpose Meet the Assignment?
Students occasionally stumble over this question. Be sure you understand your assignment and shape your specific purpose to meet it. If you have questions, check with your instructor.

Can I Accomplish My Purpose in the Time Allotted?

Most classroom speeches are quite short, ranging from four to ten minutes. That may seem like a lot of time, but you will quickly find what generations of students have discovered—time flies when you are giving a speech!

Most people speak at an average rate of 120 to 150 words a minute. This means that a six-minute speech will consist of roughly 720 to 900 words. That is not long enough to develop a highly complex topic. Here are some specific purpose statements that would defy being handled well in the time normally allotted for classroom speeches:

> To inform my audience about the rise and fall of ancient Rome.
>
> To inform my audience about the role of technology in human history.
>
> To persuade my audience to convert to Buddhism.

You are much better off with a limited purpose that you have some reasonable hope of achieving in the short span of four to ten minutes.

Is the Purpose Relevant to My Audience?

The price of retirement homes in Palm Springs might be an engrossing topic for older citizens who are in the market for such dwellings. And the quality

checklist

Specific Purpose

YES	NO	
☐	☐	1. Is the specific purpose written as a full infinitive phrase?
☐	☐	2. Does the specific purpose include a reference to the audience?
☐	☐	3. Is the specific purpose phrased as a statement rather than a question?
☐	☐	4. Is the specific purpose free of figurative language?
☐	☐	5. Is the specific purpose limited to one distinct subject?
☐	☐	6. Does the specific purpose indicate precisely what I plan to accomplish in the speech?
☐	☐	7. Does the specific purpose meet the requirements of the assignment?
☐	☐	8. Can the specific purpose be accomplished in the time allotted for the speech?
☐	☐	9. Is the specific purpose relevant to my audience?
☐	☐	10. Does the specific purpose deal with a nontrivial subject?
☐	☐	11. Is the specific purpose suitable for a nontechnical audience?

of hot lunches in the elementary schools is of great concern to the students who eat them and the parents who pay for them. But neither subject has much relevance for an audience of college students. No matter how well you construct your speeches, they are likely to fall flat unless you speak about matters of interest to your listeners.

This is not to say you must select only topics that pertain directly to the college student's daily experience. Most students have wide-ranging backgrounds, interests, ideas, and values. And most of them are intellectually curious. They can get involved in an astonishing variety of subjects. Follow your common sense and make sure *you* are truly interested in the topic. Also, when speaking on a subject that is not obviously relevant to your listeners, find a way to tie it in with their goals, values, interests, and well-being. We'll discuss how to do this in the next chapter.

Is the Purpose Too Trivial for My Audience?

Just as you need to avoid speech topics that are too broad or complicated, so you need to steer clear of topics that are too superficial. How to build a fire without matches might absorb a group of Cub Scouts, but your classmates would probably consider it frivolous. Unfortunately, there is no absolute rule for determining what is trivial to an audience and what is not. Here are some examples of specific purposes that most people would find too trivial for classroom speeches:

To inform my audience about the parts of a backpack.

To inform my audience how to tie a bow tie.

To persuade my audience that espresso is better than cappuccino.

Is the Purpose Too Technical for My Audience?

Nothing puts an audience to sleep faster than a dry and technical speech. Beware of topics that are inherently technical and of treating ordinary subjects in a technical fashion. Although you may be familiar with the principles and vocabulary of international finance or clinical psychology, most of your classmates probably are not. There are aspects of these and similar subjects that can be treated clearly, with a minimum of jargon. But if you find that you can't fulfill your specific purpose without relying on technical words and concepts, you should reconsider your purpose.

Here are some examples of specific purposes that are overly technical for most classroom speeches:

To inform my audience about the solution to Fermat's Last Theorem.

To inform my audience about the principles of neutrino physics.

To inform my audience about the methods of encryption technology.

We will discuss the details of audience analysis and adaptation in Chapter 6. For the moment, remember to make sure that your specific purpose is appropriate for your listeners. If you have doubts, ask your instructor, or circulate a questionnaire among your classmates (see pages 111–113).

Phrasing the Central Idea

WHAT IS THE CENTRAL IDEA?

The specific purpose of a speech is what you hope to accomplish. The *central idea* is a concise statement of what you *expect to say*. Sometimes it is called the thesis statement, the subject sentence, or the major thought. Whatever the term, the central idea is usually expressed as a simple, declarative sentence that refines and sharpens the specific purpose statement.

Imagine that you run into a friend on your way to speech class. She says, "I have to dash to my history lecture, but I hear you're giving a speech today. Can you tell me the gist of it in one sentence?" "Sure," you reply. "America's prison system suffers from three major problems—overcrowding of inmates, lack of effective rehabilitation programs, and high expense to taxpayers."

Your answer is the central idea of your speech. It is more precise than your topic (America's prison system) or your specific purpose statement ("To inform my audience of the three major problems facing America's prison system"). By stating exactly what the three major problems are, the central idea sums up your speech in a single sentence.

Another way to think of the central idea is as your *residual message*—what you want your audience to remember after they have forgotten everything else in the speech. Most of the time the central idea will encapsulate the main points to be developed in the body of the speech. To show how this works, let's take a few of the examples we saw earlier in this chapter and develop them from the topic, general purpose, and specific purpose to the central idea.

We can start with the speech about music therapy.

Topic:	Music therapy.
General Purpose:	To inform.
Specific Purpose:	To inform my audience about the benefits of music therapy for people with psychological or cognitive disabilities.
Central Idea:	Music therapy developed as a formal mode of treatment during the twentieth century, utilizes a number of methods, and is explained by several theories that account for its success.

Look carefully at this example. It shows how the speaker might start with a broad subject (music therapy) that becomes narrower and narrower as the speaker moves from the general purpose to the specific purpose to the central idea. Notice also how much more the central idea suggests about the content of the speech. From it we can expect the speaker to address three main points—the first summarizing the development of music therapy, the second looking at methods of music therapy, and the third exploring theories that account for the success of music therapy.

This sharpening of focus as one proceeds to the central idea is crucial. Here is another example:

Topic:	Día de los Muertos.
General Purpose:	To inform.

Specific Purpose:	To inform my audience about the history of Mexico's Día de los Muertos celebration.
Central Idea:	Día de los Muertos can be traced to the Aztecs, was moved from summer to fall by Spanish priests, and today is celebrated in a number of ways in different regions of Mexico.

This central idea is especially well worded. We can assume from it that the body of the speech will contain three main points: (1) on the Aztec origins of Día de los Muertos, (2) on how it was changed by the Spanish, and (3) on the ways it is celebrated today.

Notice in each of these examples how much more the central idea reveals about the content of the speech than does the specific purpose. This is not accidental. Often you can settle on a specific purpose statement early in preparing your speech. The central idea, however, usually emerges later—after you have done your research and have decided on the main points of the speech. The process may work like this:

As an environmental science major, Marcia Esposito had learned that many experts fear the world may face a severe water shortage by the year 2025. She decided this would make a good topic for her informative speech. Tentatively, she adopted the following specific purpose statement: "To inform my audience about the seriousness of the growing international water crisis." Then Marcia started her research.

An article in *Time* magazine, which she located through LexisNexis, explained how the population in countries such as China, India, and Pakistan is outstripping the available supply of fresh water. According to the article, 400 million Chinese do not have access to suitable drinking water, and two-thirds of India's 1.1 billion people lack the water they need.

Next Marcia found a report on the United Nations Web site about the impact of pollution on the water supply. The report stated that in developing countries "more than 90 percent of sewage and 70 percent of industrial wastewater is dumped untreated into surface water."

Then Marcia hit upon the idea of interviewing one of her environmental science professors. In addition to confirming Marcia's research about the impact of population growth and pollution, the professor mentioned the problems caused by mismanagement of water supplies. Around the world, 65 to 70 percent of the water people use is lost to waste, evaporation, and other inefficiencies.

Marcia digested all this information. Now she was ready to formulate her central idea: "Population growth, pollution, and mismanagement are creating a serious shortage of fresh water in many parts of the world."

GUIDELINES FOR THE CENTRAL IDEA

What makes a well-worded central idea? Essentially the same things that make a well-worded specific purpose statement. The central idea (1) should be expressed in a full sentence, (2) should not be in the form of a question, (3) should avoid figurative language, and (4) should not be vague or overly general.

Here, for example, are four poorly written central ideas. See if you can identify the problem with each and figure out how each might be phrased more effectively:

Unlike the specific purpose, which you need to settle on early in the speech preparation process, the central idea usually takes shape later, as a result of your research and analysis of the topic.

Ineffective: Paying college athletes a monthly salary is a good idea.

Ineffective: Problems of fad diets.

Ineffective: What are nanorobots?

Ineffective: Mexico's Yucatán Peninsula is an awesome place for a vacation.

The first is too general. To say that paying college athletes a monthly salary is a "good idea" does not convey the speaker's viewpoint sharply and clearly. What does the speaker mean by a "good idea"? A revised central idea for this speech might be:

More Effective: Because college athletes in revenue-producing sports such as football and basketball generate millions of dollars in revenue for their schools, the NCAA should allow such athletes to receive a $300 monthly salary as part of their scholarships.

The second ineffective central idea is also too general, but it suffers further from not being written as a complete sentence. "Problems of fad diets" does not reveal enough about the content of the speech to serve as the central idea. It should be rewritten as a full sentence that identifies the problems of fad diets to be discussed in the speech:

More Effective: Although fad diets produce quick weight loss, they can lead to serious health problems by creating deficiencies in vitamins and minerals and by breaking down muscle tissue as well as fat.

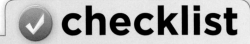

checklist

Central Idea

YES	NO	
☐	☐	1. Is the central idea written as a complete sentence?
☐	☐	2. Is the central idea phrased as a statement rather than a question?
☐	☐	3. Is the central idea free of figurative language?
☐	☐	4. Does the central idea clearly encapsulate the main points to be discussed in the body of the speech?
☐	☐	5. Can the central idea be adequately discussed in the time allotted for the speech?
☐	☐	6. Is the central idea relevant to the audience?
☐	☐	7. Is the central idea appropriate for a nontechnical audience?

The third poorly written central idea is phrased as a question rather than as a full declarative sentence. Asking "What are nanorobots?" might be a good way to catch the attention of listeners, but it does not encapsulate the main points to be developed in the speech. A more effective central idea would be:

More Effective: Microscopic in size, nanorobots are being developed for use in medicine, weaponry, and daily life.

The final ineffective central idea is flawed by its use of figurative language. To say that the Yucatán Peninsula is an "awesome" place for a vacation does not indicate what characteristics of the Yucatán Peninsula the speaker intends to discuss. A better central idea might be:

More Effective: Mexico's Yucatán Peninsula has many attractions for vacationers, including a warm climate, excellent food, and extensive Mayan ruins.

Notice that in all these examples the more effective central idea sums up the main points of the speech in a single sentence. If you are having trouble phrasing your central idea, the reason may be that you do not yet have a firm grasp on the main points of your speech.

Do not worry too much about your central idea until after you have developed the body of your speech (see Chapter 9). If, at that point, you still can't come up with a clear, concise central idea, your speech itself may not be clear or concise. Keep working on the speech until you can compose a central idea that fits the criteria just discussed. The result will be a sharper central idea and a tighter, more coherent speech.

Summary

The first step in speechmaking is choosing a topic. For classroom speeches, you can choose a subject you know well or one you research especially for the speech. If you have trouble picking a topic, you can use one of three brainstorming procedures. First, make an inventory of your hobbies, interests, skills, beliefs, and so forth. Second, use clustering to list the first topics that come to mind in several categories. Third, use an Internet subject directory, encyclopedia, or similar reference site to help you scan possible topics.

The general purpose of your speech will usually be to inform or to persuade. When your general purpose is to inform, your goal is to communicate information clearly, accurately, and interestingly. When your general purpose is to persuade, your goal is to win listeners over to your point of view.

Once you know your topic and general purpose, you must focus on a specific purpose statement that indicates precisely what your speech seeks to achieve. The specific purpose statement should (1) be a full infinitive phrase; (2) be worded as a statement, not a question; (3) avoid figurative language; (4) concentrate on one distinct idea; (5) not be vague or general.

Keep several questions in mind as you formulate your specific purpose statement: Does my purpose meet the assignment? Can I accomplish my purpose in the time allotted? Is the purpose relevant to my audience? Is the purpose too trivial or too technical for my audience?

The central idea refines and sharpens your specific purpose. It is a concise statement of what you will say in your speech, and it usually crystallizes in your thinking after you have done your research and have decided on the main points of your speech. The central idea usually encapsulates the main points to be developed in the body of your speech.

Key Terms

topic *(78)*

brainstorming *(80)*

general purpose *(82)*

specific purpose *(82)*

central idea *(89)*

residual message *(89)*

Review Questions

After reading this chapter, you should be able to answer the following questions:

1. What three brainstorming methods can you follow if you are having trouble choosing a topic for your speech?

2. What are the two general purposes of most classroom speeches? How do they differ?

connect

For further review, go to the LearnSmart study module for this chapter.

3. Why is determining the specific purpose such an important early step in speech preparation? Why is it important to include the audience in the specific purpose statement?

4. What are five tips for formulating your specific purpose?

5. What are five questions to ask about your specific purpose?

6. What is the difference between the specific purpose and the central idea of a speech? What are four guidelines for an effective central idea?

Exercises for Critical Thinking

1. Using one of the brainstorming methods described in this chapter, come up with three topics you might like to deal with in your next classroom speech. For each topic, devise a specific purpose statement suitable for the speech assignment. Make sure your specific purpose statements fit the guidelines discussed in the chapter.

2. Here are several specific purpose statements for classroom speeches. Identify the problem (or problems) with each.

    To inform my audience how to sign up for Facebook.

    To persuade my audience that the U.S. government should increase funding for stem cell research and support the development of hydrogen-fuel vehicles.

    What is an individual retirement account?

    To inform my audience why square grooves are superior to U-shaped grooves on golf clubs.

    To inform my audience about New Zealand.

    Donate blood.

    To persuade my audience that something has to be done about the problem of antibiotic-resistant bacteria.

3. Below are three sets of main points for speeches. For each set, supply the general purpose, specific purpose, and central idea.

    General Purpose:

    Specific Purpose:

    Central Idea:

    Main Points: I. You should study abroad because it will enhance your personal development.

                    II. You should study abroad because it will enhance your academic development.

                III. You should study abroad because it will enhance your career development.

General Purpose:

Specific Purpose:

Central Idea:

Main Points: I. The first event in a triathlon is swimming.
               II. The second event in a triathlon is cycling.
              III. The third event in a triathlon is running.

General Purpose:

Specific Purpose:

Central Idea:

Main Points: I. As a writer, Thomas Jefferson penned the Declaration of Independence and *Notes on the State of Virginia.*
               II. As President, Thomas Jefferson negotiated the Louisiana Purchase and approved the Lewis and Clark expedition.
              III. As an architect, Thomas Jefferson designed Monticello and the University of Virginia.

6

Analyzing the Audience

When President Barack Obama stepped to the lectern in Tucson, Arizona, on January 12, 2011, the eyes of the nation were upon him. Only four days earlier, 19 people had been gunned down at a grocery store during an open meeting for Congresswoman Gabrielle Giffords. Although Giffords survived, six people were killed. In the wake of this tragedy, Obama knew he had to reach multiple audiences, including families of the victims, residents of Arizona, and Americans in general.

He spent the first part of his speech eulogizing victims of the shooting. Then he turned to the need for reasoned public discourse that, instead of placing blame and pointing fingers, would remind Americans "of all the ways our hopes and dreams are bound together." He ended by referring to Christina Taylor Green, a nine-year-old girl who had been killed at the shooting. "I want our democracy to be as good as she imagined it," Obama stated. "All of us—we should do everything we can to make sure this country lives up to our children's expectations."

View an excerpt from Barack Obama's Tucson speech of January 12, 2011, in the online Media Library for this chapter (Video 6.1).

connect

The speech garnered almost universal praise. Historian Garry Wills called it "Obama's finest hour." Others deemed it "splendid," "inspirational," and a "remarkable display of oratory." Even Obama's critics praised the speech as "courageous," "genuine," and "pitch-perfect for the nation."

Audience-Centeredness

Obama's speech points up an important fact: Good public speakers are *audience-centered*. They know the primary purpose of speechmaking is not to browbeat the audience or to blow off steam. Rather, it is to gain a *desired response* from listeners.

Being audience-centered does not involve compromising your beliefs to get a favorable response. Nor does it mean using devious, unethical tactics to achieve your goal. As with Barack Obama, you can remain true to yourself and speak ethically while adapting your message to the goals, values, and attitudes of your audience.

To be audience-centered, you need to keep several questions in mind when you work on your speeches:

To whom am I speaking?

What do I want them to know, believe, or do as a result of my speech?

What is the most effective way of composing and presenting my speech to accomplish that aim?

The answers to these questions will influence every decision you make along the way—selecting a topic, determining a specific purpose, settling on your main points and supporting materials, organizing the message, and, finally, delivering the speech.

In many ways, adapting to an audience during a public speech is not much different from what you do in your daily social contacts. Few people would walk into a party and announce, "You know those people protesting at the administration building are way over the edge!"

People usually prefer to open controversial topics with a fairly noncommittal position. You might say, "What's going on at the administration building?" Then when you have heard and processed your companion's response, you can present your position accordingly. (You don't have to *agree* with a viewpoint different from your own, but neither do you have to hit your listeners over the head with your own opinion.)

Effective speakers seek to create a bond with their listeners by emphasizing common values and experiences. Communication scholars call this process *identification*. Obama created identification with his audience by honoring the victims of the shooting and by showing how the nation could move forward in the wake of tragedy. "For all our imperfections," he said, "we are full of decency and goodness, and . . . the forces that divide us are not as strong as those that unite us."

When you make a speech, either in class or in some other forum, keep in mind the need to be audience-centered. Think in advance about your listeners' background and interests, about their level of knowledge regarding the

audience-centeredness

Keeping the audience foremost in mind at every step of speech preparation and presentation.

identification

A process in which speakers seek to create a bond with the audience by emphasizing common values, goals, and experiences.

speech topic, and about their attitudes regarding your stance on the topic. As you develop the speech, work on explaining your ideas so they will be clear, interesting, and persuasive to the audience.

At this point, you may be nodding your head and saying, "Of course, everyone knows that. It's only common sense." But knowing a precept and putting it into practice are two different matters. The aim of this chapter is to introduce the basic principles of audience analysis and adaption. Chapters 15 and 16 will deal with those features of audience analysis unique to informative and persuasive speaking.

Your Classmates as an Audience

There is a tendency—among students and teachers alike—to view the classroom as an artificial speaking situation. In a way, it is. Your speech class is a testing ground where you can develop your communication skills before applying them outside the classroom. The most serious measure of success or failure is your grade, and that is determined ultimately by your teacher.

Because of this, it is easy to lose sight of your fellow students as an authentic audience. But each of your classmates is a real person with real ideas, attitudes, and feelings. Your speech class offers an enormous opportunity to inform and persuade other people. As one student wrote on her evaluation form at the end of her speech class, "I thought the speeches would all be phony, but they weren't. I've not only learned a lot about speaking—I've learned a lot about other things from listening to the speeches in class."

The best classroom speeches are those that take the classroom audience as seriously as a lawyer, a politician, a minister, or an advertiser takes an audience. You should consider every audience—inside the classroom and out—as worthy of your best efforts to communicate your knowledge or convictions. At the least you show respect for your listeners. At the most you could make a real difference in their lives. The following story demonstrates the latter:

Crystal Watkins gave an informative speech on the subject of small claims court, where ordinary people can press lawsuits involving up to $5,000 without lawyers. Part of her speech went like this: "It's two weeks after you have moved into a new apartment. A letter arrives from your old landlord. Expecting to get back your $800 security deposit, you joyfully tear open the envelope. Inside is a form letter explaining why your security deposit is not being refunded. What can you do about it? Nothing, right? Wrong! You can file a claim in small claims court."

Lee Callaway, one of Crystal's classmates, paid close attention. At the end of the previous term, he had run into a situation just like the one Crystal described. Not having money to hire a lawyer, he assumed he would have to forfeit his security deposit. But now, as he listened to Crystal's speech, Lee decided he would try to get his money back in small claims court. He filed suit the next week, and within a month he had his money back—thanks in part to his classmate's speech!

Most of your classroom speeches won't have this much immediate impact. Nevertheless, any topic that you handle conscientiously can influence your listeners—can enrich their experience, broaden their knowledge, perhaps change their views about something important.[1]

The Psychology of Audiences

What do you do when you listen to a speech? Sometimes you pay close attention; at other times you let your thoughts wander. People may be compelled to attend a speech, but no one can make them listen. The speaker must make the audience *choose* to pay attention.

Even when people do pay attention, they don't process a speaker's message exactly as the speaker intends. Auditory perception is always selective. Every speech contains two messages—the one sent by the speaker and the one received by the listener.

As we saw in Chapter 1, what a speaker says is filtered through a listener's frame of reference—the sum of her or his needs, interests, expectations, knowledge, and experience. As a result, we listen and respond to speeches not as they are, but as we are. Or, to borrow from Paul Simon's classic song "The Boxer," people hear what they want to hear and disregard the rest.

What do people want to hear? Very simply, they usually want to hear about things that are meaningful to them. People are *egocentric*. They pay closest attention to messages that affect their own values, beliefs, and well-being. Listeners approach speeches with one question uppermost in mind: "Why is this important to *me*?" As Harry Emerson Fosdick, the great preacher, once said: "There is nothing that people are so interested in as themselves, their own problems, and the way to solve them. That fact is . . . the primary starting point of all successful public speaking."

What do these psychological principles mean to you as a speaker? First, they mean your listeners will hear and judge what you say on the basis of what they already know and believe. Second, they mean you must relate your message to your listeners—show how it pertains to them, explain why they should care about it as much as you do. Here's an example:

> Mika Nakamura is a nutritionist who frequently gives presentations to different groups about making good food choices. Sometimes she speaks to groups of schoolchildren and their parents, sometimes to adult clubs and community organizations. Although her basic message—eat fresh, eat local—never varies, she has learned how important it is to tailor the message to her specific audience.
>
> When Mika speaks to children, her presentations are very hands-on. With the children's help, she typically prepares a nutritious and delicious shake for them to drink. Rather than telling them to eat more fruits and vegetables, she shows them a way to do it. She has learned from experience that children respond well to concrete learning.
>
> When her audience consists of working parents, Mika focuses on ways to prepare healthful food quickly and easily. For older adults with more free time, she presents more elaborate techniques and emphasizes the importance of good nutrition for healthy aging. When asked to speak to a gourmet club, she tells them about local sources of grass-fed meats and fresh fruits and vegetables.

As Mika's experience shows, you need some grasp of what your listeners know, believe, and care about. Saul Alinsky, the noted community organizer, advises, "People only understand things in terms of their experience," which means that to communicate with them, "you must get inside their experience."[2]

egocentrism

The tendency of people to be concerned above all with their own values, beliefs, and well-being.

Good speakers are audience-centered. Whether speaking formally or informally, they look for creative ways to communicate their ideas and keep their audience's attention.

Of course, you can't actually get inside another person's experience. But you can learn enough about your audience to know what you should do to make your ideas clear and meaningful. How you can do this is our next topic.

Demographic Audience Analysis

One of the ways speakers analyze audiences is by looking at demographic traits such as age; gender; religion; sexual orientation; group membership; racial, ethnic, or cultural background; and the like. This is called *demographic audience analysis*. It consists of two steps: (1) identifying the general demographic features of your audience, and (2) gauging the importance of those features to a particular speaking situation.

While demographic audience analysis can be a useful tool in understanding your audience, like all tools, it can be used improperly. When analyzing demographic information about your audience, it is essential that you avoid stereotyping. Stereotyping involves creating an oversimplified image of a particular group of people, usually by assuming that all members of the group are alike. Examples of stereotyping include the erroneous notions that all African Americans are athletic or that all Asians excel in science. Looking at demographic factors can provide important clues about your audience, but you must use those factors prudently and responsibly.

In addition, as we shall see later in this chapter, you should always combine your demographic audience analysis with situational audience analysis.

demographic audience analysis

Audience analysis that focuses on demographic factors such as age, gender, religion, sexual orientation, group membership, and racial, ethnic, or cultural background.

stereotyping

Creating an oversimplified image of a particular group of people, usually by assuming that all members of the group are alike.

The importance of any given demographic factor will vary from audience to audience depending on the occasion and the speech topic. If you keep this in mind, demographic analysis can be a valuable starting point in gauging your audience's background, interests, values, and beliefs. Here are a few of the major demographic factors you should consider.

AGE

As Aristotle noted almost 2,500 years ago and as researchers have confirmed many times since, few things affect a person's outlook more than his or her age. Of course, no age group is monolithic. There is no generation in which everyone thinks alike, buys the same products, or votes for the same political candidates. Yet each generation has more or less common values and experiences that set it apart from other generations. Whatever your age, you are a product of your world.

You can see what this means for your speeches. Suppose you address an audience of older people. If you refer to Kanye West, Ke$ha, or Rihanna, your audience may have no idea who you mean. Similarly, if you speak to an audience of young adults and casually mention Watergate, they may not know what you are talking about. Even if younger listeners do recognize the name, it will not produce the same emotional associations as in people who lived through the Watergate break-in and the subsequent resignation of President Richard Nixon.

Depending on the composition of your speech class, you may face an audience that is mostly in their late teens and early twenties. If so, you can assume a common level of age experience. On the other hand, 40 percent of college students today are age 25 or older, and some classrooms include students in their thirties, forties, and beyond. You may then have to tackle two or three generations. This will give you good practice for speeches outside the classroom, where age is usually a major factor in audience analysis.

GENDER

Question: What do you call a female doctor?
Answer: A doctor.

This probably strikes you as a strange question. Few Americans in the second decade of the 21st century identify their doctor by gender. Yet as recently as 1970, only 8 percent of doctors in the United States were women, and the phrase "female doctor" was often heard. Today, 30 percent of American doctors—and 50 percent of medical-school students—are women. The phrase "female doctor" has become extinct.

As in medicine, vocational distinctions between the sexes have been eroding for many years. Women work in construction trades, run corporations, enlist in the armed forces, and serve as college athletic directors. Men work as receptionists, nurses, flight attendants, and day-care attendants.

In addition, the "typical" composition of audiences has changed. At one time, for example, civic groups such as Kiwanis and Rotary clubs were all-male. Today most have sizable contingents of women. Parent associations, which were once composed almost solely of women, now include plenty of interested fathers. Here, as in other areas, the old stereotypes no longer apply.

What does this have to do with public speaking? Speakers who fail to take account of current gender attitudes and practices are almost certain to provoke negative reactions among some listeners, male and female alike. If you're delivering a speech about small businesses, for example, and you refer to business owners generically as "he," or to all shoppers as "she," your word choice will doubtless lead some listeners to squirm in their seats.

At the same time, it is important to recognize that men and women are not alike in all their values and beliefs. When it comes to politics, for instance, American women tend to be more concerned about issues such as education, health care, and social justice, whereas men tend to stress economics and national security. But keep in mind that these are generalizations. There are lots of women who believe that national security comes first, just as there are plenty of men who give priority to social issues. An astute speaker will be equally attuned to the differences *and* the similarities between the sexes.[3]

RELIGION

Current events around the world demonstrate that religious views are among the most emotionally charged and passionately defended of all human concerns. Even your small speech class might include a wide range of faiths, as well as atheists and agnostics. You cannot assume that your views on religion—whatever they may be—are shared by your listeners.

As the United States has become more diverse culturally, it has also become more diverse religiously. The traditional mix of Protestantism, Catholicism, and Judaism has been enriched by growing numbers of Buddhists, Muslims, Hindus, Sikhs, Russian Orthodox, and others. One leading scholar on the subject says the United States is "the most religiously diverse nation in the world."[4]

Demographic audience analysis is vital to successful public speaking in any situation. Here Tibetan Buddhists gather at a ceremony celebrating the 900th anniversary of the birth of spiritual leader Gyalwang Karmapa.

There is also great diversity within different faiths. You cannot assume that all Catholics support the official view of their church on birth control or women in the priesthood, that all Baptists are being born-again, or that all Muslims favor a subservient status for women. In matters of religion, the United States is truly a nation of many faiths, many voices, many views.

Whenever you speak on a topic with religious dimensions, be sure to consider the religious orientations of your listeners. Doing so can help you avoid potentially embarrassing pitfalls. In some cases, it may make the difference between an unsuccessful speech and a successful one.

SEXUAL ORIENTATION

Philip Ward, president of a major engineering firm, was hosting his annual awards banquet to recognize outstanding employees. After presenting all the plaques and checks, he said: "Now that we have honored these fine people for their career and community accomplishments, I would like to take a moment to recognize the spouses and partners who have supported their exceptional efforts." The room filled with applause.

After the ceremony, Ward made his way around the room shaking hands and chatting with award winners. "I want to congratulate you again on your superior design for the Houston water project," he said to Joanne Fitzpatrick.

"Thank you for the award," Joanne replied. "And I want to thank you for being sensitive to the fact that many of us are supported by partners as well as by spouses. It really meant a lot to Julie and me to feel recognized and included."

As an experienced speaker and a successful businessperson, Philip Ward is aware of the need to adapt to his audience on the basis of sexual orientation. By mentioning "partners" as well as "spouses," he took an inclusive stance acknowledging that couples can be same-sex or opposite-sex, married or unmarried.

When you work on your speeches, keep an eye out for language, examples, and other elements that may unintentionally exclude listeners with same-sex partners. The word "homosexual," for example, is considered derogatory by lesbians and gay men. So are references to a gay or lesbian "lifestyle." As there is no single heterosexual lifestyle, there is no single lesbian or gay lifestyle.

Just as audiences often include people of varying occupations, ages, races, and religions, so too do they contain people of different sexual orientations. Effective public speakers take all these demographic factors into account when preparing their remarks.

RACIAL, ETHNIC, AND CULTURAL BACKGROUND

As we saw in Chapter 1, the United States has long been a multicultural society. Populated originally by Native Americans and then by immigrants from all over the world, it is today a multiracial, multiethnic country of unmatched diversity. The majority of Americans support this diversity as a positive development in today's globalized world. Attitudes about race and ethnicity are quite different from what they were even a few decades ago.

These new attitudes are especially evident among Americans born from 1981 to 2000, often referred to as the Millennial Generation. The most racially and ethnically diverse generation in U.S. history, it is also the most tolerant of racial and ethnic differences. As time goes by, this tolerance may continue to grow as the nation becomes even more diverse.

Yet even if you are speaking to an audience composed primarily of members of the Millennial Generation, you must be sensitive to issues of race, ethnicity, and cultural background. Despite their similarities as Americans, people of European descent, blacks, Latinos, Asians, and many others have different customs and beliefs that may bear upon your speech topic.

Because we live in an age of globalization, you may also find yourself addressing listeners from countries other than your own. Not only does the United States contain a substantial percentage of people born in other lands, but more than 5 million Americans (not including those in military service) live abroad. If all those Americans were placed in one state, it would be the 20th largest state in the Union. This is one reason why employers identify the ability to communicate effectively with people of different cultural backgrounds as one of the most desirable skills for current college graduates.

Regardless of where you are speaking, be aware that some of your listeners may have racial, ethnic, or cultural perspectives that will affect their attitudes toward your speech topic. Try to gauge what those perspectives are and how they are likely to affect the audience's response to your message. Adjust your remarks so they will be as clear, suitable, and convincing as possible.

GROUP MEMBERSHIP

"Tell me thy company," says Don Quixote, "and I'll tell thee what thou art." For all our talk about rugged individualism, Americans are very group-oriented. Workers belong to unions, businesspeople to chambers of commerce. Hunters join the National Rifle Association, environmentalists the Sierra Club, feminists the National Organization for Women. Doctors enroll in the American Medical Association, lawyers in the American Bar Association. There are thousands of such voluntary organizations in the United States.

Similar groups abound on campus. Some of your classmates may belong to fraternities or sororities, some to Campus Crusade for Christ, some to the Young Republicans, some to the film society, some to the ski club, and so forth. For speeches in the classroom, as well as for those outside the classroom, the group affiliations of your audience may provide excellent clues about your listeners' interests and attitudes.

Age; gender; religion; sexual orientation; racial, ethnic, and cultural background; group membership—these are just a few of the variables to consider in demographic audience analysis. Others include occupation, economic position, social standing, education, intelligence, and place of residence. Indeed, *anything* characteristic of a given audience is potentially important to a speaker addressing that audience. For your classroom speeches, you may want to learn about your classmates' academic majors, years in school, extracurricular activities, living arrangements, and job aspirations.

Perhaps the most important thing to keep in mind about demographic audience analysis is that it is not an end in itself. Your aim is not just to list the major traits of your listeners, but to find in those traits clues about how your listeners will respond to your speech. Once you have done that, you are ready to move on to the next stage of audience analysis.

Situational Audience Analysis

Situational audience analysis usually builds on demographic analysis. It identifies traits of the audience unique to the speaking situation at hand. These traits include the size of the audience, the physical setting, and the disposition of the audience toward the subject, the speaker, and the occasion.

SIZE

Outside the classroom, the size of an audience can, with the aid of television and radio, range in the millions. Most speech classes, however, consist of between 20 and 30 people—a small- to medium-sized audience. This is a good size for beginning speakers, most of whom are terrified at the prospect of addressing a huge crowd. As you gain more experience, though, you may welcome the challenge of speaking to larger groups. Some speakers actually prefer a large audience to a small one.

No matter what size group you are addressing, bear in mind one basic principle: The larger the audience, the more formal your presentation must be. Audience size may also affect your language, choice of appeals, and use of visual aids.

PHYSICAL SETTING

Which of the following would you rather address?

> An audience assembled immediately after lunch, crammed into an overheated room with inadequate seating

> An audience assembled at 10:00 in the morning, comfortably seated in an airy, well-lighted room

Undoubtedly you chose the second option. Any of the adverse conditions listed in the first could seriously impair your audience's willingness to accept your ideas or even listen to you at all.

When you face any speaking situation, it is important to know in advance if there will be any difficulties with the physical setting. For classroom speeches, of course, you already do know. But speeches outside the classroom can present unpleasant surprises unless you do your homework beforehand.

When you are invited to speak, don't be shy about asking questions of the person who arranged the speech. If possible, look over the room a few days in advance, or else arrive early on the day of your speech to inspect the room. If it is too warm or too cold, see about adjusting the thermostat. Check the seating arrangements and the location of the lectern to be sure your audience can see you. In short, do everything you can to control the influence of physical setting on your audience.

What about circumstances you can't control? Your speech *is* scheduled directly after lunch or dinner. The room *is* too small for the audience expected. The heat *cannot* be regulated. Then you are simply going to have to work harder to adapt to these aspects of your listeners' discomfort.

Above all, don't be influenced *yourself* by the poor physical setting. If your audience sees that you are energetic, alert, and involved with your topic, chances are they will forget their discomfort and come right along with you.

DISPOSITION TOWARD THE TOPIC

As we saw in Chapter 5, you should keep your audience in mind when choosing a topic. Ideally, you will pick a topic that suits them as well as it suits you. Once you have your topic, however, you must consider in more detail their interest in the topic, knowledge about it, and attitudes toward it.

Interest

Outside the classroom, people do not often expend the time and effort to attend a speech unless they are interested in the topic. But the members of your speech class are a captive audience. Sometimes they will be deeply interested in your topic, particularly if it relates directly to them. Most of the time they will range from fairly interested to mildly curious to downright indifferent.

One of your tasks will be to assess their interest in advance and to adjust your speech accordingly. Most important, if your topic is not likely to generate great interest, you must take special steps to get your classmates involved. Here is a brief example of how to do this:

Sharon wanted to persuade her classmates to vote on a regular basis. She started by saying: "Suppose a total stranger was responsible for making life-or-death decisions about your life. You'd want to have a say in who that person was, wouldn't you? Well, total strangers do make decisions that affect you every single day—those total strangers are called members of Congress, Senators, and the President. And you can help choose all those people by doing one simple thing—voting on election day."

In the chapters that follow, we'll look closely at all the ways you can develop interest in your topic—by an arresting introduction, provocative supporting materials, vivid language, dynamic delivery, visual aids, and so forth.

Knowledge

There is often a strong correlation between interest in a topic and knowledge about it. People tend to be interested in what they know about. Likewise, they are inclined to learn about subjects that interest them. But there are exceptions. Few students know much about handwriting analysis, yet most would find it an absorbing topic. On the other hand, almost all know a lot about checking books out of the library, but few would find it a fascinating subject for a speech.

Your listeners' knowledge about your topic will to a large extent determine what you can say in your speech. If your listeners know little about your topic—whether or not they find it interesting—you will have to talk at a more elementary level. If they are reasonably well informed, you can take a more technical and detailed approach.

Attitude

The attitude of your listeners toward your topic can be extremely important in determining how you handle the material. If you know in advance the

connect
View the beginning of "Make Your Voice Heard: Get Out and Vote" in the online Media Library for this chapter (Video 6.2).

prevailing attitude among members of your audience, you can adjust your speech to address their concerns or to answer their objections. Consider the experiences of the following two students—one who did not account for listener attitude and one who did:

Jen Salerno spoke about family-leave policies in the workplace. On the basis of her research, she believed there was evidence that such policies unfairly benefited a few parents at the expense of other employees, such as single people and childless couples. Unfortunately, rather than citing her sources and acknowledging that her point of view was controversial, Jen presented her material as though it were general knowledge.

The speech was not well received. As one student commented, "You may be right in what you say, but I have trouble believing it. We've heard so much about the need for businesses to be family-friendly—can it all be wrong? I think you would have been more persuasive if you had looked at both sides of the issue rather than just your own."

Had Jen taken the skepticism of her audience into account and established the credibility of her sources, she might have made her arguments more convincing to her audience.

Compare the approach of Bryan Watts, who also espoused a controversial viewpoint:

connect

View an excerpt from "The Internet and Our Future" in the online Media Library for this chapter (Video 6.3).

Concerned about the economic woes of his state, Bryan decided to give a persuasive speech calling for a sales tax on goods purchased over the Internet. After distributing an audience-analysis questionnaire among his classmates, Bryan found that 80 percent of them opposed his plan. They gave two major reasons. First, they believed they were taxed enough already. Second, they thought an Internet sales tax would be too difficult to implement.

Although Bryan disagreed with those beliefs, he realized he could neither ignore them nor insult his classmates for holding them. He knew he would have to discuss these points logically and with hard evidence if he were to have any chance of persuading his audience.

As it turned out, Bryan did convince some members of the class to reconsider their beliefs. He could not have done so without first investigating what those beliefs were and then adapting his message to them.[5]

DISPOSITION TOWARD THE SPEAKER

Let's return for a moment to Jen's speech about family leave. Jen was a first-year student with no special background in workplace issues. It's not surprising that her classmates took her statements with a large grain of salt. But suppose Jen had been a recognized expert who had conducted research on the impact of family leave on employee attitudes and business productivity. Then her listeners would have found her much more believable. Why? Because an audience's response to a message is invariably colored by their perception of the speaker.

The more competent listeners believe a speaker to be, the more likely they are to accept what he or she says. Likewise, the more listeners believe that a speaker has their best interests at heart, the more likely they are to respond positively to the speaker's message.

We will come back to this subject in detail when we deal with strategies for persuasive speaking in Chapter 17. For now, keep in mind that your listeners will always have *some* set of attitudes toward you as a speaker. Estimating what those attitudes are and how they will affect your speech is a crucial part of situational audience analysis.

DISPOSITION TOWARD THE OCCASION

It was graduation day at Valencia High School. The mood was festive as the valedictorian spoke eloquently about the special memories of the graduating class. There was laughter when the principal recounted a well-known prank from the class picnic.

Then, Russell Merritt, the mayor, rose to say a few words. "What a pleasure it is to be here," he said. "I'm so proud of you, the graduates, and you, the parents who raised such a terrific group of kids." He continued in this vein for a couple minutes, interrupted by applause as he heaped praise on the students, their parents, their teachers, and their community.

The listeners' enthusiasm faded as Merritt began talking about building a new library to replace the town's old one. This was a controversial issue, and it was going to be voted on in an upcoming referendum. The more the mayor talked about it, the more irritated his audience became. When he concluded, he was met with grudging applause and quite a few hostile glares.

On other occasions, Merritt's remarks would not have touched off such a negative response. But graduation day was understood by the audience to be a celebratory occasion that focused on the students and their achievements. The last thing anyone expected to hear was a political speech. What angered the audience was not what the mayor said, but that he exploited the occasion for his own purposes.

No matter what the situation, listeners have fairly definite ideas about the speeches they consider appropriate. Speakers who seriously violate those expectations can almost always count on infuriating the audience.

Perhaps most important, the occasion will dictate how long a speech should be. When you are invited to speak, the chairperson will usually say how much time you have for your talk. If not, be sure to ask.

Once you know, pare down your speech so it fits easily within the allotted time. Do not exceed that time under any circumstances, for you are likely to see your audience dwindle as you drone on. (This is one reason why most teachers insist that classroom speeches be kept within the designated time limit. It provides crucial training for speeches you will give outside the classroom.)

There are other audience expectations that apply to your classroom situation. One is that speeches will conform to the assignment. Another is that speakers will observe appropriate standards of taste and decorum. Failure to adhere to these expectations may disturb your classmates and will almost certainly damage your grade.

Getting Information About the Audience

Now that you know *what* to learn about an audience, the next question is, *how* do you learn it? A person running for political office can rely on hired professional pollsters. If, as is more likely, you are invited sometime to address a particular group—say a meeting of the local Rotary club—the person who invites you can usually provide a good sketch of the audience. Ask your contact where you can find out more about the group's history and mission. If you know someone who has spoken to the same group, be sure to sound out that person.

What about your classmates as an audience? You can learn a lot about them just by observation and conversation, but you may want to know more about their knowledge and attitudes on specific speech topics. Some teachers require students to do a formal audience-analysis questionnaire for at least one of their speeches. In addition to providing information about your classroom audience, such a questionnaire gives you practice in developing the skills of audience analysis you will need for speeches after your class is over.

There are three major types of questions to choose from when developing an audience-analysis questionnaire: fixed-alternative questions, scale questions, and open-ended questions.

Fixed-alternative questions, as their name implies, offer a fixed choice between two or more responses. For example:

fixed-alternative questions

Questions that offer a fixed choice between two or more alternatives.

Do you know what the insanity plea is in the U.S. legal system?

Yes _____

No _____

Not sure _____

By limiting the possible responses, such questions produce clear, unambiguous answers. They also tend to yield superficial answers. Other techniques are needed to get beneath the surface.

Scale questions resemble fixed-alternative questions, but they allow more leeway in responding. For example:

scale questions

Questions that require responses at fixed intervals along a scale of answers.

How often do you believe the insanity plea is used in U.S. court cases?

Very seldom ————|————|————|————|———— Very often

Questions like these are especially useful for getting at the strength of a respondent's attitudes.

Open-ended questions give maximum leeway in responding. For example:

open-ended questions

Questions that allow respondents to answer however they want.

What is your opinion about the insanity plea in U.S. court cases?

Under what circumstances do you think the insanity plea is legitimate in a criminal trial?

Although open-ended questions invite more detailed responses than the other two types of questions, they also increase the likelihood of getting answers that do not give the kind of information you need.

Because each type of question has its advantages and disadvantages, many questionnaires contain all three types. Figure 6.1 (page 112) shows a questionnaire that was distributed before a classroom speech on volunteering. By using all three types of questions, the speaker did two things—elicited specific information about the audience and probed more deeply into their attitudes toward the speech topic. The results broke down as follows:

1. Roughly half of the class had not participated as a volunteer. Therefore, the speaker knew she would have to explain clearly what was involved in this kind of work.

2. Five students knew someone close to them who had benefited from volunteer work by a community, religious, or charitable organization; most

Two fixed-alternative questions establish the listeners' level of knowledge about and degree of involvement with the topic.

1. Have you ever engaged in volunteer work for a community, religious, or charitable organization?

   Yes _____
   No _____

2. Have you or anyone close to you ever benefited from the volunteer work of a community, religious, or charitable organization?

   Yes _____
   No _____
   Not sure _____

This scale question is designed to show the attitudes of listeners who have participated in volunteer work.

3. If you have engaged in volunteer work, how would you rate the experience?

   ☐ Very rewarding
   ☐ Somewhat rewarding
   ☐ Neutral
   ☐ Somewhat unrewarding
   ☐ Very unrewarding

Another scale question gauges the listeners' sense of social obligation.

4. Do you agree or disagree with the following statement? To the extent possible, people have an obligation to help those in less fortunate circumstances.

   ☐ Strongly agree
   ☐ Mildly agree
   ☐ Undecided
   ☐ Mildly disagree
   ☐ Strongly disagree

Two open-ended questions help gauge the listeners' disposition toward volunteer work. The last question is especially important. It probes the specific issues the speaker needs to address for listeners who have not engaged in volunteer work.

5. If you have worked as a volunteer, do you plan to do so again? Why or why not?

6. If you have not worked as a volunteer, what is your major reason for not doing so? Please explain.

FIGURE 6.1
Sample Questionnaire

said they were not sure. Thus the speaker could not depend on a high degree of personal involvement among the audience.

3. All but one of the students who had engaged in volunteer work rated it "very rewarding" or "somewhat rewarding." Not only would this portion of the audience be inclined to support the speaker's position, but the speaker could point to their attitude as proof that working as a volunteer is a rewarding experience.

4. Nearly 75 percent of the respondents either "strongly agreed" or "mildly agreed" that people have an obligation to help those in less fortunate circumstances. The speaker could therefore depend on an audience favorably inclined to the basic premise underlying volunteer work.

5. Answers to the fifth question—"If you have worked as a volunteer, do you plan to do so again? Why or why not?"—were interesting. All the respondents indicated that they planned to engage in volunteer work again, but most said they were not likely to do so while in college because they were too busy with other activities.

6. Nearly 90 percent of the students who had not engaged in volunteer work stated that their major reason for not doing so was a lack of time. In combination with the answers to question 5, these responses showed that the speaker would have to deal persuasively with the time issue if she were to be successful in convincing people to volunteer while they were enrolled in school.

connect

View how the speaker in Video 6.3 used an audience-analysis questionnaire in his speech (Video 6.4).

This questionnaire revealed a great deal about the listeners' knowledge, attitudes, and concerns. In putting together your own questionnaire, keep the following principles in mind:

1. Plan the questionnaire carefully to elicit precisely the information you need.
2. Use all three types of questions—fixed-alternative, scale, and open-ended.
3. Make sure the questions are clear and unambiguous.
4. Keep the questionnaire relatively brief.

Adapting to the Audience

Once you have completed the audience analysis, you should have a pretty clear picture of your listeners. But this does not guarantee a successful speech. The key is how well you *use* what you know in preparing and presenting the speech.

This point deserves special attention because it poses one of the hardest tasks facing novice speakers. Most people can identify the major characteristics of their audience, but many have trouble *adapting* their ideas to the audience. There are two major stages in the process of audience adaptation. The first occurs before the speech, as part of your preparation and rehearsal. The second occurs during the presentation of the speech itself.

AUDIENCE ADAPTATION BEFORE THE SPEECH

As we have seen, you must keep your audience in mind at every stage of speech preparation. This involves more than simply remembering who your listeners will be. Above all, it means two things: (1) assessing how your audience is likely to respond to what you say in your speech, and (2) adjusting what you say to make it as clear, appropriate, and convincing as possible.

This is not always easy to do. We are all so wrapped up in our own ideas and concerns that we have trouble seeing things from other people's perspective—especially if their perspective is different from ours. To step outside your own frame of reference and see things from another person's point of view is a real achievement.

Yet this is what a successful speaker eventually learns to do. You must submerge your own views so completely that you can adopt, temporarily, those of your listeners. When you do this, you will begin to hear your speech through the ears of your audience and to adjust it accordingly. Try to imagine what they will like, what they will dislike, where they will have doubts or questions, whether they will need more details here or fewer there, what will interest them and what will not.

At every point you must *anticipate* how your audience will respond. Put yourself in their place and respond to your speech as they would.

Here is how one student worked out his problems of audience adaptation:

> Juan Ruiz, a junior geology major, decided to give an informative speech about how earthquakes occur. From his audience analysis, he learned that only a handful of his classmates knew much about geology. Juan realized that he would have to present his speech at an elementary level and with a minimum of scientific language.
>
> As he prepared the speech, Juan kept asking himself, "How can I make this clear and meaningful to someone who knows nothing about earthquakes or geological principles?" Because he was speaking in the Midwest, he decided to begin by noting that the most severe earthquake in American history took place not in California, but at New Madrid, Missouri, in 1811. If such an earthquake happened today, it would be felt from the Rocky Mountains to the Atlantic Ocean and would flatten most of the cities in the Mississippi Valley. That, he figured, should get his classmates' attention.
>
> Throughout the body of his speech, Juan dealt only with the basic mechanics of earthquakes and carefully avoided technical terms such as "asthenosphere," "lithosphere," and "subduction zones." He also prepared PowerPoint slides to illustrate his points.
>
> To be absolutely safe, Juan asked his roommate—who was not a geology major—to listen to the speech. "Stop me," he said, "anytime I say something you don't understand." Juan's roommate stopped him four times, and at each spot Juan worked out a way to make his point more clearly. Finally, he had a speech that was interesting and perfectly understandable to his audience.

As you work on your speeches, try to keep your listeners constantly in mind. Anticipate how they will respond to your ideas. Be creative in thinking about ways to adapt your message to them. Like Juan, you will give a much better speech.

AUDIENCE ADAPTATION DURING THE SPEECH

No matter how hard you prepare ahead of time, things may not go exactly as planned on the day of your speech. For speeches in the classroom, you may find that the projector for your visual aids is not available or that another student has the same topic as you. For speeches outside the classroom, you might learn that the audience will be much larger (or smaller) than you had anticipated, or that the amount of time available for your speech has been cut in half because a previous speaker has droned on for too long.

If something like this happens to you, don't panic. Find another way to present your visual aids. Modify your introduction to mention the other student's speech on your topic. Adjust your delivery to the changed audience size. If you find that you have less time than you had planned, condense your speech to its most essential points and present them in the time available. Your listeners will sympathize with your predicament and will appreciate

In political campaigns, poll-taking helps the candidates keep track of public opinion. For classroom speeches, you can use an audience-analysis questionnaire to gauge the knowledge and opinions of your listeners.

your regard for their time. This will more than compensate for your lost speaking time.

Finally, be sure to keep an eye out during your speech for audience feedback. If your listeners are sitting forward in their chairs, looking at you with interest, and nodding their heads in approval, you can assume that things are going well. But suppose you find them frowning or responding with quizzical looks. Then you may need to back up and go over your point again, as in this example:

Brandi Michaels, an economics major, had worked diligently to make sure her speech on the U.S. trade deficit was not too technical for her classmates. She explained everything from the ground up, prepared two excellent visual aids, and practiced giving the speech to her best friend, a music major and self-confessed "economics imbecile."

On the day of Brandi's speech, everything went well until she got to her second main point, when she noticed that several of her classmates seemed puzzled by the relationship between international trade deficits and the U.S. cost of living. Knowing they would be lost for the rest of the speech if they didn't understand that relationship, Brandi paused and said, "I can see some of you are confused by my explanation. Let me try it again from a different angle."

As Brandi went through the material again, she could see her classmates nodding their heads in understanding. She could now go on with her speech, confident that her audience was ready to go with her.

Adapting to your audience is one of the most important keys to successful public speaking. Like other aspects of speechmaking, it is sometimes easier said than done. But once you master it, you'll see that it pays dividends in more personal facets of your life—when you adapt to an audience of one.

Summary

Good speakers are audience-centered. They know that the aim of speechmaking is to gain a desired response from listeners. When working on your speeches, keep three questions in mind: To whom am I speaking? What do I want them to know, believe, or do as a result of my speech? What is the most effective way of composing and presenting my speech to accomplish that aim?

To be an effective speaker, you should know something about the psychology of audiences. People are egocentric. They typically approach speeches with one question uppermost in mind: "Why is this important to *me*?" Therefore, you need to study your audience and adapt your speech to their beliefs and interests.

The first stage in learning about your audience is to identify demographic traits such as age, gender, religion, sexual orientation, group membership, and racial, ethnic, or cultural background. The second stage is identifying traits of the audience unique to the speaking situation. These traits include the size of the audience, attitudes influenced by the physical setting, and your listeners' disposition toward the topic, toward you as a speaker, and toward the occasion.

For speeches outside the classroom, you can best get information about the audience by asking the person who invites you to speak. For classroom speeches, you can learn about your audience by observation and conversation. You also can circulate an audience-analysis questionnaire.

Once you complete the audience analysis, you must adapt your speech so it will be clear and convincing to your listeners. Put yourself in their place. Try to hear the speech as they will. Anticipate questions and objections, and try to answer them in advance. When you deliver your speech, keep an eye out for audience feedback and adjust your remarks in response.

Key Terms

audience-centeredness *(98)*	situational audience analysis *(106)*
identification *(98)*	attitude *(108)*
egocentrism *(100)*	fixed-alternative questions *(111)*
demographic audience analysis *(101)*	scale questions *(111)*
stereotyping *(101)*	open-ended questions *(111)*

Review Questions

After reading this chapter, you should be able to answer the following questions:

1. Why must a public speaker be audience-centered?

2. What does it mean to say that people are egocentric? What implications does the egocentrism of audiences hold for you as a public speaker?

3. What are the six demographic traits of audiences discussed in this chapter? Why is each important to audience analysis?

4. What is situational audience analysis? What factors do you need to consider in situational audience analysis?

5. How can you get information about an audience?

6. What are the three kinds of questions used in questionnaires? Why is it a good idea to use all three in audience analysis?

7. What methods can you use to adapt your speech to your audience before the speech? During the speech?

connect

For further review, go to the LearnSmart study module for this chapter.

Exercises for Critical Thinking

1. Advertisers are usually very conscious of their audience. Choose an issue of a popular magazine such as *Time, Newsweek, Sports Illustrated, Vanity Fair, Rolling Stone,* or the like. From that issue select three advertisements to analyze. Try to determine the audience being appealed to in each advertisement, and analyze the appeals (verbal and visual) used to persuade buyers. How might the appeals differ if the ads were designed to persuade a different audience?

2. Below are three general speech topics and, for each, two hypothetical audiences to which a speech might be delivered. For each topic, write a brief paragraph explaining how you might adjust your specific purpose and message according to the demographic characteristics of the audience.

   a. *Topic:*   "Data Encryption"

   Audience #1: 50% computer science majors, 30% physics majors, 20% fine arts majors

   Audience #2: 40% business majors, 40% history majors, 20% computer science majors

   b. *Topic:*   "Sexual Assault: The Biggest Campus Crime"

   Audience #1: 80% female, 20% male

   Audience #2: 80% male, 20% female

   c. *Topic:*   "The Fall of the Berlin Wall"

   Audience #1: Day class: 70% age 18 to 22, 30% age 23 and over

   Audience #2: Evening class: 50% age 35 and over, 30% age 23 to 34, 20% age 18 to 22

3. For your next speech, design and circulate among your classmates an audience-analysis questionnaire like that discussed on pages 111–113. Use all three kinds of questions explained in the text: fixed-alternative, scale, and open-ended. After you have tabulated the results of the questionnaire, write an analysis explaining what the questionnaire reveals about your audience and what steps you must take to adapt your speech to the audience.

7

Gathering Materials

- Using Your Own Knowledge and Experience
- Doing Library Research
- Searching the Internet
- Interviewing
- Tips for Doing Research

Suppose you are planning a trip to India. You want to know the major sites so you can work out an itinerary. You also need to know what things will cost, where the hostels are located, and how the train and bus systems work. How do you go about gathering all this information?

You can talk to people who have traveled in India and get ideas from them. You can consult guide-books. You can search the Internet for information. If you have traveled to South Asia before, you can draw on that experience. Since you want your trip to be a success, you gather as much information as you can before you leave.

Gathering materials for a speech is like gathering information for any project. There are many resources available if you take advantage of them. You can interview people with specialized knowledge. You can do research on the Internet or in the library. Sometimes you can use your-self as a resource—whenever you have personal experience or above-average knowledge about a subject. Let's turn first to the resource of your own experience.

Using Your Own Knowledge and Experience

Everybody is an expert on something, whether it is video games, child care, or backpacking. As we saw in Chapter 5, we often speak best about subjects with which we are familiar. This is why many teachers encourage students to capitalize on their own knowledge and experience in developing speech topics.

When you choose a topic from your own experience, you may be tempted to depersonalize it by relying solely on facts and figures from books and the Internet. Such outside information is almost always necessary. But supplementing it with the personal touch can really bring your speeches to life.

One student, afflicted with diabetes, chose to explain how a person can live with the disease on a daily basis. He cited statistics on the incidence of diabetes in the United States, identified symptoms of the disease, and explained how it is treated. Along the way, he illustrated his points by talking about his personal experiences. Here is part of what he said:

> Being a diabetic presents a challenge one cannot afford to lose. On a personal note, I have tried not to let my diabetes affect my lifestyle. Last year, I spent nine months traveling in Central and South America. The trip was very memorable, but I had one particularly frightening experience that quickly makes you realize just how vulnerable a diabetic is. On the fifth day of a two-week excursion down the Amazon River, our canoe tipped, dumping everything into the water.
>
> Although I recovered my pack, part of its contents—including my insulin—were swallowed up by the river. Without insulin, I could not eat any food, for if I did, my blood sugar level would become too high and I could eventually go into convulsions, slip into a coma, and die. We returned back up the Amazon and traveled three days until we reached the first village and I could radio for more medicine. I was hot and hungry, but alive.

This speech has color and emotion. By drawing on his own experience, the speaker conveyed his point more meaningfully than he could have in any other way.

Even if your life stories are not that dramatic, you can still put them to work for you. By thinking over your past experiences—gathering material from yourself—you can find many supporting materials for your speeches.

Doing Library Research

Even in this age of the Internet, you will get some of the information for your speeches from the library. It contains many resources to help you find what you need, including librarians, the catalogue, reference works, and databases. We'll look at each in turn.

LIBRARIANS

Too often students waste their time wandering aimlessly in the library because they are afraid to ask for assistance. They don't want to appear stupid or to

FIGURE 7.1   Sample Catalogue Entry for a Book

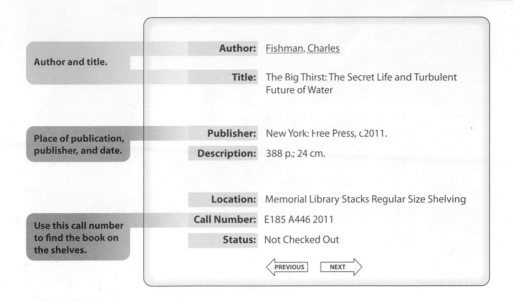

Author and title.

Author:	Fishman, Charles
Title:	The Big Thirst: The Secret Life and Turbulent Future of Water

Place of publication, publisher, and date.

Publisher:	New York: Free Press, c2011.
Description:	388 p.; 24 cm.

Use this call number to find the book on the shelves.

Location:	Memorial Library Stacks Regular Size Shelving
Call Number:	E185 A446 2011
Status:	Not Checked Out

PREVIOUS   NEXT

"bother" anyone. But would you be as sensitive about asking a doctor for help with a medical problem? Librarians are experts in their own field, trained in library use and research methods. If you have a question, don't hesitate to ask a librarian. He or she can help you find your way, locate sources, even track down a specific piece of information.

THE CATALOGUE

The catalogue lists all the books, periodicals, and other resources owned by the library. Although there are many different computer systems for library catalogues, most allow you to search for books by author, title, subject, or keyword. The catalogue also tells you whether the book you want is available or is already checked out.

Figure 7.1 above shows a sample catalogue entry for a book. The key to finding the book on the shelves is the *call number*. Once you have the call number, all you have to do is find the right section of the shelves (or stacks, as they are called in some libraries) and retrieve your book.

REFERENCE WORKS

Reference works are usually kept in a part of the library called the reference section. The right reference work can save you hours of time by putting at your fingertips a wealth of information that might be difficult to locate through the library catalogue. The major kinds of reference works you are likely to use for your speeches are encyclopedias, yearbooks, quotation books, and biographical aids.

Encyclopedias

We are all familiar with general encyclopedias such as the *Encyclopaedia Britannica*. But there are also special encyclopedias that cover their fields in more depth than do general encyclopedias. Some of the most frequently

catalogue

A listing of all the books, periodicals, and other resources owned by a library.

call number

A number used in libraries to classify books and periodicals and to indicate where they can be found on the shelves.

reference work

A work that synthesizes a large amount of related information for easy access by researchers.

used special encyclopedias are the *African American Encyclopedia,* the *Encyclopedia of Religion,* and the *McGraw-Hill Encyclopedia of Science and Technology.*

Yearbooks

As the name implies, yearbooks are published annually. They contain an amazing amount of current information that would otherwise be all but impossible to track down. Two of the most valuable yearbooks are *Facts on File* and *World Almanac and Book of Facts.*

Quotation Books

The best-known collection of quotations is *Bartlett's Familiar Quotations.* With more than 25,000 quotations from historical and contemporary figures, it has long been regarded as an indispensable source for speakers and writers alike. Other excellent quotation books include the *Oxford Dictionary of Quotations, The New Quotable Woman,* and *Ancient Echoes: Native American Words of Wisdom.*

Biographical Aids

When you need information about people in the news, you can turn to one of the many reference works that contain brief life and career facts about contemporary men and women. The most popular biographical aids are published by Who's Who, which produces such titles as *International Who's Who* and *Who's Who in America.* More specialized biographical aids include *Contemporary Black Biography, Dictionary of Hispanic Biography,* and *Who's Who Among Asian Americans.*

newspaper and periodical database

A research aid that catalogues articles from a large number of magazines, journals, and newspapers.

NEWSPAPER AND PERIODICAL DATABASES

Newspaper and periodical databases allow you to locate articles in thousands of publications, including *Time, Atlantic,* the *New York Times,* and the *Wall*

Street Journal. Type a subject in your database's search box, and citations for articles on your subject will appear on screen.

In some cases, you may get an *abstract* of the article in addition to—or instead of—the full article. Keep in mind that the abstract is only a summary of the article. You should *never* cite an article in your speech on the basis of the abstract alone. Always consult the full article.

The exact databases you can use will depend on what is available through your library. Here are three major databases; odds are that your library will have at least one of them.

> *ProQuest.* An excellent database that indexes thousands of periodicals and newspapers. Figure 7.2 below shows a sample screen from ProQuest with a magazine citation and abstract.

> *LexisNexis Academic.* This database provides full-text access to more than 45,000 information sources, including magazines, legal documents, and television broadcast transcripts. LexisNexis also furnishes articles from more than 500 U.S. and international newspapers.

> *World News Connection.* Provides full-text articles from more than 2,000 international sources, including newspapers, speeches, broadcasts, books, and reports.

ACADEMIC DATABASES

At colleges and universities around the world, experts are researching almost every aspect of the natural world and human society. Their work appears in respected, peer-reviewed journals. Academic databases make those journals available to you.

FIGURE 7.2 Sample Periodical Entry from ProQuest

Citation: includes title of article, author, name of magazine, place of publication, and date.

Drivers Not Wanted
Joe Brown. Wired. San Francisco: Jan 2011. Vol. 19, Iss. 1; pg. 94.

Related subjects. Click on these for additional articles.

Subjects:	Automobiles, Technology, Sensors, Product testing, Innovations
Source type:	Periodical
Word Count:	1695

Abstract of article. Use this to decide whether you want to read the full text.

Abstract:
Self-driving vehicles are paving the way toward truly smart cars. Engineers at Google are testing a fleet of self-driving Toyota Priuses in San Francisco. Such cars are not yet available to consumers, but results to date are impressive and reliable.

The best place to find scholarly research is in one of the following academic databases. Because each searches across different academic disciplines, you should be able to find what you need in one of the databases.

InfoTrac OneFile. Provides access to more than 100 million scholarly articles in areas from economics and sociology to science and medicine.

JSTOR. In addition to cataloguing more than 1,000 academic journals in various disciplines, JSTOR allows you to search images, letters, and other primary documents.

Google Scholar. A fast and easy way to search a broad range of scholarly literature. Advanced search tools let you narrow your search by author, publication, date, and subject matter.

Searching the Internet

The Internet has been called the world's biggest library. But unlike a library, the Internet has no central information desk, no librarians, no catalogue, and no reference section. Nor does it have a person or department in charge of determining whether materials are of high quality. You can unearth a great deal of information on the Internet, but you cannot always find the same range and depth as in a good library. This is why experts advise that you use the Internet to supplement, not to replace, library research.

In this section, we will look at ways you can go beyond browsing the Web and turn it into a powerful research tool for your speeches. After discussing search engines and other resources for conducting efficient, focused inquiries, we'll explain how to evaluate the reliability and objectivity of the research materials you find on the Web.

SEARCH ENGINES

Search engines are the key to finding materials on the Internet. There are numerous search engines, but the most widely used by far is Google. In addition to providing access to billions of Web pages, it has specialized search tools devoted to images, video, news, blogs, and finance.

The question is: How can you use Google and other search engines *systematically* to find what you need? The answer is: Develop a search strategy that will allow you to zero in precisely on the information required for your speech.

Suppose you are using Google to look for information about sports injuries among college cheerleaders. If you simply enter the word *cheerleading* in the search box, you will get a list of every document catalogued by Google that contains the word *cheerleading*—more than 45 million. Some will deal with sports injuries among college cheerleaders, but the vast majority will not. Scanning through everything to find what you need would be impossible.

How do you limit your search to get manageable results? If you type *college cheerleading* in Google's search box, you will still come up with 2.5 million citations. However, if you type "college cheerleading" in quotation marks, you will get only documents that contain the exact phrase "college cheerleading"— 312,000 in all.

Research gives speakers facts and figures to support their ideas. Gary Locke, U.S. Ambassador to China, uses a wide range of supporting materials in his addresses to domestic and international audiences alike.

This is much better, but it's still too many to go through one by one. So you narrow your search still further. This time you type the following entry into Google's search box:

"college cheerleading" + "sports injury"

The + sign limits the search to items that contain both sets of keywords, "college cheerleading" and "sports injury." This time you get a list of 1,360 documents, all of which deal specifically with sports injuries among college cheerleaders. You won't be able to look through all 1,360, but usually you don't need to go past the first few pages of results. After that, you will run into lots of repetition and lower-quality sites.

Google also allows you to narrow your search by the kind of research source that will serve you best. Once your search terms are in the Google search box, you can click on *news* at the top of the page to explore recent news stories that mention "college cheerleading" and "sports injury." You can also click on *images, videos, blogs, scholar,* or *books* to search those kinds of resources. If nothing appears for "college cheerleading" and "sports injury" in these specialized categories, try removing the quotation marks and see what happens.

Of course, you will have to adjust your search terms depending on the kind of material you're looking for, but once you learn the basic principles for doing precise, pinpointed searches, you will greatly increase your odds of finding exactly what you need for your speeches.

SPECIALIZED RESEARCH RESOURCES

Search engines are extremely helpful, but they are not the only vehicles for finding information. The following specialized resources concentrate on sites that are most likely to be helpful as you work on your speeches.[1]

Virtual Libraries

Search engines help you find what's on the Internet, but they don't evaluate the quality of the sources they retrieve. Librarians and other information specialists are working to make it easier to locate reliable, high-quality Web resources. One result of their efforts is virtual libraries—search engines that combine Internet technology with traditional library methods of assessing data.

The best virtual library on the Internet is a merger of two previous virtual libraries—Librarians' Internet Index and Internet Public Library. Now called ipl2 (www.ipl.org), this site has more than 20,000 entries organized into 12 main topics, including arts and humanities, education, and health and medical sciences (see Figure 7.3 below). In addition, ipl2 links to a large number of reference sites, as well as to a wide range of constantly evolving special collections.

Government Resources

One of the great strengths of the Internet as a research tool is the access it provides to government documents and publications. Whether you are looking for information from the federal government or from a state or local agency, chances are you can find it by starting your search at one of these Web sites:

USA.gov (www.usa.gov). One-stop shopping for all U.S. government information on the Internet. Provides links to more than 250 million Web pages from federal, state, local, and tribal governments.

Statistical Abstract (www.census.gov/compendia/statab). The standard reference source for numerical information on social, political, and economic aspects of American life. Compiled by the Census Bureau, its incredible array of facts are organized in table form.

World Factbook (www.cia.gov/library/publications/the-world-factbook). Published annually by the Central Intelligence Agency, the *World Factbook* is a rich compendium of information on every country in the world. Topics include people, government, economy, communication, transportation, and transnational issues.

FIGURE 7.3   Subject Screen from ipl2

The Special Case of Wikipedia

With more than 18 million articles, Wikipedia is the biggest encyclopedia in human history. Each month, some 400 million people access one or more of its articles, making it the seventh most visited Web site in the world.

But is Wikipedia a reliable source of information? Several years ago, it was not. Today, however, its reliability ratings are as high as those for print encyclopedias.[2] Major articles have been edited and refined over time to improve currency and accuracy. Articles still in development are flagged so readers know not to take their information at face value.

The most important thing to know about Wikipedia is that it can be a good place to *start* learning about a topic, but it is not a good place to end. Because of its convenience, Wikipedia is used by many people—including teachers and journalists—as a source of basic information. But experienced researchers know not to rely on it as their sole source of information.

One benefit of Wikipedia is that its major articles are followed by an extensive set of additional resources. Those resources include footnotes, a list of references, external links, and, in some cases, video and/or still images. If you take advantage of these resources, they will lead you to a vast amount of information beyond that in Wikipedia.

EVALUATING INTERNET DOCUMENTS

When you do research in a library, everything you find has been evaluated in one way or another before it gets to you. Books, magazines, and journals have editorial procedures to determine whether a given work should or should not be published. Once a work is published, it has to be approved by the acquisitions staff for inclusion in the library.

✔ checklist

Evaluating Internet Documents

YES	NO	
☐	☐	1. Is the author of the document clearly identified?
☐	☐	2. If the author is identified, is he or she an expert on the topic?
☐	☐	3. If the author is not an expert, can his or her opinions be accepted as objective and unbiased?
☐	☐	4. If the author is not identified, can the sponsoring organization be determined?
☐	☐	5. Does the sponsoring organization have a reputation for expertise and objectivity?
☐	☐	6. Does the document include a copyright date, publication date, or date of last revision?
☐	☐	7. If a date is included, is the document recent enough to cite in my speech?

The Internet, of course, is a very different story. Anyone with a computer and access to the Internet can share his or her opinions with a discussion group, publish an electronic newsletter, or create a personal Web page. Never has the adage been more true than when applied to the Internet: "Don't believe everything you read."

In Chapter 8, we will discuss how to judge the soundness of supporting materials in general. Here we look at three criteria you can use to help distinguish between the jewels and the junk on the Internet.[3]

Authorship

Is the author of the Web document you are assessing clearly identified? If so, what are his or her qualifications? Is the author an expert on the topic? Can her or his data and opinions be accepted as objective and unbiased? Just as you should not cite a book or magazine article without identifying the author and his or her credentials, so you should not cite an electronic work in the absence of this information.

In a book or magazine article, information about the author is usually fairly easy to find. Too often, this is not true on the Internet. If you can't find information about the author in the document itself, look for a link to the author's homepage or to another site that explains the author's credentials.

Often you can learn about an author by typing his or her name in the Google search box. If the author is an accepted authority on the subject, there's a good chance Google will turn up information about his or her credentials, publications, and affiliation.

Sponsorship

Many Web documents are published by businesses, government agencies, public-interest groups, and the like rather than by individual authors. In such cases, you must judge whether the sponsoring organization is impartial enough to cite in your speech. Is the organization objective in its research and fair-minded in its statements? Is it economically unbiased with regard to the issue under discussion? Does it have a history of accuracy and nonpartisanship?

Over the years, some organizations have developed strong reputations for their expertise and objectivity. Many of these are public-interest groups such as Consumers Union, Common Cause, and the American Cancer Society. Others include the National Archives, Centers for Disease Control, and similar government agencies. Private think tanks such as RAND, the Cato Institute, and the Brookings Institution often have definite political leanings but are usually well respected for the quality and substance of their research.

One way to gauge the credibility of an organization is to type its name into Google. If commentators have raised serious questions about an organization, those questions will usually surface in the first few pages of search results.

You can also check the *About* link on the organization's homepage. Often the resulting screen will identify the site's founders, purpose, or philosophy. If the homepage does not contain an *About* link, this may be a sign that the sponsoring organization is less than forthright and does not meet the necessary standards of objectivity and expertise.

What if you can't verify the credentials of an author or identify a credible sponsoring organization for an Internet document? The answer is easy: Don't use the document in your speech!

sponsoring organization

An organization that, in the absence of a clearly identified author, is responsible for the content of a document on the Internet.

After receiving your master's degree in education administration, you took a job at the state department of education. At the request of the governor, your section of the department has developed a new early childhood intervention program for children from impoverished households.

Now you have been asked to help publicize the program and to build support for it. You will be speaking to church groups, teachers' associations, family advocacy groups, and others with an interest in children's welfare. You want to prepare a talk that makes good use of statistics and expert testimony to demonstrate the value of early childhood education programs, especially for poor children.

As part of your research, you decide to look on the Web for supporting materials. List three reputable Web sites that provide useful statistics or testimony on the value of early childhood education. Explain why each Web site is reputable and list one statistic or expert quotation you obtain from each source.

Recency

One of the advantages of using the Internet for research is that it often has more recent information than you can find in print sources. But just because a document is on the Internet does not mean its facts and figures are up-to-the-minute.

The best way to determine the recency of an Internet document is to look for a copyright date, publication date, or date of last revision at the top or bottom of the document. If you are using a source located through a virtual library, you can usually be confident of its currency, as well as its objectivity and reliability. News, government, and academic sites also usually include the date on which a document was last updated.

Once you know the date of the document, you can determine whether it is current enough to use in your speech. This is especially important with regard to statistics, which you should never cite from an undated source, whether in print or on the Internet.

Of course, the date of a Web page is easy to change, so someone who wants to make information appear up-to-date can easily do so. But if you have already verified the credibility of the author and the sponsoring organization, you can usually assume that the date of the information is valid. If you can't find the date on which a Web document was created or last modified, search for another work whose recency you can verify.

Interviewing

Most people think of interviewing in terms of job interviews or conversations with celebrities. But there is another kind of interview—the research (or investigative) interview. Among journalists, it is a time-honored way to collect information. It is also an excellent way to gather materials for speeches.

When done well, interviewing (like many things) looks deceptively easy. In practice, it is a complex and demanding art. The principles of effective interviewing fall into three groups—what to do before the interview, what to do during the interview, and what to do after the interview.

To illustrate, we'll follow the entire interview process for a hypothetical speech about current issues in college athletics.

BEFORE THE INTERVIEW

research interview

An interview conducted to gather information for a speech.

The outcome of most interviews is decided by how well the interviewer prepares. Here are five steps you should take ahead of time to ensure a successful outcome.

Define the Purpose of the Interview

You have done Internet and library research about current issues in college athletics and have a good grasp of the major points of view. But you still have many questions about the situation at your school. You decide that the only way to get answers is to interview someone associated with the athletic program. In that decision you have begun to formulate a purpose for the interview.

Decide Whom to Interview

There are several possibilities, but you elect to start at the top—with the athletic director. That may seem a bit presumptuous, but in dealing with administrative organizations, it is usually best to go to the leaders first. They are likely to have a broad understanding of the issues. And if you need more specific information, they can get it for you or put you in touch with the right person.

Arrange the Interview

Because the athletic director is a busy person, you work out a plan for setting up the interview. Knowing that it's easier to brush off someone over e-mail or the telephone than in person, you go to the athletic office to request the interview. The athletic director agrees, and you set up the interview for three days later.

Decide Whether to Record the Interview

The major advantage of recording an interview is that it gives you an exact record you can check later for direct quotes and important facts. Even if you record the interview, however, you should still take notes by hand in case of technical malfunctions.

If the athletic director does not want the interview recorded, you will need to rely solely on your handwritten notes. Whatever you do, *never* record a conversation without the knowledge or consent of the person being interviewed. Not only is it unethical to do so, but the interviewee is bound to find out and you will only cause yourself trouble.

Prepare Your Questions

You now face the most important of your preinterview tasks—working out the questions you will ask. You should devise questions that are sensible, intelligent, and meaningful. Here are some types of questions to *avoid:*

■ Questions you can answer without the interview. (How many sports does your school offer? What is the size of its athletic budget?) Queries like these just waste the subject's time and make you look foolish. Research this information before the interview.

- Leading questions. (Opinion polls show that most Americans believe athletics today have little relation to the academic purposes of a college education. You *do* think it's a problem, too, *don't you*?).

- Hostile, loaded questions. (I think it's disgraceful that many schools spend gobs of money on salaries for football and basketball coaches. Don't you think good teachers for all students are more important than coaches for a few athletes? What do you say to *that*, hmmm?)

You need not shy away from tough questions; just phrase them as neutrally as possible and save them until near the end of the interview. That way, if your interviewee becomes irritated or uncooperative, you'll still get most of the information you want.

Although some experienced journalists conduct interviews with only a few key-word notes on the areas to be covered, you want to be sure not to forget anything during the interview. So you arrange your questions in the order you want to ask them and take the list with you to the interview.

DURING THE INTERVIEW

Every interview is unique. Because the session will seldom go exactly as you plan, you need to be alert and flexible. Here are several steps you can take to make things proceed smoothly.

Dress Appropriately and Be on Time

The athletic director has a busy schedule and is doing you a favor by agreeing to an interview, so you show up on time. Since the interview is a special occasion, you dress appropriately. This is one way of confirming that you regard the interview as serious business.

Interviewing people with expertise on your speech topic can provide valuable information. When conducting an interview, be sure to listen attentively and to take accurate notes.

Repeat the Purpose of the Interview

The athletic director invites you into the office; you exchange a few introductory remarks. Now, before you plunge into your questions, you take a moment to restate the purpose of the interview. You are more likely to get clear, helpful answers if your subject knows why you are following a certain line of questioning.

Set Up the Recorder, if You Are Using One

If your subject has agreed to being recorded, keep one principle in mind: The recorder should be as casual and inconspicuous as possible. Most cell phones now offer applications for audio recording, giving you an easy way to capture the interview.

Keep the Interview on Track

Your goal in the interview is to get answers to the questions you have prepared. Suppose, however, that in answering one of your questions, the athletic director brings up an important point that is not covered on your list of questions. Rather than ignoring the point, you decide to pursue the new issue. You pose a couple questions about it, get helpful answers, then return to your prepared questions.

Throughout the interview, you pursue new leads when they appear, improvise follow-up questions when called for, then move on again in an orderly fashion. When the interview is over, you have answers to all your prepared questions—and a lot more.

Listen Carefully

During the interview, you listen attentively to the athletic director's answers. When you don't understand something, you ask for clarification. Chances are the athletic director will have been misquoted more than once in the press, so he or she will be happy to oblige.

Don't Overstay Your Welcome

Keep within the stipulated time period for the interview, unless your subject clearly wants to prolong the session. When the interview is over, you thank the athletic director for taking the time to talk with you.

AFTER THE INTERVIEW

Although the interview is over, the interviewing process is not. You must now review and transcribe your notes.

Review Your Notes as Soon as Possible

When you leave the athletic director's office, the interview is fresh in your mind. You know what the cryptic comments and scrawls in your notes mean. But as time passes, the details will become hazy. Don't let something like this true story happen to you:

> Years ago, a prominent woman—writer and diplomat—was being interviewed by a young reporter. Among other things, the reporter asked about hobbies and leisure activities. The woman replied that she enjoyed skeet shooting and raised Siamese cats. The reporter scribbled in her notes "shoots" and "cats"—but didn't

bother to put a comma or a dash between the words. The interview was published. And ever since, that prominent woman has been trying to live down the reputation that she "shoots cats."

In reviewing your notes, try to concentrate on two things—discovering the main points that emerged during the interview and pulling out specific information that might be useful in your speech.

Transcribe Your Notes

Once you settle on the most important ideas and information from the interview, you should transcribe that material so it is in the same format as the rest of your research notes (see pages 134–136). By putting all your research notes in a consistent format, you can arrange and rearrange them easily when you start to organize your speech.[4]

Tips for Doing Research

Few people regard doing research as one of life's great joys. But there are ways to make it less tedious and more productive. Here are four ways that are guaranteed to help.

START EARLY

The biggest mistake students make when faced with a research project is waiting too long to begin. The longer you wait, the more problems you will encounter. You may find that a vital book has been checked out of the library or that you no longer have time to arrange a crucial interview. No matter what kind of research you do, you can be sure of one thing: It will *always* take longer than you expect.

Starting early also gives you plenty of time to think about what you find. In researching, you will collect much more material than you will actually use. Preparing a speech is a little like constructing a jigsaw puzzle. Once you gather the pieces, you have to decide how they fit together. The more time you give yourself, the more likely you are to get the pieces to fit just right.

MAKE A PRELIMINARY BIBLIOGRAPHY

In your research, you will run across the titles of books, magazine articles, Internet documents, and so on that look as if they might contain helpful information about your speech topic. Enter *each* item you find in your preliminary bibliography, even though you don't know whether you will use it in your speech. As a result, you may have 15 or 20 works in your preliminary bibliography. But remember that you have not yet examined all those works. Of the 15 or 20 preliminary sources, only 7 or 8 are likely to be of much use. Those final sources will be listed on the bibliography you turn in with your speech outline (see Chapter 11, page 208).

There are two major formats for citing documents in a bibliography. One comes from the Modern Language Association (MLA), the other from the

preliminary bibliography

A list compiled early in the research process of works that look as if they might contain helpful information about a speech topic.

American Psychological Association (APA). Both are widely used by communication scholars; ask your instructor which he or she prefers.

Whichever format you adopt, make sure your bibliography is clear, accurate, and consistent. Figure 7.4 (page 135) lists sample MLA and APA citations for 10 kinds of sources that are cited most frequently in student speeches.

TAKE NOTES EFFICIENTLY

Asia Marshall started her speech preparation with the best of intentions. She was excited about her topic, "Great Women of Jazz," and she started research on the Internet the same day the assignment was announced. She found several interesting sources and took some notes about them. That evening, she checked out a fascinating book about Billie Holiday and read it straight through. She didn't bother taking notes because she was sure she'd remember it all. The next day, she looked through the *Encyclopedia of Jazz* and jotted a few notes on the back of her syllabus.

Then Asia remembered that she had a test in another class. Somewhat panicked, she put aside her speech research to study. When she got back to the speech, the deadline was only four days away. She dug out her notes, but what did they mean? One said, "Medford—*important!!!*" But who or what was Medford? Asia had thought she'd remember all about the Billie Holiday book, but without notes, it was mostly a blur by now. With a sense of doom, she faced up to the fact that she would have to start over—and finish in four days.

Sound familiar? This has happened to almost everyone at least once. But once is enough. There's a better way to take research notes. Here is a method that has worked well for many students:

Take Plenty of Notes
Few things are more aggravating than trying to recall some bit of information you ran across in your research but neglected to record. The moral of Asia Marshall's story is clear: If there is even an outside chance that you may need a piece of information, make a note of it. This will take a little extra time in the short run, but in the long run it can save you much grief.

Record Notes in a Consistent Format
You should use the same format for all your research notes, whether they come from Internet sources, library documents, or personal interviews. In each case, record the note, the source of the note, and a heading indicating the subject of the note (see Figure 7.5 on page 136).

The importance of the subject heading cannot be overemphasized. It is the first step to more efficient note taking. By telling you at a glance what each note is about, it will simplify the task of organizing your notes when you start to compose the speech. Once you start using subject headings, you'll see how helpful they can be.

Make a Separate Entry for Each Note
Many students try to record all the information from one source on a single note. This is not an effective procedure because it makes your notes almost

FIGURE 7.4   Sample Bibliography Formats

Book: Single author.

MLA: Chua, Amy. *Battle Hymn of the Tiger Mother*. New York: Penguin, 2011. Print.

APA: Chua, A. (2011). *Battle hymn of the tiger mother*. New York, NY: Penguin.

Signed magazine article.

MLA: Adler, Jerry. "The Growing Menace from Superweeds." *Scientific American* May 2011: 74–79. Print.

APA: Adler, J. (2011, May). The growing menace from superweeds. *Scientific American, 304*(5), 74–79.

Signed newspaper article.

MLA: Tucker, Neely. "Your Novel Got Rejected? Join the E-Book Gold Rush!" *Washington Post* 8 May 2011: E1+. Print.

APA: Tucker, N. (2011, May 8). Your novel got rejected? Join the e-book gold rush! *The Washington Post*, pp. E1, E4.

Signed article in reference work.

MLA: Emanuel, Kerry A. "Hurricanes." *Encyclopedia of Climate and Weather*. Ed. Stephen H. Schneider, Michael Mastrandrea, and Terry L. Root. 2nd ed. New York: Oxford University Press, 2011. Print.

APA: Emanuel, K. (2011). Hurricanes. In S. H. Schneider, M. Mastrandrea, & T. L. Root (Eds.), *Encyclopedia of climate and weather* 2nd ed., (pp. 138–141). New York, NY: Oxford University Press.

Personal interview.

MLA: Hernandez, Claudia. Personal interview. 5 Oct. 2011.

APA: C. Hernandez (personal communication, October 5, 2011).

Speech or lecture.

MLA: Chung, Cindy. "The Asian Diaspora." Asian American Studies 160: Asian American History. University of Wisconsin. 16 Sept. 2011. Lecture.

APA: Chung, C. (2011, September). *The Asian diaspora*. Lecture presented in Asian American Studies 160: Asian American History. University of Wisconsin.

Television program.

MLA: "Lady Gaga and the Art of Fame." Narr. Anderson Cooper. *Sixty Minutes*. CBS. WUSA, Washington, 13 Feb. 2011. Television.

APA: Cooper, A. (Narrator). (2011). Lady Gaga and the art of fame [Television newsmagazine episode segment]. In J. Hamlin (Producer), *Sixty Minutes*. New York, NY: CBS News.

Online government publication.

MLA: United States. Dept. of Labor. Bureau of Labor Statistics. "Women at Work." Mar. 2011. *BLS Spotlight on Statistics*. Web. 9 May 2011.

APA: U.S. Department of Labor, Bureau of Labor Statistics. (2011). Women at work. In *BLS spotlight on statistics*. Retrieved from http://www.bls.gov/spotlight/2011/women

Online newspaper article.

MLA: Bowles, Scott. "Can 3-D Technology Save the Moviemaking Business?" *USA Today*. USA Today, 28 Mar. 2011. Web. 3 Apr. 2011.

APA: Bowles, S. (2011, March 28). Can 3-D technology save the moviemaking business? *USA Today*. Retrieved from http://www.usatoday.com

Online magazine article.

MLA: Conley, Dalton. "Wired for Distraction: Kids and Social Media." *Time*. Time and Cable News Network, 19 Mar. 2011. Web. 3 May 2011.

APA: Conley, D. (2011, March 19). Wired for distraction: Kids and social media. *Time, 177*(7). Retrieved from http://www.time.com

FIGURE 7.5   Sample Research Note

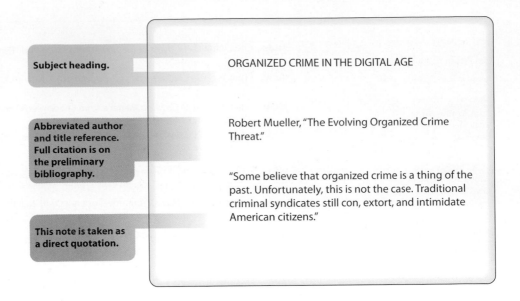

Subject heading.

ORGANIZED CRIME IN THE DIGITAL AGE

Abbreviated author and title reference. Full citation is on the preliminary bibliography.

Robert Mueller, "The Evolving Organized Crime Threat."

This note is taken as a direct quotation.

"Some believe that organized crime is a thing of the past. Unfortunately, this is not the case. Traditional criminal syndicates still con, extort, and intimidate American citizens."

impossible to review and organize. A better approach is to make a separate note for *each* quotation or piece of information you record. Although you may end up with several notes from the same document, you will find that this approach allows you to keep better track of your research.

Distinguish Among Direct Quotations, Paraphrases, and Your Own Ideas

As we saw in Chapter 2, it's easy to plagiarize accidentally by not taking careful research notes. As you do research for your speeches, be sure to use quotation marks whenever you copy the exact words of a source. If you paraphrase, rather than quote verbatim, don't forget to include the source when you record the note.

By keeping track of quotations and paraphrases, you will be able to separate your own words and ideas from those of other people. This will help you avoid the trap of inadvertent plagiarism when you put your speech together.

THINK ABOUT YOUR MATERIALS AS YOU RESEARCH

Students often approach research as a mechanical routine that simply involves gathering the materials to be used in a speech or paper. But when done properly, research can be extremely creative.

If you *think about* what you are finding in your research, you will see your topic just a little bit differently with each note you take. You will find new relationships, develop new questions, explore new angles. You will, in short, begin to write the speech in your head even as you do the research. As you learn more about the topic, you will formulate a central idea, begin to sketch out main points and supporting points, experiment with ways of

To take research notes efficiently, record them in a consistent format; make a separate entry for each note; and distinguish among direct quotations, paraphrases, and your own ideas.

organizing your thoughts. You may even change your point of view, as did this student:

Francesca Lopez began her speech preparation with this central idea in mind: "Wild animals make more interesting pets than dogs and cats." She went about her research conscientiously, spending many hours online and in the library. In the process, she came upon some disturbing information about the capture of wild animals. She read that young chimpanzees and other apes were literally snatched out of their mothers' arms, and that the mothers were afterward heard to cry almost like humans. Back in her room that night, Francesca couldn't get her mind off the baby chimpanzees.

The next day, Francesca found some more disturbing material. One source told about the extraordinarily high death rate of wild animals during shipment to the United States. Again, that night Francesca brooded about the young animals dying of fear and cold in the cargo holds of airplanes.

By the time she finished her research, Francesca's central idea was completely different. When she spoke, her central idea was "The importation of wild animals for use as pets is inhumane."

This is an example of creative research—and of critical thinking. Francesca kept her mind open, read everything she could find about her topic, and thought seriously about what she found. Because of this thoughtful approach, she changed her mind.[5]

Your own speech preparation may not cause you to reverse your position, but it should give you new insights into your topic. If you approach research in this way, you may find that the time you spend researching is the most productive of all the time you devote to preparing your speech.

Summary

There are many resources you can use when gathering information for a speech. If you have personal experience or above-average knowledge about a topic, you can use yourself as a resource. Most of the time, however, you will need outside information, which you can get in the library, on the Internet, or by interviewing people with specialized information.

Finding what you need in the library is largely a matter of knowing how to search for information. The catalogue lists all the books, periodicals, and other resources owned by the library. Databases help you find articles in magazines, newspapers, and journals. The reference section includes encyclopedias, yearbooks, biographical aids, and books of quotations. If you have trouble finding something, don't hesitate to ask a librarian.

When looking for information online, you need a search strategy that will help you find exactly what you need. Given the lack of editorial review for most documents on the Web, it is especially important to evaluate the authorship, sponsoring organization, and recency of the research materials you find there.

You can also get information by conducting a personal interview. Before the interview, you should define its purpose, decide whom you are going to interview, and prepare the interview questions. Once the interview begins, be sure to listen attentively and to take accurate notes. Afterward, review and transcribe your notes as soon as possible.

No matter what sources you draw upon in gathering information, your research will be more effective if you start early and make a preliminary bibliography to keep track of all the books, articles, and Internet documents that look as if they might be helpful. By learning to take research notes effectively, you will save yourself time and energy every step of the way. And if you think about your materials as you research, you may find that gathering materials is the most creative part of your speech preparation.

Key Terms

catalogue *(121)*

call number *(121)*

reference work *(121)*

newspaper and periodical database *(122)*

abstract *(123)*

academic database *(123)*

virtual library *(126)*

sponsoring organization *(128)*

research interview *(130)*

preliminary bibliography *(133)*

Review Questions

After reading this chapter, you should be able to answer the following questions:

1. Why is it important to draw on your own knowledge and experience in gathering materials for your speeches?
2. What are five resources for finding what you need in the library?

3. What are three criteria for evaluating the soundness of research materials that you find on the Internet?

4. What are the three stages of a research interview? What should you do in each stage to help ensure a successful interview?

5. Why is it important to start your speech research early?

6. What is a preliminary bibliography? Why is it helpful to you in researching a speech?

7. What four things should you do to take research notes efficiently?

connect

For further review, go to the LearnSmart study module for this chapter.

Exercises for Critical Thinking

1. Using one of the periodical and newspaper databases discussed on pages 122–123, find three magazine or newspaper articles on the topic of your next speech. Prepare a preliminary bibliography entry for each article. Read the full text of the articles and assess their value for your speech.

2. Using Google or another search engine, find three high-quality documents on the topic of your next speech. Prepare a preliminary bibliography entry for each document. Read the full text of the documents and assess them in light of the criteria for evaluating Internet documents discussed on pages 127–129.

3. Plan to conduct an interview for one of your classroom speeches. Be sure to follow the guidelines presented in this chapter for effective interviewing. Afterward, evaluate the interview. Did you prepare for it adequately? Did you get the information you needed? What would you do differently if you could conduct the interview again?

AFFORDABLE CA

8

Supporting Your Ideas

Examples

Statistics

Testimony

Citing Sources Orally

An avid tea drinker, Laura Kramer decided to give her first classroom speech on the health benefits of tea. Part of her speech ran like this:

"If your family medical history shows that you are likely to develop heart disease, high cholesterol, circulatory problems, or Parkinson's disease, you need to be drinking more tea. Black tea and green tea have been proven to reduce the risk of many serious health problems. I've been drinking tea for years, and I am extremely healthy. If you start drinking tea, you can be healthy too."

After the speech, Laura's classmates were polite but skeptical. As one remarked, "Laura made some interesting points, but she's no doctor. I'd be more convinced if she had provided medical evidence to back up her opinion."

Good speeches are not composed of hot air and generalizations. They need strong supporting materials to bolster the speaker's point of view. In Laura's case, there is evidence that tea is helpful in treating some ailments, but most of the claims about its health benefits have yet to be verified by research. So Laura's listeners were right to be skeptical about her vague, unsupported generalizations.

The problem with generalizations is that they don't answer the three questions listeners always ask of a speaker: "What do you mean?" "Why should I believe you?" "So what?" Consider the following statements:

General	Less General	Specific
There are lots of community colleges in the United States.	Community colleges enroll a large number of students and play a vital role in American higher education.	According to the Department of Education, there are more than 1,100 community colleges in the United States. They enroll some 12 million students each year, which is 44 percent of all U.S. undergraduates.

Which statement do you find most interesting? Most convincing? Chances are you prefer that in the right-hand column. It is sharp and specific, clear and credible—just what a speech needs to come alive.

The skillful use of supporting materials often makes the difference between a poor speech and a good one. In Chapters 15 and 17, we will look at special uses of supporting materials in informative and persuasive speeches. In this chapter, we focus on the basic kinds of supporting materials—examples, statistics, and testimony—and on general principles for using them effectively and responsibly.

supporting materials

The materials used to support a speaker's ideas. The three major kinds of supporting materials are examples, statistics, and testimony.

Examples

The attack came after daybreak. The *Delta Ranger*, a cargo ship carrying bauxite, was steaming through the ink-blue Indian Ocean about 200 miles off Somalia's coast. A crewman on the bridge spied two speedboats zooming straight at the port side of his vessel. Moments later, bullets tore into the bridge, and vapor trails from rocket-propelled grenades streaked across the bow—pirates.

These lines are from the opening of an article in *Smithsonian* magazine about modern-day pirates that prey on international shipping. It illustrates a device well known to magazine writers—and public speakers: Get the audience involved.

See how skillfully this example accomplishes the goal. It gives us a specific incident to focus on (the attack on the *Delta Ranger*). It sets the stage with details of time, place, color, and action. We can almost see ourselves on the bridge of the *Delta Ranger*, watching the pirates' speedboats and hearing their bullets tear into the ship. We would not be nearly as involved if the article had merely said, "Pirates are a serious menace to international shipping."

Research has shown that vivid, concrete examples have a strong impact on listeners' beliefs and actions.[1] Without examples, ideas often seem vague, impersonal, and lifeless. With examples, ideas become specific, personal, and lively. This is nowhere better illustrated than in the Bible and the Koran, both of which use all manner of stories, parables, and anecdotes to make abstract principles clear and compelling. There are several kinds of examples you may want to try in your speeches.

example

A specific case used to illustrate or represent a group of people, ideas, conditions, experiences, or the like.

BRIEF EXAMPLES

Brief examples—also called specific instances—may be referred to in passing to illustrate a point. The following excerpt uses a brief example to illustrate the miraculous nature of recent advances in creating artificial limbs for accident victims:

> Changes in technology have made it possible for doctors to work wonders that once seemed impossible. Roger Charter, for example, lost both his feet when they were crushed in a truck accident. Now he has new feet—made of a springy plastic alloy that duplicates a normal arch. Not only can Roger walk normally, but he can run and play sports again!

Another way to use brief examples is to pile them one upon the other until you create the desired impression. Here is how one speaker used this technique to reinforce the point that Mexican Americans have made many valuable contributions to U.S. life:

> Many of us are familiar with prominent Chicanos and Chicanas such as actress Jessica Alba, boxer Oscar De La Hoya, and guitarist Carlos Santana. But you may be less familiar with other Americans of Mexican origin who have made important contributions to U.S. society. Nancy Lopez played a crucial role in popularizing women's professional golf and won 48 tour championships. Dr. Ellen Ochoa is a former astronaut who logged more than 480 hours in space and invented several optical methods that greatly aid space exploration. Dr. Mario Molina won the 1995 Nobel Prize in Chemistry for his research on the formation and decomposition of the ozone layer.

EXTENDED EXAMPLES

Extended examples are often called narratives, illustrations, or anecdotes. By telling a story vividly and dramatically, they pull listeners into the speech. Here is such an example, from a speech by Sun Yan, a student at Fudan University in Shanghai, China. Participating in China's national English-language speech competition, Sun Yan used an extended example to illustrate the spirit of the Olympic Games:

> In the history of the Olympic Games, there have been many shining stars. Among them was a European girl. With the lapse of time, her name has faded from memory, yet her unbending spirit shall never perish. It was she who highlighted the Olympic Creed.
> In the lead though she had been, she stumbled near the terminus and her leg was injured. Competitors passed her from behind in succession until finally only her weak and lonely figure remained on the track. Doctors came and offered to take her away. Yet she refused. With the only strength left in her, she managed to get up and shuffled feebly to the endpoint with drops of blood along her trail.
> But cheers broke out. Though she failed in the race, the girl won applause from people all over the world. It was she who elucidated the Olympic creed of participation. It was she who instilled perseverance in our minds.[2]

This long example captures vividly the courage of the Olympic runner and her personification of the Olympic spirit. The speaker could merely have said,

brief example

A specific case referred to in passing to illustrate a point.

connect
View this excerpt from "Living in America" in the online Media Library for this chapter (Video 8.1).

extended example

A story, narrative, or anecdote developed at some length to illustrate a point.

connect
View this excerpt from "The Olympic Spirit" in the online Media Library for this chapter (Video 8.2).

"Olympic athletes often display great fortitude," but the story makes the point far more poignantly.

HYPOTHETICAL EXAMPLES

All the examples presented up to now have been factual; the incidents they refer to really happened. Sometimes, however, speakers will use a hypothetical example—one that describes an imaginary situation. Usually such examples are brief stories that relate a general principle.

Here is how one student used a hypothetical example to illustrate the use of honor codes to reduce cheating:

> Imagine this: You're taking your psychology exam when you notice the student sitting next to you is staring at your answers. You also see his open notebook under his desk. You feel your cheeks redden as you become angry that he may get a high score by cheating while you've worked hard to earn your grade. And you feel helpless because you think telling the professor will do nothing.
>
> But now imagine that you attend a school with an honors system. At the beginning of each exam, you sign a statement that says you will not cheat and that you accept the responsibility to report cheating. After the professor hands out the exam, she leaves the room. In this case, you have the power and the duty to report cheaters rather than feel robbed by them.
>
> Such a system has worked elsewhere and it can work at our school. Professor Donald McCabe, president of the Center for Academic Integrity, has surveyed more than 20,000 students at 70 colleges throughout the country, and his research shows that the level of cheating is significantly lower at schools with honor codes than at schools without them.

connect

View this excerpt from "College Cheating: A National Epidemic" in the online Media Library for this chapter (Video 8.3).

This hypothetical example is especially effective. The speaker creates a realistic scenario, relates it directly to her listeners, and gets them involved in the speech. In addition, she uses figures from the president of the Center for Academic Integrity to show that honor codes help reduce the incidence of cheating on college campuses. Whenever you use a hypothetical example, it is a good idea to follow it with statistics or testimony to show that the example is not far-fetched.

TIPS FOR USING EXAMPLES

Use Examples to Clarify Your Ideas

You probably use clarifying examples all the time in everyday conversation. If you were explaining to a friend about different body types, you might say, "Look at Professor Shankar. He's a typical ectomorph—tall, thin, and bony." Examples are an excellent way to clarify unfamiliar or complex ideas. They put abstract ideas into concrete terms that listeners can easily understand.

This principle works exceptionally well in speeches. Suppose you are talking about suspension bridges. You could give a technical description:

> The suspension bridge has a roadway suspended by vertical cables attached to two or more main cables. The main cables are hung on two towers and have their ends anchored in concrete or bedrock.

If your audience were made up of people familiar with structural systems, they might be able to visualize what a suspension bridge looks like. But

No matter what the occasion, personal examples are an excellent way to clarify ideas and to build audience interest. To be most effective, they should be delivered sincerely and with strong eye contact.

for listeners lacking this background, you might want to add a simple example:

Two well-known suspension bridges are the Golden Gate Bridge in San Francisco and the Brooklyn Bridge in New York.

Because almost everyone has at least seen a picture of the Golden Gate Bridge or the Brooklyn Bridge, using them as examples clarifies your meaning quickly and effectively.

Use Examples to Reinforce Your Ideas

In a speech titled "The Dangers of Cell Phones," one student dealt with the long-term health risks of cell phone use. She cited figures from the World Health Organization noting that people who use a cell phone for more than 10 years double their risk of developing brain tumors. She also discussed other problems associated with long-term exposure to cell phone radiation, including headaches, dizziness, circulatory problems, nausea, and cancer.

To reinforce her ideas, the speaker cited the example of Alan Marks, a father of three who developed a golf-ball-sized tumor in his brain from talking on his cell phone an hour a day for 23 years. She talked of Marks's health problems and of how he would have used his speakerphone or headset if he had known the perils of holding his phone next to his ear day after day, year after year.

This example was very effective. It put the medical facts about the dangers of cell phones in vivid, human terms that everyone could understand. When you use such an example, make sure it is representative—that it does not deal with rare or exceptional cases. Your listeners are likely to feel betrayed if they suspect you have chosen an atypical example to prove a general point.

connect

View this portion of "The Dangers of Cell Phones" in the online Media Library for this chapter (Video 8.4).

Use Examples to Personalize Your Ideas

People are interested in people. As social psychologist Elliot Aronson explains, "Most people are more deeply influenced by one clear, vivid, personal example than by an abundance of statistical data."[3] Whenever you talk to a general audience (such as your speech class), you can include examples that will add human interest to your speech. So far in this section, we have seen a number of such examples—the heroic Olympic runner, accident victim Roger Charter, and so on. The abstract becomes more meaningful when applied to a person. Which of the following would you be more likely to respond to?

> There are many hungry families in our community who could benefit from food donations.

Or:

> Let me tell you about Arturo. Arturo is four years old. He has big brown eyes and a mop of black hair and an empty belly. In all his four years on this earth, Arturo has never once enjoyed three square meals in a single day.

Try using examples with human interest in your speeches. You will soon discover why accomplished speakers consider them "the very life of the speech."[4]

Make Your Examples Vivid and Richly Textured

The richly textured example supplies everyday details that bring the example to life. Recall the example on page 143 of the Olympic runner. The speaker provided us with many details about the runner's bravery in the face of adverse conditions. The runner stumbles and injures her leg near the end of the race. She is passed by other competitors until she alone is left on the track. Doctors offer to help, but she refuses their assistance and shuffles to the finish line with drops of blood along her trail.

How much less compelling the example would have been if the speaker had merely said:

> One Olympic runner courageously completed her race despite being injured and exhausted.

Instead, the details let us *see* the runner as she battles through her pain and misfortune. She is much more likely to stay in our minds than a "brave runner who completed her race." The more vivid your examples, the more impact they are likely to have on your audience.

Practice Delivery to Enhance Your Extended Examples

An extended example is just like a story or narrative. Its impact depends as much on delivery as on content. Many students have discovered this the hard way. After spending much time and energy developing a splendid example, they have seen it fall flat because they did not make it vivid and gripping for listeners.

Look again at the speaker in Video 8.2. Notice how she uses her voice to increase the impact of her story about the Olympic runner. Like that speaker, you should think of yourself as a storyteller. Don't rush through your examples as though you were reading the newspaper. Use your voice to get listeners involved. Speak faster here to create a sense of action, slower there to

checklist

Using Examples

YES	NO	
☐	☐	1. Do I use examples to clarify my ideas?
☐	☐	2. Do I use examples to reinforce my ideas?
☐	☐	3. Do I use examples to personalize my ideas?
☐	☐	4. Are my examples representative of what they are supposed to illustrate or prove?
☐	☐	5. Do I reinforce my examples with statistics or testimony?
☐	☐	6. Are my extended examples vivid and richly textured?
☐	☐	7. Have I practiced the delivery of my extended examples to give them dramatic effect?

build suspense. Raise your voice in some places; lower it in others. Pause occasionally for dramatic effect.

Most important, maintain eye contact with your audience. The easiest way to ruin a fine example is to read it from your notes. As you practice the speech, "talk through" your extended examples without relying on your notes. By the day of your speech, you should be able to deliver your extended examples as naturally as if you were telling a story to a group of friends.

Statistics

We live in an age of statistics. Day in and day out we are bombarded with a staggering array of numbers: Keith Urban has sold more than 13 million albums. Drowsiness is a factor in 17 percent of U.S. traffic fatalities. Americans spend $60 billion a year on lottery tickets. The BP oil spill released more than 200 million gallons of oil into the Gulf of Mexico.

What do all these numbers mean? Most of us would be hard-pressed to say. Yet we feel more secure in our knowledge when we can express it numerically. According to Lord Kelvin, the 19th-century physicist, "When you can measure what you are speaking about, and express it in numbers, you know something about it. But when you cannot measure it, when you cannot express it in numbers, your knowledge is . . . meager and unsatisfactory." It is this widely shared belief that makes statistics, when used properly, such an effective way to clarify and support ideas.[5]

statistics

Numerical data.

Like brief examples, statistics are often cited in passing to clarify or strengthen a speaker's points. The following examples show how two students used statistics in their speeches:

To document the number of Chinese students in U.S. colleges and universities: "According to the Institute of International Education, nearly 130,000 Chinese students attended school in the United States last year—a 30 percent increase from the previous year."

To illustrate the dramatic increase in pay for professional athletes: "ESPN reports that just 20 years ago, the highest paid baseball player made $5 million. Today, the highest paid player makes more than $30 million a year."

Statistics can also be used in combination to show the magnitude or seriousness of an issue. We find a good instance of this technique in a student presentation about America's crowded roadways. To demonstrate his point that traffic congestion wastes massive amounts of time and money, the speaker cited the following figures:

According to the Urban Mobility Report from Texas A&M University, Americans collectively spend 4.2 billion hours stuck in traffic each year. All told, traffic congestion results in more than $87 billion in wasted fuel and lost productivity. That number breaks down to about $750 per traveler each year. Clearly, we are wasting far too much time and money on traffic gridlock.

This is a well-supported argument. But what if the speaker had merely said:

Traffic jams are very costly for the United States.

This statement is neither as clear nor as convincing as the one containing statistics. Of course, the audience didn't remember all the numbers, but the purpose of presenting a series of figures is to create an *overall* impact on listeners. What the audience did recall is that an impressive array of statistics supported the speaker's position.

connect

View this excerpt from "Stuck in Traffic" in the online Media Library for this chapter (Video 8.5).

UNDERSTANDING STATISTICS

In his classic book *How to Lie with Statistics,* Darrell Huff exploded the notion that numbers don't lie. Strictly speaking, they don't. But they can be easily manipulated and distorted. For example, which of the following statements is true?

a. Enriched white bread is more nutritious than whole-wheat bread because it contains as much or more protein, calcium, niacin, thiamine, and riboflavin.

b. Whole-wheat bread is more nutritious than white bread because it contains seven times the amount of fiber, plus more iron, phosphorus, and potassium.

As you might expect, *both* statements are true. And you might hear either one of them, depending on who is trying to sell you the bread.

One can play with statistics in all kinds of areas. Which of these statements is true?

a. The cheetah, clocked at 70 miles per hour, is the fastest animal in the world.

b. The pronghorn antelope, clocked at 61 miles per hour, is the fastest animal in the world.

The cheetah, right? Not necessarily. The cheetah can go faster, but only for short sprints. The antelope can maintain its high speed over a much greater distance. So which is faster? It depends on what you're measuring. Put in

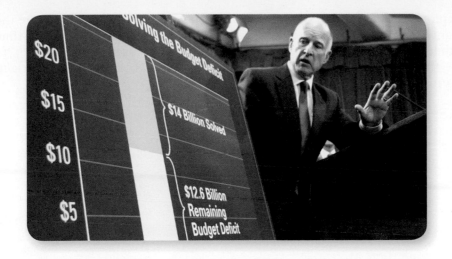

terms of human races, the cheetah would win the hundred-yard dash, but the antelope would win the marathon.

When you are dealing with money, statistics become even trickier. Consider the following facts:

a. In 1940, President Franklin D. Roosevelt earned a salary of $75,000.

b. In 1972, President Richard Nixon earned a salary of $200,000.

c. In 2010, President Barack Obama earned a salary of $400,000.

Which president was paid the most money? In purely mathematical terms, Obama is the highest earner. But a dollar today does not buy as much as it did in 1940, when Franklin Roosevelt was president. One measure of the inflation rate is the Consumer Price Index, which lets us gauge the value of the dollar in any given year against its purchasing power in 1972. If we apply the Consumer Price Index to the three presidents' salaries, we can see how much each earned in 1972 dollars:

a. In 1940, President Franklin D. Roosevelt earned a salary of $192,000.

b. In 1972, President Richard Nixon earned a salary of $200,000.

c. In 2010, President Barack Obama earned a salary of $78,000.

In other words, although Obama has the highest salary, the value of his $400,000 is less than half the value of Roosevelt's $75,000.

The point is that there is usually more to statistics than meets the eye.[6] When you track down statistics for your speeches, be sure to evaluate them in light of the following questions.

Are the Statistics Representative?

Say that on your way to class you choose ten students at random and ask them whether they favor or oppose banning recreational vehicles on public lands. Say also that six approve of such a ban and four do not. Would you then be accurate in claiming that 60 percent of the students on your campus favor banning recreational vehicles from public lands?

Of course not. Ten students is not a big enough sample. But even if it were, other problems would arise. Do the ten students interviewed accurately reflect your school's proportion of freshmen, sophomores, juniors, and seniors? Do they mirror the proportion of male and female students? Are the various majors accurately represented? What about part-time and full-time students? Students of different cultural and religious backgrounds?

In short, make sure your statistics are representative of what they claim to measure.

Are Statistical Measures Used Correctly?

Here are two groups of numbers:

Group A	Group B
7,500	5,400
6,300	5,400
5,000	5,000
4,400	2,300
4,400	1,700

mean

The average value of a group of numbers.

Let us apply to each group three basic statistical measures—the mean, the median, and the mode.

The *mean*—popularly called the average—is determined by summing all the items in a group and dividing by the number of items. The mean for group A is 5,520. For group B it is 3,960.

The *median* is the middle figure in a group once the figures are put in order from highest to lowest. The median for both group A and group B is exactly the same—5,000.

median

The middle number in a group of numbers arranged from highest to lowest.

The *mode* is the number that occurs most frequently in a group of numbers. The mode for group A is 4,400. For group B it is 5,400.

Notice the results:

	Group A	Group B
Mean	5,520	3,960
Median	5,000	5,000
Mode	4,400	5,400

mode

The number that occurs most frequently in a group of numbers.

All these measures have the same goal—to indicate what is typical or characteristic of a certain group of numbers. Yet see how different the results are, depending on which measure you use.

The differences among the various measures can be striking. For instance, the *mean* salary of local TV news anchorpersons is $75,100 a year. But the mean is inflated by the huge salaries (up to $1 million a year) paid to a few star anchors in media centers such as New York, Los Angeles, and Chicago. In contrast, the *median* salary of local news anchors is $59,000—not a sum to scoff at, but still $16,100 less than the mean.[7]

How might a speaker use these different measures? The owner of a television station would probably cite the *mean* ($75,100) to show that local news anchors are handsomely compensated for their work. An organization of news anchors might emphasize the *median* ($59,000) to demonstrate that salaries are not nearly as high as the station owner makes them out to be. Both speakers would be telling the truth, but neither would be completely honest unless she or he made clear the meaning of the statistics.

Are the Statistics from a Reliable Source?

Which is the more reliable estimate of the environmental dangers of toxic waste in a landfill—one from the U.S. Environmental Protection Agency or one compiled by the company that owns the landfill? Easy—the estimate by the EPA, which does not have a vested interest in what the figures look like. What about nutritional ratings for fast foods offered by Consumers Union (a highly respected nonprofit organization) or by Burger King? That's easy too—Consumers Union.

But now things get tougher. What about the competing statistics offered by groups for and against Medicare reform? Or the conflicting numbers tossed out by a governor and the public employee unions protesting against him? In these cases, the answer is not so clear, since both sides would present the facts according to their own partisan motives.

As a speaker, you must be aware of possible bias in the use of numbers. Since statistics can be interpreted so many ways and put to so many uses, you should seek figures gathered by objective, nonpartisan sources.

TIPS FOR USING STATISTICS

Use Statistics to Quantify Your Ideas

The main value of statistics is to give your ideas numerical precision. This can be especially important when you are trying to document the existence of a problem. Examples can bring the problem alive and dramatize it in personal terms, but your listeners may still wonder how many people the problem actually affects. In such a situation, you should turn to statistics. Research has shown that the impact of examples is enhanced when they are combined with statistics that show the examples to be typical.[8]

Suppose you are talking about the need for college students to avoid credit-card debt. Part of your speech deals with the large amount of debt the typical college student faces by the time he or she graduates. You give an example, you personalize the subject, you provide many details, as follows:

> Travis Blake left college a changed person. Not only had he earned his degree, but he had racked up almost $4,000 in credit-card debt. Travis was sure he would be able to pay off his debt once he got a full-time job. But when he received his first paycheck, he found that after paying his taxes and living expenses, he could make only the minimum monthly payment on his credit cards. Rather than getting rid of his debt, he would be paying it off for years.

Confronted with this example, a listener might think, "Poor Travis. But I'm not going to end up in his spot because I don't plan to leave college with a lot of credit-card debt." Anticipating just such a response, a sharp speaker would include figures to quantify the extent of credit-card debt among college students in general:

> According to an article last month in *USA Today*, the average credit-card debt of a graduating college student is $3,100, and new graduates spend almost 25 percent of their income on debt payments. If someone makes only the minimum monthly payment on his or her credit cards—which is what most people do—they will rack up more than $4,073 in interest charges alone before paying off their original $3,100 debt. Perhaps this explains why in the past few years

the number of people under 25 filing for bankruptcy has increased by more than 50 percent.

Now the audience is much more likely to agree that they need to keep a closer eye on their credit-card balance.

Use Statistics Sparingly

As helpful as statistics can be, nothing puts an audience to sleep faster than a speech cluttered with numbers from beginning to end. Insert statistics only when they are needed, and then make sure they are easy to grasp. Even the most attentive listener would have trouble sorting out this barrage of figures:

> According to the *World Factbook*, life expectancy in the United States ranks 50th in the world. The United States ranks 47th in the world in infant mortality. France ranks 9th. Americans spend more each year on health care than any other nation—$2.5 trillion dollars, or 17.6 percent of gross domestic product—yet the World Health Organization ranks the U.S. health care system 37th in overall performance among member nations.

Instead of drowning your audience in a sea of statistics, use only those that are most important. For example:

> According to the *World Factbook*, the United States has one of the lowest life expectancies among industrialized nations—plus one of the highest rates of infant mortality. Even though we spend more on health care than any other nation, the World Health Organization ranks 36 nations ahead of us on the overall performance of our health care system.

This second statement makes the same point as the first statement, but now the ideas are not lost in a torrent of numbers.

Identify the Sources of Your Statistics

As we have seen, figures are easy to manipulate. This is why careful listeners keep an ear out for the sources of a speaker's statistics. One student learned this by experience. In a speech titled "Tax Reform: Fact Versus Fiction," he claimed that the wealthiest 1 percent of U.S. taxpayers pay 38 percent of federal income taxes, even though they account for only 20 percent of all earned income. He also noted that the wealthiest 25 percent of Americans pay 86 percent of federal income taxes. These are startling statistics. But because the student did not say where he got them, his classmates were sure he must be wrong.

As it turned out, the figures were quite reliable. They had come from a study by the Internal Revenue Service reported in the *New York Times*. If the speaker had mentioned the source in his speech, he would have been more successful.[9]

Explain Your Statistics

Statistics don't speak for themselves. They need to be interpreted and related to your listeners. Notice how effectively one student did this in a speech about Chinese culture in the United States:

> Food is another aspect of Chinese culture that has become part of American life. According to Jennifer Lee's new book, *The Fortune Cookie Chronicles*, there

✔ checklist

Using Statistics

	YES	NO	
	☐	☐	1. Do I use statistics to quantify my ideas?
	☐	☐	2. Are my statistics representative of what they purport to measure?
	☐	☐	3. Are my statistics from reliable sources?
	☐	☐	4. Do I cite the sources of my statistics?
	☐	☐	5. Do I use statistical measures (mean, median, mode) correctly?
	☐	☐	6. Do I round off complicated statistics?
	☐	☐	7. Do I use visual aids to clarify statistical trends?
	☐	☐	8. Do I explain my statistics and relate them to the audience?

are some 43,000 Chinese restaurants in the United States. That's more than all the McDonalds, Burger Kings, and KFCs combined.

Explaining what statistics mean is particularly important when you deal with large numbers, since they are hard to visualize. How, for example, can we comprehend the size of the U.S. national debt, which is projected to hit $20 billion by 2015? We could explain that a trillion is a thousand billion and a billion is a thousand million. But millions and billions are almost as hard to visualize as trillions. Suppose, instead, we translate the huge numbers into terms a listener can relate to. Here is one speaker's solution:

> How much money is a trillion dollars? Think of it this way. If you had $1 million and spent it at the rate of $1,000 a day, you would run out of money in less than three years. If you had $1 billion and spent it at the rate of $1,000 a day, you would not run out of money for almost 3,000 years. And if you had $1 trillion and spent it at the rate of $1,000 a day, you wouldn't run out of money for nearly 3 million years!

Whenever you use statistics in your speeches, think of how you can make them meaningful to your audience. Rather than simply reciting figures about, say, the continuing destruction of the world's rainforests, find a way to bring those figures home to your audience. You might say, as did one speaker:

> According to the Rainforest Action Network, rainforest is disappearing at an alarming rate. Within the next second, we will lose an area of rainforest equal to two football fields. Within the next fifteen minutes, an area the size of this campus will be erased. By this time tomorrow, 214,000 acres, an area equivalent to the size of New York City, will be gone forever.

connect

View this excerpt from "The Rainforests: Nature's Pharmacy" in the online Media Library for this chapter (Video 8.6).

Be creative in thinking of ways to relate your statistics to your audience. This is probably the single most important step you can take to make statistics work in your speeches.

Round Off Complicated Statistics

Mount Kilimanjaro is 19,341 feet high; the official world land speed record is 763.065 miles per hour; the population of Libya is 6,461,454 people; the moon is 238,855 miles from earth.

These are intriguing figures, but they are too complicated to be readily understood by listeners. Unless there is an important reason to give exact numbers, you should round off most statistics. You might say that Mount Kilimanjaro is 19,300 feet high; the world land speed record is 763 miles per hour; the population of Libya is more than 6 million; and the moon is 239,000 miles from earth.

Use Visual Aids to Clarify Statistical Trends

Visual aids can save you a lot of time, as well as make your statistics easier to comprehend. Suppose you are discussing the declining purchasing power of the U.S. dollar over the past century. You could start by explaining that in 1913, before the United States entered World War I, the dollar was at an all-time high. It fell off during the war, but it regained value during the 1920s, and in 1933 it stood at 80 cents of its 1913 value. Beginning in the 1940s, however, the dollar started a long decline that has yet to end. By 2011, it was worth less than four cents compared to 1913.

These are interesting statistics, and you could build a good speech around them. But strung together in a few sentences they are hard to digest. Figure 8.1 shows how much more clearly the points can be made with a simple graph. We shall discuss visual aids in detail in Chapter 14. For the moment, keep in mind that they can be helpful in presenting statistical information.

FIGURE 8.1

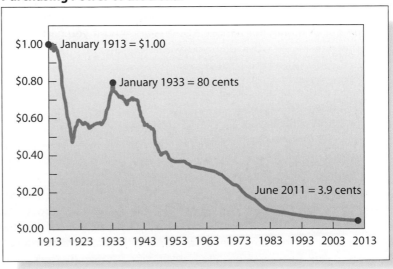

Purchasing Power of the Dollar

Testimony

Imagine that you are talking with a friend about the classes you plan to take next term. You are not sure whether to sign up for Psychology 230 or Accounting 181. Both are requirements; both meet at the same time of day. Your friend says, "I took those classes last year. They're both good, but Professor Hassam was excellent in Psych 230. If she's teaching it next term, I'd take it for sure." You check the timetable and find that Professor Hassam is indeed slated for Psychology 230. You sign up for her course.

As this story illustrates, we are often influenced by the *testimony* of other people. Just as you are likely to be swayed by your friend's recommendation about which class to take, so audiences tend to respect the opinions of people who have special knowledge or experience on the topic at hand. By quoting or paraphrasing such people, you can give your ideas greater strength and impact. The two major kinds of testimony are expert testimony and peer testimony.

testimony

Quotations or paraphrases used to support a point.

EXPERT TESTIMONY

In most speeches, you will probably rely on expert testimony—testimony from people who are acknowledged authorities in their fields. Citing the views of people who are experts is a good way to lend credibility to your speeches. It shows that you are not just mouthing your own opinions, but that your position is supported by people who are knowledgeable about the topic.[10]

Expert testimony is even more important when a topic is controversial or when the audience is skeptical about a speaker's point of view. The following story explains how one student enlisted expert testimony for a speech on phony pharmaceuticals:

expert testimony

Testimony from people who are recognized experts in their fields.

> The more Leah Giovanni researched her speech topic, the more she became convinced that the growth of fraudulent pharmaceuticals is a serious problem that requires action by the U.S. government. Yet Leah was not an expert on the subject. How could she convince her classmates to accept her ideas?
>
> Statistics helped, and so did examples. But that was not enough. To reinforce her credibility, Leah cited a wide range of experts who agreed with her—including investigative reporter Katherine Eban, author of a book on counterfeit medicines; Graham Jackson, editor of the *International Journal of Clinical Practice;* Tom Kubic, head of the Pharmaceutical Security Institute; and U.S. Representative Steve Israel of New York, who has sponsored legislation in Congress to deal with phony pharmaceuticals. By citing the views of these experts, Leah made her speech much more persuasive.

connect

View an excerpt from "Phony Pharmaceuticals" in the online Media Library for this chapter (Video 8.7).

PEER TESTIMONY

Another type of testimony often used in speeches is peer testimony—opinions of people like ourselves; not prominent figures, but ordinary citizens who have firsthand experience on the topic. This kind of testimony is especially valuable because it gives a more personal viewpoint on issues than can be gained from expert testimony.

For example, if you were speaking about the barriers faced by people with physical disabilities, you would surely include testimony from doctors and other medical authorities. But in this case, the expert testimony would be limited because it cannot communicate what it really means to have a physical

peer testimony

Testimony from ordinary people with firsthand experience or insight on a topic.

disability. To communicate that, you need a statement from someone who can speak with the voice of genuine experience—as in the following case:

> Itzhak Perlman, the world-renowned violinist whose legs are paralyzed, once said: "When you are in a wheelchair, people don't talk to you. Perhaps they think it is contagious, or perhaps they think crippled legs mean a crippled mind. But whatever the reason, they treat you like a thing."

There is no way expert testimony could express these ideas with the same authenticity and emotional impact.

QUOTING VERSUS PARAPHRASING

direct quotation

Testimony that is presented word for word.

The statement from Itzhak Perlman is presented as a direct quotation. Testimony can also be presented by paraphrasing. Rather than quoting someone verbatim, you present the gist of that person's ideas in your own words—as did one student in her speech about America's potential water crisis:

> Writing in *Audubon* magazine, Dr. Peter Bourne, president of Global Water, a nonpartisan educational group in Washington, D.C., said most Americans do not yet realize the extent and urgency of the water problem. At the present rate, he says, we are headed for a crisis that will change the way we live in every part of the nation.

paraphrase

To restate or summarize a source's ideas in one's own words.

When should you use a direct quotation as opposed to paraphrasing? The standard rule is that quotations are most effective when they are brief, when they convey your meaning better than you can, and when they are particularly eloquent, witty, or compelling. If you find a quotation that fits these criteria, then recite the quotation word for word.

Paraphrasing is better than direct quotation in two situations: (1) when the wording of a quotation is obscure or cumbersome; (2) when a quotation is longer than two or three sentences. Audiences often tune out partway through lengthy quotations, which tend to interrupt the flow of a speaker's ideas. Since the rest of the speech is in your own words, you should put longer quotations in your own words as well.

TIPS FOR USING TESTIMONY

Quote or Paraphrase Accurately

quoting out of context

Quoting a statement in such a way as to distort its meaning by removing the statement from the words and phrases surrounding it.

Accurate quotation involves three things: making sure you do not misquote someone; making sure you do not violate the meaning of statements you paraphrase; making sure you do not quote out of context.

Of these, the last is the most subtle—and the most dangerous. By quoting out of context, you can twist someone's remarks so as to prove almost anything. Take movie advertisements. A critic pans a movie with these words:

> This movie is a colossal bore. From beginning to end it is a disaster. What is meant to be brilliant dialogue is about as fascinating as the stuff you clean out of your kitchen drain.

But when the movie is advertised in the newspapers, what appears in huge letters over the critic's name? "COLOSSAL! FROM BEGINNING TO END— BRILLIANT! FASCINATING!"

Citing expert testimony is an excellent way for students to lend credibility to their speeches. It shows that the speaker's views are shared by people who have special knowledge on the topic.

This is so flagrant as to be humorous. But quoting out of context can have serious consequences. Consider the following statement by a political candidate:

Creating a national sales tax would provide needed revenue for programs such as education, health care, and national defense. Several European countries have such a tax, and it could work here. However, I do not support such a tax here—in fact, I don't support new taxes of any kind.

Now look what happens when the first part of that statement is quoted out of context by a competing candidate:

Americans already pay too much in taxes. Yet my opponent in this election has stated—and I quote: "Creating a national sales tax would provide needed revenue for programs such as education, health care, and national defense. Several European countries have such a tax, and it could work here." Well, my opponent may think new taxes are good for Europe, but they're the last thing we need in the United States.

By quoting the original statement out of context, the competing candidate has created a false impression. Such behavior is highly unethical. Be sure, when you quote or paraphrase someone, that you represent their words and ideas with complete accuracy.

Use Testimony from Qualified Sources

We have all become accustomed to the celebrity testimonial in television and magazine advertising. The professional basketball player endorses a brand of athletic shoes. The movie star praises a hair spray or shampoo. So far, so good. These are the tools of the trade for the people who endorse them.

✔ checklist

Using Testimony

YES	NO	
☐	☐	1. Do I use testimony to support my ideas?
☐	☐	2. Do I use testimony from qualified sources?
☐	☐	3. Do I use testimony from unbiased sources?
☐	☐	4. Do I distinguish between expert testimony and peer testimony?
☐	☐	5. Do I identify the sources of all testimony?
☐	☐	6. Do I quote and paraphrase all sources of testimony with complete accuracy?

But what happens when an Academy Award winner endorses a cell phone company? A tennis player represents a line of cameras? Do they know more about these products than you or I? Probably not.

Being a celebrity or an authority in one area does not make someone competent in other areas. Listeners will find your speeches much more credible if you use testimony from sources qualified *on the subject at hand*. As we have seen, this may include either recognized experts or ordinary citizens with special experience on the speech topic.

Use Testimony from Unbiased Sources

In a speech about the use of stun guns by police officers to subdue unruly students in public schools, a student said:

Steve Tuttle, a spokesman for Taser International, said in a statement that "the Taser device has been shown to be medically safe when used on children" and that there is no reason to prohibit its use when necessary to maintain security in the public schools.

As you might expect, the students' classmates were not persuaded. After all, what would you expect someone at Taser International, the leading manufacturer of stun guns, to say—that its product is unsafe and should be banned?

Careful listeners are suspicious of testimony from biased or self-interested sources. Be sure to use testimony from credible, objective authorities.

Identify the People You Quote or Paraphrase

The usual way to identify your source is to name the person and sketch his or her qualifications before presenting the testimony. The following excerpt is from a speech arguing that excessive time spent at work is harming the quality of education for many American high-school students:

In their book, *When Children Work*, psychology professors Ellen Greenberger of the University of California and Lawrence Steinberg of Temple University note that intensive levels of work among youth tend to produce higher truancy and lower grades. According to Greenberger and Steinberg, one study after another has found that working more than a few hours a week has a negative impact on teenagers' academic performance.

Had the speaker not identified Greenberger and Steinberg, listeners would not have had the foggiest idea who they are or why their opinion should be heeded.

As we saw in Chapter 2, identifying the source of testimony is also an important ethical responsibility. If you use another person's words or ideas without giving credit to that person, you will be guilty of plagiarism. This is true whether you paraphrase the original source or quote it verbatim.

Citing Sources Orally

We have mentioned more than once in this chapter the importance of citing the sources of your supporting materials. Careful listeners are skeptical. They keep an ear out both for a speaker's information and for the sources of that information.

The bibliography in your speech outline should state the sources you used in constructing the speech (see Chapter 11, page 208). But listeners do not have access to your outline. You have to identify your sources orally, as you are speaking.

Unlike a written bibliography, oral source citations do not follow a standard format. What you include depends on your topic, your audience, the kind of supporting material you are using, and the claim you are making. The key is to tell your audience enough that they will know where you got your information and why they should accept it as qualified and credible. In most cases, you will need to identify some combination of the following:

- The book, magazine, newspaper, or Web document you are citing.
- The author or sponsoring organization of the document.
- The author's qualifications with regard to the topic.
- The date on which the document was published, posted, or updated.

Here is an example of a speech citation that includes all the above:

The power of earthquakes can be seen in more than just the damage they cause. Kenneth Chang, science reporter for the *New York Times*, reported in the paper's March 13, 2011, issue that the recent quake in Japan widened the country by 13 feet. It also tilted the earth's axis and shortened the day by a couple millionths of a second.

Because this speaker was citing statistics, she needed to show that they were up-to-date and came from a credible source. In the following example, the speaker is using testimony, but notice how he also establishes the credibility of his source and the recency of his information:

Human smuggling is big business, and the U.S. government has made little headway in stopping it. Just ask Scott Hatfield, chief of the Human Smuggling

checklist

Citing Sources Orally

YES	NO	
☐	☐	1. Do I identify all the print documents cited in my speech?
☐	☐	2. Do I identify all the Web documents cited in my speech?
☐	☐	3. Do I identify the authors or sponsoring organizations of the documents I cite?
☐	☐	4. Do I establish the authors' credentials with regard to the topic?
☐	☐	5. Do I use documents from sponsoring organizations with established expertise and objectivity?
☐	☐	6. Do I include the dates on which the documents were published, posted, or updated?
☐	☐	7. Do I use a variety of methods in citing my sources?

division at Immigration and Customs Enforcement, who was quoted last month in the *Houston Chronicle:* "Any time we shut down a smuggling organization, there's always somebody to take their place."

On the other hand, if you were quoting Abraham Lincoln's Gettysburg Address of November 19, 1863, about "government of the people, by the people, for the people," you would not need to explain Lincoln's qualifications (because he is so well known) or the date of his statement (because it does not affect the relevance of his words).

The same principles apply if you are citing online sources. It is not enough to say, "As I found on the Web," or "As the Internet states." On the other hand, it is not necessary to recite the entire address of the Web page. If you are citing a specific person, you should identify him or her and the name of the Web site on which you found the information—as in this example:

In an article posted on MSNBC.com in March 2011, Harry Johns, president and chief executive of the Alzheimer's Association, states: "Alzheimer's disease doesn't just affect those with it. It invades families and the lives of everyone around them."

If you are citing an organization, rather than an individual, you need to provide the name of the organization:

The U.S. Department of Agriculture explains on its Web site that providing nutritious meals and snacks to children in low-income areas during the summer months is critical to improving the health of America's kids.

Finally, notice how skillfully the speakers quoted above blend their citations into their speeches. They do not always say "According to . . ." or "As stated by. . . ." Nor do they use words like "quote . . . unquote." Usually you

FIGURE 8.2   Sample Oral Citations

Book

William D. Schanbacher's 2010 book, *The Politics of Food*, explains that the Slow Food Movement was established "as an alternative to fast-paced life, specifically with respect to our eating habits, our knowledge of how food is produced, where it comes from, and how it affects the natural environment."

Newspaper

According to the *Los Angeles Times*, March 9, 2011, the Latino population of California is almost equal to that of the white population. Latinos make up 38 percent of the state's population, while whites compose 40 percent.

Magazine

The problems of the current kidney transplant system are explored by Amanda Glassman, director of Global Health Policy at the Center for Global Development, in last month's *Atlantic Monthly*. Glassman notes that while 87,000 Americans are on the waiting list, only 17,000 will receive a kidney transplant. More disturbing, 4,600 people will die this year because they don't receive a kidney in time.

Academic journal

A recent study published in the *Journal of Neuroscience* by researchers at Duke University demonstrates just how problematic sleep deprivation can be for compulsive gamblers. The less sleep a person has, the more he or she is willing to take big risks in the hope of a big score. And the result can be huge losses.

Organization or institution

The March 2011 report *Women in America*, prepared by the U.S. Department of Commerce and other government agencies, reveals that almost 40 percent of single women with children under the age of 18 live below the poverty line.

Interview

In an interview I conducted for this speech, Professor Lloyd Jasinski of the Political Science Department said that the impact of lobbyists has so corrupted the American political system that many people have lost their faith in government to serve the public good.

Television program

The October 10, 2010, episode of *60 Minutes* explains how much the stock exchange has changed in recent years. The majority of trades are no longer made by humans. In fact, almost 70 percent of trades are done by computers, which can buy and sell thousands of different stocks in the blink of an eye.

Web site

Overcrowding is particularly bad in the nation's community colleges. A February 9, 2011, article on *InsideHigherEd.com*, which is affiliated with the *Chronicle of Higher Education*, states that over 30 percent of community college students were not able to enroll in one or more of the classes they needed last semester because of overcrowding.

can modify your tone of voice or use brief pauses to let your listeners know when you are making a direct quotation.

In Figure 8.2 (on page 161), you will find more examples of how you can cite different kinds of sources in your speeches. Keep in mind, however, that the examples are just that—examples. They are presented to give you a fuller sense of the various methods of oral citation. You can use *any* of the methods with any of the sources. As with other aspects of public speaking, citing sources orally in your speeches is not a matter of following a rigid formula, but of adapting general principles to specific circumstances.

Summary

Good speeches need strong supporting materials to bolster the speaker's point of view. The three basic types of supporting materials are examples, statistics, and testimony.

In the course of a speech you may use brief examples—specific instances referred to in passing—and sometimes you may want to give several brief examples in a row to create a stronger impression. Extended examples are longer and more detailed. Hypothetical examples describe imaginary situations and can be quite effective for relating ideas to the audience. All three kinds of examples help clarify ideas, reinforce ideas, or personalize ideas. To be most effective, they should be vivid and richly textured.

Statistics can be extremely helpful in conveying your message as long as you use them sparingly and make them meaningful to your audience. Above all, you should understand your statistics and use them fairly. Make sure your figures are representative of what they claim to measure, that you use statistical measures correctly, and that you take statistics only from reliable sources.

Citing the testimony of experts is a good way to make your ideas more credible. You can also use peer testimony, from ordinary people who have firsthand experience on the topic. Regardless of the kind of testimony, you can either quote someone verbatim or paraphrase his or her words. Be sure to quote or paraphrase accurately and to use qualified, unbiased sources.

When citing sources in a speech, you need to let your audience know where you got your information and why they should accept it as qualified and credible. In most cases, this means identifying the document you are citing, its date of publication or posting, the author or sponsoring organization, and the author's credentials.

Key Terms

supporting materials *(142)*

example *(142)*

brief example *(143)*

extended example *(143)*

hypothetical example *(144)*

statistics *(147)*

mean *(150)*

median *(150)*

mode *(150)*

testimony *(155)*

expert testimony *(155)*

peer testimony *(155)*

direct quotation *(156)*

paraphrase *(156)*

quoting out of context *(156)*

Review Questions

After reading this chapter, you should be able to answer the following questions:

1. Why do you need supporting materials in your speeches?
2. What are the three kinds of examples discussed in this chapter? How might you use each kind to support your ideas?
3. What are five tips for using examples in your speeches?
4. Why is it so easy to lie with statistics? What three questions should you ask to judge the reliability of statistics?
5. What are six tips for using statistics in your speeches?
6. What is testimony? Explain the difference between expert testimony and peer testimony.
7. What are four tips for using testimony in your speeches?
8. What four pieces of information do you usually need to provide when making oral source citations in a speech?

connect

For further review, go to the LearnSmart study module for this chapter.

Exercises for Critical Thinking

1. Each of the following statements violates at least one of the criteria for effective supporting materials discussed in this chapter. Identify the flaw (or flaws) in each statement.

    a. As Taylor Swift stated in a recent interview, U.S. policy toward North Korea should put more emphasis on bilateral negotiations.

    b. According to *The New York Times Almanac,* California has the largest Native American population of any state in the union—421,346. Arizona is second with 294,118 and Oklahoma is third with 287,124.

    c. I don't know why rental car companies don't like to rent to people under the age of 25. My friends and I all drive a lot, and none of us has been in an accident.

    d. In a random survey conducted last month among people visiting Las Vegas casinos, 96 percent of respondents opposed limitations on gambling in the United States. Clearly, then, the American people oppose such limitations.

    e. In the words of one expert, "The state education budget has been cut so much in recent years that any further cuts will do irreparable harm to our schools and the children they serve."

    f. Figures compiled by the Bureau of Labor Statistics show that the median salary for petroleum engineers in the U.S. is $108,910. This shows that petroleum engineers average almost $109,000 a year in salary.

    g. According to a study by American Airlines, passenger satisfaction among frequent fliers is growing each year.

2. Analyze "Bursting the Antibacterial Bubble" in the appendix of sample speeches following Chapter 19. Identify the main points of the speech and the supporting materials used for each. Evaluate the speaker's use of supporting materials in light of the criteria discussed in this chapter.

9

Organizing the Body of the Speech

Organization Is Important

Main Points

Supporting Materials

Connectives

Think about shopping in a store such as Ikea, Target, or Best Buy. Many of the items for sale are *organizers*—drawer organizers, desk organizers, closet organizers, kitchen organizers, bathroom organizers, office organizers, audio and video organizers.

Why all this quest for organization? Obviously, when the objects you possess are well organized, they serve you better. Organization allows you to see what you have and to put your hands immediately on the garment, the tool, the piece of paper, the DVD you want without a frenzied search.

Much the same is true of your speeches. If they are well organized, they will serve you better. Organization allows you—and your listeners—to see what ideas you have and to put mental "hands" on the most important ones.

Organization Is Important

In a classic study, a college professor took a well-organized speech and scrambled it by randomly changing the order of its sentences. He then had a speaker deliver the original version to one group of listeners and the scrambled version to another group. After the speeches, he gave a test to see how well each group understood what they had heard. Not surprisingly, the group that heard the original, unscrambled speech scored much higher than the other group.[1]

A few years later, two professors repeated the same experiment at another school. But instead of testing how well the listeners comprehended each speech, they tested to see what effects the speeches had on the listeners' attitudes toward the speakers. They found that people who heard the well-organized speech believed the speaker to be much more competent and trustworthy than did those who heard the scrambled speech.[2]

These are just two of many studies that show the importance of organization in effective speechmaking.[3] Listeners demand coherence. Unlike readers, they cannot flip back to a previous page if they have trouble grasping a speaker's ideas. In this respect a speech is much like a movie. Just as a director must be sure viewers can follow the plot of a film from beginning to end, so must a speaker be sure listeners can follow the progression of ideas in a speech from beginning to end. This requires that speeches be organized *strategically*. They should be put together in particular ways to achieve particular results with particular audiences.

Speech organization is important for other reasons as well. As we saw in Chapter 1, it is closely connected to critical thinking. When you work to organize your speeches, you gain practice in the general skill of establishing clear relationships among your ideas. This skill will serve you well throughout your college days and in almost any career you may choose. In addition, using a clear, specific method of speech organization can boost your confidence as a speaker and improve your ability to deliver a message fluently.

The first step in developing a strong sense of speech organization is to gain command of the three basic parts of a speech—introduction, body, and conclusion—and the strategic role of each. In this chapter we deal with the body of the speech. The next chapter will take up the introduction and the conclusion.

There are good reasons for talking first about the body of the speech. The body is the longest and most important part. Also, you will usually prepare the body first. It is easier to create an effective introduction after you know exactly what you will say in the body.

The process of organizing the body of a speech begins when you determine the main points.

strategic organization

Putting a speech together in a particular way to achieve a particular result with a particular audience.

Main Points

The main points are the central features of your speech. You should select them carefully, phrase them precisely, and arrange them strategically. Here are the main points of a student speech about the uses of hypnosis:

Specific Purpose:	To inform my audience about some of the major uses of hypnosis.
Central Idea:	Three major uses of hypnosis today are to control pain in surgery, to help people stop smoking, and to help students improve their academic performance.
Main Points:	I. Hypnosis is used in surgery as an adjunct to chemical anesthesia. II. Hypnosis is used to help people stop smoking. III. Hypnosis is used to help students improve their academic performance.

These three main points form the skeleton of the body of the speech. If there are three major *uses* of hypnosis, then logically there can be three *main points* in the speech.

How do you choose your main points? Sometimes they will be evident from your specific purpose statement. Suppose your specific purpose is "To inform my audience about the development, technology, and benefits of hydrogen fuel cells." Obviously, your speech will have three main points. The first will deal with the development of hydrogen fuel cells, the second with the technology behind hydrogen fuel cells, the third with the benefits of hydrogen fuel cells. Written in outline form, the main points might be:

Specific Purpose:	To inform my audience about the development, technology, and benefits of hydrogen fuel cells.
Central Idea:	Developed as a highly efficient form of energy, hydrogen fuel cells use sophisticated technology and offer a number of economic and environmental benefits.
Main Points:	I. Hydrogen fuel cells were developed to provide a highly efficient form of energy. II. Hydrogen fuel cells produce power through an electro-chemical reaction involving hydrogen gas. III. Hydrogen fuel cells provide an economically and environmentally superior method of powering motor vehicles.

Even if your main points are not stated expressly in your specific purpose, they may be easy to project from it. Let's say your specific purpose is "To inform my audience of the basic steps in making stained-glass windows." You know each of your main points will correspond to a step in the window-making process. They might look like this in outline form:

Specific Purpose:	To inform my audience of the basic steps in making stained-glass windows.
Central Idea:	There are four steps in making stained-glass windows.
Main Points:	I. The first step is designing the window. II. The second step is cutting the glass to fit the design. III. The third step is painting the glass. IV. The fourth step is assembling the window.

You will not always settle on your main points so easily. Often they will emerge as you research the speech and evaluate your findings. Suppose your specific purpose is "To persuade my audience that our state should not approve proposals for online voting." You know that each main point in the speech will present a *reason* why online voting should not be instituted in your state. But you aren't sure how many main points there will be or what they will be. As you research and study the topic, you decide there are two reasons to support your view. Each of these reasons will become a main point in your speech. Written in outline form, they might be:

Specific Purpose: To persuade my audience that our state should not approve proposals for online voting.

Central Idea: Our state should not approve online voting because it will increase voter fraud and disfranchise people without Internet access.

Main Points: I. Our state should not approve online voting because it will increase voter fraud.

II. Our state should not approve online voting because it will disfranchise people without access to the Internet.

NUMBER OF MAIN POINTS

You will not have time in your classroom speeches to develop more than four or five main points, and most speeches will contain only two or three. Regardless of how long a speech might run, if you have too many main points, the audience will have trouble sorting them out.

If, when you list your main points, you find that you have too many, you may be able to condense them into categories. Here is a set of main points for a speech about yoga:

Specific Purpose: To inform my audience about the practice of yoga.

Central Idea: Yoga is an ancient practice that involves the whole body.

Main Points: I. Yoga breathing starts with deep inhalation.

II. Yoga breathing requires slow exhalation.

III. Yoga breathing includes prolonged pauses.

IV. Yoga breathing provides many benefits.

V. Yoga postures involve all parts of the body.

VI. Yoga postures increase flexibility.

VII. Yoga postures strengthen muscle tone.

VIII. Yoga postures demand precise movements.

connect

View an excerpt from "Yoga: Uniting Mind, Body, and Spirit" in the online Media Library for this chapter (Video 9.1).

You have eight main points—which is too many. But if you look at the list, you see that the eight points fall into two broad categories: yoga breathing and yoga postures. You might, therefore, restate your main points this way:

I. One part of practicing yoga involves proper breathing.

II. Another part of yoga involves body postures.

Research studies confirm that clear organization is vital to effective public speaking. Listeners must be able to follow the progression of ideas in a speech from beginning to end.

STRATEGIC ORDER OF MAIN POINTS

Once you establish your main points, you need to decide the order in which you will present them. The most effective order depends on three things—your topic, your purpose, and your audience. Chapters 15 and 16 will cover special aspects of organizing informative speeches and persuasive speeches. Here we look briefly at the five basic patterns of organization used most often by public speakers.

Chronological Order

Speeches arranged chronologically follow a time pattern. They may narrate a series of events in the sequence in which they happened. For example:

Specific Purpose: To inform my audience how the Great Wall of China was built.

Central Idea: The Great Wall of China was built in three major stages.

Main Points:
    I. Building of the Great Wall began during the Qin dynasty of 221–206 B.C.

    II. New sections of the Great Wall were added during the Han dynasty of 206 B.C.–220 A.D.

    III. The Great Wall was completed during the Ming dynasty of 1368–1644.

Chronological order is also used in speeches explaining a process or demonstrating how to do something. For example:

Specific Purpose: To inform my audience of the steps in laser-assisted corrective eye surgery.

Central Idea: There are three main steps in laser-assisted corrective eye surgery.

chronological order

A method of speech organization in which the main points follow a time pattern.

Main Points:	I. First, a thin layer is sliced off the surface of the eye to expose the cornea.
	II. Second, an ultraviolet laser is used to reshape the cornea.
	III. Third, the thin layer sliced off at the beginning of the surgery is reaffixed to the eye.

As this outline shows, chronological order is especially useful for informative speeches.

Spatial Order

spatial order

A method of speech organization in which the main points follow a directional pattern.

Speeches arranged in spatial order follow a directional pattern. That is, the main points proceed from top to bottom, left to right, front to back, inside to outside, east to west, or some other route. For example:

Specific Purpose:	To inform my audience about the structure of a hurricane.
Central Idea:	A hurricane is made up of three parts going from inside to outside.
Main Points:	I. At the center of a hurricane is the calm, cloud-free eye.
	II. Surrounding the eye is the eyewall, a dense ring of clouds that produces the most intense wind and rainfall.
	III. Rotating around the eyewall are large bands of clouds and precipitation called spiral rain bands.

connect

View an excerpt from "The Wrath of Hurricanes" in the online Media Library for this chapter (Video 9.2).

Or:

Specific Purpose:	To inform my audience about the three major regions in Italy.
Central Idea:	Northern, central, and southern Italy have their own identities and attractions.
Main Points:	I. Northern Italy is home to Venice and its world-famous canals.
	II. Central Italy is home to Rome and its historical treasures.
	III. Southern Italy is home to Sicily and its culinary traditions.

Spatial order, like chronological order, is used most often in informative speeches.

Causal Order

causal order

A method of speech organization in which the main points show a cause-effect relationship.

Speeches arranged in causal order organize main points so as to show a cause-effect relationship. When you put your speech in causal order, you have two main points—one dealing with the causes of an event, the other dealing with its effects. Depending on your topic, you can devote your first main point to the causes and the second to the effects, or you can deal first with the effects and then with the causes.

Suppose your specific purpose is "To persuade my audience that a growing shortage of air-traffic controllers is a serious problem for U.S. aviation." Then you would begin with the causes of the shortage and work toward its effects:

Specific Purpose:	To persuade my audience that a growing shortage of qualified air-traffic controllers is a serious problem for U.S. aviation.

The main points of a speech should be organized to communicate the speaker's message. Chronological order would work very well for a speech on the history of Mount Rushmore.

Central Idea: The growing shortage of certified air-traffic controllers threatens the safety of air travel.

Main Points:
    I. The U.S. aviation system faces a growing shortage of qualified air-traffic controllers.
    II. If this shortage continues, it will create serious problems for airline safety.

When the effects you are discussing have already occurred, you may want to reverse the order and talk first about the effects and then about their causes—as in this speech about the Mayan civilization of Central America:

Specific Purpose: To inform my audience about the possible causes for the collapse of Mayan civilization.

Central Idea: The causes for the collapse of Mayan civilization have not yet been fully explained.

Main Points:
    I. Mayan civilization flourished for over a thousand years until 900 A.D., when it mysteriously began to disintegrate.
    II. Scientists have advanced three major explanations for the causes of this disintegration.

Because of its versatility, causal order can be used for both persuasive speeches and informative speeches.

Problem-Solution Order

Speeches arranged in problem-solution order are divided into two main parts. The first shows the existence and seriousness of a problem. The second presents a workable solution to the problem. For example:

Specific Purpose: To persuade my audience that action is needed to combat the abuses of puppy mills.

connect

View an excerpt from "The Horrors of Puppy Mills" in the online Media Library for this chapter (Video 9.3).

Central Idea:	Puppy mills are a serious problem that can be solved by a combination of legislation and individual initiative.
Main Points:	I. Puppy mills are a serious problem across the United States.
	II. Solving the problem requires legislation and individual initiative.

Or:

Specific Purpose:	To persuade my audience that the electoral college should be abolished.
Central Idea:	Because the electoral college does not give equal weight to the vote of each citizen, it should be replaced with direct popular election of the President.
Main Points:	I. The electoral college is a serious problem in the U.S. political system because it does not give equal weight to each citizen's vote in electing the President.
	II. The problem can be solved by abolishing the electoral college and electing the President by popular vote.

As these examples indicate, problem-solution order is most appropriate for persuasive speeches.

Topical Order

Topical order results when you divide the speech topic into *subtopics*, each of which becomes a main point in the speech.

Let's say your topic is Josephine Baker, an African-American entertainer and social activist in the middle of the 20th century. You could organize your speech chronologically—by discussing Baker's exploits during each decade of her career. On the other hand, you could arrange the speech topically—by dividing Baker's accomplishments into categories. Then your central idea and main points might be:

Specific Purpose:	To inform my audience about the achievements of Josephine Baker.
Central Idea:	Josephine Baker was a multitalented figure in the fight for racial justice.
Main Points:	I. As an entertainer, Baker captivated audiences in Europe and America.
	II. As a spy, Baker gathered information on Nazi activities in France during World War II.
	III. As a civil rights activist, Baker worked for racial equality on a variety of fronts.

Notice how the main points subdivide the speech topic logically and consistently. Each main point isolates one aspect of Baker's achievements. But suppose your main points look like this:

problem-solution order

A method of speech organization in which the first main point deals with the existence of a problem and the second main point presents a solution to the problem.

topical order

A method of speech organization in which the main points divide the topic into logical and consistent subtopics.

I. As an entertainer, Baker captivated audiences in Europe and America.

II. As a spy, Baker gathered information on Nazi activities in France during World War II.

III. During the 1950s, Baker expanded her activities and the scope of her influence.

This would *not* be a good topical order because main point III is inconsistent with the rest of the main points. It deals with a *time period* in Baker's life, whereas main points I and II deal with fields of achievement.

The Josephine Baker example refers to an informative speech. But topical order also works for persuasive speeches. Usually the topical subdivisions are the *reasons* why a speaker believes in a certain point of view. Here, for example, are the main points for a speech on why the United States should continue its program of space exploration:

Specific Purpose: To persuade my audience that the United States should continue its program of space exploration.

Central Idea: The United States should continue its program of space exploration because it produces scientific knowledge, generates technological breakthroughs, and opens access to natural resources.

Main Points:
    I. The space program produces scientific knowledge about the nature of the solar system.

    II. The space program generates technological breakthroughs that benefit many aspects of human life.

    III. The space program opens access to natural resources that are in short supply on earth.

Because it is applicable to almost any subject and to any kind of speech, topical order is used more often than any other method of speech organization.

Using public speaking in your CAREER

You are the purchasing manager for a large jewelry manufacturer. The company's president sent you abroad to find new suppliers of base metals, including brass, copper, nickel, and aluminum. You were asked to evaluate each supplier based on the quality, availability, and cost of its products.

You have just returned from a 12-day trip to suppliers in Cambodia, China, South Korea, and the United Arab Emirates. You will present your findings and recommendations to the company's senior executives, but you're not sure how best to organize your speech.

Your major choices are chronological order, problem-solution order, and topical order. What might be the main points of your speech with each of these methods of organization? Explain which method you think would be most effective for your presentation.

TIPS FOR PREPARING MAIN POINTS

Keep Main Points Separate

Each main point in a speech should be clearly independent of the others. Compare these two sets of main points for a speech about the process of producing a Broadway play:

Ineffective

I. The first step is choosing the play.
II. The second step is selecting the cast.
III. The third step is conducting rehearsals and then performing the play.

More Effective

I. The first step is choosing the play.
II. The second step is selecting the cast.
III. The third step is conducting the rehearsals.
IV. The fourth step is performing the play.

The problem with the left-hand list is that point III contains two main points. It should be divided, as shown in the right-hand list.

Try to Use the Same Pattern of Wording for Main Points

Consider the following main points for an informative speech about the benefits of karate:

Ineffective

I. Karate gives you better mental discipline.
II. You will become physically stronger through karate.
III. Taking karate lessons will teach you self-defense.

More Effective

I. Karate improves your mental discipline.
II. Karate increases your physical strength.
III. Karate teaches you self-defense.

The set of main points on the right follows a consistent pattern of wording throughout. Therefore, it is easier to understand and easier to remember than the set on the left.

You will find that it is not always possible to use this kind of parallel wording. Some speeches just don't lend themselves to such a tidy arrangement. But try to keep the wording parallel when you can, for it is a good way to make your main points stand out from the details surrounding them.

Balance the Amount of Time Devoted to Main Points

Because your main points are so important, you want to be sure they all receive enough emphasis to be clear and convincing. This means allowing sufficient time to develop each main point. Suppose you discover that the proportion of time devoted to your main points is something like this:

I. 85 percent

II. 10 percent

III. 5 percent

A breakdown of this sort indicates one of two things. Either points II and III aren't really *main* points and you have only one main point, or points II and III haven't been given the attention they need. If the latter, you should revise the body of the speech to bring the main points into better balance.

This is not to say that all main points must receive exactly equal emphasis, but only that they should be roughly balanced. For example, either of the following would be fine:

I. 30 percent	I. 20 percent
II. 40 percent	II. 30 percent
III. 30 percent	III. 50 percent

The amount of time spent on each main point depends on the amount and complexity of supporting materials for each point.

Supporting Materials

By themselves, main points are only assertions. As we saw in Chapter 8, listeners need supporting materials to accept what a speaker says. The outline below demonstrates how supporting materials can be integrated into the body of a speech. (In Chapter 11, we'll look at requirements for a complete speech outline. For now, concentrate on how the supporting materials relate to the main points.)

I. Hypnosis is used in surgery as an adjunct to chemical anesthesia.
  A. Hypnosis reduces both the physical and psychological aspects of pain.
    1. Hypnosis can double a person's pain threshold.
    2. It also reduces the fear that intensifies physical pain.
  B. Hypnosis is most useful in cases when the patient is known to have problems with general anesthesia.
    1. Quotation from Dr. Harold Wain of the Mayo Clinic.
    2. Story of Linda Kuay.
    3. Statistics from *Psychology Today.*

II. Hypnosis is used to help people stop smoking.
  A. Many therapists utilize hypnosis to help people break their addiction to cigarettes.
    1. The U.S. Department of Health and Human Services considers hypnosis a safe and effective means of stopping smoking.
    2. Success rates are as high as 70 percent.
      a. Story of Alex Hamilton.
      b. Quotation from New York psychiatrist Dr. Herbert Spiegel.
  B. Hypnosis does not work for all smokers.
    1. A person must want to stop smoking for hypnosis to work.
    2. A person must also be responsive to hypnotic suggestion.

III. Hypnosis is used to help students improve their academic performance.
  A. Hypnosis enables people to use their minds more effectively.
    1. The conscious mind uses about 10 percent of a person's mental ability.
    2. Hypnosis allows people to tap more of their mental power.
  B. Studies show that hypnosis can help people overcome many obstacles to academic success.
    1. It improves ability to concentrate.
    2. It increases reading speed.
    3. It reduces test anxiety.

supporting materials

The materials used to support a speaker's ideas. The three major kinds of supporting materials are examples, statistics, and testimony.

In Chapter 8, we discussed the major kinds of supporting materials and how to use them. Here, we need stress only the importance of *organizing* your supporting materials so they are directly relevant to the main points they are supposed to support. Misplaced supporting materials are confusing. Here's an example:

I. There are several reasons why people immigrate to the United States.
    A. Over the years, millions of people have immigrated to the United States.
    B. Many people immigrate in search of economic opportunity.
    C. Others immigrate to attain political freedom.
    D. Still others immigrate to escape religious persecution.

The main point deals with the reasons immigrants come to the United States, as do supporting points B, C, and D. Supporting point A ("Over the years, millions of people have immigrated to the United States") does not. It is out of place and should not be included with this main point.

If you find such a situation in your own speeches, try to reorganize your supporting points under appropriate main points, like this:

I. Over the years, millions of people have immigrated to the United States.
    A. Since the American Revolution, more than 90 million people have immigrated to the United States.

✔ checklist

Main Points

YES	NO	
☐	☐	1. Does the body of my speech contain two to five main points?
☐	☐	2. Are my main points organized according to one of the following methods of organization? Chronological order Spatial order Causal order Topical order Problem-solution order
☐	☐	3. Are my main points clearly separate from one another?
☐	☐	4. As much as possible, have I used the same pattern of wording for all my main points?
☐	☐	5. Have I roughly balanced the amount of time devoted to each main point?
☐	☐	6. Is each main point backed up with strong, credible supporting materials?
☐	☐	7. Do I use connectives to make sure my audience knows when I am moving from one main point to another?

B. Today there are 38 million Americans who were born in other countries.

II. There are several reasons why people immigrate to the United States.
A. Many people immigrate in search of economic opportunity.
B. Others immigrate to attain political freedom.
C. Still others immigrate to escape religious persecution.

Now you have two supporting points to back up your "millions of people" point and three supporting points to back up your "reasons" point.

Once you have organized your main points and supporting points, you must give attention to the third element in the body of a speech—connectives.

Connectives

Emily Chen was speaking to her class about the need for medical malpractice reform. She had rehearsed the speech several times, had a well-defined central idea, three sharp main points, and strong evidence to support her position. But when Emily delivered the speech, she said "All right" every time she moved from one thought to the next. After a while, her classmates started counting. By the end of the speech, most were too busy waiting for the next "All right" to pay attention to Emily's message. Afterward, Emily said, "I never even thought about saying 'All right.' I guess it just popped out when I didn't know what else to say."

We all have stock phrases that we use to fill the space between thoughts. In casual conversation they are seldom troublesome. But in speechmaking they distract listeners by calling attention to themselves.

What Emily's speech lacked were strong *connectives*—words or phrases that join one thought to another and indicate the relationship between them. Without connectives, a speech is disjointed and uncoordinated—much as a person would be without ligaments and tendons to join the bones and hold the organs in place. Four types of speech connectives are transitions, internal previews, internal summaries, and signposts.

connective

A word or phrase that connects the ideas of a speech and indicates the relationship between them.

TRANSITIONS

Transitions are words or phrases that indicate when a speaker has just completed one thought and is moving on to another. Technically, the transitions state both the idea the speaker is leaving and the idea she or he is coming up to. In the following examples, the transitional phrases are underlined:

transition

A word or phrase that indicates when a speaker has finished one thought and is moving on to another.

Now that we have a clear understanding of the problem, let me share the solution with you.

I have spoken so far of Cesar Chavez the community organizer, but it was his work as a labor leader that truly etched his name into American history.

Keeping these points in mind about sign language, let's return to the sentence I started with and see if we can learn the signs for "You are my friend."

Notice how these phrases remind the listener of the thought just completed, as well as reveal the thought about to be developed.

INTERNAL PREVIEWS

internal preview

A statement in the body of the speech that lets the audience know what the speaker is going to discuss next.

Internal previews let the audience know what the speaker will take up next, but they are more detailed than transitions. In effect, an internal preview works just like the preview statement in a speech introduction, except that it comes in the body of the speech—usually as the speaker is starting to discuss a main point. For example:

> In discussing how Asian Americans have been stereotyped in the mass media, we'll look first at the origins of the problem and second at its continuing impact today.

After hearing this, the audience knows exactly what to listen for as the speaker develops the "problem" main point.

Internal previews are often combined with transitions. For example:

> [*Transition*]: Now that we have seen how serious the problem of faulty credit reports is, let's look at some solutions. [*Internal Preview*]: I will focus on three solutions—instituting tighter government regulation of credit bureaus, holding credit bureaus financially responsible for their errors, and giving individuals easier access to their credit reports.

You will seldom need an internal preview for each main point in your speech, but be sure to use one whenever you think it will help listeners keep track of your ideas.

INTERNAL SUMMARIES

internal summary

A statement in the body of the speech that summarizes the speaker's preceding point or points.

Internal summaries are the reverse of internal previews. Rather than letting listeners know what is coming up next, internal summaries remind listeners of what they have just heard. Such summaries are usually used when a speaker finishes a complicated or particularly important main point or set of main points. For example:

> In short, palm reading is an ancient art. Developed in China more than five thousand years ago, it was practiced in classical Greece and Rome, flourished during the Middle Ages, survived the Industrial Revolution, and remains popular today in many parts of the world.

Internal summaries are an excellent way to clarify and reinforce ideas. By combining them with transitions, you can also lead your audience smoothly into your next main point:

> [*Internal Summary*]: Let's pause for a moment to summarize what we have found so far. First, we have seen that firearm sales at gun shows too often put weapons in the hands of criminals. Second, we have seen that there is almost no accountability for gun-show dealers who sell to criminals. [*Transition*]: We are now in a position to see what can be done to close the gun-show loophole.

SIGNPOSTS

signpost

A very brief statement that indicates where a speaker is in the speech or that focuses attention on key ideas.

Signposts are very brief statements that indicate exactly where you are in the speech. Frequently they are just numbers. Here is how one student used

Experienced speakers include transitions and other connectives to help listeners keep track of their ideas. Here Adam Savage, co-host of *MythBusters*, addresses the media at the White Hose Science Fair.

simple numerical signposts to help her audience keep track of the major causes for the continuing problem of famine in Africa:

> The first cause of this problem is inefficient agricultural production.
>
> The second cause is recurrent drought in the affected countries.
>
> The final cause is mismanagement of available food resources by local leaders.

Another way to accomplish the same thing is to introduce your main points with a question, as did one student in his speech on mail-order fraud. His first main point showed that mail-order fraud continues to be a serious problem despite the growth of the Internet. He introduced it this way:

> So just how serious is the problem of mail-order fraud? Is it just a few isolated cases, or is it widespread enough to require serious measures to protect consumers?

His second main point dealt with ways to curb mail-order fraud. He introduced it by saying:

> So how can we solve this problem? Is there a way to protect the rights of legitimate mail-order companies while attacking the fraudulent ones?

Questions are particularly effective as signposts because they invite subliminal answers and thereby get the audience more involved with the speech.

Besides using signposts to indicate where you are in the speech, you can use them to focus attention on key ideas. You can do this with a simple phrase, as in the following example:

> The most important thing to remember about abstract art is that it is always based on forms in the natural world.

The underlined words alert the audience to the fact that an especially significant point is coming up. So do phrases such as these:

Be sure to keep this in mind . . .

This is crucial to understanding the rest of the speech . . .

Above all, you need to know . . .

Depending on the needs of your speech, you may want to use two, three, or even all four kinds of connectives in combination. You needn't worry too much about what they are called—whether this one is a signpost and that a transition. The important thing is to be aware of their functions. Properly applied, connectives can make your speeches more unified and coherent.

Summary

Clear organization is vital to speechmaking. Listeners demand coherence. They get only one chance to grasp a speaker's ideas, and they have little patience for speakers who ramble aimlessly from one idea to another. A well-organized speech will enhance your credibility and make it easier for the audience to understand your message.

The process of planning the body of a speech begins when you determine the main points. You should choose them carefully, phrase them precisely, and organize them strategically. Because listeners cannot keep track of a multitude of main points, most speeches should contain no more than two to five. Each should focus on a single idea, should be worded clearly, and should receive enough emphasis to be clear and convincing.

You can organize main points in various ways, depending on your topic, purpose, and audience. Chronological order follows a time pattern, whereas spatial order follows a directional pattern. In causal order, main points are organized according to their cause-effect relationship. Topical order results when you divide your main topic into subtopics. Problem-solution order breaks the body of the speech into two main parts—the first showing a problem, the second giving a solution.

Supporting materials are the backup ideas for your main points. When organizing supporting materials, make sure they are directly relevant to the main points they are supposed to support.

Connectives help tie a speech together. They are words or phrases that join one thought to another and indicate the relationship between them. The four major types of speech connectives are transitions, internal previews, internal summaries, and signposts. Using them effectively will make your speeches more unified and coherent.

Key Terms

strategic organization *(166)*
main points *(167)*
chronological order *(169)*
spatial order *(170)*
causal order *(170)*
problem-solution order *(172)*
topical order *(172)*

supporting materials *(175)*
connective *(177)*
transition *(177)*
internal preview *(178)*
internal summary *(178)*
signpost *(178)*

Review Questions

After reading this chapter, you should be able to answer the following questions:

1. Why is it important that speeches be organized clearly and coherently?

2. How many main points will your speeches usually contain? Why is it important to limit the number of main points in your speeches?

3. What are the five basic patterns of organizing main points in a speech? Which are appropriate for informative speeches? Which is most appropriate for persuasive speeches? Which is used most often?

4. What are three tips for preparing your main points?

5. What is the most important thing to remember when organizing supporting materials in the body of your speech?

6. What are the four kinds of speech connectives? What role does each play in a speech?

connect

For further review, go to the LearnSmart study module for this chapter.

Exercises for Critical Thinking

1. What organizational method (or methods) might you use to arrange main points for speeches with the following specific purpose statements?

   To inform my audience of the causes and effects of Parkinson's disease.

   To inform my audience about the major kinds of symbols used in Native American art.

   To persuade my audience that the state legislature should enact tougher laws to curb the problem of predatory lending to college students.

   To inform my audience about the major stages of the civil rights movement from 1955 to 1970.

   To inform my audience about the educational philosophy of Jean Piaget.

   To inform my audience about the geographical regions of Brazil.

2. Turn to the outline of main points and supporting materials for the speech about hypnosis on page 167. Create appropriate transitions, internal previews, internal summaries, and signposts for the speech.

3. Identify the organizational method used in each of the following sets of main points.

   I. Fraudulent charity fund-raising is a widespread national problem.
   II. The problem can be solved by a combination of government regulation and individual awareness.

   I. At the top of the rainforest is the emergent layer, where trees can be 200 feet tall.
   II. Below the emergent layer is the canopy, where vegetation is so dense that it filters out 80 percent of the sunlight.
   III. Beneath the canopy is the understory, where trees are less than 12 feet tall and grow large leaves to collect the small amount of sunlight.
   IV. At the bottom is the forest floor, where there are almost no plants because of the lack of sunlight.

   I. Sonia Sotomayor is best known as the first Hispanic justice of the U.S. Supreme Court.
   II. Sonia Sotomayor is also an accomplished communicator who has given hundreds of public speeches.

   I. Founded in 1948, NASCAR was limited primarily to the South through the 1950s and 1960s.
   II. The modern era of NASCAR began in the 1970s with the development of the points system to crown a yearly champion.
   III. Today NASCAR is one of the most popular spectator sports in America.

   I. Caused by an antibiotic-resistant strain of staphylococcus bacteria, MRSA is prevalent among college students.
   II. The effects of MRSA include skin infections, damage to internal organs, pneumonia, and, in some cases, death.

10

Beginning and Ending the Speech

The Introduction

The Conclusion

On the night of January 26, 1988, a conductor stepped to the podium at the Majestic Theatre in New York City, tapped his baton, raised his arms, and signaled the orchestra to play Moments later, American theatergoers first heard the dramatic opening chords of *The Phantom of the Opera*. Today, this scene has been repeated more than 9,500 times and *Phantom* has become the longest-running musical in Broadway history.

Like most classic musicals, *Phantom of the Opera* begins with an overture—an orchestral introduction that captures the audience's attention and gives them a preview of the music they are going to hear. Without such an introduction—if the characters simply walked onstage and began singing or speaking—the beginning of the play would seem too abrupt, and the audience would not be suitably "primed" for the entertainment.

Similarly, most musicals end with a finale, when the whole cast is onstage, elements of the dramatic plot are resolved, portions of the principal songs are recalled, and the music is brought to a dramatic climax. If there were no such conclusion, if the actors merely stopped and walked offstage, the audience would be left unsatisfied.

Just as musical plays need appropriate beginnings and endings, so do speeches. The beginning, or introduction, prepares listeners for what is to come. The conclusion ties up the speech and alerts listeners that the speech is going to end. Ideally, it is a satisfying conclusion.

In this chapter, we explore the roles played by an introduction and a conclusion in speechmaking. We also discuss techniques aimed at fulfilling those roles. If you apply these techniques imaginatively, you will take a big step toward elevating your speeches from the ordinary to the splendid.

The Introduction

First impressions are important. A poor beginning may so distract or alienate listeners that the speaker can never fully recover. Moreover, getting off on the right foot is vital to a speaker's self-confidence. What could be more encouraging than watching your listeners' faces begin to register interest, attention, and pleasure? A good introduction, you will find, is an excellent confidence booster.

In most speech situations, the introduction has four objectives:

- Get the attention and interest of your audience.
- Reveal the topic of your speech.
- Establish your credibility and goodwill.
- Preview the body of the speech.

We'll look at each of these objectives in turn.

GET ATTENTION AND INTEREST

"Unless a speaker can interest his audience at once, his effort will be a failure." So said the great lawyer Clarence Darrow. If your topic is not one of extraordinary interest, your listeners are likely to say to themselves, "So what? Who cares?" A speaker can quickly lose an audience if she or he doesn't use the introduction to get their attention and quicken their interest.

Getting the initial attention of your audience is usually easy—even before you utter a single word. After you are introduced and step to the lectern, your audience will normally give you their attention. If they don't, wait patiently. Look directly at the audience without saying a word. In a few moments all talking and physical commotion will stop. Your listeners will be attentive. You will be ready to start speaking.

Keeping the attention of your audience once you start talking is more difficult. Here are the methods used most often. Employed individually or in combination, they will help get the audience caught up in your speech.

Relate the Topic to the Audience
People pay attention to things that affect them directly. If you can relate the topic to your listeners, they are much more likely to be interested in it.

Suppose, for example, one of your classmates begins her speech like this:

Today I am going to talk about collecting postcards—a hobby that is both fascinating and financially rewarding. I would like to explain the basic kinds of collectible postcards, why they are so valuable, and how collectors buy and sell their cards.

A good introduction will get your speech off to a strong start. To be most effective, it should relate the topic to the audience and be delivered from a minimum of notes—as in this speech by British anthropologist Jane Goodall.

This is certainly a clear introduction, but it is not one to get you hooked on the speech. Now what if your classmate were to begin her speech this way—as one student actually did.

> It's Saturday morning, and you are helping clean out your grandmother's attic. After working a while, you stumble upon a trunk, open it, and discover hundreds of old postcards. Thinking about getting to the football game on time, you start tossing the cards into the trash can. Congratulations! You have just thrown away a year's tuition.

This time the speaker has used just the right bait. Chances are you will be hooked.

Even when you use other interest-arousing lures, you should *always* relate your topic to the audience. At times this will test your ingenuity, but it pays dividends. Here is an excellent example from a student speech about dreams. The speaker began by saying:

> You're being chased by an object of unspeakable horror, yet your legs can only move in slow motion. Each step takes unbearably long, and your frantic struggle to run faster is hopeless. Your pursuer gets closer, and your desperation turns to terror. You're completely helpless—eye to eye with death.
>
> Then you wake up, gasping for air, your heart pounding, your face clammy with sweat. It takes a few minutes for your heart and breathing to slow down. You reassure yourself that it was "just a dream." Soon you drift back to sleep.

By using vivid language to describe something all his classmates had experienced, the speaker made sure of an attentive audience.

connect

View the beginning of "In Your Dreams" in the online Media Library for this chapter (Video 10.1).

State the Importance of Your Topic

Presumably, you think your speech is important. Tell your audience why they should think so too. Here is how Judith Kaye, Chief Judge of the State of New York, used this method to involve her audience in a speech to the American Bar Association Center on Children and the Law:

> We know that a child is born into poverty in the United States every 36 seconds, and we see 12.8 million children living below the poverty line. . . . A child dies from neglect or abuse every six hours, a child is killed by gunfire almost every three hours, and the number of neglected or abused children each year would fill up the city of Detroit.[1]

These are striking statistics. By citing them in her introduction, Kaye emphasized the importance of her topic and captured the attention of her audience.

Clearly this technique is easy to use when discussing social and political issues such as child abuse, endangered species, terrorism, and stem cell research, but it is appropriate for other topics as well. Here is how one student handled it in a speech about starting a home aquarium:

> It is very hard to cuddle a fish. Fish won't roll over or fetch the morning paper. You won't find them curling up on your lap, chasing a ball of string, or rescuing a child from a burning building.
>
> Yet despite these shortcomings, 150 million tropical fish have found their way into 14 million American homes. Each year $60 million of tropical fish are sold in the United States, and they have earned a spot next to the all-American dog and the cuddly kitten in the hearts of millions of people. Today I would like to explain how you can start a home aquarium and discover the pleasures of owning tropical fish.

Whenever you discuss a topic whose importance may not be clear to the audience, you should think about ways to demonstrate its significance in the introduction.

Startle the Audience

One surefire way to arouse interest quickly is to startle your listeners with an arresting or intriguing statement. Everyone in the audience paid close attention after this speaker's introduction:

> Take a moment and think of the three women closest to you. Who comes to mind? Your mother? Your sister? Your girlfriend? Your wife? Your best friend? Now guess which one will be sexually assaulted during her lifetime. It's not a pleasant thought, but according to the U.S. Department of Justice, one of every three American women will be sexually assaulted sometime during her life.

Notice the buildup to the speaker's arresting statement, "Now guess which one will be sexually assaulted during her lifetime." This statement startles the audience—especially the men—and drives home at a personal level the problem of sexual assault against women.

This technique is highly effective and easy to use. Just be sure the startling introduction relates directly to the subject of your speech. If you choose a strong opening simply for its shock value and then go on to talk about something else, your audience will be confused and possibly annoyed.

Arouse the Curiosity of the Audience

People are curious. One way to draw them into your speech is with a series of statements that progressively whet their curiosity about the subject of the speech. For example:

> It is the most common chronic disease in the United States. Controllable but incurable, it is a symptomless disease. You can have it for years and never know until it kills you. Some 73 million Americans have this disease, and 300,000 will die from it before the year is out. Odds are that five of us in this class have it.
>
> What am I talking about? Not cancer. Not AIDS. Not heart disease. I am talking about hypertension—high blood pressure.

By building suspense about his subject, the speaker pulls his audience into the speech. Notice how much less effective the introduction would have been if he had simply said, "Today I am going to talk about high blood pressure."

Question the Audience

Asking a *rhetorical question* is another way to get your listeners thinking about your speech. Sometimes a single question will do:

> How would you respond if a loved one was the victim of terrorism?

> What would you think if you went to the doctor because you were ill and she told you to watch *Modern Family* as part of your treatment?

In other circumstances, you may want to pose a series of questions, each of which draws the audience deeper and deeper into the speech. Here is how one speaker used this method:

> Have you ever spent a sleepless night studying for an exam? Can you remember rushing to finish a term paper because you waited too long to start writing it? Do you often feel overwhelmed by all the things you have to get done at school? At work? At home?
>
> If so, you may be the victim of poor time management. Fortunately, there are proven strategies you can follow to use your time more effectively and to keep control of your life.

When using this technique, be sure to pause for just a moment after each question. This adds dramatic impact and gives the question time to sink in. The audience, of course, will answer mentally— not out loud.

rhetorical question

A question that the audience answers mentally rather than out loud.

Begin with a Quotation

Another way to arouse the interest of your audience is to start with an attention-getting quotation. You might choose your quotation from Shakespeare or Confucius, from the Bible or Talmud, from a poem, song, or film. Here is how one student used a humorous quotation to begin a speech about the need for political reform in the U.S. Congress:

> Mark Twain once said, "It could probably be shown by facts and figures that there is no distinctly American criminal class except Congress."

You need not use a famous quotation. The following made an effective introduction for a speech about bird watching:

"It is a moment I will never forget. I glimpsed a flash of color in the thicket, and then I saw it—a Bachman's Warbler, one of the rarest birds in all of America. I was so excited I could barely keep my binoculars from shaking."

This statement was made by my father. He is just one of the millions of people who have discovered the joys of bird-watching.

Notice that both of the quotations used here as examples are relatively short. Opening your speech with a lengthy quotation is a sure way to set your audience yawning.

Tell a Story

We all enjoy stories—especially if they are provocative, dramatic, or suspenseful. Consider the story one student told to open his remarks about the devastating earthquake and tsunami that struck Japan on March 11, 2011:

A young couple clutched their four-month-old baby girl as a tidal wave smashed into their home in northern Japan. The wave, caused by a massive 9.0 earthquake earlier in the day, was simply too powerful. It ripped the baby girl

✔ checklist

Speech Introduction

YES	NO	
☐	☐	1. Do I gain the attention and interest of my audience by using one or more of the methods discussed in this chapter?
☐	☐	2. Do I relate the speech topic to my audience?
☐	☐	3. Do I clearly reveal the topic of my speech?
☐	☐	4. Do I establish my credibility to speak on this topic?
☐	☐	5. If my topic is controversial, do I take steps to establish my goodwill toward the audience?
☐	☐	6. Do I define any key terms that will be necessary for the audience to understand the rest of my speech?
☐	☐	7. Do I provide a preview statement of the main points to be covered in the body of the speech?
☐	☐	8. Is the introduction limited to 10–20 percent of my entire speech?
☐	☐	9. Have I worked out the language of my introduction in detail?
☐	☐	10. Have I practiced the delivery of my introduction so I can present it fluently, confidently, and with strong eye contact?

As you research your speeches, keep an eye out for quotations, stories, and other materials you can use to craft an introduction that will capture the attention of your listeners.

from the arms of her parents and carried her off amidst piles of debris. The parents could not stop weeping at the thought of their dead child.

Three days later, rescue workers were combing through mounds of wood, metal, and rock when they heard a faint cry. Working frantically, they pulled the lost baby out of the rubble—alive. "Her discovery put a new energy into the search," one of her rescuers told a local news crew in a story later reported by *Time* magazine.

Not everyone was as fortunate as that little girl—or as the parents who were reunited with her. But as Japan tried to overcome the devastation, any sign of hope was welcomed with open arms.

Like many good introductions, this one does a double job—it arouses the interest of the audience and gets listeners emotionally involved in the speech.

You can also use stories based on your personal experience. Here is how one pre-med student used such a story. She began by recounting the first time she observed doctors performing surgery in the operating room:

There I stood, wearing a surgical mask, in the middle of a large, brightly lit room. In the center of the room were five figures huddled over a table. I found it difficult to see since everything was draped in blue sheets, yet I didn't dare take a step toward the table.

Then one of the figures called to me, "Angela, get over here and take a closer look." My knees buckled as I walked through the sterile environment. But eventually I was there, standing over an unconscious body in the operating room.

The effectiveness of any story—especially a personal one—hinges on the speaker's delivery as well as on the content. As you can see from the excerpt of this speech on Video 10.2 in the online Media Library for this chapter, the speaker uses pauses, eye contact, and changes in her tone of voice to help draw her audience into the speech. See if you can do the same in your introduction.

The seven methods discussed above are the ones used most often by student speakers to gain attention and interest. Other methods include referring to the occasion, inviting audience participation, using audio equipment or visual aids, relating to a previous speaker, and beginning with humor. For any

connect

View the beginning of "Hoping to Heal" in the online Media Library for this chapter (Video 10.2).

given speech, try to choose the method that is most suitable for the topic, the audience, and the occasion.

REVEAL THE TOPIC

In the process of gaining attention, be sure to state clearly the topic of your speech. If you do not, your listeners will be confused. And once they are confused, your chances of getting them absorbed in the speech are almost nil.

This is a basic point—so basic that it may hardly seem worth mentioning. Yet you would be surprised how many students need to be reminded of it. You may hear speeches in your own class in which the topic is not clear by the end of the introduction. So you will know what to avoid, here is such an introduction, presented in a public speaking class:

> Imagine taking a leisurely boat ride along a peaceful waterway. The sun is high in the sky, reflecting brightly off the ripples around you. The banks are lush with mangrove and cypress trees. You see a stately pelican resting on a low-lying branch. You grab your camera, snap a shot, and check the result. The picture is perfect. But will it be perfect in the future?

What is the topic of this speech? Nature photography? No. Birding? No. Tourism in the tropics? No. The student was talking about efforts to restore the natural beauty of the Florida Everglades. But she did not make that clear to her audience. Suppose, instead, she had begun her speech differently:

> Alligators, panthers, otters, brown pelicans—these and other creatures have lost 50 percent of their habitat in south Florida over the past few decades. Now, however, there is an $8 billion program to preserve their home in the Florida Everglades. The largest restoration effort in the history of the world, it will rejuvenate one of America's most diverse ecosystems and protect it for future generations.

This opening would have provided a way to get the audience's attention, but it also would have related directly to the speech topic. If you beat around the bush in your introduction, you may lose your listeners. Even if they already know your topic, you should restate it clearly and concisely at some point in the introduction.

ESTABLISH CREDIBILITY AND GOODWILL

Besides getting attention and revealing the topic, there is a third objective you may need to accomplish in your introduction—establishing your credibility and goodwill.

Credibility is mostly a matter of being qualified to speak on a given topic—and of being *perceived* as qualified by your listeners. Here is how one student established her credibility on the subject of weight lifting without sounding like a braggart:

credibility

The audience's perception of whether a speaker is qualified to speak on a given topic.

> Once seen as an exclusively male activity, weight lifting has crossed the gender barrier—and with good reason. Regardless of whether you are male or female, weight lifting can give you a sense of strength and power, enhance your self-esteem, and make you look and feel better.
> I started lifting weights when I was in high school, and I have kept at it for the past eight years. I have also taught weight lifting in several health clubs, and I am a certified instructor through the Aerobics and Fitness Association of America.

Telling a story is an excellent way to gain attention in a speech introduction. The story should be clearly relevant to the topic and should be delivered expressively with strong eye contact.

Using some of my experience, I would like to explain the basic kinds of weights and how to use them properly.

Whether or not you lift weights, you will probably be more interested in the speech when you realize that the speaker knows what she is talking about.

Your credibility need not be based on firsthand knowledge and experience. It can come from reading, from classes, from interviews, from friends—as in these cases:

I have been interested in the myth of Atlantis for several years, and I have read a number of books and articles about it.

The information I am going to share with you today comes mostly from my biology class and an interview with Reyna Vasquez of the local Audubon Society.

Whatever the source of your expertise, be sure to let the audience know.

Establishing your *goodwill* is a slightly different challenge. It is often crucial outside the classroom, where speakers have well-established reputations and may be identified with causes that arouse hostility among listeners. In such a situation, the speaker must try to defuse that hostility right at the start of the speech.

Occasionally you may have to do the same thing in your classroom speeches. Suppose you advocate a potentially unpopular position. You will need to make a special effort to ensure that your classmates will consider your point of view. This is how one student tried to minimize her classmates' opposition in the introduction of a speech urging them to change the way they use their cell phones:

Now, don't worry, I'm not going to try to persuade you to abandon your constant companion. I still use mine on a regular basis, and I probably always will. But I do hope to persuade you to make one simple change in the way you use your cell phone—a change that will protect your health and could even make the difference between a long life and premature death.

goodwill

The audience's perception of whether the speaker has the best interests of the audience in mind.

connect

View this portion of "The Dangers of Cell Phones" in the online Media Library for this chapter (Video 10.3).

The speaker was clear about her intentions and reasonable in her expectations. By the end of the introduction, the audience knew she had their best interests at heart.

PREVIEW THE BODY OF THE SPEECH

As we saw in Chapter 3, most people are poor listeners. Even good listeners need all the help they can get in sorting out a speaker's ideas. One way to help your listeners is to tell them in the introduction what they should listen for in the rest of the speech. Here is an excellent example, from a speech by U.S. Secretary of Defense Robert Gates at the U.S. Military Academy, West Point, on February 25, 2011:

preview statement

A statement in the introduction of a speech that identifies the main points to be discussed in the body.

> Today, I'd like to focus on three interrelated issues—the future of conflict and the implications for the Army; how best to institutionalize the diverse capabilities that will be required; and the kinds of officers the Army will need for the 21st century.[2]

After this introduction, there was no doubt about Gates's topic or the main points he would cover in his speech.

In some types of persuasive speeches, you may not want to reveal your central idea until later in the speech. But even in such a situation you must be sure your audience is not left guessing about the main points they should listen for as the speech unfolds. Nearly always, you should include a *preview statement* like the following:

connect

View these preview statements from student speeches in the online Media Library for this chapter (Video 10.4).

> The goal of my speech today is to inform you about Ramadan—specifically its history and practices. In the end, I hope you'll have a better understanding of this sacred time for Muslims in the United States and around the globe.

> I am convinced that we need to take action to combat the problem of phony pharmaceuticals. Later in my speech, I'll share a plan with you for curbing the spread of these dangerous drugs. But let's start by taking a closer look at the problem.

Preview statements such as these serve another purpose as well. Because they usually come at the very end of the introduction, they provide a smooth lead-in to the body of the speech. They signal that the body of the speech is about to begin.

There is one other aspect you may want to cover in previewing your speech. You can use your introduction to give specialized information—definitions or background—that your listeners will need if they are to understand the rest of the speech. Often you can do this very quickly, as in the following example:

> A triathlon is a race made up of three different events completed in succession. The events are usually swimming, biking, and running, though canoeing is sometimes substituted for one of these.

In other circumstances, you may have to explain an important term in more detail. Here is how one student handled the problem in a speech about the Underground Railroad used by slaves to escape from the South before the Civil War:

The term "Underground Railroad" was first used about 1830. But in fact, the Underground Railroad was neither underground nor a railroad. It was an informal network that provided runaway slaves food, clothing, directions, and places to hide on their escape routes to the North and to Canada.

Why was it called the Underground Railroad? Because of its secrecy and because many of the people involved used railroad terms as code words. Hiding places, for example, were called "stations," and people who helped the slaves were called "conductors." Over the years, the Underground Railroad helped thousands of slaves make their way from bondage to freedom.

SAMPLE INTRODUCTION WITH COMMENTARY

So far we have seen many excerpts showing how to fulfill the various objectives of an introduction. Now here is a complete introduction from a student speech. The side comments indicate the principles used in developing the introduction.

View this introduction in the online Media Library for this chapter (Video 10.5).

Surrounded by Stuff

COMMENTARY	SPEECH
The speaker uses a story to gain attention. This story works particularly well because it is richly detailed and is high in human interest. The frequent use of "you" helps relate the story to the audience.	For my Aunt Josefina, life can be empty, even though she's surrounded by tons of stuff. Walking into her living room, you'll see stacks of magazines and newspapers, piles of clean and dirty laundry, and boxes of collectible figurines. But you won't find a place to sit down. In her kitchen, you'll see towers of dishes, scores of empty two-liter bottles, and over a dozen trash bags. But you won't see a kitchen table.
Now the speaker reveals her topic and defines the meaning of hoarding. The way she gradually reveals Aunt Josefina's malady helps build the audience's interest. Her personal involvement with the topic increases her credibility and goodwill.	Some people say Aunt Josefina is lazy. Others say she's just dirty. But my family and I know the truth: Aunt Josefina suffers from a mental disorder known as Collyer's Syndrome, or disposophobia. But you probably know it by its most common name: compulsive hoarding. Those who suffer from compulsive hoarding can't bring themselves to get rid of anything. It doesn't matter if the things are valuable; it only matters that they hold on to them.
The speaker uses statistics to show the importance of her topic. Mentioning her research for the speech further bolsters her credibility.	Over the years, my family and I have become painfully aware of what life is like for a compulsive hoarder. But until researching the topic for this speech, I had no idea how widespread the disorder was. Gail Steketee and Randy Frost, authors of *Stuff: Compulsive Hoarding and the Meaning of Things,* report that anywhere from 6 million to 15 million Americans are compulsive hoarders.
The introduction ends with a clear preview of the main points to be discussed in the body.	Today I would like to introduce you to the world of compulsive hoarding. I will show you the seriousness of the problem, the impact it can have on individuals and families, and the ways it can be treated.

TIPS FOR THE INTRODUCTION

1. Keep the introduction relatively brief. Under normal circumstances it should not constitute more than 10 to 20 percent of your speech.

2. Be on the lookout for possible introductory materials as you do your research. File them with your notes so they will be handy when you are ready for them.

3. Be creative in devising your introduction. Experiment with two or three different openings and choose the one that seems most likely to get the audience interested in your speech.

4. Don't worry about the exact wording of your introduction until you have finished preparing the body of the speech. After you have determined your main points, it will be much easier to make final decisions about how to begin the speech.

5. Work out your introduction in detail. Some teachers recommend that you write it out word for word; others prefer that you outline it. Whichever method you use, practice the introduction over and over until you can deliver it smoothly from a minimum of notes and with strong eye contact.

6. When you present the speech, don't start talking too soon. Make sure the audience has quieted down and is focused on you before you begin. Establish eye contact with the audience, smile, and then launch into your opening words. Give yourself every chance to make sure your introduction has the desired impact.

The Conclusion

"Great is the art of beginning," said Longfellow, "but greater the art is of ending." Longfellow was thinking of poetry, but his insight is equally applicable to public speaking. Many a speaker has marred an otherwise fine speech by a long-winded, silly, or antagonistic conclusion. Your closing remarks are your last chance to drive home your ideas. Moreover, your final impression will probably linger in your listeners' minds. Thus you need to craft your conclusion with as much care as your introduction.

No matter what kind of speech you are giving, the conclusion has two major functions:

- To let the audience know you are ending the speech.
- To reinforce the audience's understanding of, or commitment to, the central idea.

Let us look at each.

SIGNAL THE END OF THE SPEECH

It may seem obvious that you should let your audience know you are going to stop soon. However, you will almost certainly hear speeches in your class in which the speaker concludes so abruptly that you are taken by surprise. Too sudden an ending leaves the audience puzzled and unfulfilled.

How do you let an audience know your speech is ending? One way is through what you say. "In conclusion," "My purpose has been," "Let me end by saying"—these are all brief cues that you are getting ready to stop.

You can also let your audience know the end is in sight by your manner of delivery. The conclusion is the climax of a speech. A speaker who has carefully built to a peak of interest and involvement will not need to say anything like "in conclusion." By use of the voice—its tone, pacing, intonation, and rhythm—a speaker can build the momentum of a speech so there is no doubt when it is over.

One method of doing this has been likened to a musical crescendo. As in a symphony in which one instrument after another joins in until the entire orchestra is playing, the speech builds in force until it reaches a zenith of power and intensity.[3] (This does *not* mean simply getting louder and louder. It is a combination of many things, including vocal pitch, choice of words, dramatic content, gestures, pauses—and possibly loudness.)

The conclusion is your last chance to drive home your ideas. Here Geena Davis concludes her keynote address at the Spark Summit rally at Hunter College in New York City.

A superb example of this method is the memorable conclusion to Martin Luther King's "I've Been to the Mountaintop," the speech he delivered the night before he was assassinated in April 1968. Speaking to an audience of 2,000 people in Memphis, Tennessee, he ended his speech with a stirring declaration that the civil rights movement would succeed despite the many threats on his life:

Like anybody, I would like to live a long life. Longevity has its place, but I'm not concerned about that now. I just want to do God's will, and he's allowed me to go up to the mountain, and I've looked over and I've seen the Promised Land. I may not get there with you, but I want you to know tonight that we as a people will get to the Promised Land. So I'm happy tonight. I'm not worried about anything; I'm not fearing any man. Mine eyes have seen the glory of the coming of the Lord.

Another effective method might be compared to the dissolve ending of a concert song that evokes deep emotions: "The song seems to fade away while the light on the singer shrinks gradually to a smaller and smaller circle until it lights only the face, then the eyes. Finally, it is a pinpoint, and disappears with the last note of the song."[4] Here is a speech ending that does much the same thing. It is from General Douglas MacArthur's moving farewell to the cadets at the U.S. Military Academy:

In my dreams I hear again the crash of guns, the rattle of musketry, the strange, mournful mutter of the battlefield. But in the evening of my memory always I come back to West Point. Always there echoes and re-echoes: duty, honor, country.

Today marks my final roll call with you. But I want you to know that when I cross the river, my last conscious thoughts will be of the Corps, and the Corps, and the Corps.

I bid you farewell.

crescendo ending

A conclusion in which the speech builds to a zenith of power and intensity.

connect

View the ending of Martin Luther King's "I've Been to the Mountaintop" in the online Media Library for this chapter (Video 10.6).

Your degree in civil engineering has served you well and you are now the chief city planner for a major metropolis. After studying the issue for more than a year, you and the planning commission have decided that the best way to relieve the city's growing traffic congestion is to build a new downtown freeway. Unfortunately, there is no way to build the freeway without knocking down a number of houses and businesses.

Not surprisingly, the neighborhood association that represents the area through which the new freeway will run has expressed a number of concerns about the proposal. Because of your excellent public speaking skills, you have been chosen to represent the city at a meeting of the neighborhood association. You know that if your speech is to be persuasive, you must use the introduction to establish your credibility and goodwill so your listeners will be willing to listen receptively to what you say in the body.

Write a draft of your introduction. Be sure to address all four functions of a speech introduction discussed in this chapter.

The final words fade like the spotlight, bringing the speech to an emotional close.

You may think that you couldn't possibly end a speech with that much pathos—and you'd be right. MacArthur was an eloquent speaker discussing a grave issue with extraordinary poignance. This combination rarely occurs. But that doesn't mean you can't use the dissolve ending effectively. One student used it with great effect in a speech about the immigrant experience in the United States. During the body of the speech, the student spoke about the numbers of immigrants and the challenges they faced. Then, in her conclusion, she created a moving dissolve ending by evoking the emotional images of her grandfather's arrival in the United States:

> On a recent trip to Ellis Island, where my grandfather first stepped on American soil, I saw his name etched into the wall along with the names of tens of thousands of other immigrants. I saw the entry hall where he lined up to process his forms. I saw the room where he underwent a physical examination. I sensed the fear and insecurity he must have felt. But I could also sense his excitement as he looked forward to life in a land of opportunity—a land he came to think of as home.

dissolve ending

A conclusion that generates emotional appeal by fading step by step to a dramatic final statement.

Both the crescendo and the dissolve endings must be worked out with great care. Practice until you get the words and the timing just right. The benefits will be well worth your time.

REINFORCE THE CENTRAL IDEA

The second major function of a conclusion is to reinforce the audience's understanding of, or commitment to, the central idea. There are many ways to do this. Here are the ones you are most likely to use.

Summarize Your Speech

Restating the main points is the easiest way to end a speech. One student used this technique effectively in his persuasive speech about the AIDS epidemic in Africa:

> In conclusion, we have seen that the AIDS epidemic is having a devastating effect on African society. An entire adult generation is slowly being wiped out. An entirely new generation of AIDS orphans is being created. Governments in the nations most afflicted have neither the resources nor the expertise to counter the epidemic. Many African economies are being crippled by the loss of people in the workplace.
>
> Before it's too late, the United Nations and developed countries need to increase their efforts to halt the epidemic and bring it under control. The lives and well-being of tens of millions of people hang in the balance.

connect

View the conclusion of "AIDS in Africa: A World Crisis" in the online Media Library for this chapter (Video 10.7).

The value of a summary is that it explicitly restates the central idea and main points one last time. But as we shall see, there are more imaginative and compelling ways to end a speech. They can be used in combination with a summary or, at times, in place of it.

End with a Quotation

A quotation is one of the most common and effective devices to conclude a speech. Here is a fine example, from a speech on volunteering for Big Brothers or Big Sisters:

> None of us have the extra time that we'd like. But whatever time you can spare, you'll be making a world of difference in the life of an underprivileged child. In the words of the poet Henry Wadsworth Longfellow, "Give what you have. To someone, it may be better than you dare to think."

The closing quotation is particularly good because its urgency is exactly suited to the speech. When you run across a *brief* quotation that so perfectly captures your central idea, keep it in mind as a possible conclusion.

Make a Dramatic Statement

Rather than using a quotation to give your conclusion force and vitality, you may want to devise your own dramatic statement. Some speeches have become famous because of their powerful closing lines. One is Patrick Henry's legendary "Liberty or Death" oration. It takes its name from the final sentences Henry uttered on March 23, 1775, as he exhorted his audience to resist British tyranny:

> Is life so dear, or peace so sweet, as to be purchased at the price of chains and slavery? Forbid it, Almighty God! I know not what course others may take; but as for me, give me liberty, or give me death.

Although your classroom speeches are not likely to become famous, you can still rivet your listeners—as Henry did—with a dramatic concluding statement. What follows is a particularly striking example, from a speech on suicide prevention. Throughout the speech, the student referred to a friend

checklist

Speech Conclusion

YES	NO	
☐	☐	1. Do I signal that my speech is coming to an end?
☐	☐	2. Do I reinforce my central idea by:
		Summarizing the main points of my speech
		Ending with a quotation
		Making a dramatic statement
		Referring to the introduction
☐	☐	3. Is the conclusion limited to 5–10 percent of my entire speech?
☐	☐	4. Have I worked out the language of my conclusion in detail?
☐	☐	5. Have I practiced the delivery of my conclusion so I can present it fluently, confidently, and with strong eye contact?

who had tried to commit suicide the previous year. Then, in the conclusion, she said:

> My friend is back in school, participating in activities she never did before—and enjoying it. I'm happy and proud to say that she's still fighting for her life and even happier that she failed to kill herself. Otherwise, I wouldn't be here today trying to help you. You see, I am my "friend," and I'm more than glad to say I've made it.

As you can imagine, the audience was stunned. The closing lines brought the speech to a dramatic conclusion. The speaker made it even more effective by pausing just a moment before the last words and by using her voice to give them just the right inflection.

Refer to the Introduction

An excellent way to give your speech psychological unity is to conclude by referring to ideas in the introduction. Here is how one student used the method in her speech about carbon monoxide poisoning:

Introduction   It was supposed to be a time of celebration. Five friends had gathered in a south Florida hotel room to celebrate a birthday. Juchen Martial, one of the five, was turning nineteen. But the day after the birthday party, a maid passing by the hotel room glanced through a window and saw five dead bodies. All five friends had been killed.

Their killer was silent, invisible, odorless, and tasteless. Their killer was carbon monoxide. The friends had left their car running in a carport directly beneath their hotel room. Carbon monoxide seeped into the room and took their lives—as it does the lives of 400 people a year in the United States.

In the body of her speech, the student looked in detail at the problem of carbon monoxide poisoning and explained ways to head off the problem. Then, in her closing words, she tied the whole speech together by returning to the story described in her introduction:

Conclusion   Remember those five friends I mentioned in the introduction of my speech? Their deaths were tragic and unnecessary. I hope the information I have provided today will help you avoid their fate. By understanding where carbon monoxide comes from, by recognizing the warning signs of carbon monoxide poisoning, and by following the simple preventive steps I've discussed, you can make sure that you don't fall victim to the silent killer.

connect

View the beginning and ending of "The Silent Killer" in the online Media Library for this chapter (Video 10.8).

Summarizing the speech, ending with a quotation, making a dramatic statement, referring to the introduction—all these techniques can be used separately. But you have probably noticed that speakers often combine two or more in their conclusions. Actually, all four techniques can be fused into one—for example, a dramatic quotation that summarizes the central idea while referring to the introduction.

One other concluding technique is making a direct appeal to your audience for action. This technique applies only to a particular type of persuasive speech, however, and will be discussed in Chapter 16. The four methods covered in this chapter are appropriate for all kinds of speeches and occasions.

SAMPLE CONCLUSION WITH COMMENTARY

How do you fit these methods together to make a conclusion? Here is an example, from the speech about compulsive hoarding whose introduction we looked at earlier (page 195).

connect

View this conclusion in the online Media Library for this chapter (Video 10.9).

⌄⌄ COMMENTARY	⌄⌄ CONCLUSION
The speaker gives an excellent summary of her speech. This is particularly important when speaking to inform because it gives you one last chance to make sure the audience remembers your main points.	Today we have seen that compulsive hoarding is a serious mental disorder whose effects can be devastating for individuals and families. It's also difficult to treat, which means that millions of Americans are left living a life of clutter and chaos.
By referring to her Aunt Josefina, whom she had mentioned in her introduction, the speaker unifies the entire speech. The quotation from Aunt Josefina and the speaker's final sentence end the speech on a strong note.	My Aunt Josefina is one of those people. She says: "People look at my apartment and know I have a problem. I look at my apartment and know I have a problem. I'm trying to get it under control, but it's a really long road." For my Aunt Josefina and millions of others, the good news is that understanding the problem is the first step toward conquering all the stuff.

TIPS FOR THE CONCLUSION

1. As with the introduction, keep an eye out for possible concluding materials as you research and develop the speech.

2. Conclude with a bang, not a whimper. Be creative in devising a conclusion that hits the hearts and minds of your audience. Work on several possible endings, and select the one that seems likely to have the greatest impact.

3. Don't be long-winded. The conclusion will normally make up no more than 5 to 10 percent of your speech.

4. Don't leave anything in your conclusion to chance. Work it out in detail, and give yourself plenty of time to practice delivering it. Many students like to write out the conclusion word for word to guarantee it is just right. If you do this, make sure you can present it smoothly, confidently, and with feeling—without relying on your notes or sounding wooden. Make your last impression as forceful and as favorable as you can.

Summary

First impressions are important. So are final impressions. This is why speeches need strong introductions and conclusions.

In most speech situations you need to accomplish four objectives with your introduction—get the attention and interest of the audience, reveal the topic of your speech, establish your credibility and goodwill, and preview the body of the speech. Gaining attention and interest can be done in several ways. You can show the importance of your topic, especially as it relates to your audience. You can startle or question your audience or arouse their curiosity. You can begin with a quotation or a story.

Be sure to state the topic of your speech clearly in your introduction so the audience knows where the speech is going. Establishing credibility means that you tell the audience why you are qualified to speak on the topic at hand. Establishing goodwill may be necessary if your point of view is unpopular. Previewing the body of the speech helps the audience listen effectively and provides a smooth lead-in to the body of the speech.

The first objective of a speech conclusion is to let the audience know you are ending, which you can do by your words or by your manner of delivery. The second objective of a conclusion is to reinforce your central idea. You can accomplish this by summarizing the speech, ending with a quotation, making a dramatic statement, or referring to the introduction. Sometimes you may want to combine two or more of these techniques. Be creative in devising a vivid, forceful conclusion.

Key Terms

rhetorical question (189)

credibility (192)

goodwill (193)

preview statement (194)

crescendo ending (197)

dissolve ending (198)

Review Questions

After reading this chapter, you should be able to answer the following questions:

1. What are the four objectives of a speech introduction?
2. What are seven methods you can use in the introduction to get the attention and interest of your audience?
3. Why is it important to establish your credibility at the beginning of your speech?
4. What is a preview statement? Why should you nearly always include a preview statement in the introduction of your speech?
5. What are six tips for your introduction?
6. What are the major functions of a speech conclusion?
7. What are two ways you can signal the end of your speech?
8. What are four ways to reinforce the central idea when concluding your speech?
9. What are four tips for your conclusion?

connect

For further review, go to the LearnSmart study module for this chapter.

Exercises for Critical Thinking

1. Here are six speech topics. Explain how you might relate each to your classmates in the introduction of a speech.

Social Security	laughter
coffee	steroids
illiteracy	blood donation

2. Think of a speech topic (preferably one for your next speech in class). Create an introduction for a speech dealing with any aspect of the topic you wish. In your introduction, be sure to gain the attention of the audience, to reveal the topic and relate it to the audience, to establish your credibility, and to preview the body of the speech.

3. Using the same topic as in Exercise 2, create a speech conclusion. Be sure to let your audience know the speech is ending, to reinforce the central idea, and to make the conclusion vivid and memorable.

11

Outlining the Speech

The Preparation Outline

The Speaking Outline

Think what might happen if you tried to build a house without a floor plan or an architect's blueprint. You install a cathedral ceiling so you can have big windows and a huge ceiling fan, but the roof is so high it blocks your bedroom window upstairs. You put in sliding doors to the yard, but they can't be opened because they're too close to the fireplace to slide back without hitting it. You think it's a wonderful idea to have almost no interior walls. But when the first snowfall comes, your (unsupported) roof collapses.

Plans and blueprints are essential to architecture. So, too, are outlines essential to effective speeches. An outline is like a blueprint for your speech. It allows you to see the full scope and content of your speech at a glance. By outlining, you can judge whether each part of the speech is fully developed, whether you have adequate supporting materials for your main points, and whether the main points are properly balanced. An outline helps you make sure that related items are together, that ideas flow from one to another, that the structure of your speech will "stand up"—and not collapse.

Probably you will use two kinds of outlines for your speeches—one very detailed, for the planning stage, and one very brief, for the delivery of the speech.

The Preparation Outline

The preparation outline is just what its name implies—an outline that helps you prepare the speech. Writing a preparation outline means putting your speech together—deciding what you will say in the introduction, how you will organize the main points and supporting materials in the body, and what you will say in the conclusion.

GUIDELINES FOR THE PREPARATION OUTLINE

preparation outline

A detailed outline developed during the process of speech preparation that includes the title, specific purpose, central idea, introduction, main points, subpoints, connectives, conclusion, and bibliography of a speech.

Over the years, a relatively uniform system for preparation outlines has developed. It is explained below and is exemplified in the sample outline on pages 211–213. You should check with your teacher to see exactly what format you are to follow.

State the Specific Purpose of Your Speech

The specific purpose statement should be a separate unit that comes before the outline itself. Including the specific purpose makes it easier to assess how well you have constructed the speech to accomplish your purpose.

Identify the Central Idea

Some teachers prefer that the central idea be given immediately after the purpose statement. Others prefer that it be given and identified in the text of the outline. Check to see which your teacher wants.

Label the Introduction, Body, and Conclusion

If you label the parts of your speech, you will be sure that you indeed *have* an introduction and conclusion and have accomplished the essential objectives of each. Usually the names of the speech parts are placed in the middle of the page or in the far left margin. They are technical labels only and are not included in the system of symbolization used to identify main points and supporting materials.

Use a Consistent Pattern of Symbolization and Indentation

In the most common system of outlining, main points are identified by Roman numerals and are indented equally so as to be aligned down the page. Subpoints (components of the main points) are identified by capital letters and are also indented equally so as to be aligned with each other.

Beyond this, there may be sub-subpoints and even sub-sub-subpoints. For example:

    I. Main point
       A. Subpoint
       B. Subpoint
          1. Sub-subpoint
          2. Sub-subpoint
             a. Sub-sub-subpoint
             b. Sub-sub-subpoint

```
II. Main point
   A. Subpoint
      1. Sub-subpoint
      2. Sub-subpoint
   B. Subpoint
      1. Sub-subpoint
      2. Sub-subpoint
```

The clear *visual framework* of this outline immediately shows the relationships among the ideas of the speech. The most important ideas (main points) are farthest to the left. Less important ideas (subpoints, sub-subpoints, and so on) are progressively farther to the right. This pattern reveals the structure of your entire speech.

Once you have organized the body of your speech (see Chapter 9), you should have identified the main points. You need only flesh out your outline with subpoints and sub-subpoints, as necessary, to support the main points. But suppose, as sometimes happens, you find yourself with a list of statements and are not sure which are main points, which are subpoints, and so forth. Such a list might look like this:

There were 13 people at the Last Supper—Jesus and his 12 disciples.

Many superstitions revolve around numbers.

In the United States, 13 is often omitted in the floor numbering of hotels and skyscrapers.

The number 13 has meant bad luck as long as anyone can remember.

Which statement is the main point? The second statement ("Many superstitions revolve around numbers"), which is broader in scope than any of the other statements. This would be one of the main ideas of your speech. The fourth statement is the subpoint; it immediately supports the main point. The other two statements are sub-subpoints; they illustrate the subpoint. Rearranged properly, they look like this:

```
I. Many superstitions revolve around numbers.
   A. The number 13 has meant bad luck as long as anyone can
      remember.
      1. There were 13 people at the Last Supper—Jesus and his
         12 disciples.
      2. In the United States, 13 is often omitted in the floor numbering
         of hotels and skyscrapers.
```

Above all, remember that all points at the same level should immediately support the point that is just above and one notch to the left in your outline.

State Main Points and Subpoints in Full Sentences

Below are two sets of main points and subpoints for the same speech on the life of Martin Luther King.

Ineffective	More Effective
I. Montgomery	I. King began his civil rights career in the Montgomery bus boycott of 1955–1956.
II. 1960s	II. King's greatest triumphs came during the early 1960s.
A. Birmingham	A. In 1963, he campaigned against segregation in Birmingham, Alabama.
B. March	B. Later that year, he participated in the famous march on Washington, D.C.
1. 200,000	1. More than 200,000 people took part.
2. "Dream"	2. King gave his "I Have a Dream" speech.
C. Prize	C. In 1964, he received the Nobel Peace Prize.
III. Final years	III. King faced great turmoil during his final years.
A. Criticized	A. He was criticized by more militant blacks for being nonviolent.
B. Vietnam	B. He protested against the war in Vietnam.
C. Assassination	C. He was assassinated in Memphis, Tennessee, on April 4, 1968.

connect

For help formatting your outlines, use the automated Outline Tool in the online Speech Tools for this chapter.

The sample at left might serve as a speaking outline, but it is virtually useless as a preparation outline. It gives only vague labels rather than distinct ideas. It does not indicate clearly the content of the main points and subpoints. Nor does it reveal whether the speaker has thought out his or her ideas. But there is no concern about any of these matters with the outline on the right.

In sum, a skimpy preparation outline is of little value. Stating your main points and subpoints in full sentences will ensure that you develop your ideas fully.

Label Transitions, Internal Summaries, and Internal Previews

One way to make sure you have strong transitions, internal summaries, and internal previews is to include them in the preparation outline. Usually they are not incorporated into the system of symbolization and indentation but are labeled separately and inserted in the outline where they will appear in the speech.

Attach a Bibliography

bibliography

A list of all the sources used in preparing a speech.

You should include with the outline a bibliography that shows all the books, magazines, newspapers, and Internet sources you consulted, as well as any interviews or field research you conducted.

The two major bibliographic formats are those developed by the Modern Language Association (MLA) and the American Psychological Association (APA). Both are widely used by communication scholars; ask your instructor which he or she prefers. No matter which format you adopt, make sure your statement of sources is clear, accurate, and consistent. For help, turn to page 135

As blueprints are essential to architecture, so outlines are essential to speechmaking. Developing an outline helps ensure that the structure of your speech is clear and coherent.

in Chapter 7, where you will find sample citations for the kinds of sources used most frequently in classroom speeches.

Give Your Speech a Title, if One Is Desired

In the classroom you probably do not need a title for your speech unless your teacher requires one. In some other situations, however, a speech title is necessary—as when the speech is publicized in advance or is going to be published. Whatever the reason, if you do decide to use a title, it should (1) be brief, (2) attract the attention of your audience, and (3) encapsulate the main thrust of your speech.

A good title need not have what Madison Avenue would call "sex appeal"—lots of glitter and pizzazz. By the same token, there is certainly nothing wrong with a catchy title—as long as it is germane to the speech. Here are two groups of titles. Those on the left are straightforward and descriptive. Those on the right are figurative alternatives to the ones on the left.

Group I	Group II
Gambling Addiction	Against All Odds
The Rage to Diet	The Art of Wishful Shrinking
Living with Deafness	The Sounds of Silence
Unsafe Drinking Water	Toxins on Tap

Which group do you prefer? There are advantages and disadvantages to both. Those in the first group clearly reveal the topic, but they are not as provocative as those in the second group. Those in the second group are sure to arouse interest, but they do not give as clear an idea of what the speeches are about.

There is one other kind of title you should consider—the question. Phrasing your title as a question can be both descriptive and provocative. Using

checklist

Preparation Outline

YES	NO	
☐	☐	1. Does my speech have a title, if one is required?
☐	☐	2. Do I state the specific purpose before the text of the outline itself?
☐	☐	3. Do I state the central idea before the text of the outline itself?
☐	☐	4. Are the introduction, body, and conclusion clearly labeled?
☐	☐	5. Are main points and subpoints written in full sentences?
☐	☐	6. Are transitions, internal summaries, and internal previews clearly labeled?
☐	☐	7. Does the outline follow a consistent pattern of symbolization and indentation?
☐	☐	8. Does the outline provide a clear visual framework that shows the relationships among the ideas of my speech?
☐	☐	9. Does the bibliography identify all the sources I consulted in preparing the outline?
☐	☐	10. Does the bibliography follow the format required by my instructor?

this method, we can construct a third set of titles combining the virtues of groups I and II:

Group III

Do You Really Think You Can Beat the Odds?

Diets: How Effective Are They?

Can You See What I'm Saying?

Is Your Water Safe to Drink?

Sometimes you will choose a title for your speech very early. At other times you may not find one you like until the last minute. Either way, try to be resourceful about creating titles for your speeches. Experiment with several and choose the one that seems most appropriate.

SAMPLE PREPARATION OUTLINE WITH COMMENTARY

The following outline for a six-minute informative speech illustrates the principles just discussed. The commentary explains the procedures used in organizing the speech and writing the outline. (Check with your teacher to see if she or he wants you to include a title with your outline.)

Service Dogs

COMMENTARY

Stating your specific purpose and central idea as separate units before the text of the outline makes it easier to judge how well you have constructed the outline to achieve your purpose and to communicate your central idea.

Labeling the introduction marks it as a distinct section that plays a special role in the speech.

The opening gets attention and, as it progresses, reveals the topic of the speech.

Here the speaker establishes his credibility and previews the main points to be discussed in the body.

Including transitions ensures that the speaker has worked out how to connect one idea to the next. Notice that the transition is not included in the system of symbolization and indentation used for the rest of the speech.

Labeling the body marks it as a distinct part of the speech.

Main point I is phrased as a full sentence. The two subpoints of main point I are shown by the capital letters A and B and are also written in full sentences to ensure that the speaker has thought them out fully.

The progressive indentation shows visually the relationships among main points, subpoints, and sub-subpoints.

OUTLINE

Specific Purpose: To inform my audience about three major kinds of service dogs.

Central Idea: Guide dogs, assistance dogs, and seizure-alert dogs make a huge difference in the lives of their owners.

Introduction

I. Most of us hardly think about simple tasks such as turning on the television or walking across the street.
   A. But for many Americans with disabilities, these tasks are anything but simple.
   B. They could not be accomplished without service dogs.
II. According to the Americans with Disabilities Act, a service dog is any dog specially trained to assist an individual with a disability.
III. In researching this speech, I learned how indispensable service dogs are for millions of Americans.
IV. Today I will introduce you to three types of service dogs—guide dogs, assistance dogs, and seizure-alert dogs.

(*Transition:* Let's start by looking at guide dogs.)

Body

I. Once referred to as Seeing Eye dogs, guide dogs help the visually impaired navigate their surroundings.
   A. As explained in the 2010 *Handbook on Animal-Assisted Therapy,* guide dogs receive intensive training.
      1. Professional training lasts at least 5 months.
      2. Another month of training occurs after a dog is assigned to its owner.
      3. The result is a dog worth from $15,000 to $50,000.
   B. Guide Dogs of America is a major trainer of U.S. guide dogs.
      1. Its Web site says the group provides 50 trained dogs free of charge each year.
      2. It also notes that there are 7,000 guide dogs currently working in the U.S.

(*Transition:* Like guide dogs, assistance dogs are invaluable for those who need them.)

The transition shows how the speaker will get from main point I to main point II.

Like main point I, main point II is phrased as a full sentence.

(*Transition:* Like guide dogs, assistance dogs are invaluable for those who need them.)

II. Assistance dogs perform routine tasks for people with physical disabilities.
  A. These dogs' skills are truly amazing.
    1. They help people put on clothes, unload the washing machine, and pick up items on the floor.
    2. They also open and close doors, gather the mail, and manipulate keys and cell phones.
    3. In fact, they can do almost anything that is needed to help their owners with daily tasks.
  B. Assistance dogs are invaluable to their owners.
    1. Dr. Alice Blue-McLendon, of the Texas A&M College of Veterinary Medicine, notes that these dogs help their owners achieve a new sense of freedom and independence.
    2. Phil Day, owner of a black Labrador provided by Dogs for the Disabled, says: "I wouldn't be without an assistance dog; they help on so many different levels."

Points below the level of subpoint are indicated by Arabic numerals and lowercase letters. Sometimes they are not written as full sentences. Check to see what your teacher prefers.

(*Transition:* Now that we have looked at guide dogs and assistance dogs, let's turn to seizure-alert dogs.)

The transition indicates that the speaker is moving to his next main point.

This main point, like the first two, is stated as a full sentence.

III. Seizure-alert dogs warn owners with epilepsy when a seizure is about to occur.
  A. These dogs can sense a seizure from several seconds to 45 minutes before it occurs, says John Ensminger, author of *Service and Therapy Dogs in American Society.*
  B. How seizure-alert dogs acquire this ability is a mystery.
    1. Dogs cannot be trained to anticipate seizures.
    2. Some are born with the power and some are not.
    3. There are two major theories to explain the dogs' power.
      a. One theory holds that dogs anticipate seizures through their sensitivity to slight changes in nonverbal behavior.
      b. Another theory says they detect minor chemical changes through their acute sense of smell.

Notice the pattern of subordination in this section. Subpoint B states that how seizure-alert dogs acquire their ability is a mystery. Sub-subpoint 3 notes that there are two major theories to explain the dogs' power. Because items a and b expand upon the theories point, they are subordinated to it.

Conclusion

Labeling the conclusion marks it as a distinct part of the speech.

Summarizing the main points is standard procedure in an informative speech. The speaker's final line reinforces his central idea.

I. As we have seen, service dogs provide vital support for people with physical disabilities.
II. I have focused on guide dogs, assistance dogs, and seizure-alert dogs.
III. For their owners, these dogs are much more than "man's best friend"—they are a new way of life.

Bibliography

This is the final bibliography. It lists the sources actually used in writing the speech and is shorter than the preliminary bibliography compiled in the early stages of research. (See Chapter 7 for a discussion of the preliminary bibliography.)

This bibliography follows the 2009 Modern Language Association (MLA) format. Check with your instructor to see what format you should use for your bibliography.

United States. Dept. of Justice. *Americans with Disabilities Act*. 14 Jan. 2008. Web. 15 Apr. 2011.

Dogs for the Disabled. Dogs for the Disabled, 2010. Web. 17 Apr. 2011.

Ensminger, John J. *Service and Therapy Dogs in American Society*. Springfield: Charles C. Thomas, 2010. Print.

Fine, Aubrey H., ed. *Handbook on Animal-Assisted Therapy*, 3rd ed. London: Academic Press, 2010. Print.

Guide Dogs of America. Guide Dogs of America, 2011. Web. 18 Apr. 2011.

Veterinary Medicine and Biomedical Sciences. "Assistance Dogs: Offering a New Sense of Freedom." *Pet Talk. Texas A&M News and Information Services*. Texas A&M University, 25 Feb. 2011. Web. 17 Apr. 2011.

The Speaking Outline

"I was never so excited by public speaking before in my life," wrote one listener in 1820 after listening to Daniel Webster. "Three or four times I thought my temples would burst with the gush of blood. . . . I was beside myself, and am so still."[1]

Such reactions were not unusual among Webster's audiences. He thrilled two generations of Americans with his masterful orations. Incredible as it seems today, he did so while speaking for several hours at a time, often without using any notes! A reporter once asked how he managed this. "It is my memory," Webster said. "I can prepare a speech, revise and correct it in my memory, then deliver the corrected speech exactly as finished."[2]

Few people have Webster's remarkable powers of memory. Fortunately, it is no longer customary to speak from memory. Today most people speak extemporaneously—which means the speech is carefully prepared and practiced in advance, but much of the exact wording is selected while the speech is being delivered (see Chapter 13). Your speeches will probably be of this type. You should know, then, about the *speaking outline*—the most widely recommended form of notes for extemporaneous speeches.

The aim of a speaking outline is to help you remember what you want to say. In some ways, it is a condensed version of your preparation outline. It should contain key words or phrases to jog your memory, as well as essential statistics and quotations that you don't want to risk forgetting. But it should also include material *not* in your preparation outline—especially cues to direct and sharpen your delivery.

Most speakers develop their own variations on the speaking outline. As you acquire more experience, you, too, should feel free to experiment. But for now, your best bet is to follow the basic guidelines below and to use the sample speaking outline on pages 216–217 as your model.

speaking outline

A brief outline used to jog a speaker's memory during the presentation of a speech.

GUIDELINES FOR THE SPEAKING OUTLINE

Follow the Visual Framework Used in the Preparation Outline

Your speaking outline should use the same visual framework—the same symbols and the same pattern of indentation—as your preparation outline. This will make it much easier to prepare the speaking outline. More important, it will allow you to see instantly where you are in the speech at any given moment while you are speaking. You will find this a great advantage. As you speak, you will look down at your outline periodically to make sure you are covering the right ideas in the right order.

Compare the following two versions of a partial speaking outline. They are from an informative speech about the history of the U.S. women's rights movement.

Ineffective	More Effective
I. 1840–1860	I. 1840–1860
A. World Anti-Slavery Convention	A. World Anti-Slavery Convention
B. Seneca Falls convention	B. Seneca Falls convention
1. Lucretia Mott	1. Lucretia Mott
2. Elizabeth Cady Stanton	2. Elizabeth Cady Stanton
3. Declaration of Sentiments	3. Declaration of Sentiments
II. 1900–1920	II. 1900–1920
A. National American Woman Suffrage Association	A. National American Woman Suffrage Association
1. Founding	1. Founding
2. Objectives	2. Objectives
B. Nineteenth Amendment	B. Nineteenth Amendment
1. Campaign	1. Campaign
2. Ratification	2. Ratification

The wording of both outlines is exactly the same. But the visual framework of the one on the right makes it easier to take in at a glance and reduces the odds of the speaker losing her or his place.

Make Sure the Outline Is Legible

Your speaking outline is all but worthless unless it is instantly readable at a distance. When you make your outline, use large lettering, leave extra space between lines, provide ample margins, and write or type on only one side of the paper.

Some speakers put their notes on index cards. Most find the 3 × 5 size too cramped and prefer the 4 × 6 or 5 × 8 size instead. Other people write their speaking outlines on regular paper. Either practice is fine, as long as your notes are immediately legible to you while you are speaking.

As with personal finance expert Suze Orman, many experienced speakers are more comfortable with a brief set of notes, or no notes at all, which allows them to communicate directly with the audience.

Keep the Outline as Brief as Possible

If your notes are too detailed, you will have difficulty maintaining eye contact with your audience.

Using public speaking in your CAREER

As the defense attorney in a car theft case, you need to prepare your closing argument to the jury before it begins its deliberations. After reviewing evidence from the trial, you decide to stress the following points to demonstrate the innocence of your client:

a. The stolen car was found abandoned three hours after the theft with the engine still warm; at the time the car was found, your client was at the airport to meet the flight of a friend who was flying into town.

b. Lab analysis of muddy shoe prints on the floor mat of the car indicates that the prints came from a size 13 shoe; your client wears a size 10.

c. Lab analysis shows the presence of cigarette smoke in the car, but your client does not smoke.

d. The only eyewitness to the crime, who was 50 feet from the car, said the thief "looked like" your client; yet the eyewitness admitted that at the time of the theft she was not wearing her glasses, which had been prescribed for improving distance vision.

e. The car was stolen at about 1 P.M.; your client testified that he was in a small town 250 miles away at 11 A.M.

f. In a statement to police, the eyewitness described the thief as blond; your client has red hair.

As you work on the outline of your speech, you see that these points can be organized into three main points, each with two supporting points. Compose an outline that organizes the points in this manner.

A detailed outline will tempt you to look at it far too often, as one student discovered:

> Angela Rossi was speaking about the benefits of Pilates. She had prepared the speech thoroughly and practiced it until it was nearly perfect. But when she delivered the speech in class, she referred constantly to her detailed notes. As a result, her delivery was choppy and strained. After the speech, Angela's classmates remarked on how often she had looked at her notes, and she was amazed. "I didn't even know I was doing it," she said. "Most of the time I wasn't even paying attention to the outline. I knew the speech cold."

Many students have had the same experience. "As long as I have plenty of notes," they feel, "disaster will not strike." In fact, most beginning speakers use too many notes. Like Angela, they don't need all of them to remember the speech, and they find that too many notes can actually interfere with good communication.

To guard against this, keep your speaking outline as brief as possible. It should contain key words or phrases to help you remember major points, subpoints, and connectives. If you are citing statistics, you will probably want to include them in your notes. Unless you are good at memorizing quotations, write them out fully as well. Finally, there may be two, three, or four key ideas whose wording is so important that you want to state them in simple complete sentences. The best rule is that your notes should be the *minimum* you need to jog your memory and keep you on track.

Give Yourself Cues for Delivering the Speech

A good speaking outline reminds you not only of *what* you want to say but also of *how* you want to say it. As you practice the speech, you will decide that certain ideas and phrases need special emphasis—that they should be spoken more loudly, softly, slowly, or rapidly than other parts of the speech. You will also determine how you want to pace the speech—how you will control its timing, rhythm, and momentum. But no matter how you work these things out ahead of time, no matter how often you practice, it is easy to forget them once you get in front of an audience.

The solution is to include in your speaking outline *delivery cues*—directions for delivering the speech. One way to do this is by underlining or otherwise highlighting key ideas that you want to be sure to emphasize. Then, when you reach them in the outline, you will be reminded to stress them. Another way is to jot down on the outline explicit cues such as "pause," "repeat," "slow down," "louder," and so forth. Both techniques are good aids for beginning speakers, but they are also used by most experienced speakers.

delivery cues

Directions in a speaking outline to help a speaker remember how she or he wants to deliver key parts of the speech.

SAMPLE SPEAKING OUTLINE WITH COMMENTARY

Below is a sample speaking outline for a six-minute informative talk about service dogs. By comparing it with the preparation outline for the same speech on pages 211–213, you can see how a detailed preparation outline is transformed into a concise speaking outline.

⌄⌄⌄ COMMENTARY	⌄⌄⌄ OUTLINE
	Eye Contact!! *Slow Down*

These comments remind the speaker to establish eye contact and not to race through the speech.	I. Don't think about simple tasks—tv, crossing street.
	    A. Not simple for Americans with disabilities.
	    B. Cannot be accomplished without service dogs.
	II. ADA: Service dog is specially trained to assist person with a disability.

Including the main points of the introduction helps keep the speaker on track at the start of the speech.	III. Researched speech; learned dogs indispensable. IV. Today—guide dogs, assistance dogs, seizure-alert dogs. (Let's start with guide dogs.)
It's usually a good idea to pause briefly before launching into the first main point. This is another way of signaling that you are moving from the introduction to the body.	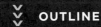 *—Pause—*

Body

I. Help visually impaired navigate surroundings.
  A. Training: 2010 *Handbook on Animal-Assisted Therapy.*
    1. Professional training—5 months.
    2. Another month—with owner.
    3. Dogs worth $15,000 to $50,000.
  B. Guide Dogs of America trains U.S. dogs.
    1. Web site: free of charge to 50 people a year.
    2. 7,000 guide dogs in U.S.

(Like guide dogs, assistance dogs invaluable.)

II. Routine tasks for people with physical disabilities.
  A. <u>Amazing</u> skills.
    1. Clothes, washing machine, items on floor.
    2. Doors, mail, keys, cell phones.
    3. <u>Almost anything</u> needed for daily tasks.
  B. Invaluable to owners.
    1. Dr. Alice Blue-McLendon, Texas A&M Veterinary Medicine: help owners achieve freedom and independence.
    2. Phil Day: black Lab owner: "I wouldn't be without an assistance dog; they help on <u>so many</u> different levels."

(Now turn to seizure-alert dogs.)

III. Warn owners with epilepsy before seizures occur.
  A. Several seconds to 45 minutes warning: John Ensminger, *Service and Therapy Dogs in American Society.*
  B. How dogs do this is a mystery.
    1. Cannot be trained to anticipate seizures.
    2. Some born with power and some not.
    3. Two major theories explaining power.
      a. Anticipate seizures through nonverbal behavior.
      b. Detect minor chemical changes through smell.

—Pause—

Conclusion

I. As we have seen, service dogs support people with physical disabilities.
II. Focused today on guide dogs, assistance dogs, and seizure-alert dogs.
III. Service dogs are more than "man's best friend"—they are a new way of life.

Most speakers label the body of the speech in the speaking outline as well as in the preparation outline.

Throughout the outline, key words are used to jog the speaker's memory. Because the final wording of an extemporaneous speech is chosen at the moment of delivery, it will not be exactly the same as that in the preparation outline.

Inserting transitions makes sure the speaker doesn't forget them.

Underlining reminds the speaker to stress key words or ideas.

Quotations are usually written out in full in the speaking outline.

Sources of statistics or testimony should be included in the speaking outline to make sure the speaker identifies them in the speech.

Notice how the body of the speech follows the same visual format as the preparation outline. This makes the outline easy to read at a glance.

It's usually a good idea to pause before entering the conclusion.

Including key ideas and phrases from the conclusion jogs the speaker's memory and ensures that the speech will end as planned.

Summary

Outlines are essential to effective speeches. By outlining, you make sure that related ideas are together, that your thoughts flow from one to another, and that the structure of your speech is coherent. You will probably use two kinds of outlines for your speeches—the detailed preparation outline and the brief speaking outline.

In the preparation outline, you state your specific purpose and central idea; label the introduction, body, and conclusion; and designate transitions, internal summaries, and internal previews. You should identify main points, subpoints, and sub-subpoints by a consistent pattern of symbolization and indentation. Your teacher may require a bibliography with your preparation outline.

The speaking outline should contain key words or phrases to jog your memory, as well as essential statistics and quotations. Make sure your speaking outline is legible, follows the same visual framework as your preparation outline, and includes cues for delivering the speech.

Key Terms

preparation outline *(206)*

visual framework *(207)*

bibliography *(208)*

speaking outline *(213)*

delivery cues *(216)*

Review Questions

After reading this chapter, you should be able to answer the following questions:

1. Why is it important to outline your speeches?

2. What is a preparation outline? What are the eight guidelines discussed in this chapter for writing a preparation outline?

3. What is a speaking outline? What are four guidelines for your speaking outline?

connect

For further review, go to the LearnSmart study module for this chapter.

Exercises for Critical Thinking

1. In the left-hand column on page 219 is a partially blank outline from a speech about the Golden Gate Bridge. In the right-hand column, arranged in random order, are the subpoints to fill in the outline. Choose the appropriate subpoint for each blank in the outline.

Outline	Subpoints
I. More than 20 years passed from the time the Golden Gate Bridge was proposed to the time it opened.	Today, those towers make it the world's third tallest suspension bridge.
A.	Construction finally began in 1933 and ended in 1937.
B.	The span between its towers is 4,200 feet.
C.	At the time it was built, the Golden Gate was also the longest suspension bridge in the world.
D.	In 1923, the State of California passed legislation authorizing construction of the bridge.
II. Now 75 years old, the Golden Gate Bridge remains a marvel of modern engineering.	Its two towers rise almost 750 feet above the waters of the Pacific Ocean.
A.	Once construction of the bridge was authorized, it took ten years to approve the design and financing.
1.	That span makes it the ninth longest suspension bridge in the world today.
2.	
B.	At the time it was built, the Golden Gate was the tallest suspension bridge in the world.
1.	
2.	The bridge was originally proposed in 1916 but faced years of legal hurdles.

2. From the preparation outline on the Golden Gate Bridge you constructed in Exercise 1, create a speaking outline that you might use in delivering the speech. Follow the guidelines for a speaking outline discussed in this chapter.

12

Using Language

Contrary to popular belief, language does not mirror reality. It does not simply describe the world as it is. Instead, language helps create our sense of reality by giving meaning to events. The words we use to label an event determine to a great extent how we respond to it.

For example, if you see the medical use of stem cells as "immoral," as "scientifically irresponsible," and as a "violation of human life," you will likely oppose it. But if you see the medical use of stem cells as "moral," as "scientifically responsible," and as a way to "alleviate pain and suffering," you will likely support it.

What separates these two viewpoints? Not the capabilities of modern medicine; not the conditions of people with genetic disorders; not the medical procedures of using stem cells. All those are the same for both sides. The difference is in the *meaning* given to them by the words that label them.[1]

Words are the tools of a speaker's craft. They have special uses, just like the tools of any other profession. Have you ever watched a carpenter at work? The job that would take you or me a couple of hours is done by the carpenter in 10 minutes—with the right tools. You can't drive a nail with a screwdriver or turn a screw with a hammer. It is the same with public speaking. You must choose the right words for the job you want to do.

Good speakers are aware of the meaning of words—both their obvious and their subtle meanings. They also know how to use language accurately, clearly, vividly, appropriately, and inclusively. This chapter will explore each of these areas.

Meanings of Words

denotative meaning

The literal or dictionary meaning of a word or phrase.

Words have two kinds of meanings—denotative and connotative. *Denotative* meaning is precise, literal, and objective. It describes the object, person, place, idea, or event to which the word refers. One way to think of a word's denotative meaning is as its dictionary definition. For example, denotatively, the noun "school" means "a place, institution, or building where instruction is given."

Connotative meaning is more variable, figurative, and subjective. The connotative meaning of a word is what the word suggests or implies. For instance, the connotative meaning of the word "school" includes all the feelings, associations, and emotions that the word touches off in different people. For some people, "school" might connote personal growth, childhood friends, and a special teacher. For others, it might connote frustration, discipline, and boring homework assignments.

connotative meaning

The meaning suggested by the associations or emotions triggered by a word or phrase.

Connotative meaning gives words their intensity and emotional power. It arouses in listeners feelings of anger, pity, love, fear, friendship, nostalgia, greed, guilt, and the like. Speakers, like poets, often use connotation to enrich their meaning. For example:

Terrorists neither listen to reason nor engage in reasoning with others. Their aim is to generate fear—to frighten people into submission. They measure success by the magnitude of the fear they generate through brutal, savage acts of violence. Terrorists are prepared to kill to further whatever cause they claim to be pursuing. And the heinousness of these murders is accentuated by the fact that terrorists murder without passion. They murder with cool deliberation and deliberate planning. They are utterly amoral.

The underlined words in this passage have powerful connotations that are almost certain to produce a strong emotional revulsion to terrorism.

Here, in contrast, is another version of the same statement—this time using words with a different set of connotations:

Terrorists do not seek to negotiate with their opponents. They seek victory by using political and psychological pressure, including acts of violence that may endanger the lives of some people. To the terrorist, ultimate objectives are more important than the means used to achieve them.

With the exception of "terrorist," the words in this statement are less likely to evoke an intensely negative response than those in the first statement.

Which statement is preferable? That depends on the audience, the occasion, and the speaker's purpose. Do you want to stir up your listeners' emotions, rally them to some cause? Then select words with more intense

Words are the tools of the speaker's craft. Good speakers use them accurately and correctly. They also use language that will be clear, vivid, and appropriate for their listeners.

connotative meanings. Or are you addressing a controversial issue and trying to seem completely impartial? Then stick with words that touch off less intense reactions. Choosing words skillfully for their denotative and connotative meanings is a crucial part of the speaker's craft.

Using Language Accurately

Using language accurately is as vital to a speaker as using numbers accurately is to an accountant. One student found this out the hard way. In a speech about America's criminal justice system, he referred several times to "criminal *persecution*." What he meant, of course, was "criminal *prosecution*." This one error virtually ruined his speech. As one of his classmates said, "How can I believe what you say about our courts when you don't even know the difference between prosecution and persecution?"

Fortunately, such outright blunders are relatively rare among college students. However, we all commit more subtle errors—especially using one word when another will capture our ideas more precisely. Every word has shades of meaning that distinguish it from every other word. As Mark Twain said, "The difference between the right word and the almost right word is the difference between lightning and the lightning bug."

If you look in a thesaurus, you'll find the following words given as synonyms:

education   knowledge   expertise

All mean roughly the same thing—special grasp of a subject matter or skill. But all these words have different shades of meaning. See if you can fill in the best word to complete each of the sentences below:

1. Because he won a scholarship to a top university, Enrique received an excellent _____.

2. Sophia acquired her _____ of Chinese history by reading a number of books on the subject.

3. Ebony's _____ as a business consultant comes from having worked with many clients over the years.

thesaurus

A book of synonyms.

The best answers for the three statements are:

1. education   2. knowledge   3. expertise

Each of the words means something a little different from the others, and each says something special to listeners.

As you prepare your speeches, ask yourself constantly, "What do I *really* want to say? What do I *really* mean?" When in doubt, consult a dictionary or thesaurus to make sure you have the best words to express your ideas.

Using Language Clearly

People are different. What makes perfect sense to some may be gobbledygook to others. You cannot assume that what is clear to you is clear to your audience. Listeners, unlike readers, cannot turn to a dictionary or reread an author's words to discover their meaning. A speaker's meaning must be *immediately* comprehensible; it must be so clear that there is no chance of misunderstanding. You can ensure this by using familiar words, by choosing concrete words over abstract words, and by eliminating verbal clutter.

USE FAMILIAR WORDS

One of the biggest barriers to clear speech is using big, bloated words where short, sharp ones will do the job better.[2] This is especially true when it comes to technical language that may be familiar to the speaker but not to the audience. Yet, if you work at it, you will almost always be able to translate even the most specialized topic into clear, familiar language.

Here, for instance, are two passages explaining the devastating effects of a pregnant woman's drinking on her unborn child. The first passage is technically accurate, but it contains too many obscure words.

The deleterious effects of alcohol on the unborn child are very serious. When a pregnant mother consumes alcohol, the ethanol in the bloodstream easily crosses the placenta from mother to child and invades the amniotic fluid. This can produce a number of abnormal birth syndromes, including central-nervous-system dysfunctions, growth deficiencies, a cluster of facial aberrations, and variable major and minor malformations.

Well-informed listeners can probably figure out "deleterious effects," "central-nervous-system dysfunctions," and "facial aberrations." But these terms don't create sharp mental images of what the speaker is trying to say.

Here, in contrast, is the second passage. It is utterly clear and shows what can be done with work, imagination, and a healthy respect for everyday words:

When the expectant mother drinks, alcohol is absorbed into her bloodstream and distributed throughout her entire body. After a few beers or a couple of martinis, she begins to feel tipsy and decides to sober up. She grabs a cup of coffee, two aspirin, and takes a little nap. After a while she'll be fine.

But while she sleeps, the fetus is surrounded by the same alcoholic content as its mother had. After being drowned in alcohol, the fetus begins to feel the effect. But it can't sober up. It can't grab a cup of coffee. It can't grab a couple of aspirin. For the fetus's liver, the key organ in removing alcohol from the blood, is just not developed. The fetus is literally pickled in alcohol.[3]

This kind of plain talk is what listeners want. You cannot go wrong by following the advice of Winston Churchill to speak in "short, homely words of common usage." If you think big words (or a lot of words) are needed to impress listeners, bear in mind that the Gettysburg Address—considered the finest speech in the English language—contains 271 words, of which 251 have only one or two syllables.

CHOOSE CONCRETE WORDS

Concrete words refer to tangible objects—people, places, and things. They differ from abstract words, which refer to general concepts, qualities, or attributes. "Carrot," "pencil," "nose," and "door" are concrete words. "Humility," "science," "progress," and "philosophy" are abstract words.

Of course, few words are completely abstract or concrete. "Apple pie" is concrete, but in the United States, the phrase also has abstract values of patriotism and conventional morals. Usually, the more specific a word, the more concrete it is. Let us say you are talking about basketball. Here are several words and phrases you might use:

physical activity	abstract/general
sports	
basketball	
professional basketball	
Kobe Bryant	concrete/specific

concrete words

Words that refer to tangible objects.

abstract words

Words that refer to ideas or concepts.

As you move down the list, the words become less abstract and more concrete. You begin with a general concept (physical activity), descend to one type of activity (sports), to a particular sport (basketball), to a division of that sport (professional basketball), to one specific professional basketball player (Kobe Bryant).

Although abstract words are necessary to express certain kinds of ideas, they are much easier to misinterpret than are concrete words. Also, concrete words are much more likely to claim your listeners' attention. Suppose you make a speech about bed bugs, which are plaguing people from coast to coast. Here are two ways you could approach the subject—one featuring abstract words, the other concrete words:

Abstract Words

Bed bugs are highly newsworthy in the United States. They affect people regardless of social strata, demographic group, or region of the country. They are found in a wide range of social locations, some of which one might not expect. No matter where one lives, bed bugs are a growing problem.

Concrete Words

In recent months, bed bugs have made headlines across the country, affecting the rich and the poor, the clean and the dirty, the East Coast, the West Coast, and every place in between.

connect

View this excerpt from "The Plague of Bed Bugs" in the online Media Library for this chapter (Video 12.1).

In New York City, bed bugs have been found in fancy hotels, crowded subways, even the Victoria's Secret store on Lexington Avenue. In Los Angeles, they have infiltrated public housing and posh Beverly Hills neighborhoods alike. In college towns, they are almost everywhere—dorm rooms, apartments, restaurants, movie theaters, bars, even sports arenas.

Bed bugs are becoming a pest of epidemic proportions.

Notice how much more persuasive the second version is. A speech dominated by concrete words will almost always be clearer, more interesting, and easier to recall than one dominated by abstract words.

ELIMINATE CLUTTER

Cluttered speech has become a national epidemic. Whatever happened to such simple words as "before," "if," and "now"? When last seen they were being routed by their cluttered counterparts: "prior to," "in the eventuality of," and "at this point in time." By the same token, why can't politicians say, "We have a crisis," instead of saying, "We are facing a difficult crisis situation that will be troublesome to successfully resolve"?

This type of clutter forces listeners to hack through a tangle of words to discover the meaning. When you make a speech, keep your language lean and lively. Beware of using several words where one or two will do. Avoid flabby phrases. Let your ideas emerge sharply and firmly. Above all, watch out for redundant adjectives and adverbs. Inexperienced speakers (and writers) tend to string together two or three synonymous adjectives, such as "a learned and educated person" or "a hot, steamy, torrid day."

Here is part of a student speech that has been revised to eliminate clutter:

> Sitting Bull was one of the most important ~~and significant of all~~ Native American leaders. He was born in ~~the year of~~ 1831 near Grand River, in ~~an area that is now part~~ *present-day* ~~of the state of~~ South Dakota. A fearless ~~and courageous~~ warrior, he ~~ended up being~~ *was* elected chief of the Hunkpapa Sioux in 1867. In the following years, he also attracted a large ~~and numerous~~ following among the ~~tribes of the~~ Cheyenne and Arapaho. He is best known ~~to people in this day and age~~ *today* for his ~~instrumental~~ role in ~~helping to lead the defeat of~~ *defeating* General Custer at the Battle of Little Big Horn in 1876. Although eventually ~~required against his will~~ *forced* to live ~~his life~~ on the Standing Rock Reservation in South Dakota, he never surrendered ~~to anyone~~ his dignity or his ~~personal~~ devotion to the Sioux way of life.

Notice how much cleaner and easier to follow the revised version is. No longer are the speaker's ideas hidden in a thicket of wasted words.

This kind of pruning is easy once you get the knack of it. The hardest part—and it is often very hard—is recognizing clutter and forcing yourself to

clutter

Discourse that takes many more words than are necessary to express an idea.

Even when discussing technical subjects, effective speakers such as Nobel Prize-winning economist Paul Krugman look for ways to communicate their ideas in clear, familiar language.

throw away the unnecessary words. Watch for clutter when you write your speech outlines. Be prepared to revise the outline until your ideas emerge clearly and crisply.

You can also help eliminate clutter by practicing your speeches with a digital recorder. As you play the speech back, keep an ear out not just for flabby phrases but for verbal fillers such as "you know," "like," and "really." Practice delivering the speech again, this time making a special effort to trim it of wasted or distracting words. This will not only make you a better public speaker, but it will also help you present ideas more effectively in meetings, conversations, and group discussions.[4]

Using Language Vividly

Just as you can be accurate without being clear, so you can be both accurate and clear without being interesting. Here, for example, is how Martin Luther King *might have* phrased part of his great "I Have a Dream" speech:

Turning back is something we cannot do. We must continue to work against police brutality, segregated housing, disfranchisement, and alienation. Only when these problems are solved will we be satisfied.

Here is what King *actually* said:

We cannot turn back. There are those who ask the devotees of civil rights, "When will you be satisfied?" We can never be satisfied as long as the Negro is the victim of the unspeakable horrors of police brutality. We can never be satisfied as long as our bodies, heavy with the fatigue of travel, cannot gain lodging in the motels of the highways and the hotels of the cities. . . . We cannot be satisfied as long as a Negro in Mississippi cannot vote and a Negro in New York believes he has nothing for which to vote.

No, no, we are not satisfied, and we will not be satisfied until justice rolls down like waters and righteousness like a mighty stream.

Much more stirring, isn't it? If you want to move people with your speeches, use vivid, animated language. Although there are several ways to do this, two of the most important are imagery and rhythm.

IMAGERY

imagery

The use of vivid language to create mental images of objects, actions, or ideas.

One sign of a good novelist is the ability to create word pictures that let you "see" the haunted house, or "hear" the birds chirping on a warm spring morning, or "taste" the hot enchiladas at a Mexican restaurant.

Speakers can use imagery in much the same way to make their ideas come alive. Three ways to generate imagery are by using concrete words, simile, and metaphor.

Concrete Words

As we saw earlier in this chapter, choosing concrete words over abstract words is one way to enhance the clarity of your speeches. Concrete words are also the key to effective imagery. Consider the following excerpt from Ronald Reagan's famous address commemorating the 40th anniversary of D-Day. Speaking at the scene of the battle, Reagan dramatically recounted the heroism of the U.S. Rangers who scaled the cliffs at Pointe du Hoc to help free Europe from Hitler's stranglehold:

connect

View this excerpt from Ronald Reagan's speech at Pointe du Hoc in the online Media Library for this chapter (Video 12.2).

> We stand on a lonely, windswept point on the northern shore of France. The air is soft, but 40 years ago at this moment, the air was dense with smoke and the cries of men, and the air was filled with the crack of rifle fire and the roar of cannon.
>
> At dawn, on the morning of the 6th of June, 1944, 225 Rangers jumped off the British landing craft and ran to the bottom of these cliffs. . . . The Rangers looked up and saw the enemy soldiers—at the edge of the cliffs shooting down at them with machine guns and throwing grenades. And the American Rangers began to climb. They shot rope ladders over the face of these cliffs and began to pull themselves up.
>
> When one Ranger fell, another would take his place. When one rope was cut, a Ranger would grab another and begin his climb again. They climbed, shot back, and held their footing. Soon, one by one, the Rangers pulled themselves over the top, and in seizing the firm land at the top of these cliffs, they began to seize back the continent of Europe.

Concrete words call up mental impressions of sights, sounds, touch, smell, and taste. In Reagan's speech, we do not merely learn that the U.S. Rangers helped win the battle of D-Day. We visualize the Rangers landing at the foot of the cliffs. We see them fighting their way up the cliffs in the face of enemy grenades and machine guns. We hear the crack of rifle fire and the cries of the soldiers. The concrete words create images that pull us irresistibly into the speech.

Simile

simile

An explicit comparison, introduced with the word "like" or "as," between things that are essentially different yet have something in common.

Another way to create imagery is through the use of simile. Simile is an explicit comparison between things that are essentially different yet have something in common. It always contains the words "like" or "as." Here are some examples from student speeches:

> Walking into my grandparents' home when I was a child was like being wrapped in a giant security blanket.

Audience-oriented speakers put a premium on clear, vivid, uncluttered language. They give a great deal of thought to finding just the right words to express their ideas.

Air pollution is eating away at the monuments in Washington, D.C., like a giant Alka-Seltzer tablet.

These are bright, fresh similes that clarify and vitalize ideas. Some similes, however, have become stale through overuse. Here are a few:

fresh as a daisy	hungry as a bear
fit as a fiddle	busy as a bee
strong as an ox	happy as a lark

Such *clichés* are fine in everyday conversation, but you should avoid them in speechmaking. Otherwise, you are likely to be "dull as dishwater" and to find your audience "sleeping like a log"!

cliché

A trite or overused expression.

Metaphor

You can also use metaphor to create imagery in your speeches. Metaphor is an implicit comparison between things that are essentially different yet have something in common. Unlike simile, metaphor does not contain the words "like" or "as." For example:

America's cities are the windows through which the world looks at American society. (Henry Cisneros)

With globalization, the same sea washes all of humankind. We are all in the same boat. There are no safe islands. (Kofi Annan)

metaphor

An implicit comparison, not introduced with the word "like" or "as," between two things that are essentially different yet have something in common.

These are both brief metaphors. Sometimes, however, a speaker will develop a longer metaphor. Here is an excellent example, from Al Gore's speech accepting the Nobel Peace Prize for his efforts to help the world deal with climate change:

The earth has a fever. And the fever is rising. The experts have told us it is not a passing affliction that will heal by itself. We asked for a second opinion.

And a third. And a fourth. And the consistent conclusion, restated with increasing alarm, is that something basic is wrong.

When used effectively, metaphor—like simile—is an excellent way to bring color to a speech, to make abstract ideas concrete, to clarify the unknown, and to express feelings and emotions.[5]

RHYTHM

Language has a rhythm created by the choice and arrangement of words. Speakers, like poets, sometimes seek to exploit the rhythm of language to enhance the impact of their words. Winston Churchill was a master at this. Here is a passage from one of his famous speeches during World War II. To emphasize its cadence, the passage has been printed as if it were poetry rather than prose:

connect

View this excerpt from Winston Churchill's speech of June 12, 1941, in the online Media Library for this chapter (Video 12.3).

We cannot tell what the course
   of this fell war will be. . . .
We cannot yet see
   how deliverance will come,
or when it will come.
   But nothing is more certain
than that every trace of Hitler's footsteps,
   every stain of his infected and corroding fingers,
will be sponged and purged
   and, if need be,
blasted from the surface of the earth.

The impact of the passage was heightened by Churchill's superb delivery; but even by themselves the words take on an emphatic rhythm that reinforces the message. You can see why one observer said that Churchill "mobilized the English language and sent it into battle."[6]

A speech, however, is not a poem. You should never emphasize sound and rhythm at the expense of meaning. The aim is to think about ways you can use the rhythm and flow of language to enhance your meaning. Although you may never have paid much conscious attention to this subject, you can develop an ear for vocal rhythms by study and practice. What's more, you can easily begin now to use four basic stylistic devices employed by Churchill and other fine speakers to improve the rhythm of their prose.

Parallelism

The first device is parallelism—the similar arrangement of a pair or series of related words, phrases, or sentences. For example:

Rich and poor, intelligent and ignorant, wise and foolish, virtuous and vicious, man and woman—it is ever the same, each soul must depend wholly on itself. (Elizabeth Cady Stanton)

The effects of parallelism are perhaps best illustrated by seeing what happens when it is absent. For instance, compare this statement:

I speak as a Republican. I speak as a woman. I speak as a United States Senator. I speak as an American. (Margaret Chase Smith)

Since graduating from college, you have developed a successful business that is located near the campus. As part of its plan to involve more alumni and community members in college affairs, the school has asked you to speak with new students during registration week for the fall term. In the opening section of your speech, you want the audience to feel what you felt the first few days you were on campus as a new student. The best strategy, you decide, is to present two or three similes that complete the sentence "Beginning college is like. . . ." Write your similes.

with this one:

> I speak as a Republican. I speak as a woman. I speak as a United States Senator. And I am also addressing you as an American.

The first statement is clear, consistent, and compelling. The second is not. By violating the principle of parallel structure, its final sentence ("And I am also addressing you as an American") destroys the progression begun by the preceding three sentences. It turns a strong, lucid, harmonious statement into one that is fuzzy and jarring.

Repetition

Repetition means reiterating the same word or set of words at the beginning or end of successive clauses or sentences. For example:

> *If not* now, when? *If not* us, who? *If not* together, how? (Gordon Brown)

> *We do not* give up. *We do not* quit. *We do not* allow fear or division to break our spirit. (Barack Obama)

As you can see, repetition usually results in parallelism. In addition to building a strong cadence, it also unifies a sequence of ideas, emphasizes an idea by stating it more than once, and helps create a strong emotional effect.

repetition

Reiteration of the same word or set of words at the beginning or end of successive clauses or sentences.

Alliteration

The third device you can use to enhance the rhythm of your speeches is alliteration. The most common method of alliteration is repeating the initial consonant sound of close or adjoining words. For example:

> *P*eace is essential for *p*rogress, but *p*rogress is no less essential for *p*eace. (Liaquat Ali Khan)

> Nothing great is accomplished without *c*ooperation, *c*ompromise, and *c*ommon *c*ause. (Ban Ki-moon)

By highlighting the sounds of words, alliteration catches the attention of listeners and can make ideas easier to remember. Used sparingly, it is a marvelous

alliteration

Repetition of the initial consonant sound of close or adjoining words.

way to spruce up your speeches. Used to excess, however, it can be laughable and draw too much attention, so that listeners get more involved in listening for the next alliteration than in absorbing the content of the speech.

Antithesis

antithesis

The juxtaposition of contrasting ideas, usually in parallel structure.

Finally, you might try using antithesis—the juxtaposition of contrasting ideas, usually in parallel structure. For example:

> Ask not what your country can do for you; ask what you can do for your country. (John F. Kennedy)

> Let us never negotiate out of fear. But let us never fear to negotiate. (John F. Kennedy)

It is no accident that both of these examples are from speeches by President Kennedy. Antithesis was one of his favorite language devices, and the one he used in his most memorable phrases. Because it nearly always produces a neatly turned phrase, it is a fine way to give your speeches a special touch of class.

You may be thinking that imagery and rhythm are too fancy for ordinary speeches like yours. This is not true. Take a look at the following excerpt from one student's speech about the Massachusetts 54th, the regiment of African-American soldiers during the Civil War featured in the movie *Glory:*

connect

View this excerpt from "The Massachusetts 54th" in the online Media Library for this chapter (Video 12.4).

> To join an army that didn't believe in you. To fight with an army who didn't like you. To die for an army that didn't respect you. This was the Massachusetts 54th. Today they lay where they died, on the beaches of South Carolina. Colonel Shaw and his men were piled together in a mass grave, which has since been covered by the shifting tides of the Atlantic. A small statue stands in Boston—a reminder of their sacrifice.
>
> Bravery, patriotism, and sacrifice. These are qualities of the Massachusetts 54th. With the help of their efforts, along with all the other black regiments that followed them, slavery did eventually come to an end.

This is vivid, moving language. The imagery is sharp and poignant, the rhythm strong and insistent. Think of how you can do similar things in your own speeches.

Using Language Appropriately

Here is part of a famous oration given by John Hancock in 1774, during the American Revolution. Speaking of the British soldiers who killed five Americans in the Boston Massacre, Hancock exclaimed:

> Ye dark designing knaves, ye murderers, parricides! How dare you tread upon the earth, which has drank in the blood of slaughtered innocents shed by your wicked hands? . . . Tell me, ye bloody butchers, ye villains high and low, ye wretches, do you not feel the goads and stings of conscious guilt pierce through your savage bosoms?

This is certainly vivid language—and Hancock's audience loved it. But can you imagine speaking the same way today? In addition to being accurate,

Language needs to be appropriate to a speaker's topic, as well as to the audience. A speech on Laser Radial sailing would use more action-oriented words than a speech about theories of psychology.

clear, and vivid, language should be appropriate—to the occasion, to the audience, to the topic, and to the speaker.

APPROPRIATENESS TO THE OCCASION

Language that is appropriate for some occasions may not be appropriate for others. As a simple example, a coach might address the football team as "you guys" (or worse!), whereas the speaker in a more formal situation would begin with "distinguished guests." Try reversing these two situations, and see how ridiculous it becomes. It's only common sense to adjust your language to different occasions.

APPROPRIATENESS TO THE AUDIENCE

Appropriateness also depends on the audience. If you keep this in mind, it will help you greatly when dealing with technical topics. When addressing an audience of physicians, you might use the word "parotitis" to refer to a viral disease marked by the swelling of the parotid glands. Your audience would know just what you meant. But when talking to a nonmedical audience, such as your classmates, the appropriate word would be "mumps."

You should be especially careful to avoid language that might offend your audience. Off-color humor or profanity might be appropriate in a comedy routine, but most listeners would find it offensive in a formal public speech. Remember, speakers are expected to elevate and polish their language when addressing an audience.

Of course, you cannot always be sure of how listeners will respond to what you say. When it comes to appropriateness, you will seldom go wrong by erring on the side of caution. (Put simply, "erring on the side of caution" means "when in doubt—don't.")

APPROPRIATENESS TO THE TOPIC

Language should also be appropriate to the topic. You would not use metaphor, antithesis, and alliteration when explaining how to change a bicycle tire. But you might use all three in a speech honoring U.S. soldiers who have died in defense of their country. The first topic calls for straightforward description and explanation. The second calls for special language skills to evoke emotion, admiration, and appreciation.

APPROPRIATENESS TO THE SPEAKER

No matter what the occasion, audience, or topic, language should also be appropriate to the speaker. Every public speaker develops his or her own language style.

"Terrific," you may be thinking. "I have my own style too. I feel more comfortable using abstract words, slang, and technical jargon. That's *my* way of speaking." But to say that language should be appropriate to the speaker does not justify ignoring the other needs for appropriateness. There is a difference between one's everyday style and one's *developed* style as a public speaker. Accomplished speakers have developed their speaking styles over many years of trial, error, and practice. They have *worked* at using language effectively.

You can do the same if you become language-conscious. One way to develop this consciousness is to read and listen to effective speakers. Study their techniques for achieving accuracy, clarity, and vividness, and try to adapt those techniques to your own speeches. But do not try to "become" someone else when you speak. Learn from other speakers, blend what you learn into your own language style, and seek to become the best possible you.

A Note on Inclusive Language

inclusive language

Language that does not stereotype, demean, or patronize people on the basis of gender, race, religion, disability, sexual orientation, or other factors.

As the United States has become more diverse, our language has evolved to reflect that diversity. Regardless of the situation, audiences expect public speakers to use inclusive language that is respectful of the different groups that make up American society. They also expect speakers to avoid stereotypes based on age, race, gender, disability, and other factors.

Today a number of principles for inclusive language have become so widespread that no aspiring speaker (or writer) can afford to ignore them. Here are a few of the most important.

Avoid the Generic "He"

Ineffective: Each time a surgeon walks into the operating room, *he* risks being sued for malpractice.

generic "he"

The use of "he" to refer to both women and men.

More Effective: Each time a surgeon walks into the operating room, *he or she* risks being sued for malpractice.

Often, a more graceful alternative is to pluralize. For example:

More Effective: Whenever surgeons walk into the operating room, *they* risk being sued for malpractice.

Avoid the Use of "Man" When Referring to Both Men and Women

Ineffective: If a large comet struck the Earth, it could destroy all of mankind.

More Effective: If a large comet struck the Earth, it could destroy all human life.

Avoid Stereotyping Jobs and Social Roles by Gender

Ineffective: Being a small businessman in the current economic climate is not easy.

More Effective: Being a small businessperson in the current economic climate is not easy.

Sometimes you can solve this problem with a simple twist in sentence construction. For example:

More Effective: Owning a small business is not easy in the current economic climate.

Use Names That Groups Use to Identify Themselves

One of the most fundamental ways of showing respect for others is to refer to them by the names they use to identify themselves and to avoid names they consider offensive.

Ineffective: Despite progress in recent years, homosexuals still face many forms of discrimination.

More Effective: Despite progress in recent years, lesbians and gay men still face many forms of discrimination.

Ineffective: The Paralympics show what handicapped people can accomplish in the athletic arena.

More Effective: The Paralympics show what people with disabilities can accomplish in the athletic arena.

Like many other aspects of American life, issues of inclusive language can sometimes be confusing. Language is alive and constantly evolving, so what is considered inclusive today may shift down the road. If you have questions in any particular case, check the Internet for the most up-to-date information. Using inclusive and respectful language is not a matter of political correctness, but it is a matter of P.C.—personal courtesy.[7]

Summary

Good speakers have respect for language and how it works. As a speaker, you should be aware of the meanings of words and know how to use language accurately, clearly, vividly, and appropriately.

Words have two kinds of meanings—denotative and connotative. Denotative meaning is precise, literal, and objective. Connotative meaning is more variable, figurative, and subjective. It includes all the feelings, associations, and emotions that a word touches off in different people.

Using language accurately is vital to a speaker. Never use a word unless you are sure of its meaning. If you are not sure, look up the word in a dictionary. As you prepare your speeches, ask yourself constantly, "What do I *really* want to say? What do I *really* mean?" Choose words that are precise and accurate.

Using language clearly allows listeners to grasp your meaning immediately. You can ensure this by using words that are known to the average person and require no specialized background, by choosing concrete words in preference to more abstract ones, and by eliminating verbal clutter.

Using language vividly helps bring your speech to life. One way to make your language more vivid is through imagery, which you can develop by using concrete language, simile, and metaphor. Another way to make your speeches vivid is by exploiting the rhythm of language with parallelism, repetition, alliteration, and antithesis.

Using language appropriately means adapting to the particular occasion, audience, and topic at hand. It also means developing your own language style instead of trying to copy someone else's.

The subject of inclusive language can be complex, but a number of inclusive usages have become so widely accepted that no aspiring speaker can afford to ignore them. They include avoiding the generic "he," dropping the use of "man" when referring to both men and women, refraining from stereotyping jobs and social roles by gender, and using names that groups use to identify themselves.

Key Terms

denotative meaning *(222)*

connotative meaning *(222)*

thesaurus *(223)*

concrete words *(225)*

abstract words *(225)*

clutter *(226)*

imagery *(228)*

simile *(228)*

cliché *(229)*

metaphor *(229)*

rhythm *(230)*

parallelism *(230)*

repetition *(231)*

alliteration *(231)*

antithesis *(232)*

inclusive language *(234)*

generic "he" *(234)*

Review Questions

After reading this chapter, you should be able to answer the following questions:

1. How does language help create our sense of reality?

2. What is the difference between denotative and connotative meaning? How might you use each to convey your message most effectively?

3. What are four criteria for using language effectively in your speeches?

4. What are three things you should do to use language clearly in your speeches?

5. What are two ways to bring your speeches to life with vivid, animated language?

6. What does it mean to say you should use language appropriately in your speeches?

7. Why is it important for a public speaker to use inclusive language? What four usages of inclusive language have become so widely accepted that no speaker can afford to ignore them?

connect

For further review, go to the LearnSmart study module for this chapter.

Exercises for Critical Thinking

1. Arrange each of the sequences below in order, from the most abstract word to the most concrete word.

    a. housing complex, building, dining room, structure, apartment

    b. *Mona Lisa,* art, painting, creative activity, portrait

    c. automobile, vehicle, Ferrari, transportation, sports car

2. Rewrite each of the following sentences using clear, familiar words.

    a. My employment objective is to attain a position of maximum financial reward.

    b. All professors at this school are expected to achieve high standards of excellence in their instructional duties.

    c. In the eventuality of a fire, it is imperative that all persons evacuate the building without undue delay.

3. Each of the statements below uses one or more of the following stylistic devices: metaphor, simile, parallelism, repetition, alliteration, antithesis. Identify the device (or devices) used in each statement.

    a. "We are a people in a quandary about the present. We are a people in search of our future. We are a people in search of a national community." (Barbara Jordan)

    b. "The vice presidency is the sand trap of American politics. It's near the prize, and designed to be limiting." (Howard Fineman)

    c. "People the world over have always been more impressed by the power of our example than by the example of our power." (Bill Clinton)

    d. "America is not like a blanket—one piece of unbroken cloth, the same color, the same texture, the same size. America is more like a quilt—many patches, many sizes, and woven and held together by a common thread." (Jesse Jackson)

4. Analyze Martin Luther King's "I Have a Dream" in the appendix of sample speeches that follows Chapter 19. Identify the methods King uses to make his language clear, vivid, and appropriate. Look particularly at King's use of familiar words, concrete words, imagery, and rhythm.

californiawo

Delivery

If you were to record one of Conan O'Brien's comedy routines, memorize it word for word, and stand up before your friends to recite it, would you get the same response O'Brien does? Not very likely. And why not? Because you would not *deliver* the jokes as O'Brien does. Of course, the jokes are basically funny. But Conan O'Brien brings something extra to the jokes—his manner of presentation, his vocal inflections, his perfectly timed pauses, his facial expressions, his gestures. All these are part of an expert delivery. It would take you years of practice—as it took O'Brien—to duplicate his results.

No one expects your speech class to transform you into a multimillion-dollar talk show host. Still, this example demonstrates how important delivery can be to any public speaking situation. Even a mediocre speech will be more effective if it is presented well, whereas a wonderfully written speech can be ruined by poor delivery.

This does not mean dazzling delivery will turn a mindless string of nonsense into a triumphant oration. You cannot make a good speech without having something to say. But having something to say is not enough. You must also know *how* to say it.

Speech delivery is a matter of *nonverbal communication.* It is based on how you use your voice and body to convey the message expressed by your words. There is a great deal of research showing that the impact of a speaker's words is powerfully influenced by his or her nonverbal communication. In this chapter, we will explain how you can use nonverbal communication to deliver your speeches effectively and to increase the impact of your verbal message.

What Is Good Delivery?

Wendell Phillips was a leader in the movement to abolish slavery in the United States during the 1800s. Some people considered him the greatest speaker of his time. The following story suggests one reason why:

> Shortly before the Civil War an Andover student, learning that Phillips was to lecture in Boston, made a 22-mile pilgrimage on foot to hear him. At first the trip seemed hardly worthwhile, for the student discovered that Phillips was not an orator in the grand manner, but spoke in an almost conversational style. He stood on the platform, one hand lightly resting on a table, talked for what seemed to be about 20 minutes, concluded, and sat down. When the student looked at his watch, he found to his astonishment that he had been listening for an hour and a half![1]

Good delivery does not call attention to itself. It conveys the speaker's ideas clearly, interestingly, and without distracting the audience. Most audiences prefer delivery that combines a certain degree of formality with the best attributes of good conversation—directness, spontaneity, animation, vocal and facial expressiveness, and a lively sense of communication.

Speech delivery is an art, not a science. What works for one speaker may fail for another. And what succeeds with today's audience may not with tomorrow's. You cannot become a skilled speaker just by following a set of rules in a textbook. In the long run, there is no substitute for experience. But take heart! A textbook *can* give you basic pointers to get you started in the right direction.

When you plan your first speech (or your second or third), you should concentrate on such basics as speaking intelligibly, avoiding distracting mannerisms, and establishing eye contact with your listeners. Once you get these elements under control and begin to feel fairly comfortable in front of an audience, you can work on polishing your delivery to enhance the impact of your ideas. Eventually, you may find yourself able to control the timing, rhythm, and momentum of a speech as skillfully as a conductor controls an orchestra.

Methods of Delivery

There are four basic methods of delivering a speech: (1) reading verbatim from a manuscript, (2) reciting a memorized text, (3) speaking impromptu, and (4) speaking extemporaneously. Let us look at each.

READING FROM A MANUSCRIPT

Certain speeches *must* be delivered word for word, according to a meticulously prepared manuscript. Examples include a Pope's religious proclamation, an engineer's report to a professional meeting, or a President's message to Congress. In such situations, absolute accuracy is essential. Every word of the speech will be analyzed by the press, by colleagues, perhaps by enemies. In the case of the President, a misstated phrase could cause an international incident.

manuscript speech

A speech that is written out word for word and read to the audience.

Although it looks easy, delivering a speech from manuscript requires great skill. Some people do it well. Their words "come alive as if coined on the spot."[2] Others ruin it every time. Instead of sounding vibrant and conversational, they come across as wooden and artificial. They falter over words, pause in the wrong places, read too quickly or too slowly, speak in a monotone, and march through the speech without even glancing at their audience. In short, they come across as *reading to* their listeners, rather than *talking with* them.

If you are in a situation where you must speak from a manuscript, practice aloud to make sure the speech sounds natural. Work on establishing eye contact with your listeners. Be certain the final manuscript is legible at a glance. Above all, reach out to your audience with the same directness and sincerity that you would if you were speaking extemporaneously.

RECITING FROM MEMORY

Among the feats of the legendary orators, none leaves us more in awe than their practice of presenting even the longest and most complex speeches entirely from memory. Nowadays it is no longer customary to memorize any but the shortest of speeches—toasts, congratulatory remarks, acceptance speeches, introductions, and the like.

If you are giving a speech of this kind and want to memorize it, by all means do so. However, be sure to memorize it so thoroughly that you will be able to concentrate on communicating with the audience, not on trying to remember the words. Speakers who gaze at the ceiling or stare out the window trying to recall what they have memorized are no better off than those who read dully from a manuscript.

SPEAKING IMPROMPTU

An impromptu speech is delivered with little or no immediate preparation. Few people choose to speak impromptu, but sometimes it cannot be avoided. In fact, many of the speeches you give in life will be impromptu. You might be called on suddenly to "say a few words" or, in the course of a class discussion, business meeting, or committee report, want to respond to a previous speaker.

impromptu speech

A speech delivered with little or no immediate preparation.

When such situations arise, don't panic. No one expects you to deliver a perfect speech on the spur of the moment. If you are in a meeting or discussion, pay close attention to what the other speakers say. Take notes of major points with which you agree or disagree. In the process, you will automatically begin to formulate what you will say when it is your turn to speak.

Whenever you are responding to a previous speaker, try to present your speech in four simple steps: First, state the point you are answering. Second, state the point you wish to make. Third, support your point with appropriate statistics, examples, or testimony. Fourth, summarize your point. This four-step method will help you organize your thoughts quickly and clearly.

If time allows, sketch a quick outline of your remarks on a piece of paper before you rise to speak. This will help you remember what you want to say and will keep you from rambling.

If the situation calls for you to speak from a lectern, walk to it calmly, take a deep breath or two (not a visible gasp), establish eye contact with your audience, and begin speaking. No matter how nervous you are inside, do your best to look calm and assured on the outside.

Once you begin speaking, maintain eye contact with the audience. Help the audience keep track of your ideas with signposts such as "My first point is . . . ; second, we can see that . . . ; in conclusion, I would like to say . . . ." By stating your points clearly and concisely, you will come across as organized and confident.

As with other kinds of public speaking, the best way to become a better impromptu speaker is to practice. You can do this on your own. Simply choose a topic on which you are already well informed, and give a one- or two-minute impromptu talk on some aspect of that topic. Any topic will do, no matter how serious or frivolous it may be. You don't even need an audience—you can speak to an empty room. Better yet, speak to a digital recorder and play it back to hear how you sound. The purpose is to gain experience in pulling your ideas together quickly and stating them succinctly.

SPEAKING EXTEMPORANEOUSLY

In popular usage, "extemporaneous" means the same as "impromptu." But technically the two are different. Unlike an impromptu speech, which is delivered off-the-cuff, an extemporaneous speech is carefully prepared and practiced in advance. In presenting the speech, the extemporaneous speaker uses only a brief set of notes or a speaking outline to jog the memory (see Chapter 11). The exact wording is chosen at the moment of delivery.

This is not as hard as it sounds. Once you have your outline (or notes) and know what topics you are going to cover and in what order, you can begin to practice the speech. Every time you run through it, the wording will be slightly different. As you practice the speech over and over, the best way to present each part will emerge and stick in your mind.

The extemporaneous method has several advantages. It gives more precise control over thought and language than does impromptu speaking; it offers greater spontaneity and directness than does speaking from memory or from a full manuscript; and it is adaptable to a wide range of situations. It also encourages the conversational quality audiences look for in speech delivery.

"Conversational quality" means that no matter how many times a speech has been rehearsed, it still *sounds* spontaneous. When you speak extemporaneously—and have prepared properly—you have full control over your ideas, yet you are not tied to a manuscript. You are free to establish strong eye contact, to gesture naturally, and to concentrate on talking *with* the audience rather than declaiming *to* them.

For an example of extemporaneous delivery, look at Video 13.1 in the online Media Library for this chapter. The student is demonstrating how to breathe when doing yoga. She clearly has rehearsed a great deal, and she

extemporaneous speech

A carefully prepared and rehearsed speech that is presented from a brief set of notes.

conversational quality

Presenting a speech so it sounds spontaneous no matter how many times it has been rehearsed.

Extemporaneous speeches are prepared ahead of time, but the exact words are chosen at the moment of presentation. This allows for more direct delivery than does reading from a manuscript.

knows what she wants to say, but she has not memorized the speech. She has a brief set of speaking notes in case she needs them, but she is not tied to the notes. Rather, she selects her words as she goes along, maintains strong eye contact with the audience, and has excellent conversational quality.

Like thousands of previous students, you can become adept at speaking extemporaneously by the end of the term. As one student commented in looking back at his class: "At the start, I never thought I'd be able to give my speeches without a ton of notes, but I'm amazed at how much progress I've made. It's one of the most valuable things I learned in the entire class."

Most experienced speakers prefer the extemporaneous method, and most teachers emphasize it. Later in this chapter (pages 251–252), we'll look at a step-by-step program for practicing your extemporaneous delivery.

connect™

View an excerpt from "Yoga: Uniting Mind, Body, and Spirit" in the online Media Library for this chapter (Video 13.1).

The Speaker's Voice

What kind of voice do you have? Is it rich and resonant like Morgan Freeman's? Soft and alluring like Scarlett Johansson's? Loud and irritating like Dick Vitale's? Whatever the characteristics of your voice, you can be sure it is unique. Because no two people are exactly the same physically, no two people have identical voices.

A golden voice is certainly an asset for a public speaker, but some of the most famous speakers in history have had undistinguished voices. Abraham Lincoln had a harsh and penetrating voice; Winston Churchill suffered from a slight lisp and an awkward stammer. Like them, you can overcome natural disadvantages and use your voice to the best effect. Lincoln and Churchill learned to *control* their voices. You can do the same thing.

The aspects of voice you should work to control are volume, pitch, rate, pauses, vocal variety, pronunciation, articulation, and dialect.

VOLUME

volume

The loudness or softness of the speaker's voice.

At one time, a powerful voice was essential for an orator. Today, electronic amplification allows even a soft-spoken person to be heard in any setting. But in the classroom you will speak without a microphone. When you do, be sure to adjust your voice to the acoustics of the room, the size of the audience, and the level of background noise. If you speak too loudly, your listeners will think you boorish. If you speak too softly, they will not understand you.

Remember that your own voice always sounds louder to you than to a listener. Soon after beginning your speech, glance at the people farthest away from you. If they look puzzled, are leaning forward in their seats, or are otherwise straining to hear, you need to talk louder.

PITCH

pitch

The highness or lowness of the speaker's voice.

inflections

Changes in the pitch or tone of a speaker's voice.

monotone

A constant pitch or tone of voice.

Pitch is the highness or lowness of a speaker's voice. The faster sound waves vibrate, the higher their pitch; the slower they vibrate, the lower their pitch.

Changes in pitch are known as *inflections*. Inflection is what makes the difference between the "Aha!" triumphantly exclaimed by Sherlock Holmes upon discovering a seemingly decisive clue and the "Aha" he mutters when he learns the clue is not decisive after all. If you were to read the preceding sentence aloud, your voice would probably go up in pitch on the first "Aha" and down on the second.

In ordinary conversation, we instinctively use inflections to convey meaning and emotion. People who do not are said to speak in a *monotone*, a trait whose only known benefit is to cure insomnia in one's listeners.

Although few people speak in an absolute monotone, with no variation whatever in pitch, many fall into repetitive pitch patterns that are just as hypnotic. You can guard against this by recording your speeches as you practice them. If all your sentences end on the same inflection—either upward or downward—work on varying your pitch patterns to fit the meaning of your words.

RATE

rate

The speed at which a person speaks.

Rate refers to the speed at which a person talks. People in the United States usually speak at a rate between 120 and 150 words per minute, but there is no uniform rate for effective speechmaking. Franklin Roosevelt spoke at 110 words per minute, John Kennedy at 180. Martin Luther King opened his "I Have a Dream" speech at 92 words per minute and finished it at 145. The best rate of speech depends on several things—the vocal attributes of the speaker, the mood she or he is trying to create, the composition of the audience, and the nature of the occasion.

Two obvious faults to avoid are speaking so slowly that your listeners become bored or so quickly that they lose track of your ideas. Novice speakers are particularly prone to racing through their speeches at a frantic rate. Fortunately, this is usually an easy habit to break, as is the less common one of crawling through one's speech at a snail's pace.

The key in both cases is becoming aware of the problem and concentrating on solving it. Use a recording device to check how fast you speak. Pay special attention to rate when practicing your speech. Finally, be sure to include reminders about delivery on your speaking outline so you won't forget to make the adjustments when you give your speech in class.

PAUSES

Learning how and when to pause is a major challenge for most beginning speakers. Even a moment of silence can seem like an eternity. As you gain more poise and confidence, however, you will discover how useful the pause can be. It can signal the end of a thought unit, give an idea time to sink in, and lend dramatic impact to a statement. "The right word may be effective," said Mark Twain, "but no word was ever as effective as a rightly timed pause."

Developing a keen sense of timing is partly a matter of common sense, partly a matter of experience. You will not always get your pauses just right at first, but keep trying. Listen to accomplished speakers to see how they use pauses to modulate the rate and rhythm of their messages. Work on pauses when you practice your speeches.

Make sure you pause at the end of thought units and not in the middle. Otherwise, you may distract listeners from your ideas. Most important, do not fill the silence with "uh," "er," or "um." These *vocalized pauses* can create negative perceptions about a speaker's intelligence and often make a speaker appear deceptive.[3]

VOCAL VARIETY

Just as variety is the spice of life, so is it the spice of public speaking. A flat, listless, unchanging voice is as deadly to speechmaking as a flat, listless, unchanging routine is to daily life. When giving a speech, you should strive for vocal variety—changes in rate, pitch, and volume that will give your voice interest and expressiveness.

For an excellent example of vocal variety, look at Video 13.2 in the online Media Library for this chapter. The speaker, Sajjid Zahir Chinoy, was born and raised in Bombay, India, before coming to the United States to attend college at the University of Richmond. At the end of his senior year, Chinoy was selected as the student commencement speaker in a campus-wide competition. He spoke of the warm reception he received at Richmond and of how cultural differences can be overcome by attempting to understand other people.

pause

A momentary break in the vocal delivery of a speech.

vocalized pause

A pause that occurs when a speaker fills the silence between words with vocalizations such as "uh," "er," and "um."

vocal variety

Changes in a speaker's rate, pitch, and volume that give the voice variety and expressiveness.

The best rate of speech depends partly on the mood a speaker wants to create. To communicate the excitement of thoroughbred horse racing, you would probably speak at a faster-than-normal rate.

connect

View an excerpt from "Questions of Culture" in the online Media Library for this chapter (Video 13.2).

At the end of his speech, Chinoy received thunderous applause—partly because of what he said, but also because of how he said it. Addressing the audience of 3,000 people without notes, he spoke extemporaneously with strong eye contact and excellent vocal variety. The speech was so inspiring that the main speaker, Harvard psychiatrist Robert Coles, began his presentation by paying tribute to Chinoy. "I've been to a number of commencements," said Coles, "but I've never heard a speech quite like that!"

How can you develop a lively, expressive voice? Above all, by approaching every speech as Chinoy approached his—as an opportunity to share with your listeners ideas that are important to you. Your sense of conviction and your desire to communicate will give your voice the same spark it has in spontaneous conversation.

PRONUNCIATION

We all mispronounce words now and again. Here, for example, are four words with which you are probably familiar. Say each one aloud.

pronunciation

The accepted standard of sound and rhythm for words in a given language.

genuine	arctic
err	nuclear

Very likely you made a mistake on at least one, for they are among the most frequently mispronounced words in the English language. Let's see:

Word	Common Error	Correct Pronunciation
genuine	gen-u-wine	gen-u-win
arctic	ar-tic	arc-tic
nuclear	nu-cu-lar	nu-cle-ar
err	air	ur

Every word leads a triple life: it is read, written, and spoken. Most people recognize and understand many more words in reading than they use in ordinary writing, and about three times as many as occur in spontaneous speech.[4] This is why we occasionally stumble when speaking words that are part of our reading or writing vocabularies. In other cases, we may mispronounce the most commonplace words out of habit.

The problem is that we usually don't *know* when we are mispronouncing a word. If we are lucky, we learn the right pronunciation by hearing someone else say the word properly or by having someone gently correct us in private. If we are unlucky, we mispronounce the word in front of a roomful of people, who may raise their eyebrows, groan, or laugh.

All of this argues for practicing your speech in front of as many trusted friends and relatives as you can corner. If you have any doubts about the proper pronunciation of certain words, be sure to check a dictionary.

ARTICULATION

Articulation and pronunciation are not identical. Sloppy articulation is the failure to form particular speech sounds crisply and distinctly. It is one of several causes of mispronunciation, but you can articulate a word sharply and still mispronounce it. For example, if you say the "s" in "Illinois" or the "p" in "pneumonia," you are making a mistake in pronunciation, regardless of how precisely you articulate the sounds.

Among college students, poor articulation is more common than ignorance of correct pronunciation. We know that "let me" is not "lemme," that "going to" is not "gonna," that "did you" is not "didja," yet we persist in articulating these words improperly. Here are some other common errors in articulation you should work to avoid:

Word	Misarticulation
ought to	otta
didn't	dint
don't know	dunno
have to	hafta
want to	wanna
will you	wilya

If you have sloppy articulation, work on identifying and eliminating your most common errors. Like other bad habits, careless articulation can be broken only by persistent effort—but the results are well worth it. As Shakespeare advised, "Mend your speech a little, lest you may mar your fortunes."

DIALECT

Most languages have dialects, each with a distinctive accent, grammar, and vocabulary. Dialects are usually based on regional or ethnic speech patterns. The United States has four major regional dialects—Eastern, New England, Southern, and General American. We also have multiple ethnic dialects. As the nation has become more diverse culturally, it has also become more diverse linguistically.[5]

Linguists have concluded that no dialect is inherently better or worse than another. Dialects are not linguistic badges of superiority or inferiority. They are usually shaped by our regional or ethnic background, and every dialect is "right" for the community of people who use it.

When is a given dialect appropriate in public speaking? The answer depends above all on the composition of your audience. Heavy use of any dialect—regional or ethnic—can be troublesome when the audience does not share that dialect. In such a situation, the dialect may cause listeners to make negative judgments about the speaker's personality, intelligence, and competence. This is why professional speakers have been known to invest large amounts of time (and money) to master the General American dialect used by most television news broadcasters.

Does this mean you must talk like a television news broadcaster if you want to be successful in your speeches? Not at all. Regional or ethnic dialects do not pose a problem as long as the audience is familiar with them and finds them appropriate. When speaking in the North, for example, a southern politician may avoid regional dialect. But when addressing audiences in the South, the same politician may intentionally include regional dialect as a way of creating common ground with listeners.

Although not strictly speaking a matter of dialect, the proficiency of non-native speakers of English often arises in the speech classroom. Fortunately, teachers and students alike usually go out of their way to be helpful and encouraging to international students and others for whom English is not the primary language. Over the years, many non-native speakers of English have found speech class a supportive environment in which to improve their proficiency in spoken English.[6]

The Speaker's Body

Imagine yourself at a party. During the evening you form impressions about the people around you. Jonte seems relaxed and even-tempered, Nicole tense and irritable. Kyndra seems open and straightforward, Bekah hostile and evasive. Amin seems happy to see you; Seth definitely is not.

How do you reach these conclusions? To a surprising extent, you reach them not on the basis of what people say with words, but because of what they say with their posture, gestures, eyes, and facial expressions. Suppose you are sitting next to Amin, and he says, "This is a great party. I'm really glad to be here with you." However, his body is turned slightly away from you, and he keeps looking at someone across the room. Despite what he says, you know he is *not* glad to be there with you.

Much the same thing happens in speechmaking. Posture, facial expression, gestures, eye contact—all affect the way listeners respond to a speaker. How we use these and other body motions to communicate is the subject of a fascinating area of study called kinesics. One of its founders, Ray Birdwhistell, estimated that more than 700,000 physical signals can be sent through bodily movement. Studies have shown that these signals have a significant impact on the meaning communicated by speakers.

Research has also confirmed what the Greek historian Herodotus observed more than 2,400 years ago: "People trust their ears less than their eyes." When a speaker's body language is inconsistent with his or her words, listeners often believe the body language rather than the words.[7] Here are the major aspects of physical action that will affect the outcome of your speeches.

kinesics

The study of body motions as a systematic mode of communication.

PERSONAL APPEARANCE

If you were Lady Gaga, you could show up to make an MTV Music Video Award presentation speech wearing a bizarre creation that left little to the imagination. If you were Albert Einstein, you could show up to address an international science conference wearing wrinkled trousers, a sweater, and tennis shoes. While the members of your audience would certainly comment on your attire, your reputation would not be harmed. In fact, it might be enhanced. You would be one of the few, the very few, who live outside the rules, who are expected to be unusual.

Now imagine what would happen if the president of a corporation showed up to address a stockholders' meeting attired like Lady Gaga, or if the President of the United States spoke on national television wearing wrinkled clothes and tennis shoes. Both presidents would soon be looking for work. Barring the occasional eccentric, every speaker is expected by her or

Good speakers use a lively voice to bring their ideas to life. They also use gestures, eye contact, and facial expressions to create a bond with their audience.

his audience to exhibit a personal appearance in keeping with the occasion of the speech.

Many studies have confirmed that personal appearance plays an important role in speechmaking.[8] Listeners always see you before they hear you. Just as you adapt your language to the audience and the occasion, so should you dress and groom appropriately. Although the force of your speech can sometimes overcome a poor impression created by personal appearance, the odds are against it. Regardless of the speaking situation, you should try to evoke a favorable first impression.

MOVEMENT

Novice speakers are often unsure about what to do with their body while giving a speech. Some pace back and forth across the podium, shift their weight from one foot to the other, fidget with their notes, or jingle coins in their pockets. Still others turn into statues, standing rigid and expressionless from beginning to end.

Such quirks usually stem from nervousness. If you are prone to distracting mannerisms, your teacher will identify them so you can work on controlling them. With a little concentration, these mannerisms should disappear as you become more comfortable speaking in front of an audience.

As important as how you act during the speech is what you do just *before* you begin and *after* you finish. As you rise to speak, try to appear calm, poised, and confident, despite the butterflies in your stomach. When you reach the lectern, don't lean on it, and don't rush into your speech. Give yourself time to get set. Arrange your notes just the way you want them. Stand quietly as you wait to make sure the audience is paying attention. Establish eye contact with your listeners. Then—and only then—should you start to talk.

When you reach the end of your speech, maintain eye contact for a few moments after you stop talking. This will give your closing line time to sink in. Unless you are staying at the lectern to answer questions, collect your notes and return to your seat. As you do so, maintain your cool, collected demeanor. Whatever you do, don't start to gather your notes before you have finished talking, and don't cap off your speech with a huge sigh of relief or some remark like, "Whew! Am I glad that's over!"

When practicing your speeches, spend a little time rehearsing how you will behave at the beginning and at the end. It is one of the easiest—and one of the most effective—things you can do to improve your image with an audience.

GESTURES

Few aspects of delivery cause students more anguish than deciding what to do with their hands. "Should I clasp them behind my back? Let them hang at my sides? Rest them on the lectern? And what about gesturing? When should I do that—and how?" Even people who use their hands expressively in everyday conversation seem to regard them as awkward appendages when speaking before an audience.

Over the years, more nonsense has been written about gesturing than any other aspect of speech delivery. Adroit gestures *can* add to the impact of a speech; but effective speakers do not need a vast repertoire of gestures. Some accomplished speakers gesture frequently, others hardly at all. The primary rule is this: Whatever gestures you make should not distract from your message. They should *appear* natural and spontaneous, help clarify or reinforce your ideas, and be suited to the audience and occasion.

Gesturing tends to work itself out as you acquire experience and confidence. For now, make sure your hands do not upstage your ideas. Avoid flailing them about, wringing them together, or toying with your rings. Once you have eliminated these distractions, forget about your hands. Think about communicating with your listeners, and your gestures will take care of themselves—just as they do in conversation.

EYE CONTACT

The eyes have been called "the windows of the soul." We look to them to help gauge a speaker's truthfulness, intelligence, attitudes, and feelings.

Although patterns of eye contact in everyday conversation vary from culture to culture, there is wide agreement across cultures on the importance of eye contact in public speaking. In most circumstances, one of the quickest ways to establish a communicative bond with your listeners is to look at them personally and pleasantly. Avoiding their gaze is one of the surest ways to lose them.

Speakers in the United States who fail to establish eye contact are perceived as tentative or ill at ease and may be seen as insincere or dishonest. It is no wonder, then, that teachers urge students to look at the audience 80 to 90 percent of the time they are talking. You may find this disconcerting at first. But after one or two speeches, you should be able to meet the gaze of your audience fairly comfortably.

It isn't enough just to look at your listeners; *how* you look at them also counts. Beware of the tendency to gaze intently at one part of the audience while ignoring the rest. In speech class, some students look only at the section of the room where the teacher is sitting. Others avoid looking anywhere near the teacher and focus on one or two sympathetic friends. You should try to establish eye contact with your whole audience.

When addressing a small audience such as your class, you can usually look briefly from one person to another. For a larger group, you can scan the

---

gestures

Motions of a speaker's hands or arms during a speech.

eye contact

Direct visual contact with the eyes of another person.

Research shows that eye contact is one of the most important elements in speech delivery. As with figure skating champion Michelle Kwan, you want your eyes to convey confidence, sincerity, and conviction.

audience rather than try to engage the eyes of each person individually. No matter what the size of your audience, you want your eyes to convey confidence, sincerity, and conviction.

Look at Video 13.3 in the online Media Library for this chapter to see a fine example of eye contact. The speaker is telling her classmates how they can become volunteers for the Special Olympics. Notice how she uses her eyes to connect with her listeners at a personal level. This is the kind of strong communication you should strive for in your speeches.[9]

Practicing Delivery

Popular wisdom promises that practice makes perfect. This is true, but only if we practice properly. You will do little to improve your speech delivery unless you practice the right things in the right ways. Here is a five-step method that has worked well for many students:

connect

View an excerpt from "Making a Difference Through the Special Olympics" in the online Media Library for this chapter (Video 13.3).

1. Go through your preparation outline *aloud* to check how what you have written translates into spoken discourse. Is it too long? Too short? Are the main points clear when you speak them? Are the supporting materials distinct, convincing, interesting? Do the introduction and conclusion come across well? As you answer these questions, revise the speech as needed.

2. Prepare your speaking outline. In doing so, be sure to follow the guidelines in Chapter 11. Use the same visual framework as in the preparation outline. Make sure the speaking outline is easy to read at a glance. Give yourself cues on the outline for delivering the speech.

3. Practice the speech aloud several times using only the speaking outline. Be sure to "talk through" all examples and to recite in full all quotations and statistics. If your speech includes visual aids, use them as you practice. The first couple of times, you will probably forget something or make a mistake, but don't worry. Keep going and complete the speech as well as you can. Concentrate on gaining control of the *ideas;* don't try to learn the speech word for word. After a few tries you should be able to get through the speech extemporaneously with surprising ease.

4. Now begin to polish and refine your delivery. Practice the speech in front of a mirror to check for eye contact and distracting mannerisms. Record the speech to gauge volume, pitch, rate, pauses, and vocal variety. Most important, try it out on friends, roommates, family members—anyone who will listen and give you an honest appraisal. Because your speech is designed for people rather than for mirrors or recorders, you need to find out ahead of time how it goes over with people.

5. Finally, give your speech a dress rehearsal under conditions as close as possible to those you will face in class. Some students like to try the speech a couple times in an empty classroom the day before the speech is due. No matter where you hold your last practice session, you should leave it feeling confident and looking forward to speaking in your class.

If this or any practice method is to work, you must start early. Don't wait until the night before your speech to begin working on delivery. A single practice session—no matter how long—is rarely enough. Allow yourself *at least* a couple of days, preferably more, to gain command of the speech and its presentation.

Answering Audience Questions

If you have ever watched a press conference or heard a speaker answer questions after a talk, you know the question-and-answer session can make or break a presentation. A speaker who handles questions well can strengthen the impact of his or her speech. On the other hand, a speaker who evades questions or shows annoyance will almost certainly create the opposite effect.

The question-and-answer session is a common part of public speaking, whether the occasion is a press conference, business presentation, public hearing, or classroom assignment. An answer to a question is often the final word an audience hears and is likely to leave a lasting impression.

PREPARING FOR THE QUESTION-AND-ANSWER SESSION

The first step to doing well in a question-and-answer session is to take it as seriously as the speech itself. The two major steps in preparing are working out answers to possible questions and practicing the delivery of those answers.

Formulate Answers to Possible Questions

Once you know that your presentation will include questions from the audience, you should be thinking about possible questions even as you are writing your speech. If you practice your speech in front of friends, family, or coworkers, ask them to jot down questions. Keep track of all the questions and formulate answers. Write your answers in full to make sure you have thought them through completely.

If you are giving a persuasive speech, be sure to work out answers to objections the audience may have to your proposal. No matter how careful you are to deal with those objections in your speech, you can be sure they will come up in the question-and-answer session.

If you are speaking on a topic with technical aspects, be ready to answer specialized inquiries about them, as well as questions that seek clarification, in nontechnical terms. You might even prepare a handout that you can distribute afterward for people who want more information.

Practice the Delivery of Your Answers

You would not present a speech to a room full of people without rehearsing. Neither should you go into a question-and-answer session without practicing the delivery of your answers.

One possibility is to have a friend or colleague listen to your presentation, ask questions, and critique your answers. This method is used by political candidates and business leaders before debates or press conferences. Another possibility is to record your answers to anticipated questions, play them back, and revise them until they are just right.

As you rehearse, work on making your answers brief and to the point. Many simple questions can be answered in 30 seconds, and even complex ones should usually be answered in a minute or two. If you practice answering questions beforehand, you will find it much easier to keep to these time limits.

Of course, there is no way to predict every question you will receive. But if you go into the question-and-answer period fully prepared, you will be able to adapt to whatever occurs.

MANAGING THE QUESTION-AND-ANSWER SESSION

If you have ever watched a skillful speaker field questions from the audience, you know there is an art to managing a question-and-answer session. Entire books have been written on this subject, but the following suggestions will help get you started on the right foot.

Using public speaking in your CAREER

Utilizing your business degree and computer savvy, you have made a success of the online marketing company you started after graduating from college. Now in its third year, the company has prepared a proposal to design the e-commerce site for a major sporting goods retailer. In your 30-minute presentation to the retailer's management team, you will review the homepage designs, site maps, and security protocols.

You notice on the agenda that another 30 minutes has been allotted after your presentation for questions and answers. Knowing from your previous experience with clients how important the Q&A session can be, you want to be sure you are ready for it. What steps will you take to prepare?

Approach Questions with a Positive Attitude

A positive attitude will help you answer questions graciously and respectfully. Try to view questions from the audience as signs of genuine interest and a desire to learn more about your subject. If someone asks about a point that seems clear to you, don't respond by saying, "I discussed that at the beginning of my talk," or "The answer seems obvious." Instead, use moments like these to reiterate or expand upon your ideas.

A speaker who adopts a sharp or defensive tone while answering questions will alienate many people in the audience. Even if you are asked a hostile question, keep your cool. Avoid the temptation to answer defensively, sarcastically, or argumentatively. Most people in the audience will respect you for trying to avoid a quarrel.

Listen Carefully

It's hard to answer a question well if you don't listen carefully to it. Give the questioner your full attention. When faced with an unclear or unwieldy question, try to rephrase it by saying something like, "If I understand your question, it seems to me that you are asking. . . ." Another option is simply to ask the audience member to repeat the question. Most people will restate it more succinctly and clearly.

Direct Answers to the Entire Audience

When you are being asked a question, look at the questioner. Direct your answer, however, to the entire audience. Make occasional eye contact with the questioner as you answer, but speak primarily to the audience as a whole. If you speak just to the questioner, the rest of your audience may drift off.

When speaking to a large audience, repeat or paraphrase each question after it is asked. This involves the entire audience and ensures that they know the question. In addition, repeating or paraphrasing the question gives you a moment to frame an answer before you respond.

Be Honest and Straightforward

If you don't know the answer to a question, say so. Don't apologize, don't evade, and most important, don't try to bluff. Do, however, let the questioner know that you take the question seriously. Offer to check into the answer as soon as possible after the speech. If a more knowledgeable person is at hand, ask if she or he knows the answer.

Stay on Track

It's easy to get diverted or lose control of time in a lively question-and-answer session. Unless there is a moderator, the speaker is responsible for keeping things on track. Allow one follow-up question from each person, and don't let yourself be dragged into a personal debate with any questioner. If someone attempts to ask more than two questions, respond graciously yet firmly by saying, "This is an interesting line of questioning, but we need to give other people a chance to ask questions."

Sometimes, a listener will launch into an extended monologue instead of posing a question. When this happens, you can retain control of the situation by saying something like, "Those are very interesting ideas, but do you have a specific question I can answer?" If the person persists, offer to talk individually with him or her after the session.

Question-and-answer sessions are an important part of public speaking around the globe. Here Mike Weightman of the International Atomic Energy Agency talks with reporters in Tokyo, Japan, about the nuclear power plant crippled in the 2011 earthquake and tsunami.

On some occasions, the length of the question-and-answer session is pre-determined. On other occasions, it's up to the speaker. Make sure you allow enough time to get through issues of major importance, but don't let things drag on after the momentum of the session has started winding down. As the end approaches, offer to respond to another question or two. Then wrap things up by thanking the audience for its time and attention.[10]

Summary

Speech delivery is a matter of nonverbal communication. It is based on how you use your voice and body to convey the message expressed by your words. Rather than calling attention to itself, effective delivery conveys the speaker's ideas clearly, engagingly, and without distracting the audience.

There are four basic methods of delivering a speech: reading verbatim from a manuscript, reciting a memorized text, speaking impromptu, and speaking extemporaneously. When speaking extemporaneously, you will have a brief set of notes or a speaking outline and will choose the exact wording of your speech at the moment of delivery.

To use your voice effectively you should work on controlling your volume, pitch, rate, pauses, vocal variety, pronunciation, articulation, and dialect. Volume is the relative loudness of your voice, and pitch is the relative highness or lowness. Rate refers to the speed at which you talk. Pauses, when carefully timed, can add punch to your speech, but you should avoid vocalized pauses ("er," "um," and the like).

Vocal variety refers to changes in volume, pitch, rate, and pauses, and is crucial to making your voice lively and animated. You also need correct pronunciation and distinct articulation. Avoid heavy use of dialect in situations where the audience does not share the dialect or will find it inappropriate.

Posture, personal appearance, facial expression, gestures, and eye contact also affect the way listeners respond to speakers. Dress and groom appropriately, use gestures and bodily movement to enhance your message, and make eye contact with your listeners.

You should practice all these aspects of delivery along with the words of your speech. Start your practice sessions early so you will have plenty of time to gain command of the speech and its presentation.

If your speech includes a question-and-answer session, anticipate the most likely questions, prepare answers to them, and practice delivering those answers. During the question-and-answer period, listen carefully to the questions, approach them positively, and respond to them briefly, graciously, and straightforwardly. Direct your answers to the full audience, rather than to the questioner alone, and make sure to end the session in a timely fashion.

Key Terms

nonverbal communication *(240)*

manuscript speech *(241)*

impromptu speech *(241)*

extemporaneous speech *(242)*

conversational quality *(242)*

volume *(244)*

pitch *(244)*

inflections *(244)*

monotone *(244)*

rate *(244)*

pause *(245)*

vocalized pause *(245)*

vocal variety *(245)*

pronunciation *(246)*

articulation *(247)*

dialect *(247)*

kinesics *(248)*

gestures *(250)*

eye contact *(250)*

Review Questions

After reading this chapter, you should be able to answer the following questions:

1. What is nonverbal communication? Why is it important to effective public speaking?

2. What are the elements of good speech delivery?

3. What are the four methods of speech delivery?

4. What are the eight aspects of voice usage you should concentrate on in your speeches?

5. What are four aspects of bodily action you should concentrate on in your speeches?

6. What are the five steps you should follow when practicing your speech delivery?

7. What steps should you take when preparing for a question-and-answer session? What should you concentrate on when responding to questions during the session?

Exercises for Critical Thinking

1. An excellent way to improve your vocal variety is to read aloud selections from poetry that require emphasis and feeling. Choose one of your favorite poems that falls into this category, or find one by leafing through a poetry anthology.

   Practice reading the selection aloud. As you read, use your voice to make the poem come alive. Vary your volume, rate, and pitch. Find the appropriate places for pauses. Underline the key words or phrases you think should be stressed. Modulate your tone of voice; use inflections for emphasis and meaning.

   For this to work, you must overcome your fear of sounding affected or "dramatic." Most beginning speakers do better if they exaggerate changes in volume, rate, pitch, and expression. This will make you more aware of the ways you can use your voice to express a wide range of moods and meanings. Besides, what sounds overly "dramatic" to you usually does not sound that way to an audience. By adding luster, warmth, and enthusiasm to your voice, you will go a long way toward capturing and keeping the interest of your listeners.

   If possible, practice reading the selection into a digital recorder. Listen to the playback. If you are not satisfied with what you hear, practice the selection some more and record it again.

2. Watch a 10-minute segment of a television drama with the sound turned off. What do the characters say with their dress, gestures, facial expressions, and the like? Do the same with a television comedy. How do the nonverbal messages in the two shows differ? Be prepared to report your observations in class.

3. Attend a speech on campus. You may choose either a presentation by a guest speaker from outside the college or a class session by a professor who has a reputation as a good lecturer. Prepare a brief report on the speaker's delivery.

   In your report, first analyze the speaker's volume, pitch, rate, pauses, vocal variety, pronunciation, and articulation. Then evaluate the speaker's personal appearance, bodily action, gestures, and eye contact. Explain how the speaker's delivery added to or detracted from what the speaker said. Finally, note at least two techniques of delivery used by the speaker that you might want to try in your next speech.

Using Visual Aids

Diagnosed with high blood pressure when he was in high school, Devin Marshall decided to give his persuasive speech on the excessive amount of salt in the American diet. On the day of his speech, he brought to class a large box, which he set on the table next to him. This immediately aroused the curiosity of his audience. Devin took from the box a container of Morton Salt, a measuring cup, and two plates. Then he began his speech.

First, he explained the monthly salt consumption recommended by the American Medical Association. To illustrate, he measured a cup of salt onto one plate and showed it to the audience. Next, he gave statistics about how much salt the average American consumes in a month. Again, as he spoke, he measured. When he was finished measuring, the second plate had three cups, almost two pounds of salt.

Finally, Devin said, "Now let's multiply that amount by 12 and see how much salt we eat over the course of a year." And he began taking out of the box one container of Morton Salt after another, until he had piled up a pyramid of 14 containers, or nearly 24 pounds of salt!

As the old saying tells us, one picture is worth a thousand words. Can you picture 2 pounds of salt? Or 24 pounds of salt? You could if you had watched Devin measure out the salt and stack up the Morton containers. This dramatic visual evidence brought home Devin's point more forcefully than would have been possible with words alone.

People find a speaker's message more interesting, grasp it more easily, and retain it longer when it is presented visually as well as verbally. In fact, when used properly, visual aids can enhance almost *every* aspect of a speech. An average speaker who uses visual aids will come across as better prepared, more credible, and more professional than a dynamic speaker who does not use visual aids. Visual aids can even help you combat stage fright. They heighten audience interest, shift attention away from the speaker, and give the speaker greater confidence in the presentation as a whole.[1]

For all these reasons, you will find visual aids of great value in your speeches. In this chapter, we will concentrate primarily on visual aids suitable for classroom speeches, but the same principles apply in all circumstances. For speeches outside the classroom—in business or community situations, for instance—you should have no difficulty if you follow the suggestions given here.

Let us look first at the kinds of visual aids you are most likely to use, then at guidelines for preparing visual aids, and finally at guidelines for using visual aids.

Kinds of Visual Aids

OBJECTS AND MODELS

Bringing the object of your speech to class can be an excellent way to clarify your ideas and give them dramatic impact. If your specific purpose is "To inform my audience how to choose the right ski equipment," why not bring the equipment to class to show your listeners? Or suppose you want to inform your classmates about the Peruvian art of doll making. You could bring several dolls to class and explain how they were made.

Some objects, however, cannot be used effectively in classroom speeches. Some are too big. Others are too small to be seen clearly. Still others may not be available to you. If you were speaking about a rare suit of armor in a local museum, you could, theoretically, transport it to class, but it is most unlikely that the museum would let you borrow it.

If the object you want to discuss is too large, too small, or unavailable, you may be able to work with a model. For an example, check Video 14.1 in the online Media Library for this chapter. The speaker is talking about CPR, which he demonstrates on a training dummy he borrowed from the local Red Cross.

connect™

View an excerpt from "CPR" in the online Media Library for this chapter (Video 14.1).

PHOTOGRAPHS AND DRAWINGS

In the absence of an object or a model, you may be able to use photographs or drawings. Neither, however, will work effectively unless they are large enough for the audience to see without straining. Normal-size photos are too small to be seen clearly without being passed around—which only diverts the

audience from what you are saying. The same is true of photographs and drawings in books.

The most effective way to show drawings and photographs is with Power-Point. Notice, for example, how the speaker in Video 14.2 uses PowerPoint to present a photograph of the famous Incan ruins at Machu Picchu in Peru. No other method of showing the photograph would work as well.

For another example, take a look at Figure 14.1 (below), which shows a drawing used in a speech about the kinds of problems faced by people who have dyslexia. It allowed the speaker to translate complex ideas into visual terms the audience could grasp immediately.

GRAPHS

Audiences often have trouble grasping a complex series of numbers. You can ease their difficulty by using graphs to show statistical trends and patterns.

connect

View an excerpt from "Machu Picchu: City of the Gods" in the online Media Library for this chapter (Video 14.2).

graph

A visual aid used to show statistical trends and patterns.

FIGURE 14.1

This si wɦat a qerƨon with dyƨlexia mihgt ƨe wɦem reding this ƨentnce.

FIGURE 14.2

Percentage of Personal Spending

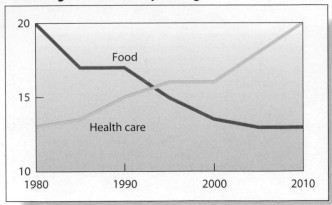

The most common type is the *line graph*. Figure 14.2 (above) shows such a graph, used in a speech about the rising cost of health care. If you look at Video 14.3 in the online Media Library for this chapter, you can see how the speaker explained the graph. She said:

> As you can see from this graph, based on figures from the U.S. government, health care continues to eat away at our budgets. Since 1980, it's risen from 13 percent of personal spending to 20 percent. Compare that to what we spend on food. In 1980, 20 percent of personal spending was on food; today it is 13 percent. That's right, over the past three decades health care has completely changed places with food as the largest category of personal expense.

connect

View the presentation of this graph in "America's Continuing Health Care Crisis" in the online Media Library for this chapter (Video 14.3).

The *pie graph* is best suited for illustrating simple distribution patterns. Figure 14.3 (below) shows how one speaker used a pie graph to help listeners

FIGURE 14.3

Women in the Work Force

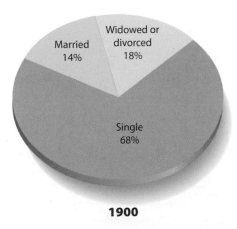

1900

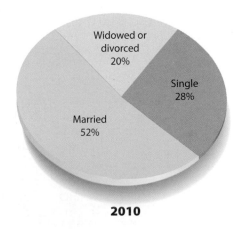

2010

FIGURE 14.4

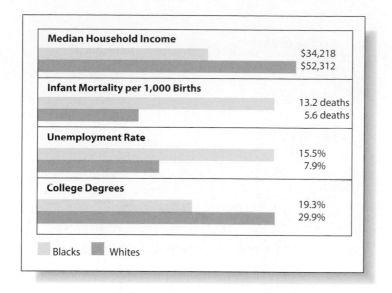

Median Household Income
$34,218
$52,312

Infant Mortality per 1,000 Births
13.2 deaths
5.6 deaths

Unemployment Rate
15.5%
7.9%

College Degrees
19.3%
29.9%

Blacks   Whites

bar graph

A graph that uses vertical or horizontal bars to show comparisons among two or more items.

visualize changes in marital status among working women in the past century. The graph on the left shows the percentages of working women who were single, married, and widowed or divorced in 1900. The graph on the right shows percentages for the same groups in 2010.

Because a pie graph is used to dramatize relationships among the parts of a whole, you should keep the number of different segments in the graph as small as possible. A pie graph should ideally have from two to five segments; under no circumstances should it have more than eight.

The *bar graph* is a particularly good way to show comparisons among two or more items. It also has the advantage of being easy to understand, even by people who have no background in reading graphs.

Figure 14.4 (above) is an example of a bar graph from a speech titled "The Politics of Race in America." It shows visually the relative standing of whites and blacks with respect to median household income, infant mortality, unemployment, and college education. By using a bar graph, the speaker made her points more vividly than if she had just cited the numbers orally.[2]

CHARTS

Charts are particularly useful for summarizing large blocks of information. One student, in a speech titled "The United States: A Nation of Immigrants," used a chart to show the leading regions of the world for U.S. immigrants (Figure 14.5, page 264). These are too many categories to be conveyed in a pie graph. By listing them on a chart, the speaker made it easier for listeners to keep the information straight. Look at Video 14.4 in the online Media Library for this chapter to see how the student presented the chart during her speech.

The biggest mistake made by beginning speakers when using a chart is to include too much information. As we will discuss later, visual aids should be clear, simple, and uncluttered. Lists on a chart should rarely exceed seven or eight items, with generous spacing between items. If you cannot fit everything on a single chart, make a second one.

connect

View an excerpt from "The United States: A Nation of Immigrants" in the online Media Library for this chapter (Video 14.4).

FIGURE 14.5

Region of Birth	Percent of U.S. Immigrants
Asia	36 percent
Mexico	14 percent
Europe	11 percent
Caribbean	11 percent
South America	10 percent
Africa	9 percent
Central America	5 percent
Other	4 percent

chart

A visual aid that summarizes a large block of information, usually in list form.

VIDEO

If you are talking about the impact caused by a low-speed automobile accident, what could be more effective than showing slow-motion video of crash tests? Or suppose you are explaining the different kinds of roller coasters found in amusement parks. Your best visual aid would be a video showing those coasters in action.

Despite its advantages, however, adding video to a speech can cause more harm than good if it is not done carefully and expertly. First, make sure the clip is not too long. While a 30-second video can illustrate your ideas in a memorable way, anything much longer will distract attention from the speech itself. Second, make sure the video is cued to start exactly where you want it. Third, if necessary, edit the video to the precise length you need so it will blend smoothly into your speech. Fourth, beware of low-resolution video that may look fine on a computer but is blurry and distorted when projected on a screen or monitor.

THE SPEAKER

Sometimes you can use your own body as a visual aid—by illustrating how a conductor directs an orchestra, by revealing the secrets behind magic tricks, by showing how to perform sign language, and so forth. In addition to clarifying a speaker's ideas, doing some kind of demonstration helps keep the audience involved. It also can reduce a speaker's nervousness by providing an outlet for extra adrenaline.

Doing a demonstration well requires special practice to coordinate your actions with your words and to control the timing of your speech. You can see an excellent example on Video 14.5 in the online Media Library for this chapter. After talking about the role of proper breathing in yoga, the speaker demonstrates three yoga poses. Notice how clearly she explains each pose, communicates directly with the audience, and maintains eye contact throughout her demonstration.

Special care is required if you are demonstrating a process that takes longer to complete than the time allotted for your speech. If you plan to show

connect

View an excerpt from "Yoga: Uniting Body, Mind, and Spirit" in the online Media Library for this chapter (Video 14.5).

Sometimes a speaker can use her or his body as a visual aid, as in this speech on yoga. Such a speech requires careful practice to coordinate the speaker's actions and words while maintaining eye contact with the audience.

a long process, you might borrow the techniques of television chefs. They work through most of the steps in making a perfect marinated chicken, but they have a second, finished chicken ready to show you at the last minute.

POWERPOINT

PowerPoint allows you to integrate a variety of visual aids—including charts, graphs, photographs, and video—in the same talk. Depending on the technological resources at your school, you may be able to use PowerPoint in your speech class. If so, it will provide training for speeches outside the classroom—especially in business settings, where PowerPoint presentations are made every day.

Later in this chapter, we will look at guidelines for preparing and presenting visual aids effectively. In the process, we'll pay special attention to what you can do to create and deliver high-quality PowerPoint slides. For now, consider the following factors when thinking about employing PowerPoint in your speeches.

Pluses and Minuses of PowerPoint

When used well, PowerPoint is a great boon to communication. Unfortunately, it is not always used well. Too often speakers allow it to dominate their presentations, wowing the audience with their technical proficiency while losing the message in a flurry of sounds and images. As technology expert Herb Lovelace states, it sometimes seems that "the fancier the PowerPoint presentation, the less valuable the ideas being presented."[3]

At the other extreme are speakers who throw their presentations together carelessly, assuming that using PowerPoint will magically produce a superb speech. Plodding through one poorly designed slide after another with little or no eye contact with the audience, these speakers would be better off if they had never heard of PowerPoint.

Another problem is that some speakers use PowerPoint to illustrate every point of their talk, so the speaker is virtually reading the speech to the audience as the words appear on screen. This is no more effective than reading dully from a manuscript, and it seldom produces genuine communication.

Planning to Use PowerPoint

If you are going to employ PowerPoint effectively, you need a clear idea of exactly why, how, and when to use it. Rather than putting everything you say on screen for the audience to read, you need to choose which aspects of your speech to illustrate. This requires careful planning.

The first step is deciding where you can use PowerPoint to greatest advantage. After you have finished developing the speech, think about where you might employ PowerPoint to clarify or strengthen your ideas. Rather than using slides to illustrate every thought, look for spots where it will genuinely enhance your message.

One student, for example, used PowerPoint in a speech about puppy mills. After documenting the number of puppy mills in America and describing their cruelty, he said, "But you can see for yourself what the dogs have to endure." He then showed several photographs demonstrating the terrible conditions of dogs in puppy mills. The photographs provided powerful visual evidence to back up the speaker's claims.

For another example, look at Video 14.7, in which the speaker discusses Georges Seurat's famous painting *Sunday Afternoon on the Island of la Grand Jatte.* The speaker uses a series of PowerPoint slides to show details of the painting that could not have been seen otherwise. He also does an excellent job of explaining each slide as he goes along.

As you plan your speeches, think how you can use PowerPoint to enhance your ideas. At the same time, remember that too many visuals—or poor visuals—can do more harm than good. Be creative and resourceful without allowing PowerPoint to overpower your entire speech.

connect

View an excerpt from "The Horrors of Puppy Mills" in the online Media Library for this chapter (Video 14.6).

connect

View an excerpt from "Georges Seurat and the Art of Pointillism" in the online Media Library for this chapter (Video 14.7).

Using public speaking in your CAREER

As a veterinarian and owner of a small-animal practice, you work closely with your local humane society to help control a growing population of unwanted dogs and cats. You and your staff devote many hours annually in free and reduced-cost medical services to animals adopted from the society. Now you have been asked to speak to the city council in support of legislation proposed by the society for stronger enforcement of animal licensing and leash laws.

In your speech, you plan to include statistics that (1) compare estimates of the city's dog population with the number of licenses issued during the past five years and (2) show the small number of citations given by local law enforcement for unleashed pets during the same period of time. Knowing from your college public speaking class how valuable visual aids can be in presenting statistics, you decide to illustrate one set of statistics with a chart and the other with a graph.

For which set of statistics will a chart be more appropriate? For which set will a graph be more appropriate? Of the three kinds of graphs discussed in this chapter—bar, line, pie—which will work best for your statistics, and why?

Guidelines for Preparing Visual Aids

Whether you are creating visual aids by hand or with PowerPoint, the following guidelines will help you design aids that are clear and visually appealing.

PREPARE VISUAL AIDS WELL IN ADVANCE

Preparing visual aids well in advance has two advantages. First, it means you will have the time and resources to devise creative, attractive aids. Second, it means you can use them while practicing your speech. Visual aids are effective only when they are integrated smoothly with the rest of the speech. If you lose your place, drop your aids, or otherwise stumble around when presenting them, you will distract your audience and shatter your concentration.

KEEP VISUAL AIDS SIMPLE

Visual aids should be simple, clear, and to the point. If you look back at the aids presented earlier in this chapter, you will see that all of them are clear and uncluttered. They contain enough information to communicate the speaker's point, but not so much as to confuse or distract the audience.[4]

When using PowerPoint, limit your slides to a manageable amount of information, and beware of the tendency to go overboard. It is possible to create a graphic that displays two charts, a photograph, and ten lines of text in five different typefaces with 250 colors. But who would be able to read it?

MAKE SURE VISUAL AIDS ARE LARGE ENOUGH

A visual aid is useless if no one can see it. Keep in mind the size of the room in which you will be speaking and make sure your aid is big enough to be seen easily by everyone. As you prepare the aid, check its visibility by moving to a point as far away from it as your most distant listener will be sitting.

If you are using PowerPoint, make sure your text and images are easy for everyone in your audience to see. By making sure your visual aid is large enough, you will avoid having to introduce it with the comment "I know some of you can't see this, but . . ."

What about using all capital letters? That might seem a great way to ensure that your print is large enough to be read easily. But research has shown that a long string of words in ALL CAPS is actually harder to read than is normal text. Reserve ALL CAPS for titles or for individual words that require special emphasis.

USE A LIMITED AMOUNT OF TEXT

When displaying text on visual aids, follow this general rule: Briefer is better. Succinct phrases containing only essential key words will help listeners grasp your basic point and process the information as you're speaking.

Brevity is especially important when using PowerPoint. One of the biggest mistakes people make with PowerPoint is putting too much text on a single

FIGURE 14.6

Mystery of Easter Island

▸ Coast of Chile

▸ Discovered
April 5, 1722

slide. A general rule for slides that contain only text is to include no more than a half-dozen lines of type. If you are combining text with images, you may need to limit yourself to fewer lines to keep the text from getting too small. If you have a number of important points to cover, spread them out over multiple slides.

Figure 14.6 (above) shows a slide from a speech about Easter Island, famous for its mysterious statues of unknown origin. Notice that the slide is not bogged down with information, presenting only an image of the statues, as well as a title and text identifying the location of Easter Island and the date it was discovered by Europeans. Because the slide is simple and clear, the speaker was able to present it succinctly and move to her next point.

USE FONTS EFFECTIVELY

font

A complete set of type of the same design.

Not all fonts are suitable for visual aids. For the most part, you should avoid decorative fonts such as those on the left in Figure 14.7 (page 269). Those on the right of the figure, however, will help make your aids audience-friendly.

Using fonts effectively can make a huge difference in your PowerPoint slides. In general, keep the following guidelines in mind when selecting fonts for your presentation:

- Choose fonts that are clear and easy to read.
- Avoid using ALL CAPS because they are difficult to read.
- Don't use more than two fonts on a single slide—one for the title or major heading and another for subtitles or other text.
- Use the same fonts on all your slides.
- Put titles and major headings in 44- to 36-point type; make subheads and other text 32- to 24-point.

FIGURE 14.7

Ineffective	More Effective
Blackmoor	Arial
Bradley Hand	Baskerville
Cracked	Cambria
ECCENTRIC	Courier
Handwriting	Gill Sans
ROSEWOOD	Optima
SchoolHouse	Times New Roman
Snell Roundhand	Verdana

If you use one of PowerPoint's built-in themes, you can be confident that the fonts, which have been preselected according to the design of the theme, are clear, legible, and consistent.

USE COLOR EFFECTIVELY

When used effectively, color can dramatically increase the impact of a visual aid. The key words, of course, are "when used effectively." Some colors do not work well together. Red and green are a tough combination for anyone to read, and they look the same to people who are color-blind. Many shades of blue and green are too close to each other to be easily differentiated—as are orange and red, blue and purple.

You can use either dark print on a light background or light print on a dark background, but in either case make sure there is enough contrast between the background and the text so listeners can see everything clearly. Avoid such colors as yellow on a white background or purple on a red background.

Also, stick to a limited number of colors and use them consistently. Use one color for background, one color for titles, and one color for other text throughout all your slides. This consistency will unify the slides and give your speech a professional appearance.

USE IMAGES STRATEGICALLY

One of the benefits of PowerPoint is the ease with which it allows you to include photographs, charts, graphs, and other images, including video. Unfortunately, some speakers are prone to adding images simply because it is easy, rather than because it is essential for communicating their message. You should *never* add images of any sort to a PowerPoint slide unless they are truly needed. There is a great deal of research showing that extraneous images distract listeners and reduce comprehension of the speaker's point.[4]

In addition to keeping your slides free of extraneous images, keep these guidelines in mind:

- Make sure images are large enough to be seen clearly.
- Choose high-resolution images that will project without blurring.
- Keep graphs and charts clear and simple.

- In most cases, include a title above charts and graphs so the audience knows what they are viewing.
- Edit video so it is integrated seamlessly into your slides.[5]

Guidelines for Presenting Visual Aids

No matter how well designed your visual aids may be, they will be of little value unless you display them properly, discuss them clearly, and integrate them effectively with the rest of your presentation. Here are seven guidelines that will help you get the maximum impact out of your visual aids.

DISPLAY VISUAL AIDS WHERE LISTENERS CAN SEE THEM

Check the speech room ahead of time to decide exactly where you will display your visual aids. If you are displaying an object or a model, be sure to place it where it can be seen easily by everyone in the room. If necessary, hold up the object or model while you are discussing it.

Once you have set the aid in the best location, don't undo all your preparation by standing where you block the audience's view of the aid. Stand to one side of the aid, and point with the arm nearest it. Using a pen, a ruler,

✔ checklist

Preparing Visual Aids

YES	NO	
☐	☐	1. Have I prepared my visual aids well in advance?
☐	☐	2. Are my visual aids clear and easy to comprehend?
☐	☐	3. Does each visual aid contain only the information needed to make my point?
☐	☐	4. Are my visual aids large enough to be seen clearly by the entire audience?
☐	☐	5. Do the colors on my visual aids work well together?
☐	☐	6. Is there a clear contrast between the lettering and background on my charts, graphs, and drawings?
☐	☐	7. Do I use line graphs, pie graphs, and bar graphs correctly to show statistical trends and patterns?
☐	☐	8. Do I limit charts to no more than eight items?
☐	☐	9. Do I use fonts that are easy to read?
☐	☐	10. Do I use a limited number of fonts?

PowerPoint is an excellent way to show visual aids if it is used properly. Here linguist Steven Pinker uses PowerPoint during a lecture at the British Museum in London, England.

or some other pointer will allow you to stand farther away from the visual aid, thereby reducing the likelihood that you will obstruct the view.

If you are using a projection screen, check ahead of time to make sure it is not located where you will cast a shadow on it while you are speaking. If necessary, move the lectern to the side of the screen.

AVOID PASSING VISUAL AIDS AMONG THE AUDIENCE

Once visual aids get into the hands of your listeners, you are in trouble. At least three people will be paying more attention to the aid than to you—the person who has just had it, the person who has it now, and the person waiting to get it next. By the time the visual aid moves on, all three may have lost track of what you are saying.

Nor do you solve this problem by preparing a handout for every member of the audience. They are likely to spend a good part of the speech looking over the handout at their own pace, rather than listening to you. Although handouts can be valuable, they usually just create competition for beginning speakers.

Every once in a while, of course, you will want listeners to have copies of some material to take home. When such a situation arises, keep the copies until after you've finished talking and distribute them at the end. Keeping control of your visual aids is essential to keeping control of your speech.

DISPLAY VISUAL AIDS ONLY WHILE DISCUSSING THEM

Just as circulating visual aids distracts attention, so does displaying them throughout a speech. If you are using an object or a model, keep it out of sight until you are ready to discuss it. When you finish your discussion, place the object or model back out of sight.

The same principle applies to PowerPoint slides. They should be visible only while you are discussing them. You can accomplish this by adding blank slides as needed, so the audience's attention will not be diverted by the previous slide. It is also a good idea to add a blank slide at the end of your presentation, so your last content slide will not continue to be exposed after you have finished discussing it.

FIGURE 14.8

EXPLAIN VISUAL AIDS CLEARLY AND CONCISELY

Visual aids don't explain themselves. Like statistics, they need to be translated and related to the audience. For example, Figure 14.8 (above) is an excellent visual aid, but do you know what it represents? Probably not, unless you've kept up on the latest statistics of U.S. drunk-driving deaths. But even then, the full meaning of the map may not be clear until it is explained to you.

A visual aid can be of enormous benefit—but only if the viewer knows what to look for and why. Unfortunately, speakers often rush over their visual aids without explaining them clearly and concisely. Be sure to adapt your visual aids to the audience. Don't just say "As you can see . . ." and then pass quickly over the aid. Tell listeners what the aid means. Describe its major features. Spell out the meaning of charts and graphs. Interpret statistics and percentages. Remember, a visual aid is only as useful as the explanation that goes with it.

As you can see from Video 14.8 in the online Media Library for this chapter, the speaker who used the map of drunk-driving deaths discussed above did an excellent job explaining how each color on the map corresponds to a different per-capita death rate. Having used the map during her practice sessions, she was able to integrate it into the speech smoothly and skillfully—and to maintain eye contact with the audience throughout her discussion of it. You should strive to do the same when you present visual aids in your speeches.

TALK TO YOUR AUDIENCE, NOT TO YOUR VISUAL AID

When explaining a visual aid, it is easy to break eye contact with your audience and speak to the aid. Of course, your listeners are looking primarily at the aid, and you will need to glance at it periodically as you talk. But if you keep your eyes fixed on the visual aid, you may lose your audience. By keeping eye contact with your listeners, you will also pick up feedback about how the visual aid and your explanation of it are coming across.

connect

View an excerpt from "The Tragedy of Drunk Driving" in the online Media Library for this chapter (Video 14.8).

PRACTICE WITH YOUR VISUAL AIDS

This chapter has mentioned several times the need to practice with visual aids, but the point bears repeating. No matter what kind of visual aid you choose, be sure to employ it when you practice. Go through the speech multiple times, rehearsing how you will show your aids, the gestures you will make, and the timing of each move. In using visual aids, as in other aspects of speechmaking, there is no substitute for preparation.

If you are using PowerPoint, don't just click the mouse casually or rush quickly over your words when you practice. Make sure you know exactly when you want each slide to appear and disappear, and what you will say while each is on screen. Mark your speaking notes with cues that will remind you when to display each slide and when to remove it.

Rehearse with the mouse, keyboard, or iPad until you can use them without looking down for more than an instant when advancing your slides. Also concentrate on presenting the speech without looking back at the screen to see what is being projected. There is nothing wrong with glancing at the screen now and again as you explain your slides, but remember to address your remarks to the audience, not to the screen.

Given all the things you have to work on when practicing a speech with PowerPoint, you need to allow extra time for rehearsal. So get an early start and give yourself plenty of time to ensure that your delivery is as impressive as your slides.[6]

 **checklist**

Presenting Visual Aids

YES	NO	
☐	☐	1. Have I checked the speech room to decide where I can display my visual aids most effectively?
☐	☐	2. Have I practiced presenting my visual aids so they will be clearly visible to everyone in the audience?
☐	☐	3. Have I practiced presenting my visual aids so they are perfectly timed with my words and actions?
☐	☐	4. Have I practiced keeping eye contact with my audience while presenting my visual aids?
☐	☐	5. Have I practiced explaining my visual aids clearly and concisely in terms my audience will understand?
☐	☐	6. If I am using handouts, have I planned to distribute them after the speech rather than during it?
☐	☐	7. Have I double-checked all equipment to make sure it works properly?
☐	☐	8. If I am using PowerPoint, do I have a backup of my slides that I can take to the speech with me?

CHECK THE ROOM AND EQUIPMENT

For classroom speeches, you will already be familiar with the room and equipment. If any of the technology fails, a technician can make the necessary adjustments. For speeches outside the classroom, however, the situation is very different. There is wide variation among computers and projectors, as well as among rooms equipped with multimedia connections. Even if you have used PowerPoint on previous occasions, you need to check the setup in the room where you will be speaking.

If possible, look at the room and equipment before the day of your speech. Hook up your computer to make sure everything works properly. If you are using a computer that is installed in the room, bring your slides on a flash drive so you can see how they work with that computer. If your presentation includes audio or video, double-check them using the room's audiovisual system. Arrange ahead of time to have a technician present so he or she can take care of any problems.

Sometimes, of course, it is not possible to visit the room before the day of your speech. In that case, plan to arrive an hour early to familiarize yourself with the equipment and to make sure it's working properly. Never assume that everything will be "just fine." Instead, assume that things will not be fine and that they need to be checked ahead of time. You will save yourself the embarrassment of having your speech delayed, cut short, or even canceled because of faulty equipment or unforeseen technical complications.

Finally, if you are using PowerPoint, *always* bring a backup of your slides on a flash drive even if you plan on using your own computer during the speech.

This may all seem like a lot of fuss and bother, but anyone who has given speeches with PowerPoint—or any other kind of visual aid—will tell you that it is absolutely essential.

Summary

There are many kinds of visual aids. Most obvious is the object about which you are speaking, or a model of it. Diagrams, sketches, and other kinds of drawings are valuable because you can design them to illustrate your points exactly. Photographs should be large enough to be seen clearly by all your listeners. Graphs are an excellent way to illustrate any subject dealing with numbers, while charts are used to summarize large blocks of information. Video can be useful as a visual aid, but it needs to be carefully edited and integrated into the speech. You can act as your own visual aid by performing actions that demonstrate processes or ideas.

If you use PowerPoint, plan carefully why, how, and when you will utilize it. Rather than putting everything you say on screen for your audience to read, use PowerPoint only when it will genuinely enhance your message.

No matter what kind of visual aid you use, you need to prepare it carefully. You will be most successful if you prepare your aids well in advance, keep them simple, make sure they are large enough to be seen clearly, and use a limited amount of text. If you are creating visual aids on a computer, use fonts, color, and images strategically and effectively.

In addition to being designed with care, visual aids need to be presented skillfully. Avoid passing visual aids among the audience. Display each aid only while you are talking about it, and be sure to place it where everyone can see it without straining. When presenting a visual aid, maintain eye contact with your listeners and explain the aid clearly and concisely. If you are using PowerPoint, make sure you check the room and equipment prior to the time of delivery. Above all, practice with your visual aids so they fit into your speech smoothly and expertly.

Key Terms

graph *(261)*

line graph *(262)*

pie graph *(262)*

bar graph *(263)*

chart *(264)*

font *(268)*

Review Questions

After reading this chapter, you should be able to answer the following questions:

1. What are the major advantages of using visual aids in your speeches?
2. What kinds of visual aids might you use in a speech?
3. What factors should you consider when planning to use PowerPoint in a speech?
4. What guidelines are given in the chapter for preparing visual aids?
5. What guidelines are given in the chapter for presenting visual aids?

connect

For further review, go to the LearnSmart study module for this chapter.

Exercises for Critical Thinking

1. Watch a how-to television program (a cooking show, for example) or the weather portion of a local newscast. Notice how the speaker uses visual aids to help communicate the message. What kinds of visual aids are used? How do they enhance the clarity, interest, and retainability of the speaker's message? What would the speaker have to do to communicate the message effectively without visual aids?

2. Consider how you might use visual aids to explain each of the following:

   a. How to perform the Heimlich maneuver to help a choking victim.

   b. The proportion of the electorate that votes in major national elections in the United States, France, Germany, England, and Japan, respectively.

   c. Where to obtain information about student loans.

   d. The wing patterns of various species of butterflies.

   e. The increase in the amount of money spent by Americans on health care since 1985.

   f. How to change a bicycle tire.

   g. The basic equipment and techniques of rock climbing.

3. Plan to use visual aids in at least one of your classroom speeches. Be creative in devising your aids, and be sure to follow the guidelines discussed in the chapter for using them. After the speech, analyze how effectively you employed your visual aids, what you learned about the use of visual aids from your experience, and what changes you would make in using visual aids if you were to deliver the speech again.

15

Speaking to Inform

Types of Informative Speeches: Analysis and Organization

Guidelines for Informative Speaking

Sample Speech with Commentary

Hayley Walden is the chief designer at a fast-growing company that creates and sells stylish, innovative knitwear. On a bright Tuesday in October, Hayley begins her workday by talking to a colleague from technical support about the computer problems she has been having. She demonstrates what goes wrong when she boots up and details the problems with the internal backup system.

Later that morning, Hayley has a long meeting with other members of her design team. They discuss their new line of products for the spring, going over everything from the manufacturing process to the marketing campaign. As the other staff members talk, Hayley takes careful notes and asks questions to make sure she understands every aspect of the spring product launch.

In the afternoon, Hayley rushes to a meeting with company executives, including the president, so she can report on what the design team discussed earlier in the day. She reviews the manufacturing process for the new knits, discusses the distribution chain for the company's goods, and explains different options for marketing a new line of spring jackets. Afterward, the president compliments Hayley for giving such a clear presentation. "Anyone who can communicate that well," the president says, "is going to go a long way in this company."

Hayley doesn't consider herself a "public speaker," but much of her job involves absorbing and communicating information clearly and effectively. Although Hayley is just a single person, her experience is not unusual. In one survey, graduates from five U.S. colleges were asked to rank the speech skills most important to their jobs. They rated informative speaking number one. In another survey, 62 percent of the respondents said they used informative speaking "almost constantly."[1]

Public speaking to inform occurs in a wide range of everyday situations. The business manager explains next year's budget. The architect reviews plans for a new building. The union leader informs members about a new contract. The church worker outlines plans for a fund drive. There are endless situations in which people need to inform others. Competence in this form of communication will prove valuable to you throughout your life.

One of your first classroom assignments probably will be to deliver an informative speech in which you will act as a lecturer or teacher. You may describe an object, show how something works, report on an event, explain a concept. Your aim will be to convey knowledge and understanding—not to advocate a cause. Your speech will be judged in light of three general criteria:

Is the information communicated accurately?

Is the information communicated clearly?

Is the information made meaningful and interesting to the audience?

In this chapter, we will look at four types of informative speeches and the basic principles of informative speaking. Along the way, we will apply various general principles discussed in previous chapters.

Types of Informative Speeches: Analysis and Organization

There are many ways to classify informative speeches. Here we focus on the kinds you are most likely to give in your speech class: (1) speeches about objects, (2) speeches about processes, (3) speeches about events, and (4) speeches about concepts.

SPEECHES ABOUT OBJECTS

As the word is used here, "objects" include anything that is visible, tangible, and stable in form. Objects may have moving parts or be alive; they may include places, structures, animals, even people. Here are examples of subjects for speeches about objects:

e-book readers	Susan B. Anthony
service dogs	titanium
human eye	Golden Gate Bridge

You will not have time to tell your classmates everything about any of these subjects. Instead, you will choose a specific purpose that focuses on

informative speech

A speech designed to convey knowledge and understanding.

object

Anything that is visible, tangible, and stable in form.

one aspect of your subject. Working from the topics presented above, the following are examples of good specific purpose statements for informative speeches about objects:

> To inform my audience about three major kinds of service dogs.

> To inform my audience about the role of Susan B. Anthony in the U.S. women's rights movement.

> To inform my audience what to look for when buying an e-book reader.

Notice how precise these statements are. As we saw in Chapter 5, you should select a specific purpose that is not too broad to achieve in the allotted time. "To inform my audience about Pablo Picasso" is far too general for a classroom speech. "To inform my audience about the major contributions of Pablo Picasso to modern art" is more precise and is a purpose you could reasonably hope to achieve in a brief talk.

If your specific purpose is to explain the history or evolution of your subject, you will put your speech in *chronological* order. For example:

Specific Purpose:	To inform my audience about the major achievements of Frederick Douglass.
Central Idea:	Although born in slavery, Frederick Douglass became one of the greatest figures in American history.
Main Points:	I. Douglass spent the first 20 years of his life as a slave in Maryland.
	II. After escaping to the North, Douglass became a leader in the abolitionist movement to end slavery.
	III. During the Civil War, Douglass helped establish black regiments in the Union Army.
	IV. After the war, Douglass was a tireless champion of equal rights for his race.

If your specific purpose is to describe the main features of your subject, you may organize your speech in *spatial* order:

Specific Purpose:	To inform my audience about the design of the St. Louis Arch.
Central Idea:	The St. Louis Arch is divided into three sections, each with its own attractions.
Main Points:	I. The base of the St. Louis Arch houses a visitor's center with a museum, two movie theaters, and retail outlets.
	II. The middle of the St. Louis Arch contains a high-speed tram that carries visitors from the base to the top.
	III. The top of the St. Louis Arch has an observation deck 630 feet above the ground.

As often as not, you will find that speeches about objects fall into *topical* order. For example:

Specific Purpose:	To inform my audience about the four major elements of a Japanese garden.

Central Idea:	The four major elements of a Japanese garden are stones, sand, water, and plants.
Main Points:	I. The first element of a Japanese garden is stones, which symbolize mountains and islands.
	II. The second element of a Japanese garden is sand, which symbolizes the sea or other vast areas.
	III. The third element of a Japanese garden is water, which symbolizes purity and life.
	IV. The fourth element of a Japanese garden is plants, which symbolize life and the changing seasons.

No matter which of these organizational methods you use—chronological, spatial, or topical—be sure to follow the guidelines discussed in Chapter 9: (1) limit your speech to between two and five main points; (2) keep main points separate; (3) try to use the same pattern of wording for all main points; (4) balance the amount of time devoted to each main point.

SPEECHES ABOUT PROCESSES

process

A systematic series of actions that leads to a specific result or product.

A process is a systematic series of actions that leads to a specific result or product. Speeches about processes explain how something is made, how something is done, or how something works. Here are examples of good specific purpose statements for speeches about processes:

To inform my audience how U.S. currency is made.

To inform my audience how to write an effective job resumé.

To inform my audience how hurricanes develop.

As these examples suggest, there are two kinds of informative speeches about processes. One kind explains a process so that listeners will *understand* it better. Your goal is to have your audience know the steps of the process and how they relate to one another. If your specific purpose is "To inform my audience how a nuclear power plant works," you will explain the basic procedures of a nuclear power plant. You will not instruct your listeners on how they can *operate* a nuclear power plant.

A second kind of speech explains a process so listeners will be better able to *perform* the process themselves. Your goal in this kind of speech is to have the audience learn a skill. Suppose your specific purpose is "To inform my audience how to take pictures like a professional photographer." You will present photographic techniques and show your listeners how they can utilize them. You want the audience to be able to *use* the techniques as a result of your speech.

Both kinds of speeches about processes may require visual aids. At the very least, you should prepare a chart outlining the steps or techniques of your process. In some cases you will need to demonstrate the steps or techniques by performing them in front of your audience. One student did sleight-of-hand magic tricks to show the techniques behind them. Another executed elementary tai chi maneuvers. In each case, the demonstration not only clarified the speaker's process, but captivated the audience as well. (If you are using visual aids of any kind, be sure to review Chapter 14.)

Informative speeches can be organized in many ways. A speech on the history of Renaissance art would likely be in chronological order, while a speech on techniques of painting would fall into topical order.

When informing about a process, you will usually arrange your speech in *chronological* order, explaining the process step by step from beginning to end. For example:

Specific Purpose: To inform my audience about the major rituals of a traditional Bengali wedding in India.

Central Idea: A traditional Bengali wedding consists of a series of rituals that take place before, during, and after the wedding ceremony.

Main Points:
   I. Pre-wedding rituals include giving gifts to the bride and groom and dressing the bride in traditional fashion.
   II. Rituals during the wedding ceremony include an exchange of garlands between the bride and groom, the chanting of mantras, and the giving away of the bride by her uncle.
   III. Post-wedding rituals include a celebration at the home of the bride's family, a reception at the home of the groom's family, and the formal exit of the bride and groom.

Sometimes, rather than moving through a process step by step, you will focus on the major principles or techniques involved in performing the process. Then you will organize your speech in *topical* order. Each main point will deal with a separate principle or technique. For example:

Specific Purpose: To inform my audience of the common methods used by stage magicians to perform their tricks.

Central Idea: Stage magicians use two common methods to perform their tricks—mechanical devices and sleight of hand.

Main Points: I. Many magic tricks rely on mechanical devices that may require little skill by the magician.

II. Other magic tricks depend on the magician's skill in fooling people by sleight-of-hand manipulation.

Concise organization is especially important in speeches about processes. You must make sure each step is clear and easy to follow. If your process has more than four or five steps, group the steps into units to limit the number of main points. For example, in a speech explaining how to set up a home aquarium, a student presented the following main points:

    I. First you must choose the size of your tank.
    II. Then you must determine the shape of your tank.
    III. You must also decide how much you can afford to pay for a tank.
    IV. Once you have the tank, you need a filter system.
    V. A heater is also absolutely necessary.
    VI. You must also get an air pump.
    VII. Once this is done, you need to choose gravel for the tank.
    VIII. You will also need plants.
    IX. Other decorations will round out the effects of your aquarium.
    X. Now you are ready to add the fish.
    XI. Freshwater fish are the most common.
    XII. Saltwater fish are more expensive and require special care.

Not surprisingly, this was too much for the audience to follow. The speaker should have organized the points something like this:

I. The first step in establishing a home aquarium is choosing a tank.
    A. The size of the tank is important.
    B. The shape of the tank is important.
    C. The cost of the tank is important.

II. The second step in establishing a home aquarium is equipping the tank.
    A. You will need a filter system.
    B. You will need a heater.
    C. You will need an air pump.
    D. You will need gravel.
    E. You will need plants.
    F. You may also want other decorations.

III. The third step in establishing a home aquarium is adding the fish.
    A. Freshwater fish are the most common for home aquariums.
    B. Saltwater fish are more expensive and require special care.

The subpoints cover the same territory as the original twelve points, but three main points are much easier to understand and remember.

SPEECHES ABOUT EVENTS

event

Anything that happens or is regarded as happening.

The *Random House Dictionary* defines an event as "anything that happens or is regarded as happening." By this definition, the following are examples of suitable subjects for informative speeches about events:

Festival of the Sun	sleep deprivation
cyberterrorism	Battle of Little Big Horn
therapeutic massage	Olympic Games

As usual, you will need to narrow your focus and pick a specific purpose you can accomplish in a short speech. Here are examples of good specific purpose statements for informative speeches about events:

To inform my audience about the events at Peru's Festival of the Sun ceremony.

To inform my audience about the major types of therapeutic massage.

To inform my audience about what occurred at the Battle of Little Big Horn.

There are many ways to discuss events. If your specific purpose is to recount the history of an event, you will organize your speech in *chronological* order, relating the incidents one after another in the order they occurred. For example:

Specific Purpose: To inform my audience about the history of the Paralympics.

Central Idea: Olympic-style games for athletes with physical disabilities have made great strides since the first competition more than 60 years ago.

Main Points:
    I. What would eventually become the Paralympics began in 1948 with a sports competition in Great Britain involving World War II veterans with spinal cord injuries.
    II. In 1952, the event expanded when athletes from the Netherlands took part.
    III. In 1960, the first Paralympic Games for international athletes took place in Rome.
    IV. In 2001, an agreement was signed officially holding the Paralympic Games alongside the summer and winter Olympic Games.

You can approach an event from almost any angle or combination of angles—features, origins, implications, benefits, future developments, and so forth. In such cases, you will put your speech together in *topical* order. And you should make sure your main points subdivide the subject logically and consistently. For instance:

Specific Purpose: To inform my audience about three aspects of the Mardi Gras celebration in New Orleans.

Central Idea: The Mardi Gras celebration in New Orleans is renowned for its parades, costumes, and food.

Main Points:
    I. The parades are lavish events that take place over the course of several weeks.

    II. The costumes include disguises, medallions, and the official Mardi Gras colors of purple, green, and gold.

    III. The food features Cajun and Creole dishes common to southern Louisiana.

SPEECHES ABOUT CONCEPTS

Concepts include beliefs, theories, ideas, principles, and the like. They are more abstract than objects, processes, or events. The following are examples of subjects for speeches about concepts:

Confucianism	nutritional theories
original-intent doctrine	philosophies of education
string theory	numerology

Taking a few of these general subjects, here are some specific purpose statements for speeches about concepts:

To inform my audience about the basic principles of Confucianism.

To inform my audience about the doctrine of original intent in constitutional interpretation.

To inform my audience about different philosophies of education in Asia and the United States.

Speeches about concepts are usually organized in *topical* order and focus on the main features or aspects of your concept. For example:

Specific Purpose: To inform my audience about the basic principles of non-violent resistance.

Central Idea: The basic principles of nonviolent resistance stress using moral means to achieve social change, refusing to inflict violence on one's enemies, and using suffering as a social force.

Main Points:
    I. The first major principle of nonviolent resistance is that social change must be achieved by moral means.

    II. The second major principle of nonviolent resistance is that one should not inflict violence on one's enemies.

    III. The third major principle of nonviolent resistance is that suffering can be a powerful social force.

Another approach is to define the concept you are dealing with, identify its major elements, and illustrate it with specific examples. An excellent instance of this came in a student speech about film theory:

Specific Purpose: To inform my audience about different approaches to film theory.

Central Idea: Approaches to film theory include auteur theory, structuralist theory, and genre theory.

The need to convey information effectively exists in all cultures. Here tea-servers dressed in traditional clothes learn the art of the tea ceremony in Sichuan Province, China.

Main Points: I. Auteur theory focuses on the director's creative vision in the construction of a film.

II. Structuralist theory focuses on how film conveys meaning through the use of codes and conventions.

III. Genre theory focuses on patterns across major types of films such as drama, comedy, science fiction, and the like.

Speeches about concepts are often more complex than other kinds of informative speeches. When dealing with concepts, pay special attention to avoiding technical language, to defining terms clearly, and to using examples and comparisons to illustrate the concepts.

Look, for example, at Video 15.1 in the online Media Library for this chapter, which presents an excerpt from a student speech about the Chinese philosophy of Confucianism. Notice how the student defines Confucianism and then explains its unifying principle of *jen*. If you give an informative speech about a concept, give special thought to how you can make that concept clear and comprehensible to your listeners.

connect

View an excerpt from "Confucianism" in the online Media Library for this chapter (Video 15.1).

The lines dividing speeches about objects, processes, events, and concepts are not absolute. Some subjects could fit into more than one category, depending on how you develop the speech. For example, a speech about the destruction of ancient Pompeii by the eruption of Mount Vesuvius would probably deal with its subject as an event, but a speech on what causes volcanoes to erupt would most likely treat its subject as a process. The important step is to decide whether you will handle your subject as an object, a process, an event, or a concept. Once you do that, you can develop the speech accordingly.

Regardless of how you approach your topic, be sure to give listeners plenty of help in sorting out facts and ideas. One way is by using enough transitions, internal previews, internal summaries, and signposts (see Chapter 9). Another way is to follow the old maxim "Tell 'em what you're going to say; say it; then tell 'em what you've said." In other words, preview the main points of your speech in the introduction and summarize them in the conclusion. This will make your speech easier to understand and easier to remember.

Guidelines for Informative Speaking

All the previous chapters of this book relate to the principles of informative speaking. Selecting a topic and specific purpose, analyzing the audience, gathering materials, choosing supporting details, organizing the speech, using words to communicate meaning, delivering the speech—all must be done effectively if an informative speech is to be a success. Here we emphasize six additional points that will help make yours a success.

DON'T OVERESTIMATE WHAT THE AUDIENCE KNOWS

In a speech about meteorology, a student said, "If modern methods of weather forecasting had existed in 1900, the Galveston hurricane disaster would never have taken place." Then he was off to other matters, leaving his listeners to puzzle over what the Galveston hurricane was, when it happened, and what kind of destruction it wreaked.

The speaker assumed his audience already knew these things. But they were not experts on meteorology or on American history. Even those who had heard of the hurricane had only a fuzzy notion of it. Only the speaker knew that the hurricane, which killed more than 6,000 people when it unexpectedly struck on September 8, 1900, is still the deadliest natural disaster in American history.

As many speakers have discovered, it is easy to overestimate the audience's stock of information. In most informative speeches, your listeners will be only vaguely knowledgeable (at best) about the details of your topic. You cannot *assume* they will know what you mean. Rather, you must be *sure* to explain everything so thoroughly that they cannot help but understand. As you work on your speech, always consider whether it will be clear to someone who is hearing about the topic for the first time.

Suppose you are talking about bulletproof vests. Surely all of your classmates have heard of bulletproof vests, but most probably don't know how the vests work. How will you tell them? Here's one way:

> Ballistic vests, more commonly known as bulletproof vests, are pieces of personal body armor that protect human beings from damage incurred by explosively propelled projectiles. How? Intricately woven synthetic fibers such as Kevlar form a powerful mesh that laterally disperses a projectile's kinetic energy while at the same time deforming the projectile and stopping its momentum.

To someone who knows a lot about physics or textiles, this is probably perfectly clear. But someone who does not may get lost along the way. The tone of the statement is that of a speaker reviewing information already familiar to the audience—not of a speaker introducing new information.

Here, in contrast, is another explanation of bulletproof vests:

So how do bulletproof vests actually stop bullets? Let me explain with an example.

Imagine a police officer investigating a strange noise down a dark alley. He startles a drug dealer trying to make a sale, and before he knows it, bang! Luckily, the officer was wearing his bulletproof vest.

Instead of entering the officer's body, the bullet enters layer upon layer of strong, tightly woven fibers. Because of their strength and intricate pattern, the fibers begin to twist and deform the bullet. The fibers are so strong that they flatten the bullet out and absorb its energy. While the bullet may go through a couple layers of fabric, it stops well before going through the entire vest.

Thanks to these strong, tightly woven fibers, our police officer lives to put the drug dealer in cuffs.

This explanation is clear and simple. Its tone is that of a teacher unraveling a new subject.

Is it too simple? Not at all. The test of a good speaker is to communicate even the most complex ideas clearly and simply. Anyone can go to a book and find a learned-sounding definition of a bulletproof vest. But to say in plain English how a bulletproof vest works—that takes hard work and creative thinking.

Also, remember that readers can study a printed passage again and again until they extract its meaning, but listeners don't have that luxury. They must understand what you say in the time it takes you to say it. The more you assume they know about the topic, the greater your chances of being misunderstood.

RELATE THE SUBJECT DIRECTLY TO THE AUDIENCE

The British dramatist Oscar Wilde arrived at his club after the disastrous opening-night performance of his new play.

"Oscar, how did your play go?" asked a friend.

"Oh," Wilde quipped, "the play was a great success, but the audience was a failure."

Speakers have been known to give much the same answer in saving face after a dismal informative speech. "Oh," they say, "the speech was fine, but

In business as in other areas of life, effective informative speakers personalize their ideas and relate them directly to the audience.

the audience just wasn't interested." And they are at least partly right—the audience *wasn't* interested. But there is no such thing as a fine speech that puts people to sleep. It is the speaker's job to get listeners interested—and to keep them interested.

Informative speakers have one big hurdle to overcome. They must recognize that what is fascinating to them may not be fascinating to everybody. Once you have chosen a topic that could possibly be interesting to your listeners, you should take special steps to relate it to them. You should tie it in with their interests and concerns.

Start in the introduction. Instead of saying,

> I want to talk with you about chili peppers,

you could say:

connect

View this excerpt from "The Hidden World of Chili Peppers" in the online Media Library for this chapter (Video 15.2).

> Imagine your mouth burning like wildfire, your eyes squirting out uncontrollable tears, and your face red and sweating profusely. Are you sick? No. You just took a bite of a screaming hot chili pepper. Congratulations. You're partaking in a world-wide tradition that has been spicing up lives and diets for thousands of years.

But don't stop with the introduction. Whenever you can, put your listeners into the body of the speech. After all, nothing interests people more than themselves. Find ways to talk about your topic in terms of your listeners. Bring your material home to them. Get it as close to them as possible.

Here's an example. Let's say you are explaining how bed bugs spread from person to person and location to location. You have plenty of facts and could recite them like this:

> High-traffic areas provide ideal environmental conditions for bed bugs to spread. High-density locations such as dormitories, apartment buildings, and transportation terminals are among the most likely places to find bed bugs. Because bed bugs are attracted to items that allow them to hide, they often attach themselves to clothing, backpacks, purses, and the like. Bed bugs also thrive in cluttered locations that have a lot of items lying about.

This is valuable information, but it is not related to the audience. Let's try again:

connect

View this excerpt from "Don't Let the Bed Bugs Bite" in the online Media Library for this chapter (Video 15.3).

> Bed bugs spread most rapidly in places that have lots of people coming and going. If *you* live in the dorms or an apartment, if *you* travel through airports, train stations, and bus stations, or if *you* stay in hotels and motels, *you're* passing through prime breeding grounds for bed bugs.
>
> Bed bugs are like tiny hitchhikers. They'll insert themselves in *your* clothes, *your* luggage, *your* purse, *your* backpack, *your* coat—anything that has fabric and folds.
>
> Bed bugs are also drawn to locations where they can hide easily. So the more clutter *you* have in *your* environment, the more bed bugs will like to be *your* tiny companions.

Look at the frequent use of "you" and "your." The facts are the same, but now they are pointed directly at the audience. Research shows that using personal terms such as "you" and "your" in an informative speech significantly increases audience understanding of the speaker's ideas.[2]

DON'T BE TOO TECHNICAL

What does it mean to say that an informative speech is too technical? It may mean the subject matter is too specialized for the audience. Any subject can be popularized—but only up to a point. The important thing for a speaker to know is what can be explained to an ordinary audience and what cannot.

Say your subject is power amplifiers. It's no trick to demonstrate how to operate an amplifier (how to turn it on and off, adjust the volume, set the tone and balance controls). It's also relatively easy to explain what an amplifier does (it boosts the sound received from a DVD, iPod, or live performance). But to give a full scientific account of how an amplifier works cannot be done in any reasonable time unless the audience knows the principles of audio technology. The material is just too technical to be understood by a general audience.

Even when the subject matter is not technical, the language used to explain it may be. Every activity has its jargon, whether it be golf (bogey, wedge, match play); chemistry (colloid, glycogen, heavy water); or financial analysis (covered call, reverse bid, toehold acquisition). If you are talking to a group of specialists, you can use technical words and be understood. But you must do all you can to avoid technical words when informing a general audience such as your speech class.

Here, for instance, are two statements explaining stem cells and the roles they can play in the human body. The first is heavily laden with specialized language that would have little impact on ordinary listeners:

Most multicellular organisms contain stem cells that reinvigorate themselves through the process of mitotic cellular division. Stem cells in early embryos represent basic units of life in higher organisms, while adult stem cells in somatic tissues

Using public speaking in your CAREER

As a financial planner at a local investment firm, you have been asked to speak to a group of recent college graduates about long-term financial planning. After considering what recent college graduates need to know about saving for their future, you decide to organize your presentation around four general stages of investing:

1. The early years of investing, which include putting aside small amounts of money that will grow over time.
2. The years of acquisition, which include balancing investments with large expenses such as raising children and paying a mortgage.
3. The years of accumulation, which include putting away

as much money as possible in anticipation of retirement.
4. The retirement years, which include living off of savings and adjusting investments as needed.

As you look over these stages of investing, you think back to the public speaking course you took in college. You remember that informative speakers should relate their speech directly to the audience, should not be too technical, should not overestimate what the audience knows about the subject, and should be creative. How might each of these guidelines influence your presentation to recent college graduates? Be specific.

represent cellular stores capable of regenerating tissue and maintaining organ functions. Both are characterized by properties that permit accurate in vivo cell copying.

The second statement is perfectly understandable and shows how technical information can be made clear to the average person:

> According to the National Institutes of Health, stem cells are general cells that have the potential to develop into any of the more than 200 different kinds of cells in the human body. Basically, they turn into a cell that has a specific job to do.
>
> For example, stem cells might become muscle cells that help rebuild damaged tissue. They might become red blood cells that help deliver oxygen to different tissues. Or they might become brain cells that help the nervous system function. No matter what type of cells need assistance, stem cells can come to the rescue and replenish the cells our bodies need.
>
> The Genetics Learning Center at the University of Utah explains it like this: Stem cells are like actors waiting for a casting call. Just as an actor waits to find out his or her next role, stem cells wait for signals from the body that tell them what to become. Once they get those signals, they begin to change into specific cells with specific jobs to do.

Much clearer, isn't it? The only specialized words in the whole passage are "stem cells." The rest of the language is straightforward, the ideas easy to grasp. This is what you should strive for in your informative speeches.

AVOID ABSTRACTIONS

"My task," said the novelist Joseph Conrad, "is, before all, to make you see." And make the reader see is just what Conrad did. Witness this passage, in which Conrad describes the aftermath of an explosion aboard a ship:

> The first person I saw was Mahon, with eyes like saucers, his mouth open, and the long white hair standing straight on end round his head like a silver halo. . . . I stared at him in unbelief, and he stared at me with a queer kind of shocked curiosity. I did not know that I had no hair, no eyebrows, no eyelashes, that my young mustache was burnt off, that my face was black, one cheek laid open, my nose cut, and my chin bleeding.[3]

A speech is not a novel. Still, many informative speeches would be vastly improved by the novelist's bent for color, specificity, and detail.

One way to avoid abstractions is through *description*. When we think of description, we usually think of external events such as the explosion described by Conrad. But description is also used to communicate internal feelings. Here is how one student tried to convey to his audience the sensations he experienced when he first began sky diving:

> As we wait for the plane to climb to the jump altitude of 12,000 feet, my mind races with a frenzied jumble of thoughts: "OK, this is the moment you've been waiting for. It's going to be great. Am I really going to jump out of an airplane from 12,000 feet? What if something goes wrong? Can I still back out? Come on now, don't worry. It'll be fine."

Even if we have not been sky diving, we have all had the same kinds of emotions on similar occasions. So what happened next?

connect

View this excerpt from "The Promise of Stem Cells" in the online Media Library for this chapter (Video 15.4).

description

A statement that depicts a person, event, idea, or the like with clarity and vividness.

Now it is time to jump. My palms are sweating and my heart is pounding so hard I think it may burst. "Get ready," yells the instructor. As I jump into the blue, I wonder, "What am I doing here?"

Yes—and then what?

The blast of air resistance blows me backward like a leaf at the mercy of an autumn wind. In about 10 seconds my body levels out and accelerates to a speed of 120 miles an hour. The air supports my body like an invisible flying carpet. There is no sound except for the wind rushing around my face. Any fears or doubts I had are gone in the exhilaration of free flight. Every nerve in my body is alive with sensation; yet I am overcome by a peaceful feeling and the sense that I am at one with the sky.

As we listen to the speaker we share his thoughts, feel his heart pound, and join his exhilaration as he floats effortlessly through the sky. The vivid description lends reality to the speech and draws us further in.

Another way to escape abstractions is with *comparisons* that put your subject in concrete, familiar terms. Do you want to convey what would happen if a comet or large asteroid struck the earth? You could say this:

> If a comet or large asteroid struck the earth, the impact would be devastating.

comparison

A statement of the similarities among two or more people, events, ideas, etc.

True, but the statement is vague and abstract. It does not communicate your meaning clearly and concretely. Now suppose you add this:

> To give you an idea how devastating the impact would be, it would be like all the nuclear bombs in the world going off at one spot.

Now you have made the abstract specific and given us a sharp new slant on things.

Like comparison, *contrast* can put an idea into concrete terms. Suppose you want to make the point that a person's chances of winning a state lottery are extremely low. You could say, "The odds, for example, of winning a state lottery are an astronomical 14 million to 1." The word "astronomical" suggests that you consider 14 million to 1 long odds, but long in comparison to what? One speaker offered this contrast:

contrast

A statement of the differences among two or more people, events, ideas, etc.

> The odds of picking the correct six-digit sequence in a typical state lottery are 14 million to 1. In contrast, the odds of getting hit by lightning are only 700,000 to 1. The odds of dying in a car accident are 6,000 to 1. In other words, the odds are much stronger that you will get hit by lightning or be killed in a car crash than that you will win the jackpot in a state lottery.

This puts an abstract fact into meaningful perspective.

PERSONALIZE YOUR IDEAS

Listeners want to be entertained as they are being enlightened.[4] Nothing takes the edge off an informative speech more than an unbroken string of facts and figures. And nothing enlivens a speech more than personal illustrations. Whenever possible, you should try to *personalize* your ideas and dramatize them in human terms.

personalize

To present one's ideas in human terms that relate in some fashion to the experience of the audience.

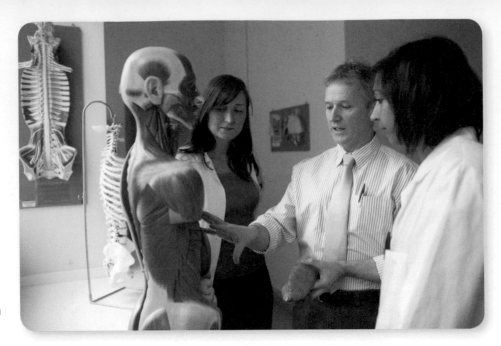

Informative speeches take place in a wide range of situations. Here a doctor explains a point about human anatomy to medical students.

Let's say you are talking about autism, the developmental disability marked by impaired communication and interaction skills. You would surely note that the condition affects 1 in every 500 children, occurs four times more frequently in males than in females, and is most prevalent among Caucasians. You would also note that the symptoms of autism include abnormal introversion, severely limited use of language, repetitive behaviors, avoidance of eye contact, loss of emotional control, and passive responses to affection.

But these are dry facts and figures. If you really want to get your audience involved, you will weave in some examples of children who suffer from autism. One speaker began by telling about Sam, her autistic nephew:

My nephew Sam was the delight of our family when he was born, the first grandchild of my parents. He cooed and babbled, smiled at his mom and dad, grasped for the playthings around his crib. At family dinners on Sunday, we took turns holding him in our arms, feeding him, and singing him to sleep. He seemed like any normal infant in a secure and loving home.

Then shortly before his second birthday we began to notice unusual behaviors. Sam avoided looking us in the eye, did not seem interested in learning words, played endlessly with the same toy, rocked back and forth in his chair for hours at a time, and was easily frustrated. My sister took him to a specialist, who gave the dreaded diagnosis: Sam was autistic.

During the body of the speech, the speaker mentioned Sam twice more to illustrate different aspects of autism. Then, at the end of the speech, she brought Sam's story to a hopeful conclusion:

We have seen that autism is a very serious disorder whose causes are not well understood and whose effects on families and the lives of the children themselves can be devastating. But we have also seen that early diagnosis and early intervention can help to modify and even turn around the symptoms of autism.

I am happy to say that Sam has benefited from such intervention. From the time he was two, he has been taught "normal" behavior patterns through aggressive therapy. Now he is able to participate in his class at the local school. He is also more responsive and affectionate at home. Sam continues to be our delight.

It was a powerful ending. By putting a human face on a familiar topic, the speaker took autism out of the realm of statistics and medical jargon and brought it home in personal terms.

connect

View this excerpt from "Autism: Heartbreak and Hope" in the online Media Library for this chapter (Video 15.5).

BE CREATIVE

Whether you are seeking alternatives to technical language, avoiding abstractions, personalizing ideas, or adapting to the audience's knowledge about the topic, you need to be creative in thinking about ways to achieve your objectives. A good informative speech is not an oral encyclopedia article. Like any other kind of speech, it requires a healthy dose of creativity.

If you look back at the examples on the previous few pages, you will see that all of them involve creative thinking by the speaker. As in these examples, creativity is often a matter of using language imaginatively and resourcefully. But creativity can involve *any* aspect of an informative speech, including visual aids—as can be seen in the speech on medical robots that is reprinted on pages 294–296.

Part of the speech deals with orderly robots, which transport medicine, food, and lab supplies around the hospital without a human by their side. The robots navigate by using "light whiskers"—invisible beams of sonar, infrared, and laser that constantly scan the environment to avoid collisions. Because the light whiskers are invisible, the speaker needed to find a way to make them visible for his audience. He did so by using a PowerPoint slide in which colored lines representing the light whiskers popped on screen in perfect coordination with the speaker's words. As you can see from Video 15.6, it was an effective—and creative—solution.

If, like this speaker, you think creatively when constructing your informative speech, you are much more likely to be successful.

connect

View this excerpt from "Medical Robots: From Science Fiction to Science Fact" in the online Media Library for this chapter (Video 15.6).

Sample Speech with Commentary

The following classroom speech provides an excellent example of how to apply the guidelines for informative speaking discussed in this chapter. Notice how the speaker takes what could be a dry, technical topic and makes it interesting. Also pay attention to how crisply the speech is organized and to how the speaker uses well-chosen supporting materials and visual aids to develop his ideas. You can view the speech in the online Media Library for this chapter.

connect

View "Medical Robots: From Science Fiction to Science Fact" in the online Media Library for this chapter (Video 15.7).

Medical Robots: From Science Fiction to Science Fact

 SPEECH

The speaker starts with a richly detailed extended example that captures attention and interest.

Maureen Schrader lay on the operating table at Saint Barnabas Medical Center in Livingston, New Jersey. Four mechanical arms moved with precision over her abdomen. In one arm was a high-definition camera. The other three contained small surgical instruments that made a five-centimeter incision just below her ribcage. It was a tiny opening, but it was big enough to put a new kidney into Maureen's body.

As the speaker continues his opening example, he reveals that the mechanical arms mentioned in the first paragraph are actually robotic arms controlled by a surgeon.

At no point during the surgery did the surgeon actually touch Maureen. In fact, he sat several feet away peering into a monitor and holding what looked like video game controls. But the work of his hands was digitally recorded and sent to the robotic arms, which mimicked his every movement. The robot became an extension of the surgeon, and together they transplanted the kidney.

Here the speaker relates the topic to his audience, establishes his credibility, previews the main points to be discussed in the body of the speech, and provides a transition statement to the body.

Robots in the operating room are now a reality, and the next operation you or a family member undergoes may well involve a robot. But surgery is just one of the areas in which robots are changing modern medicine. As a pre-med student interested in becoming a surgeon, I've long been fascinated with medical robots. After researching the topic for this speech, I'd like to introduce you to the world of medical robots. We'll take a look at three kinds of robots in particular—orderly robots, remote-presence robots, and surgical robots. Let's begin with orderly robots.

Now the speaker moves into his first main point, dealing with orderly robots. He illustrates the point by focusing on the TUG robot.

Orderly robots help hospital staff accomplish routine tasks. Their primary function is to transport medicine, food, and lab supplies—and to do so without a human by their side. Here is one of the most popular orderly robots—the TUG, or tug robot—which, according to its manufacturer, can be found in more than 100 hospitals in the United States alone.

As you can see from the video of this speech, the speaker uses a creative visual aid to help his audience visualize the "light whiskers" used by TUG robots.

A September 2010 story in *Discovery News* explains how the robot works. Relying on a digital map of the hospital, the robot moves from room to room picking up and dropping off supplies. It senses people and obstacles by what are called "light whiskers"—invisible beams of sonar, infrared, and laser. These light whiskers are represented by the colored lines you see in this drawing. They constantly scan the environment to avoid collisions.

The speaker uses expert testimony to explain the benefits of orderly robots. Notice how he identifies the person he is quoting and his credentials before presenting the testimony.

TUG robots can also communicate with one another about the most efficient route to a location given current hallway conditions. They are highly efficient and make fewer delivery errors than people. Mark Weigel, director of food services at Bethesda Memorial Hospital in Maryland, notes that the TUG robot "never argues with patients, takes no breaks, is always polite and always on time."

The speaker moves into his second main point. He begins with a concise definition of remote-presence robots.

But orderly robots are not the only robots transforming modern medicine. Remote-presence robots allow a doctor to visit with a patient even when the doctor is not in the same room. "Remote presence" means that the doctor can be present with the patient even when the doctor is in a remote location.

The word "imagine" helps draw the audience further into the speech. A photograph shows exactly what a RP-7 remote-presence robot looks like.

Imagine you're sitting in a hospital room when in comes this—the RP-7. A 2009 story in *U.S. News & World Report* explains that physicians can pilot these robots from a laptop located anywhere in the hospital or in the world. A screen, camera, microphone, and speaker system—like the ones you see in this photograph—allow the doctor to interview the patient. Hospital staff can even attach medical devices such as electronic stethoscopes to the robot so the doctor can review a patient's vital signs.

Notice how the speaker identifies the source of his statistics and rounds off the numbers.

According to a 2010 article in *Hospital Management,* the RP-7 is used in more than 250 U.S. hospitals and has performed more than 100,000 clinic sessions. They are particularly useful in hospitals with a high patient-to-doctor ratio.

A transition at the beginning of this paragraph signals that the speaker is moving to his third main point. He again uses credible, well-chosen statistics to quantify his ideas.

In addition to orderly robots and remote-presence robots, a third kind of robot is transforming modern medicine. Surgical robots, like the kind I mentioned at the start of my speech, are increasingly being used in operating rooms around the world. Most popular is the one you see here—the da Vinci. According to a 2010 article in the *Miami Herald,* there are more than 1,400 da Vinci robots in hospitals worldwide, and they're used in more than 200,000 operations every year.

This paragraph provides an excellent example of how to explain visual aids and of how to communicate technical information in clear, nontechnical language.

How does da Vinci work? Intuitive Surgical, maker of da Vinci, explains that the surgeon controls the robot from a remote terminal. You can see the terminal in this photograph. Usually, the terminal is a few feet away, as in the photograph. But it can be as far as thousands of miles away, so a surgeon in San Francisco can operate on a patient in Miami. The surgeon controls the robot's arms utilizing an interactive 3-D imaging system. But make no mistake: Even though the robot is touching the patient, the surgeon is always in control.

Because the speaker is not a surgeon, he relies on expert testimony to explain the benefits of da Vinci surgical robots. As in other parts of the speech, his dynamic delivery creates a strong bond with his audience.

Doctors love da Vinci because it dramatically improves the quality of surgical procedures. Dr. Jeffrey Wolf, a head-and-neck surgeon at the University of Maryland Medical Center, states that da Vinci "gives us unprecedented access with really good 3-D visualization. . . . We're now able to perform intricate surgeries in a very small space with great dexterity." Da Vinci also reduces the risk of postsurgery complications, allows for faster healing, and helps patients leave the hospital sooner.

"In conclusion" signals that the speaker is coming to the end of his speech. He then summarizes the main points developed in the body.

In conclusion, we've seen that medical robots are playing an increasingly important role in modern medicine. Whether they're running errands for hospital employees, helping physicians connect with their patients, or acting as a surgeon's eyes and hands, medical robots have brought the future into the present.

The speaker ends on a strong note by stating that medical robots are now a matter of science fact, rather than of science fiction.

So the next time you find yourself at the hospital, keep your eyes peeled for the kind of technological marvels that used to exist only in science fiction. Medical robots are now a matter of science fact.

Summary

Speaking to inform occurs in a wide range of everyday situations. Improving your ability to convey knowledge effectively will be valuable to you throughout your life.

Informative speeches may be grouped into four categories—speeches about objects, speeches about processes, speeches about events, and speeches about concepts.

Objects include places, structures, animals, even people. Speeches about objects usually are organized in chronological, spatial, or topical order. A process is a series of actions that work together to produce a final result. Speeches about processes explain how something is made, how something is done, or how something works. The most common types of organization for speeches about processes are chronological and topical.

An event is anything that happens or is regarded as happening. Speeches about events are usually arranged in chronological or topical order. Concepts include beliefs, theories, ideas, and principles. Speeches about concepts are often more complex than other kinds of informative speeches, and they typically follow a topical pattern of organization.

No matter what the subject of your informative speech, be careful not to overestimate what your audience knows about it. Explain everything so thoroughly that they can't help but understand. Avoid being too technical. Make sure your ideas and your language are fully comprehensible to someone who has no specialized knowledge about the topic.

Equally important, recognize that what is fascinating to you may not be fascinating to everybody. It is your job to make your informative speech interesting and meaningful to your audience. Find ways to talk about the topic in terms of your listeners. Avoid too many abstractions. Use description, comparison, and contrast to make your audience *see* what you are talking about. Try to personalize your ideas and dramatize them in human terms. Finally, be creative in thinking of ways to communicate your ideas.

Key Terms

informative speech *(278)*

object *(278)*

process *(280)*

event *(282)*

concept *(284)*

description *(290)*

comparison *(291)*

contrast *(291)*

personalize *(291)*

Review Questions

After reading this chapter, you should be able to answer the following questions:

1. What are the four types of informative speeches discussed in the chapter? Give an example of a good specific purpose statement for each type.

2. Why must informative speakers be careful not to overestimate what the audience knows about the topic? What can you do to make sure your ideas don't pass over the heads of your listeners?

3. What should you do as an informative speaker to relate your topic directly to the audience?

4. What two things should you watch out for in making sure your speech is not overly technical?

5. What are three methods you can use to avoid abstractions in your informative speech?

6. What does it mean to say that informative speakers should personalize their ideas?

7. Why is it important for informative speakers to be creative in thinking about ways to communicate their ideas?

connect

For further review, go to the LearnSmart study module for this chapter.

Exercises for Critical Thinking

1. Below is a list of subjects for informative speeches. Your task is twofold: (a) Select four of the topics and prepare a specific purpose statement for an informative speech about each of the four. Make sure your four specific purpose statements include at least one that deals with its topic as an object, one that deals with its topic as a process, one that deals with its topic as an event, and one that deals with its topic as a concept. (b) Explain what method of organization you would most likely use in structuring a speech about each of your specific purpose statements.

hobbies	sports	education
animals	music	media
science	cultural customs	technology

2. Analyze "Ramadan" in the appendix of sample speeches that follows Chapter 19. Identify the specific purpose, central idea, main points, and method of organization. Evaluate the speech in light of the guidelines for informative speaking discussed in this chapter.

16

Speaking to Persuade

Ramon Trujillo started that particular school day by stopping at the library to return an overdue book. "Look," he explained to the librarian, "I know this book was due last week, but I was sick with the flu and couldn't even get out of bed. Do I still have to pay the fine? I can get you a note from the doctor if you need one." The librarian hemmed and hawed. Then he said, "Okay. You don't have a record of any other fines. Just this once."

With a sigh of relief, Ramon went on to his morning classes. At noon he was dashing across campus when a friend stopped him. "How about some lunch?" she asked. "I really can't," replied Ramon. "I have to stand at the table and get signatures on the tuition petition. I'll see you later, though."

During the afternoon, Ramon went to his job at a computer sales company. He arrived just in time for the weekly staff meeting, where he presented his ideas on how to increase customer satisfaction. "One thing I've noticed," he said, "is that most people don't realize they have only 14 days to return unopened merchandise for a full refund. Most stores have a 30-day return policy, and I know we've lost some customers because ours is shorter. Changing it might be

299

inconvenient at first, but it will definitely help business in the long run." After listening to Ramon, the sales manager said, "I've always thought 14 days was plenty of time, but you've convinced me that we ought to change. Let's give it a try."

If you asked Ramon how he spent his day, he might say, "I returned a book, I went to class, I worked the tuition-petition table, I had a staff meeting at my job." In fact, he spent a large part of his day *persuading*—persuading people to do things they were reluctant to do or that had not occurred to them.

The Importance of Persuasion

persuasion

The process of creating, reinforcing, or changing people's beliefs or actions.

Persuasion is the process of creating, reinforcing, or changing people's beliefs or actions.[1] The ability to speak (and write) persuasively will benefit you in every part of your life, from personal relations to community activities to career aspirations. When economists added up the number of people—lawyers, sales representatives, public relations specialists, counselors, administrators, and others—whose jobs depend largely on persuading people to adopt their point of view, they concluded that persuasion accounts for 26 percent of the U.S. gross domestic product![2]

Understanding the principles of persuasion is also vital to being an informed citizen and consumer. By age 20, the average American has been exposed to 1 million television commercials—an average of 150 every day. Politicians and advertisers, salespeople and interest groups, fund-raisers and community activists—all vie for your attention, votes, money, time, and support. The more you know about persuasion, the more effective you can be in using your powers of critical thinking to assess the barrage of persuasive messages you are exposed to every day.

Although persuasion has been studied for more than 2,000 years, it is still the subject of lively debate among scholars. There are a number of scientific models of the persuasive process and a wide range of respected theories about how persuasion works. In this chapter and the next, we will explore the principles of persuasion as they apply to public speaking.

When you speak to persuade, you act as an advocate. Your job is to get listeners to agree with you and, perhaps, to act on that belief. Your goal may be to defend an idea, to refute an opponent, to sell a program, or to inspire people to action. Because persuasive speakers must communicate information clearly and concisely, you will need all the skills you used in speaking to inform. But you will also need new skills that take you from giving information to affecting your listeners' attitudes, beliefs, or actions.

Ethics and Persuasion

No matter what the speaking situation, you need to make sure your goals are ethically sound and that you use ethical methods to communicate your ideas. Meeting these obligations can be especially challenging when you speak to persuade. Would you be willing to shade the truth "just a bit" if it would guarantee a successful speech? How about juggling statistics, doctoring quotations, passing off opinions as facts, or pandering to prejudice and stereotypes?

Unfortunately, there is no shortage of speakers—and other persuaders—who are willing to take ethical shortcuts to achieve their objectives. Yet, as Martin Luther King stated years ago, it is not possible to bring about a truly beneficial result by using unethical methods. Maintaining the bond of trust with listeners is also vital to a speaker's credibility. As in other kinds of public speaking, the ideal of effective persuasion is the good person speaking well.

When you work on your persuasive speech, keep in mind the guidelines for ethical speaking discussed in Chapter 2. Make sure your goals are ethically sound and that you can defend them if they are questioned or challenged. Study the topic thoroughly so you won't mislead your audience through shoddy research or muddled thinking. Learn about all sides of an issue, seek out competing viewpoints, and get your facts right.

But knowing the facts is not enough. You also need to be honest in what you say. There is no place in ethical speechmaking for deliberately false or deceptive statements. Also be on guard against more subtle forms of dishonesty such as quoting out of context, portraying a few details as the whole story, and misrepresenting the sources of facts and figures. Take care to present statistics, testimony, and other kinds of evidence fairly and accurately.

Keep in mind as well the power of language and use it responsibly. Show respect for the rights of free speech and expression, and stay away from name-calling and other forms of abusive language. Finally, check the section of Chapter 17 that discusses the role of emotional appeal (pages 342–346). Make sure that any emotional appeal you use is appropriate to the topic and that you build your speech on a firm base of facts and logic before appealing to your audience's emotions. Aim at the highest standards and construct your speech so it will be both convincing *and* ethically sound.[3]

The Psychology of Persuasion

Persuasion is a psychological process. It occurs in a situation where two or more points of view exist. The speaker supports Social Security reform, but many listeners do not. The speaker considers cloning immoral, but some in the audience think it is justified in certain circumstances. The different points of view may be completely opposed, or they may simply be different in degree. Whichever the case, there must be a disagreement, or else there would be no need for persuasion.

THE CHALLENGE OF PERSUASIVE SPEAKING

Of all the kinds of public speaking, persuasion is the most complex and the most challenging. Your objective is more ambitious than in speaking to inform, and audience analysis and adaptation become much more demanding. In some persuasive speeches, you will deal with controversial topics that touch on your listeners' basic attitudes, values, and beliefs. This may increase their resistance to persuasion and make your task more difficult.

It is much easier, for example, to explain the history of capital punishment than to persuade an audience either that capital punishment should be abolished or that it should be reinstituted in every state. In the persuasive speech you must contend not only with your audience's knowledge of capital punishment but also with their attitudes toward crime and justice, their beliefs about the deterrent value of capital punishment, and their values about the taking of human life. Lines of argument that work with one part of the audience may fail with—or even upset—another part. What seems perfectly logical to some listeners may seem wildly irrational to others. No matter how expert you are on the topic, no matter how skillfully you prepare the speech, no matter how captivating your delivery—some listeners will not agree with you.

This does not mean persuasion is impossible. It does mean you should have a realistic sense of what you can accomplish. You can't expect a group of die-hard Democrats to become Republicans or a steak lover to turn vegetarian as a result of one speech.

In every persuasive speech, you will face some listeners who are strongly in favor of your position, some who are neutral, and some who are adamantly opposed. If listeners are neutral or only moderately committed one way or another, you can realistically hope your speech will move at least some of them toward your side. If listeners are strongly opposed to your viewpoint, you can consider your speech a success if it leads even a few to reexamine their views.

When thinking about the range of persuasive responses, you may find it helpful to visualize listeners on a scale such as that shown in Figure 16.1 below. Persuasion involves any movement by a listener from left to right on the scale, no matter where the listener begins and no matter how great or small the movement.[4]

How successful you are in any particular persuasive speech will depend above all on how well you tailor your message to the values, attitudes, and beliefs of your audience. In Chapter 6, we considered the general principles of audience analysis and adaptation. Here we emphasize two additional principles that are crucial to the psychology of persuasion. The first deals with how listeners process and respond to persuasive messages. The second pertains to the target audience for persuasive speeches.

HOW LISTENERS PROCESS PERSUASIVE MESSAGES

We often think of persuasion as something a speaker does *to* an audience. In fact, persuasion is something a speaker does *with* an audience. Listeners do not just sit passively and soak in everything the speaker has to say. Instead, they engage in a mental give-and-take with the speaker. While they listen, they assess the speaker's credibility, delivery, supporting materials,

FIGURE 16.1

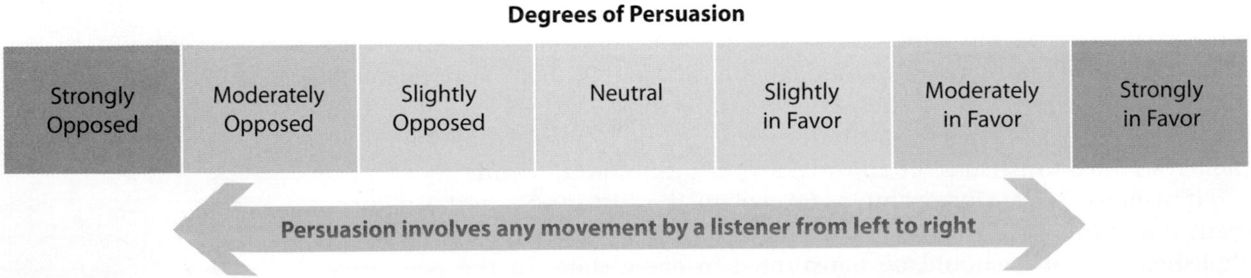

Degrees of Persuasion

Strongly Opposed	Moderately Opposed	Slightly Opposed	Neutral	Slightly in Favor	Moderately in Favor	Strongly in Favor

Persuasion involves any movement by a listener from left to right

No matter what the situation, a persuasive speaker needs to adapt to the target audience. Here British Prime Minister David Cameron speaks to a local group in Flintshire, North Wales.

language, reasoning, and emotional appeals. They may respond positively at one point, negatively at another. At times they may argue, inside their own minds, with the speaker. This mental give-and-take is especially vigorous when listeners are highly involved with the topic and believe it has a direct bearing on their lives.[5]

In a sense, the psychological interaction between a speaker and audience during a persuasive speech is similar to what happens vocally during a conversation—as in this example:

Karma: It's much better to adopt a dog from a shelter than to buy a dog from a breeder. Adoption saves dogs that might otherwise be euthanized.

Robyn: It's true that adoption saves some animals' lives, but many of the dogs in shelters have behavioral problems. A person who adopts a dog like that might be seriously bitten. A person with small children doesn't want to take chances.

Karma: Most shelters today screen animals carefully before they release them for adoption. They also screen owners; for example, they allow only experienced dog owners to adopt large, active dogs.

Robyn: Still, when you adopt a dog, you don't know about its early training, health problems, or other things that would help you take the best care of it. If you go to a breeder, you know exactly what you're getting.

Karma: That's true, but to me the biggest concern is to rescue a dog that might otherwise be put to sleep, and to give a dog that's been mistreated a chance at a happy life.

Much the same kind of interaction might occur during a persuasive speech, except that the listener would respond internally rather than out loud.

mental dialogue with the audience

The mental give-and-take between speaker and listener during a persuasive speech.

What does this mean to you as a speaker? It means you must think of your persuasive speech as a kind of *mental dialogue* with your audience. You must anticipate possible objections the audience will raise to your point of view and answer them in your speech. You cannot convert skeptical listeners unless you deal directly with the reasons for their skepticism.

As you prepare your persuasive speech, put yourself in the place of your audience and imagine how they will respond. Be as tough on your speech as your audience will be. Every place they will raise a question, answer it. Every place they will have a criticism, deal with it. Every place they will see a hole in your argument, fill it. Leave nothing to chance.[6]

THE TARGET AUDIENCE

Unfortunately, no matter how carefully you plot your speech, you will seldom be able to persuade all your listeners. Like most audiences, yours will probably contain some listeners who are hostile to your position, some who favor it, some who are undecided, and some who just don't care. You would like to make your speech equally appealing to everyone, but this is rarely possible. Most often you will have a particular *part* of the whole audience that you want to reach with your speech. That part is called the *target audience*.

target audience

The portion of the whole audience that the speaker most wants to persuade.

Advertising gives us an effective model. Successful commercials are aimed at particular segments of the market. Mutual funds are now directing many of their advertisements at women. Why? Because more and more women are investing in the stock market. Beer commercials, on the other hand, are directed at men because they drink the most beer.

For your classroom speeches, you don't have the sophisticated research capability of a large advertising agency. But as we saw in Chapter 6, you can use questionnaires to find out where your classmates stand on your speech topic. This is your equivalent of market research. Once you know where your target audience stands, you can tailor your speech to fit their values and concerns—aim at the target, so to speak.

Here, for example, is how one student, Amy Shapiro, determined her target audience for a persuasive speech urging her classmates to pass on the gift of life by signing organ donor cards:

> There are 22 students in my audience. My audience-analysis questionnaires show that 3 are opposed to donating their organs under any circumstances. I can't persuade them no matter what I say. My questionnaires also show that 4 have already signed organ donor cards. I don't need to persuade them. The other 15 students could be persuaded if they knew more about the need for organ donors and about how the process works. They are my target audience.

Not only did Amy pinpoint her target audience, she also knew from her audience-analysis questionnaire the issues she would have to discuss to be convincing:

> The members of my target audience break down this way: 7 give "fear of being pronounced dead prematurely" as their main reason for not signing organ cards; 5 are concerned about their body being "cut up or disfigured"; and 3 cite religious reasons for their opposition. The questionnaires also show that 8 of the 15 don't fully understand the need for organ donors.

With all this information, Amy was able to put together a first-rate speech that focused on her classmates' attitudes and beliefs about signing organ donor cards. As a result, she was able to convince several of her classmates to sign cards.

In the next chapter, we'll discuss the methods you can use to hit the target in your persuasive speeches. In the rest of this chapter, we focus on the three major kinds of persuasive speeches and how to organize them most effectively.

Persuasive Speeches on Questions of Fact

WHAT ARE QUESTIONS OF FACT?

What college basketball team has won the most games since 1990? Who was the first African American to sit on the U.S. Supreme Court? How far is it from Los Angeles to Cairo? These questions of fact can be answered absolutely. The answers are either right or wrong.

But many questions of fact cannot be answered absolutely. There is a true answer, but we don't have enough information to know what it is. Some questions like this involve prediction: Will the economy be better or worse next year? Who will win the Super Bowl this season?

Other questions deal with issues on which the facts are murky or inconclusive. What will happen next in the Middle East? Is sexual orientation genetically determined? No one knows the final answers to these questions, but that doesn't stop people from speculating about them or from trying to convince other people that they have the best possible answers.

question of fact

A question about the truth or falsity of an assertion.

ANALYZING QUESTIONS OF FACT

In some ways, a persuasive speech on a question of fact is similar to an informative speech. But the two kinds of speeches take place in different kinds of situations and for different purposes.

The situation for an informative speech is *nonpartisan*. The speaker acts as a lecturer or a teacher. The aim is to give information as impartially as possible, not to argue for a particular point of view.

On the other hand, the situation for a persuasive speech on a question of fact is *partisan*. The speaker acts as an advocate. The aim is not to be impartial, but to present one view of the facts as persuasively as possible. The speaker may mention competing views of the facts, but only to refute them.

For example, consider the assassination of John F. Kennedy. After 50 years, there is still much debate about what really happened in Dallas on November 22, 1963. Did Lee Harvey Oswald act alone, or was he part of a conspiracy? How many shots were fired at President Kennedy and from what locations? If there was a conspiracy, who was involved in it? The informative speaker would recite the known facts on both sides of these questions without drawing a conclusion about which side is correct. The persuasive speaker, however, would draw a conclusion from the known facts and try to convert listeners to his or her point of view.

If there were no possibility of dispute on questions of fact, there would be no need for courtroom trials. In a criminal trial there is usually at least one known fact—a crime has been committed. But did the defendant commit the crime? The prosecuting attorney tries to persuade the jury that the defendant is guilty. The defense attorney tries to persuade the jury that the defendant is innocent. The jury must decide which view of the facts is more persuasive.[7]

ORGANIZING SPEECHES ON QUESTIONS OF FACT

Persuasive speeches on questions of fact are usually organized *topically*. Suppose, for example, that you want to convince your classmates that an earthquake of 9.0 or above on the Richter scale will hit California within the next ten years. Each main point in your speech will present a *reason* why someone should agree with you:

Specific Purpose:	To persuade my audience that an earthquake of 9.0 or above on the Richter scale will hit California in the next ten years.
Central Idea:	There are three good reasons to believe that an earthquake of 9.0 or above on the Richter scale will hit California in the next ten years.
Main Points:	I. California is long overdue for a major earthquake.
	II. Many geological signs indicate that a major earthquake may happen soon.
	III. Experts agree that an earthquake of 9.0 or above could strike California any day.

To take another example, suppose you are trying to persuade your classmates that the plays attributed to William Shakespeare were not actually written by him. Your specific purpose, central idea, and main points might be:

Specific Purpose:	To persuade my audience that William Shakespeare did not write the plays attributed to him.
Central Idea:	There is considerable evidence that the plays attributed to William Shakespeare were actually written by Francis Bacon or Edward de Vere.
Main Points:	I. Biographical and textual evidence suggest that William Shakespeare did not write the plays attributed to him.
	II. Historical evidence indicates that Shakespeare's plays were probably written by either Sir Francis Bacon or Edward de Vere, 17th Earl of Oxford.

Notice in these examples that the speaker's purpose is limited to persuading the audience to accept a particular view of the facts. Sometimes, however, the dispute that gives rise to a persuasive speech will go beyond a question of fact and will turn on a question of value.

Many persuasive speeches revolve around questions of fact. Here U.S. Surgeon General Regina Benjamin discusses her report on the dangers of tobacco use.

Persuasive Speeches on Questions of Value

WHAT ARE QUESTIONS OF VALUE?

What is the best movie of all time? Is cloning morally justifiable? What are the ethical responsibilities of journalists? Such questions not only involve matters of fact, but they also demand *value judgments*—judgments based on a person's beliefs about what is right or wrong, good or bad, moral or immoral, proper or improper, fair or unfair.

Take the issue of cloning. It can be discussed at a purely factual level by asking such questions as "What are the scientific methods of cloning?" Or "What are the laws about cloning in different countries?" These are factual questions. The answers you reach are independent of your belief about the morality of cloning.

But suppose you ask, "Is it morally justifiable to clone human beings?" Or "Is it ethically acceptable to clone human cells in an effort to cure diseases such as AIDS and cancer?" Now you are dealing with questions of value. How you answer will depend not only on your factual knowledge about cloning, but also on your moral values.

ANALYZING QUESTIONS OF VALUE

Contrary to what many people think, questions of value are not simply matters of personal opinion or whim. If you say, "I enjoy bicycle riding," you do not have to give a reason why you enjoy it. You are making a statement about your personal taste. Even if bicycle riding were the most unpleasant activity ever invented, it could still be one of your favorites.

> **question of value**
>
> A question about the worth, rightness, morality, and so forth of an idea or action.

On the other hand, if you say, "Bicycle riding is the ideal form of land transportation," you are making a statement about a question of value. Whether bicycling is the ideal form of land transportation does not depend on your own likes and dislikes. To defend the statement, you cannot say, "Bicycle riding is the ideal form of land transportation because I like it."

Instead, you must *justify* your claim. The first step is to define what you mean by an "ideal form of land transportation." Do you mean a mode of transportation that gets people where they want to go as fast as possible? That is relatively inexpensive? That is fun? Nonpolluting? Beneficial for the user? In other words, you must establish your *standards* for an "ideal form of land transportation." Then you can show how bicycle riding measures up against those standards.

Whenever you give a speech on a question of value, be sure to give special thought to the standards for your value judgment.

ORGANIZING SPEECHES ON QUESTIONS OF VALUE

Persuasive speeches on questions of value are almost always organized *topically*. The most common approach is to devote your first main point to establishing the standards for your value judgment and your second main point to applying those standards to the subject of your speech.

Think back for a moment to the speech about bicycle riding as the ideal form of land transportation. If you organized this speech in topical order, your first main point would identify the standards for an ideal form of land transportation. Your second main point would show how biking measures up against those standards. Here is how your specific purpose, central idea, and main points might look:

Specific Purpose: To persuade my audience that bicycle riding is the ideal form of land transportation.

Central Idea: Bicycle riding is the ideal form of land transportation because it is faster than walking or running, is nonpolluting, and promotes the health of the rider.

Main Points: I. An ideal form of land transportation should meet three major standards.
       A. It should be faster than running or walking.
       B. It should be nonpolluting.
       C. It should be beneficial for the person who uses it.

       II. Bicycle riding meets all these standards for an ideal form of land transportation.
       A. Bicycle riding is faster than walking or running.
       B. Bicycle riding is not a source of air, land, water, or noise pollution.
       C. Bicycle riding is extremely beneficial for the health of the rider.

When you speak on a question of value, you must make sure to justify your judgment against some identifiable standards. In the following example, notice how the speaker devotes her first main point to judging capital punishment against moral standards and her second main point to judging it against legal standards:

Specific Purpose:	To persuade my audience that capital punishment is morally and legally wrong.
Central Idea:	Capital punishment violates both the Bible and the U.S. Constitution.
Main Points:	I. Capital punishment violates the biblical commandment "Thou shalt not kill."
	II. Capital punishment violates the constitutional ban on "cruel and unusual punishment."

As you can see, speeches on questions of value may have strong implications for our actions. A person who is persuaded that capital punishment is morally and legally wrong is more likely to support legislation abolishing the death penalty. But speeches on questions of value do not argue directly for or against particular courses of action. Once you go beyond arguing right or wrong to arguing that something should or should not be done, you move from a question of value to a question of policy.

Persuasive Speeches on Questions of Policy

WHAT ARE QUESTIONS OF POLICY?

Questions of policy arise daily in almost everything we do. At home we debate what to do during spring vacation, whether to buy a new television, which movie to see on the weekend. At work we discuss whether to ask for a raise, what strategy to use in selling a product, how to improve communication between management and employees. As citizens we ponder whether to vote for or against a political candidate, what to do about airport security, how to promote economic growth.

All these are questions of policy because they deal with specific courses of action. Questions of policy inevitably involve questions of fact. (How can we decide whether to vote for a candidate unless we know the facts of her or his stand on the issues?) They may also involve questions of value. (The policy you favor on abortion will be affected by whether you think abortion is moral or immoral.) But questions of policy *always* go beyond questions of fact or value to decide whether something should or should not be done.

When put formally, questions of policy usually include the word "should," as in these examples:

> What measures should be taken to protect the United States against terrorist attacks?
>
> Should the electoral college be abolished?
>
> What steps should be taken to reduce America's dependence on foreign oil?

question of policy

A question about whether a specific course of action should or should not be taken.

TYPES OF SPEECHES ON QUESTIONS OF POLICY

When you speak on a question of policy, your goal may be either to gain passive agreement or to motivate immediate action from your listeners. Deciding which goal you want to achieve will affect almost every aspect of your speech.

Speeches to Gain Passive Agreement

speech to gain passive agreement

A persuasive speech in which the speaker's goal is to convince the audience that a given policy is desirable without encouraging the audience to take action in support of the policy.

If your goal is passive agreement, you will try to get your audience to agree with you that a certain policy is desirable, but you will not necessarily encourage the audience to do anything to enact the policy. For example, suppose you want to persuade people that the United States should abolish the electoral college and elect the President by direct popular vote. If you seek passive agreement, you will try to get your audience to concur, but you will not urge them to take any action right now to help change presidential election procedures.

Here are some specific purpose statements for policy speeches that seek passive agreement:

> To persuade my audience that there should be stricter safety standards on amusement-park rides.
>
> To persuade my audience that the United States should put greater emphasis on solar power to meet the country's energy needs.
>
> To persuade my audience that a balanced-budget amendment should be added to the U.S. Constitution.

In each case, the speaker's aim is to convince listeners that the speaker's policy is necessary and practical. The speaker is not trying to get listeners to take action in support of the policy.

Speeches to Gain Immediate Action

speech to gain immediate action

A persuasive speech in which the speaker's goal is to convince the audience to take action in support of a given policy.

When your goal is immediate action, you want to do more than get your listeners to nod their heads in agreement. You want to motivate them to action—to sign a petition for abolishing the electoral college, to campaign for lower tuition, to contribute to a fund drive, and so forth.

Here are some examples of specific purpose statements for policy speeches that seek immediate action:

> To persuade my audience to give time to Big Brothers or Big Sisters.
>
> To persuade my audience to vote in the next student election.
>
> To persuade my audience to begin a regular exercise program.

Some experts say you should seek action from your audience whenever possible. Although it is much easier to evoke passive agreement than to elicit action, the listener is not making much of a commitment by thinking, "Sure, I agree with you." Within a day or two that same listener may forget entirely about your speech—and about her or his agreement with it.

Action, however, reinforces belief. A great deal of research shows that if you can persuade a listener to take some kind of action—even if it is no more than signing a petition, putting a bumper sticker on a car, or attending a meeting— you have gained a more serious commitment. Once a listener acts on behalf of a speaker's position, she or he is more likely to remain committed to it.[8]

When you call for action in a persuasive speech, you should make your recommendations as specific as possible. Don't just urge listeners to "do something." Tell them exactly what to do and how to do it.

For an excellent example, look at Video 16.1 in the online Media Library for this chapter. The speaker's aim was to convince her classmates to donate time to the Special Olympics. After talking about the mission of Special

connect

View this excerpt from "Making a Difference Through the Special Olympics" in the online Media Library for this chapter (Video 16.1).

Persuasive speeches on questions of policy are given whenever people debate specific courses of action. Such speeches can seek either passive agreement or immediate action.

Olympics, the need for volunteers, and the rewarding feelings experienced by volunteers, she explained how students can get involved for whatever amount of time they are able to commit at the moment. She also brought along brochures with additional information to pass out after her speech. When you construct your persuasive speech, remember that the more specific your instructions, the more likely it is that your call to action will succeed.[9]

ANALYZING QUESTIONS OF POLICY

Regardless of whether your aim is to elicit passive agreement or to gain immediate action, you will face three basic issues whenever you discuss a question of policy—need, plan, and practicality.

Need

There is no point in arguing for a policy unless you can show a need for it:

Is there a need for more student parking on campus?

Is there a need for the school district to institute single-sex classrooms?

Is there a need for a national ID card in the United States?

Your first step is to convince listeners that there is a serious problem with things as they are. People are not inclined to adopt a new policy unless they are convinced that the old one is not working. This is why the *burden of proof* always rests with the speaker who advocates change. (Of course, you may be defending present policy, in which case you will argue that there is *no* need to change—that things are already working as well as can be expected.)

Plan

The second basic issue of policy speeches is plan. Once you have shown that a problem exists, you must explain your plan for solving it:

What can we do to get more student parking on campus?

What topics should be taught in single-sex classrooms? Are single-sex classrooms appropriate for all grade levels?

What information should be included on a national ID card? Who will be responsible for collecting the information and creating the cards?

need

The first basic issue in analyzing a question of policy: Is there a serious problem or need that requires a change from current policy?

burden of proof

The obligation facing a persuasive speaker to prove that a change from current policy is necessary.

plan

The second basic issue in analyzing a question of policy: If there is a problem with current policy, does the speaker have a plan to solve the problem?

connect

View this excerpt from "The Horrors of Puppy Mills" in the online Media Library for this chapter (Video 16.2).

Answering such questions is especially important if you call for a new policy. It's easy to complain about problems; the real challenge is developing solutions.

In most classroom speeches, you will not have time to describe your plan in detail, but you should at least identify its major features. Look, for example, at the plan section in the speech on puppy mills in the online Media Library for this chapter. First, the speaker proposes legal measures to punish dog breeders that do not take proper care of their animals. Second, he presents four steps that individual listeners can take when buying a dog to make sure they are not supporting puppy mills. The speech would have been much less persuasive if the speaker had not spelled out the major features of his plan.

Practicality

The third basic issue of policy speeches is practicality. Once you have presented a plan, you must show that it will work. Will it solve the problem? Or will it create new and more serious problems?

> Building a multilevel parking garage on campus would provide more student parking, but the cost would require a sharp increase in tuition.
>
> Creating single-sex classrooms would be academically beneficial for some students, but it could reinforce gender stereotypes and return education to a separate-but-equal status.
>
> A national ID card might be an easy way for people to verify their identity for security purposes, but it could also infringe on civil liberties and give the government too much personal information about individuals.

practicality

The third basic issue in analyzing a question of policy: Will the speaker's plan solve the problem? Will it create new and more serious problems?

These are significant concerns. Whenever you advocate a new policy, you must be prepared to show that it is workable. No matter how serious a problem may be, listeners usually want some assurance that a speaker's plan will actually solve the problem.[10]

One way to provide this assurance is to show that a plan similar to yours has been successfully implemented elsewhere. For example, Video 16.3 in the online Media Library for this chapter shows an excerpt from a student speech calling for tougher measures to reduce smoking in the speaker's state. As you view the video, notice how the speaker points to the success of a similar plan in California as evidence that it will work in her state.

connect

View this excerpt from "The Most Dangerous Habit" in the online Media Library for this chapter (Video 16.3).

If you oppose a shift in policy, one of your major arguments will be that the change is impractical—that it will create more problems than it can solve. For example, critics of raising the federal minimum wage in the United States say it would overburden small businesses and lead to greater unemployment. Other opponents argue that a high minimum wage puts American companies at a disadvantage when competing against foreign companies. If listeners accept these arguments, they will probably decide that the United States should not raise the federal minimum wage.

How much of your speech should you devote to need, to plan, and to practicality? The answer depends on your topic and your audience. For example, if your audience is not aware of the health and environmental problems caused by the use of antibacterial chemicals in household products, you will have to give much of your time to need before covering plan and practicality. On the other hand, if your listeners already know about the problems caused by antibacterial household products, you can quickly remind them of need and then devote most of your speech to plan and practicality.

ORGANIZING SPEECHES ON QUESTIONS OF POLICY

Effective organization is crucial when you speak on a question of policy. Although any of the basic patterns of organization explained in Chapter 9 can be used, four special patterns are especially valuable for policy speeches. They are problem-solution order, problem-cause-solution order, comparative advantages order, and Monroe's motivated sequence.

Problem-Solution Order

If you advocate a change in policy, your main points often will fall naturally into problem-solution order. In the first main point you demonstrate the need for a new policy by showing the extent and seriousness of the problem. In the second main point you explain your plan for solving the problem and show its practicality. For example:

Specific Purpose:	To persuade my audience that the U.S. Congress should pass legislation curbing the spread of phony pharmaceuticals.
Central Idea:	Because phony pharmaceuticals are a serious problem in the United States, Congress should pass legislation ensuring that the medications we buy are safe.
Main Points:	I. The spread of phony pharmaceuticals is a serious problem.
	A. Phony pharmaceuticals are one of the most profitable areas of criminal activity in the world.
	B. The spread of phony pharmaceuticals is producing serious health risks in the United States.
	II. Solving the problem of phony pharmaceuticals requires action by the federal government.
	A. Congress should pass legislation targeting the spread of phony pharmaceuticals and imposing strict penalties for violators.
	B. Experts believe that such legislation will go a long way toward solving the problem.

> **problem-solution order**
>
> A method of organizing persuasive speeches in which the first main point deals with the existence of a problem and the second main point presents a solution to the problem.

connect™

View an excerpt from "Phony Pharmaceuticals" in the online Media Library for this chapter (Video 16.4).

You can use the problem-solution format just as easily to organize a speech opposing a change in policy. In such a speech your job is to defend the current system and to attack your opponents' proposed policy. Thus in the first main point you might argue that there is *not* a need for change. In the second main point you might show that even if there were a serious problem, the suggested new policy would *not* solve it and would create serious problems of its own. For example:

Specific Purpose:	To persuade my audience that the city council should not pass legislation merging the police and fire departments.
Central Idea:	Merging the police and fire departments is neither necessary nor practical.
Main Points:	I. Merging the police and fire departments is not necessary.
	A. Under the current system, the police department has developed a reputation for excellence that has made it a model for departments in other cities,
	B. The fire department is equally well-respected for doing its job quickly and efficiently.

II. Besides being unnecessary, merging the police and fire departments is highly impractical.
   A. Rather than saving the city money, merging the departments would increase costs.
   B. Merging the departments would also harm morale and reduce the high level of performance we expect from our police force and firefighters.

Problem-Cause-Solution Order

problem-cause-solution order

A method of organizing persuasive speeches in which the first main point identifies a problem, the second main point analyzes the causes of the problem, and the third main point presents a solution to the problem.

For a variation on problem-solution order, you might arrange your speech in problem-cause-solution order. This produces a speech with three main points—the first identifying a problem, the second analyzing the causes of the problem, and the third presenting a solution to the problem. For example:

Specific Purpose: To persuade my audience that action is required to deal with the problem of childhood obesity.

Central Idea: Childhood obesity is a serious problem that can be controlled by changes in diet and exercise.

Main Points:
I. Childhood obesity is a major problem in the United States.
   A. Childhood obesity continues to grow at a rapid pace.
   B. Obesity is producing serious health problems among children.

II. There are two major causes of the increase in childhood obesity.
   A. The first cause is dietary.
   B. The second cause is physical inactivity.

III. Solving the problem requires dealing with both causes.
   A. Parents and schools must make sure that children are eating healthy foods.
   B. Parents and schools must also make sure that children get enough exercise.

connect

View an excerpt from "The Epidemic of Childhood Obesity" in the online Media Library for this chapter (Video 16.5).

Some teachers prefer this method of organization because it requires a speaker to identify the causes of the problem. This in turn makes it easier to check whether the proposed solution will get at the causes of the problem.

Comparative Advantages Order

comparative advantages order

A method of organizing persuasive speeches in which each main point explains why a speaker's solution to a problem is preferable to other proposed solutions.

When your audience already agrees that a problem exists, you can devote your speech to comparing the advantages and disadvantages of competing solutions. In such a situation, you might put your speech in comparative advantages order, devoting each main point to explaining why your solution is preferable to other proposed solutions.

Suppose you want to convince your audience that automakers should put greater emphasis on developing hydrogen fuel-cell cars than gas-electric hybrid cars. Using comparative advantages order, you would compare hydrogen cars with gas-electric hybrid cars and show why the former are a better choice. Your specific purpose, central idea, and main points might look like this:

Specific Purpose: To persuade my audience that automakers should put greater emphasis on developing hydrogen fuel-cell cars than gas-electric cars.

Because it follows the process of human thinking, Monroe's motivated sequence is especially useful for persuasive speakers who seek immediate action from their listeners.

Central Idea: Unlike gas-electric cars, hydrogen cars run entirely without gasoline and do not emit air-polluting exhaust.

Main Points: I. Unlike hybrid cars, hydrogen cars run entirely without gasoline.

II. Unlike hybrid cars, hydrogen cars do not emit any air-polluting exhaust.

Monroe's Motivated Sequence

Developed in the 1930s by Alan Monroe, a professor of speech at Purdue University, the motivated sequence is tailor-made for policy speeches that seek immediate action. The sequence has five steps that follow the psychology of persuasion:

1. *Attention.* First, you gain the attention of your audience by using one or more of the methods described in Chapter 10: relating to the audience, showing the importance of the topic, making a startling statement, arousing curiosity or suspense, posing a question, telling a dramatic story, or using visual aids.

2. *Need.* Next, you make the audience feel a need for change. You show there is a serious problem with the existing situation. It is important to state the need clearly and to illustrate it with strong supporting materials. By the end of this step, listeners should be so concerned about the problem that they are psychologically primed to hear your solution.

3. *Satisfaction.* Having aroused a sense of need, you satisfy it by providing a solution to the problem. You present your plan and show how it will work. Be sure to offer enough details about the plan to give listeners a clear understanding of it.

4. *Visualization.* Having given your plan, you intensify desire for it by visualizing its benefits. The key to this step is using vivid imagery to show your listeners how *they* will profit from your policy. Make them *see* how much better conditions will be once your plan is adopted.

> **Monroe's motivated sequence**
>
> A method of organizing persuasive speeches that seek immediate action. The five steps of the motivated sequence are attention, need, satisfaction, visualization, and action.

5. *Action.* Once the audience is convinced your policy is beneficial, you are ready to call for action. Say exactly what you want the audience to do—and how to do it. Then conclude with a final stirring appeal that reinforces their commitment to act.

Many speakers prefer the motivated sequence because it is more detailed than problem-solution order. It follows the process of human thinking and leads the listener step by step to the desired action. One indication of its effectiveness is that it is widely used by people who make their living by persuasion—especially advertisers. The next time you watch television, pay close attention to the commercials. You will find that many of them follow the motivated sequence.

Try using the motivated sequence when you want to spur listeners to action. You should find it easy and effective, as did one student who used it in a speech urging classmates to work for passage of a local tenants' rights bill. Here are the highlights of his speech:

Attention:	Have you ever had cockroaches running through the cupboards in your apartment? Have you shivered in the cold because the furnace was broken? Or waited months for the security deposit you never got back even though you left your apartment as clean as when you moved in?
Need:	Throughout this city students and other tenants are being victimized by unresponsive and unethical landlords. Just last year more than 200 complaints were filed with the city housing department, but no action has been taken against the landlords.
Satisfaction:	These problems could be solved by passing a strong tenants' rights bill that defines the rights of tenants, specifies the obligations of landlords, and imposes strict penalties for violators.
Visualization:	Such bills have worked in a number of college communities across the nation. If one were passed here, you would no longer have to worry about substandard conditions in your apartment. Your landlord could not violate the terms of your lease or steal your security deposit.
Action:	A tenants' rights bill has been proposed to the city council. You can help get it passed by signing the petition I will pass around after my speech. I also urge you to circulate petitions among your friends and to support the bill when it is debated in the city council next week. If we all work together, we can get this bill through the council.

Monroe's motivated sequence is perfectly compatible with the standard method of outlining discussed in Chapter 11. The following outline shows how one speaker incorporated the sequence into a speech urging her classmates to change the way they use their cell phones:

Specific Purpose: To persuade my audience to use their cell phones in a way that will protect their health.

Central Idea:	You can avoid the long-term health risks of cell phone use by making some simple changes.

Introduction

Attention:	I. Your cell phone is your constant companion. You use it everywhere you go, day and night.
	II. But what if your constant companion is dangerous? What if it's hazardous to your health?
	III. After doing extensive research, I hope to persuade each of you to use your cell phone in a manner that will protect your health.

connect

View an excerpt from "The Dangers of Cell Phones" in the online Media Library for this chapter (Video 16.6).

Body

Need:	I. Although cell phones are safe in the short run, they pose serious long-term health risks.
	A. Using a cell phone exposes you to radiation that builds up over time.
	B. More and more scientists are warning about the long-term dangers of cell phone use.
	C. Even cell phone manufacturers warn against keeping phones too close to the body.
Satisfaction:	II. You can guard against these risks by making simple changes in the way you use your cell phone.
	A. Above all, do not press your cell phone against your head while talking.
	B. Get in the habit of using ear buds or your phone's internal speaker.

Using public speaking in your CAREER

After earning your teaching certificate, you landed a job in one of the best public school districts in the state. You've excelled in the classroom, and evaluations of your teaching are consistently outstanding.

But the newly announced state budget means drastic cuts for the district. Either 100 teachers will be laid off, or every teacher will have to accept a 10 percent pay cut. Because the newest teachers are the first to be fired, and you have been on the job for only three years, you know that the only way to keep your position is if all teachers agree to the pay cut. What's more, laying off 100 teachers will mean more students in each classroom, and that will harm the quality of education.

In one week, the school superintendent will hold an open meeting for teachers to voice their opinions. You plan on arguing for the pay cut, but you're unsure of how to organize your speech. Which of the following methods of organization will be most effective, and why: problem-solution, comparative advantages, Monroe's motivated sequence?

Visualization:	III. These changes will help protect your health.
	A. You can use your cell phone without long-term health risks.
	B. You will avoid the fate of people who have developed cancer and other conditions from prolonged cell phone use.

Conclusion

Action:	I. So I encourage each of you to make these changes starting today.
	II. Make sure your constant companion is not endangering your health.

Try using the motivated sequence when you seek immediate action from your listeners. Over the years it has worked for countless speakers—and it can work for you as well.

Sample Speech with Commentary

View "Phony Pharmaceuticals" in the online Media Library for this chapter (Video 16.7).

The following persuasive speech deals with a question of policy and provides an excellent example of problem-solution structure. As you read the speech, notice how the speaker deals with the issues of need, plan, and practicality. Notice also how she uses strong, well-chosen supporting materials to back up her point of view. Finally, observe how clear and uncluttered the speech is. There are few wasted words and the ideas progress cleanly and crisply. You can view the speech in the online Media Library for this chapter.

Phony Pharmaceuticals

COMMENTARY	SPEECH
The speaker captures attention by showing three PowerPoint slides and asking the audience questions about them.	Take a look at these two pills. Do you notice a difference between them? How about these two? Do you see a difference here? How about these?
Notice how the speaker uses "you" throughout her opening to relate the topic directly to her listeners.	To the naked eye, these pills are indistinguishable. But at a chemical level, they are very, very different. In each case, the pill on the left is real; it will help you get better. The pill on the right is counterfeit. It will not help you get better. In some cases, it may even kill you.

The speaker presents expert testimony to define phony pharmaceuticals and to show why they can be harmful.

Katherine Eban, author of *Dangerous Doses: How Counterfeiters Are Contaminating America's Drug Supply,* explains that phony pharmaceuticals are drugs that have been diluted, drugs in which the active ingredient has been replaced with something else, or drugs that have been relabeled to appear stronger than they truly are. Taking a phony pharmaceutical means that you do not receive the medicine you need to get better, and the results can be deadly.

The speaker establishes her credibility by stating that she has a personal connection to the topic and has done substantial research on it. She closes the introduction by stating her central idea and previewing the body of her speech.

I first became aware of this issue after my younger sister received a phony drug for her asthma last summer. Fortunately, the error was discovered before it caused her any lasting harm. But I've been concerned about the issue ever since, and I did a great deal of research on it for this speech. As a result, I am convinced that we need to take action now to combat the problem of phony pharmaceuticals. Later in my speech, I'll share with you my plan for curbing the spread of these dangerous drugs. But let's start by taking a closer look at the problem.

This speech is organized in problem-solution order. Here the speaker starts the problem main point by identifying some of the harmful ingredients found in phony pharmaceuticals.

Phony pharmaceuticals are dangerous because of the health risks they pose. According to Graham Jackson, editor of the *International Journal of Clinical Practice,* counterfeit drugs include ingredients such as boric acid, leaded road paint, floor polish, shoe polish, talcum powder, and cement powder. But that's not all. There's also brick dust, chalk, nickel, and arsenic. Ingesting too much boric acid or floor polish can make you sick; leaded road paint and arsenic can kill you.

The speaker uses an example to illustrate the dangers of phony pharmaceuticals.

In one highly publicized case, 81 people in the United States died in 2008 because they took a counterfeit version of the blood thinner heparin. As reported by CNN, the phony heparin was originally manufactured outside the United States using a cheap sulfate that proved deadly. After slipping past all regulatory checks, it ended up in the United States, with tragic results.

The speaker presents statistics and testimony to show how widespread the problem of phony pharmaceuticals is. Notice how she relates her statistics to the audience.

The U.S. government's Bureau of International Information Programs estimates that 700,000 people around the world will die this year from phony pharmaceuticals—almost three times the number of people who live here in Madison. In fact, Roger Bate, of the American Enterprise Institute, reports that "trafficking in counterfeit drugs has become one of the world's fastest-growing criminal enterprises."

Here, as elsewhere, the speaker cites recent, credible sources and identifies them clearly. The quotation from Tom Kubic is especially effective.

Phony pharmaceuticals are so widespread that they have become big business. The FDA estimates that they will bring in close to $75 billion in revenue this year alone—up from $40 billion only a few years ago. Tom Kubic, head of the Pharmaceutical Security Institute, told *USA Today* in September 2010 that criminals "can make more money in counterfeit drugs than they can in heroin."

A transition moves the speaker into the solution portion of her speech, in which she presents a concise, four-step plan to deal with phony pharmaceuticals.

As the speaker proceeds, she uses a signpost to introduce each part of her plan.

As you can see from the video of this speech, the speaker highlights each point in her plan with a PowerPoint slide.

The rhetorical question at the end of this paragraph invites the audience to draw the same conclusion as the speaker.

Here, as throughout the speech, the speaker uses her voice, gestures, and eye contact to help communicate her ideas and to establish a bond with the audience.

The speaker presents a quotation to show the practicality of her plan. Establishing practicality is always important in a persuasive speech on a question of policy.

The speaker signals the beginning of her conclusion and restates her central idea.

In addition to using language from her introduction, the speaker returns to the PowerPoint slides with which she opened the speech. This makes for a strong ending and gives the speech a sense of psychological unity.

Given the rewards of the counterfeit drug trade, the problem will only get worse in the coming years unless we take steps to bring it under control. The solution I propose is similar to House Resolution 2726, which is under consideration by the U.S. Congress. There are four steps to this solution.

First, criminal penalties for drug counterfeiters should be increased from three years in prison, which is the current limit, to no limit at all. If a drug peddler kills someone with phony pharmaceuticals, the punishment should fit the crime.

Second, the Food and Drug Administration should have the authority to recall prescription drugs. Right now, the FDA can encourage drug manufacturers to issue a recall, but it has no power to issue a recall on its own. To get phony pharmaceuticals off the street, recall authority needs to rest with a central agency that will act quickly and uniformly.

Third, the FDA should be given the resources for spot-checking the chemical makeup of prescription medication. We have health inspectors for food, why not have inspectors for prescription drugs?

Fourth, legitimate drug manufacturers should be required to implement track-and-trace technology. As explained in the *New York Times,* this technology stamps each bottle and pill with a unique code tied to a secure, centralized database. The code allows pharmacies and distributors to determine whether drugs are legitimate or phony, plus the route the drugs took to get to store shelves.

Representative Steve Israel of New York, sponsor of House Resolution 2726, says these four steps will "ensure that the domestic drug supply chain is secure for every American." It "will crack down on counterfeiting and increase the penalties for the outlaws who are compromising our health." The time has come for Congress to pass this vital legislation.

In conclusion, phony pharmaceuticals are pervasive and dangerous. By implementing the solution I have outlined, we will be able to control this public-health menace.

You have the right to know that the medication you're taking is real. You have the right to know that your next trip to the drugstore will be a safe one. And you have the right to know that what you see is what you get.

Summary

Persuasion is the process of creating, reinforcing, or changing people's beliefs or actions. When you speak to persuade, you act as an advocate. The ability to speak persuasively will benefit you in every part of your life, from personal relations to community activities to career aspirations.

How successful you are in any persuasive speech depends on how well you tailor your message to your listeners' values, attitudes, and beliefs. You should think of your speech as a mental dialogue with your audience. Identify your target audience, anticipate objections they may raise to your point of view, and answer those objections in your speech.

Persuasive speeches may center on questions of fact, value, or policy. When giving a persuasive speech about a question of fact, your role is akin to that of a lawyer in a courtroom trial. You will try to get your listeners to accept your view of the facts.

Questions of value involve a person's beliefs about what is right or wrong, good or bad, moral or immoral, ethical or unethical. When speaking about a question of value, you must justify your opinion by establishing standards for your value judgment. Speeches on questions of value do not argue directly for or against particular courses of action.

Once you go beyond arguing right or wrong to urging that something should or should not be done, you move to a question of policy. When you speak on a question of policy, your goal may be to evoke passive agreement or to spark immediate action. In either case, you will face three basic issues—need, plan, and practicality. How much of your speech you devote to each issue will depend on your topic and your audience.

There are several options for organizing speeches on questions of policy. If you advocate a change in policy, your main points will often fall naturally into problem-solution order or into problem-cause-solution order. If your audience already agrees that a problem exists, you may be able to use comparative advantages order. Whenever you seek immediate action from listeners, you should consider a more specialized organizational pattern known as Monroe's motivated sequence.

Regardless of your topic or method of organization, you need to make sure your goals are ethically sound and that you use ethical methods to persuade your audience.

Key Terms

persuasion *(300)*

mental dialogue with the audience *(304)*

target audience *(304)*

question of fact *(305)*

question of value *(307)*

question of policy *(309)*

speech to gain passive agreement *(310)*

speech to gain immediate action *(310)*

need *(311)*

burden of proof *(311)*

plan *(311)*

practicality *(312)*

problem-solution order *(313)*

problem-cause-solution order *(314)*

comparative advantages order *(314)*

Monroe's motivated sequence *(315)*

Review Questions

After reading this chapter, you should be able to answer the following questions:

1. What is the difference between an informative speech and a persuasive speech? Why is speaking to persuade more challenging than speaking to inform?

2. What does it mean to say that audiences engage in a mental dialogue with the speaker as they listen to a speech? What implications does this mental give-and-take hold for effective persuasive speaking?

3. What is the target audience for a persuasive speech?

4. What are questions of fact? How does a persuasive speech on a question of fact differ from an informative speech? Give an example of a specific purpose statement for a persuasive speech on a question of fact.

5. What are questions of value? Give an example of a specific purpose statement for a persuasive speech on a question of value.

6. What are questions of policy? Give an example of a specific purpose statement for a persuasive speech on a question of policy.

7. Explain the difference between passive agreement and immediate action as goals for persuasive speeches on questions of policy.

8. What are the three basic issues you must deal with when discussing a question of policy? What will determine the amount of attention you give to each of these issues in any particular speech?

9. What four methods of organization are used most often in persuasive speeches on questions of policy?

10. What are the five steps of Monroe's motivated sequence? Why is the motivated sequence especially useful in speeches that seek immediate action from listeners?

connect

For further review, go to the LearnSmart study module for this chapter.

Exercises for Critical Thinking

1. Look back at the story of Ramon Trujillo at the beginning of this chapter (page 299). Like Ramon, most people do a certain amount of persuading every day in normal conversation. Keep a journal of your communication activities for an entire day, making special note of all instances in which you tried to persuade someone else to your point of view. Choose one of those instances and prepare a brief analysis of it.

   In your analysis, answer the following questions: (1) Who was the audience for your persuasive effort? (2) What were the "specific purpose" and the "central idea" of your persuasive message? (3) Did you rehearse your persuasive message ahead of time, or did it arise spontaneously from the situation? (4) Were you successful in achieving your specific purpose? (5) If you faced the same situation again, what strategic changes would you make in your persuasive effort?

2. Below are four specific purposes for persuasive speeches. In each case explain whether the speech associated with it concerns a question of fact, a question of

value, or a question of policy. Then rewrite the specific purpose statement to make it appropriate for a speech about one of the other two kinds of questions. For instance, if the original purpose statement is about a question of policy, write a new specific purpose statement that deals with the same topic as either a question of fact or a question of value.

Example:

Original statement: To persuade my audience that it is unfair for judges to favor natural parents over adoptive parents in child custody disputes. (question of value)

Rewritten statement: To persuade my audience that the courts should establish clear guidelines for settling disputes between adoptive parents and natural parents in child custody cases. (question of policy)

a. To persuade my audience that a national sales tax should be adopted to help reduce the national debt.

b. To persuade my audience that it is unethical for doctors to receive money from pharmaceutical companies to promote their products.

c. To persuade my audience that violence in video games is a major cause of violent behavior among teenagers.

d. To persuade my audience to join Teach for America.

3. Choose a topic for a persuasive speech on a question of policy. Create two specific purpose statements about that topic—one for a speech to gain passive agreement, another for a speech to motivate immediate action. Once you have the specific purpose statements, explain how the speech seeking immediate action would differ in structure and persuasive appeals from the speech seeking passive agreement. Be specific.

4. Analyze the sample speech with commentary at the end of this chapter ("Phony Pharmaceuticals," pages 318–320). Because this is a speech on a question of policy, pay special attention to how the speaker deals with the basic issues of need, plan, and practicality. Does the speaker present a convincing case that a serious problem exists? Does she offer a clear plan to solve the problem? Does she demonstrate that the plan is practical?

5. Select a television commercial that is organized according to Monroe's motivated sequence. Prepare a brief analysis in which you (a) identify the target audience for the commercial and (b) describe each step in the motivated sequence as it appears in the commercial.

17

Methods of Persuasion

Building Credibility

Using Evidence

Reasoning

Appealing to Emotions

Sample Speech with Commentary

Persuasion is big business. Thousands of authors and consultants promise to teach you the one key secret to persuading people to do what you want. Dan Lok claims to reveal "forbidden psychological tactics" that will "give you an unfair advantage in dealing with people." Chris St. Hilaire offers "simple strategies to seduce audiences and win allies." Kevin Dutton claims to have discovered "a single, definitive formula" for "a mysterious, previously unidentified, superstrain of persuasion." These people all charge thousands of dollars for their seminars, hundreds for videos and motivational books. Companies and individuals flock—and pay—to read and hear what they have to say.

It sounds good, but can any of these people really have the "one key secret" to persuasion? Probably not. Persuasion is too complicated for that. Yet, as the number of books, seminars, and videos on the subject shows, there is a perpetual fascination with the strategies and tactics of effective persuasion.

What makes a speaker persuasive? Why do listeners accept one speaker's views and reject those of another? How can a speaker motivate listeners to act in support of a cause, a campaign, or a candidate? People have been trying to answer these questions for thousands of years—from the ancient Greek philosopher Aristotle to modern-day communication researchers. Although many answers have been given, we can say that listeners will be persuaded by a speaker for one or more of four reasons:

Because they perceive the speaker as having high *credibility*.

Because they are won over by the speaker's *evidence*.

Because they are convinced by the speaker's *reasoning*.

Because their *emotions* are touched by the speaker's ideas or language.

In this chapter we will look at each of these. We will not discover any magical secrets that will make you an irresistible persuasive speaker. But if you learn the principles discussed in this chapter, you will greatly increase your odds of winning the minds and hearts of your listeners.

Building Credibility

Here are two sets of imaginary statements. Which one of each pair would you be more likely to believe?

The U.S. State Department needs major changes in organization to fulfill its mission in the 21st century. (Hillary Clinton)

The State Department does not need any major organizational changes in the near future. (Johnny Depp)

The key to acting is to push your character as far as you can without making the character unbelievable. (Johnny Depp)

The key to acting is to learn your lines and hit your cues regardless of the character you are playing. (Hillary Clinton)

ethos

The name used by Aristotle for what modern students of communication refer to as credibility.

Most likely you chose the first in each pair of statements. If so, you were probably influenced by your perception of the speaker. You are more likely to respect the judgment of Clinton, Secretary of State under President Barack Obama, when she speaks about the organization of the State Department, and to respect the judgment of Depp, acclaimed for his many screen roles, when he speaks about methods of acting. Some teachers call this factor *source credibility*. Others refer to it as *ethos*, the name given by Aristotle.

FACTORS OF CREDIBILITY

Many things affect a speaker's credibility, including sociability, dynamism, physical attractiveness, and perceived similarity between speaker and audience. Above all, though, credibility is affected by two factors:

- *Competence*—how an audience regards a speaker's intelligence, expertise, and knowledge of the subject.
- *Character*—how an audience regards a speaker's sincerity, trustworthiness, and concern for the well-being of the audience.

The more favorably listeners view a speaker's competence and character, the more likely they are to accept what the speaker says. No doubt you are familiar with this from your own experience. Suppose you take a course in economics. The course is taught by a distinguished professor who has published widely in prestigious journals, who sits on a major international commission, and who has won several awards for outstanding research. In class, you hang on this professor's every word. One day the professor is absent; a colleague from the Economics Department—fully qualified but not as well known—comes to lecture instead. Possibly the fill-in instructor gives the same lecture the distinguished professor would have given, but you do not pay nearly as close attention. The other instructor does not have as high credibility as the professor.

It is important to remember that credibility is an attitude. It exists not in the speaker, but in the mind of the audience. A speaker may have high credibility for one audience and low credibility for another. A speaker may also have high credibility on one topic and low credibility on another. Looking back to our imaginary statements, most people would more readily believe Johnny Depp speaking about acting than Johnny Depp speaking about the organization of the State Department.

TYPES OF CREDIBILITY

Not only can a speaker's credibility vary from audience to audience and topic to topic, but it can also change during the course of a speech—so much so that we can identify three types of credibility:

- *Initial credibility*—the credibility of the speaker before she or he starts to speak.
- *Derived credibility*—the credibility of the speaker produced by everything she or he says and does during the speech itself.
- *Terminal credibility*—the credibility of the speaker at the end of the speech.[1]

All three are dynamic. High initial credibility is a great advantage for any speaker, but it can be destroyed during a speech, resulting in low terminal credibility. The reverse can also occur, as in the following example:

Randall Washington is the information technology manager for a major textbook publisher. Soon after taking the job, he began implementing a new content management system for the company's Web site. He assumed there would be some glitches, but they turned out to be much worse than anything he had imagined. It took nine months to get the new system working properly, and even then people continued to grumble about the confusing interface and unpredictable behavior of the Web site.

A year later, the publishing company decided to purchase new tablet computers that would allow employees to interact more efficiently with data on the internal network. The president of the company asked Randall to take charge of buying the computers and training the staff in their use.

When Randall outlined his plans at a weekly staff meeting, he had low initial credibility. Everyone remembered the content management system, and they were reluctant to go through the same problems again. But Randall realized this and was prepared.

He began by reminding everyone that the president had authorized him to purchase tablet computers that would make their jobs easier and improve office communications. He then acknowledged that he had told them the same thing about the content management system—an admission that drew a laugh and

---

credibility

The audience's perception of whether a speaker is qualified to speak on a given topic. The two major factors influencing a speaker's credibility are competence and character.

initial credibility

The credibility of a speaker before she or he starts to speak.

derived credibility

The credibility of a speaker produced by everything she or he says and does during the speech.

terminal credibility

The credibility of a speaker at the end of the speech.

helped everyone relax. Finally, he explained that he had checked with several other companies that used the same devices, and they all reported that the computers worked flawlessly.

Throughout his presentation, Randall's approach was "I know the content management system was a disaster, and I've worked hard to make sure it doesn't happen again." By the time he finished, most staff members were eager to begin using their tablet computers. Randall had achieved high terminal credibility.

In every speech you give you will have some degree of initial credibility, which will be strengthened or weakened by your message and how you deliver it. And your terminal credibility from one speech will affect your initial credibility for the next one. If your audience sees you as sincere and competent, they will be much more receptive to your ideas.

ENHANCING YOUR CREDIBILITY

How can you build your credibility in your speeches? At one level, the answer is frustratingly general. Since everything you say and do in a speech will affect your credibility, you should say and do *everything* in a way that will make you appear capable and trustworthy. In other words—give a brilliant speech and you will achieve high credibility!

The advice is sound, but not all that helpful. There are, however, some specific ways you can boost your credibility while speaking. They include explaining your competence, establishing common ground with the audience, and speaking with genuine conviction.

Explain Your Competence

One way to enhance your credibility is to advertise your expertise on the speech topic. Did you investigate the topic thoroughly? Then say so. Do you have experience that gives you special knowledge or insight? Again, say so.

Here is how two students revealed their qualifications. The first stressed her study and research:

> Before I studied antibacterial products in my public-health class, I always used antibacterial soaps and antibacterial all-surface cleaner for my apartment. I also know from my class survey that 70 percent of you use antibacterial soaps, cleaners, or other products. But after learning about the subject in class and reading research studies for this speech, I'm here to tell you that, try as we might, we cannot build a bubble between ourselves and germs with antibacterial products and that these products actually create more problems than they solve.

The second student emphasized her background and personal experience:

> Most of us have no idea what it means to be poor and hungry. But before returning to school last year, I spent three years working at local assistance centers. I can't tell you everything I have seen. But on the basis of what I can tell you, I hope you will agree with me that government help for the poor and needy must be maintained.

Both speakers greatly increased their persuasiveness by establishing their credibility.

A speaker's credibility has a powerful impact on how his or her speech is received. One way to boost your credibility is to deliver your speeches expressively and with strong eye contact.

Establish Common Ground with Your Audience

Another way to bolster your credibility is to establish common ground with your audience. You do not persuade listeners by assaulting their values and rejecting their opinions. As the old saying goes, "You catch more flies with honey than with vinegar." The same is true of persuasion. Show respect for your listeners. You can make your speech more appealing by identifying your ideas with those of your audience—by showing how your point of view is consistent with what they believe.[2]

Creating common ground is especially important at the start of a persuasive speech. Begin by identifying with your listeners. Show that you share their values, attitudes, and experiences. Get them nodding their heads in agreement, and they will be much more receptive to your ultimate proposal. Here is how a businesswoman from Massachusetts, hoping to sell her product to an audience in Colorado, began her persuasive speech:

> I have never been in Colorado before, but I really looked forward to making this trip. A lot of my ancestors left Massachusetts and came to Colorado nearly 150 years ago. Sometimes I have wondered why they did it. They came in covered wagons, carrying all their possessions, and many of them died on the journey. The ones who got through raised their houses and raised their families. Now that I've seen Colorado, I understand why they tried so hard!

The audience laughed and applauded, and the speaker was off to a good start.

Now look at a different approach, used in a classroom speech favoring a tuition increase at the speaker's school—an unpopular point of view with his classmates. He began by saying:

> As we all know, there are many differences among the people in this class. But regardless of age, major, background, or goals, we all share one thing in common—we're all concerned about the quality of education at this school. And that quality is clearly in danger.
>
> The economic crisis has hit every aspect of life, and education is no exception. Budgets are shrinking, faculty salaries are falling, student services are disappearing,

creating common ground

A technique in which a speaker connects himself or herself with the values, attitudes, or experiences of the audience.

connect

View this excerpt from "Let's Protect the Quality of Our Education" in the online Media Library for this chapter (Video 17.2).

and we are being crowded out of classes we need to take. Whether we like it or not, we have a problem—a problem that affects each of us.

There are no easy answers, but one thing that will help solve the problem is an increase in tuition. I don't like it any more than you do, but sometimes we have to do what is necessary to protect the quality of our education.

By stressing common perceptions of the problem, the student hoped to get off on the right foot with his audience. Once that was done, he moved gradually to his more controversial ideas.

Deliver Your Speeches Fluently, Expressively, and with Conviction

There is a great deal of research to show that a speaker's credibility is strongly affected by his or her delivery. Moderately fast speakers, for example, are usually seen as more intelligent and confident than slower speakers. So too are speakers who use vocal variety to communicate their ideas in a lively, animated way. On the other hand, speakers who consistently lose their place, hesitate frequently, or pepper their talk with "uh," "er," and "um" are seen as less competent than speakers who are poised and dynamic.[3]

All of this argues for practicing your persuasive speech fully ahead of time so you can deliver it fluently and expressively. In addition to being better prepared, you will take a major step toward enhancing your credibility. (Review Chapter 13 if you have questions about speech delivery.)

Speaking techniques aside, the most important way to strengthen your credibility is to deliver your speeches with genuine conviction. President Harry Truman once said that in speaking, "sincerity, honesty, and a straightforward manner are more important than special talent or polish." If you wish to convince others, you must first convince yourself. If you want others to believe and care about your ideas, you must believe and care about them yourself. Your spirit, enthusiasm, and conviction will carry over to your listeners.

Using Evidence

Evidence consists of supporting materials—examples, statistics, testimony—used to prove or disprove something. As we saw in Chapter 8, most people are skeptical. They are suspicious of unsupported generalizations. They want speakers to justify their claims. If you hope to be persuasive, you must support your views with evidence. Whenever you say something that is open to question, you should give evidence to prove you are right.

Evidence is particularly important in classroom speeches because few students are recognized as experts on their speech topics. Research has shown that speakers with very high initial credibility do not need to use as much evidence as do speakers with lower credibility. For most speakers, though, strong evidence is absolutely necessary. It can enhance your credibility, increase both the immediate and long-term persuasiveness of your message, and help "inoculate" listeners against counterpersuasion.[4]

Evidence is also crucial whenever your target audience opposes your point of view. As we saw in Chapter 16, listeners in such a situation will mentally argue with you—asking questions, raising objections, and creating counterarguments to "answer" what you say. The success of your speech will depend partly on how well you anticipate these internal responses and give evidence to refute them.

evidence

Supporting materials used to prove or disprove something.

You may want to review Chapter 8, which shows how to use supporting materials. The following case study illustrates how they work as evidence in a persuasive speech.

HOW EVIDENCE WORKS: A CASE STUDY

Let's say one of your classmates is talking about the harmful effects of repeated exposure to loud music and other noises. Instead of just telling you what she thinks, the speaker offers strong evidence to prove her point. Notice how she carries on a mental dialogue with her listeners. She imagines what they might be thinking, anticipates their questions and objections, and gives evidence to answer the questions and resolve the objections.

She begins this way:

As college students we are exposed to loud music and other noise all the time. We go to parties, clubs, and concerts where the volume is so loud we have to shout so the person next to us can hear what we are saying. We turn our iPods so high they can be heard halfway across the room. And we seldom give it a second thought. But we should, because excessive noise can have a serious impact on our health and well-being.

How do you react? If you already know about the problems caused by noise pollution, you probably nod your head in agreement. But what if you don't know? Or don't agree? If you enjoy rock concerts and listening to your iPod at high volumes, you probably don't *want* to hear about it. Certainly you will not be persuaded by a general statement about exposure to loud music. Mentally you say to the speaker, "How do you know? Can you prove it?"

Anticipating just such a response, the speaker gives evidence to support her point:

The American Medical Association reports that 36 million Americans have some degree of hearing loss, and that 17 million of those cases are caused by too much exposure to loud noise.

"That's unfortunate," you may think. "But everyone loses some hearing as they grow old. Why should I be concerned about it now?" The speaker answers:

In an alarming trend, more and more victims of noise-induced deafness are adolescents and even younger children. According to the American Academy of Audiology, 12 percent of children in the United States between ages 6 and 19 have some hearing damage from amplified music and other sources. Audiologist Dean Garstecki, head of the hearing-impairment program at Northwestern University, says, "We've got 21-year-olds walking around with hearing-loss patterns of people 40 years their senior."

"These are impressive facts," you say to yourself. "Luckily, I haven't noticed any problems with my hearing. When I do, I'll just be careful until it gets better." Keeping one step ahead of you, the speaker continues:

The problem with hearing loss is that it creeps up on you. *Sierra* magazine notes that today's hard-rock fans won't notice the effects of their hearing loss for another 15 years. And then it will be too late.

"What do you mean, too late?" you ask mentally. The speaker tells you:

Unlike some physical conditions, hearing loss is irreversible. Loud noise damages the microscopic hairs in the inner ear that transmit sound to the auditory nerve. Once damaged, those hairs can never recover and can never be repaired.

"I didn't know that," you say to yourself. "Is there anything else?"

One last point. Repeated exposure to loud music and other noise does more than damage your hearing. The Hearing Loss Association of America reports that excessive noise has been linked to such problems as stress, high blood pressure, chronic headaches, learning disorders, even heart disease. It's easy to see why Jill Lipoti, chief of Rutgers University's Noise Technical Assistance Center, warns that "noise affects more people than any other pollutant."

Now are you convinced? Chances are you will at least think about the possible consequences the next time you are set to pump up the volume on your iPod. Maybe you will use earplugs at a rock concert. You may even begin to reassess your whole attitude toward noise pollution. Why? Because the speaker supported each of her claims with evidence. You should try to do the same in your persuasive speeches.

TIPS FOR USING EVIDENCE

Any of the supporting materials discussed in Chapter 8—examples, statistics, testimony—can work as evidence in a persuasive speech. As we saw in that chapter, there are guidelines for using each kind of supporting material regardless of the kind of speech you are giving. Here we look at four special tips for using evidence in a persuasive speech.

Use Specific Evidence

No matter what kind of evidence you employ—statistics, examples, or testimony—it will be more persuasive if you state it in specific rather than general terms.[5] In the speech about noise pollution, for instance, the speaker did not say, "Lots of people suffer from hearing loss." That would have left the audience wondering how many "lots" amounts to. By saying "36 million Americans have some degree of hearing loss," the speaker made her point much more effectively. She also enhanced her credibility by showing she had a firm grasp of the facts.

Use Novel Evidence

Evidence is more likely to be persuasive if it is new to the audience.[6] You will gain little by citing facts and figures that are already well known to your listeners. If they have not persuaded your listeners already, they will not do so now. You must go beyond what the audience already knows and present striking new evidence that will get them to say, "Hmmm, I didn't know *that*. Maybe I should rethink the issue." Finding such evidence usually requires hard digging and resourceful research, but the rewards are worth the effort.

Use Evidence from Credible Sources

Listeners find evidence from competent, credible sources more persuasive than evidence from less qualified sources.[7] Above all, listeners are suspicious of evidence from sources that appear to be biased or self-interested. In assessing

Persuasive speeches need strong evidence to convince skeptical listeners. Finding the best evidence often takes hard digging, but it is well worth the effort.

the current state of airline safety, for example, they are more likely to be persuaded by testimony from impartial aviation experts than from the president of American Airlines. If you wish to be persuasive, rely on evidence from objective, nonpartisan sources.

Make Clear the Point of Your Evidence

When speaking to persuade, you use evidence to prove a point. Yet you would be surprised how many novice speakers present their evidence without making clear the point it is supposed to prove. A number of studies have shown that you cannot count on listeners to draw, on their own, the conclusion you want them to reach.[8] When using evidence, be sure listeners understand the point you are trying to make.

Notice, for example, how the speaker in Video 17.3 in the online Media Library for this chapter drives home the point of her evidence about the number of motor vehicle fatalities involving teenage drivers:

According to the National Highway Traffic Safety Administration, while teenagers make up 7 percent of the nation's licensed drivers, they represent 14 percent of all motor vehicle fatalities. The NHTSA reports that last year 3,657 drivers aged 16 to 20 were killed in automobile accidents. In addition to killing the drivers, these same accidents took the lives of 2,384 teenage passengers. But these accidents didn't affect teenagers alone. They also took the lives of 2,625 people aged 21 or older.

So the total number of people killed last year in automobile accidents involving teenage drivers was 8,666—almost exactly the number of full-time students at this campus.

Evidence is one element of what Aristotle referred to as *logos*—the logical appeal of a speaker. The other major element of logos is reasoning, which works in combination with evidence to help make a speaker's claims persuasive.

connect
View this excerpt from "Putting the Brakes on Teenage Driving" in the online Media Library for this chapter (Video 17.3).

logos

The name used by Aristotle for the logical appeal of a speaker. The two major elements of logos are evidence and reasoning.

checklist

Evidence

YES	NO	
☐	☐	1. Are all my major claims supported by evidence?
☐	☐	2. Do I use sufficient evidence to convince my audience of my claims?
☐	☐	3. Is my evidence stated in specific rather than general terms?
☐	☐	4. Do I use evidence that is new to my audience?
☐	☐	5. Is my evidence from credible, unbiased sources?
☐	☐	6. Do I identify the sources of my evidence?
☐	☐	7. Is my evidence clearly linked to each point that it is meant to prove?
☐	☐	8. Do I provide evidence to answer possible objections the audience may have to my position?

Reasoning

The story is told about Hack Wilson, a hard-hitting outfielder for the Brooklyn Dodgers baseball team in the 1930s.[9] Wilson was a great player, but he had a fondness for the good life. His drinking exploits were legendary. He was known to spend the entire night on the town, stagger into the team's hotel at the break of dawn, grab a couple hours sleep, and get to the ballpark just in time for the afternoon game.

This greatly distressed Max Carey, Wilson's manager. At the next team meeting, Carey spent much time explaining the evils of drink. To prove his point, he stood beside a table on which he had placed two glasses and a plate of live angleworms. One glass was filled with water, the other with gin—Wilson's favorite beverage. With a flourish Carey dropped a worm into the glass of water. It wriggled happily. Next Carey plunged the same worm into the gin. It promptly stiffened and expired.

A murmur ran through the room, and some players were obviously impressed. But not Wilson. He didn't even seem interested. Carey waited a little, hoping for some delayed reaction from his wayward slugger. When none came, he prodded, "Do you follow my reasoning, Wilson?"

"Sure, skipper," answered Wilson. "It proves that if you drink gin, you'll never get worms!"

And what does this story prove? No matter how strong your evidence, you will not be persuasive unless listeners grasp your reasoning.

Reasoning is the process of drawing a conclusion based on evidence. Sometimes we reason well—as when we conclude that ice particles forming

Reasoning is an important part of persuasive speaking. In a legal trial, for example, neither the prosecution nor the defense is likely to sway the jury unless their reasoning is clear and convincing.

on the trees may mean the roads will be slippery. Other times we reason less effectively—as when we conclude that spilling salt will bring bad luck. Most superstitions are actually no more than instances of faulty reasoning.

Reasoning in public speaking is an extension of reasoning in other aspects of life. As a public speaker, you have two major concerns with respect to reasoning. First, you must make sure your own reasoning is sound. Second, you must try to get listeners to agree with your reasoning. Let us look, then, at four basic methods of reasoning and how to use them in your speeches.

reasoning

The process of drawing a conclusion on the basis of evidence.

REASONING FROM SPECIFIC INSTANCES

When you reason from specific instances, you progress from a number of particular facts to a general conclusion.[10] For example:

reasoning from specific instances

Reasoning that moves from particular facts to a general conclusion.

Fact 1:   My physical education course last term was easy.

Fact 2:   My roommate's physical education course was easy.

Fact 3:   My brother's physical education course was easy.

Conclusion: Physical education courses are easy.

As this example suggests, we use reasoning from specific instances daily, although we probably don't realize it. Think for a moment of all the general conclusions that arise in conversation: Politicians are corrupt. Professors are bookish. Dorm food is awful. Where do such conclusions come from? They come from observing particular politicians, professors, dormitories, and so on.

The same thing happens in public speaking. The speaker who concludes that unethical banking practices are common in the United States because several major banks have been guilty of fraud in recent years is reasoning from specific instances. So is the speaker who argues that anti-Semitism is increasing on college campuses because there have been a number of attacks on Jewish students and symbols at schools across the nation.

Such conclusions are never foolproof. No matter how many specific instances you give (and you can give only a few in a speech), it is always possible that an exception exists. Throughout the ages people observed countless white swans in Europe without seeing any of a different color. It seemed an undeniable fact that all swans were white. Then, in the 19th century, black swans were discovered in Australia![11]

When you reason from specific instances, beware of jumping to conclusions on the basis of insufficient evidence. Make sure your sample of specific instances is large enough to justify your conclusion.

Also make sure the instances you present are fair, unbiased, and representative. (Are three physical education courses *enough* to conclude that physical education courses in general are easy? Are the three courses *typical* of most physical education courses?)

Finally, reinforce your argument with statistics or testimony. Because you can never give enough specific instances in a speech to make your conclusion irrefutable, you should supplement them with testimony or statistics demonstrating that the instances are representative.

REASONING FROM PRINCIPLE

Reasoning from principle is the opposite of reasoning from specific instances. It moves from the general to the specific.[12] When you reason from principle, you progress from a general principle to a specific conclusion. We are all familiar with this kind of reasoning from statements such as the following:

1. All people are mortal.
2. Socrates is a person.
3. Therefore, Socrates is mortal.

This is a classic example of reasoning from principle. You begin with a general statement ("All people are mortal"), move to a minor premise ("Socrates is a person"), and end with a specific conclusion ("Socrates is mortal").

reasoning from principle

Reasoning that moves from a general principle to a specific conclusion.

Speakers often use reasoning from principle when trying to persuade an audience. One of the clearest examples from American history is Susan B. Anthony's famous speech "Is It a Crime for a U.S. Citizen to Vote?" Delivered on numerous occasions in 1872 and 1873, at a time when women were legally barred from voting, Anthony's speech reasoned along the following lines:

1. The United States Constitution guarantees all U.S. citizens the right to vote.
2. Women are U.S. citizens.
3. Therefore, the United States Constitution guarantees women the right to vote.

This argument progresses from a general principle ("The United States Constitution guarantees all U.S. citizens the right to vote") through a minor premise ("Women are U.S. citizens") to a conclusion ("Therefore, the United States Constitution guarantees women the right to vote").

When you use reasoning from principle in a speech, pay special attention to your general principle. Will listeners accept it without evidence? If not, give evidence to support it before moving to your minor premise. You may also need to support your minor premise with evidence. When both the general principle and the minor premise are soundly based, your audience will be much more likely to accept your conclusion.

CAUSAL REASONING

There is a patch of ice on the sidewalk. You slip, fall, and break your arm. You reason as follows: "*Because* that patch of ice was there, I fell and broke my arm." This is an example of causal reasoning, in which someone tries to establish the relationship between causes and effects.

As with reasoning from specific instances, we use causal reasoning daily. Something happens and we ask what caused it to happen. We want to know the causes of chronic fatigue syndrome, of the football team's latest defeat, of our roommate's peculiar habits. We also wonder about effects. We speculate about the consequences of chronic fatigue syndrome, of the star quarterback's leg injury, of telling our roommate that a change is needed.

As any scientist (or detective) will tell you, causal reasoning can be tricky. The relationship between causes and effects is not always clear. For example, the fact that one event happens after another does not mean that the first is the cause of the second. The closeness in time of the two events may be entirely coincidental. If a black cat crosses your path and five minutes later you fall and break your arm, you needn't blame your accident on the poor cat.

You also need to beware of assuming that events have only one cause. In fact, most events have several causes. What causes the economy to boom or bust? Interest rates? Gas prices? Tax policy? Labor costs? Consumer confidence? World affairs? *All* these factors—and others—affect the economy. When you use causal reasoning, be wary of the temptation to attribute complex events to single causes.

ANALOGICAL REASONING

When arguing from analogy, a speaker compares two similar cases and infers that what is true for one case is also true for the other: For example:

> If you're good at tennis, you will probably be good at Ping-Pong.

Although playing Ping-Pong is not exactly the same as playing tennis, the two are close enough that the speaker is on firm ground in concluding that being skilled at one significantly increases the odds of being skilled at the other.

Analogical reasoning is used frequently in persuasive speeches—especially when the speaker is dealing with a question of policy. When arguing for a new policy, you should find out whether it has been tried elsewhere. You may be able to claim that your policy will work because it has worked in like circumstances. Here is how one speaker used reasoning from analogy to support her claim that controlling handguns will reduce violent crime in the United States:

> Will my policy work? The experience of foreign countries suggests it will. In England, guns are tightly regulated; even the police are unarmed, and the murder rate is trivial by American standards. Japan has even fewer guns than England, and its crime rate is lower than England's. On the basis of these comparisons, we can conclude that restricting the ownership of guns will control crime and murder rates in America.

By the same token, if you argue against a change in policy, you should check whether the proposed policy—or something like it—has been implemented elsewhere. Here, too, you may be able to support your case by reasoning from analogy—as did one speaker who opposed gun control:

Advocates of gun control point to foreign countries such as England and Japan to prove their case. But the key to low personal violence in these and other countries is the peaceful character of the people, not gun control laws. Switzerland, for example, has a militia system; more than 1 million automatic rifles and military pistols are sitting at this moment in Swiss homes. Yet Switzerland's murder rate is only 8 percent of ours. In other words, cultural factors are more important than gun control when it comes to violent crime.

As these examples illustrate, argument from analogy can be used on both sides of an issue. You are more likely to persuade your audience if the analogy shows a truly parallel situation.

FALLACIES

fallacy

An error in reasoning.

A fallacy is an error in reasoning. As a speaker, you need to avoid fallacies in your speeches. As a listener, you need to be alert to fallacies in the speeches you hear.

Logicians have identified more than 125 different fallacies. Here we look at 10 that you should guard against.

Hasty Generalization

hasty generalization

A fallacy in which a speaker jumps to a general conclusion on the basis of insufficient evidence.

Hasty generalization is the most common fallacy in reasoning from specific instances. It occurs when a speaker jumps to a conclusion on the basis of too few cases or on the basis of atypical cases. For example:

Throughout American history, military leaders have always made excellent Presidents. Look at the examples of George Washington, Andrew Jackson, and Dwight Eisenhower.

Washington, Jackson, and Eisenhower are widely regarded as outstanding chief executives, but are these examples enough to conclude that military leaders *always* make excellent Presidents? In fact, they are not. James Buchanan and Ulysses S. Grant were both highly decorated military leaders during the 19th century, but they are usually rated among the nation's worst Presidents. An accurate statement would be:

Throughout American history, military leaders have sometimes made excellent Presidents—as with Washington, Jackson, and Eisenhower.

This statement is factually correct and avoids the fallacy of hasty generalization.

False Cause

false cause

A fallacy in which a speaker mistakenly assumes that because one event follows another, the first event is the cause of the second.

The fallacy of false cause is often known by its Latin name, *post hoc, ergo propter hoc,* which means "after this, therefore because of this." In other words, the fact that one event occurs after another does not mean that the first is the cause of the second. The closeness in time of the two events may be entirely coincidental—as in this case:

In addition to using evidence to support their ideas, effective persuasive speakers rely on research to help them avoid fallacies that may undermine their credibility and persuasiveness.

When a team from the NFC wins the Super Bowl, economic growth during the next year is stronger than when a team from the AFC wins the Super Bowl. Therefore, if we want economic growth, we should root for a team from the NFC to win this year's Super Bowl.

There may be a slight correlation between economic growth and which conference wins the Super Bowl, but there is no *causal* connection between the two events. Whether the American economy rises or falls is not dependent on who wins the Super Bowl.

Invalid Analogy

As we saw on pages 337–338, when reasoning from analogy, a speaker concludes that what is true in one case is also true in another. An invalid analogy occurs when the two cases being compared are not essentially alike. For example:

invalid analogy

An analogy in which the two cases being compared are not essentially alike.

Employees are like nails. Just as nails must be hit on the head to get them to work, so must employees.

This statement is obviously fallacious. No one in his or her right mind can seriously think that employees, which are human beings, can be compared with inanimate objects such as nails.

But what about the following statement:

In Great Britain, the general election campaign for Prime Minister lasts less than three weeks. Surely we can do the same with the U.S. presidential election.

At first glance, this analogy may seem perfectly sound. But are the British and American political systems enough alike to warrant the conclusion? Not really. The United States is much larger than Great Britain and its party system operates much differently. As a result, the factors that allow Great Britain to conduct campaigns for Prime Minister in less than three weeks are not present in the United States. The analogy is not valid.

As this example suggests, determining whether an analogy is valid or invalid is not always easy, but doing so is important for speakers and listeners alike.

Bandwagon

How often have you heard someone say, "It's a great idea—everyone agrees with it"? This is a classic example of the bandwagon fallacy, which assumes that because something is popular, it is therefore good, correct, or desirable.

Much advertising is based on the bandwagon fallacy. The fact that more people use Tylenol than Advil does not prove that Tylenol is a better pain-killer. Tylenol's popularity could be due to clever marketing. The question of which product does a better job reducing pain is a medical issue that has nothing to do with popularity.

The bandwagon fallacy is also evident in political speeches. Consider the following statement:

> The governor must be correct in his approach to social policy; after all, the polls show that 60 percent of the people support him.

This statement is fallacious because popular opinion cannot be taken as proof that an idea is right or wrong. Remember, "everyone" used to believe that the world is flat and that space flight is impossible.

Red Herring

The name of this fallacy comes from an old trick used by farmers in England to keep fox hunters and their hounds from galloping through the crops. By dragging a smoked herring with a strong odor along the edge of their fields, the farmers could throw the dogs off track by destroying the scent of the fox.

A speaker who uses a red herring introduces an irrelevant issue in order to divert attention from the subject under discussion. For instance:

> How dare my opponents accuse me of political corruption at a time when we are working to improve the quality of life for all people in the United States.

What does the speaker's concern about the quality of life in the United States have to do with whether he or she is guilty of political corruption? Nothing! It is a red herring used to divert attention away from the real issue.

Ad Hominem

Latin for "against the man," *ad hominem* refers to the fallacy of attacking the person rather than dealing with the real issue in dispute. For instance:

> The head of the commerce commission has a number of interesting economic proposals, but let's not forget that she comes from a very wealthy family.

By impugning the commissioner's family background rather than dealing with the substance of her economic proposals, the speaker is engaging in an *ad hominem* attack.

Sometimes, of course, a person's character or integrity can be a legitimate issue—as in the case of a police chief who violates the law or a corporate president who swindles stockholders. In such cases, a speaker might well raise questions about the person without being guilty of the *ad hominem* fallacy.

Either-Or

Sometimes referred to as a false dilemma, the either-or fallacy forces listeners to choose between two alternatives when more than two alternatives exist. For example:

> The government must either raise taxes or eliminate services for the poor.

This statement oversimplifies a complex issue by reducing it to a simple either-or choice. Is it true that the only choices are to raise taxes or to eliminate services for the poor? A careful listener might ask, "What about cutting the administrative cost of government or eliminating pork-barrel projects instead?"

You will be more persuasive as a speaker and more perceptive as a listener if you are alert to the either-or fallacy.

Slippery Slope

The slippery slope fallacy takes its name from the image of a boulder rolling uncontrollably down a steep hill. Once the boulder gets started, it can't be stopped until it reaches the bottom.

A speaker who commits the slippery slope fallacy assumes that taking a first step will lead inevitably to a second step and so on down the slope to disaster—as in the following example:

> Now that the TSA is allowed to use full body scanners and invasive pat-downs before letting us through security, it's only a matter of time before they strip-search every man, woman, and child who wants to fly on a plane.

If a speaker claims that taking a first step will lead inevitably to a series of disastrous later steps, he or she needs to provide evidence or reasoning to support the claim. To assume that all the later steps will occur without proving that they will is to commit the slippery slope fallacy.

Appeal to Tradition

Appeal to tradition is fallacious when it assumes that something old is automatically better than something new. For example:

> I don't see any reason to abolish the electoral college. It has been around since the adoption of the U.S. Constitution in 1787, and we should keep it as long as the United States continues to exist.

There are good arguments on both sides of the debate over abolishing the electoral college. However, to conclude that the electoral college should be kept forever solely because it has always been a part of the U.S. Constitution commits the fallacy of appeal to tradition.

Just because a practice, an institution, or an idea is old does not automatically make it better. Its value should be based on its contributions to society, not on its age. If tradition were the sole measure of value, we would still have slavery, women would not be able to vote, and people would undergo surgery without anesthesia.

As the service manager for a local home improvement company, you have been pleased to see your company expand its size and scope, but you don't want that growth to come at the expense of customer service. In particular, you're worried about losing touch with one of the company's key demographics—women, who make up 55 percent of your customer base. To prevent this from happening, you have developed a plan for a range of personalized services targeted at women, including one-on-one teaching of do-it-yourself skills and free in-home consultations.

When you present your plan at a meeting of the company's management team, you listen as one executive argues in opposition. Among his points are the following: (1) If your plan is adopted, customers will expect more and more special services and eventually will demand free installation of flooring and carpeting; (2) Because a majority of the management team opposes your plan, it must not be a good idea; (3) One of your competitors tried a customer service plan specifically for women, but it did not succeed; therefore, your plan is doomed to failure.

In your response to the executive, you will point out the fallacy in each of his points. What are those fallacies?

Appeal to Novelty

appeal to novelty

A fallacy which assumes that something new is automatically better than something old.

The fallacy of appeal to novelty is the opposite of appeal to tradition. Appeal to novelty assumes that because something is new, it is therefore superior to something that is older. For example:

> Our church should adopt the 2011 New International Version of the Bible because it is 400 years newer than the King James Version.

The fact that the New International Version of the Bible is newer than the King James Version (completed in 1611), does not *automatically* make it better. There are many reasons why a church might prefer the New International Version, but the speaker should *explain* those reasons, rather than assuming that one version is better than another simply because it is new.

Advertisers often commit the fallacy of appeal to novelty. They tout their latest products as "new and improved," yet we know from experience that new does not always mean improved. As always, we need to look carefully at the claim and make sure it is based on sound reasoning.[13]

Appealing to Emotions

Effective persuasion often requires emotional appeal. As the Roman rhetorician Quintilian stated, "It is feeling and force of imagination that make us eloquent."[14] By adding "feeling" and the "force of imagination" to your logical arguments, you can become a more compelling persuasive speaker.

WHAT ARE EMOTIONAL APPEALS?

Emotional appeals—what Aristotle referred to as *pathos*—are intended to make listeners feel sad, angry, guilty, afraid, happy, proud, sympathetic, reverent, or the like. These are often appropriate reactions when the question is one of value or policy. As George Campbell wrote in his *Philosophy of Rhetoric*, "When persuasion is the end, passion also must be engaged."[15]

Below is a list of some of the emotions evoked most often by public speakers. Following each emotion are a few examples of subjects that might stir that emotion:

- *Fear*—of serious illness, of natural disasters, of sexual assault, of personal rejection, of economic hardship.

- *Compassion*—for the physically disabled, for battered women, for neglected animals, for starving children, for victims of AIDS.

- *Pride*—in one's country, in one's family, in one's school, in one's ethnic heritage, in one's personal accomplishments.

- *Anger*—at terrorists and their supporters, at business leaders who act unethically, at members of Congress who abuse the public trust, at landlords who exploit student tenants, at vandals and thieves.

- *Guilt*—about not helping people less fortunate than ourselves, about not considering the rights of others, about not doing one's best.

- *Reverence*—for an admired person, for traditions and institutions, for one's deity.

There are many other emotions and many other subjects that might stir them. However, this brief sample should give you an idea of the kinds of emotional appeals you might use to enhance the message of your persuasive speech.

Emotional appeals often make a persuasive speech more compelling. Such appeals should always be used ethically and should not be substituted for facts and logic.

GENERATING EMOTIONAL APPEAL

Use Emotional Language

As we saw in Chapter 12, one way to generate emotional appeal is to use emotion-laden words. Here, for instance, is part of the conclusion from a student speech about the challenges and rewards of working as a community volunteer with young children:

> The promise of America sparkles in the eyes of every child. Their dreams are the glittering dreams of America. When those dreams are dashed, when innocent hopes are betrayed, so are the dreams and hopes of the entire nation. It is our duty—to me, it is a sacred duty—to give all children the chance to learn and grow, to share equally in the American dream of freedom, justice, and opportunity.

The underlined words and phrases have strong emotional power, and in this case they produced the desired effect. Be aware, however, that packing too many emotionally charged words into one part of a speech can call attention to the emotional language itself and undermine its impact. The emotion rests in your audience, not in your words. Even the coldest facts can touch off an emotional response if they strike the right chords in a listener.

Develop Vivid Examples

Often a better approach than relying on emotionally charged language is to let emotional appeal grow naturally out of the content of your speech. The most effective way to do this is with vivid, richly textured examples that pull listeners into the speech.

Here is how one speaker used a vivid example for emotional appeal. She was speaking about the malaria epidemic in Africa. Here is what she might have said, stripping the content of emotional appeal:

> Malaria is one of the biggest problems facing Africa. Many die from it every day. If the rest of the world doesn't help, the malaria epidemic will only get worse.

connect

View this excerpt from "The Tragedy of Malaria" in the online Media Library for this chapter (Video 17.4).

What she actually said went something like this:

> Nathan was only five years old when the fever struck him. At first, no one knew what was wrong. No one knew that parasites inside his body had infected his red blood cells. No one knew those cells were clumping together, choking the flow of blood through his body and damaging his vital organs. No one knew his kidneys would soon fail and seizures would begin. No one knew he would wind up in a coma.
>
> The parasites in Nathan's body came from a mosquito bite, a bite that gave him malaria. And Nathan is not alone. The World Health Organization tells us the horrible truth: In Africa, a child dies from malaria every 30 seconds.

People who listen to a speech like that will not soon forget it. They may well be moved to action—as the speaker intends. The first speech, however, is not nearly as compelling. Listeners may well nod their heads, think to themselves "good idea"—and then forget about it. The story of Nathan and his tragic fate gives the second speech emotional impact and brings it home to listeners in personal terms.

Speak with Sincerity and Conviction

Ronald Reagan was one of the most effective speakers in U.S. history. Even people who disagreed with his political views often found him irresistible. Why? Partly because he seemed to speak with great sincerity and conviction.

What was true for Reagan is true for you as well. The strongest source of emotional power is your conviction and sincerity. All your emotion-laden words and examples are but empty trappings unless *you* feel the emotion yourself. And if you do, your emotion will communicate itself to the audience through everything you say and do—not only through your words, but also through your tone of voice, rate of speech, gestures, and facial expressions.

ETHICS AND EMOTIONAL APPEAL

Much has been written about the ethics of emotional appeal in speechmaking. Some people have taken the extreme position that ethical speakers should avoid emotional appeal entirely. To support this view, they point to speakers who have used emotional appeal to fan the flames of hatred, bigotry, and fanaticism.

There is no question that emotional appeals can be abused by unscrupulous speakers for detestable causes. But emotional appeals can also be wielded by honorable speakers for noble causes—by Winston Churchill to rouse the world against Adolf Hitler and the forces of Nazism, by Martin Luther King to call for racial justice. Few people would question the ethics of emotional appeal in these instances.

Nor is it always possible to draw a sharp line between reason and emotional appeal. Think back to the story of Nathan, the five-year-old boy who was infected with malaria. The story certainly has strong emotional appeal. But is there anything unreasonable about it? Or is it irrational for listeners to respond to it by donating to anti-malarial causes? By the same token, is it illogical to be compassionate for victims of natural disasters? Angered by corporate wrongdoing? Fearful about cutbacks in student aid? Reason and emotion often work hand in hand.

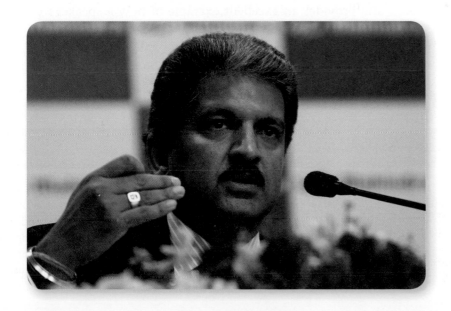

Emotional language and vivid examples can help generate emotional appeal, but neither will be effective unless the speaker talks with genuine sincerity and conviction.

One key to using emotional appeal ethically is to make sure it is appropriate to the speech topic. If you want to move listeners to act on a question of policy, emotional appeals are not only legitimate but perhaps necessary. If you want listeners to do something as a result of your speech, you will probably need to appeal to their hearts as well as to their heads.

On the other hand, emotional appeals are usually inappropriate in a persuasive speech on a question of fact. Here you should deal only in specific information and logic. Suppose someone charges your state governor with illegal campaign activities. If you respond by saying, "I'm sure the charge is false because I have always admired the governor," or "I'm sure the charge is true because I have always disliked the governor," then you are guilty of applying emotional criteria to a purely factual question.

Even when trying to move listeners to action, you should never substitute emotional appeals for evidence and reasoning. You should *always* build your persuasive speech on a firm foundation of facts and logic. This is important not just for ethical reasons, but for practical ones as well. Unless you prove your case, careful listeners will not be stirred by your emotional appeals. You need to build a good case based on reason *and* kindle the emotions of your audience.[16]

When you use emotional appeal, keep in mind the guidelines for ethical speechmaking discussed in Chapter 2. Make sure your goals are ethically sound, that you are honest in what you say, and that you avoid name-calling and other forms of abusive language. In using emotional appeal, as in other respects, your classroom speeches will offer a good testing ground for questions of ethical responsibility.

Sample Speech with Commentary

connect

View "The Dangers of Cell Phones" in the online Media Library for this chapter (Video 17.5).

The following persuasive speech deals with a question of policy and is organized according to Monroe's motivated sequence. As you read the speech, notice how the speaker utilizes the methods of persuasion discussed in this chapter as she moves through each step of the motivated sequence. The speech also provides an excellent example of how a speaker's delivery can enhance his or her credibility and emotional appeal—as you can see by watching Video 17.5 in the online Media Library for this chapter.

The Dangers of Cell Phones

 COMMENTARY

 SPEECH

The first step in Monroe's motivated sequence is gaining attention, which the speaker does by arousing curiosity about the audience's "constant companion." The heavy use of "you" and "your" also draws the audience into the speech.

It's your constant companion. It's in your pocket, in your bag, in your hands, or against your head. You use it at home, in class, at the gym, before you go to sleep at night and first thing when you wake up in the morning. I'm talking, of course, about your cell phone. According to my class survey, everyone in this room has a cell phone, and all of us use it dozens of times every day.

The speaker's questions keep the audience involved while revealing the topic of the speech. The quotation from Devra Davis, an expert on cell phone radiation, underscores the importance of the topic.

The speaker establishes her credibility by referring to the research she has done for the speech.

By stating that she is not arguing against cell phones in general, the speaker encourages the audience to listen with an open mind. She ends the introduction with a transition to the body of her speech.

The speaker moves into the need step of Monroe's motivated sequence. She makes clear that she will focus on the long-term dangers of cell phone radiation.

Because most listeners were skeptical about the dangers of cell phones, the speaker cites high-quality sources to show how harmful heavy cell phone use can be. As in other parts of the speech, she clearly identifies each source.

This paragraph builds upon the previous one and presents additional evidence about the dangers of prolonged cell phone use.

But what if your constant companion is dangerous? What if it's hazardous to your health? Evidence is piling up that long-term use of cell phones can lead to tissue damage, tumors, and even brain cancer. Given that there are well over 4 billion people worldwide using cell phones, we're looking at a problem of potentially staggering magnitude. According to Devra Davis, epidemiologist and author of the 2010 book *Disconnect: The Truth About Cell Phone Radiation,* we may be watching "an epidemic in slow motion."

I'd never thought much about the possible perils of cell phones before I saw a CBS News report on the subject earlier this year. But doing extensive research for this speech made me realize that cell phones do in fact pose a danger to our health.

Now, don't worry, I'm not going to try to persuade you to abandon your constant companion. I still use mine on a regular basis, and I probably always will. But I do hope to persuade you to make one simple change in the way you use your cell phone—a change that will protect your health and could even make the difference between a long life and premature death. But first, let's look more closely at the health risks posed by cell phones.

Those risks stem from the fact that cell phones emit small amounts of radiation that, over time, can damage tissue. Every time you use your cell phone, you expose yourself to that radiation. The amount is miniscule in comparison to that given off by x-ray machines—about one one-billionth of the intensity. However, Ronald Herberman of the University of Pittsburgh Cancer Institute explains that the problem with cell phone radiation is not how much is emitted at a single time, but how much we are exposed to with repeated use day after day, year after year.

It's this long-term use of cell phones that has led researchers to warn about their danger. In one study, for example, the World Health Organization tracked 10,000 cell phone users over the course of 10 years. As reported in the *New York Times* on November 13, 2010, the data in this study indicated that subjects who used a cell phone 10 or more years doubled the risk of developing brain tumors.

Other studies have reached the same conclusion. Perhaps most important is a study in the *Journal of Occupational and Environmental Medicine* that surveyed all the previous research on cell phone use. It found "a consistent pattern of increased risk" for developing brain tumors among people who used cell phones for more than 10 years.

A vivid example reinforces the statistics and testimony cited in the previous paragraphs.

Alan Marks is one of those people. A 58-year-old real estate developer and father of three, he talked on his cell phone an hour a day for 23 years. Two years ago, doctors found a golf-ball-sized tumor in his brain. "There's no question what caused it," he says. "It was my cell phone."

The speaker cites evidence to show that the example of Alan Marks is not atypical.

And Alan Marks isn't the only person to conclude that he's sick because of his cell phone. Ann Gittleman's 2010 book *Zapped,* which deals at length with the health problems of cell phones, catalogues people who developed blinding headaches, dizziness, circulatory problems, nausea, and cancer from the kind of radiation emitted by cell phones.

By citing the usage guidelines provided by cell phone makers themselves, the speaker seeks to dispel any remaining skepticism about cell phone radiation.

Still not convinced about the potential dangers posed by your constant companion? Take a look, then, inside the thick manual that comes with your phone. You'll see that all cell phone manufacturers warn against keeping the phone right next to your body. Apple, for example, recommends keeping the iPhone five-eighths of an inch away from your body. Makers of the BlackBerry recommend that you keep their phone a full inch away. Cell phone manufacturers don't publicize this information widely, but they clearly recognize that their products are potentially hazardous.

This paragraph begins with a transition into the satisfaction section of the speech. As you can see from the video, the speaker's delivery is extemporaneous, personable, and conversational.

So what's the solution? As I said earlier, it's not to stop using cell phones altogether. I still use mine on a regular basis, and I can't imagine being without it—and I'm sure you can't imagine being without yours. You can, however, take seriously the risks of cell phones and find a way to minimize those risks. Time and again, experts point out that the single most effective way to reduce the risk is not to press your cell phone against your head while using it. Since the phone emits radiation, the closer you put it to your head, the more radiation you expose yourself to.

Here the speaker states the key element in her plan. She enhances her credibility by noting that she follows the plan when using her own phone.

At the very least, you should hold the phone one-half an inch to one full inch away from your ear. But ideally, you should get in the habit of not putting it up to your head at all. I now use my earbuds almost every time I use my phone. Another option is to use your speakerphone.

Having explained her plan, the speaker moves into the visualization section. Returning to the example of Alan Marks gives the speech a sense of unity. The quotation from Marks is highly effective.

As with breaking any habit, changing the way you talk on your cell phone may be slightly inconvenient at first but will soon become second nature. You'll be able to enjoy all the benefits of your constant companion without suffering the fate of Alan Marks. If Marks had known the dangers of prolonged cell phone use, he would have done things a lot differently. "I wouldn't have held it to my head," he says. "I would have used the headset. I would have used the speakerphone. . . . And I would not have had the problems I had."

The speaker begins the action section of her speech. Once again, she relates to the audience by using "you" and your."

So please get in the habit of keeping your cell phone away from your ear when talking, and encourage your friends and family to do the same. Start today, with your next phone call, and continue every day in the future.

As you can see from the video of this speech, the speaker ends by holding her cell phone to her head. This visually reinforces the central idea and makes for a dramatic ending.

We can avoid the slow-motion epidemic that doctors and scientists are warning us about—as long as we remember to keep this away from this.

Summary

Listeners accept a speaker's ideas for one or more of four reasons—because they perceive the speaker as having high credibility, because they are won over by the speaker's evidence, because they are convinced by the speaker's reasoning, or because they are moved by the speaker's emotional appeals.

Credibility is affected by many factors, but the two most important are competence and character. The more favorably listeners view a speaker's competence and character, the more likely they are to accept her or his ideas. Although credibility is partly a matter of reputation, you can enhance your credibility during a speech by establishing common ground with your listeners, by letting them know why you are qualified to speak on the topic, and by presenting your ideas fluently and expressively.

If you hope to be persuasive, you must also support your views with evidence—examples, statistics, and testimony. Regardless of what kind of evidence you use, it will be more persuasive if it is new to the audience, stated in specific rather than general terms, and from credible sources. Your evidence will also be more persuasive if you state explicitly the point it is supposed to prove.

No matter how strong your evidence, you will not be persuasive unless listeners agree with your reasoning. In reasoning from specific instances, you move from a number of particular facts to a general conclusion. Reasoning from principle is the reverse—you move from a general principle to a particular conclusion. When you use causal reasoning, you try to establish a relationship between causes and effects. In analogical reasoning, you compare two cases and infer that what is true for one is also true for the other.

Whatever kind of reasoning you use, avoid fallacies such as hasty generalization, false cause, invalid analogy, appeal to tradition, and appeal to novelty. You should also be on guard against the red herring, slippery slope, bandwagon, *ad hominem,* and either-or fallacies.

Finally, you can persuade your listeners by appealing to their emotions. One way to generate emotional appeal is by using emotion-laden language. Another is to develop vivid, richly textured examples. Neither, however, will be effective unless you feel the emotion yourself and communicate it by speaking with sincerity and conviction.

As with other methods of persuasion, your use of emotional appeal should be guided by a firm ethical rudder. Although emotional appeals are usually inappropriate in speeches on questions of fact, they are legitimate—and often necessary—in speeches that seek immediate action on questions of policy. Even when trying to move listeners to action, however, you should never substitute emotional appeals for evidence and reasoning.

Key Terms

ethos *(326)*
credibility *(327)*
initial credibility *(327)*
derived credibility *(327)*
terminal credibility *(327)*
creating common ground *(329)*
evidence *(330)*
logos *(333)*
reasoning *(335)*
reasoning from specific instances *(335)*
reasoning from principle *(336)*
causal reasoning *(337)*
analogical reasoning *(337)*

fallacy *(338)*
hasty generalization *(338)*
false cause *(338)*
invalid analogy *(339)*
bandwagon *(340)*
red herring *(340)*
ad hominem (340)
either-or *(341)*
slippery slope *(341)*
appeal to tradition *(341)*
appeal to novelty *(342)*
pathos *(343)*

Review Questions

After reading this chapter, you should be able to answer the following questions:

1. What is credibility? What two factors exert the most influence on an audience's perception of a speaker's credibility?
2. What are the differences among initial credibility, derived credibility, and terminal credibility?
3. What are three ways you can enhance your credibility during your speeches?
4. What is evidence? Why do persuasive speakers need to use evidence?
5. What are four tips for using evidence effectively in a persuasive speech?
6. What is reasoning from specific instances? Why is it important to supplement reasoning from specific instances with testimony or statistics?
7. What is reasoning from principle? How is it different from reasoning from specific instances?
8. What is causal reasoning? Why is the relationship between causes and effects not always clear?
9. What is analogical reasoning? Why is analogical reasoning frequently used in persuasive speeches on questions of policy?
10. What are the ten logical fallacies discussed in this chapter?
11. What is the role of emotional appeal in persuasive speaking? Identify three methods you can use to generate emotional appeal in your speeches.

connect

For further review, go to the LearnSmart study module for this chapter.

Exercises for Critical Thinking

1. Research has shown that a speaker's initial credibility can have great impact on how the speaker's ideas are received by listeners. Research has also shown that a speaker's credibility will vary from topic to topic and audience to audience. In the left-hand column below is a list of well-known public figures. In the right-hand column is a list of potential speech topics. Assume that each speaker will be addressing your speech class.

   For each speaker, identify the topic in the right-hand column on which she or he would have the highest initial credibility for your class. Then explain how the speaker's initial credibility might be affected if the speaker were discussing the topic in the right-hand column directly across from her or his name.

Speaker	Topic
Hillary Clinton	Life in the NFL
Jon Stewart	The Future of Social Networking
Mark Zuckerberg	Pop Music and the Cult of Celebrity
Lady Gaga	Diplomacy in the 21st Century
Peyton Manning	The Comedy of Politics

2. Identify the kind of reasoning used in each of the following statements. What weaknesses, if any, can you find in the reasoning of each?

   a. According to a study by the American Medical Association, men with bald spots have three times the risk of heart attack as men with a full head of hair. Strange as it may seem, it looks as if baldness is a cause of heart attacks.

   b. We can see from its work all around the world that Women for Women International is a worthy charitable organization. It has helped women in Rwanda operate sewing machines and make clothing. It has given women in Kosovo the skills to operate businesses in their communities. It has shown women in the Democratic Republic of Congo how to create and market ceramics.

   c. The United States Constitution guarantees all citizens the right to bear arms. Gun control legislation infringes on the right of citizens to bear arms. Therefore, gun control legislation is contrary to the Constitution.

   d. Almost every industrialized nation in the world except for the United States has a national curriculum and national tests to help ensure that schools throughout the country are meeting high standards of education. If such a system can work elsewhere, it can work in the United States.

3. Over the years there has been much debate about the role of emotional appeal in public speaking. Do you believe it is ethical for public speakers to use emotional appeals when seeking to persuade an audience? Do you feel there are certain kinds of emotions to which an ethical speaker should not appeal? Why or why not? Be prepared to explain your ideas in class.

4. Analyze "The Horrors of Puppy Mills" in the appendix of sample speeches that follows Chapter 19 (pages A7–A9). Pay special attention to the speaker's credibility, evidence, reasoning, and emotional appeal. View the video of the speech in the online Media Library for this chapter so you can also assess the speaker's delivery and use of visual aids.

18

Speaking on Special Occasions

Speeches of Introduction

Speeches of Presentation

Speeches of Acceptance

Commemorative Speeches

pecial occasions are the punctuation marks of day-to-day life, the high points that stand out above ordinary routine. Christenings, weddings, funerals, graduations, award ceremonies, inaugurals, retirement dinners—all these are occasions, and they are very special to the people who take part in them. Nearly always they are occasions for speechmaking. A close friend proposes a toast to the bride and groom; the sales manager presents an award to the sales representative of the year; a family member delivers a moving eulogy to the deceased. These speeches help give the occasion its "specialness." They are part of the ceremonial aura that marks the event.

Speeches for special occasions are different from the speeches we have considered so far in this book. They may convey information or persuade, but that is not their primary purpose. Rather, they aim to fit the special needs of a special occasion. In this chapter we look at the most common special occasions and the kinds of speeches appropriate for each.

Speeches of Introduction

"Distinguished guests, the President of the United States." If you are ever in a situation in which you have to introduce the President, you will need no more than the eight words that begin this paragraph. The President is so well known that any further remarks would be inappropriate and almost foolish.

Most of the time, however, a speech of introduction will be neither this brief nor this ritualized. If you are introducing another speaker, you will need to accomplish three purposes in your introduction:

Build enthusiasm for the upcoming speaker.

Build enthusiasm for the speaker's topic.

Establish a welcoming climate that will boost the speaker's credibility.

A good speech of introduction can be a delight to hear and can ease the task of the main speaker. Usually you will say something about the speaker and the topic—in that order. Following are some guidelines for speeches of introduction.

Be Brief

During World War I, Lord Balfour, Great Britain's foreign secretary, was to be the main speaker at a rally in the United States. But the speaker introducing him gave a 45-minute oration on the causes of the war. Then, almost as an afterthought, he said, "Now Lord Balfour will give his address." Lord Balfour rose and said, "I'm supposed to give my address in the brief time remaining. Here it is: 10 Carleton Gardens, London, England."[1]

Everyone who has ever sat through a long-winded introduction knows how dreary it can be. The purpose of a speech of introduction is to focus attention on the main speaker, not on the person making the introduction. A speech of introduction will usually be no more than two to three minutes long, and may be shorter if the speaker is already well known to the audience.

Make Sure Your Remarks Are Completely Accurate

Many an introducer has embarrassed himself or herself, as well as the main speaker, by garbling basic facts. Always check with the speaker ahead of time to make sure your introduction is accurate in every respect.

Above all, get the speaker's name right. If the speaker's name is at all difficult—especially if it involves a foreign pronunciation—practice saying it in advance. However, don't practice so much that you frighten yourself about getting it wrong. This was the plight of an announcer whose gaffe is now a classic: "Ladies and gentlemen, the President of the United States—Hoobert Heever!"

Adapt Your Remarks to the Occasion

In preparing your introduction, you may be constrained by the nature of the occasion. Formal occasions require formal speeches of introduction. If you were presenting a guest speaker at an informal business meeting, you might be much more casual than at a formal banquet.

Adapt Your Remarks to the Main Speaker

No matter how well it is received by the audience, a speech of introduction that leaves the main speaker feeling uncomfortable has failed in part of its purpose. How can you make a main speaker uncomfortable? One way is to overpraise the person—especially for his or her speaking skills. Never say, "Our speaker will keep you on the edge of your seat from beginning to end!" You create a set of expectations that are almost impossible to fulfill.

Another way to create discomfort is by revealing embarrassing details of the speaker's personal life or by making remarks that are in poor taste. An introducer may think this line is funny: "Why, I've known Anita Fratello since she was 10 years old and so fat that everybody called her Blimpo!" To the speaker, however, the statement will probably not be a bit funny and may be painful.

Adapt Your Remarks to the Audience

Just as you adapt other speeches to particular audiences, so you need to adapt a speech of introduction to the audience you are facing. Your aim is to make *this* audience want to hear *this* speaker on *this* subject. If the speaker is not well known to the audience, you will need to establish her or his credibility by recounting some of the speaker's main achievements and explaining why she or he is qualified to speak on the topic at hand. But if the speaker is already personally known to the audience, it would be absurd to act as if the audience had never heard of the person.

Also, you will want to tell each audience what *it* wants to hear—to give the kind of information that is interesting and accessible to the members of that audience. If you were introducing the same speaker to two different groups, some of the information in the speeches of introduction might be the same, but it would be slanted differently.

Suppose, for example, that J. K. Rowling, author of the Harry Potter series, is going to address two groups—an audience of elementary-school children and an audience of educators at the International Reading Association. The introduction to the schoolchildren might go like this:

> Children, we have a very important guest today. You know her by the character she has created—Harry Potter. What you don't know is all the hard work that goes into writing the books that we all love to read. Today she is going to tell us how she came up with the idea of Harry Potter and his friends and how she goes about writing her books. Let's give a big round of applause to J. K. Rowling.

But the introduction to the International Reading Association would be along these lines:

> Ladies and gentlemen, it is my privilege to introduce to you today the world's best-selling author. We are all well acquainted with her Harry Potter series that has captured the imagination of children—and more than a few adults—around the globe.
>
> Many of us know the remarkable story of her writing life: The inspiration for Harry Potter came on a train ride from Manchester to London in 1990. Over the next few years, she compiled notes as the story took shape in her mind. The bulk of the writing took place when she was a single mother on public assistance in

Edinburgh. She was teaching French to teenagers in the mid-1990s when she heard that the first Harry Potter book had been accepted for publication. The rest is literary history.

She will be telling us this afternoon more about what inspired her fascinating story of wizardry, where she gets her ideas, and what kinds of books she wants to write next. Please give a warm welcome to J. K. Rowling.

Try to Create a Sense of Anticipation and Drama

You may have noticed one detail shared by the two speeches introducing J. K. Rowling: In both cases the speaker's name was saved for last. This is a convention in speeches of introduction. While there may occasionally be a good reason to break the convention, usually you will avoid mentioning the speaker's name until the final moment—even when the audience knows exactly whom you are discussing. By doing this you build a sense of drama, and the speaker's name comes as the climax of your introduction.

Often you will find yourself in the situation of introducing someone who is fairly well known to the audience—a classmate, a colleague at a business meeting, a neighbor in a community group. Then you should try to be creative and cast the speaker in a new light. Talk to the speaker beforehand and see if you can learn some interesting facts that are not generally known—especially facts that relate to the speaker's topic.

Above all, if you expect to be creative and dramatic, be sure to practice your speech of introduction thoroughly. You should be able to deliver it extemporaneously, with sincerity and enthusiasm.

Speeches of Presentation

speech of presentation

A speech that presents someone a gift, an award, or some other form of public recognition.

Speeches of presentation are given when someone receives a gift, an award, or some other form of public recognition. Usually such speeches are brief. They may be no more than a mere announcement ("And the winner is . . .") or be up to four or five minutes in length.

The main purpose of a speech of presentation is to tell the audience why the recipient is receiving the award. Point out his or her contributions, achievements, and so forth. Do not deal with everything the person has ever done. Focus on achievements related to the award, and discuss these achievements in a way that will make them meaningful to the audience.

Depending on the audience and the occasion, you may also need to discuss two other matters in a speech of presentation. First, if the audience is not familiar with the award, you should explain it briefly. Second, if the award was won in a public competition and the audience knows who the losers are, you might take a moment to praise the losers.

On page 357 is a sample speech of presentation. It was delivered by President Bill Clinton in presenting the Congressional Gold Medal to former South African President Nelson Mandela at a ceremony in the Rotunda of the United States Capitol in Washington, D.C. Because the Congressional Gold Medal is a special honor bestowed by the U.S. Congress, there are no public competitors for the award. Thus Clinton did not need to say anything about the "losers." His speech focused on Mandela's battle against apartheid and his efforts to promote reconciliation among the people of South Africa.

PRESENTING THE CONGRESSIONAL GOLD MEDAL

Bill Clinton

To my friend, President Mandela, Americans as one today, across all the lines that divide us, pay tribute to your struggle, to your achievement, and to the inspiration you have given us to do better. Today we offer a man who has received the Nobel Prize the highest honor within the gift of this country. . . .

Those of us who share his vision and lift him up in honor today owe it to him to build a permanent partnership between Americans and Africans—for the education of our children, for the solution of our problems, for the resolution of our differences, for the elevation of what is best about us all. . . .

In forgiving those who imprisoned him, he reminded us of the most fundamental lesson of all—that in the end apartheid was a defeat of the heart, the mind, the spirit. It was not just a structure outside and jail houses within which people were kept; it was a division of the mind and soul against itself. We owe it to Nelson Mandela not simply to give him this award, but to live by the lesson he taught us and to tear down every last vestige of apartheid in our own hearts—everything that divides us, one from another.

For those of us who have been privileged to know this remarkable man, no medal, no award, no fortune, nothing we could give him could possibly compare to the gift he has given to us and to the world. The only gift that is true recompense is to continue his mission and to live by the power of his profound and wonderful example.

Now, as prescribed by the law, it is my privilege to present the Congressional Gold Medal to President Nelson Mandela.

Speeches for special occasions are part of the ceremonial aura that makes certain events special, as in these remarks by Army Staff Sergeant Salvatore A. Giunta receiving the Congressional Medal of Honor.

Speeches of Acceptance

The purpose of an acceptance speech is to give thanks for a gift or an award. When giving such a speech, you thank the people who are bestowing the award and recognize the people who helped you gain it.

The acceptance speech below is the companion piece to the speech of presentation by Bill Clinton. It was delivered by Nelson Mandela in accepting the Congressional Gold Medal, and it exemplifies the major traits of a good acceptance speech—brevity, humility, and graciousness.[2]

connect

View an excerpt from Nelson Mandela's acceptance speech in the online Media Library for this chapter (Video 18.1).

ACCEPTING THE CONGRESSIONAL GOLD MEDAL

Nelson Mandela

Thank you. President Clinton, Mr. Speaker, distinguished members of the Senate and the House, ladies and gentlemen. . . .

It has been my great privilege to serve a people whose bondage to an inhuman system evoked the solidarity of all those who love freedom and justice, a people whose triumph over the divisions of racist doctrine has given new life to humanity's hope for a world without hatred and discrimination. I am conscious that in bestowing the Congressional Gold Medal upon me you are evoking these bonds between our nations and paying tribute to the whole South African nation for its achievements in realizing our shared ideals.

It is in that spirit that I humbly accept the award, aware at the same time of the great honor you do me by using me as the vehicle of a unique distinction conferred by this hallowed institution of American democracy. As one who has dedicated his life to the pursuit of unity, I am moved by the consensus in your nation's regard for the achievements of my people. And I feel a great pride in the fact that with a few citizens of other countries who have received this high honor, the name of an African is now added. . . .

The award with which you honor me today is an expression of the common humanity that binds us, one person to another, nation to nation, and people of the north to people of the south. I receive it with pride as a symbol of partnership for peace, prosperity, and equity as we enter the new millennium. I thank you.

Commemorative Speeches

Commemorative speeches are speeches of praise or celebration. Eulogies, Fourth of July speeches, and dedications are examples of commemorative speeches. Your aim in such speeches is to pay tribute to a person, a group of people, an institution, or an idea.

As in an informative speech, you probably will have to give the audience information about your subject. After all, the audience must know *why* your subject is praiseworthy. As in other speeches, you may draw on examples, testimony, even statistics to illustrate the achievements of your subject.

Your fundamental purpose in a commemorative speech, however, is not to inform your listeners but to *inspire* them—to arouse and heighten their appreciation of or admiration for the person, institution, or idea you are praising. If you are paying tribute to a person, for example, you should not simply recount the details of the person's life. Rather, you should penetrate to the *essence* of your subject and generate in your audience a deep sense of respect.

When speaking to commemorate, you want to express feelings, to stir sentiments—joy and hope when a new building is dedicated, anticipation and good wishes at a commencement celebration, lament and consolation at a funeral, admiration and respect at a testimonial dinner. A commemorative speech is like an impressionist painting—"a picture with warm colors and texture capturing a mood or a moment."[3]

But while the painter works with brush and colors, the commemorative speaker works with language. Of all the kinds of speeches, none depends more on the creative and subtle use of language. Some of the most memorable speeches in history, including Abraham Lincoln's Gettysburg Address, have been commemorative. We continue to find such speeches meaningful and inspiring largely because of their eloquent use of language.

One of the most effective commemorative speakers in recent history was President Ronald Reagan. After the explosion of the space shuttle *Challenger* in 1986, Reagan delivered a nationally televised eulogy to the astronauts killed in the blast. Below are two versions of Reagan's closing lines. The first is what he *might* have said, stripping the text of its warm emotional content and poignant language:

Like Francis Drake, the great explorer of the oceans, the *Challenger* astronauts gave their lives for a cause to which they were fully dedicated. We are honored by them, and we will not forget them. We will always remember seeing them for the last time this morning as they prepared for their flight.

Here is what Reagan *actually* said:

There's a coincidence today. On this day 390 years ago, the great explorer Francis Drake died aboard ship off the coast of Panama. In his lifetime the great frontiers were the oceans, and an historian later said, "He lived by the sea, died on it, was buried in it." Well, today we can say of the *Challenger* crew: Their dedication was, like Drake's, complete.

The crew of the space shuttle *Challenger* honored us by the manner in which they lived their lives. We will never forget them, nor the last time we saw them, this morning, as they prepared for their journey and waved goodbye and "slipped the surly bonds of earth" to "touch the face of God."

The final words—"'slipped the surly bonds of earth' to 'touch the face of God'"—are especially effective. Drawn from a sonnet called "High Flight" that

connect

View the ending of Ronald Reagan's eulogy to the *Challenger* astronauts in the online Media Library for this chapter (Video 18.2).

many pilots keep with them, they ennoble the deaths of the astronauts and end the speech on an eloquent, moving, and poetic note.

When speaking to commemorate, your success will depend on your ability to put into language the thoughts and emotions appropriate to the occasion. It is easy—too easy—to fall back on clichés and trite sentiments. Your challenge will be to use language imaginatively to invest the occasion with dignity, meaning, and honest emotion.

In doing so, you may want to utilize the special resources of language discussed in Chapter 12. Metaphor, simile, parallelism, repetition, antithesis, alliteration—all are appropriate for commemorative speeches. Some highly acclaimed commemorative speeches—including Martin Luther King's "I Have a Dream" and John Kennedy's inaugural address—are distinguished by their creative use of such devices.

commemorative speech

A speech that pays tribute to a person, a group of people, an institution, or an idea.

Confronted with the evocative speeches of a Kennedy or a King, you may decide that the speech of commemoration is far beyond your abilities. But other students have delivered excellent commemorative speeches—not immortal, perhaps, but nonetheless dignified and moving.

Look, for example, at "My Crazy Aunt Sue" in the appendix of sample speeches that follows Chapter 19. The speaker's aim was to pay tribute to her aunt, who for years had battled rheumatoid arthritis. Although the speaker provides basic information about aunt Sue and her physical condition, the speech does not recount all the details of her life. Instead, it focuses on her courage, her sense of humor, and her refusal to complain about her fate. The speaker provides enough details to let us see why aunt Sue is so commendable, but not so many as to slow the pace of the speech.

The speaker also uses vivid language, repetition, and parallel structure to give the speech the kind of formal tone appropriate for a commemorative speech. You can see this even in the opening lines:

connect

View "My Crazy Aunt Sue" in the online Media Library for this chapter (Video 18.3).

> The strongest person I know cannot peel a potato. The strongest person I know has trouble putting on her makeup. The strongest person I know needs a special key holder to turn the key in her car's ignition.

In addition to arousing curiosity about the subject of the speech, these lines have a simple elegance that comes partly from the repetition of "The strongest person I know" at the start of each sentence. Consider, in contrast, how much less effective the opening would have been if the speaker had said:

> My aunt Sue can't peel a potato, has trouble putting on her makeup, and needs a special key holder to turn the key in her car's ignition.

These lines convey the same information, but not with the same effect.

For another example, consider the student commemorative speech printed on page 361. The subject is Elie Wiesel—humanitarian, Nobel Peace Prize winner, and tireless campaigner for international justice. Notice how the speaker uses the repetition of "A-7713" to capture attention at the beginning and to give the speech artistic unity at the end. Also notice how he tells us enough about Wiesel to know why he is praiseworthy without getting bogged down in biographical details.

ELIE WIESEL

A-7713. His new name, the graffiti stamped on his skin. A-7713, a concentration camp tattoo. At age fifteen, A-7713 was taken from his home by the Nazis and sent to Auschwitz, one of the twentieth century's most potent symbols of evil. Here A-7713 witnessed the deaths of thousands of human beings, including his mother and younger sister. Somehow, A-7713 survived, and when World War II ended, he put his pain and grief to work making sure the world did not forget the Holocaust and making sure another Holocaust did not take place.

Today, the world knows A-7713 as Elie Wiesel, noted speaker and lecturer, author of more than 40 books, and recipient of the Presidential Medal of Freedom, the Congressional Gold Medal, and the Nobel Peace Prize, among others. Elie Wiesel is an eloquent, fearless, selfless leader who took the evils of Auschwitz as motivation to improve the world.

An eloquent leader, Elie Wiesel uses the power of language to confront the problems of humanity. Through compelling prose and brutal honesty, he explains that we cannot root out evil unless we recognize it and battle it wherever it exists. In his classic book, *Night,* he says of Auschwitz: "Never shall I forget that night, the first night in camp, which turned my life into one long night, seven times cursed and seven times sealed. Never shall I forget that smoke. Never shall I forget the little faces of the children, whose bodies I saw turned into wreaths of smoke beneath a silent blue sky." Haunting words that remind us of the reality of evil.

A fearless leader no less than an eloquent one, Elie Wiesel has spent 40 years battling the evils that continue to plague our planet. To the Miskito Indians of Nicaragua, displaced from their homeland, he brought inspiring words of strength and compassion. To men and women facing apartheid in South Africa, he brought a powerful denunciation of racial segregation and violence. To Cambodian refugees suffering from starvation and disease, he brought food and the promise of a new beginning. And to those of us who follow his work, he continues to provide inspiration.

A selfless leader as much as an eloquent and fearless one, Elie Wiesel has consistently put the needs of others before his own. With every award, his modesty stands side by side with his achievements. As he stated in his Nobel Prize acceptance speech, "Neutrality helps the oppressor, never the victim. Silence encourages the tormentor, never the tormented. . . . Wherever men and women are persecuted because of their race, religion, or political views, that place must—at that moment—become the center of the universe."

Today, at 80 years of age, Elie Wiesel continues to fight against the night. Through all his trials and all his triumphs, the tattoo remains: A-7713, a constant reminder of evil, injustice, and indifference. In battling these forces, Elie Wiesel has shown the kind of moral leadership too often lacking in today's world.

There is no better way to conclude than to quote his own words: "There may be times when we are powerless to prevent injustice, but there must never be a time when we fail to protest. . . . What these victims need above all is to know that they are not alone, that we are not forgetting them, that while their freedom depends on ours, the quality of our freedom depends on theirs."

connect

View "Elie Wiesel" in the online Media Library for this chapter (Video 18.4).

Summary

In this chapter we have considered speeches of introduction, speeches of presentation, speeches of acceptance, and commemorative speeches.

Your job in a speech of introduction is to build enthusiasm for the main speaker and to establish a welcoming climate. Keep your remarks brief, make sure they are accurate, and adapt them to the audience, the occasion, and the main speaker.

Speeches of presentation are given when someone receives a gift or an award. The main theme of such a speech is to acknowledge the achievements of the recipient. The purpose of an acceptance speech is to give thanks for a gift or an award. When delivering such a speech, you should thank the people who are bestowing the award and recognize the contributions of people who helped you gain it. Be brief, humble, and gracious.

Commemorative speeches are speeches of praise or celebration. Your aim in such a speech is to pay tribute to a person, a group of people, an institution, or an idea. A commemorative speech should inspire the audience, and its success will depend largely on how well you put into language the thoughts and feelings appropriate to the occasion.

Key Terms

speech of introduction *(354)*

speech of presentation *(356)*

acceptance speech *(358)*

commemorative speech *(360)*

Review Questions

After reading this chapter, you should be able to answer the following questions:

connect

For further review, go to the LearnSmart study module for this chapter.

1. What are the three purposes of a speech of introduction? What guidelines should you follow in preparing such a speech?

2. What is the main theme of a speech of presentation? Depending on the audience and occasion, what two other themes might you include in such a speech?

3. What are the three major traits of a good acceptance speech?

4. What is the fundamental purpose of a commemorative speech? Why does a successful commemorative speech depend so much on the creative and subtle use of language?

Exercises for Critical Thinking

1. Attend a speech on campus. Pay special attention to the speech introducing the main speaker. How well does it fit the guidelines discussed in this chapter?

2. Observe several speeches of presentation and acceptance—at a campus awards ceremony or on a television program such as the Academy Awards, Grammy Awards, Emmy Awards, or Tony Awards. Which speeches do you find most effective? Least effective? Why?

3. Analyze "Elie Wiesel" (page 361) in light of the criteria for commemorative speaking presented in this chapter.

19

Speaking in Small Groups

The publisher of a national sports magazine asked Mike Lee, the new head of the human resources department, to organize an October retreat for the magazine's editorial staff. Mike went to work on setting a date, finding a place to stay, and creating an agenda for the retreat.

Mike was very pleased with his plan. He thought he had taken everyone's needs into account. But when he explained his plan at the magazine's next staff meeting, no one seemed happy.

"The date you set for the retreat is over Halloween," said the editorial manager. "I know you don't have children, but no one with kids is going to want to be away at that time."

The administrative assistant responded next. "Do you realize," she said, "that the hotel you booked is the same one we used for a retreat five years ago? It was a disaster! The food was awful, the meeting rooms were uncomfortable, and the tech support was nonexistent."

Next a member of the magazine's junior editorial staff said, "I see that all the sessions involve members of the senior editorial staff. Did you mean to exclude all the younger editors? Don't you think we're important to the magazine?"

Finally, the managing editor said, "I wish you had checked with me at some point. I could have warned you about the hotel, the conflict with Halloween, and the need to include junior staff."

What went wrong? Mike did not have enough time or resources on his own to create a successful retreat. If a group, instead of a single person, had been assigned to plan the retreat, the problems might have been averted. One person could have taken charge of looking into the best dates, another of finding accommodations, a third of coordinating with other staff members about who should be included in the retreat, and so forth. The plan would have taken *all* factors into account.

Of course, you may have heard the old saying that "a camel is a horse designed by a committee." If you have ever been part of a group that seemed to get nothing done, you may be inclined to say, "Oh, let one person decide and get it over with." The problem in such cases, however, is not that there is a group, but that the group is not functioning properly. A great deal of research shows that if members of a group work well together, they can almost always resolve a problem better than a single person.[1]

This chapter deals with speaking in a particular kind of group—the problem-solving small group.

What Is a Small Group?

dyad

A group of two people.

small group

A collection of three to twelve people who assemble for a specific purpose.

problem-solving small group

A small group formed to solve a particular problem.

As its name implies, a small group has a limited number of members. The minimum number is three. (A group of two persons is called a *dyad*, and it operates quite differently from a group of three or more.) There is some difference of opinion about the maximum number of people who constitute a small group. Most experts set the maximum number at seven or eight; some go as high as twelve. The important point is that the group must be small enough to allow free discussion among all members. In small-group communication, all participants are potentially speakers *and* listeners.

Members of a small group assemble for a specific purpose. Several shoppers milling around the clothing section of a department store are not a small group, even if they speak to one another or comment about high prices and poor service. But if those same shoppers decided to meet together and prepare a formal complaint to the store manager about high prices and poor service, they would then constitute a small group.

A *problem-solving small group* is formed to solve a particular problem. Such groups exist in every area of life. Business groups consider ways of increasing sales. Church groups discuss how to raise funds and provide for the needy. Groups of parents work on improving day-care facilities. You will almost surely be a member of many problem-solving small groups during your life.

Although speaking in a small group is not the same as public speaking, it involves similar skills. Members of a small group influence one another through communication. As a participant in a small group, you might influence your colleagues by giving them important information, by encouraging them to speak, by convincing them to change their minds, even by getting them to end a meeting of the group. All other members of the group have the same opportunity to influence you through effective communication.[2]

Leadership in Small Groups

We have said that small groups often make better decisions than do individuals. To do so, however, they need effective leadership.

KINDS OF LEADERSHIP

Sometimes there is *no specific leader.* In such a situation, members of effective groups tend to have equal influence. When a need for leadership arises, any of the members can—and one probably will—provide the necessary leadership. A typical instance might be a class project, in which you and several classmates are working together. From time to time, each of you will help the group move toward its goal by suggesting when and where to meet, by outlining the strengths and weaknesses of a certain viewpoint, by resolving disagreements among other members, and so forth.

A group may have an *implied leader.* For example, if a business meeting includes one vice president and several subordinates, the vice president becomes the implied leader. The same is true if one member of the group is a specialist in the topic at hand and the others are not. Members will likely defer to the person with the highest rank or greatest expertise.

Even when a group starts out leaderless, there may be an *emergent leader.* This is a person who, by ability or by force of personality, or just by talking the most, takes a leadership role. The emergence of a leader may or may not be desirable. If the group is stalemated or has dissolved into bickering or making jokes, an emergent leader can put it back on track. There is a danger,

leadership

The ability to influence group members so as to help achieve the goals of the group.

implied leader

A group member to whom other members defer because of her or his rank, expertise, or other quality.

Small groups require effective leadership to accomplish their goals. Some groups have a designated leader, while others have an implied leader or an emergent leader.

however, that the emergent leader may not be the most effective leader but merely the most assertive personality.

Finally, there may be a *designated leader*—a person elected or appointed as leader when the group is formed. A group that meets for only one session should almost always have a designated leader who takes care of the procedural tasks and serves as spokesperson. Likewise, a formal committee will usually have a designated chairperson. The chair can perform leadership functions or delegate them, but he or she remains in charge.

A group may or may not need a specific leader, but it always needs *leadership*. When all members of the group are skilled communicators, they can take turns at providing leadership even if the group has a designated or implied leader. As you develop group communication skills, you should be prepared to assume a leadership role whenever necessary.[3]

FUNCTIONS OF LEADERSHIP

An effective leader helps the group reach its goals by fulfilling three overlapping sets of needs—procedural needs, task needs, and maintenance needs.

Procedural Needs

Procedural needs can be thought of as the "housekeeping" requirements of the group. They include:

Deciding when and where the group will meet.

Reserving the room, checking the number of chairs, making sure the heat or air conditioning is turned on.

Setting the agenda of each meeting.

Starting the meeting.

Taking notes during the meeting.

Preparing and distributing any written handouts needed for the meeting.

Summarizing the group's progress at the end of the meeting.

If there is a designated leader, he or she can attend to these needs or assign one or more group members to do so. Otherwise, members of the group must split the procedural responsibilities.

Task Needs

Task needs are substantive actions necessary to help the group complete the particular task it is working on. They include:

Analyzing the issues facing the group.

Distributing the workload among the members.

Collecting information.

Soliciting the views of other members.

Keeping the group from going off on a tangent.

Playing devil's advocate for unpopular ideas.

Formulating criteria for judging the most effective solution.

Helping the group reach consensus on its final recommendations.

All members should help the group satisfy its task needs. The best small groups are those in which each person contributes fully to accomplishing the group's objective.

Maintenance Needs

Maintenance needs involve interpersonal relations in the group. They include such factors as:

maintenance needs

Communicative actions necessary to maintain interpersonal relations in a small group.

How well members get along with one another.

How willing members are to contribute to the group.

Whether members are supportive of one another.

Whether members feel satisfied with the group's accomplishments.

Whether members feel good about their roles in the group.

If interpersonal problems dominate discussion, the group will have a difficult time working together and reaching a decision. A leader can do much to create and sustain supportive communication in the group. By helping group members handle conflict, by working out differences of opinion, by reducing interpersonal tension, by encouraging participation from all members, by being alert to personal feelings, and by promoting solidarity within the group, a leader can make a tremendous contribution toward helping the group achieve its goals.

Responsibilities in a Small Group

Every member of a small group must assume certain responsibilities, which can be divided into five major categories: (1) commit yourself to the goals of your group; (2) fulfill individual assignments; (3) avoid interpersonal conflicts; (4) encourage full participation; (5) keep the discussion on track. Some of these responsibilities involve leadership roles, but all five are so important that each participant should take them as personal obligations, regardless of the group's leadership.

COMMIT YOURSELF TO THE GOALS OF YOUR GROUP

For a group to succeed, members must align their personal goals with the group's goal. This sounds obvious, but it is not always easy. When you are working with other students on a class project, the group goal—and most likely the goal of each member—is to get a good grade. There is a strong incentive for members to cooperate and commit themselves to completing the task.

Problems arise when one or more members have personal goals that conflict with the group's goal. Here is the kind of situation that can occur:

Sherri Baines is a member of the committee to buy new equipment for the local newspaper's employee cafeteria. Because the budget is very tight, the committee's goal is to get the best equipment for the lowest price. But unknown to the other members of the group, Sherri's son-in-law is a salesman for a distributor of high-priced kitchen appliances. Privately, Sherri has reasoned that if she can sway the committee toward that company, her son-in-law will get a large commission. Sherri does not mention this fact to the group. Instead, she argues that quality—not price—should be the determining factor in the purchase. The group process breaks down because Sherri will not surrender her private goal.

This is an extreme example, but there can be more subtle kinds of private goals, as in the following case:

Carlos and Rachel are part of a group, and Carlos would like to be on closer terms with Rachel. To impress her, he may agree with everything she says, regardless of whether he really shares her views. Consequently, Carlos's expressed views are not his actual views. In short, Carlos has a *hidden agenda* in the group meeting. The group's agenda is to solve the problem, but Carlos's agenda is to go out with Rachel.

hidden agenda

A set of unstated individual goals that may conflict with the goals of the group as a whole.

Group members may have all sorts of hidden agendas. One may be experiencing personal problems—lowered grades, a breakup with a friend, or just a bad day. Another may have a commitment to a different group whose goals conflict with those of the present group. A third may want to take charge of the group for reasons of personal power, regardless of the group's task.

Remember that what one member of a group does affects all the other members. You should not try to advance your own interests or boost your own ego at the expense of the group and its goals. Beware of hidden agendas—whether yours or someone else's—and participate with a positive spirit.

FULFILL INDIVIDUAL ASSIGNMENTS

As mentioned earlier, one of the advantages of the group process is that it divides the workload among several people. But unless every member fulfills his or her assignments, the group's entire project may fail—as in the following example:

Several years ago, one student group decided that as a class project they would bring Easter baskets to the patients in the children's ward of a local hospital. After the project had been approved, assignments were given out. Stoya would coordinate with the hospital authorities. Corrine would handle fund-raising for the needed supplies. Jesse would supervise the egg-decorating team. Liu would be responsible for buying baskets and chocolate bunnies. Justin would arrange for transportation.

Everybody completed their assignments except Justin, who was busy writing a term paper. He asked a friend to pick up a bus schedule and assumed everything would be fine. On Easter morning, the group assembled at the bus stop, loaded down with baskets for the children. And they waited and waited. After an hour Justin called the bus company, only to discover that the buses did not run on holidays. By the time Justin had made other arrangements to get to the hospital, visiting hours were over, and the group could not get in.

No matter what other assignments they may have, *all* members of a group have one very critical assignment—listening. First, it helps you understand what is happening in the group. And unlike a public speaking situation, you can stop the speaker and ask for clarification at any point. Second, listening helps you evaluate the merits of the speaker's position. Third, listening provides support for the speaker and helps create a positive climate for discussion. Without effective listening, no group is going to make much progress.

AVOID INTERPERSONAL CONFLICTS

If groups were made up of robots, there would be no interpersonal conflicts. But groups are made up of people with likes and dislikes, animosities and prejudices, and very different personalities. It is vital to the group process that disagreements be kept on a task level, rather than on a personal level.

Suppose you disagree with another member's idea. Disagreement on the personal level could sound like this: "That's the most stupid idea I ever heard of! Do you realize how much money it would cost to do that?" But on the task level, disagreement is aimed at the *idea*, not the person: "Potentially that's a very good solution, but I'm not sure we have enough money to accomplish it."

No matter what the group, personal antagonism leaves a bad taste in everyone's mouth and harms the performance of the group. It's essential that someone take a leadership role and bring the discussion back to the relevant issues. Let's say you are part of a committee charged with setting up a speakers' series on your campus. The discussion might go like this:

Anton: We definitely should have Representative Hightower speak on campus. He has been very active in protecting the environment.

Minh: That liberal? He could care less what we pay for a gallon of gas. And forget about economic development with him.

Anton: So you support more offshore drilling? You're willing to destroy our coastlines so the oil companies can rake in more profits?

Minh: It's people like you that have made us dependent on foreign sources of oil—which threatens our prosperity and national security by making us vulnerable to economic blackmail from abroad.

Leader: Just a minute. This might make a good subject for our speakers' series. We can ask both Representative Hightower and a spokesperson for one of the oil companies to debate each other.

This is not to say that members of a group should never disagree. In fact, a serious problem occurs when members get along so well and are so concerned about maintaining the harmony of the group that they will not disagree with one another about anything. When this happens, there is no chance to reach the best decision by exploring an array of perspectives, opinions, and information. The aim is not for groups to avoid conflict but to keep it at the task level so it will not degenerate into personal feuding.[4]

ENCOURAGE FULL PARTICIPATION

If a group is to work effectively, all members must contribute fully and share their ideas with one another. Every member of a group should take responsibility for encouraging other members to participate. You can do this, first of all, by listening attentively. After all, how would you like to speak in a group where everybody else appears bored or distracted?

If there are one or two quiet members in the group, you can draw them into the discussion by asking their opinions and showing interest in their ideas. When a member speaks, you can say, "I never knew that; can you tell us more about it?" Conversely, try to avoid negative comments that will squelch a speaker before he or she has finished—comments like "Oh, no, that never works" or "What a terrible idea." Supportive comments create goodwill among group members and make everyone feel free to discuss their ideas without ridicule or embarrassment.

If you are shy or afraid your ideas will be taken too critically, you may be unwilling to participate at first. To overcome your diffidence, remember that your contribution is necessary to the group. At the very least, you can help provide a supportive environment for discussion by listening, reacting, and encouraging the free exchange of ideas.

KEEP THE DISCUSSION ON TRACK

In some groups the discussion proceeds like a stream-of-consciousness exercise. Here is a hypothetical example in which a town planning board is considering installing a new traffic light at a busy intersection:

Sharif: You know, we're going to have trouble getting cars to come to a full stop even if we do put in a traffic light.

Delany: Tell me about it! I came through there yesterday and hit my brakes, and the car just kept going. Maybe I need the brakes adjusted, though.

Mike: Get ready to pay through the nose. I had a brake job on my car last week, and it was nearly twice as much as last time.

Austin: That's nothing. Have you looked at lawnmowers lately? And if you think lawnmowers are high. . . .

Kym: Who mows lawns? I had my yard planted with ground cover and put gravel over the rest. It's . . .

Leader: Excuse me, folks, but weren't we talking about the *traffic light*?

Every member has a responsibility to keep the discussion on track and to intervene if the group wanders too far afield. There is nothing wrong with a little casual conversation, but it shouldn't be allowed to get out of hand. When working in a problem-solving group, make sure the group's ultimate goal is always in the forefront. Do your best to see that discussion proceeds in an orderly fashion from one point to the next and that the group does not get bogged down in side issues.

On the other hand, you need to guard against the tendency to progress to a solution too quickly, without thoroughly exploring the problem. If you feel your group is taking the easy way out and jumping at an easy solution, try to make the other members aware of your concern. By suggesting that they talk about the problem in more detail, you may bring out vital information or ideas.

There are systematic ways to keep the discussion on track and to avoid hasty group decisions. Research shows that if your group follows a tested method of decision making, it will have a better chance of reaching a satisfactory outcome.[5] We turn, therefore, to the most common decision-making technique for small groups—the reflective-thinking method.

In effective small groups, all members participate fully and interact with each other. They also feel that their contributions are respected and valued by the full group.

The Reflective-Thinking Method

The reflective-thinking method is derived from the writings of the American philosopher John Dewey. It offers a step-by-step process for discussion in problem-solving groups and consists of five steps: (1) defining the problem; (2) analyzing the problem; (3) establishing criteria for solving the problem; (4) generating potential solutions; (5) selecting the best solution. As we look at these steps, we'll illustrate each by following a single group through the entire reflective-thinking process.

reflective-thinking method

A five-step method for directing discussion in a problem-solving small group.

DEFINE THE PROBLEM

Before a problem-solving group can make progress, it must know exactly what problem it is trying to solve. Defining the problem for group discussion is akin to settling on a specific purpose for a speech. Unless it is done properly, everything that follows will suffer.

The best way to define the problem is to phrase it as a question of policy. As we saw in Chapter 16, questions of policy inquire about the necessity or practicality of specific courses of action. They typically include the word "should." For example:

question of policy

A question about whether a specific course of action should or should not be taken.

What measures should our school take to improve on-campus security for students?

What steps should the federal government take to deal with the federal budget deficit?

What policy should the United States adopt with respect to the exploitation of child labor in other countries around the world?

When phrasing the question for discussion, your group should follow several guidelines. First, make sure the question is as clear and specific as possible. For example:

Ineffective: What should be done about fraudulent charities?

More Effective: What should the government do to control the activities of fraudulent charities?

Second, phrase the question to allow for a wide variety of answers. Be especially wary of questions that can be answered with a simple yes or no. For example:

Ineffective: Should the city build a new elementary school?

More Effective: What steps should the city take to deal with increasing enrollment in the elementary schools?

Third, avoid biased or slanted questions. For example:

Ineffective: How can we keep the campus bookstore from ripping off students?

More Effective: What changes, if any, should be made in the pricing policies of the campus bookstore?

Fourth, make sure you pose a single question. For example:

Ineffective: What revisions should the college consider in its admissions requirements and in its graduation requirements?

More Effective: What revisions should the college consider in its admissions requirements?

More Effective: What revisions should the college consider in its graduation requirements?

To clarify this first step of the reflective-thinking method, let's see how our model problem-solving group defined the problem:

As a class project, the group set out to discuss the problem of rising costs for attending college. Following the reflective-thinking method, they began by defining the problem. After several false starts, they phrased the problem this way: "What steps should our school take to reduce student costs for attending college?"

ANALYZE THE PROBLEM

After the problem has been defined, the group begins to analyze it. Too often, groups (like individuals) start mapping out solutions before they have a firm grasp of what is wrong. This is like a doctor prescribing treatment before fully diagnosing the patient's ailment. If your group investigates the problem as thoroughly as possible, you will be in a much better position to devise a workable solution.

In analyzing the problem, pay particular attention to two questions. First, how severe is the problem? Investigate its scope. Determine how many people it affects. Assess what might happen if it is not resolved. Second, what are the causes of the problem? Check the history of the problem and learn what factors contributed to it.

As you might imagine, analyzing the problem requires research. Effective group decisions depend on having the best information available. You can get this information in the same way you gather materials for a speech. Sometimes you can rely on your own knowledge and experience. More often, you need to get information from other sources—by looking on the Internet, by interviewing someone with expertise on the topic, or by working in the library (see Chapter 7). When meeting with your group, make sure you have done the research assigned to you so you can offer complete and unbiased information.

Let's return now to our sample group and see how it analyzed the problem of rapidly escalating student costs for attending college:

The group talked first about the severity of the problem. Tuition had risen dramatically, as had outlays for books and incidentals. One member found statistics showing that the cost of attending college had more than doubled in the past 10 years. Another provided evidence that average annual costs were now close to $15,000 for students at in-state public colleges and universities, and roughly $35,000 for students at private schools.

To determine the causes of the problem, the group researched articles about the rise in student costs for attending college across the nation. They also interviewed an economics professor and the head of the student aid program on campus. After studying the matter thoroughly, the group identified several major causes, including administrative costs, faculty salaries, the price of textbooks, and increased living expenses.

ESTABLISH CRITERIA FOR SOLUTIONS

If you planned to buy a car, how would you proceed? You would probably not just walk into a showroom and buy whatever appealed to you on the spur of the moment. You would most likely decide ahead of time what kind of car you wanted, what options it should have, and how much money you could spend. That is, you would establish *criteria* to guide you in deciding exactly which car to buy.

criteria

Standards on which a judgment or decision can be based.

You should do the same thing in group discussion. Once your group has analyzed the problem, you should not jump immediately to proposing solutions. Instead, you should establish criteria—standards—for responsible solutions. You should work out (and write down) exactly what your solutions must achieve and any factors that might limit your choice of solutions.

To get a better idea of how this stage of the reflective-thinking method works, let's look at the cost-cutting group we have been following:

After some discussion, the group established these criteria for possible solutions: (1) The solution should significantly reduce students' costs. (2) The solution should come into force at the start of the next school year. (3) The solution should not hurt the prestige of the college. (4) The cost of the solution should be minimal and should be paid by the administration. (5) The human resources needed to implement the solution should come from administrative personnel already working on the school's staff. (6) The solution should involve only actions controlled by the college—not matters controlled by outside individuals or agencies.

GENERATE POTENTIAL SOLUTIONS

Once your group has the criteria firmly in mind, you are ready to discuss solutions. Your goal at this stage is to come up with the widest possible range of potential solutions—not to judge the solutions. One member of the group should be responsible for writing down all the solutions proposed at this time.

Many groups find the technique of *brainstorming* helpful in this stage. In Chapter 5, we discussed how brainstorming can work for an individual in choosing a speech topic. Here brainstorming is expanded to the whole group.

The best approach is to begin by having each member of the group write down all the possible solutions he or she can think of. One person should then consolidate the individual lists into a master list. The group should discuss the master list to make sure potential solutions have not been overlooked.

At this stage, members often "piggyback" new ideas onto ideas on the master list. For example, if one suggestion is "Establish food co-ops," a group member might say, "Yes, and we could establish clothing co-ops, too." One member should write down these new ideas and add them to the master list. The brainstorming process continues until the group cannot think of any more solutions.

Brainstorming in this fashion has two advantages. First, it encourages creativity. Research shows that beginning with written lists usually produces more and higher-quality ideas than relying solely on oral discussion.[6] Second, this method of brainstorming encourages equal participation. Having each member create his or her own list makes it less likely that one or two members will dominate the process or that anyone will hold back ideas for fear of being hooted down.

Let's see how our cost-cutting group handled this stage:

> By brainstorming, the group came up with the following possible solutions: (1) reduce the number of required books for each course; (2) cut some of the "fat" from the administrative staff; (3) make all professors teach more courses; (4) approach landlords about stabilizing rent and utility costs; (5) establish food

brainstorming

A method of generating ideas by free association of words and thoughts.

Working in a small group requires many of the skills involved in public speaking. Formal presentations may occur during a group's deliberations or when the group presents its report.

and clothing co-ops; (6) increase financial aid; (7) decrease the amount of money available for faculty research; (8) boycott businesses around the campus where price markups are highest; (9) increase out-of-state tuition; (10) decrease dormitory expenses; (11) organize fund-raising programs with the student government; (12) redirect some money from construction of new buildings to student aid. This was a good yield from a brainstorming session—12 solid suggestions.

SELECT THE BEST SOLUTION

After all potential solutions have been listed, it is time to evaluate them. The best way to proceed is to discuss each solution with regard to the criteria established earlier, then move to the next solution, and so on. This orderly process ensures that all potential solutions receive equal consideration.

As each potential solution is discussed, the group should try to reach *consensus*. A consensus decision is one that all members accept, even though the decision may not be ideal in the eyes of every member. Because it usually results in superior decisions as well as in a high degree of unity within the group, consensus is the ideal of group decision making. It comes about when members have been so cooperative that they reach a common decision through reasoning, honest exchange of ideas, and full examination of the issues.

consensus

A group decision that is acceptable to all members of the group.

 **checklist**

Reflective-Thinking Method

YES	NO	
☐	☐	1. Did the group clearly define the problem for discussion?
☐	☐	2. Did the group phrase the question for discussion as a question of policy?
☐	☐	3. Did the group phrase the question for discussion as clearly as possible?
☐	☐	4. Did the group phrase the question for discussion so as to allow for a wide variety of answers?
☐	☐	5. Did the group phrase the question for discussion in an unbiased manner?
☐	☐	6. Did the group phrase the question for discussion as a single question?
☐	☐	7. Did the group analyze the problem thoroughly before attempting to map out solutions?
☐	☐	8. Did the group establish criteria for an ideal solution to the problem before discussing specific solutions?
☐	☐	9. Did the group brainstorm to generate a wide range of potential solutions to the problem?
☐	☐	10. Did the group evaluate each potential solution in light of the criteria for an ideal solution?
☐	☐	11. Did the group make a determined effort to reach consensus with regard to the best solution?
☐	☐	12. Did the group achieve consensus?

Like most ideals, consensus can be difficult to achieve. If there are different viewpoints, members of the group will often try to find the easiest way to resolve the differences. Sometimes a member will call for a vote, which is very agreeable to those holding a majority opinion but not so pleasant for those in the minority. Resorting to a vote does resolve the immediate conflict, but it may not result in the best solution. Moreover, it weakens unity in the group by fostering factions and perhaps by creating bitterness among the members who lose the vote. A group should vote only when it has failed in every other attempt to agree on a solution.

What kind of final decision did our model cost-cutting group reach? Let's see:

> The cost-cutting group had 12 possible solutions to evaluate. Three were rejected because they violated the group's criterion that an acceptable solution must involve only actions controlled directly by the college.
>
> Three more solutions were rejected because they were economically impractical. Increasing financial aid would hurt many students because the funds would have to come from student fees. Raising out-of-state tuition would drive away too many out-of-state students. And decreasing dorm costs would make it impossible to provide minimally acceptable services.
>
> The proposal to reduce funds for faculty research was also rejected since most research money comes from government, corporations, and foundations. Finally, the suggestion to reduce administrative "fat" was rejected as too costly because a group would have to be established to audit all administrative duties.
>
> After refining the suggestions, the group finally reached consensus on a solution that included the following provisions: (1) A student should not have to spend more than $200 on required books for any single course. (2) The university should authorize the student government to organize food, book, and clothing co-ops. (3) The student government should conduct five fund-raising projects each academic year. (4) Each professor should teach one more class a year.

Once consensus has been reached, the group is ready to present its findings.[7]

Presenting the Recommendations of the Group

The work of a problem-solving group does not end with the last stage of the reflective-thinking process. Once a group has agreed on its recommendations, it usually needs to present them to somebody. A business group might report to the president of the company or to the board of directors. A presidential commission reports to the President and to the nation at large. A classroom group reports to the instructor and to the rest of the class. The purpose of such reports is to present the group's recommendations clearly and convincingly.

Sometimes a group will prepare a formal written report. Often, however, the written report is supplemented with—or replaced by—an oral report, a symposium, or a panel discussion.

ORAL REPORT

An oral report is much the same in content as a written report. If the group has a designated leader, she or he will probably deliver the report. Otherwise, the group will select one person for the job.

If you are picked to present your group's report, you should approach it as you would any other speech. Your task is to explain the group's purpose, procedures, and recommendations. Your report should have three main sections. The introduction will state the purpose of the report and preview its main points. The body will spell out the problem addressed by your group, the criteria set for a solution, and the solution being recommended. The conclusion will summarize the main points and, in some cases, urge that the group's recommendations be adopted.

oral report

A speech presenting the findings, conclusions, or decisions of a small group.

As with any other speech, you should adapt your report to the audience. Use supporting materials to clarify and strengthen your ideas, and consider whether visual aids will enhance your message. Make sure your language is accurate, clear, vivid, and appropriate. Rehearse the report so you can deliver it fluently and decisively. Afterward, you—and possibly other members of the group—may be called on to answer questions from the audience.

SYMPOSIUM

A symposium consists of a moderator and several speakers seated together in front of an audience. If the group presenting the symposium has a designated leader, she or he will typically be the moderator. The moderator's job is to introduce the topic and the speakers. Each speaker delivers a prepared speech on a different aspect of the topic. After the speeches, there may be a question-and-answer session.

symposium

A public presentation in which several people present prepared speeches on different aspects of the same topic.

The symposium is often used for group reports in speech classes. One way to organize it is to have each member of the group present a brief talk sketching the group's work and decisions during one stage of the reflective-thinking process. Another way is to have each speaker deal with a major issue relating to the discussion topic. A group dealing with capital punishment, for example, might have one speaker present the group's conclusion on the issue of whether capital punishment is an effective deterrent to crime, another speaker present the group's position on the morality of capital punishment, and so forth.

All the speeches should be carefully planned. They should also be coordinated with one another to make sure the symposium reports on all important aspects of the group's project.

PANEL DISCUSSION

A panel discussion is essentially a conversation in front of an audience. The panel should have a moderator, who introduces the topic and the panelists. Once the discussion is under way, the moderator may interject questions and comments as needed to focus the discussion. The panelists speak briefly, informally, and impromptu. They talk to each other, but loudly enough for the audience to hear. As with a symposium, a panel discussion may be followed by a question-and-answer session.

panel discussion

A structured conversation on a given topic among several people in front of an audience.

Because of its spontaneity, a panel discussion can be exciting for participants and audience alike. But, unfortunately, that spontaneity inhibits systematic presentation of a group's recommendations. Thus the panel discussion is seldom used by problem-solving groups, although it can work well for information-gathering groups.

If you are a participant in a panel discussion, beware of the common fallacy that no serious preparation is required. Although you will speak impromptu, you need to study the topic ahead of time, analyze the major issues, and map out the points you want to make. An effective panel discussion also requires planning by the moderator and panelists to decide what issues will be discussed and in what order. Finally, all panelists must be willing to share talking time, so the discussion is not monopolized by one or two people.

Whatever method your group uses to present its findings, you will benefit from the public speaking guidelines given throughout this book. The techniques of effective speech remain the same whether you are one person addressing an audience, part of a small group of people working to solve a problem, or a participant in a symposium or a panel discussion.[8]

Summary

A small group consists of three to twelve people assembled for a specific purpose. A problem-solving small group is formed to solve a particular problem. When such a group has effective leadership, it usually makes better decisions than do individuals by themselves.

Most groups have a designated leader, an implied leader, or an emergent leader. Some groups have no specific leader, in which case all members of the group must assume leadership responsibilities. An effective leader helps a group reach its goals by fulfilling procedural needs, task needs, and maintenance needs.

Apart from leadership, all members of a group have five basic responsibilities. You should commit yourself to the goals of your group, fulfill your individual assignments, avoid interpersonal conflict within the group, encourage full participation by all members, and help keep the group on track.

Your group will also be more successful if it follows the reflective-thinking method, which offers a step-by-step process for decision making in problem-solving groups. The method consists of five steps: (1) defining the problem as clearly and specifically as possible; (2) analyzing the problem to determine its severity and causes; (3) establishing criteria for evaluating solutions; (4) generating a wide range of potential solutions; (5) selecting the best solution or solutions.

Once your group has agreed on its recommendations, it usually has to make an oral report or participate in a symposium or a panel discussion. Whichever kind of oral presentation your group gives will call for skills of effective speechmaking.

Key Terms

dyad (366)

small group (366)

problem-solving small group (366)

leadership (367)

implied leader (367)

emergent leader (368)

designated leader (368)

procedural needs (368)

task needs (368)

maintenance needs (369)

hidden agenda (370)

reflective-thinking method (373)

question of policy (373)

criteria (375)

brainstorming (376)

consensus (377)

oral report (379)

symposium (379)

panel discussion (379)

Review Questions

After reading this chapter, you should be able to answer the following questions:

1. What is a small group? What is a problem-solving small group?
2. What are the four kinds of leadership that may occur in a small group? Explain the three kinds of needs fulfilled by leadership in a small group.
3. What are the five major responsibilities of every participant in a small group?
4. What are the stages of the reflective-thinking method? Explain the major tasks of a group at each stage.
5. What are the three methods for presenting orally the recommendations of a problem-solving group?

connect

For further review, go to the LearnSmart study module for this chapter.

Exercises for Critical Thinking

1. Identify the flaw (or flaws) in each of the following questions for a problem-solving group discussion. Rewrite each question so it conforms to the criteria discussed in the chapter for effective discussion questions.

   a. What should be done to prevent the utterly ridiculous shortage of new computers for students at this school?

   b. What should be done about child abuse?

   c. What should our state government do to reduce homelessness and to combat drunk driving?

   d. Should the federal government institute a national sales tax to help reduce the national debt?

2. If possible, arrange to observe a problem-solving small group in action. You might attend a meeting of your city council, the school board, the zoning commission, a local business, a church committee. To what extent does the discussion measure up to the criteria for effective discussion presented in this chapter? What kind of leadership does the group have, and how well does the leader (or leaders) fulfill the group's procedural needs, task needs, and maintenance needs? How do the other members meet their responsibilities? What aspects of the meeting are handled most effectively? Which are handled least effectively?

3. Identify a relatively important decision you have made in the last year or two. Try to reconstruct how you reached that decision. Now suppose you could remake the decision following the reflective-thinking method. Map out what you would do at each stage of the method. Do you still reach the same decision? If not, do you believe the reflective-thinking method would have led you to a better decision in the first place?

4. Attend a symposium or panel discussion on campus. Prepare a brief analysis of the proceedings. First, study the role of the moderator. How does she or he introduce the topic and participants? What role does the moderator play thereafter? Does she or he help guide and focus the panel discussion? Does she or he summarize and conclude the proceedings at the end?

Second, observe the participants. Are the speeches in the symposium well prepared and presented? Which speaker (or speakers) do you find most effective? Least effective? Why? Do participants in the panel discussion share talking time? Does their discussion appear well planned to cover major aspects of the topic? Which panelist (or panelists) do you find most effective? Least effective? Why?

Speeches for Analysis and Discussion

Appendix

I HAVE A DREAM

Martin Luther King, Jr.

Martin Luther King's "I Have a Dream" is widely regarded as a masterpiece. It was delivered August 28, 1963, to some 200,000 people who had come to Washington, D.C., to participate in a peaceful demonstration to further the cause of equal rights for African Americans. King spoke from the steps of the Lincoln Memorial, in the "symbolic shadow" of Abraham Lincoln, and the crowd filled the vast area between the Memorial and the Washington Monument. In addition, millions of Americans watched the speech on television or listened to it on the radio.

Like most ceremonial addresses, "I Have a Dream" is relatively short. Although it took King only 16 minutes to deliver the speech, he prepared it more carefully than any other speech in his career to that time. His purpose was to set forth as succinctly and as eloquently as possible the guiding principles of the civil rights movement, and to reinforce the commitment of his listeners to those principles.

One of the most interesting features of this speech is King's use of language to make the abstract principles of liberty and equality clear and compelling. Throughout, King relies on familiar, concrete words that create sharp, vivid images. He uses many more metaphors than do most speakers, but they are appropriate to the occasion and help to dramatize King's ideas. Finally, King makes extensive use of repetition and parallelism to reinforce his message and to enhance the momentum of the speech.

If you have heard a recording of "I Have a Dream," you know its impact was heightened by King's delivery. In his rich baritone voice, marked by the fervor of the crusader and modulated by the cadences of the Southern Baptist preacher, King gained the total involvement of his audience. As William Robert Miller says, "The crowd more than listened, it participated, and before King had reached his last phrase, a torrent of applause was already welling up."

The text of this speech is transcribed from a recording and is reprinted with permission of Joan Daves. Copyright 1963 by Martin Luther King, Jr.

1 I am happy to join with you today in what will go down in history as the greatest demonstration for freedom in the history of our nation.

2 Five score years ago, a great American, in whose symbolic shadow we stand today, signed the Emancipation Proclamation. This momentous decree came as a great beacon light of hope to millions of Negro slaves, who had been seared in the flames of withering injustice. It came as a joyous daybreak to end the long night of their captivity.

3 But one hundred years later, the Negro still is not free. One hundred years later, the life of the Negro is still sadly crippled by the manacles of segregation and the chains of discrimination. One hundred years later, the Negro lives on a lonely island of poverty in the midst of a vast ocean of material prosperity. One hundred years later, the Negro is still languished in the corners of American society and finds himself an exile in his own land. And so we've come here today to dramatize a shameful condition.

4 In a sense we've come to our nation's Capitol to cash a check. When the architects of our republic wrote the magnificent words of the Constitution and the Declaration of Independence, they were signing a promissory

note to which every American was to fall heir. This note was a promise that all men—yes, black men as well as white men—would be guaranteed the unalienable rights of life, liberty, and the pursuit of happiness.

5 It is obvious today that America has defaulted on this promissory note insofar as her citizens of color are concerned. Instead of honoring this sacred obligation, America has given the Negro people a bad check—a check which has come back marked "insufficient funds."

6 But we refuse to believe that the bank of justice is bankrupt. We refuse to believe that there are insufficient funds in the great vaults of opportunity of this nation. And so we've come to cash this check—a check that will give us upon demand the riches of freedom and the security of justice.

7 We have also come to this hallowed spot to remind America of the fierce urgency of now. This is no time to engage in the luxury of cooling off or to take the tranquilizing drug of gradualism. Now is the time to make real the promises of democracy. Now is the time to rise from the dark and desolate valley of segregation to the sunlit path of racial justice. Now is the time to lift our nation from the quicksands of racial injustice to the solid rock of brotherhood. Now is the time to make justice a reality for all of God's children.

8 It would be fatal for the nation to overlook the urgency of the moment. This sweltering summer of the Negro's legitimate discontent will not pass until there is an invigorating autumn of freedom and equality. Nineteen sixty-three is not an end, but a beginning. Those who hope that the Negro needed to blow off steam and will now be content will have a rude awakening if the nation returns to business as usual. There will be neither rest nor tranquility in America until the Negro is granted his citizenship rights. The whirlwinds of revolt will continue to shake the foundations of our nation until the bright day of justice emerges.

9 But there is something that I must say to my people, who stand on the warm threshold which leads into the palace of justice. In the process of gaining our rightful place, we must not be guilty of wrongful deeds. Let us not seek to satisfy our thirst for freedom by drinking from the cup of bitterness and hatred.

10 We must forever conduct our struggle on the high plane of dignity and discipline. We must not allow our creative protest to degenerate into physical violence. Again and again we must rise to the majestic heights of meeting physical force with soul force.

11 The marvelous new militancy which has engulfed the Negro community must not lead us to a distrust of all white people. For many of our white brothers, as evidenced by their presence here today, have come to realize that their destiny is tied up with our destiny. They have come to realize that their freedom is inextricably bound to our freedom. We cannot walk alone.

12 As we walk, we must make the pledge that we shall always march ahead. We cannot turn back. There are those who are asking the devotees of civil rights, "When will you be satisfied?" We can never be satisfied as long as the Negro is the victim of the unspeakable horrors of police brutality. We can never be satisfied as long as our bodies, heavy with the fatigue of travel, cannot gain lodging in the motels of the highways and the hotels of the cities. We cannot be satisfied as long as the Negro's basic mobility is from a smaller ghetto to a larger one. We can never be satisfied as long as our children are stripped of their selfhood and robbed of their dignity by signs stating "For Whites Only." We cannot be satisfied as long as a Negro in Mississippi

cannot vote and a Negro in New York believes he has nothing for which to vote. No, no, we are not satisfied, and we will not be satisfied until justice rolls down like waters, and righteousness like a mighty stream.

13 I am not unmindful that some of you have come here out of great trials and tribulations. Some of you have come fresh from narrow jail cells. Some of you have come from areas where your quest for freedom left you battered by the storms of persecution and staggered by the winds of police brutality. You have been the veterans of creative suffering. Continue to work with the faith that unearned suffering is redemptive.

14 Go back to Mississippi, go back to Alabama, go back to South Carolina, go back to Georgia, go back to Louisiana, go back to the slums and ghettos of our Northern cities, knowing that somehow this situation can and will be changed. Let us not wallow in the valley of despair.

15 I say to you today, my friends, so even though we face the difficulties of today and tomorrow, I still have a dream. It is a dream deeply rooted in the American dream.

16 I have a dream that one day this nation will rise up and live out the true meaning of its creed, "We hold these truths to be self-evident, that all men are created equal."

17 I have a dream that one day on the red hills of Georgia the sons of former slaves and the sons of former slaveowners will be able to sit down together at the table of brotherhood.

18 I have a dream that one day even the state of Mississippi, a state sweltering with the heat of injustice, sweltering with the heat of oppression, will be transformed into an oasis of freedom and justice.

19 I have a dream that my four little children will one day live in a nation where they will not be judged by the color of their skin but by the content of their character. I have a dream today.

20 I have a dream that one day, down in Alabama, with its vicious racists, with its governor having his lips dripping with the words of interposition and nullification, one day right there in Alabama little black boys and black girls will be able to join hands with little white boys and white girls as sisters and brothers. I have a dream today.

21 I have a dream that one day every valley shall be exalted, every hill and mountain shall be made low, the rough places will be made plane and the crooked places will be made straight, and the glory of the Lord shall be revealed, and all flesh shall see it together.

22 This is our hope. This is the faith that I go back to the South with. With this faith we will be able to hew out of the mountain of despair a stone of hope. With this faith we will be able to transform the jangling discords of our nation into a beautiful symphony of brotherhood. With this faith we will be able to work together, to pray together, to struggle together, to go to jail together, to stand up for freedom together, knowing that we will be free one day.

23 This will be the day—this will be the day when all of God's children will be able to sing with new meaning, "My country 'tis of thee, sweet land of liberty, of thee I sing. Land where my fathers died, land of the pilgrim's pride, from every mountainside, let freedom ring." And if America is to be a great nation, this must become true.

24 So let freedom ring from the prodigious hilltops of New Hampshire. Let freedom ring from the mighty mountains of New York. Let freedom ring from the heightening Alleghenies of Pennsylvania!

25 Let freedom ring from the snowcapped Rockies of Colorado! Let freedom ring from the curvaceous slopes of California!

26 But not only that. Let freedom ring from Stone Mountain of Georgia!

27 Let freedom ring from Lookout Mountain of Tennessee!

28 Let freedom ring from every hill and molehill of Mississippi. From every mountainside, let freedom ring.

29 And when this happens, when we allow freedom ring—when we let it ring from every village and every hamlet, from every state and every city—we will be able to speed up that day when all of God's children, black men and white men, Jews and Gentiles, Protestants and Catholics, will be able to join hands and sing in the words of the old Negro spiritual, "Free at last! Free at last! Thank God almighty, we are free at last!"

RAMADAN

Choosing a topic based on one's personal experience can be an excellent decision, especially when the speaker supplements her or his existing knowledge with additional research—as in the following informative presentation on the Muslim holy month of Ramadan. As you read, notice how crisply the speech is organized, how the speaker relates her topic to the audience, and how she explains each aspect of Ramadan clearly and engagingly.

The speech also provides an instructive example of extemporaneous delivery, which you can see by watching the video in the online Media Library for this appendix. The speaker maintains strong eye contact with the audience and refers to her notes only as needed. Despite her nerves, she comes across as poised and confident. Her gestures are natural and spontaneous, and her voice conveys a strong sense of communication.

View "Ramadan" in the online Media Library for this appendix (Video A.1).

1 This past month, more than one billion people around the world skipped lunch every day. They ate no food of any kind and drank no liquid of any kind from sunup to sunset. They did this every day during the month, and they do the same thing every year. I myself did it. Why? Last month was a time for tending to the mind, the body, and the spirit. Last month was the Muslim holy month of Ramadan.

2 I'm sure most of you have heard of Ramadan, but you may not know a lot about it. Ramadan refers to the ninth month in the Islamic calendar, when Muslims fast from sunrise to sunset. But Ramadan is much more than a time of fasting. As Tariq Ramadan, author of *Western Muslims and the Future of Islam,* explains, Ramadan is a time when "believers strengthen their faith and spirituality while developing their sense of social justice."

3 As a practicing Muslim, I have observed Ramadan my entire life. My parents moved to the United States from Pakistan shortly before I was born, and I remember going to the mosque as a child and breaking my fast at the end of the day with my family and friends. Nowadays, I get together with other students here on campus.

4 The goal of my speech today is to inform you about Ramadan—specifically its history and practices. In the end, I hope you'll have a better understanding of this sacred time for Muslims in the United States and around the globe. Let's begin by exploring the history of Ramadan.

5 Ramadan can be traced back 1,400 years to the Middle East and the beginnings of the Quran. As explained in Karen Armstrong's *Islam: A Short History,* in 610 A.D. the Prophet Mohammed embarked on a spiritual journey through the desert in what is now Saudi Arabia. At one point in this journey, Muslims believe, Allah spoke to Mohammed through the archangel Gabriel—the same Gabriel of the Jewish and Christian scriptures.

6 This is when the Prophet Mohammed received the first verses of the Quran. Gabriel told Mohammed to remember the revelation by observing a holy time every year. In the years after this journey, the Prophet Mohammed and his followers made the ninth month of the Muslim year the month of Ramadan.

7 The word "Ramadan" literally means "scorcher" in Arabic, because it was in the intense heat of the summer that the Prophet Mohammed encountered Gabriel. But unlike the Western calendar, the Islamic calendar follows the cycles of the moon and contains only 354 days. As a result, Ramadan always begins approximately ten days before it began the previous year. So, for example, this year Ramadan came on August 11th. Next year, it will come on August 1st.

8 Now let's take a look at what Muslims do during this holy month. The practices of Ramadan center on fasting, prayer, and charity.

9 Fasting is one of the five pillars of Islam, and it becomes especially important during Ramadan. The Ramadan fast, known as the *Sawm,* begins at sunrise and ends at sunset. Seyyed Nasr, author of *Islam: Religion, History, and Civilization,* explains that "the fast is required of all Muslims, male and female, from the age of adolescence until one no longer possesses the physical strength to undertake it." The only exceptions are for the sick, the elderly, travelers, and pregnant women.

10 At the end of daylight hours, Muslims break the fast with *Iftar*—the evening meal, during which families, friends, and communities gather. As Donna Bowen and Evelyn Early explain in their book *Everyday Life in the Muslim Middle East, Iftar* usually begins with eating a date, which is what the Prophet Mohammed is said to have done. After eating a date and drinking water, my family would eat the *Iftar* dinner my mother cooked for us. We would always marvel that even though she was fasting and couldn't taste what she was cooking, she still somehow got the spices just right.

11 Prayer is also central to Ramadan. Muslims traditionally pray five times a day, but during Ramadan prayer is encouraged even more. Ramadan prayers are often tied to oral readings of the Quran—a practice known as *Tarawih.* The goal is to read and recite the entire Quran over the course of the month.

12 In addition to fasting and prayer, charity plays a key role in Ramadan. *Iftars* are often organized and funded by the wealthy as a way of feeding the poor and the needy. Also, many Muslims increase their charitable giving during the month. At the end of Ramadan, my family donates to charity and we also exchange gifts like Christians do on Christmas.

13 If you think about it, the main purpose of Ramadan is the same as most religious holidays—spiritual development. Christians and Jews gather regularly to commemorate their histories, to enact certain rituals, and to feel closer to God. Muslims do the same thing during Ramadan.

14 Today, we've explored the history of Ramadan and its practices—fasting, prayer, and charity. I'd like to leave you with the traditional greeting that Muslims utter during this holy month: "Ramadan Kareem," which means

"Ramadan is generous." Less than a year from now, when the next Ramadan comes around, I hope you'll have a better understanding of why it is so sacred for one billion people around the world.

15 Thank you.

THE HORRORS OF PUPPY MILLS

Seventy-five million dogs are owned as pets in the United States, and 7 to 9 million puppies are purchased each year at a total cost of close to $1 billion. Most come from legitimate breeders who take good care of their animals. Two to four million, however, come from puppy mills, large-scale operations run solely for profit with no concern for the animals' physical or emotional welfare. After explaining the problem of puppy mills, the following persuasive speech presents a solution that combines legislative action with individual initiative.

In addition to reading the speech, you can watch it in the online Media Library for this appendix. As you watch, notice how the speaker uses PowerPoint to present visual evidence of the conditions animals are subjected to in puppy mills. Do you think the speech would have been as effective without this kind of evidence? All in all, does the speaker convince you that puppy mills are a serious problem? Does he present a clear and workable solution? How well does he use the methods of persuasion presented in Chapter 17?

connect

View "The Horrors of Puppy Mills" in the online Media Library for this appendix (Video A.2).

1 A cold, dark room. It smells disgusting. The creatures in front of you shake uncontrollably, packed one on top of another in tiny wire cages. To eat, they have only crumbs in front of them, and to drink, only a dirty bowl of water. Many have eye problems, ear problems, diseases, and infections. They've never been groomed. They've never been for a walk. And they've never seen the sun.

2 For too many dogs across America, this is how life begins—in a puppy mill. Puppy mills, as defined by the Humane Society of the United States, are "mass dog-breeding operations" that take place in "shockingly poor conditions." Puppy-mill breeders produce puppies for profit—only for profit—with little or no concern for the physical, social, or emotional needs of the dogs.

3 As a dog lover, I was shocked to discover the horrors of puppy mills across the country as I researched this speech. I know from my audience-analysis questionnaires that most of you had a dog or another pet while you were growing up and that you believe they should be treated humanely. Today I'll show you that puppy mills are not treating their animals humanely and I'll suggest some ways of solving the problem.

4 Puppy mills have been around for a long time, but they've grown dramatically in recent years. The Humane Society estimates that there are more than 10,000 puppy mills currently operating in the United States. According to Stephanie Shain, the Society's Director of Outreach for Companionable Animals, of the 7 to 9 million dogs sold in this country each year, 2 to 4 million come from puppy mills. That's double the number from only a decade ago.

5 Rather than producing the healthy, happy pets that millions of families dream of, puppy mills produce dogs with canine herpes, respiratory infections, parasites, seizures, and E. coli. Dogs that are lucky enough to escape these diseases often have rotten teeth, missing eyes or limbs, hip disorders, skin problems, and a host of other deformities.

6 In addition to suffering from physical problems, dogs in puppy mills are often emotionally unstable. Some are dangerously violent and aggressive. Others are apathetic and lack any desire to interact with people or animals. Because of the overcrowding in puppy mills, some animals literally go crazy and chew off the ears, legs, and tails of other dogs.

7 But you can see for yourself what the dogs have to endure. Here's a picture of a puppy mill provided by the U.S. Humane Society. As you can see, the cages are stacked one on top of another and the dogs are packed into the cages like sardines into a can. The dogs are not let out to go to the bathroom, so the cages are filled with waste and become breeding grounds for the diseases I mentioned earlier in my speech.

8 You can get a better sense of how disgusting puppy mills are from this photo, taken after the dogs were removed by animal protection officials. You can see how narrow the cages are and how they're crammed one against the other. You can see the filth and debris everywhere.

9 Finally, take a look at a couple individual dogs. The first one came from a puppy mill here in Wisconsin. It was so malnourished that it couldn't stand up by itself, and it had lost the fur on almost all of its body.

10 The next dog was in even worse shape. Covered with its own filth, it had a rash of infections and diseases and had lost the sight in one eye. Like other puppy-mill dogs, it never saw a veterinarian until it was rescued.

11 It's time that we stop the horrors of puppy mills and help dogs and dog owners alike. Solving the problem requires action on two fronts—legislation and individual initiative.

12 The first step is for new laws that will put puppy mills out of business. Current laws, such as the Animal Welfare Act, are ineffective at best. This law only regulates a small number of breeders, leaving countless puppy mills to operate under the radar.

13 Here's the legislation I propose. It's based on a combination of proposals that have been presented in several states. All dog breeders who produce more than 30 puppies a year should be required to register with their state's Department of Agriculture, which would inspect dog-breeding facilities just as the health department inspects restaurants.

14 Breeders with dogs in substandard conditions would be dealt with accordingly. A first offense would result in a fine of $3,000. A second offense would result in a fine of $5,000 and 30 days in jail. A third offense would result in a fine of $10,000 and 90 days in jail, plus permanent loss of the breeder's license in every state of the union.

15 But legislation alone won't do the job. You and I also have a part to play. We have to take the profit out of puppy mills by making sure we don't purchase dogs produced by puppy mills. We can do this by following guidelines laid out by the Humane Society.

16 First, consider adopting a dog from a trusted animal shelter instead of buying a new dog. The animal shelter will make sure the dog is free of physical and behavioral problems.

17 Second, if you decide to buy a new dog, visit the breeder's premises. If the breeder refuses to let you see the premises, or wants to meet you somewhere else, don't buy from that breeder.

18 Third, don't buy a dog from a pet store. The Humane Society has found that most dogs in pet stores actually come from puppy mills.

19 And fourth, don't be fooled by advertising. Just because an ad promises that a dog has been, quote, "family raised" or has a "health certificate,"

doesn't mean it's true. This is especially important when it comes to the Internet, where there is no way to verify the health of a dog or the trustworthiness of a breeder.

20 In conclusion, I'd like you to imagine your own pet—no matter what kind of animal it might be—living even one day in the conditions endured by dogs in puppy mills. Then imagine your pet living in those conditions day after day, week after week, month after month. Surely you would not want this for your own pet.

21 Yet even as we sit here, millions of dogs are suffering from the horrors of puppy mills. It's time to stop puppy-mill breeders from profiting on their cruelty. Even if, as the movie title says, all dogs go to heaven, we should not allow them to start their lives in hell.

BURSTING THE ANTIBACTERIAL BUBBLE

During the past several years, the use of household antibacterial products has grown dramatically in the United States. Today Americans spend millions of dollars on everything from antibacterial soaps and hand wipes to tissues, sponges, shampoos, and even children's toys that have been treated with antibacterial chemicals.

The following persuasive speech argues that these products do not provide the benefits they claim and may, in fact, be contributing to long-term health and environmental problems. As a solution, the speaker recommends that the U.S. Food and Drug Administration institute regulations governing the use of antibacterial products and that consumers avoid using these products.

In addition to reading this speech, you can watch the video in the online Media Library for this appendix. Study how the speaker uses examples, statistics, and testimony to support her position. Does she convince you that the heavy use of antibacterial products is a serious problem? Does she present an effective solution to the problem? How could she have made the speech more convincing?

connect

View "Bursting the Antibacterial Bubble" in the online Media Library for this appendix (Video A.3).

1 In the film *The Boy in the Plastic Bubble,* a boy born with a deficient immune system is forced to live in a germ-free environment to prevent him from contracting infections. His room is sealed against bacteria and viruses, his food is specially prepared, and his only human contact comes in the form of gloved hands.

2 Today millions of Americans are trying to build a bubble around themselves and their families to keep out germs. The bubble is not made of plastic, however, but of billions of dollars worth of antibacterial hand wipes, tissues, soaps, and sponges.

3 Before I studied antibacterial products in my public health class, I always used antibacterial hand soaps and antibacterial all-surface cleaner for my apartment. I also know from my class survey that 70 percent of you use antibacterial soaps, cleaners, and other products.

4 But after learning about the subject in class and reading research studies for this speech, I'm here to tell you that, try as we might, we cannot build a bubble between ourselves and germs with antibacterial products and that these products actually create more problems than they solve. After looking at the problems created by antibacterial products, we'll explore some solutions.

5 The place to begin is by noting that antibacterial products are popping up just about everywhere. The next time you go to the store, try to find a liquid soap that is not antibacterial. According to the Alliance for the Prudent Use of Antibiotics, 75 percent of all liquid soaps and 33 percent of all bar soaps are antibacterial.

6 In fact, there are more than 1,000 antibacterial household products on the market. In addition to all the soaps and cleaning products, there are also antibacterial cotton swabs, tons of antibacterial shampoos, and this antibacterial cutting board from Williams Sonoma. You can even get antibacterial socks, mouthwash, toothpaste, and, to protect you while away from home, this travel toothbrush with antibacterial bristles.

7 The *Boston Globe* reports that larger items such as mattresses, countertops, high chairs, and even children's toys have been coated with antibacterial chemicals. *The New York Times* calls the antibacterial craze "the biggest marketing coup since bottled water."

8 There's no doubt that antibacterial products are popular with consumers, but there is a great deal of doubt about whether they're effective in stopping the spread of germs. Elaine Larson, associate dean of the Columbia University School of Nursing, studied 238 families who used antibacterial products and found that they were just as likely to get fevers, sore throats, coughs, rashes, and stomach problems as families who used regular products. Larson's findings are echoed by Eric Kupferberg, associate director of the Harvard School for Public Health, who states: "Antimicrobial products don't significantly eliminate the number of germs you encounter on a daily basis."

9 Nor do antibacterial products prevent the transmission of diseases such as colds and flus. Why? Because these illnesses come from viruses, not from bacteria. Antibacterial products don't kill viruses. As Dr. Larson explains, "Most of the infections healthy people get are colds, flu, and diarrhea caused by viruses"—none of which can be prevented by the use of antibacterial products.

10 Not only do antibacterial products fail to deliver what they promise, but they actually increase your chances of getting sick. According to Stuart Levy, a professor of microbiology and medicine at Tufts University, excessive use of antibacterial products in the home can make children more likely to develop allergies and asthma.

11 In addition, people who use antibacterial products may become more susceptible to infections. Dr. James Chin, a research scientist in New South Wales, Australia, says: "The way we stay healthy is by low-dose exposure to bacteria and viruses. You need to exercise your immune system in the same way you need to exercise your muscles to be fit. If you don't do that, your immune system doesn't have a chance to do battle when it engages with an infection."

12 The problems caused by antibacterial products are so serious that Dr. Myron Genel, chairman of the American Medical Association's council on scientific affairs, fears one result may be the creation of antibiotic-resistant bacteria "that are largely untreatable because they are resistant to existing drugs."

13 And that's not all. Besides being ineffective at preventing diseases and being potentially dangerous to our health, antibacterial household products also appear to harm the environment. Rolf Halden of Johns Hopkins University School of Public Health reports that each year the United States releases into the water supply more than 2 million pounds of the active chemicals in antibacterial soaps.

14 The U.S. Geological Survey reports that chemicals from antibacterial products are winding up in streams and groundwater from the Denver area to remote locations in the Rocky Mountains. These chemicals are known to pollute the water supply, disrupt fish reproduction and growth, and, because they do not decompose quickly, remain active for years and years.

15 Now that we've seen the seriousness of the problem, let's look at some solutions.

16 First, we need federal legislation regulating the use of household antibacterial products. Just as the Food and Drug Administration has regulations controlling the use of antibiotics, so, too, should it institute regulations controlling the use of antibacterial products.

17 We don't let people purchase antibiotics without a doctor's prescription, and there's no reason we should allow makers of soap, tissues, hand wipes, toothbrushes, and other products to add powerful antibacterial agents without oversight from the Food and Drug Administration. Given the problems being caused by these products, it is time for the federal government to take action.

18 Second, we all need to take action as consumers. Most obviously, we need to stop buying these products. The best way to avoid germs, says the Centers for Disease Control, is to wash your hands for 10 to 15 seconds with plain soap and water.

19 In fact, a study at the University of North Carolina found that washing your hands with soap and water is more effective at getting rid of germs than using antibacterial hand wipes. Emily Sickbert-Bennett, a public epidemiologist and co-author of the study, explains that when you use soap and water, the germs go down the drain, but with waterless antibacterial hand wipes, "you never rinse your hands. You are just rubbing a chemical into your hand and letting it dry."

20 In conclusion, Americans spend millions of dollars every year on products that promise to "kill germs on contact." But as we have seen today, the antibacterial craze is a marketing coup rather than a proven way of stopping either the spread of germs or the incidence of colds, flus, and other virus-borne illnesses. Worse, these products appear to contribute to health problems, and they are creating environmental problems in the U.S. water supply. The federal government should start regulating these products and we, as consumers, should stop throwing our money away on them.

21 We need to resist the false notion that we can use these products to create a bubble around ourselves to keep out germs and disease. Instead, we can burst the bubble of marketers who are selling us a false bill of goods and then we can thoroughly wash our hands of the whole mess.

MY CRAZY AUNT SUE

The aim of a commemorative speech is to pay tribute to a person, a group of people, an institution, or an idea. In the following student speech, the speaker commemorates her aunt Sue and her heroic battle against the debilitating disease of rheumatoid arthritis.

As you read the speech, notice that it is not a biography that simply recounts the details of aunt Sue's life. Instead, it focuses on her courage, her sense of humor, and her refusal to complain about her fate. The speaker provides enough details to make clear why her aunt is so commendable, but her ultimate purpose

connect
View "My Crazy Aunt Sue" in the online Media Library for this appendix (Video A.4).

is to inspire the audience rather than to inform it. The speaker also uses vivid language, repetition, and parallel structure to give the speech the kind of formal tone appropriate for a commemorative speech.

In addition to reading this speech, you can view it in the online Media Library for this appendix.

1 The strongest person I know cannot peel a potato. The strongest person I know has trouble putting on her makeup. The strongest person I know needs a special key holder to turn the key in her car's ignition.

2 For the past 15 years, my 47-year-old aunt Sue has been living with rheumatoid arthritis, a painfully debilitating disease in which the joints of the body become intensely inflamed due to the immune system's activity. Yet despite the daily torments of this disease, my aunt Sue is stronger than any woman or man I have ever met.

3 Not a moment passes that my aunt Sue is not confronted with this demon of a disease and reminded of her disability through the pills she must take and the pain she must endure. It hurts to stand, it hurts to walk, it hurts to sit. After an infinite number of failed medications, aunt Sue is now undergoing her most aggressive treatment, which includes weekly oral chemotherapy. After half a dozen surgeries, her frail body is in need of still more.

4 And yet despite all of this, I can't recall ever hearing her complain about her fate. After all the indignities and inconveniences her illness has thrown at her, my aunt Sue still finds the energy to devote much of her time not to herself, but to those less fortunate than her. This past Thanksgiving, for example, she helped organize a dinner for more than 500 poor and homeless people. My aunt Sue, who has her medications put in non-childproof containers so she can open them, helped coordinate a dinner for those in need.

5 The picture I have painted of my aunt Sue thus far is of a kind woman, a determined woman, a warmhearted woman whose own suffering seems inconsequential when compared to that of others. This is all completely true, but there is something else about my aunt Sue that makes me admire her so. Actually, it's what makes me love her as much as I do.

6 At five feet two inches, and 105 pounds, with the spunk of a teenager, she introduces herself as "Crazy Sue"—and sometimes I'd have to agree with her. Somehow she is able to approach this demonic disease with a sense of humor. And not just any sense of humor. My aunt Sue is one of the funniest people I know.

7 Years ago, when the disease began to hit her really hard, one of the attorneys at her law firm asked why she was limping. She told him she fell off a trapeze performing her weekend hobby—and he believed her! Following an ankle sprain and further complications, her ankle became deformed and the arch of her foot completely collapsed. Whereas most people would wallow in their misery, aunt Sue calls it her "cartoon foot."

8 My aunt Sue has made a positive impression on countless people throughout her life, but I hope she knows how much of an impression she has made on me—and how much I admire her.

9 I complain about trudging through the snow to class, but I'm walking pain free. I complain about driving my friends around town, but I'm steering the wheel pain free. I complain about the final exams I'll have to write, but I have the mobility in my wrist to write pain free. I have learned from my aunt Sue that I need to do a better job about being happy for the things that I have, rather than worrying about the not-so-perfect things in my life.

10 Aunt Sue may call herself crazy, but I call her phenomenal—a joy to be around and a reminder that having a physical disability in no way diminishes a person's spirit or inner beauty.

QUESTIONS OF CULTURE

Sajjid Zahir Chinoy

Seldom does a student commencement address upstage the featured speaker—especially when that speaker is a Pulitzer Prize winner from Harvard University. Yet that is exactly what happened when Sajjid Zahir Chinoy spoke to his fellow graduates at the University of Richmond on May 12, 1996.

Born and raised near Bombay, India, Chinoy was selected to speak as the result of a campuswide competition. After describing the jumble of emotions that filled his mind as he came to the United States to attend school, he spoke movingly of the warm reception he received in Richmond and of how cultural differences can be overcome by attempting to understand other people.

Addressing his audience of 3,000 people extemporaneously and without notes, Chinoy received thunderous applause, and his remarks were widely reported in the press. His speech was so inspiring that the main speaker, Harvard psychiatrist Robert Coles, began his address by paying tribute to Chinoy. "I've been to a number of commencements," said Coles, "but I've never heard a speech quite like that."

The text of this speech has been transcribed from a video recording and is reprinted with permission from Sajjid Zahir Chinoy and the University of Richmond. A video is available in the online Media Library for this appendix.

connect

View "Questions of Culture" in the online Media Library for this appendix (Video A.5).

1 Distinguished guests, faculty, staff, students, ladies and gentlemen, and, most of all, the Class of 1996:

2 I can visualize the scene again and again: 11:30 P.M., Saturday night, the fifteenth of August, 1992, Bombay International Airport, India. I was leaving home for the University of Richmond. And as I said that final good-bye to my parents, my family, and my friends; and as I saw hope, expectation, even a tinge of sadness, in their eyes; and as I stepped aboard the Boeing 747 in front, I knew my life had changed forever.

3 The next 36 hours on board the aircraft were a time of questions, of concerns, of tremendous uncertainty.

4 Had I made the right choice in leaving home? Had I made the right choice in leaving my parents, my family, my home? Had I made the right choice in leaving my country, my culture, my background? Had I made the right choice in choosing the University of Richmond?

5 And then, of course, there was that one nagging question, that one overriding concern: As one of only three Indian students on a Richmond campus of 3,000, would I ever fit in?

6 My country was different. My culture was different. My experiences were different. My background was different. My language was different. My accent was different. Would I ever fit in?

7 And so here I was, high above the clouds, grappling with questions of culture, of interaction, of ethnicity. What I didn't know was that 30,000 feet

below, on the ground, the world was faced with these very same questions—the question of culture, the question of interaction, the question of ethnicity.

8 And so whether my aircraft took off from Bombay, where the Hindus and the Muslims lived together in a most fragile peace; or whether my aircraft was over Africa, where the Hutus and Tutsis of Rwanda and Burundi had long-standing animosity; or whether my aircraft was over Bosnia, where the Serbs, the Croats, the Muslims, and the Bosnians had broken yet another truce, the question was the same—could different cultures ever come together to reinforce one another?

9 Ladies and gentlemen, after that bumpy aircraft ride, this young Indian student had found his answer. He had been witness to the four most spectacular years of his life at the University of Richmond. The academics were great; the extracurriculars were great; his graduate plans were great.

10 But what left an indelible impact on his mind was none of this. No, instead it was those special moments, those moments of human interaction, those human relationships that can never quite be translated into words:

11 The time this young Indian student spent his first Thanksgiving dinner with his debate team coach. That Thanksgiving evening when I ate my first American turkey and saw my first American football game, not knowing the difference between a tackle and a touchdown. And yet, all of a sudden, just like that, this very different Indian student had become an inherent part of the great American tradition of giving thanks.

12 The time I spent my first Christmas Eve with my journalism professor. That Christmas evening when the relationship wasn't of a faculty member and a student anymore, but of two buddies who fought fiercely over every point in Ping-Pong.

13 The time I had a long and honest talk with an American friend on the eve of a calculus exam. I didn't learn much calculus that night, but what I did learn was that as different as we are—different countries, different cultures, different continents—inherently we are still the same.

14 The time in December 1992 when India was hit by communal riots, when violence and bloodshed were but a few hundred yards from my family and my home, and when my fantastic roommate from my freshman year sat up the entire night, giving me hope, strength, and courage at every step.

15 Yes, four years after that bumpy aircraft ride, I have found the answer to the question of culture.

16 I have found that it has taken just a little understanding, just a little sensitivity, just a little open-mindedness, just a little empathy on the part of this community—this University of Richmond community—to change my life like never before.

17 I have found that it makes no difference what culture you follow, what your background is, what your experiences are, what language you speak, what accent you have. The commonality of the human bond far transcends these superficial differences.

18 And yet look around at the world today. Look around at the very regions that were faced with the same question of culture that I was faced with four years ago.

19 Look at Bosnia, where, between 1992 and 1996, 300,000 people had been slaughtered—Bosnians, Serbs, Croats, Muslims—all because they came from a slightly different heritage or culture or history.

20 Look at Bombay, India. In one maddening week in 1992, 2,000 Indians—Hindus and Muslims—lost their lives fighting with one another. They fought

over a mosque; they fought over a structure made of brick and mortar. Two thousand human beings lost their lives.

21 Look at Africa, where, between 1992 and 1996, 1 million Hutus and Tutsis lost their lives. Just comprehend that for a moment. Between the time you were a freshman and a senior, 1 million lost their lives fighting over culture, over history, over background.

22 Yes, just look at the madness. The world has fought hard to highlight its differences. We have forgotten our inherent similarities. All because what was missing was a little understanding. Just a little sensitivity. Just a little open-mindedness. Just a little empathy.

23 Two similar questions of culture in 1992. Two diametrically opposite results in 1996.

24 And so, to the Class of 1996, I say go and distinguish yourselves like never before. Go get the best of jobs, the most rewarding of careers. Go to the best of graduate programs. And make a real difference in your communities.

25 But not for one moment, not for one moment, ever forget the memory of these four years—the memory that just a little understanding, just a little sensitivity, just a little open-mindedness, just a little empathy on your part can mean the difference between complete despair for one young boy in Bosnia and remarkable hope for another young boy at Richmond.

26 Thank you.

Notes

Chapter 1

[1] Pericles, quoted in Richard Whately, *Elements of Rhetoric,* 7th ed. (London: John W. Parker, 1846), p. 10.

[2] *Raising the Bar: Employers' Views on College Learning in the Wake of the Economic Downturn* (Washington, DC: Hart Research Associates, 2010); "Communication Tops Skills Sought by Employers," *Training,* October 11, 2010, www.training.com. May 12, 2011.

[3] Dave McGinn, "Me? Public Speaking?" *Globe and Mail*, December 1, 2009, p. L1.

[4] Quoted in Emily Driscoll, "Um, Like, Whatever: College Grads Lack Verbal Skills," Foxbusiness.com, March 4, 2011. April 6, 2011.

[5] George A. Kennedy, *Comparative Rhetoric: An Historical and Cross-Cultural Introduction* (New York: Oxford University Press, 1998).

[6] Geoffrey Brewer, "Snakes Top List of Americans' Fears," Gallup News Service, February 2001; Alex Blyth, "How to Get the Most Out of Public Speaking Training," *Training Magazine* (June 14, 2006), p. 7.

[7] A. M. Ruscio, T. A. Brown, W. T. Chiu, J. Sareen, M. B. Steain, and R. C. Kessler, "Social Fears and Social Phobia in the USA: Results from the National Comorbidity Survey Replication," *Psychological Medicine* (January 2008), pp. 15–28.

[8] Cicero, *De Oratore,* trans. E. W. Sutton (Cambridge, MA: Harvard University Press, 1942), p. xxvi.

[9] Digby Jones, "Public Speaking Tests the Nerves of Most Directors," *Birmingham Post,* August 25, 2003.

[10] Elayne Snyder, *Speak for Yourself—With Confidence* (New York: New American Library, 1983), p. 113.

[11] Sharon Aschaiek, "Conquer Your Fear of Public Speaking," *Toronto Sun,* March 16, 2005.

[12] A number of studies have shown that taking a public speaking course is effective in reducing stage fright. See Graham D. Bodie, "A Racing Heart, Rattling Knees, and Ruminative Thoughts: Defining, Explaining, and Treating Public Speaking Anxiety," *Communication Education,* 59 (2010), pp. 70–105.

[13] Lilly Walters, *Secrets of Successful Speakers* (New York: McGraw-Hill, 1993), pp. 32–36.

[14] See Steven Ungerleider, *Mental Training for Peak Performance,* rev. ed. (Emmaus, PA: Rodale Books, 2005).

[15] Joe Ayres, Tim Hopf, Michael T. Hazel, Debbie M. A. Sonandre, and Tanichya K. Wongprasert, "Visualization and Performance Visualization: Applications, Evidence, and Speculation," in John A. Daly et al. (eds.), *Avoiding Communication: Shyness, Reticence, and Communication Apprehension,* 3rd ed. (Cresskill, NJ: Hampton Press, 2009), pp. 375–394.

[16] Dick Cavett, quoted in Steve Allen, *How to Make a Speech* (New York: McGraw-Hill, 1986), p. 10.

[17] For more detail on the ideas in this paragraph, see Michael T. Motley, *Overcoming Your Fear of Public Speaking: A Proven Method* (Boston: Houghton Mifflin, 1998).

[18] Chris R. Sawyer and Ralph R. Behnke, "Reduction in Public Speaking State Anxiety During Performance as a Function of Sensitization Processes," *Communication Quarterly,* 50 (2002), pp. 110–121.

[19] For more detail on the dimensions of critical thinking, see M. Neil Browne and Stuart M. Keeley, *Asking the Right Questions: A Guide to Critical Thinking,* 9th ed. (Upper Saddle River, NJ: Pearson Education, 2010).

[20] For other models of the speech communication process, see Stephen W. Littlejohn and Karen A. Foss, *Theories of Human Communication,* 10th ed. (Long Grove, IL: Waveland Press, 2011); Em Griffin, *A First Look at Communication Theory,* 8th ed. (New York: McGraw-Hill, 2012).

[21] Herman Melville, *Redburn: His First Voyage* (New York: Harper and Brothers, 1850), p. 214.

[22] William B. Gudykunst and Young Yun Kim, *Communicating with Strangers: An Approach to Intercultural Communication,* 4th ed. (New York: McGraw-Hill, 2003), p. 4.

[23] For more detail on gestures and other aspects of intercultural communication, see Judith N. Martin and Thomas K. Nakayama, *Intercultural Communication in Contexts,* 5th ed. (New York: McGraw-Hill, 2010).

[24] Adapted from Roger E. Axtell (ed.), *Do's and Taboos Around the World,* 3rd ed. (New York: John Wiley and Sons, 1993), p. 41.

[25]Myron W. Lustig and Jolene Koester, *Intercultural Competence: Interpersonal Communication Across Cultures,* 6th ed. (Boston: Allyn and Bacon, 2010), pp. 149–152.

[26]For more on multiculturalism and communication, see Shang Liu, Zala Volčič, and Cindy Gallois, *Introducing Intercultural Communication: Global Cultures and Contexts* (Thousand Oaks, CA: Sage, 2011).

Chapter 2

[1]Richard L. Johannesen, Kathleen S. Valde, and Karen E. Whedbee, *Ethics in Human Communication,* 6th ed. (Prospect Heights, IL: Waveland Press, 2008), p. 14.

[2]Johannesen, Valde, and Whedbee, *Ethics in Human Communication,* p. 13.

[3]See, for example, Vincent Ryan Ruggiero, *Thinking Critically About Ethical Issues,* 7th ed. (New York: McGraw-Hill, 2008).

[4]Haig A. Bosmajian, *The Language of Oppression* (Lanham, MD: University Press of America, 1983), p. 5.

[5]See Steven J. Heyman, *Free Speech and Human Dignity* (New Haven, CT: Yale University Press, 2008).

[6]Thomas L. Tedford and Dale A. Herbeck, *Freedom of Speech in the United States,* 6th ed. (State College, PA: Strata Publishing, 2009), pp. 173–180.

[7]Kenneth Blanchard and Norman Vincent Peale, *The Power of Ethical Management* (New York: Ballantine Books, 1988), p. 64.

[8]For an excellent guide to ethical decision making, see Ronald A. Howard and Clinton D. Korver, *Ethics for the Real World* (Boston: Harvard Business Press, 2008).

[9]*MLA Handbook for Writers of Research Papers,* 7th ed. (New York: Modern Language Association of America, 2009), p. 52.

[10]Merry Firschein, "School Chief Calls Speech 'An Error in Judgment,'" *The Record,* June 2, 2007; "Superintendent's Speech Stirs Talk of Plagiarism," *New York Times,* June 2, 2007; Merry Firschein, "Teachers Worried About Boss's Last Year," *The Record,* June 13, 2007.

[11]Bruce Perry, *Malcolm: The Life of the Man Who Changed Black America* (Tarrytown, NY: Station Hill, 1991), p. 380.

[12]The credo is available at www.natcom.org/Default.aspx?id=134&terms=credo.

[13]See www.natcom.org/Default.aspx?id=134 & terms=credo.

Chapter 3

[1]Larry Barker and Kittie Watson, *Listen Up: What You've Never Heard About the Other Half of Every Conversation* (New York: St. Martin's, 2001), p. 5.

[2]Michael P. Nichols, *The Lost Art of Listening,* 2nd ed. (New York: Guilford, 2009).

[3]See Lyman K. Steil and Richard K. Bommelje, *Listening Leaders: The Ten Golden Rules to Listen, Lead, and Succeed* (Edina, MN: Beaver's Pond Press, 2004).

[4]Judi Brownell, *Listening: Attitudes, Principles, and Skills,* 4th ed. (Boston: Allyn and Bacon, 2010), p. 9.

[5]Jan Flynn, Tuula-Riitta Valikoski, and Jennie Grau, "Listening in the Business Context: Reviewing the State of Research," *International Journal of Listening,* 22 (2008), pp. 141–151; Laura A. Janusik, "Listening Pedagogy: Where Do We Go From Here?" in Andrew D. Wolvin (ed.), *Listening and Human Communication in the 21st Century* (West Sussex, UK: Blackwell, 2010), pp. 193–194.

[6]See, for example, Melissa L. Beall, Jennifer Gill-Rosier, Jeanine Tate, and Amy Matten, "State of the Context: Listening in Education," *International Journal of Listening,* 22 (2008), pp. 123–132.

[7]Andrew W. Wolvin and Carolyn Gwynn Coakley, *Listening,* 5th ed. (Dubuque, IA: Brown and Benchmark, 1995), pp. 223–396.

[8]Brownell, *Listening: Attitudes, Principles, and Skills,* p. 84.

[9]Louis Nizer, *My Life in Court,* repr. ed. (Whitefish, MT: 2010), pp. 297–298.

[10]Adapted from Lyman K. Steil, Larry L. Barker, and Kittie W. Watson, *Effective Listening* (Reading, MA: Addison-Wesley, 1983).

[11]George H. Putnam, *Abraham Lincoln* (New York: Putnam, 1909), pp. 44–45.

[12]M. Scott Peck, *The Road Less Traveled: A New Psychology of Love, Traditional Values, and Spiritual Growth,* 25th anniversary ed. (New York: Touchstone Books, 2003), p. 127.

[13]Jack Hayes, "Fifty Years of Meteorological Advances," *Vital Speeches,* 77 (2011), pp. 27–30.

[14]See Ralph G. Nichols and Leonard A. Stevens, *Are You Listening?* (New York: McGraw-Hill,

1957), pp. 113–114. This classic work still has much of value to say about its subject.

[15]On some of the other challenges involved in note taking, see Annie Piolat, Thierry Olive, and Ronald T. Kellogg, "Cognitive Effort During Note Taking," *Applied Cognitive Psychology,* 19 (2005), pp. 291–312.

[16]See, for example, Tamas Makany, Jonathan Kemp, and Itiel E. Dror, "Optimizing the Use of Note-Taking as an External Cognitive Aid for Increasing Learning," *British Journal of Educational Technology,* 40 (2009), pp. 619–635.

Chapter 6

[1]Seeing the speech classroom as a real audience is also important because it engages students in a form of rhetorical activity that is vital to participatory democracy. See Rosa A. Eberly, "Rhetoric and the Anti-Logos Doughball: Teaching Deliberating Bodies the Practices of Participatory Democracy," *Rhetoric and Public Affairs,* 5 (2002), p. 296.

[2]Saul Alinsky, *Rules for Radicals* (New York: Random House, 1971), p. 81.

[3]For a broader discussion of gender issues in communication, see Julia T. Wood, *Gendered Lives: Communication, Gender, and Culture,* 9th ed. (Boston: Wadsworth, 2011).

[4]Diana L. Eck, *A New Religious America* (New York: HarperCollins, 2001), p. 4.

[5]Research shows that speakers are usually more persuasive when they attempt to refute opposing arguments rather than ignoring them. See Richard M. Perloff, *The Dynamics of Persuasion: Communication and Attitudes in the 21st Century,* 4th ed. (New York: Routledge, 2010), pp. 185–186.

Chapter 7

[1]For more detail on Internet research, see Randolph Hock, *The Extreme Searcher's Internet Handbook: A Guide for the Serious Searcher,* 3rd ed. (Medford, NJ: CyberAge Books, 2010).

[2]See, for example, Adam R. Brown, "Wikipedia as a Data Source for Political Scientists: Accuracy and Completeness of Coverage," *PS: Political Science and Politics,* 44 (2011), pp. 339–343; Don Fallis, "Toward an Epistemology of Wikipedia," *Journal of the American Society for Information Science and Technology,* 59 (2008), pp. 1662–1674.

[3]These criteria are adapted from Sheridan Libraries, "Evaluating Information Found on the Internet," *Johns Hopkins University.* Web. April 14, 2011.

[4]For more information on various interview types and situations, see Charles J. Stewart and William B. Cash, Jr., *Interviewing: Principles and Practices,* 13th ed. (New York: McGraw-Hill, 2011).

[5]For an interesting study that confirms the extent to which the process of researching and developing speeches can affect the beliefs and attitudes of student speakers, see Barbara Mae Gayle, "Transformations in a Civil Discourse Public Speaking Class: Speakers' and Listeners' Attitude Change," *Communication Education,* 53 (2004), pp. 174–184.

Chapter 8

[1]See, for example, Kathryn Greene, Shelly Campo, and Smita C. Banerjee, "Comparing Normative, Anecdotal, and Statistical Risk Evidence to Discourage Tanning Bed Use," *Communication Quarterly,* 58 (2010), pp. 111–132.

[2]I would like to thank *21st Century* and *China Daily* for permission to include this excerpt from Sun Yan's speech in the online Media Library for this edition of *The Art of Public Speaking.*

[3]Elliot Aronson, *The Social Animal,* 10th ed. (New York: Worth, 2008), pp. 92–93.

[4]This point was made by James A. Winans in his classic *Speech-Making* (New York: Appleton-Century-Crofts, 1922), p. 141.

[5]Over the years, there has been much debate over whether statistics or examples have more impact on listeners. For a recent study that addresses this subject, see Hans Hoeken and Lettica Hustinx, "When Is Statistical Evidence Superior to Anecdotal Evidence in Supporting Probability Claims? The Role of Argument Type," *Human Communication Research,* 35 (2009), pp. 491–510.

[6]Joel Best, *Stat-Spotting: A Guide to Identifying Dubious Data* (Berkeley: University of California Press, 2008), provides a fascinating look at the use and misuse of statistics. For a more technical approach, see Neil J. Salkind, *Statistics for People Who (Think They) Hate Statistics,* 4th ed. (Thousand Oaks, CA: Sage, 2011).

[7]Bob Papper, "2010 Salary Survey: News Salaries Stabilize," Radio Television Digital News Association. *RTDNA.* Web. 15 April 2011.

[8]M. Allen, R. Bruflat, R. Fucilla, M. Kramer, S. McKellips, D. J. Ryan, and M. Spiegelhoff, "Testing the Persuasiveness of Evidence: Combining Narrative and Statistical Forms," *Communication Research Reports,* 17 (2000), pp. 331–336.

[9]For research confirming the importance of citing sources when presenting evidence, see Rodney A. Reynolds and J. Lynn Reynolds, "Evidence," in James Price Dillard and Michael Pfau (eds.), *The Persuasion Handbook: Developments in Theory and Practice* (Thousand Oaks, CA: Sage, 2002), pp. 429–430.

[10]Richard M. Perloff, *The Dynamics of Persuasion: Communication and Attitudes in the 21st Century,* 4th ed. (New York: Routledge, 2010), pp. 251–254.

Chapter 9

[1]Ernest C. Thompson, "An Experimental Investigation of the Relative Effectiveness of Organizational Structure in Oral Communication," *Southern Speech Journal,* 26 (1960), pp. 59–69.

[2]Harry Sharp, Jr., and Thomas McClung, "Effects of Organization on the Speaker's Ethos," *Speech Monographs,* 33 (1966), pp. 182–183.

[3]See, for example, B. Scott Titsworth, "Students' Notetaking: The Effects of Teacher Immediacy and Clarity," *Communication Education,* 53 (2004), pp. 305–320; Joseph L. Chesebro, "Effects of Teacher Clarity and Nonverbal Immediacy on Student Learning, Receiver Apprehension, and Affect," *Communication Education,* 52 (2003), pp. 135–147.

Chapter 10

[1]Judith S. Kaye, "Gathering Dreams and Giving Them Life," *Vital Speeches,* 73 (2007), pp. 239–242.

[2]Robert M. Gates, "About the Institution You Will Someday Lead," *Vital Speeches,* 77 (2011), pp. 138–142.

[3]Dorothy Sarnoff, *Speech Can Change Your Life* (Garden City, NY: Doubleday, 1970), p. 189.

[4]Sarnoff, *Speech Can Change Your Life,* p. 190.

Chapter 11

[1]Robert T. Oliver, *History of Public Speaking in America* (Boston: Allyn and Bacon, 1965), p. 143.

[2]Oliver, *History of Public Speaking,* p. 145.

Chapter 12

[1]For an authoritative exploration of the multiple functions of language, see David Crystal, *The Cambridge Encyclopedia of Language,* 3rd ed. (New York: Cambridge University Press, 2010).

[2]Dorothy Sarnoff, *Speech Can Change Your Life* (New York: Doubleday, 1970), p. 71.

[3]Annmarie Mungo, "A Child Is Born," *Winning Orations, 1980* (Mankato, MN: Interstate Oratorical Association, 1980), pp. 49–50.

[4]See Joseph Williams and Gregory G. Colomb, *Style: Lessons in Clarity and Grace,* 10th ed. (New York: Longman, 2010), for more on the principles of verbal clarity.

[5]James Geary, *I Is an Other: The Secret Life of Metaphor and How It Shapes the Way We See the World* (New York: Harper, 2011), provides a highly readable exploration of the role of metaphor in human expression.

[6]Edward Bliss, Jr. (ed.), *In Search of Light: The Broadcasts of Edward R. Murrow, 1938–1961* (New York: Knopf, 1967), p. 276.

[7]Rosalie Maggio, *Talking About People: A Guide to Fair and Accurate Language* (Phoenix, AZ: Oryx Press, 1997), p. 26.

Chapter 13

[1]Irving Bartlett, *Wendell Phillips: Boston Brahmin* (Boston: Beacon Press, 1961), p. 192.

[2]A. Craig Baird, *Rhetoric: A Philosophical Inquiry* (New York: Ronald Press, 1965), p. 207.

[3]Daniel J. O'Keefe, *Persuasion: Theory and Research,* 2nd ed. (Thousand Oaks, CA: Sage, 2002), p. 185.

[4]Dorothy Sarnoff, *Speech Can Change Your Life* (Garden City, NY: Doubleday, 1970), p. 73.

[5]See Walt Wolfram and Ben Ward (eds.), *American Voices: How Dialects Differ from Coast to Coast* (Malden, MA: Blackwell, 2006), for a collection of readings on dialects in the United States.

[6]Consult Kenneth C. Crannell, *Voice and Articulation,* 5th ed. (Boston: Wadsworth, 2012), for more detail on all aspects of voice production.

[7]Mark L. Knapp and Judith A. Hall, *Nonverbal Communication in Human Interaction,* 7th ed. (Boston: Wadsworth, 2010), pp. 12–15.

[8]Richard M. Perloff, *The Dynamics of Persuasion: Communication and Attitudes in the 21st Century,* 4th ed. (New York: Routledge, 2010), pp. 178–181.

[9]For more on delivery, plus other aspects of public speaking, see Garr Reynolds, *The Naked Presenter* (Berkeley, CA: New Riders, 2011); Scott Berkun, *Confessions of a Public Speaker* (Sebastopol, CA: O'Reilly Media, 2010).

[10]Thomas F. Calcagni, *Tough Questions—Good Answers: Taking Control of Any Interview* (Sterling, VA: Capital Books, 2008), provides many practical tips on managing question-and-answer sessions.

Chapter 14

[1]For a compendium of research on these subjects, see Richard E. Mayer (ed.), *Multimedia Learning* (New York: Cambridge University Press, 2009).

[2]See Stephen Few, *Now You See It: Simple Visualization Techniques for Quantitative Analysis* (Oakland, CA: Analytics Press, 2009), for a revealing look at the art of statistical graphics.

[3]Herbert W. Lovelace, "The Medium Is More Than the Message," *Informationweek.com* (July 16, 2001), p. 74.

[4]See, for example, Richard E. Mayer and Cheryl I. Johnson, "Revising the Redundancy Principle in Multimedia Learning," *Journal of Educational Psychology,* 100 (2008), pp. 380–386.

[5]Nancy Duarte, *Slideology: The Art and Science of Creating Great Presentations* (Sebastopol, CA: O'Reilly Books, 2008), provides a wealth of insight on designing high-impact visual aids.

[6]For more tips on the effective use of visual aids, see Garr Reynolds, *Presentation Zen: Simple Ideas on Presentation and Delivery* (Berkeley, CA: New Riders Press, 2008).

Chapter 15

[1]John R. Johnson and Nancy Szczupakiewicz, "The Public Speaking Course: Is It Preparing Students with Work-Related Public Speaking Skills?" *Communication Education,* 36 (1987), pp. 131–137; Andrew D. Wolvin and Diana Corley, "The Technical Speech Communication Course: A View from the Field," *Association for Communication Administration Bulletin,* 49 (1984), pp. 83–91.

[2]Richard E. Mayer, Sherry Fennell, Lindsay Farmer, and Julie Campbell, "A Personalization Effect in Multimedia Learning: Students Learn Better When Words Are in Conversational Style Rather Than Formal Style," *Journal of Educational Psychology,* 96 (2004), pp. 389–395.

[3]Joseph Conrad, "Youth: A Narrative," in Samuel Hynes (ed.), *Collected Stories of Joseph Conrad* (Hopewell, NJ: Ecco Press, 1991), p. 166.

[4]James Humes, *Roles Speakers Play* (New York: Harper and Row, 1976), p. 25.

Chapter 16

[1]There are many competing definitions of persuasion. Mine is drawn from Gerald R. Miller, "On Being Persuaded: Some Basic Distinctions," in James Price Dillard and Michael Pfau (eds.), *The Persuasion Handbook: Developments in Theory and Practice* (Thousand Oaks, CA: Sage, 2002), pp. 3–16.

[2]Amanda Bennett, "Economics + Meeting = A Zillion Causes and Effects," *Wall Street Journal,* January 10, 1995, B1.

[3]See Richard L. Johannesen, Kathleen S. Valde, and Karen E. Whedbee, *Ethics in Human Communication,* 6th ed. (Prospect Heights, IL: Waveland Press, 2008), for a full look at communication ethics.

[4]Adapted from Herbert W. Simons and Jean G. Jones, *Persuasion in Society,* 2nd ed. (New York: Routledge, 2011), p. 46.

[5]This view of the interaction between speaker and listener reflects cognitive processing models of persuasion in general and the Elaboration Likelihood Model in particular. For a concise explanation of the latter, see Em Griffin, *A First Look at Communication Theory,* 8th ed. (New York: McGraw-Hill, 2012), pp. 205–216.

[6]There is a great deal of research confirming the need for persuasive speakers to answer potential objections to their arguments. See John A. Banas and Stephen A. Rains, "A Meta-Analysis of Research on Inoculation Theory," *Communication Monographs,* 77 (2010), pp. 282–311.

[7]For a superb look at the research on courtroom persuasion, see John C. Reinard, "Persuasion in the Legal Setting," in Dillard and Pfau, *Persuasion Handbook,* pp. 543–602.

[8]Richard M. Perloff, *The Dynamics of Persuasion: Communication and Attitudes in the 21st Century,* 4th ed. (New York: Routledge, 2010), pp. 259–261.

[9]Daniel J. O'Keefe, *Persuasion: Theory and Research,* 2nd ed. (Thousand Oaks, CA: Sage, 2002), pp. 218–219.

[10]See, for example, Amber Marie Reinhart, Heather M. Marshall, Thomas Hugh Feeley, and Frank Tutzauer, "The Persuasive Effects of Message Framing in Organ Donation: The Mediating Role of Psychological Reactance," *Communication Monographs,* 74 (2007), pp. 229–255.

Chapter 17

[1]James C. McCroskey, *An Introduction to Rhetorical Communication,* 9th ed. (Boston: Allyn and Bacon, 2006), pp. 84–96.

[2]Rachel A. Smith and Edward L. Fink, "Compliance Dynamics Within a Simulated Friendship Network I: The Effects of Agency, Tactic, and Node Centrality," *Human Communication Research,* 36 (2010), pp. 232–260.

[3]Richard M. Perloff, *The Dynamics of Persuasion: Communication and Attitudes in the 21st Century,* 4th ed. (New York: Routledge, 2010), pp. 210–213.

[4]See John A. Banas and Stephen A. Rains, "A Meta-Analysis of Research on Inoculation Theory," *Communication Monographs,* 77 (2010), pp. 282–311.

[5]John C. Reinard, "The Empirical Study of the Persuasive Effects of Evidence: The Status After Fifty Years of Research," *Human Communication Research*, 15 (1988), pp. 37–38.

[6]See, for example, Michael T. Stephenson, "Examining Adolescents' Responses to Antimarijuana PSAs," *Human Communication Research,* 29 (2003), pp. 343–369.

[7]Rodney A. Reynolds and J. Lynn Reynolds, "Evidence," in James Price Dillard and Michael Pfau (eds.), *The Persuasion Handbook: Developments in Theory and Practice* (Thousand Oaks, CA: Sage, 2002), pp. 429–430.

[8]Daniel J. O'Keefe, *Persuasion: Theory and Research,* 2nd ed. (Thousand Oaks, CA: Sage, 2002), pp. 216–218.

[9]Adapted from James C. Humes, *A Speaker's Treasury of Anecdotes About the Famous* (New York: Harper and Row, 1978), p. 131.

[10]In classical systems of logic, reasoning from particular facts to a general conclusion was known as induction. Contemporary logicians, however, have redefined induction as any instance of reasoning in which the conclusion follows from its premises with probability, regardless of whether the reasoning moves from specific instances to a general conclusion or from a general premise to a specific conclusion. In this scheme, reasoning from specific instances is one kind of inductive argument—as are causal reasoning and analogical reasoning. See, for example, Nancy M. Cavender and Howard Kahane, *Logic and Contemporary Rhetoric: The Use of Reason in Everyday Life,* 11th ed. (Belmont, CA: Wadsworth, 2010).

[11]Lionel Ruby, *The Art of Making Sense* (Philadelphia: Lippincott, 1954), p. 261.

[12]In classical systems of logic, reasoning from a general premise to a specific conclusion was known as deduction. But just as contemporary logicians have redefined induction (see note 10), they have redefined deduction as any instance of reasoning in which the conclusion follows from its premises with certainty. Some deductive arguments move from general premises to a specific conclusion, but others move from specific premises to a general conclusion. Many speech textbooks confuse reasoning from principle, which is one form of deduction, with deductive reasoning in general.

[13]For more on fallacies and methods of reasoning, see Douglas Walton, *Informal Logic: A Pragmatic Approach,* 2nd ed. (Cambridge: Cambridge University Press, 2008).

[14]H. E. Butler (trans.), *The Institutio Oratoria of Quintilian* (Cambridge, MA: Harvard University Press, 1961), IV, p. 141.

[15]George Campbell, *The Philosophy of Rhetoric,* ed. Lloyd F. Bitzer (Carbondale, IL: Southern Illinois University Press, 1988), p. 77.

[16]Research on fear appeals, for example, has demonstrated that messages devoted exclusively to arousing fear in the audience are usually less effective than messages that combine fear appeals with reasonable explanations of how to eliminate or cope with the source of fear. For an excellent review of that research, see Perloff, *Dynamics of Persuasion,* pp. 194–207.

Chapter 18

[1]James C. Humes, *Roles Speakers Play* (New York: Harper and Row, 1976), p. 8.

[2]For both speeches, see "Remarks by President Clinton and President Nelson Mandela at Presentation of the Congressional Gold Medal to

President Nelson Mandela," September 23, 1998. (http://clinton4.nara.gov/WH/New/html/19980923-977.html) May 20, 2011.

[3]Humes, *Roles Speakers Play,* pp. 33–34, 36.

Chapter 19

[1]Gloria J. Galanes and Katherine Adams, *Effective Group Discussion: Theory and Practice,* 13th ed. (New York: McGraw-Hill, 2010), pp. 233–235.

[2]See Charlan Jeanne Nemeth and Jack A. Goncalo, "Influence and Persuasion in Small Groups," in Timothy C. Brock and Melanie C. Green (eds.), *Persuasion: Psychological Insights and Perspectives*, 2nd ed. (Thousand Oaks, CA: Sage, 2005), pp. 171–194, for a helpful review of scholarship on this subject.

[3]For more on the many dimensions of group leadership, see John W. Gastil, *The Group in Society* (Thousand Oaks, CA: Sage 2010), pp. 139–166.

[4]For more on dealing with conflict in small groups, see Scott A. Myers and Carolyn Anderson, *The Fundamentals of Small Group Communication* (Thousand Oaks, CA: Sage, 2008), pp. 199–215.

[5]Charles Pavitt and Kelly K. Johnson, "Scheidel and Crowell Revisited: A Descriptive Study of Group Proposal Sequencing," *Communication Monographs,* 69 (2002), pp. 19–32.

[6]For research on this subject, see Michele H. Jackson and Marshall Scott Poole, "Idea-Generation in Naturally Occurring Contexts: Complex Appropriation of Simple Group Procedure," *Human Communication Research,* 29 (2003), pp. 560–591.

[7]For further reading on research in small-group communication, see Marshall Scott Poole and Andrea B. Hollingshead (eds.), *Theories of Small Groups: Interdisciplinary Perspectives* (Thousand Oaks, CA: Sage, 2005).

[8]For more on small-group oral presentations, see Katherine Adams and Gloria J. Galanes, *Communicating in Groups: Applications and Skills,* 8th ed. (New York: McGraw-Hill, 2009), pp. 292–314.

Photo Credits

Chapter 1
Page 2: Courtesy of Geoffrey Canada and Harlem Children's Zone; 7: © ULTRA.F/Photodisc/Getty Images; 11: Photo by Eric Kayne/Getty Images; 14: Photo by Dan Perry, Atlanta; 17: © Image Source/Getty Images; 19: © Image Source/Getty Images; 23: © Reuters; 25: © Brand X Pictures/PunchStock

Chapter 2
Page 28: © Bryan Bedder/Getty Images; 33: © Zuma Wire World Photos/Newscom; 35: U.S. Navy photo by MC3 Travis K. Mendoza; 39: JGI/Jamie Grill/Blend Images/Getty Images; 41: Ingram Publishing; 43: © AP Photo/Joseph Kaczmarek

Chapter 3
Page 46: © Marius Becker/dpa/Corbis; 51: LWA/Dann Tardif/Blend Images/Getty Images; 55: © Terry Vine/Blend Images/Corbis; 59: © Oliver Berg/dpa/Corbis

Chapter 4
Page 65: Photo by Jemal Countess/WireImage/Getty Images

Chapter 5
Page 76: © Wolfgang Kaehler; 79: Digital Vision/Getty Images; 83: UpperCut Images/Getty Images; 85: © AP Photo/Statesman Journal, Kobbi R. Blair; 91: © Erik Isakson/Getty Images

Chapter 6
Page 96: © Kevork Djansezian/Getty Images; 101: © Ron Sachs/CNP/Corbis; 103: DESHAKALYAN CHOWDHURY/AFP/Getty Images; 109: © Reena Rose Sibayan/The Jersey Journal/Landov; 110: DreamPictures/Getty Images; 115: © AP Photo/Minnesota Daily, Mark Vancleave

Chapter 7
Page 118: © Chris Hill/National Geographic Society/Corbis; 122: PhotoAlto/Sigrid Olsson/Getty Images; 125: © Zhang Jun/XinHua/Xinhua Press/Corbis; 129: Thinkstock/Jupiterimages; 131: © Tim Pannell/Corbis; 137: moodboard/photolibrary

Chapter 8
Page 140: © Roger L. Wollenberg/UPI/Landov; 145: © Joe Skipper/Reuters; 149: Ken James/Bloomberg/Getty Images

Chapter 9
Page 164: Thomas Hawk/Flickr/Getty Images; 169: © Mike Kepka/San Francisco Chronicle/Corbis; 171: © JupiterImages/Thinkstock/Alamy; 173: © Image Source/Corbis; 179: © UPI/Kevin Dietsch /Landov

Chapter 10
Page 184: AFP Photo/Dimitar Dilkoff/Newscom; 187: © Patrick Kovarik/AFP/Getty Images; 191: Inti St Clair/Blend Images/Getty Images; 193: Diego Tuson/AFP/Getty Images; 197: Charles Eshelman/FilmMagic/Getty Images; 198: © Image Source/Corbis

Chapter 11
Page 204: © Mike Kemp/Rubberball; 205: (far right) © Rachel Epstein/PhotoEdit; 209: © Fancy/photolibrary; 214: © Dr. Billy Ingram/WireImage/Getty Images; 215: © Stockbyte

Chapter 12
Page 220: Olivier Douliery/ABACAUSA.com/Newscom; 223: © Sipa Press/Newscom; 227: © Tim Shaffer/Reuters/Landov; 229: © Mark Costantini/San Francisco Chronicle/Corbis; 231: Dave and Les Jacobs/Blend Images LLC.; 233: © Richard Langdon/Getty Images

Chapter 13
Page 238: © Michael Buckner/Getty Images; 243: © Brooks Kraft/Corbis; 245: © Jonathan Newton/The Washington Post/Getty Images; 249: © Rick Friedman/Corbis; 251: Courtesy of Southern Vermont College and Michelle Kwan; 253: Stockbyte/Getty Images; 255: © FRANCK ROBICHON/POOL/epa/Corbis

Chapter 14
Page 258: Courtesy of Kris Krüg/Flickr; 261: © Jim Zuckerman/Corbis; 265: Mannic Media/McGraw-Hill, Inc.; 266: The McGraw-Hill Companies, Inc./Andrew Resek, photographer; 271: © ZUMA Press/Newscom

Chapter 15
Page 276: © EPA/Monica M. Davey/Photolibrary; 281: © WpN/Photoshot; 285: © China Photos/Getty Images; 287: © The Star-Ledger/Jerry McCrea/The Image Works; 289: © Stockbyte; 292: © Cultura RF/Getty Images

Index

Metaphor, 229–230
Millennial Generation, 104–105
Mode, 150
Models, as visual aids, 260
Modern Language Association (MLA) format, 133, 135
Monotone, 244
Monroe, Alan, 315
Monroe's motivated sequence, 315–317
Multiculturalism. *See* Cultural diversity
"My Crazy Aunt Sue" (speech), 360, A11–A13

N

Nadal, Rafael, 10
Name-calling, 34–35, 43
National Communication Association, 42, 44
Need
  in Monroe's motivated sequence, 315–317
  in questions of policy, 311
Nervousness
  acquiring speaking experience to overcome, 10–11
  methods to deal with, 11–15, 71
  nature of, 9–10
  positive, 10
  positive thinking to deal with, 12
New England dialect, 247
Newspaper databases, 122–123
Nonverbal communication
  body movement and, 249–250
  cultural diversity and, 23
  explanation of, 240
  eye contact as, 15, 70, 249–251, 272
  gestures as, 23, 70, 250
  personal appearance as, 248–249
  role of, 248
  during speech delivery, 70–71, 240
Notes
  for extemporaneous speech, 68–69
  interview, 132–133
  research, 134, 136
Note taking
  guidelines for, 134, 136
  during interviews, 132–133
  key-word outline system for, 59–60
  when listening, 58–60

O

Obama, Barack, 97–98
Objects
  explanation of, 278
  speeches about, 278–280
  as visual aids, 260
O'Brien, Conan, 239
Occasion
  appropriate language for, 233
  appropriate remarks for, 354
  audience disposition toward, 109–110
Open-ended questions, 111, 112
Oral reports, 378–379
Organization
  critical thinking and, 16–17
  of main points, 166–175 (*See also* Main points)
  of parts of speech, 66–67
  for persuasive presentation, 7
  strategic, 166
  of supporting material, 175–177 (*See also* Supporting materials)
  use of connectives for, 177–180
Organizational methods
  causal, 170–171
  chronological, 66, 169–170, 279, 281
  comparative advantages, 314–315
  Monroe's motivated sequence, 315–317
  problem-cause-solution, 314
  problem-solution, 171–172, 313–314
  spatial, 170, 279
  topical, 66, 172–173, 279–281, 283, 284, 306, 308
Outlines. *See* Preparation outlines; Speaking outlines
Out-of-context quotations, 156–157

P

Panel discussions, 379–380
Parallelism, 230–231
Paraphrases
  explanation of, 40, 156
  identify sources of, 136, 158–159
  quotations vs., 156
Passive agreement, 310
Patchwork plagiarism, 38
Pathos, 343
Pauses, in speech, 245
Peer testimony, 155–156
Perfection, expectations of, 13–14
Pericles, 4

Periodical databases, 122–123
Perry, Bruce, 39
Personal appearance
  focusing on, 52, 53, 56
  for interviews, 131
  nervousness and, 13
  of speakers, 248–249
Personal inventory, 80
Personalize, 291–293
Persuasion
  building credibility for, 326–330
  challenges related to, 301–302
  degrees of, 302
  emotional appeals for, 342–346
  ethics and, 300–301
  explanation of, 300
  importance of, 300
  psychology of, 301–305, 315–316
  reasoning for, 334–342
  use of evidence for, 330–333
Persuasive speeches
  examples of, 318–320, 346–349
  how listeners process, 302–304
  on questions of fact, 305–306
  on questions of policy, 309–318
  on questions of value, 307–309
  situations for, 305
  target audience for, 304–305
Phillips, Wendell, 240
Philosophy of Rhetoric (Campbell), 343
"Phony Pharmaceuticals" (speech), 318–320
Photographs, 260–261
Physical setting, 106–107, 274
Pie graphs, 262–263
Pitch, 244
Pizan, Christine de, 6
Plagiarism
  explanation of, 37
  global, 37
  incremental, 38–40
  Internet and, 40–41
  methods to avoid, 136
  patchwork, 38
Plan, in questions of policy, 311–312
Plato, 30
Policy questions, 309–318
Pollak, Lindsey, 5
Positive nervousness, 10. *See also* Nervousness
Positive thinking, 12
Post hoc, ergo propter hoc, 338–339

Essentials of Health Policy and Law

Second Edition

Joel B. Teitelbaum, JD, LLM

George Washington University
School of Public Health and Health Services
Department of Health Policy
Washington, DC

Sara E. Wilensky, JD, PhD

The George Washington University
School of Public Health and Health Services
Department of Health Policy
Washington, DC

JONES & BARTLETT
LEARNING

BP45

World Headquarters
Jones & Bartlett Learning
5 Wall Street
Burlington, MA 01803
978-443-5000
info@jblearning.com
www.jblearning.com

Jones & Bartlett Learning books and products are available through most bookstores and online booksellers. To contact Jones & Bartlett Learning directly, call 800-832-0034, fax 978-443-8000, or visit our website, www.jblearning.com.

Substantial discounts on bulk quantities of Jones & Bartlett Learning publications are available to corporations, professional associations, and other qualified organizations. For details and specific discount information, contact the special sales department at Jones & Bartlett Learning via the above contact information or send an email to specialsales@jblearning.com.

This publication is designed to provide accurate and authoritative information in regard to the Subject Matter covered. It is sold with the understanding that the publisher is not engaged in rendering legal, accounting, or other professional service. If legal advice or other expert assistance is required, the service of a competent professional person should be sought.

Production Credits
Publisher: Michael Brown
Editorial Assistant: Kayla Dos Santos
Production Manager: Tracey McCrea
Senior Marketing Manager: Sophie Fleck Teague
Manufacturing and Inventory Control Supervisor: Amy Bacus

Composition: Publishers' Design and Production Services, Inc.
Cover Design: Scott Moden
Cover Image: © Architect of the Capitol
Printing and Binding: Edwards Brothers Malloy
Cover Printing: Edwards Brothers Malloy

Some images in this book feature models. These models do not necessarily endorse, represent, or participate in the activities represented in the images.
The Architect of the Capitol or the United States Congress do not endorse this product.

To order this product, use ISBN: 978-1-4496-5330-9

Library of Congress Cataloging-in-Publication Data
Teitelbaum, Joel Bern.
   Essentials of health policy and law / Joel Teitelbaum, Sara Wilensky. — 2nd ed.
      p. cm.
   Includes bibliographical references and index.
   ISBN 978-1-4496-0473-8 (pbk.)
1.   Medical policy—United States—Textbooks. 2. Medical laws and legislation--United States—Textbooks. I. Wilensky, Sara E. II. Title.
   RA395.A3T45 2013
   362.1—dc23
                                                                                                2011039512

6048

Printed in the United States of America
16   15   14   13   10   9   8   7   6   5   4

11/5/13

Contents

Prologue

The second edition of *Essentials of Health Policy and Law* is a textbook on health reform. Building on the core content and engaging style of the first edition, this edition is heavily influenced by the 2010 passage of the Patient Protection and Affordable Care Act, the most far-reaching effort at national health reform in generations. Professors Joel Teitelbaum and Sara Wilensky are both experienced in analyzing and communicating about the Affordable Care Act, and this edition benefits from their expertise. Beyond the issue of health reform, *Essentials of Health Policy and Law, Second Edition* takes a broad approach to the study of health policy and law and provides a coherent framework for grappling with important healthcare, public health, and bioethical issues in the United States.

Health policies and laws have become an inescapable and critical component of our everyday lives. The accessibility, cost, and quality of health care; the country's preparedness for disasters; the safety of the food, water, and medications we consume; the right to make individual decisions about one's own health and well-being; and scores of other important issues are at the heart of health policy and law. Health policies and laws have a strong and lasting effect on our quality of lives as individuals and on our safety and welfare as a nation.

Professors Teitelbaum and Wilensky do a marvelous job of succinctly describing not only the policy- and lawmaking machinery and the always-evolving healthcare and public health systems, but also the ways in which policy and law affect health care and public health, and vice versa. They have a unique ability to make complex issues accessible to various readers, including those without a background in health care or public health. Their training as policy analysts and lawyers

shines through as they systematically describe and analyze the complex field of health policy and law and provide vivid examples to help make sense of it. Equally apparent is their wealth of experience teaching health policy and law at both the undergraduate and graduate levels. Between them, they have designed and taught many health policy and/or law courses, supplemented the content of health policy and law by integrating writing and analytic skills into their courses, designed a Bachelor of Science degree program in public health, and received teaching awards for their efforts. Readers of this textbook are the beneficiaries of their experience, enthusiasm, and commitment, as you will see in the pages that follow.

Essentials of Health Policy and Law, Second Edition stands on its own as a text. Even so, the accompanying *Essential Readings in Health Policy and Law* provides abundant illustrations of the development, influence, and consequences of health policies and laws. The carefully selected articles, legal opinions, and public policy documents in the supplemental reader will allow students to delve deeper into the topics and issues explored in this book.

I am pleased that *Essentials of Health Policy and Law* is a part of the *Essential Public Health* series. From the earliest stages of the series' development, Professors Teitelbaum and Wilensky have played a central role. They have closely coordinated efforts with other series authors to ensure that the series provides a comprehensive approach with only intended overlap. This is well illustrated by the addition in this edition of a glossary, which required careful efforts to ensure consistency of terminology across the series, and by the numerous other additions and revisions that have taken place with the publication of this second edition. A fuller description of these additions and revisions can be found in the Preface.

I am confident that you will enjoy reading and greatly benefit from *Essentials of Health Policy and Law*. Whether you are studying public health, public policy, healthcare administration, or a field within the clinical health professions, this textbook is a key component of your education.

Richard Riegelman, MD, MPH, PhD
Editor, *Essential Public Health* Series

Preface

Health policy and law are matters of national and local focus and concern. Public opinion polls, media coverage, and policy debates at all levels of government and in private industry attest to the important place that health care and public health hold in the minds of the American public, policymakers, and lawmakers. The constant attention showered on health policy-related topics also highlights their complexity, which stems from multiple factors.

First, like most challenging public policy problems, pressing health policy questions simultaneously implicate politics, law, ethics, and social mores, all of which come with their own set of competing interests and advocates. Second, health policy debates often involve deeply personal matters pertaining to one's quality—or very definition—of life, philosophical questions about whether health care should be a market commodity or a social good, or profound questions about how to appropriately balance population welfare with closely guarded individual freedoms and liberties. Third, it is often not abundantly clear how to begin tackling a particular health policy problem. For example, is it one best handled by the medical care system, the public health system, or both? Which level of government—federal or state—has the authority or ability to take action? Should the problem be handled legislatively or through regulatory channels? The final ingredient that makes health policy problems such a complex stew is the rapid developments often experienced in the areas of healthcare research, medical technology, and public health threats. Generally speaking, this kind of rapid evolution is a confounding problem for the usually slow-moving American policy- and lawmaking machinery.

Broadly defined, the goal of health policy is to promote and protect the health of individuals and of populations bound by common circumstances. Because the legal system provides the formal structure through which public policy—including health policy—is debated, effectuated, and interpreted, law is an indispensable component of the study of health policy. Indeed, law is inherent to the expression of public policy: major changes to policies often demand the creation, amendment, or rescission of laws. As such, students studying policy must learn about the law, legal process, and legal concepts.

The range of topics fairly included under the banner of "health policy and law" is breathtaking. For example, what effect is healthcare spending having on national and state economies? How should finite financial resources be allocated between health care and public health? How can we ensure that the trust funds established to account for Medicare's income and disbursements remain solvent in the future as an enormous group of Baby Boomers becomes eligible for program benefits? What kind of return (in terms of quality of individual care and the overall health of the population) should we expect from the staggering amount of money we collectively spend on health? Should individuals have a legal entitlement to health insurance? How best to attack extant health disparities based on race, ethnicity, and socioeconomic status? What policies will best protect the privacy of personal health information in an increasingly electronic medical system? Can advanced information technology systems improve the quality of individual and population health? Should the right to have an abortion continue to be protected under the federal Constitution? Should physician assistance in dying be promoted as a laudable social value? Will mapping the human genome lead to discrimination based on underlying health status? How prepared is the country for natural and man-made catastrophes, like pandemic influenza or bioterrorism attacks? What effect will chronic diseases, such as diabetes and obesity-related conditions, have on healthcare delivery and financing? How best to harness advancing scientific findings for the benefit of the public's health?

As seen from this partial list of questions, the breadth of issues encountered in the study of health policy and law is virtually limitless, and we do not grapple with all of the preceding questions in this book. We do, however, introduce you to many of the policies and laws that give rise to them, provide an intellectual framework for thinking about how to address them going forward, and direct you to additional relevant readings. Given the prominent role played by policy and law in the health of all Americans, and the fact that the Institute of Medicine recommends that students of public health and other interdisciplinary subjects (for example, public policy or medicine), receive health policy and law training,[1] the aim of this book is to help you understand the broad context of American health policy and law, the essential issues impacting and flowing out of the healthcare and public health systems, and how health policies and laws are influenced and formulated. Think of this textbook as an extended manual—introductory, concise, and straightforward—to the seminal issues in American health policy and law, and thus as a jumping off point for discussion, reflection, research, and analysis. To further assist with those pursuits, this book is accompanied by *Essential Readings in Health Policy and Law* (Jones and Bartlett Publishers, 2008), a compilation of carefully selected readings meant to allow for deeper analysis of issues covered in this textbook, as well as some issues not covered due to space constraints.

The health policy and law landscape has changed dramatically since publication of the first edition of this textbook in 2007 as a result of the Patient Protection and Affordable Care Act (known as the Affordable Care Act, or ACA), which was passed by Congress after a historic debate and signed into law by President Barack Obama in March 2010. The ACA has been hailed as the most important set of changes to American health insurance since the 1965 enactment of Medicare and Medicaid and, over time, this hugely complex law could effectively reorder most aspects of the healthcare system.

At its core, the ACA represents two landmark achievements in health policy: major reform of the private health insurance market and, relatedly, a redistribution of resources to groups and individuals who, by virtue of indigence and/or illness, have historically been excluded from the health insurance market and/or healthcare system. Although, in the end, the approach taken was to build on the existing public and private health insurance coverage system rather than tossing out the system in existence to replace it with something else, such as a government-sponsored single payer insurance system, the ACA nonetheless made sweeping reforms with an eye toward achieving near-universal health insurance coverage by 2019. Indeed, if fully implemented, the ACA will move the nation toward a more affordable, equitable, and stable insurance system, not only for the 32 million individuals who are expected to gain insurance, but also for the tens of millions of people who no longer face the threat of a loss or lapse of coverage.

Although the ACA is most properly understood as a series of policy and legal decisions aimed at transforming health insurance coverage, the law includes dozens of other important reforms and new programs unrelated to insurance. For example, more efficient and higher quality health care, population health, healthcare access, long-term care, the health workforce, health disparities, community health centers, healthcare fraud and abuse, comparative effectiveness research, health information technology, and more all receive attention by the ACA.

The key to the many reforms put forward in the ACA is a reordering of the relationships that lie at the heart of the healthcare system. Individuals, providers, insurers, employers, governments, and others will be forced to alter normative behaviors in response to the policy and legal decisions underpinning the law. These changes are described in relevant places throughout this book, but we provide here a few examples. Most notable is the ACA's requirement that individuals carry "minimum essential health coverage" or face specified financial penalties. This "individual mandate," as it is known, is perhaps the most important provision in the ACA, because it creates a new and large pool of premium-paying individuals that operates as the *quid pro quo* to insurers. Insurers are now forced to accept individuals—whom to this point they have deemed "uninsurable" because they are relatively unhealthy—as insured beneficiaries. For individuals unable to attain the type of minimum coverage mandated by the ACA, subsidies are made available.

A second change key to health system reordering is a series of reforms that prohibit or curtail commonplace practices on the part of health insurers and health plans. These include: prohibiting the use of preexisting condition exclusions and

---

[1] Kristine Gebbie et al., eds., *Who Will Keep the Public Healthy?: Educating Public Health Professionals for the 21st Century* (Washington, DC: The National Academies Press, 2003), 95–98.

discriminatory enrollment practices based on an individual's health status; guaranteeing the availability of health insurance and the renewability of an individual's existing insurance; requiring coverage of certain preventive screening and immunization services recommended by the federal government; and guaranteeing coverage for dependent children who are under age 26. A third key shift is the ACA's creation of state health insurance "exchanges" and expansion of Medicaid eligibility standards. The state exchanges were established for the purpose of giving individuals and small groups an opportunity to purchase health insurance products from a heavily regulated (and therefore relatively stable) market. The Medicaid expansion will for the first time cover all U.S. citizens and legal immigrants with incomes below 133% of the Federal Poverty Level.

A final word, for now, about the ACA and its implementation. As described in Chapter 9, passage of the ACA was anything but smooth. The law passed by the slimmest of margins after months of rancorous debate, and backlash against the law after its passage was swift and forceful. At the time of this writing, dozens of states, individuals, and organizations have lodged lawsuits against various aspects of the ACA, and these lawsuits are slowly cropping up through trial and appellate courts across the country. The most heavily litigated issue—the constitutionality of the individual mandate—is widely expected to reach the U.S. Supreme Court in 2012 or 2013, and several other courts could rule on various legal challenges to the ACA in ways that may affect, to one degree or another, implementation of the law. The outcomes of these lawsuits will no doubt be discussed in both the national media and in the health policy and law courses in which you register, and they will be devoted space in the pages of this book in future editions. Whatever the outcome of these individual cases, however, we urge readers not to lose sight of an important principle: whether the ACA ultimately survives wholly intact or undergoes changes as a result of courts' interpretation of it is largely beside the point; the more important point is that the ACA has put the country on a path toward a more just, equitable, and accessible health system.[2]

A second significant change since 2007 that is relevant to this textbook and the entire *Essentials of Public Health* series has occurred in the field of public health education. Since

the initial publication of this textbook, the Association of American Colleges and Universities (AAC&U) has worked with public health educational associations, including the Association of Schools of Public Health (ASPH) and the Association for Prevention Teaching and Research (APTR), and with the Council of Colleges of Arts and Sciences (CCAS), to develop the Educated Citizen and Public Health Initiative.[3] This initiative seeks to integrate public health perspectives into a comprehensive liberal education framework and to develop and organize publications, presentations, and resources to help faculty develop public health curricula in the nation's colleges and universities. As a result, public health perspectives generally, and health policy and law specifically, are increasingly being integrated into courses as diverse as political science, history, sociology, public policy, and a range of courses that prepare students for the health professions. We seek in this second edition to make the material as accessible to these diverse audiences as possible.

As a result of the changes just described and also in response to comments we received from users of the original textbook, this edition of *Essentials of Health Policy and Law* has undergone many revisions. Among them are new chapters covering the healthcare and public health systems generally, the ACA, and public health preparedness policy; expanded content in the chapter on healthcare quality; expanded content around agency rulemaking in a health context; revisions to several chapters to reflect the ACA's influence; a newly included glossary; updated figures, tables, timelines, and discussion questions; a reordering of some of the chapters to enhance the flow of the topics covered; and more.

Part I of this textbook includes five preparatory chapters. Chapter 1 describes the influential role of policy and law in health care and public health and introduces various conceptual frameworks through which the study of health policy and law can take place. The chapter also illustrates why it is important to include policy and law in the study of health care and public health. However, an advanced exploration of health policy and law in individual and population health necessitates both a basic and practical comprehension of policy and law in general—including the policymaking process and the workings of the legal system—and an understanding of the nation's somewhat fragmented health care and public health systems. Thus, Chapter 2 discusses both the meaning of policy and the policymaking process, including the basic functions, structures, and powers of the legislative and executive branches of government and the respective roles of

[2] For readers interested in closely following implementation of the ACA, we recommend *http://www.healthreformgps.org*, a website dedicated to analysis of the ACA and its implementation. In the interest of full disclosure, one of the authors (Teitelbaum) is part of the Health Reform GPS project team at the George Washington University's Department of Health Policy responsible for the content found at the site.

[3] For information about the Initiative, visit *http://www.aacu.org/public_health/index.cfm*.

the federal and state governments in policymaking. Chapter 3 then describes the meaning and sources of law and several key features of the American legal system, including the separation of powers doctrine, federalism, the role of courts, and due process. Chapter 4 provides an overview of the healthcare system, including basic information on healthcare finance, access, and quality, and examples of how the U.S. system differs from those in other first-world nations. Part I closes with an overview, in Chapter 5, of the public health system, including its evolution and core functions.

Part II offers several chapters focusing on key substantive health policy and law issues. The opening chapter examines the ways in which the law creates, protects, and restricts individual rights in the contexts of health care and public health, including a discussion of laws (such as Medicaid and Medicare) that aim to level the playing field where access to health care is concerned. The chapter also introduces the "no-duty" to treat principle, which holds that there is no general legal duty on the part of physicians to provide care and which rests at the heart of the legal framework pertaining to healthcare rights and duties. Chapters 7 and 8 cover the fundamentals of health insurance and health economics, respectively, and set up a subsequent thematic discussion in Chapters 9 and 10. Specifically, Chapter 7 describes the function of risk and uncertainty in health insurance, defines the basic elements of health insurance, discusses important health policy issues relating to health insurance, and more; Chapter 8 explains why it is important for health policymakers to be familiar with basic economic concepts, the basic tenets of supply, demand, and markets, and the way in which health insurance affects economic conditions.

The focus of Chapter 9 is on health reform, including the ACA. The chapter discusses the reasons why for decades the United States failed to achieve national health reform prior to the ACA, why the ACA passed given this history, and what the ACA aims to achieve. Chapter 10 explains how the federal and state policymakers have created health insurance programs for individuals and populations who otherwise might go without health insurance coverage. The basic structure, administration, financing, and eligibility rules of the three main U.S. public health insurance programs—Medicaid, the State Children's Health Insurance Program, and Medicare—are discussed, as are key health policy questions relating to each program. Chapter 11 reflects on several important policy and legal aspects of healthcare quality, including the advent of provider licensure and accreditation of health facilities (both of which represent quality control through regulation), the evolution of the standard of care, tort liability for healthcare providers and insurers, preventable medical errors, and, with the ACA as the focal point, improving healthcare quality through quality improvement and provider incentive programs. Part II concludes with a chapter on public health preparedness policy, including discussions about how to define preparedness, the types of public health threats faced by the United States, policy responses to these threats, and an assessment of where the country stands in terms of preparedness. The textbook concludes in Part III by teaching the basic skills of health policy analysis. Because the substance of health policy can only be understood as the product of an infinite number of policy choices as to whether and how to intervene in many types of health policy problems, Chapter 13 explains how to structure and write a short health policy analysis, which is a tool frequently used by policy analysts when they assess policy options and discuss rationales for their health policy recommendations.

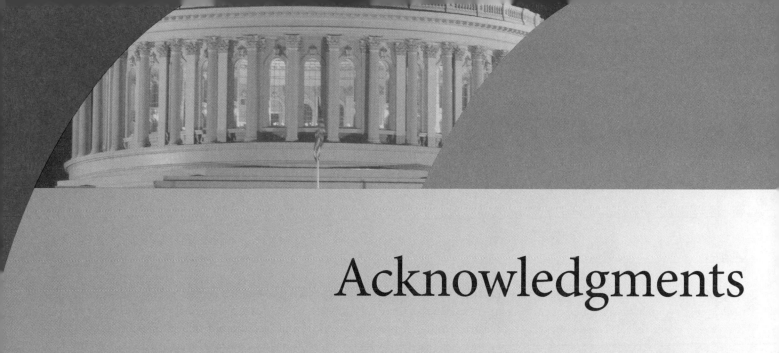

Acknowledgments

We are grateful to many people who generously contributed their guidance, assistance, and encouragement to us during the writing of this book. At the top of the list is Dr. Richard Riegelman, Founding Dean of the George Washington University (GW) School of Public Health and Health Services and Professor of Epidemiology and Biostatistics, Medicine, and Health Policy. The *Essential Public Health* series was his brainchild, and his stewardship of the project as Series Editor made our involvement in it both enriching and enjoyable. We are indebted to him for his guidance and confidence.

We single out one other colleague for special thanks: Sara Rosenbaum, the Harold and Jane Hirsh Professor of Health Law and Policy and the Founding Chair of GW's Department of Health Policy, has been a wonderful mentor, colleague, and friend for many years. We are indebted to her for supporting our initial decision to undertake the writing of this textbook.

At various times during the writing of the first and second editions of this book we have been blessed by the help of several stellar research assistants. The first edition could not have been completed without V. Nelligan Coogan, Mara B. McDermott, Sarah E. Mutinsky, Dana E. Thomas, and Ramona Whittington. Brittany Plavchak and Julia Roumm were essential to the completion of this edition. To all of them we send our deep appreciation for their research assistance and steady supply of good cheer.

Our gratitude extends also to Mike Brown, publisher at Jones & Bartlett Learning, for his encouragement, and to his staff, for their technical expertise and patience.

Finally, we wish to thank those closest to us. Sara gives special thanks to Trish Manha—her life-partner, cheerleader, reviewer, and constant supporter—and to Sophie, the newest addition to their family. Sophie's impending arrival served as an excellent impetus to finish the second edition manuscript on time and showed Sara and Trish how much can be accomplished without sleeping. Joel sends special thanks to his family: Laura Hoffman, Jared Teitelbaum, and Layna Teitelbaum, his favorite people and unending sources of joy and laughter.

About the Authors

Joel Teitelbaum, JD, LLM, is Associate Professor and Vice Chair for Academic Affairs in the Department of Health Policy, and Managing Director of the Hirsh Health Law and Policy Program, at the George Washington University (GW) School of Public Health and Health Services (SPHHS) in Washington, DC. In his role as Vice Chair for Academic Affairs, Professor Teitelbaum provides comprehensive oversight and coordination of all the Department's academic activities, including graduate degree programs, faculty recruitment, curriculum development, faculty teaching development and classroom evaluation processes, and faculty and student support services. As Managing Director of the Hirsh Health Law and Policy Program, he provides day-to-day oversight of a program designed to foster an interdisciplinary approach to the study of health law, health policy, health care, and public health through educational and research opportunities for law students, health professions students, and practicing lawyers.

Professor Teitelbaum teaches a graduate health services law course, a graduate healthcare civil rights course, and an undergraduate survey course on health law. He has also taught courses on public health law, minority health policy, and long-term care law and policy. In 2009, he became the first member of the SPHHS faculty to win the GW-wide Bender Teaching Award. He also received an SPHHS Excellence in Teaching Award for his graduate coursework and in 2007 he was inducted into the ASPH/Pfizer Public Health Academy of Distinguished Teachers.

Professor Teitelbaum has authored or co-authored many articles, book chapters, policy papers, and reports on civil rights issues in health care, insurance law and policy, health reform and its implementation, and behavioral healthcare quality, and he has directed or managed many health law and policy research projects. In 2000, he was co-recipient of The Robert Wood Johnson Foundation Investigator Award in Health Policy Research, which he used to explore the creation of a new framework for applying Title VI of the 1964 Civil Rights Act to the modern healthcare system.

He is heavily involved in GW service activities: Among other things, he has served as Chair of the Medical Center Faculty Senate's Executive Committee; Chair of the SPHHS Curriculum Committee; Chair of the Department's Appointments, Promotion, and Tenure Committee; and Co-Chair of the committee that created and implemented GW's Bachelor of Science degree in public health. He is also a faculty advisor to Health Leads DC (formerly Project HEALTH).

Professor Teitelbaum is a member of Delta Omega, the national honor society recognizing excellence in the field of public health; the American Constitution Society for Law and Policy; the American Society of Law, Medicine, and Ethics; and the Society for American Law Teachers.

Sara Wilensky, JD, PhD, is Special Services Faculty for Undergraduate Education in the Department of Health Policy at the George Washington University School of Public Health and Health Services in Washington, DC. She is also the Director of the SPHHS Undergraduate Program in Public Health.

Doctor Wilensky teaches a health policy analysis course and health systems overview course required of all students in the in the Master of Public Health–Health Policy degree program, as well as the introductory health policy course required of all undergraduate students majoring in public health. She has been the principal investigator or co-principal investigator on numerous health policy research projects relating to a variety of topics, such as Medicaid coverage, access and financing; community health centers; childhood obesity; HIV preventive services; financing of public hospitals; and data sharing barriers and opportunities between public health and Medicaid agencies.

As Director of the Undergraduate Program in Public Health, Dr. Wilensky is responsible for the day-to-day management of the program, including implementation of the dual BS/MPH program. In addition, she is responsible for faculty oversight, course scheduling, new course development, and student satisfaction.

Doctor Wilensky is involved with several GW service activities: She has taught a service learning in public health course in the undergraduate program, she has been heavily involved in making GW's Writing in the Disciplines program part of the undergraduate major in public health, and she is the advisor to students receiving a Master in Public Policy or a Master in Public Administration with a focus on health policy from GW's School of Public Policy and Public Administration.

Prior to joining GW, Dr. Wilensky was a law clerk for federal Judge Harvey Bartle, III in the Eastern District of Pennsylvania, and worked as an associate at the law firm of Cutler and Stanfield, LLP in Denver, Colorado.

Contributors

Chapter 5: *Public Health Institutions and Systems*
Richard Riegelman, MD, PhD, MPH
The George Washington University
Washington, DC

Chapter 12: *Public Health Preparedness Policy*
Rebecca Katz, PhD
The George Washington University
Washington, DC

PART I

Setting the Stage

An Overview of Health Policy and Law

Part I of this textbook includes five chapters aimed at preparing you for the substantive health policy and law discussions in Chapters 6–12 and the skills-based discussion of policy analysis in Chapter 13. Chapter 1 describes generally the role of policy and law in health care and public health and introduces conceptual frameworks for studying health policy and law. Chapter 2 describes the meaning of policy and the policymaking process. Chapter 3 provides an overview of the meaning and sources of law and of several important features of the legal system. Part I closes with overviews of the U.S. healthcare system (Chapter 4) and public health system (Chapter 5).

CHAPTER 1

Understanding the Role of and Conceptualizing Health Policy and Law

INTRODUCTION

In this chapter, we introduce the role played by policy and law in the health of individuals and populations and describe three conceptual frameworks with which you can approach the study of health policy and law. Later, we narrow our focus, providing a measure of clarity in an area that is neither readily discernable—even to those who use and work in the health care and public health systems—nor easily redrawn by those who shape them through policy and law.

The goals of this chapter are to describe why it is important to include policy and law in the study of health care and public health and how you might conceptualize health policy and law when undertaking your studies. To achieve these goals, we first briefly discuss the vast influence of policy and law in health care and public health. You will have a much better feel for how far policy and law reach into these areas as you proceed, but we dedicate a few pages here to give you a sense of why it is critical to examine policy and lawmaking as part of your broader health studies. We then describe three ways to conceptualize health policy and law. As you will discover, the three conceptual frameworks are interwoven, with no one framework dominating the discussion.

ROLE OF POLICY AND LAW IN HEALTH CARE AND PUBLIC HEALTH

The forceful influence of policy and law on the health of individuals and populations is undeniable. Policy and law have always been fundamental in shaping the practice of individual health care in the United States and to achieving both everyday and landmark public health improvements.

Centuries-old legal principles have, since this country's inception, provided the bedrock on which healthcare quality laws are built, and today the healthcare industry is regulated in many different ways. Indeed, federal and state policy and law shape virtually all aspects of the healthcare system, from structure and organization, to service delivery, to financing, and to administrative and judicial oversight. Whether pertaining to the accreditation and certification of individual or institutional healthcare providers, requirements to provide care under certain circumstances, the creation of public insurance programs, the regulation of private insurance systems, or any other number of issues, policy and law drive the healthcare system to a degree unknown by most people.

In fact, professional digests that survey and report on the subjects of health policy and law typically include in their pages information on topics like the advertising and marketing of health services and products, the impact of health expenditures on federal and state budgets, antitrust concerns, healthcare contracting, employment issues, patents, taxation, healthcare discrimination and disparities, consumer protection, bioterrorism, health insurance, prescription drug regulation, physician-assisted suicide, biotechnology, human subject research, patient privacy and confidentiality, organ availability and donation, and more. Choices made by policymakers and decisions handed down through the legal system impact how we approach, experience, analyze, and research all of these and other specific aspects of the healthcare system.

Once you have read the next four preparatory chapters—one on policy and the policymaking process, one on law and the legal system, and one each covering the structure and organization of the healthcare and public health systems—and begin to digest the substantive chapters that follow them, the full force of policy and law in shaping the individual healthcare system will unfold. For now, simply keep in the back of your mind the fact that policy and law heavily influence the way in which health care is accessed, medicine is practiced, treatments are paid for, and much more.

The role of policy and law in public health is no less important than in individual health care, but the influence of policy and law in the field of public health is less frequently articulated. In fact, policy and law have long played a seminal role in everyday public health activities (think, for example, of food establishment inspections, occupational safety standards, policies related to health services for persons with chronic health conditions such as diabetes, and policies and laws affecting the extent to which public health agencies are able to gauge whether individuals in a community suffer from certain health conditions), as well as in many historic public health accomplishments such as water and air purification, reduction in the spread of communicable diseases through compulsory immunization laws, reduction in the number of automobile-related deaths through seatbelt and consumer safety laws, and several others.[a] Public health professionals and students quickly learn to appreciate that combating public health threats requires both vigorous policymaking and adequate legal powers. Additionally, in recent years, enhanced fears about bioterrorism and new and emerging infectious diseases have only increased the public's belief that policy and law are important tools in creating an environment in which people can achieve optimal health and safety.

Of course, policies and laws do not always cut in favor of what many people believe to be in the best interests of public health and welfare. A policy or law might, for example, favor the economic interests of a private, for-profit company over the residents of the community in which the company is located.[b] Why? Because one main focus of policy and law in the realm of public health is on locating the appropriate balance between public regulation of private individuals and corporations and the ability of those same parties to exercise

rights that allow them to function free of overly intrusive government intervention. Achieving this balance is not easy for policymakers. Not all interested parties agree on things like the extent to which car makers should alter their operations to reduce environmentally harmful auto emissions, or the degree to which companies should be limited in advertising cigarettes, or whether gun manufacturers should be held liable in cases where injuries or killings result from the negligent use of their products.

How do policymakers and the legal system reach a (hopefully) satisfactory public health/private right balance? The competing interests at the heart of public health are mainly addressed through two types of policies and laws: those that define the functions and powers of public health agencies, and those that aim to directly protect and promote health.[c] State-level policymakers and public health officials create these types of policies and laws through what are known as their *police powers*. These powers represent the inherent authority of state and local governments to regulate individuals and private business in the name of public health promotion and protection. The importance of police powers cannot be overstated; it is fair to say that they are the most critical aspect of the sovereignty that states retained at the founding of the country, when the colonies agreed to a governmental structure consisting of a strong national government. Furthermore, the reach of police powers should not be underestimated, particularly since they permit public health authorities to coerce private interests to engage in (or refrain from) activities in the name of public health and welfare. However, states do not need to exercise their police powers in order to affect or engage in public health-related policymaking. Because the public's health is impacted by many social, economic, and environmental factors, public health agencies also conduct policy-relevant research, disseminate information aimed at helping people engage in healthy behaviors, and establish collaborative relationships with healthcare providers and purchasers and with other government policymaking agencies.

Federal policy and law also play a role in public health. Although the word "health" never appears in the U.S. Constitution, the document confers powers on the federal government—to tax and spend, for example—that allow it to engage in public health promotion and disease prevention activities. For example, the power to tax (or establish exemptions from taxation) allows Congress to incentivize healthy behaviors, as witnessed by the heavy taxes levied on packages of cigarettes; the power to spend enables Congress to establish executive branch public health agencies and to allocate public health-specific funds to states and localities.

CONCEPTUALIZING HEALTH POLICY AND LAW

You have just read about the importance of taking policy and law into account when studying health care and public health. The next step is to begin thinking about how you might conceptually approach the study of health policy and law.

There are multiple ways to conceptualize the many important topics that fall under the umbrella of health policy and law. We introduce three conceptual frameworks in this section: one premised on the broad topical domains of health policy and law, one based on prevailing historical factors, and one focused on the individuals and entities impacted by a particular policy or legal determination (see Box 1-1).

BOX 1-1 Three Conceptual Frameworks for Studying Health Policy and Law

Framework 1. Study based on the broad TOPICAL DOMAINS of:

a. Health care

b. Public health

c. Bioethics

Framework 2. Study based on HISTORICALLY DOMINANT SOCIAL, POLITICAL, AND ECONOMIC PERSPECTIVES:

a. Professional autonomy

b. Social contract

c. Free market

Framework 3. Study based on the perspectives of KEY STAKEHOLDERS:

a. Individuals

b. The public

c. Healthcare professionals

d. Federal and state governments

e. Managed care and traditional insurance companies

f. Employers

g. The pharmaceutical industry

h. The research community

i. Interest groups

j. Others

We draw on these frameworks to various degrees in this text. For example, the topical domain approach of Framework 1 is on display in the sections about individual rights in health care and public health and healthcare quality policy and law. Framework 2's focus on historical perspectives is highlighted in the health reform section and the government health insurance programs section. Finally, Framework 3, which approaches the study of health policy and law from the perspectives of key stakeholders, is discussed in the policy and the policymaking process section. We turn now to a description of each framework.

The Three Broad Topical Domains of Health Policy and Law

One way to conceptualize health policy and law is as consisting of three large topical domains. One domain is reserved for policy and law concerns in the area of *healthcare,* another for issues arising in the *public health* arena, and the last for controversies in the field of *bioethics.* As you contemplate these topical domains, bear in mind that they are not individual silos whose contents never spill over into the others. Indeed, this sort of spillage is common (and, as noted, is one reason why fixing health policy problems can be terribly complicated). We briefly touch on each domain below.

Health Care Policy and Law

In the most general sense, this domain is concerned with an individual's access to care (e.g., what policies and laws impact an individual's ability to access needed care?), the quality of the care the person received (e.g., was it appropriate, cost-effective, and non-negligent?), and how the person's care is going to be financed (e.g., is the person insured?). However, "access," "quality," and "financing" are themselves rather large sub-domains, with their own sets of complex policy and legal issues, and in fact it is common for students to take semester-long policy and/or law courses focused on just one of these sub-domains.

Public Health Policy and Law

The second large topical domain is that of public health policy and law. A central focus here is on why and how the government regulates private individuals and corporations in the name of protecting the health, safety, and welfare of the general public. Imagine, for example, that the federal government was considering a blanket policy decision to vaccinate individuals across the country against the deadly smallpox disease, believing that the decision was in the best interests of national security. Would this decision be desirable from a national policy perspective? Would it be legal? If the program's desirability and legality are not immediately clear, how would you go about analyzing and assessing them? These are the kinds of questions with which public health policy and law practitioners and scholars grapple.

Bioethics

Finally, there is the *bioethics* domain to health policy and law. Strictly speaking, the term "bioethics" is used to describe ethical issues raised in the context of medical practice or biomedical research. More comprehensively, bioethics can be thought of as the point at which public policy, law, individual morals, societal values, and medicine intersect. The bioethics domain houses some of the most explosive questions in health policy, including the morality and legality of abortion, conflicting values around the meaning of death and the rights of individuals nearing the end of life, and the policy and legal consequences of mapping the human genetic code.

Social, Political, and Economic Historical Context

Dividing the substance of health policy and law into broad topical categories is only one way to conceptualize them. A second way to consider health policy and law is in historical terms, based on the social, political, and economic views that dominate a particular era.[d] Considered this way, health policy and law have been influenced over time by three perspectives, all of which are technically active at any given time, but each of which has eclipsed the others during specific periods in terms of political, policy, and legal outcomes. These perspectives are termed *professional autonomy, social contract,* and *free market.*[e]

Professional Autonomy Perspective

The first perspective, grounded in the notion that the medical profession should have the authority to regulate itself, held sway from approximately 1880 to 1960, making it the most dominant of the three perspectives in terms of both the length of time it held favored status and its effect in the actual shaping of health policy and law. This model is premised on the idea that physicians' scientific expertise in medical matters should translate into legal authority to oversee essentially all aspects of delivering health care to individuals—in other words, according to proponents of the physician autonomy model, legal oversight of the practice of medicine should be delegated to the medical profession itself. While this perspective remained dominant, policy- and lawmakers were generally willing to allow physicians to control the terms and amount of payments

for rendered healthcare services, the standards under which medical licenses would be granted, the types of patients they would treat, the type and amount of information to disclose to patients, and the determination as to whether their colleagues in the medical profession were negligent in the treatment of their patients.

Social Contract Perspective

The second perspective that informs a historical conceptualization of health policy and law is that of the "modestly egalitarian social contract."[f] This paradigm overshadowed its competitors, and thus guided policy decision making, from roughly 1960 to 1980, a time notable in U.S. history for social progressiveness, civil rights, and racial inclusion. At the center of this perspective is the belief that complete physician autonomy over the delivery and financing of health care is potentially dangerous in terms of patient care and healthcare expenditures, and that public policy and law can and sometimes should enforce a "social contract" at the expense of physician control. Put differently, this perspective sees physicians as just one of several stakeholders (including but not limited to patients, employers, and society) that lay claim to important rights and interests in the operation of the healthcare system. Health policies and laws borne of the social contract era centered on enhancing access to health care (e.g., through the Examination and Treatment for Emergency Medical Conditions and Women in Labor Act), creating new health insurance programs (Medicare and Medicaid were established in 1965), and passing anti-discrimination laws (one of the specific purposes of Title VI of the federal 1964 Civil Rights Act was wiping out healthcare discrimination based on race).

Free Market Perspective

The final historical perspective—grounded in the twin notions of the freedom of the marketplace and of market competition—became dominant in the 1990s and continues with force today. It contends that the markets for healthcare services and for health insurance operate best in a deregulated environment, and that commercial competition and consumer empowerment will lead to the most efficient healthcare system. Regardless of the validity of this claim, this perspective argues that the physician autonomy model is falsely premised on the idea of scientific expertise, when in fact most healthcare services deemed "necessary" by physicians have never been subjected to rigorous scientific validation (think of the typical treatments for the common cold or a broken leg). It further argues that even the modest version of the social contract that heavily influenced health policy and law during the civil rights generation is overly regulatory. Furthermore, market competition proponents claim that both other models are potentially inflationary, since in the first case self-interest will lead autonomous physicians to drive up the cost of their services, and in the second instance public insurance programs like Medicare would lead individuals to seek unnecessary care.

To tie a couple of these historical perspectives together and examine (albeit in somewhat oversimplified fashion) how evolving social and economic mores have influenced health policy and law, consider the example of Medicaid, the joint federal–state health insurance program for low-income individuals. In 1965, Medicaid was borne out of the prevailing societal mood that it was an important role of government to expand legal expectations among the poor and needy. Its creation exemplified a social contract perspective, which in the context of health promotes the view that individuals and society as a whole are important stakeholders in the healthcare and public health systems. Medicaid entitled eligible individuals to a set of benefits which, according to courts during the era under consideration, was the type of legal entitlement that could be enforced by beneficiaries when they believed their rights under the program were infringed.

These societal expectations and legal rights and protections withstood early challenges during the 1970s, as the costs associated with providing services under Medicaid resulted in state efforts to roll back program benefits. Then, in the 1980s, Medicaid costs soared higher, as eligibility reforms nearly doubled the program's enrollment and some providers (e.g., community health centers) were given higher payments for the Medicaid services they provided. Still, the social contract perspective held firm, and the program retained its essential egalitarian features.

As noted above, however, the gravitational pull of the social contract theory weakened as the 1980s drew to a close. This, coupled with the fact that Medicaid spending continued to increase in the 1990s, led to an increase in the number of calls to terminate program members' legal entitlement to benefits.[g] Also in the 1990s, federal and state policymakers dramatically increased the role of private managed care companies in both Medicaid and Medicare, an example of the trend toward free market principles described above.

Key Stakeholders

A third way to conceptualize health policy and law issues is in terms of the stakeholders whose interests are impacted by certain policy choices or by the passage or interpretation of a law. For example, imagine that in the context of interpreting a state statute regulating physician licensing, your state's highest court ruled that it was permissible for a physician to not treat a patient even though the doctor had been serving as the patient's family physician. What stakeholders could be impacted by this result? Certainly the patient, and other patients whose treatment may be colored by the court's decision. Obviously the doctor, and other doctors practicing in the same state, could be impacted by the court's conclusion. What about the state legislature? Perhaps it unintentionally drafted the licensing statute in ambiguous fashion, which led the court to determine that the law conferred no legal responsibility on the physician to respond to a member of a family that was part of the doctor's patient load. Or maybe the legislature is implicated in another way—maybe it drafted the law with such clarity that no other outcome was likely to result, but the citizenry of the state was outraged because its elected officials have created public policy out of step with constituents' values. Note how this last example draws in the perspective of another key stakeholder—the broader public.

Of course, patients, healthcare providers, governments, and the public are not the only key stakeholders in important matters of health policy and law. Managed care and traditional insurance companies, employers, the pharmaceutical industry, the medical device industry, the research community, interest groups, and others all may have a strong interest in various policies or laws under debate.

CONCLUSION

The above descriptions of the roles played by policy and law in the health of individuals and populations, and of the ways to conceptualize health policy and law, were cursory by design. But what we hope is apparent to you at this early stage is the fact that the study of policy and law is essential to the study of both health care and public health. Consider the short list of major problems with the U.S. health system as described in a 2005 book edited and written by a group of leading scholars: the coverage and financing of health care, healthcare quality, health disparities, and threats to population health.[h] All of the responses and fixes to these problems—and to many other healthcare- and public health-related concerns—will invariably and necessarily involve creative policymaking and rigorous legal reform (and indeed, the 2010 Patient Protection and Affordable Care Act, about which you will read in various sections, addressed each of these topics to one degree or another). This fact is neither surprising nor undesirable: Policy and law have long been used to effectuate positive social change. Since the founding of this country, the fields of health care and public health have experienced this phenomenon, and given the many serious problems playing out in these arenas right now, there is little reason to expect that policy and law will not be two of the primary drivers of health-related reform in the years ahead.

Policy and legal considerations are not only relevant in the context of major healthcare and public health problems going forward, however—they are critical to the daily functioning of the health system, and to the health and safety of individuals and communities across a range of everyday life events. Consider pregnancy and childbirth, for example. There are approximately 11,000 births each day in this country, and society views pregnancy and childbirth as more or less normal and unremarkable events. In fact, the process of becoming pregnant, accessing and receiving high-quality prenatal health care, and experiencing a successful delivery is crucial not only to the physical, mental, and emotional health and well-being of individuals and families, but to the long-term economic and social health of the nation. It also implicates a dizzying number of interesting and important policy questions. Consider the following:

- Should there be a legal right to health care in the context of pregnancy and, if so, should that right begin at the point of planning to get pregnant, at the moment of conception, at the point of labor, or at some other point?
- Regardless of legal rights to care, how should the nation finance the cost of pregnancy care? Should individuals and families be expected to save enough money to pay out-of-pocket for what is a predictable event? Should the government help subsidize the cost of prenatal care? If so, in what way? Should care be subsidized at the same rate for everyone, or should subsidy levels be based on financial need?
- Regarding the quality of care, what is known about the type of obstetrical care women should receive, and how do we know they are getting that care? Given the importance of this type of care, what policy steps are taken to assure that the care is sound? What should the law's response be when a newborn or pregnant woman is harmed through an act of negligence? When should clinician errors be considered preventable and their commission thus tied to a public policy response? And what should the response be?
- What should the legal and social response be to prospective parents who act in ways risky to the health of a fetus? Should there be no societal response because the prospective parents' actions are purely a matter of

individual right? Does it depend on what the actions are?
- Is it important to track pregnancy and birth rates through public health surveillance systems? Why or why not? If it is an important function, should the data tracking be made compulsory or voluntary?
- How well does the public health system control known risks to pregnancies, both in communities and in the workplace?
- Finally, who should answer these questions? The federal government? States? Individuals? Should courts play a role in answering some or all of them and, if so, which ones? Whose interests are implicated in each question, and how do these stakeholders affect the policymaking process?

There are scores of topics—pregnancy and childbirth among them—that implicate a range of complex health policy questions, and these are the types of questions this text prepares you to ask and address. Before you turn your attention to the essential principles, components, and issues of health policy and law, however, you must understand something about policy and law generally, and about the organization and purposes of the healthcare and public health systems. The next two chapters provide a grounding in policy and law and supply the basic information needed to study policy and law in a health context. There, we define policy and law; discuss the political and legal systems; introduce the administrative agencies and functions at the heart of the government's role in health care and public health; and more. With this information at your disposal, you will be better equipped to think through some of the threshold questions common to many policy debates, including: which sector—public, private, or not-for-profit (or some combination of them)—should respond to the policy problem?; if government responds, at what level—federal or state—should the problem be addressed?; what branch of government is best-suited to address—or more attuned to—the policy issue?; when the government takes the lead in responding to a policy concern, what is the appropriate role of the private and not-for-profit sectors in also attacking the problem?; and what legal barriers might there be to the type of policy change being contemplated? Once you have the knowledge to be able to critically assess these types of questions, you will be able to focus more specifically on how the healthcare and public health systems operate in the United States, and on the application of policy and law to critical issues in health care and public health.

ENDNOTES

a. See, e.g., Wendy E. Parmet, "Introduction: The Interdependency of Law and Public Health," in *Law in Public Health Practice*, eds. Richard A. Goodman et al. (Oxford, England: Oxford University Press, 2003).

b. For a non-fictional and utterly engrossing example of the ways in which law and legal process might stand in the way of effective public health regulation, we recommend Jonathan Harr, *A Civil Action* (New York, NY: Vintage Books, 1995).

c. See, e.g., Larry O. Gostin, Jeffrey P. Koplan, and Frank P. Grad, "The Law and the Public's Health: The Foundations," in *Law in Public Health Practice*, eds. Richard A. Goodman et al. (Oxford, England: Oxford University Press, 2003).

d. The particular historical framework described here was developed to apply to health care, rather than public health. We do not mean to imply, however, that it is impossible to consider public health from an historical, or evolutionary, vantage point. In fact, it is fair to say that public health practice may have just entered its third historical phase. Throughout the 1800s and most of the 1900s, protection of the public's health occurred mainly through direct regulation of private behavior. In the latter stages of the 20th century, strict reliance on regulation gave way to an approach that combined regulation with chronic disease management and public health promotion, an approach that necessitated a more active collaboration between public health agencies and healthcare providers and purchasers.

Now, it appears that public health professionals are adding to this revised practice model another strategic initiative: building collaborative relationships with policymaking agencies whose responsibilities are not directly related to public health—for example, agencies whose primary fields are transportation or agriculture.

e. The discussion of these perspectives is guided by Rand E. Rosenblatt, Sylvia A. Law, and Sara Rosenbaum, *Law and the American Health Care System* (Westbury, CT: The Foundation Press, Inc., 1997), 24–35; and Rand E. Rosenblatt, "The Four Ages of Health Law," *Health Matrix: Journal of Law-Medicine.* 2004;14:15.

f. Rand E. Rosenblatt, Sylvia A. Law, and Sara Rosenbaum, *Law and the American Health Care System*, 2. The authors write that the American social contract lags behind those of other developed countries, and thus use the phrase "modestly egalitarian" in describing it.

g. By 2005, proponents of weakening Medicaid-enrolled persons' entitlement to program benefits had made significant strides: Congress passed a law called the Deficit Reduction Act that, among other things, granted states the ability to redefine the benefits and services to which Medicaid beneficiaries are entitled.

h. David Mechanic, Lynn B. Rogut, David C. Colby, and James R. Knickman, eds., *Policy Challenges in Modern Health Care* (New Brunswick, NY: Rutgers University Press, 2005), 10.

CHAPTER 2

Policy and the Policymaking Process

LEARNING OBJECTIVES

By the end of this chapter, you will be able to:

- Describe the concepts of policy and policymaking
- Describe the basic function, structure, and powers of the legislative branch of government
- Describe the basic function, structure, and powers of the executive branch of government
- Explain the role of federal and state governments in the policymaking process
- Explain the role of interest groups in the policymaking process

INTRODUCTION

The first steps for any student of health policy are to understand what policy is generally and to learn about the policymaking process. It is vital to consider policy questions in the particular context in which they arise, both in terms of the general politics of the issue and the values and powers of the policymaker. As you will discover, there is no single definition of policy. Even so, this chapter arms you with the information needed to know what issues to consider when thinking about a public policy problem, how to account for a variety of competing policy views, and what policy options are possible given the political process in the United States.

The chapter first defines what policy is and then moves to a discussion of the policymaking process by examining the roles and powers of two of the political branches of government—the legislative and executive branches. As part of this discussion, we introduce you to federal and state agencies

that make up the healthcare and public health bureaucracy. We conclude with a discussion about the roles of interest groups in policymaking and the influence they wield in the policymaking process.

DEFINING POLICY

In this section we consider various aspects of what we mean by the term *policy*. Before delving into the policymaking process, we identify which issues fall within the realm of a public policy decision and, generally, what kinds of decisions might be made by policymakers.

Identifying Public Problems

Scholars have defined policy in many different ways. Consider a few of them:

Authoritative decisions made in the legislative, executive, or judicial branches of government that are intended to direct or influence the actions, behaviors, and decisions of others.[1(p243)]

A course of action adopted and pursued by a government, party, statesman, or other individual or organization.[2(p124)]

Authoritative decisions and guidelines that direct human behavior toward specific goals either in the private or the public sector.[3(p125)]

The differences in these definitions raise several important issues. The first question to consider is whether private actors make policy or whether policymaking is an activity for the government only. The first definition refers only to governmental policymakers, the second definition allows for both public and private policymakers, and the third definition is unclear on this issue. Of course, the government is a key player in any policy field, and it is certainly true that decisions by government entities represent public policy. However, in this text we also focus on private actors who make policy, such as commercial insurance companies, private employers, influential individuals, and others who can all be part of health policy. For example, when a major health insurance company decides to cover obesity prevention measures, or when the Bill and Melinda Gates Foundation provides grants to develop crops that are high in essential vitamins and minerals to improve the nutrition of people in developing countries, they are making health policy decisions.

Regardless of whether the policymaker is a public or private figure, it is necessary that the decision being made is an *authoritative* decision. These are decisions made by an individual or group with the power to implement the decision, and there are a variety of levels where these kinds of decisions can take place. For example, within government, authoritative decisions may be made by the president, cabinet officials, agency heads, members of Congress, governors, state legislatures, public health commissioners, and many others.

But all decisions by public and private individuals or entities are not necessarily policy decisions. The key issue to determining whether a "decision" represents a "policy" is whether the question at hand is an individual concern or a public policy problem. A public policy problem goes beyond the individual sphere and affects the greater community. Whereas an individual might decide to take advantage of employer-sponsored health insurance, a public policy question is whether all employers should be required to offer health insurance to their employees. Whereas an individual might decide to purchase a generic (as opposed to a brand name) drug to save money, a public policy question is whether patients should be induced to buy less expensive generic drugs. When deciding whether something is a public policy decision, the focus is not only on who is making a decision, but also on what kind of decision is being made.

Furthermore, just because a problem is identified as a public policy problem does not necessarily mean the only solution involves government intervention. For example, consider the problem of an influenza vaccine shortage. Although there are government-oriented solutions to this problem, such as expanding public research and development or creating production incentives (through tax cuts or subsidies) to encourage private manufacturers to produce more vaccine, other solutions may rely solely on private actors. Private companies may

decide to invest in the research and development of new ways to produce vaccines, or to build new plants to increase production capacity, because they believe they can make a profit in the long run. Just as private individuals and entities can make policy decisions for their own benefit, they can also play a central role in solving public policy problems. A lengthier discussion about options for solving public policy problems and arguments for and against government intervention is found in a review of health economics.

Structuring Policy Options

Considered broadly, there are different ways to approach public policy problems. For example, some policy options are voluntary, whereas others are mandatory. It is important to recognize that authoritative decisions do not always *require* others to act or refrain from acting in a certain way. Some of the most important and effective policies are those that provide incentives to others to change their behavior. Indeed, the power of persuasion is very important to public officials, particularly at the federal level, which is limited in its ability to force states and individuals to take certain actions. This stems from the fact that the 10th Amendment of the U.S. Constitution limits Congress and the executive branch to specific powers and reserves all other powers for the states. However, members of the federal government may use their enumerated powers, such as those to tax and spend, to persuade states and others to act in desired ways.

For example, the Constitution does not give the legislative or executive branches the power to protect the public's health, meaning that the area is primarily within the purview of states to regulate. As a result, Congress and the president cannot require states to create emergency preparedness plans. Yet, Congress may provide incentives to states to do so by offering them federal money in return for state preparedness plans that meet certain criteria established by the federal government.

In addition, it is important to remember that inaction can also be a policy decision. Deciding to do nothing may be a decision to keep a prior decision in place or not to engage in a new issue. For example, a governor could decide against trying to change a restrictive abortion law or a state legislature could choose not to pass a law expanding the allowable scope of practice for nurse practitioners. Both of these inactions result in important policy decisions that will affect the choices and opportunities available to individuals, advocacy organizations, and others.

This brief discussion about policy has raised several important issues to consider when identifying policy options. The next section provides a detailed discussion of the policymaking process, providing you with the background knowledge necessary to identify and understand the roles and powers of various policymakers.

PUBLIC POLICYMAKING STRUCTURE AND PROCESS

The public policymaking structure refers to the various branches of government and the individuals and entities within each branch that play a role in making and implementing policy decisions. In this section, we review the structure, powers, and constituency of these branches, with a focus on the U.S. House of Representatives, the U.S. Senate, and various commissions and agencies that assist Congress, the president, White House staff, and federal executive branch administrative agencies. In addition to reviewing the policymaking structure, we discuss the processes used by these various individuals and entities for making public policy decisions.

State-Level Policymaking

The federal government does not have a monopoly on policymaking. Indeed, important policy decisions are regularly made at the state level as well, especially in the healthcare arena. However, because state governments are similar to the federal government in many ways, the policymaking duties and powers that we discuss below can often be applied to a state-level analysis. At the same time, there is a significant amount of variation in how states structure their legislative and executive branches, agencies, and offices, and it is not possible to review the differences that exist among all 50 states. Accordingly, after a brief discussion of state-level policymaking, this chapter focuses primarily on the federal policymaking structure and process.

Like the federal government, each state has three branches of government. State legislatures pass laws, appropriate money within the state, and conduct oversight of state programs and agencies. States also have their own judiciary with trial and appellate courts. The governor is the head of the state executive branch and can set policy, appoint cabinet members, and use state administrative agencies to issue regulations that implement state laws. Although there are limits to a state's power to regulate healthcare issues, state regulation is an extremely important aspect of health policy. Just a few examples of the healthcare matters states can regulate include provider licensing, accreditation, some aspects of health insurance, and most public health concerns.

At the same time, it is also important to realize that all state governments are not exactly alike. The governor has more power in some states than others, agencies are combined

in different ways among the states, state legislatures may meet annually or biannually, state legislators may be full-time or part-time employees, and so on. Because these differences exist, it is essential for policy analysts to understand the specific structure of the state in which their client resides.

Furthermore, there are important differences between the federal government and the states. Unlike the federal government, almost all states are required to have a balanced budget, and most states cannot borrow money for operating expenses. These rules mean that states must act to raise revenue or cut programs if they project that their budget will be in deficit by the end of the fiscal year. In addition, in 2008, 30 states had at least one tax and expenditure limit rule that restricts the growth of government revenues or spending to a fixed numerical target, sometimes using changes in population level or the inflation rate as guideposts. In addition, 16 states require a legislative supermajority or voter approval to raise taxes (a supermajority means that more than a simple majority—over 50%—is required; for example, a two-thirds majority vote could be required).[4] As a result, state officials may be more likely than federal officials to make the difficult choice to either limit programs or cut resources from one program to fund another.

As is evident from this brief discussion, state level policymaking is both a rich area for discussion and a difficult area to make generalizations about because each state is unique. Having highlighted some of the key differences and similarities among the states and between the states and the federal government, we now turn to the legislative and executive branches of the federal government.

The Federal Legislative Branch

Article 1 of the U.S. Constitution makes Congress the lawmaking body of the federal government by granting it "All legislative Powers" and the right to enact "necessary and proper laws" to effectuate its prerogatives.[5] Congressional responsibilities are fulfilled by the two chambers of Congress, the Senate and the House of Representatives ("the House"). The Constitution grants specific powers to Congress, including but not limited to the power to levy taxes, collect revenue, pay debts, provide for the general welfare, regulate interstate and foreign commerce, establish federal courts inferior to the Supreme Court, and declare war.[6] The Senate has the specific power to ratify treaties and confirm nominations of public officials.

The Senate consists of two elected officials from each state, for a total of 100 senators.[a] Each senator is elected in a statewide vote for a six-year term, whereas representatives in the House sit for two-year terms. Due to the lengthy term of its members, the Senate is considered less volatile and more concerned with long-term issues than the House. A senator must be at least 30 years old, a U.S. citizen for at least nine years, and a resident of the state he or she is seeking to represent.[7]

The House includes 435 members allocated proportionally based on the population of the 50 states, with each state guaranteed at least one representative.[b] For example, in 2010, California was allotted 53 representatives, while Vermont had only 1. Due to the proportionality rule, members from larger states dominate the House and often hold leadership positions.[8] Members of the House are elected by voters in congressional districts and serve two-year terms. They must be at least 25 years old, a U.S. citizen for at least seven years, and a resident of the state where the election takes place.[9]

Leadership Positions

Leadership roles in Congress are determined by political party affiliation, with the party in the majority gaining many advantages. The vice president of the United States is also the president of the Senate and presides over its proceedings. In the vice president's absence, which is common given the other obligations of the office, the president pro tempore, a mostly ceremonial position, presides over the Senate. In most cases the vice president is not a major player in Senate voting, but with the power to break a tie vote, the vice president wields an important power. The Speaker of the House ("Speaker") presides over that chamber and has the authority to prioritize and schedule bills, refer bills to committees, and name members of joint and conference committees. Other than the vice president's senatorial role, leadership positions in Congress are not elected by the voters, but determined by the members from the party who have been elected to Congress. Other key Congressional leadership positions include:

Senate majority leader—Speaks on behalf of the majority party, schedules floor action and bills, works on committees, directs strategy, and tries to keep the party united.

House majority leader—Works with the Speaker to direct party strategy and set the legislative schedule.

House and senate minority leaders—Speak on behalf of the minority party, direct strategy, and try to maintain party unity; as members of the minority, they do not have the legislative duties of the majority leader/Speaker.

House and senate majority and minority whips—Track important legislation, mobilize members to support leadership positions, keep a count of how party members are planning to vote, and generally assist their leaders in managing their party's legislative priorities.

Committees

Committees have been referred to as the "workhorses" of Congress; they are where many key decisions are made and legislative drafting takes place. Given the vast array of issues that Congress contends with in any given legislative session, it is impossible for every member to develop expertise on every issue. Although members vote on bills that cover a wide range of issues, members often concentrate on the areas relevant to the committees on which they serve.

Committees have a variety of important roles, including drafting and amending legislation; educating members on key issues; shepherding the committee's legislation on the floor when it goes before a vote by all the members of one chamber; working with the president, his administration, and lobbyists to gain support for a bill; holding hearings; and conducting oversight of executive branch departments, agencies, commissions, and programs within their purview. Committee members often gain expertise in the areas covered by their committees, and other members often rely on their advice when making voting decisions.

Standing committees are generally permanent committees with specified duties and powers. There are 20 standing committees in the House and 17 in the Senate. House committees tend to be larger than those in the Senate, with about 40 members per committee. Some committees have *authorization* jurisdiction, allowing them to create programs and agencies. Other committees have *appropriation* authority, meaning they are responsible for funding various programs and agencies. Standing committees also have *oversight* authority, meaning they monitor how programs are run and funds are spent. Each chamber of Congress has established specific oversight committees for some programs and issues that cut across committee jurisdiction, as well as committees that review the efficiency and economy of government actions.[10(pp2–3)]

Not surprisingly, some of the most powerful and popular committees are those that deal with appropriating money. These include:

House Ways and Means and Senate Finance committees—These committees have jurisdiction over legislation concerning taxes, tariffs, and other revenue-generating measures, and over entitlement programs such as Medicare and Social Security. The Constitution requires all taxation and appropriations bills to originate in the House, and House rules require all tax bills to go through the Ways and Means committee.

House and Senate Appropriations committees—These committees have responsibility for writing federal spending bills.

House and Senate Budget committees—These committees are tasked with creating the overall budget plan that helps guide tax and appropriation committee work.

House Rules committee—This committee has jurisdiction over the rules and order of business in the House, including rules for the floor debates, amendments, and voting procedures. Unlike in the Senate, all House bills must go to the House Rules committee before reaching the House floor for a vote by all representatives.

Table 2-1 identifies the key health committees and subcommittees and their health-related jurisdictions.

Congressional Commissions and Staff Agencies

Although the committee system helps members of Congress focus on particular areas, members often need assistance with in-depth research and policy analysis. Commissions and staff agencies provide members with information they might not otherwise have the time to gather and analyze. There are too

---

TABLE 2-1 Key Health Committees and Subcommittees

Senate Committee	Health-Related Jurisdiction
Finance Committee: Subcommittee on Health Care	Department of Health and Human Services • Centers for Medicare and Medicaid Services (Medicare, Medicaid, State Children's Health Insurance Program) • Administration for Children and Families Department of the Treasury • Group health plans under the Employee Retirement Income Security Act
Appropriations Committee: Subcommittee on Labor, Health and Human Services, Education and Related Agencies	Department of Health and Human Services • Office of Public Health Service • National Institutes of Health • Centers for Disease Control and Prevention • Health Resources and Services Administration • Substance Abuse and Mental Health Services Administration • Agency for Healthcare Research and Quality Occupational Safety and Health Review Commission Social Security Administration
Appropriations Committee: Subcommittee on Agriculture, Rural Development and Related Services	Department of Health and Human Services Food and Drug Administration
Appropriations Committee: Subcommittee on Interior, Environment and Related Agencies	Department of Health and Human Services • Indian Health Services • Agency for Toxic Substances and Disease Registry
Health, Education, Labor, and Pensions Committee: Subcommittee on Public Health	Bioterrorism and Public Health Preparedness Department of Health and Human Services • Food and Drug Administration • Centers for Disease Control and Prevention • National Institutes of Health • Administration on Aging • Substance Abuse and Mental Health Services Administration • Agency for Healthcare Research and Quality
Committee on Agriculture, Nutrition and Forestry: Subcommittee on Research, Nutrition and General Legislation	• Food stamps • National school lunch program • School breakfast program • Special milk program for children • Special supplemental nutrition program for women, infants and children (WIC)

(Continues)

TABLE 2-1 Key Health Committees and Subcommittees *(Continued)*

House Committee	Health-Related Jurisdiction
Committee on Ways and Means: Subcommittee on Health	Social Security Act • Maternal and Child Health block grant • Medicare • Medicaid • Peer review of utilization and quality control of health care organizations
Appropriations Committee: Subcommittee on Labor, Health and Human Services, Education and Related Agencies	Department of Health and Human Services • Office of Public Health Service • National Institutes of Health • Centers for Disease Control and Prevention • Health Resources and Services Administration • Substance Abuse and Mental Health Services Administration • Agency for Healthcare Research and Quality Occupational Safety and Health Review Commission Social Security Administration
Appropriations Committee: Subcommittee on Agriculture, Rural Development and Related Services	Department of Health and Human Services • Food and Drug Administration
Appropriations Committee: Subcommittee on Interior, Environment and Related Agencies	Department of Health and Human Service • Indian Health Services • Agency for Toxic Substances and Disease Registry
Energy and Commerce Committee: Subcommittee on Health	Department of Health and Human Services • Medicaid

many commissions and agencies to list here, but a few key ones include:

- **Congressional Budget Office**—Provides Congress with cost estimates of bills and federal mandates to state and local governments, as well as forecasts economic trends and spending levels.
- **Government Accountability Office**—An independent, nonpartisan agency that studies how federal tax dollars are spent and advises Congress and executive agencies about more efficient and effective ways to use federal resources.
- **Congressional Research Service**—The public policy research service that conducts nonpartisan, objective research on legislative issues.
- **Medicare Payment Advisory Commission**—An independent federal commission that gives Congress advice on issues relating to the Medicare program, including payment, access to care, and quality of care.

How Laws Are Made

One way that members of Congress indicate their policy preferences is by passing laws that embody their values and the values of their constituents. This is a lengthy process, with many steps along the way that could derail a bill (see Figure 2-1).

Before a committee considers a bill, it must be introduced by a member of Congress. Once this occurs, the Speaker refers the bill to one or more committees in the House, and the majority leader does the same in the Senate. The bill may die in committee if there is not sufficient support for it, although there are rarely invoked procedures that allow a bill to be reported to the full chamber even without committee approval. While the bill is in committee, members may hold hearings on it or "mark up" the bill by changing or deleting language in the proposed bill or by adding amendments to it. If a majority of the committee members approves a bill, it goes to the full chamber (House or Senate, depending on where the bill originated).

The full House or Senate then debates the merits of the bill and puts it to a vote. If a majority does not support the bill, it dies on the chamber floor. If a majority supports the bill, it is sent to the other chamber for consideration. The second chamber may pass the exact same bill or a different version of the bill. If the second chamber does not pass any version of the bill, it dies on the chamber floor and no version of the bill moves forward. If the second chamber passes an identical bill, it goes directly to the president for consideration.

FIGURE 2-1 How a Bill Becomes a Law.

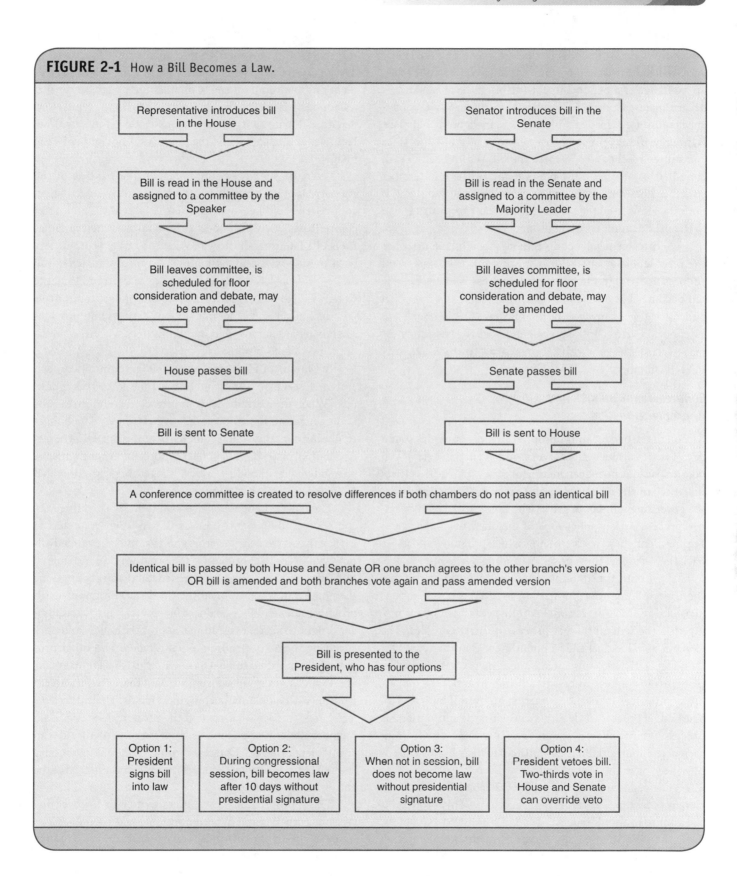

If there are differences in the bills passed by the House and Senate, the two chambers must reach a consensus through an exchange of amendments for the bill to have a chance of becoming law. Consensus building is facilitated by a "conference committee" made up of members from both chambers. If the committee cannot reach a consensus, the bill dies. If the committee reaches a consensus, the bill is sent back to each chamber for a vote on the new version of the bill. If either chamber does not approve of it, the bill dies at that point. If both the House and the Senate pass the new version, it is sent to the president for consideration.

The president may choose to sign the bill into law, or the president may choose to veto the bill. If the president chooses not to sign the bill while Congress is in session, the bill becomes law after 10 days; if Congress is not in session and the bill goes unsigned, the bill dies (this is referred to as a "pocket veto"). If the president vetoes the bill, Congress may override the veto with approval of a two-thirds majority in each chamber.

Congressional Budget and Appropriations Process[11,12]

Although the budget and appropriation processes may sound dry, it is about much more than numbers and charts. If you take a close look at budget documents, they include narratives that discuss why certain programs are being funded and what the government hopes to achieve by doing so. In many ways, this process is a key policy tool for members of Congress and the president; they are able to show which programs and issues have their support through their funding decisions.

Given both the amount of money involved in running the United States (over $3 trillion in 2011) and the various jurisdictions of congressional committees, it is not surprising that the federal budget process is fairly complex. The Congressional Budget and Impoundment Control Act of 1974 ("Budget Act") and subsequent amendments were passed by Congress to create a process that brings together the numerous committees involved in crafting an overall budget plan. The budget process works in concert with the appropriations process, which involves congressional passage of bills from each of the appropriations committees to distribute the funds provided for in the overall budget.

The president is required to submit a budget proposal to Congress by the first Monday in February. This proposal is the administration's request; it is not binding on Congress. Each chamber then passes a *budget resolution*, identifying how the chamber would spend federal money delineated by different categories of spending (e.g., defense, agriculture,

transportation). Members from each chamber then meet to develop a single *conference report* reflecting a consensus agreement on the overall budget. Congress then passes a *concurrent budget resolution*, which is binding upon the House and Senate as a blueprint for revenue collection and spending. However, it is not a law and the president is not bound by the budget resolution.

Over the six weeks subsequent to the passage of the concurrent budget resolution, the House and Senate budget committees hold hearings to discuss the budget, and other committees review the budget as it pertains to their jurisdiction. The latter committees provide the budget committees with their "views and estimates" of appropriate spending and/or revenue levels for the upcoming year. In addition, the Congressional Budget Office provides the budget committees with its budget and economic outlook reports and provides the budget and appropriations committees with its analysis of the president's proposal.

In March, the House and Senate budget committees each craft a budget plan during public meetings known as "markups." When the markups are complete, each committee sends a budget resolution to its respective chamber. The budget resolution contains a budget total, spending breakdown, reconciliation instructions, budget enforcement mechanisms, and statements of budget policy. Budget totals are provided as aggregates and as committee allocations.

The federal budget includes two types of spending: *discretionary* and *mandatory*. Discretionary spending refers to money that is set aside for programs that must be funded annually in order to continue—if the programs are not funded by Congress, they will not receive federal dollars to continue their operations. For example, the Head Start program, which provides early childhood education services, is a discretionary program that relies on annual appropriations. Mandatory spending refers to spending on entitlement and other programs that must be funded as a matter of law. For example, the Medicaid program is an entitlement that provides health insurance to eligible low-income individuals. The *authorizing legislation* (the law that created the program) for Medicaid includes eligibility rules and benefits. Because Medicaid is an entitlement program, Congress must provide enough money so the Medicaid agency can meet the obligations found in the authorizing legislation.

The appropriations committees write bills to cover discretionary spending. These committees make their decisions based on the amount of funds available and any *reconciliation instructions*, which direct the appropriate authorizing committee to make changes in the law for mandatory spending programs to meet budgetary goals. Appropriations bills and reconciliation instructions must be signed by the president to become law.

Members of the House and Senate have the opportunity to make changes to the work of the budget committees. Once the House and Senate pass their own versions of the budget resolution, they establish a conference committee to resolve any differences. Once the differences are resolved, each full chamber votes on the compromise budget.

Congress often does not meet Budget Act deadlines (shown in Table 2-2). If the appropriations bills are not passed by every October 1—the beginning of the fiscal year—Congress may pass a *continuing resolution* that allows the government to continue to spend money. If Congress does not pass a continuing resolution or if the president vetoes it, all nonessential activities of federal agencies must stop until additional funds are provided.

Constituents

With the wide array of issues they take on, members of Congress may have an equally wide array of constituents to be concerned about when making policy decisions. Clearly, members are concerned about pleasing the voters who elect them. Even though there may be a variety of policy views to consider, members often prioritize their home constituents. In addition to courting their home-state voters, members often try to court independents or voters from the opposing party in their home state to strengthen their appeal. High approval

ratings deter challengers from trying to take an incumbent's congressional seat and allow members of Congress more leeway to pursue their goals and policies.

Although concern for their home-state base may be their first priority, representatives and senators often need to be concerned about supporting their party's position on issues. Today, elected federal politicians are usually affiliated with the Democratic or Republican Party, and voters may be influenced by the party's stance on issues. Also, if the balance of power between the two parties is close in Congress, the parties usually cannot afford to have members defect from their party's positions. Members' concern regarding keeping their party strong is magnified if they hold leadership positions in Congress or are considering running for national office.

Finally, the views of the president may be important for members to consider, depending on whether the member and the president share the same party, the particular issue involved, and the president's popularity. Members who are in the same party as the sitting president have incentive to help the president remain popular because they will likely advance many of the same policies. In addition, presidents are often prodigious fundraisers and campaigners who may be able to assist members during election season. Even when members disagree with the president, the president's power to affect their influence in Congress may be a deterrent to opposing the president. Of course, if the president is exceedingly popular, it is difficult for members of either party to oppose presidential policy goals.

TABLE 2-2 Federal Budget Process Timeline

First Monday in February	President submits budget proposal to Congress.
March	House completes its budget resolution.
April	Senate completes its budget resolution.
April 15	House and Senate complete concurrent budget resolution.
May	Authorizing committees develop reconciliation language when necessary and report legislation to budget committees. House and Senate develop conference report on reconciliation, which is voted on by each chamber.
June 10	House concludes reporting annual House appropriations bills.
June 15	If necessary, Congress completes reconciliation legislation.
June 30	House completes its appropriations bills.
September 30	Senate completes its appropriations bills. House and Senate complete appropriations conference reports and vote separately on the final bills.
October 1	Fiscal year begins.

Source: Adapted from House Committee on the Budget Majority Caucus, Basics of the Budget Process. 107th Cong. Briefing Paper. 2001.

The Federal Executive Branch

Article 2 of the U.S. Constitution establishes the executive branch and vests executive power in the most well-known member of the branch, the president.[13] Of course, the president does not act alone in running the executive branch. Presidents rely on Executive Office agencies and staff such as the Council of Economic Advisors and Office of Management and Budget, as well as policy development offices such as the National Security Council and Domestic Policy Council (see Box 2-1 for a description of one such office). In addition, there are 15 cabinet departments led by individuals selected by the president (subject to Senate confirmation) and additional non cabinet-level agencies, all of which are responsible for, among other duties, interpreting and implementing the laws passed by Congress. All of these advisors identify issues to be addressed and formulate policy options for the president to consider. In theory, all of these parts of the executive branch work in furtherance of the goals set by the president.

The Presidency

The president is the head of the federal executive branch. As powerful as that may sound, the country's founders created three distinct branches of government and limited the president's power in order to ensure that no single individual gained too much control over the nation. As you will see, in some ways the president is very powerful, and in other ways his power is quite limited.

Although there have been third-party candidates for president in the past, generally speaking our country now operates on a two-party system, with the Democratic and Republican Parties as the major parties. Each party selects a candidate for president who represents the party in the election. Presidents (and their vice presidents) are elected through a nationwide vote to serve a four-year term. An individual is limited to serving two four-year terms as president, which may or may not be consecutive.[14,c] To be eligible for election, candidates must be at least 35 years old, a natural-born citizen of the United States, and a resident of the country for at least 14 years.

Presidents have many roles. As the unofficial *Chief of State*, the president is seen as the symbol of the country and its citizens.[15(p40)] As the official *Chief Executive Officer*, the president manages the cabinet and executive branch. The president also holds the position of *Commander in Chief of the Armed Forces*, and as such is the top ranking military official in the country. The U.S. Constitution vests the president with other powers, such as the ability to appoint judges to the federal courts, sign treaties with foreign nations, and appoint ambassadors as liaisons to other countries. These powers are all subject to the advice and consent of the Senate.[15(p41)]

Agenda Setting   A key tool of the presidency is the ability to put issues on the national agenda and offer a recommended course of action: "[F]raming agendas is what the presidency is all about."[16(p371)] Presidents help set the national agenda because of the role of the president as the country's leader and the amount of media attention given to presidential actions, decisions, and policy recommendations. Unlike many other politicians or interest groups, the president does not have to work hard to receive media coverage. Whether it is the annual State of the Union address, release of the president's budget proposal, a major speech, a press conference, a photo shoot with a foreign leader, or the release of a report, the president's message is continually publicized. In addition, the president's message can be delivered by the vice president, cabinet officers, and party leaders in Congress.

The notion of appealing directly to the country's citizens to focus on a particular issue and to influence legislative debates is referred to as "going public." In going public, presidents try to use support from the American people to gain the attention of Congress and sway votes on policy decisions. Because members of Congress are highly concerned about pleasing their constituency to improve their chance for re-election, "the president seeks the aid of a third party—the public—to force other politicians to accept his preferences."[17(p3)]

BOX 2-1 Office of Management and Budget (OMB)

The Office of Management and Budget (OMB) reports directly to the president and plays an important role in policy decisions. OMB is responsible for preparing the presidential budget proposal, which includes reviewing agency requests, coordinating agency requests with presidential priorities, working with Congress to draft appropriation and authorization bills, and working with agencies to make budget cuts when needed. In addition to these budgetary functions, OMB provides an estimate of the cost of regulations, approves agency requests to collect information, plays a role in coordinating domestic policy, and may act as a political intermediary on behalf of the president. OMB also has an oversight and evaluation function over select federal agencies as a result of the Government Performance and Results Act, which requires agencies to set performance goals and have their performance evaluated.

Sometimes it may be advantageous for the president to place an item on the policy agenda in a less public manner. For example, if a policy is controversial with the general public or if members of the president's party disagree with a proposal, it may be more effective to promote a policy behind the scenes. The president, either directly or through intermediaries, can carefully let members of Congress know which policies are favored. Using combinations of promises of favors and threats to members' interests, the president may be able to influence the outcome of policy debates in Congress even without going public.

In addition to deciding whether to approach Congress publicly or behind the scenes, the president must choose whether to present a preferred policy decision with more or less detail. A policy can be presented broadly through principles or general guidelines, or specifically through proposed legislation that is presented to Congress. Each method for conveying the president's goals has pros and cons. If a policy choice is presented in a broad manner, Congress may interpret the policy in a way that the president dislikes. However, if the president presents Congress with a specific proposal or draft legislation, Congressional members may view the president as infringing upon their role as the legislative body and resist working with him.

Whether presidents are successful in placing policy issues on the national agenda and having them resolved in accordance with their preferences depends in part on how much "political capital" a president has available. Political capital is defined as the strength of the president's popularity and of his party, in Congress and in other contexts. Members of Congress are more likely to support a popular president who has the ability to mobilize the public's support, improve members' standing by association with the president and the president's party, and raise money for their campaigns.

Even the most popular president cannot always dictate what issues are on the national agenda, however. Events and decisions outside the president's control often influence what topics most concern the nation. The terrorist attacks of September 11, 2001, the subsequent anthrax scare, and the subway and bus bombings in London and Madrid all served to place combating terrorism at the top of the policy and political agenda during the George W. Bush Administration. Concerns about an avian flu epidemic and numerous food recalls put public health and food safety issues on the national agenda. The devastation wrought by the BP oil spill in the Gulf of Mexico made improved responses to environmental disasters a high priority for a short time. Recently, however, all other issues have been dwarfed by concerns about the federal deficit, high unemployment, and a lagging economy. Thus, even the most popular presidents must be responsive to national and international events that may be beyond their control.

Presidential Powers   As noted earlier, if Congress passes legislation the president dislikes, he has the power to veto it, thereby rejecting the bill. However, the president does not have to actually use the veto to shape policy. The president may be able to persuade Congress to change a piece of legislation simply by threatening to veto it, especially if it is a law that is only expected to pass by a slim majority. In general, vetoes are used infrequently, with presidents vetoing only 3% of all legislation since George Washington was president.[15(p43)]

Presidents also have the power to issue executive orders. These are legally binding orders that the president gives to federal administrative agencies under the control of the Executive Office. In general, these orders are used to direct federal agencies and their officials in how they implement specific laws. Executive orders are controversial because under our system of government, Congress, not the executive, is tasked with making laws. In addition, significant policy decisions can be accomplished by using executive orders. For example, an executive order was used by President Truman to integrate the armed forces, by President Eisenhower to desegregate schools, by President Clinton to designate 1.7 million acres in southern Utah as a national monument, and by President George W. Bush to create the federal Office of Homeland Security (which subsequently became a cabinet-level department when Congress established it through legislation).

If Congress believes an executive order is contrary to congressional intent, it has two avenues of recourse. It can amend the law at issue to clarify its intent and effectively stamp out the executive order that is now clearly contrary to the law. (Bear in mind that because the president may veto any bill, in effect it takes a two-thirds majority of Congress to override an executive order.) As an alternative, Congress may challenge the executive order in court, claiming that the president's actions exceed his constitutional powers.

Constituents   From this description of the presidency, it is evident that presidents have several layers of constituents to consider when making policy choices. Certainly, the president represents every citizen and the country as a whole as the only nationally elected official (along with the vice president) in the nation. However, the president is also a representative of a particular political party and therefore must consider the views of that party when making policies. The party's views may be evident from the party platform, policies supported by party leadership in Congress, and voters who identify themselves as party members. In addition, the president must keep in mind the foreign policy duties of the office. Depending on the issue, it may be important for the president to take into account the views of other nations or international organizations, such as the United Nations or the World Health Organization.

How does the president decide which policies to pursue? Presidents are driven by multiple goals. They want "their policies to be adopted, they want the policies they put in place to last, and they want to feel they helped solve the problems facing the country."[4(p82)] In addition, presidents often speak of wanting to leave a legacy or ensure their place in history when they leave office.

Given the vast array of constituents that presidents must consider, the president's policy decision-making process involves several layers. As shown in Figure 2-2, presidents consult their agency staff to identify problems, decide which problems are priorities, determine what solutions are available to address those problems, and choose the policy option that is the preferred course of action. In addition, the president's staff interacts with members of Congress and other political players to gauge their support for or opposition to various policies. Of course, how the media portrays both problems and potential solutions can be an important ingredient in whether politicians and the general public support the president's initiatives.

In addition, which policies presidents choose to promote may depend in part on when policy decisions are made. First-term presidents must satisfy their constituents if they hope to be re-elected. Although all presidents want to see their favored policies implemented throughout their time in office, second-term presidents may be more willing to support more controversial goals because they cannot run for re-election. Yet, second-term presidents may also be constrained by the desire to keep their party in power, even though another individual will hold the presidential office.

Administrative Agencies

When studying the structure of our government, it is common to review Congress, the presidency, and the court system. Administrative agencies, however, are often overlooked despite the power they wield over the way our country is run.

Structurally, almost all administrative agencies are part of the executive branch, and thus under the power and control of the president. Practically, administrative agencies often work out of the public's eye to implement the laws passed by Congress and the executive orders signed by the president.

Federal agencies fall into two main categories: executive department agencies and independent agencies. Executive department agencies are under the direct control of the

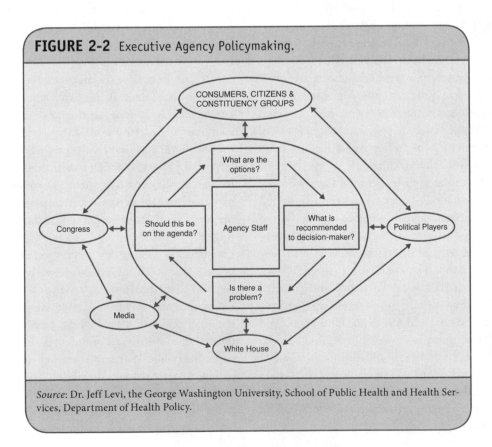

FIGURE 2-2 Executive Agency Policymaking.

Source: Dr. Jeff Levi, the George Washington University, School of Public Health and Health Services, Department of Health Policy.

president, and department heads serve at the pleasure of the president. These departments include the 15 cabinet-level departments and their subunits; some of the more well-known executive departments are the Department of Health and Human Services, the Department of Education, the Treasury Department, the Department of State, the Department of Defense, and the Department of Homeland Security. Independent agency heads are appointed by the president and confirmed by the Senate. They serve a fixed term and may only be removed "for cause," meaning there must be a legitimate reason to fire them. Examples of independent agencies include the Securities and Exchange Commission, the U.S. Postal Service, and the National Labor Relations Board.

Overall, the president fills approximately 2,400 federal jobs.[4(p160)] In general, these political appointees have short tenures, lasting an average of two years.[4(p161)] When the administration changes hands after an election, new appointees are usually selected to run the agencies. The daily operations of agencies are run by career civil servants, public employees who do not necessarily come and go with each administration but who often remain at an agency for years, gaining expertise and institutional knowledge about the agencies in which they work. Frequently, there may be tension between the goals of the political appointee and those of the career bureaucrat, who may have the advantage of familiarity with members of Congress and who knows that the political appointee is likely to be replaced in a few years.

Administrative agencies can be created by statute, internal department reorganization, or presidential directive.[15(p50)] However they are initially created, agencies must have statutory authority in order to receive appropriations from Congress and act with the force of law. This statutory authority, or enabling statute, outlines the agency's responsibilities and powers.

Agency Powers   By necessity, statutes are usually written broadly. Congress does not have the time or expertise to include every detail about how a new program should operate or how a new department will be structured. It is up to the executive branch agency to fill in the details, and it does so by issuing policy statements, developing rules, and promulgating regulations.

For example, in 2001, Congress passed the Medicare, Medicaid, and SCHIP Benefits Improvement and Protection Act, which included a new Medicaid reimbursement system for federally qualified health centers called the Prospective Payment System.[18] Basically, the statute mandated that every health center calculate a baseline per-visit cost that was the average of their 1999 and 2000 costs. Under the act, health center reimbursement rates would be determined each year by the baseline rate plus an inflationary factor called the Medicare Economic Index, adjusted to account for any increase or decrease in a health center's change in scope of service. That was all the statute said. It was up to the Center for Medicare and Medicaid Services (CMS), the federal agency in charge of the Medicaid program, to work out the details. CMS had the choice of issuing regulations, policy notices, information sheets, or the like to flesh out the broadly worded statute.

Many questions were left unresolved by the statute. For example, if the center opened in 2000, how would its baseline be calculated? What if there was an extraordinary event in 1999 or 2000, like a hurricane, that severely damaged a health center—would that affect the baseline calculation? What does a change of scope of service mean? Does it count as a change in scope of service if the health center adds a few dentists to its current dental practice, or would it have to add a new service in order to trigger the statutory definition? Who determines whether a change in scope of service occurred? The health center? The state Medicaid agency? The regional Medicaid office? CMS? As you can imagine, the list of questions that results from broadly written statutes is almost endless. Agencies are usually the ones that provide the answers.

Promulgating regulations is the most important and powerful role of agencies. Agency regulations have the force of law and must be obeyed, just as one obeys a law passed by the legislative branch. Yet, an agency's power to create rules and regulations is not unlimited. The thing being regulated must be within the power of the agency to regulate, as defined by the agency's enabling statute. Sometimes it is not clear whether an agency has acted in an area that is beyond the scope of its authorizing law. In those cases, a court may be the final arbiter of whether the agency acted properly.

In addition, agencies must follow the requirements set forth in the Administrative Procedure Act (APA).[19] The APA contains detailed requirements compelling agencies to issue a notice of their intent to issue a new rule or change an existing rule, and provide for and respond to public comments on the proposed rule. Some agencies are also required to hold hearings and develop rules based on the evidence presented in those hearings.[4(p172)] It is important to know that the APA creates procedural standards that require an agency to follow a particular *process* when promulgating regulations, but that the APA does not relate to the *substance* of the regulations. As long as an agency follows the necessary notice and comment requirements of the APA, it has wide latitude to issue rules within its scope of power, even if many of the public comments opposed the proposed rules. If an agency does not follow the APA requirements, interested parties may sue the agency in court to force compliance with the law.

Constituents Agency heads, since they are not elected, do not have constituents in the same way that the president and members of Congress do. In theory, as members of the executive branch, agency heads should only be concerned with the wishes of the president. In reality, however, that is not always the case. Some presidents have firmer control of their departments than others. If the president gives the departments and agencies broad discretion to make policy decisions, the agencies may have few policy constraints. Practically, however, agency heads want their operation to run smoothly, which includes having a good working relationship with the individuals or entities regulated by that agency. If an agency antagonizes the people or groups being regulated, they might reach out to their congressional representatives to try to change or limit the agency's personnel or authority. In addition, because Congress appropriates funds to and maintains oversight of many agencies, agency heads are well served by taking Congress' interests into account.

Table 2-3 summarizes the general public policymaking machinery. We next turn our attention to the specific parts of the government bureaucracy that operate in the health arena.

THE HEALTH BUREAUCRACY

The Federal Government

Although several federal agencies have health-related responsibilities, the three most significant health agencies are the Department of Health and Human Services (HHS), the Department of Defense (DOD), and the Department of Veterans Affairs (VA). HHS houses many of the major public health insurance programs and health services that provide care,

information, and more to millions of U.S. residents; the DoD and VA operate health insurance programs specifically for military personnel and their families.

Department of Health and Human Services

HHS includes hundreds of programs that cover activities as varied as medical and social science research, preschool education services, substance abuse and prevention services, and health insurance programs, just to name a few. As shown in Figure 2-3, the department has 11 operating divisions. The main purpose of each agency is described in Table 2-4.

Each operating division has numerous bureaus or divisions that operate health programs. For example, the HIV/AIDS Bureau (HAB) is one of six bureaus in HRSA. The HIV/AIDs Bureau implements the Ryan White CARE Act,[20] which provides health care to individuals with HIV and AIDS. Similarly, the FDA has eight offices or centers; the one whose job is perhaps most well-known to the general public is the Center for Drug Evaluation and Research, which is responsible for testing and approving new drugs before they can be sold to the public. These are just two examples of the many sub-agency units that perform vital functions in our federal health care bureaucracy.

HHS also includes numerous offices that assist the Secretary of HHS in running the department. The Assistant Secretary of Health is the principal advisor to the HHS secretary on public health matters. This individual oversees the U.S. Public Health Service (PHS), the Commissioned Corps (health professionals used for both emergency responses and as health promoters), and the Office of Public Health and Sciences (OPHS). PHS employs both commissioned corps members and civilians to run its public health programs.

TABLE 2-3 Summary of Public Policymaking Entities

	Congress	President	Administrative Agencies
Main Function	Legislative body	Chief executive of the country	Implement statutes through rulemaking
Main Tools/Powers	Support/oppose legislation Appropriations Oversight	Agenda setting Persuasion Propose solutions Budget proposals Executive orders	Create regulations Provide information
Constituents	Voters in state or district Voters in nation if in leadership role or have national aspirations Party President	Nation (all voters) Public who voted for the president Party Other nations International organizations	President Congress Individuals and entities regulated or served by the agency

FIGURE 2-3 Department of Health and Human Services Organizational Chart.

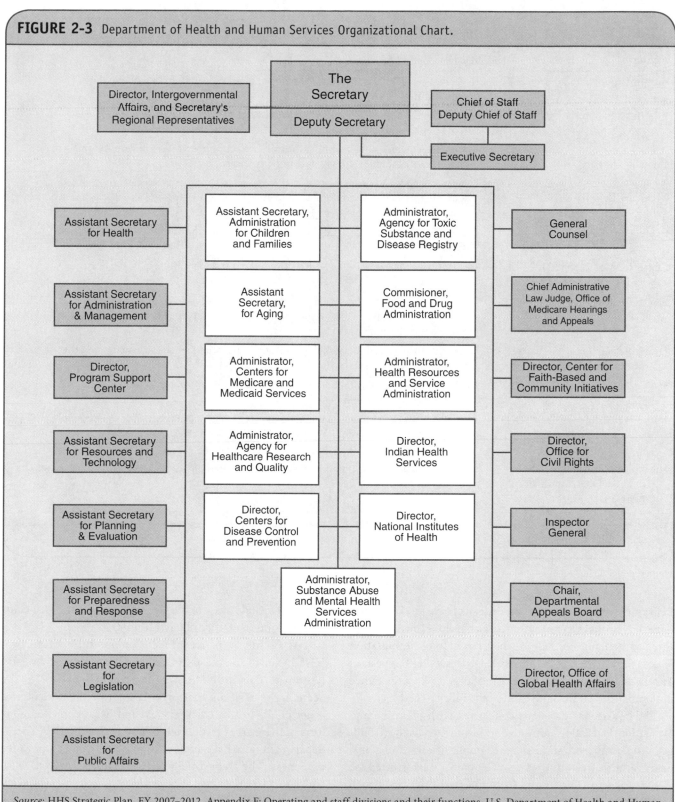

Source: HHS Strategic Plan, FY 2007–2012. Appendix F: Operating and staff divisions and their functions. U.S. Department of Health and Human Services website. Available at http://aspe.hhs.gov/hhsplan/2007/hhasplanpdf/hhsplanappE.pdf. Accessed July 25, 2011.

TABLE 2-4 Department of Health and Human Services Agencies

Agency	Main Purpose of Agency
Administration for Children and Families (ACF)	To promote economic and social well-being of families, children, individuals, and communities.
Administration on Aging (AoA)	To promote the dignity and independence of older people, and to help society prepare for an aging population.
Agency for Healthcare Research and Quality (AHRQ)	To support, conduct, and disseminate research that improves access to care and the outcomes, quality, cost, and utilization of healthcare services.
Agency for Toxic Substances and Disease Registry (ATSDR)	To serve the public by using the best science, taking responsive public health actions, and providing trusted health information to prevent harmful exposure and diseases related to toxic substances.
Centers for Disease Control and Prevention (CDC)	To promote health and quality of life, by preventing and controlling disease, injury, and disability.
Center for Medicare and Medicaid Services (CMS)	To ensure effective, up-to-date healthcare coverage and to promote quality of care for beneficiaries.
Food and Drug Administration (FDA)	To rigorously assure the safety, efficacy, and security of human and veterinary drugs, biological products, and medical devices, and assure the safety and security of the Nation's food supply, cosmetics, and products that emit radiation.
Health Resources and Services Administration (HRSA)	To provide the national leadership, program resources, and services needed to improve access to culturally competent, quality health care.
Indian Health Service (IHS)	To raise the physical, mental, social, and spiritual health of American Indians and Alaska Natives to the highest level.
National Institutes of Health (NIH)	To employ science in pursuit of fundamental knowledge about the nature and behavior of living systems and the application of that knowledge to extend healthy life and reduce the burdens of illness and disability.
Substance Abuse and Mental Health Services Administration (SAMHSA)	To build resilience and facilitate recovery for people with or at risk for substance abuse and mental illness.

Source: HHS Strategic Plan, FY 2007–2012. Appendix F: Operating and staff divisions and their functions. U.S. Department of Health and Human Services website. Available at http://aspe.hhs.gov/hhsplan/2007/hhsplanpdf/hhsplanappE.pdf. Accessed July 25, 2011.

PHS employees also work in the Bureau of Prisons, U.S. Coast Guard, National Oceanic and Atmospheric Administration, Environmental Protection Agency, Division of Immigration Health Services, and U.S. Marshal Services. OPHS consists of 11 offices, including the Office of the Surgeon General, Office of Population Affairs, and Office of Minority Health.

HHS also has divisions concerned with planning and evaluation, legislation, administration and management, budget and finance, program support, public affairs, and global health affairs. In 2001, President George W. Bush created the Center for Faith-Based and Community Initiatives, which strives to increase participation by faith-based community organizations in providing health and human services.[21] Offices concerned with the legality and efficiency of the department's

activities include those of the General Counsel and Inspector General, and the Office of Civil Rights.

As a result of the recent focus on preventing terrorism, HHS includes an Assistant Secretary for Preparedness and Response. This individual is the principal advisor to the Secretary of HHS on matters relating to bioterrorism and other public health emergencies, and helps coordinate efforts in these areas at all levels of government. Other federal departments also have a role in public health emergency preparedness. The Department of Homeland Security (DHS), which includes the Federal Emergency Management Agency (FEMA), is tasked with preparing for and coordinating the federal response to emergencies, whether due to natural or man-made disasters. The CDC houses the Strategic National

Stockpile of emergency pharmaceutical supplies. Other agencies, such as the Environmental Protection Agency (EPA), DoD, and VA, play significant roles in emergency preparedness and response.

Department of Veterans Affairs and Department of Defense

Any veteran who does not receive a dishonorable discharge is potentially eligible for healthcare services through the Veterans Health Administration (VHA). The VHA is the largest healthcare delivery system in the country, with hundreds of medical centers, nursing homes, and outpatient clinics that serve over 1 million patients each year.[22(p357)]

VHA-sponsored health plans offer a wide array of preventive, ambulatory, and hospital services as well as medications and medical and surgical supplies. VHA providers are organized into integrated networks aimed at providing cost-effective services based on local need. There are no premiums (monthly payments) for the plan, but veterans have to make co-payments (a charge per visit) unless they are exempt based on disability or income level. Unlike most healthcare plans, the VHA system is completely portable, meaning that veterans can access VHA facilities anywhere in the country.

Veterans who wish to receive care through the VHA must enroll in the program. Because the VHA receives an annual appropriation from Congress, it may not have sufficient funds to pay for all of the care demanded by eligible veterans. For that reason, the VHA uses a priority system to ensure that veterans who are low-income or have service-related disabilities can be enrolled into a plan. Other veterans may have to wait to be enrolled if there are insufficient funds. In addition, priority in accessing care is given to enrolled veterans who need care for service-related disabilities or have a sufficiently severe service-related disability and need care for any health concern. Veterans not in a priority group may have to wait to see an appropriate provider once they are enrolled.

Although veterans may receive care through VHA, they are not required to do so. If eligible, they may choose to obtain services through other public or private healthcare programs or health insurance plans. They may also choose to receive some services through VHA and others from non-VHA programs or plans.

The VHA does not provide coverage to veterans' family members, but the DoD does through its TRICARE program. TRICARE provides healthcare services to current and retired military personnel and their families. TRICARE offers a variety of plans with various eligibility requirements and costs to the patient.

State and Local Governments

As discussed earlier, the Constitution gives states primary responsibility for protecting the public's health. States have health-related agencies that deal with health financing, aging, behavioral health, environmental health, children and family services, veterans, facility licensing and standards, provider credentialing, and more. Although all states have agencies that generally cover the same functions, their structure, responsibilities, and lines of authority vary greatly.

With the variation among state agencies, it is not surprising that there are significant differences across the states in terms of their approach to public health and health services needs. All states have agencies to run their Medicaid and SCHIP programs, as well as other state-specific health services programs. Although a review of enabling statutes and mission statements found that only one-fifth of states address most of the concepts identified by PHS as essential public health functions, most states cover the traditional public health tasks such as surveillance, investigation, and education.[23(p154)]

Local public health agencies (LPHA) carry out the public health functions of the state. Most commonly, LPHAs are formed, managed by, and report to a local government, such as a county commission or local board of health. This structure provides LPHAs with significant latitude to interpret and implement state statutes. In some states, the state and local governments jointly oversee the LPHA.

LPHAs may provide services directly or, as is increasingly common, may contract or provide support to others who perform the services. The services provided by LPHAs vary considerably, though there is an emphasis on addressing communicable diseases, environmental health, and children's health issues. LPHAs often provide services such as immunizations, community assessments, epidemiology and surveillance, food safety and inspections, and tuberculosis testing. Some, but not all, also provide diabetes care, glaucoma screening, substance abuse treatment, mental health services, and more.[23(pp160–161)]

INTEREST GROUPS

Before leaving the discussion of policy, the policymaking process, and the health bureaucracy, we must say a few words about interest groups. *Interest group* is a general term used for a wide variety of organizations that are created around a particular issue or population and have the goal of influencing policy and educating others about their views and concerns.[4(p117)] Interest groups are different from most of the other stakeholders that have been discussed because interest groups do not have the power to make policy. Although members of the executive and legislative branches of government have a key role in determining which policies are adopted, interest groups have the limited, but still significant, role of trying to influence the decisions of policymakers.

There are many types of interest groups, including trade associations, think tanks, advocacy groups, and lobbying firms. A few examples include the Pharmaceutical Research and Manufacturers of America, whose mission is to "conduct effective advocacy for public policies that encourage discovery of important new medicines for patients by pharmaceutical/biotechnology research companies"[24]; the National Association of Public Hospitals, which has as its goal to "provide national, regional and local advocacy on behalf of public and other hospitals and health systems, conduct research and analysis, and provide a host of related services needed by our members"[25]; the Center for Budget and Policy Priorities, which "conducts research and analysis to help shape public debates over proposed budget and tax policies and to help ensure that policymakers consider the needs of low-income families and individuals . . . in these debates"[26]; the AARP, which is "dedicated to enhancing quality of life for all as we age . . . through information, advocacy and service"[27]; and the Heritage Foundation, which has as its goal to "formulate and promote conservative public policies based on the principles of free enterprise, limited government, individual freedom, traditional American values, and a strong national defense."[28]

Just as members of Congress do not have the time or ability to become experts in every issue that comes before them, the same is true for the average citizen. Many people do not have the time and ability to learn about all of the issues that are important to them, develop proposals, rally public support for their positions, monitor current activity, lobby to add or remove issues from the agenda, and reach out to politicians who make policy decisions. Instead, interest groups take on those duties: "Their job is to make the case for their constituents before government, plying the halls of Congress, the executive branch, the courts, and the offices of other interest groups to provide a linkage between citizens and government."[4(p119)]

Interest Group Powers

Interest groups do not have the power to pass laws. However, they can influence policy in a variety of ways throughout the policymaking process. For example, recall all the steps it takes for a bill to become a law. Anywhere along that continuum is an opportunity for interest groups to make their case. The first step for interest groups is often to commission research that they use to support their position. This can be most important in the early stages of policy development, when politicians might have an open mind about various proposals.[4(p131)] However, it does not matter how much information a group has if it is not able to gain access to the decision makers. Even a few minutes with a politician may be a few more minutes than the opposition has to make its case directly to a decision maker.[4(p131)] Finally, interest groups need to develop a persuasive argument, a way to frame the issue that convinces politicians to agree with their view of a policy matter.

Interest groups have a variety of tools at their disposal when developing strategies for lobbying. They may initiate a *grassroots* campaign, asking their members to contact their representatives with a particular message. Because interest group members are the voters with the power to re-elect public officials, strong grassroots campaigns can be quite effective. Or, they may try a *grasstops* strategy and harness the influence of community leaders and other prominent individuals,[4(p139)] or, they may join with other interest groups to create coalitions and strengthen their influence through numbers. Interest groups may start a media campaign to align public sentiment with their goals. Of course, providing candidates with money, often through political action committees, is a time-honored way to try to influence the outcome of policy debates.

Whatever methodology they use, interest groups are an important part of the policymaking process. One researcher has called interest groups an "indispensable" part of making policy decisions.[29(p85)] They provide a way to give a voice to their members, who may not otherwise feel able to participate effectively in the policymaking process.

CONCLUSION

This journey through the policymaking process in the United States was intended to provide you with an understanding of policy and a context for your discussions and analysis of health policy issues. It is vital that you become familiar with both the nature of policy and the institutions that make and influence policy. As you have seen, the definition of policy is subject to much debate, yet it is necessary to define what policy means before attempting to engage in policy analysis. We have also walked through the specific duties and powers of the executive and legislative branches of the federal government and included key points about state-level policymaking as well. Finally, all policy students must be aware of and understand the influence of interest groups. They have and use numerous opportunities to influence the policymaking process, and their strength and concerns must be accounted for when analyzing policy issues. As you move further into health policy study, use the information provided in this overview to help you think about and frame your own policy positions.

REFERENCES

1. Longest BB Jr. *Health Policy Making in the United States*. 2nd ed. Chicago, IL: Health Administration Press; 1998.

2. Subcommittee on Health and Environment of the Committee on Interstate Commerce, U.S. House of Representatives. *A Discursive Dictionary of Health Care*. Washington, DC: GPO; 1976.

3. Hanley BE. Policy development and analysis. In: Leavitt JK, Mason DJ, Chaffee MW, eds. *Policy and Politics in Nursing and Health Care*. 3rd ed. Philadelphia, PA: WB Saunders; 1998:125–138.

4. Weissert CS, Weissert WG. *Governing Health: The Politics of Health Policy*. 2nd ed. Baltimore, MD: Johns Hopkins University Press; 2002.

5. U.S. Const. art. 1, § 1; U.S. Const. art. 1, § 8.

6. U.S. Const. art. 1, § 1.

7. U.S. Const. art. 1, § 3.

8. U.S. Const. art. 1, § 3.

9. U.S. Const. art. 1, § 2.

10. Schneider J. The committee system in the U.S. Congress. *Congressional Research Service*. Washington, DC: Library of Congress; 2003.

11. Senate Committee on the Budget. *The Congressional Budget Process: An Explanation*. 105th Cong., 2nd sess. Committee Print 67; 1998.

12. House Committee on the Budget Majority Caucus. *Basics of the Budget Process*. 107th Cong. Briefing Paper; 2001.

13. U.S. Const., art. 2, § 1.

14. U.S. Const., amend. XXII, §1.

15. Committee on House Administration. *Our American Government*. House Concurrent Res. 221. 106th Cong., 2nd sess.; 2000. H. Doc. 216.

16. Davidson RH. The presidency and the Congress. In: Nelson M, ed. *The Presidency and the Political System*. Washington, DC: Congressional Quarterly Press; 1984.

17. Kernell S. *Going Public: New Strategies of Presidential Leadership*. 3rd ed. Washington, DC: CQ Press; 1997.

18. Publ L No. 106-554, relevant sections codified at 42 U.S.C. § 1396a(a).

19. 5 U.S.C. §500.

20. Ryan White Comprehensive AIDS Resources Emergency Act of 1990, amended in 1996 and 2000, 42 U.S.C 300ff.

21. Executive Order No. 13198, *Code of Federal Regulations*, title 3, sec. 750–752 (2002).

22. Sultz HA, Young KM. *Health Care USA: Understanding Its Organization and Delivery*. 3rd ed. Gaithersburg, MD: Aspen; 2001.

23. Turnock BJ. *Public Health: What It Is and How It Works*. 3rd ed. Sudbury, MA: Jones and Bartlett; 2004.

24. Pharmaceutical Research and Manufacturing Association. *About pharma*. Available at http://www.phrma.org/about/about-phrma. Accessed July 25, 2011.

25. National Association of Public Hospitals. *About NAPH*. Available at http://www.naph.org/Main-Menu-Category/About-NAPH/NAPH-Mission .aspx. Accessed July 25, 2011.

26. Center for Budget and Policy Priorities. *About us*. Available at http://www.cbpp.org/about/. Accessed July 25, 2011.

27. American Association of Retired Persons. *Overview*. Available at http://www.aarp.org. Accessed July 25, 2011.

28. The Heritage Foundation. *About Heritage*. Available at http://www .heritage.org/about. Accessed July 25, 2011.

29. Lindbloom C. *The Policy-Making Process*. Englewood Cliffs, NJ: Prentice-Hall; 1980.

ENDNOTES

a. Under Article 1 of the Constitution, Congress has jurisdiction over the District of Columbia. Both the Senate and the House have committees that oversee some governmental functions of the District. The District elects two "shadow senators" who are allowed to lobby Congress on issues but who do not have voting rights. In terms of representation, this places the District in a position similar to other political bodies administered by the United States, such as Puerto Rico, the U.S. Virgin Islands, and American Samoa. The District's shadow senators (and a shadow representative in the House) were created by the citizens of the District in anticipation of the passage of the 1978 District of Columbia Voting Rights amendment to the U.S. Constitution, which would have granted the District the same voting rights as the states. The amendment never passed, but the District government has maintained the shadow positions nonetheless.

b. In addition to the 435 representatives, Puerto Rico has a resident commissioner, and the District of Columbia, Guam, the U.S. Virgin Islands, and American Samoa each has a delegate who is allowed to sponsor legislation and vote in committees, but may not vote on the House floor. The citizens of the District of Columbia also elect a nonvoting shadow representative.

c. In circumstances where the president serves two years or less of the term of another president, an individual may hold office for 10 years.

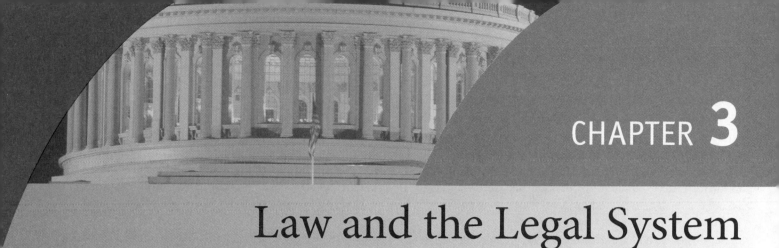

CHAPTER 3

Law and the Legal System

LEARNING OBJECTIVES

By the end of this chapter, you will be able to:

- Describe the role of law in everyday life
- Define the term *law*
- Identify the various sources of law
- Describe key features of the legal system

"It is perfectly proper to regard and study the law simply as a great anthropological document."

—Former U.S. Supreme Court Justice
Oliver Wendell Holmes[1(p 444)]

INTRODUCTION

The importance and complexity of law and the legal system in the United States cannot be overstated. Law's importance stems from its primary purpose: to function as the main tool with which we organize ourselves as an advanced, democratic society. The complexity of law and the legal process is a function of the multiple sources of law that may apply to any one of the millions of actions and interactions that occur daily in society, the division of legal authority between the federal and state governments and among the branches within them, the language the law and its players use to express themselves,[a] and more. For all its complexity, however, there is also an undeniable pervasiveness and openness when it comes to law. We are not left to wonder where it comes from or how it is made. Generally speaking, we are privy to lawmakers' rationales for the laws they write and to judges' reasoning for their legal opinions, just as we are generally privy to the process by which

law is made, and once made, laws are not hidden from us; to the contrary, they are discussed in the media and catalogued in books and online services available for public consumption. (Indeed, one is *expected* to know what the law is, since its violation can have potentially severe consequences.) If you want to know more about law than the average person, you can study it formally in law and other schools, or you can consult with one of the million or so lawyers in practice today. In other words, although law is complicated, it is equally accessible in a way that may not be clear at first blush.

Furthermore, beyond the law's sheer pervasiveness lies another simplicity: As the quotation at the outset of this chapter implies, the study of law is in essence the study of human beings, particularly their evolving customs, beliefs, and value systems. Because law is the key tool with which we regulate social behavior, it stands to reason that it also reflects our foremost values and normative standards. Indeed, law "takes an understanding, a norm, an attitude, and hardens it into muscle and bone"[4(p29)]; however, this is subject to change, for as our society evolves, so too does our law. A relevant example of legal evolution can be seen in the updating of state public health laws, which before the tragic events of September 11, 2001 and the subsequent anthrax scare had not been updated in most states for over a century. Soon after the 2001 attacks, however, many states, concerned about new risks to the public's health, reviewed and overhauled these laws.[5]

This chapter begins by briefly considering the role law plays in everyday life, and then turns to defining law and describing its multiple sources. It then discusses several key features of the legal system, including the separation of government powers, federalism, the role of courts, due process, and more.

For some, reading this chapter may bring to mind a course you have taken or a book you have read on civics or government. In this case, the chapter should serve as a helpful refresher. For those of you new to the study of law, consider the following pages a condensed, but important, introduction to one of the most critical and influential aspects of the society in which you live. In either event, this chapter is designed to better position you to understand the law's application to the specific fields of health care and public health and to digest the health policy and law concepts discussed in this textbook.

THE ROLE OF LAW

The law reaches into nearly every corner of American life. Its impact is inescapable from the moment you wake up to the time you go back to sleep at night (and perhaps beyond, if your community has a curfew or other means of controlling activity and noise after dark). Have you ever stopped to think about the regulations pertaining to the flammability of the mattress you sleep on, or the safety of the water you shower with, cook with, and drink? How about the consumer protection laws regulating the quality of the food you eat throughout the day, and the quality of the establishments that serve it? Then there are the laws pertaining to the safety of the cars, buses, and subways you travel in each day, and the traffic laws that control their movement. You encounter laws daily pertaining to the environment, property ownership, the workplace, civil rights, copyright, energy, banking, and much more. And these are just the laws implicated by the relatively mundane actions of day-to-day life. Steering into activities that are not as common—say, international travel, or adoption, or being admitted to a hospital—you encounter the law swiftly and noticeably. If you need final proof of the ubiquitous nature of law, pick up today's newspaper and count how many stories have some sort of legal angle to them. Then do it tomorrow and the next day. What you will almost certainly find is that a great majority of the stories concern law or legal process.

The law's pervasive nature is no surprise, given the important societal role we assign to it—namely, to serve as the tool with which we govern our relationships with one another, our government, and society at large. A society as sprawling and complex as ours needs formal, enforceable rules of law to provide a measure of control (for example, the need to regulate entities or actions that are potentially dangerous or invidious—a polluting power plant, or acts of discrimination based on race or gender). Furthermore, many people believe that law should be used not just to organize and control the society in which we live, but to achieve a more just society; in other words, according to this view, the country's key organizing principle should not simply be grounded in law, but rather grounded in a legal system designed to affirmatively produce outcomes based on fairness, justice, and equality.[6]

The main way the law governs the many kinds of relationships in society is to recognize and establish enforceable legal rights and responsibilities that guide those relationships, and to create the institutions necessary to define and enforce them. Take constitutional law, for example. Constitutions are charters establishing governments and delineating certain individual and governmental rights and obligations. However, constitutional provisions are triggered only when one party to a relationship works for or on behalf of the government, whether federal or state. Thus, constitutional law governs the relationship between individuals and their government—not, for example, the relationship between two private parties, even when one party's actions are clearly discriminatory or wrongful. Thus, it takes affirmative action by a governmental actor to trigger constitutional protections. So, although it would be a violation of a public school student's First Amendment right to be forced by his principal to pray in class, forced prayer in private schools passes constitutional muster.

A legal right (constitutional or otherwise) denotes a power or privilege that has been guaranteed to an individual under the law, not merely something that is claimed as an interest or something that is a matter of governmental discretion. Conceptually, legal rights derive from the fact that the government sometimes creates what are called individual "property rights"—a generic term referring to an entitlement to personal or real property—for specified groups of persons.[7] Importantly, legal rights also presuppose that their *enforcement* can be achieved through public institutions, including state and federal courts, because a person's ability to secure a remedy when a legal right is infringed (e.g., denied, reduced, or terminated) goes to the very heart of what it means to be "entitled" to something. Indeed, whether particular healthcare benefits rise to the level of being a legal "right," and whether the healthcare right can be enforced in court, are two of the most fundamental legal questions in the area of healthcare law. For example, the federal Medicare program for the aged and disabled confers on eligible individuals not only the right to healthcare services, but also the ability to enforce their right to benefits when program violations occur.

THE DEFINITION AND SOURCES OF LAW
Defining "Law"

Although many legal scholars agree on the general function of law in society, there is far less consensus on how to define "the law." As with many legal terms, there are several plausible interpretations of what is meant by the law, and thus there is no single way to correctly define it. For example, Black's Law Dictionary includes the following definitions in its primary entry:

> That which is laid down, ordained, or established. A rule or method according to which phenomena or actions co-exist or follow each other. Law, in its generic sense, is a body of rules of action or conduct prescribed by controlling authority, and having binding legal force. That which must be obeyed and followed by citizens subject to sanctions or legal consequences is a law.[3(p 884)]

However, even these commonly accepted definitions are not entirely satisfactory, because "a body of rules" that "must be obeyed" in the face of "sanctions or legal consequences" necessarily envisions a process by which the rules are created, disseminated, enforced, violated, disputed, interpreted, applied, revised, and so on. Considered in this way, "the law" essentially amounts to a "legal system"—and a system, by definition, entails regularly interacting or interdependent parts and subparts coming together to form a functional, unified whole. As you read this text, think of "the law" not just as words on a page or as codified statutes or regulations, but as the many interacting parts that are involved in drafting those words and statutes in the first place, and in bringing them to life once they have been enacted as laws. Note that this broad conceptualization of law as a system squares nicely with the primary purpose of law described above, since there must, by necessity, be a sizeable system in place if law is going to carry out its role as the primary organizing tool in society. This broad definition of law also encompasses key legal doctrines, like separation of powers and federalism, described later in this chapter.

Sources of Law

Regardless of the breadth of the definition attached to the term *law*, there is an essential truth to the fact that at the core of the nation's expansive legal system lays a body of enforceable written rules meant to maintain order, define the outer limits of our interactions with one another and with our governments, and delineate legal rights and responsibilities. These rules derive from several sources, which collectively are called *primary* sources of law. The sources of primary legal authority include constitutions, statutes, regulations, and common (i.e., judge-made) law. There are also *secondary* sources of law, which are not laws in the technical sense, but rather are a collection of treatises, law review articles, reports, legal encyclopedias, and more that analyze, interpret, and critique

primary laws. This section discusses each of the four types of primary sources of law.

Constitutions

A constitution is a charter that both establishes a government and delineates fundamental rights and obligations of that government and of individuals who fall within the territory covered by the constitution. In this country, there is a federal constitution and separate constitutions in each of the 50 states. The Constitution of the United States, completed in 1787 and subsequently ratified in each of the original 13 states, took effect in 1789. It provided for a federal union of sovereign states, and a federal government divided into three branches (legislative, executive, and judicial) to operate the union. This governmental structure was not easily agreed upon. Prior to the creation of the federal Constitution, the colonies of the American War of Independence first adopted, in 1777, the Articles of Confederation, which represented the first formal governing document of the United States and which were ratified in 1781. However, a defining feature of the Articles was a weak national government; fairly quickly, a movement for a stronger central government took hold, the colonies elected to throw out their original plan, and the Constitutional Convention—and with it the Constitution—was born.

The federal Constitution is rather short and, for the most part, quite general. One explanation for this is that the framers of the Constitution viewed it as a "document for the ages" that needed to include enduring principles to serve a growing, evolving society that has certainly proved to be more complex than it was at the time of the Constitution's ratification. In the words of former U.S. Supreme Court Justice Robert Jackson, the Constitution is a compilation of "majestic generalities" that collect meaning over a span of many years.[8]

But the fact that some of the most important constitutional provisions are written in broad terms leads to many thorny legal controversies, because there are many competing approaches and theories as to how courts should interpret ambiguous constitutional phrases. Broadly speaking, the leading approaches to constitutional interpretation include the "living constitution," the "moral constitution," "originalism," and "strict constructionism." The living constitution model reflects a belief that the broadly written Constitution should be interpreted to reflect current moral, political, and cultural values in society, not the values that were predominant at the time of the Constitution's ratification. Under this view, the meaning of the Constitution is not fixed, but instead evolves along with society. Moral constitutionalists infuse their interpretation of constitutional law with principles of moral philosophy. Originalism, technically, is an umbrella term referring to a small group of constitutional interpretation theories, all of which share a common belief that constitutional provisions have a fixed and knowable meaning. For example, "original intent," one well-known theory under the originalism umbrella, adheres to the position that constitutional interpretation should be consistent with the intent of the Constitution's original drafters. Finally, strict constructionists limit their interpretation to the Constitution's actual words and phrases, and decline to consider contextual factors such as shifts in societal values or the commentaries or intent of the framers. The most well-known interpretational controversy in the area of health pertains to the breadth and reach of the due process clause of the federal Constitution's 14th Amendment, which prohibits states from depriving "any person of life, liberty, or property, without due process of law."[9] This provision rests at the heart of the Supreme Court's "right to privacy" jurisprudence, including the right to obtain an abortion. For readers interested in theories of constitutional interpretation, there is a vast body of literature at your disposal.[10]

One of the general principles underpinning the Constitution is that citizens should not be subjected to arbitrary and oppressive government. Given that the Constitution was drafted on the heels of the Revolutionary War, this is no surprise. But one consequence of the prevailing mood of the framers toward the reach of a national government is that they drafted the Constitution with an eye toward limiting federal government, as opposed to viewing the Constitution as a vehicle for extending benefits to the public—in other words, that "[t]he men who wrote the Bill of Rights were not concerned that government might do too little for the people but that it might do too much to them."[11] This helps explain why several key constitutional provisions were drafted in "negative" terms—the First Amendment prohibits government from abridging free speech, the Fourth Amendment makes unreasonable searches illegal—rather than as conferring positive rights, like a generalized right to receive healthcare services. At the same time, the First and Fourth Amendments, along with eight others, make up the Bill of Rights, a series of important, specifically guaranteed rights in the Constitution the framers believed to be inalienable.[12]

In addition to the federal Constitution, each state has its own constitution. All state constitutions are like the federal one in that they provide for the organizational structure of the particular state's government, and all contain some measure of a state bill of rights. Here the similarities can end, however. Although state constitutions cannot limit or take away rights conferred by the U.S. Constitution (or by federal statutes), some state constitutions go further than federal law in conferring rights or extending protections. For example,

under current U.S. Supreme Court case law, the death penalty does not always violate the federal Constitution, but the Massachusetts Supreme Court has ruled that the death penalty is prohibited under the state's constitution in every instance. Maryland's constitution requires that a jury be unanimous in order to convict a person of a crime, a standard that differs from federal criminal law. Furthermore, state constitutions are amended much more easily and frequently than their federal counterpart. For instance, Georgia's constitution has undergone some 650 amendments.[4(p34)] Compare this with the fact that the language of the federal Constitution has not been dramatically altered since its inception—there have been just 27 amendments, and the 10 that make up the Bill of Rights were all added by 1791.

Statutes

Statutes are laws written by legislative bodies at all levels of government (federal, state, county, city) that, generally speaking, command or prohibit something. It is the fact of their being legislatively created that sets them apart from other sources of law, because legislatures are understood as creating laws that are forward-looking and apply to large numbers of people. Indeed, the two hallmarks of statutes are their prospectivity and generality. These hallmarks result mainly from the fact that legislatures are in the "regulation business" across an enormous array of issues, and as a result, legislators often lack both the time and the substantive expertise to regulate other than in broad fashion.

Because statutes tend to be written as broad policy statements (and because words on a page can never communicate intent with absolute accuracy), there are few statutes that are utterly unambiguous. This, coupled with the fact that our evolving society continuously presents situations that may not have been foreseeable at the time a statute was written, results in the need for courts to interpret and apply general statutes to millions of specific legal cases or controversies. This practice is called "statutory construction." Although it is a tenet of the separation of powers doctrine (discussed later in the section on key features of the legal system) that legislatures represent the law-making branch of government and the judiciary's role is to interpret law, it is commonly understood that judges and courts "make" law as well through statutory construction, because the continual interpretation and application of broad policy statements (i.e., statutes) can put a "gloss" on the original product, potentially altering its meaning over time.

As discussed more fully below in the section on federalism, state legislatures have greater ability than does Congress to use statutes to regulate across a broad range of issues, pursuant to states' plenary authority under the Constitution. For instance, the number of state statutes regarding population health and safety (e.g., disease control and prevention, the creation of public health agencies, the ability of governors to classify public health emergencies) far exceeds congressional output on the same topic. Notwithstanding states' broader regulatory power, however, federal statutes have primacy over conflicting state statutes.

Administrative Regulations

The fact that statutes are written in broad generalities has another consequence beyond their need to be interpreted and applied in vast numbers of unique instances: Specific regulations must be written to assist with the implementation of statutory directives and to promote statutes' underlying policy goals. This is where administrative agencies of the executive branch of government come in. Because these federal and state agencies—the U.S. Department of Health and Human Services, the U.S. Department of Labor, the California Department of Social Services, the Wisconsin Department of Commerce, and so on—are organized and created to deal with specific policy subject matters, they have more time and expertise than Congress or state legislatures to enforce statutes and promulgate regulations, rules, and orders necessary to carry out statutory prerogatives. It is important to note that assuming the process for creating the regulations was itself legal, and provided that the regulations do not stray beyond the intent of the enacted statute, regulations have the full force of law.

Administrative law is critically important in the area of health policy and law.[13] For example, consider the Medicaid program, which functions primarily as a health insurance program for low-income individuals. The Medicaid statute embodies Congress' intentions in passing the law, including standards pertaining to program eligibility, benefits, and payments to participating healthcare providers. Yet there are literally thousands of administrative regulations and rules pertaining to Medicaid, which over the past 40 years have become the real battleground over the stability and scope of the program. In a very real sense, the Medicaid regulations passed by the federal Department of Health and Human Services and state-level agencies are what bring the program to life and give it vitality. This "operationalizing" function of administrative law can be seen across a wide spectrum of important health issues, including the reporting of infectious diseases, the development of sanitation standards, and the enforcement of environmental laws.[14]

In order to be lawful, regulations must be proposed and established in a way that conforms to the requirements of the federal Administrative Procedure Act of 1946 (APA),[15] which provides procedural restrictions for agency rulemaking and adjudication. Compared to state administrative procedure acts, which tend to be technical and detailed, the APA is broad and sweeping, thus relatively more ambiguous and open to various interpretations by federal courts.[16] Once Congress delegates rulemaking authority to an executive branch agency via a statute (known as the "enabling statute"), the APA dictates how the agency must go about promulgating specific rules and regulations, unless the statute itself specifies the procedure an agency must follow. If the enabling statute dictates a formal rulemaking process, the APA requires the agency to follow cumbersome procedures, and it can only adopt rules after a trial-like hearing on the proposed rule. If Congress does not specify in an enabling statute how an agency must adopt rules, the APA permits the agency to follow a more informal rulemaking process. This requires the agency to publish the proposed rule in the *Federal Register* (the official daily publication for rules, proposed rules, and notices of Federal agencies) and provide an opportunity for the public to comment on the proposed rule. The agency must take the comments under consideration (though it need not revise the proposed rule in response to them), and once it settles on a final rule, it must be published in the *Code of Federal Regulations* (which houses permanent federal regulations under 50 separate titles representing broad areas subject to federal oversight).

In delegating authority to an agency through an enabling statute, Congress must provide an "intelligible principle" that the agency can (and must) follow. That said, the amount of direction and discretion given to agencies varies widely. For example, the enabling statute for the Occupational Health and Safety Administration provides broad discretion by delegating the authority to create and enforce workplace safety standards.[17] Contrast this with the Americans with Disabilities Act, which has very specific provisions and does not allow agencies much discretion when implementing and enforcing the statutory language.

In addition to the power of rulemaking, Congress may also delegate adjudicatory and enforcement powers to administrative agencies. Adjudicatory power refers to claims of public rights, which are claims that involve private persons as one party and the government as the other party (excluding criminal cases). Congress may set up a court, known as an administrative court, within an agency to adjudicate these claims. Because these courts are located in the executive, rather than judicial, branch of government, they are not subject to the same rules and procedures as traditional courts, although they still must provide for the rights and protections prescribed by the Bill of Rights (e.g., the right to legal counsel). Administrative hearings are often much less formal than judicial trials: there are no juries, and although some evidence may be gathered through witness testimony, the majority of evidence derives from written reports. Decisions by Administrative Law Judges (known as ALJs) often do not represent the final word on the matter being adjudicated, as these decisions are subject to approval or rejection by the agency's lead official, or by a traditional (judicial branch) federal court. At the same time, federal courts generally apply a deferential standard of review to administrative decisions, reviewing only to see whether an agency has acted in an "arbitrary and capricious" manner.

The third type of authority granted to agencies by Congress is that of enforcement. As this authority already inherently resides in the executive branch under the federal Constitution, Congress uses its power to specify which agencies have authority to enforce certain statutes and substantive areas of law.

Once Congress grants power to agencies to promulgate rules, adjudicate claims, and enforce statues, its ability to constrain agency action is limited. Because agencies are located in the executive branch, they are under the control of the President and Congress is limited to passing a new statute overturning the questioned agency action or investigating agency action for impropriety and making public the information obtained from the investigation.

Common Law

In each of the prior discussions about constitutions, statutes, and administrative regulations, we pointed out the generality and ambiguity of much of law, and the corresponding responsibility of courts to interpret and apply law to specific cases. It is via the common law—essay-like opinions written by appellate courts articulating the bases for their decisions in individual cases—that courts carry out this responsibility. Common law is also referred to as case law, judge-made law, or decisional law.

Common law is central to legal systems in many countries, particularly those that were territories or colonies of England, which is how the United States came to rely on common law as part of its legal system. Both historically and in modern times, case law is premised on the traditions and customs of society, the idea being that courts could continuously (and relatively efficiently, compared to the legislative process) interpret and apply law in such a way as to match the values of a society undergoing constant evolution. At the same time, the common law is heavily influenced by legal precedent and the doctrine of *stare decisis*, which refers to the legal principle that prior case law decisions should be accorded great deference and should not be frequently overturned. The

importance and function of *stare decisis* in American law is discussed later in the section detailing the role courts play in maintaining stability in the law.

Although courts are expected to overturn their own prior decisions only in rare circumstances and lower courts can never overturn decisions by higher courts that have jurisdiction over them, legislatures can modify or even overturn common law decisions interpreting statutes and regulations. Imagine that the U.S. Supreme Court interpreted a federal civil rights statute as protecting individuals from intentional acts of race discrimination, but not from conduct that has the unintended effect of discriminating against racial minorities. If Congress disagreed with the Court's interpretation of the statute, it could effectively overturn the Court's decision by amending the statute to make it clear that the law was intended to prohibit intentional discrimination *and* presumably neutral acts that nonetheless resulted in unintended discrimination. However, because the judicial branch has final authority to determine whether statutes violate the federal Constitution, Congress would be powerless to overturn a federal court decision that ruled the same civil rights statute unconstitutional.

Notice the "checks and balances" at play in this example, with one branch of government acting as a restraint on another. In the next section, we discuss the separation of powers doctrine—including checks and balances—and other key features of the legal system. But first, see Table 3-1, which provides a summary of the sources of law.

KEY FEATURES OF THE LEGAL SYSTEM

Recall the earlier description of the law as something more than just words on a page, something more than statutes and constitutional provisions. Although the laws themselves are obviously critical, they are just one component of a complex, interacting legal system that creates the laws in the first instance and brings them to life after they hit the pages of legal code books, texts, and treatises.

All legal systems rest on unique principles, traditions, and customs. This section describes a handful of the most important features and principles of the U.S. legal system, including the separation of powers doctrine, federalism, the role and structure of federal and state courts, judicial review, due process, and constitutional standards of review.

Separation of Powers

This country's government, both federal and state, has an underpinning structure of three independent and equally powerful branches, a fact that sets it apart from parliamentary systems of government—such as those found in Canada,

TABLE 3-1 Summary of the Primary Sources of American Law

Source of Law	Key Points
Constitutions	Establish governments and delineate fundamental rights and obligations of government and individuals. There is a federal constitution and separate constitutions in each state. Federal constitution restrains government more than it confers individual rights; however, the Bill of Rights specifically guarantees several important individual rights. The Supreme Court has the final word on the constitutionality of laws created by the political branches of government.
Statutes	Created by legislatures at all levels of government. Two hallmarks: prospectivity and generality. As broad policy statements, statutes are often ambiguous as applied to specific cases or controversies, requiring courts to interpret them through the practice of statutory construction. State legislatures can use statutes to regulate across a broader range of issues than can Congress; however, federal statutes have primacy over conflicting state statutes.
Regulations	Created by executive branch administrative agencies to implement statutes and clarify their ambiguities. Play a particularly critical role in health policy and law.
Common Law	Court opinions interpreting and applying law to specific cases. Also referred to as case law, judge-made law, or decisional law. Based on the traditions and customs of society, yet heavily influenced by legal precedent and the doctrine of *stare decisis*.

Germany, the United Kingdom, and many other countries—in which the legislature appoints the executive. The legal doctrine that supports the arrangement of shared governance among multiple branches is the *separation of powers* doctrine. This doctrine is considered one of the most important aspects of both federal and state constitutional design. The framers of the U.S. Constitution were well aware that nothing was more likely to foster tyrannical government than the concentration of governing powers in one individual or political party. To guard against a concentration of political power, the framers did two related things: they divided governmental powers and responsibilities among separate, co-equal branches, and they structured the elections of officials for the two political branches of government (legislative and executive) so that they would take place at different intervals and through different mechanisms (e.g., the President is elected through the electoral college system, whereas members of Congress are not).

Inherent in the separation of powers doctrine is the important concept of checks and balances. "Checks" refers to the ability and responsibility of one branch of government to closely monitor the actions of the other two, including when one branch grasps at an amount of power not envisioned by the Constitution. The "balance" at work in the separation of powers framework prevents one branch from exerting power in an area of responsibility that is the province of another branch.

The constitutional doctrine of separation of powers represents, in the words of one legal scholar, an "invitation to struggle for the privilege"[18(p171)] of governing the country. (Alexis de Tocqueville, a French philosopher and political theorist who studied American government in the 1830s, viewed the concept of checks and balances in much starker terms: "The president, who exercises a limited power, may err without causing great mischief in the state. Congress may decide amiss without destroying the union, because the electoral body in which the Congress originates may cause it to retract its decision by changing its members. But if the Supreme Court is ever composed of imprudent or bad men, the union may be plunged into anarchy or civil war."[19(p152)]) For example, at the time of this writing, a debate is taking place in the media and between Congress and President Barack Obama over the meaning of separation of powers and the appropriate role of checks and balances in the context of the nation's soaring debt and the appropriateness of raising the debt ceiling. Some columnists and policymakers maintain that the President can act unilaterally to raise the debt ceiling and allow the federal government to borrow more money, while others argue that such a move is beyond the scope of presidential power.

Throughout this text, there are health policy and law questions that distinctly highlight our government's divided powers. For instance, how will the struggle between the Executive Branch and some members of Congress over implementation of the Affordable Care Act—the former attempting to implement the law quickly and thoroughly, the latter trying to thwart implementation through fiscal, policy, and legal channels—play out? And how has the Supreme Court applied its constitutional right to privacy jurisprudence to the matter of abortion in response to federal and state legislative enactments? As you consider these and other health policy and law questions from a separation of powers angle, consider the peculiar roles of each branch of government, taking into account their duties, powers, and limitations. Through this prism, continually reflect on which governmental body is best equipped to effectively respond to health policy problems.[20]

Federalism: Allocation of Federal and State Legal Authority

In the legal system, the powers to govern, make and apply law, and effectuate policy choices are not just apportioned among three governmental branches at both the federal and state levels; they are also divided *between* the federal government and the governments of the various states. This division of authority—which also plays a key role in the development of health policies and laws—is referred to as *federalism*. Like the separation of powers doctrine, federalism derives from the U.S. Constitution.

Under the Constitution, the federal government is one of limited powers, while the states more or less retain all powers not expressly given to the federal government. In essence, this was the deal consented to by the states at the time our federal republic was formed: They agreed to surrender certain enumerated powers (like foreign affairs) to the federal government in exchange for retaining many aspects of sovereignty.

The Constitution's 10th Amendment states that "the powers not delegated to the United States by the Constitution . . . are reserved to the States respectively."[21] For example, because the Constitution does not explicitly define the protection and promotion of the public's health as a power of the federal government, public health powers are primarily held by the states. (In fact, compared to the federal government, the states handle the vast majority of all legal matters in this country. Consider just a sampling of typical legal affairs overseen by state government: marriages, divorces, and adoptions; law enforcement and criminal trials; schooling; driving, hunting, medical, and many other licenses; consumer protection; and much more.[4(pp10–11)] Furthermore, 97% of all litigation occurs in state courts.[22]) As a result, all states regulate the area of public health through what are known as their "police powers," which allow state and local governments to (among other things) legislate to protect the common good. Examples of the kinds of laws passed under this authority include childhood

immunization standards, infectious disease data collection mandates, and environmental hazard regulations. Furthermore, under the 10th Amendment, states historically have had the power to regulate the practice of medicine and the licensing of hospitals and other health care institutions.

Recall, however, that the federal government also plays a role in regulating health care and public health. The national government's enumerated powers include the ability to tax, spend, and regulate interstate commerce, all of which have been utilized in ways to improve health care and promote public health. For example, Congress has used its taxing power to increase the cost of cigarettes (in the hopes of driving down the number of smokers) and to generate funds for programs such as Medicare, and congressional spending powers are the legal cornerstone for federal health programs like Medicaid. Furthermore, the sharing of power under the 10th Amendment notwithstanding, the Constitution's supremacy clause declares that federal laws—the Constitution, statutes, and treaties—are the "supreme" law of the land, and thus preempt state laws that conflict with them.[23]

While federalism is built solidly into the nation's political branches through separate federal and state legislatures and executives, it is also on display in the structure of U.S. courts. There are both federal and state court systems, and each has unique authority and jurisdiction: federal courts are limited to ruling only in certain kinds of cases, including those involving federal constitutional or statutory law, those in which the United States is a party to the lawsuit, and those specified by statutory law; state courts, by contrast, have jurisdiction to hear just about any case (unless explicitly precluded from doing so by federal statute), including those over which federal courts also have jurisdiction. State court jurisdiction includes cases implicating state statutory and regulatory law, the state constitution, and the U.S. Constitution.

Over the years, defining the boundaries of federalism (i.e., defining the federal government's sphere of authority and determining the scope of state sovereignty) has been a contentious legal and political issue. At the dawn of the country's independence, after the colonies scrapped the Articles of Confederation in favor of a stronger central government, the Supreme Court decided federalism cases with a nod toward expansive national powers (much to the dislike of some states). Two famous cases make the point. In the 1819 case of *McCulloch v. Maryland*,[24] the Supreme Court enhanced the power of the U.S. government by establishing the principle that federal governmental powers are not strictly limited to those expressly provided for in the Constitution. At issue in the case was whether Congress had the power to charter a national bank to help the federal government shoulder wartime debt. In 1824, the Court for the first time had the opportunity to review the Constitution's commerce clause (which grants Congress the authority to regulate interstate commerce) in the case of *Gibbons v. Ogden*,[25] which resulted from a decision by the state of New York to grant a monopoly to a steamboat operator for a ferry between New York and New Jersey. Again, the Court ruled broadly in favor of the federal government, stating that the commerce clause reserved exclusively to Congress the power to regulate interstate navigation.

By the mid-1800s, however, this approach to defining the relative power of the federal and state governments gave way to one that was more deferential to states and more willing to balance their sovereign interests against the interests of the federal government. This approach, in turn, lost ground during the New Deal and civil rights eras, both of which were marked by an acceptance of federal authority to provide social services and regulate the economy. The arrival of Ronald Reagan's presidency in 1981 marked yet another turning point in the evolution of federalism. For eight years, the Reagan administration acted to restrict national authority over the states, a process that took on even more force after the Republican Party took control of Congress in the mid-90s. Indeed, since the early 1980s and continuing into the new millennium, a defining feature of federalism has been the purposeful devolution of authority and governance over social and economic policy from the federal government to state legislators and regulators.

The Role of Courts

Elsewhere, we have discussed the structure and powers of two of the political branches of government: the legislative and executive branches. The third branch is that of the judiciary, made up of justices, judges, magistrates, and other "adjudicators" in two separate court systems—one federal, one state. Although the federal and state court systems have critically distinctive authority, they do not look very different structurally. The federal court system has three tiers, with cases proceeding from the lowest-level court (a trial court) to two separate, higher-level courts (appellate courts). Federal trial courts are called district courts, and they exist in varying numbers in each state, with the size of the state determining the actual number of "districts," and thus the number of federal trial courts. In total, there are nearly 100 federal district courts. After a district court renders a decision, the losing party to a lawsuit is entitled to appeal the decision to a federal circuit court of appeals. There are 13 U.S. circuit courts of appeals—12 with jurisdiction over designated multi-state geographic regions, or "circuits," and a court of appeals for the federal circuit (residing in Washington, DC), which has

nationwide appellate jurisdiction over certain kinds of cases, such as patent and international trade disputes. For many individuals, losing a case in a federal circuit court represents the end of the line for their case, since litigants have no entitlement to have their case heard by the U.S. Supreme Court, the highest court in the country. Although parties have a right to *petition* the Supreme Court to hear their case, at least four of the nine justices on the Court must agree to grant the petition. Although the Supreme Court is undeniably the most important court in the country in terms of its authority, it by no means renders the most decisions. The Supreme Court grants approximately 150 petitions annually, whereas the 13 circuit courts collectively decide approximately 62,000 cases annually. This fact is more than trivial; it effectively means that in the huge majority of federal cases, lower appellate courts, and not the Supreme Court, have final say over the scope and meaning of federal law.

As mentioned, each state also has its own court system, most of which are organized like the federal system: one trial court, followed by two separate appellate courts (generally termed "[name of state] court of appeals" and "[name of state] supreme court"). However, some state systems provide for only one appellate court. State systems also tend to include courts that are "inferior" even to their general trial courts; these handle relatively minor disputes (think of the small claims courts frequently shown on daytime television). Furthermore, state trial courts are sometimes divided by specialty, so that certain courts hear cases that involve only family matters, juvenile matters, and the like.

Within the federal and state court system hierarchy, appellate courts have two powers unavailable to trial courts: reviewing lower court decisions to determine whether there were errors of law made during the trial that necessitate a new one, and establishing legal precedents that lower courts are bound to follow. But appellate courts lack trial courts' powers to actually conduct trials, including empanelling juries, hearing testimony from witnesses, reviewing evidence, and the like. Instead, appellate reviews are limited to the written record created at trial by the lower court.

Adjudication refers to the legal process of resolving disputes. It is in the context of resolving specific legal disputes that the judiciary interprets and applies the law, and also indirectly "makes" law under its common law authority. The results of adjudication are the common law decisions described earlier. Because U.S. courts are generally not permitted to issue advisory opinions, courts effectively only act in response to a specific "case or controversy" brought before them. (Where permitted, advisory opinions are released by courts not in response to a particular legal dispute, but in response to a request from another branch of government regarding the interpretation or permissibility of a particular law. Federal courts are bound from issuing advisory opinions because the Supreme Court has ruled that constitutional provisions establishing the federal courts prevent them from reviewing hypothetical or moot disputes. Although a couple exceptions exist, state courts are likewise prohibited from issuing advisory opinions.) This essentially means that in order for a court to rule in a particular case, an individual initiating a lawsuit must assert an enforceable legal right, a measurable violation of that right, actual damage or harm, and a court-fashioned remedy that could appropriately respond to the lawsuit.

Courts play a vital role in the legal system. This role stems in large part from their responsibility to determine what, ultimately, the Constitution means, permits, and prohibits. In discharging this responsibility, courts are asked to protect and enforce individual legal rights, determine whether the political branches of government have acted in a way that violates the Constitution, and maintain stability in the law through the application of legal precedent. The judicial branch is viewed as uniquely able to fulfill these key responsibilities, at least at the federal level, because it is the branch of government most insulated from politics: Federal judges are appointed, not elected, and granted life tenure under the Constitution to shield them from political influences that might otherwise interfere with their impartially.[b] Most state judges, however, are now subject to popular election,[22] either at the time of initial selection or subsequently, when it is determined whether they will be retained as judges.[c]

Enforcing Legal Rights

As described earlier, two main functions of the legal system are to establish legal rights and to create institutions to enforce those rights. The primary enforcers of individual legal rights, and those in the best position to create remedies for their violation, are the courts. For example, the federal courts (and the Supreme Court in particular) were critical to the success of the civil rights movement, during which time federal judges expansively interpreted civil rights laws and maintained close oversight of the implementation of their rulings. At the same time, however, the Supreme Court has not often been at the forefront of advancing individual rights. Certainly, there have been times when the Court has played an enormous role in advancing societal expectations with respect to individual equality—*Brown v. Board of Education*[26] being the most obvious example—but this decision, and a few others, are actually quite anomalous, and the Court has been more a follower of evolving attitudes and expectations.

Among the most important rights courts are expected to uphold and enforce is the constitutional right to *due process*, which protects individuals from arbitrary and unfair treatment at the hands of government. Both the Fifth and Fourteenth Amendments to the Constitution make clear that no person can be deprived of "life, liberty, or property, without due process of law," with the Fifth Amendment applying to the federal government and the Fourteenth applying to the states. An important component of due process is the principle that when government establishes a legal right or entitlement for individuals, it may not then decide to deny the right or entitlement unfairly.

When courts consider due process claims, they are often thought of as reviewing *how* laws operate and *why* laws have been established in the first place. This results from the fact that the due process clause has been interpreted by the Supreme Court as including *procedural* due process (the "how") and *substantive* due process (the "why"). Procedural due process requires that laws be enacted and applied fairly and equitably, including procedural fairness when individuals challenge government infringements on their life, liberty, or property. Thus, due process requirements might be triggered if a law is too vague or is applied unevenly, if government threatens to withdraw a previously granted license, or if an individual's public benefits are withheld. For example, before a physician can lose his state-granted license to practice medicine, the state must provide the physician advance notice of the termination and a formal hearing before an impartial examiner with all the usual legal trappings (right to legal representation, right to present evidence in one's defense, right to appeal the examiner's decision, etc.). Similarly, Medicaid beneficiaries must be given notice of, and an opportunity to challenge, benefit coverage denials made by a managed care company participating in the Medicaid program. And the courts' most well-known jurisprudence in the area of health-related due process rights concerns abortion, specifically whether federal and state laws impermissibly infringe on the right to terminate a pregnancy, which is part of the right to "liberty" under the due process clause.

But that clause has been interpreted by courts to require more than just procedural fairness when a law deprives an individual of life, liberty, or property; it also requires that government provide a sound reason for having invaded personal freedoms in the first place. This is termed *substantive due process*. This form of due process serves as a proscription against arbitrary government activity. For instance, when states have been unable to adequately explain the reasoning behind statutes requiring involuntary confinement of mentally ill individuals who were not dangerous to themselves or others, courts ruled the laws unconstitutional on substantive due process grounds. Substantive due process is unquestionably more controversial than its procedural counterpart, because many critics argue that the former gives courts unrestrained power to invalidate, on constitutional grounds, government actions with which they simply disagree. In other words, some view this form of due process "as a potentially limitless warrant for judges to impose their personal values on the Constitution."[27(p474)]

Reviewing the Actions of the Political Branches

An important piece of the separation of powers puzzle, and one that grants the courts wide authority to enforce individual legal rights in this country, is the doctrine of *judicial review*. Judicial review refers to the power of the courts to declare laws unconstitutional and to determine whether the actions of the legislative and executive branches of government are lawful. The theory behind judicial review is that, as the branch of government most independent of the political process, courts can pass judgment on the actions of the political branches free of partisanship.

Judicial review has its roots in the famous 1803 case of *Marbury v. Madison*,[28] in which the Supreme Court ruled that it had the power to review acts of Congress and determine their constitutionality. The facts of the case are fascinating. In 1800, Thomas Jefferson won the presidential election, besting incumbent John Adams. In the final days of President Adams's term, the Federalist-controlled Congress passed, and Adams signed into law, a statute called the Judiciary Act of 1801. Among other things, the law created several new judgeships, and the idea was to fill the new judicial posts with Federalists before Jefferson assumed the presidency. Among the new judicial appointments made by Adams and approved by the Senate before Jefferson took office were 42 justices of the peace, including one for William Marbury. Prior to Jefferson's taking office, Marbury's commission was signed by Adams and by John Marshall—who at the time was Secretary of State under Adams—but not delivered. After his inauguration, Jefferson ruled that Marbury's commission (and those of several other Adams-appointed justices of the peace) were invalid because they had not been delivered during the Adams presidency, and therefore directed his new Secretary of State, James Madison, to withhold delivery. Marbury sued to force delivery of his commission, petitioning the Supreme Court directly to issue a *writ of mandamus*, which is an order by a court compelling a government officer to perform his duties.

Marbury was able to ask the Court directly for the writ because the recently enacted Judiciary Act also authorized the Supreme Court to issue writs of mandamus.

The Supreme Court's decision in *Marbury v. Madison*[d] first established the important principle that for every violation of a legal right, there must be a corresponding legal remedy. With this principle in place, the Court ruled that Marbury was in fact entitled to his commission and to a legal remedy for Jefferson's decision to withhold it, "since [Marbury's] commission was signed by the President, and sealed by the secretary of state . . . and the law creating the office, gave the officer a right to hold for five years, independent of the executive, the appointment[.] To withhold his commission, therefore, is an act deemed by the court not warranted by law, but violative of a vested legal right."[29]

The *Marbury* Court then did something monumental: It established and justified the power of judicial review. This outcome flowed from the fact that Marbury had filed his legal petition directly with the Supreme Court, and the Court needed to determine whether Congress acted constitutionally in granting the Court power under the Judiciary Act to issue writs of mandamus as a matter of "original jurisdiction." (Original jurisdiction refers to cases on which the court rules before any other court does so, contrasted with situations in which the court reviews a decision of a lower court, which is called "appellate jurisdiction.")

It was not apparent that the mandamus component of the new Judiciary Act was constitutional because Article III of the Constitution—which established the judicial branch of the federal government, including the Supreme Court—says that "In all Cases affecting Ambassadors, other public Ministers and Consuls, and those in which a State shall be a Party, the Supreme Court shall have original Jurisdiction. In all the other Cases [subject to Supreme Court jurisdiction], the Supreme Court shall have appellate Jurisdiction, both as to Law and Fact, with such Exceptions, and under such Regulations as the Congress shall make."[30] Interpreting this clause, Chief Justice Marshall determined the Court could issue a writ of mandamus under the Constitution only as an exercise of appellate—but not original—jurisdiction, and that Congress had no power to modify the Court's original jurisdiction. As a result, the Court held that the Judiciary Act of 1801 was in conflict with Article III, and thus unconstitutional.

Marbury represented the first time the Supreme Court exercised the power of judicial review and declared unconstitutional a law passed by Congress. Over the years, the Court has exercised this power sparingly, exclaiming in 1867 that although it clearly had the authority to strike down congressional legislation repugnant to the Constitution, this "duty is one of great delicacy, and only to be performed where the repugnancy is clear, and the conflict unreconcilable."[31] For example, the Supreme Court invalidated few congressional acts in the first 50 years after *Marbury*, although the pace picked up somewhat after that, to an average of about one invalidation every two years. During William Rehnquist's term as Chief Justice (1986–2005), however, the Court ruled unconstitutional more than 30 laws or statutory provisions, with most of these decisions occurring between 1995 and 2005. This up-tick in the Court's use of its most powerful judicial review tool has led to a discussion about the Court's proper place in the separation of powers framework. As one opinion piece exclaimed, "[d]eclaring an act of Congress unconstitutional is the boldest thing a judge can do. That's because Congress, as an elected legislative body representing the entire nation, makes decisions that can be presumed to possess a high degree of democratic legitimacy."[32(pA19)]

When determining whether a statute violates the Constitution, courts necessarily take into account the subject of the regulation and Congress' purpose in regulating. Certain kinds of laws—say, affirmative action laws, or a law that classifies people on the basis of their gender—require a greater level of governmental justification and thus are held to a higher constitutional *standard of review*. In other words, these laws are scrutinized more closely by the Court and thus stand a greater chance of failing the constitutionality test.

By way of example, the Supreme Court has developed a tiered standard of review framework for equal protection jurisprudence. Under the Constitution's equal protection clause, states are prohibited from denying "to any person within its jurisdiction the equal protection of the laws."[33] The Court employs one of three standards when it reviews whether a particular law satisfies this constitutional mandate. The first, termed *rational basis* or *rational relations* review, is applied to everyday legislation pertaining to things like public safety, tax rates, and consumer protection and thus is the review standard most frequently used. It is nearly impossible for a law to run afoul of this standard, because as long as the challenged statute is *rationally* related to *any* legitimate government purpose in passing the law, it will be upheld as constitutional.

The second standard is that of *intermediate* review. This is the Court's choice when the measure under review classifies individuals or groups on, for example, the basis of gender. The assumption here—and the point of the heightened review standard—is that when politicians legislate with gender (or another potentially baseless characteristic) in mind, there is a greater likelihood they are doing so for nefarious reasons.

In order to pass constitutional muster under intermediate review, a statute must serve an *important* government objective and be *substantially* related to that objective. A good deal of legislation reviewed under this standard is found to be unconstitutional.

Finally, the Court has at its disposal in equal protection lawsuits a review standard known as *strict scrutiny*. The Court reserves this standard for laws that tread on fundamental constitutional rights (defined in part as those that are firmly established in American tradition), including an individual's right to be free of governmental discrimination on the basis of race. In theory, otherwise discriminatory laws that are *necessary* to achieve a *compelling* government interest—meaning that the law in question is the least discriminatory way to meet the legislature's compelling objective—can survive this intense form of scrutiny. However, of all the equal protection claims measured against this standard, only one survivor has emerged—when the Supreme Court permitted the federal government to intern individuals of Japanese descent during World War II[34]—and now it is almost universally agreed that this decision was terribly off the mark.[35]

Maintaining Stability in the Law

In addition to enforcing legal rights and passing on the constitutionality of actions of the two political branches of government, courts are expected to maintain a measure of stability, continuity, and predictability in the law. This expectation derives from the idea that those subject to the law should not have to contend with continuous swings in the direction law takes. In theory, the relatively nonpolitical judicial branch of government is in the best position to bring this expectation to fruition.

The way courts implement their responsibility to maintain legal stability is through application of *stare decisis*, a Latin legal term meaning "let it stand." *Stare decisis* is a policy of the courts to stand by existing legal precedent; that is, where rules of law have been established in prior judicial decisions, these decisions should be adhered to in subsequent cases where the questions of law and fact are substantially similar to those in the original case. Stability in the law is considered so important that *stare decisis* is usually applied, and the original judicial decision given deference, *even when the original decision is subsequently determined to be wrongly decided or not legally sound*. This is especially true where the original decision is an old one on which society has come to rest, as opposed to a relatively young decision with few deep roots in terms of societal expectations. The role of legal precedent has been described in this way:

Legal doctrines are shaped like family trees. Each generation of decisions is derived from ones that came before as, over time, each branch of the law grows and spreads or, occasionally, withers and dies away. The most recent decisions almost always draw their strength by tracing back through an ancestral line, choosing among parents, uncles, and cousins according to the aptness of their bloodlines. Rarely, a branch of doctrine is disowned, repudiated, and left vestigial until perhaps revived in another legal era.[27(p77)]

At the same time, legal precedent is not completely sacred, and prior decisions are sometimes reconsidered and, on occasion, overturned. For instance, changes in societal values might outweigh strict application of *stare decisis*, as was the case with the Supreme Court's 1954 decision in *Brown v. Board of Education* to overturn the invidious idea of "separate but equal" from the Court's 1896 decision in *Plessy v. Ferguson*.[36] *Stare decisis* is, however, generally understood to trump mere changes in a court's makeup. In other words, courts are expected to remain anchored to precedential rules of law even when current individual members may not be.[e] Indeed, in a well-known Supreme Court case, former Justice John Marshall Harlan II once wrote:

A basic change in the law upon a ground no firmer than a change in our membership invites the popular misconception that this institution is little different from the two political branches of the Government. No misconception could do more lasting injury to this Court and to the system which it is our abiding mission to serve.[37]

CONCLUSION

This chapter led you on a short journey through the complex world of the legal system. Along the way, you visited several of its essential elements and doctrines: legal rights, the various types of law, separation of powers, federalism, judicial review, and more. To be sure, the trip was abbreviated and in some cases concepts were oversimplified, but above all this is a function of needing to concisely cover a complex and expansive topic.

As you encounter myriad health policy and law topics and concepts that are complex in their own right, bearing in mind a few important details about law might help you achieve a greater measure of clarity. First, law's primary purpose is to organize and control an ever-changing, ever-expanding,

ever-more-complex society, and it does this in part by regulating a variety of relationships among parties with oftentimes competing interests (e.g., individual citizen and government; patient and physician; beneficiary and public program or private insurance company; physician and managed care organization; individual and her family). This helps explain why in the context of a specific relationship, one party has a legal right and the other party has a legal responsibility to refrain from acting in a way that infringes that legal right. It also helps explain why an individual can justifiably claim a particular legal right in the context of one specific relationship, but not in others (for example, a patient who believes that he has been treated negligently might have a legitimate legal claim against the physician who provided his care, but not against the hospital where the care was provided).

A second detail worth reflecting on periodically is that law is established, enforced, interpreted, and applied by human beings, and thus one must accept that law and the legal process comprise a certain amount of imperfection. This helps explain why statutes and regulations are sometimes difficult to understand; why laws are sometimes enforced sporadically or not at all; why reasonable jurists can disagree about the intended meaning of statutory and constitutional provisions; and why law is too often applied unevenly, or inequitably.

Finally, bear in mind the fact that laws and the broader legal system are reflective of the beliefs and values of the society from which they flow. This *fait accompli*, perhaps more than anything else, provides an object lesson in the role of law across a wide range of subjects, including matters related to health care and public health.

REFERENCES

1. Holmes OW. Law in science and science in law. *Harvard Law Rev.* 1899;12:443–444.
2. Friedman LM. Law and its language. *George Wash Univ Law Rev.* 1964;33:563, 567.
3. Black HC, et al. *Black's Law Dictionary*. 6th ed. St. Paul, MN: West; 1990.
4. Friedman LM. *Law in America: A Short History*. New York, NY: The Modern Library; 2002.
5. Center for Law and the Public's Health, Georgetown and Johns Hopkins Universities, Available at http://www.publichealthlaw.net/ Resources /Modellaws.htm#TP.
6. Smith SD. Reductionism in legal thought. *Columbia Law Rev.* 1991;91:68,73–75.
7. Reich CA. The new property. *Yale Law J.* 1964;73:733.
8. *Fay v. New York*, 332 U.S. 261, 282 (1947) (Jackson, J., concurring).
9. U.S. Const. amend. XIV, § 1.
10. See, e.g., Thomas E. Baker, "Constitutional Theory in a Nutshell," *William and Mary Bill of Rights Journal* 13 (2004): 57; Richard H. Fallon, Jr., "How to Choose a Constitutional Theory," *California Law Review* 87 (1999): 535.

11. *Jackson v. City of Joliet*, 715 F.2d 1200, 1203 (7th Cir. 1983).

12. For an overview of the Bill of Rights in a public health context, see Lawrence O. Gostin, *Public Health Law: Power, Duty, Restraint* (Berkeley, CA: University of California Press, 2000), 62–65.

13. For a full description of the intertwined nature of administrative and health law, see Timothy Stoltzfus Jost, "Health Law and Administrative Law: A Marriage Most Convenient," *Saint Louis University Law Journal* 49 (2004): 1.

14. Mensah GA, et al. Law as a tool for preventing chronic diseases: expanding the spectrum of effective public health strategies. *Prev Chronic Dis: Public Health Res Pract Policy.* 2004;1(2):1–6.

15. 5 U.S.C. § 551 et seq.

16. For an in-depth discussion of the relationship between the APA and state administrative procedures, see Arthur Bonfield, *The Federal APA and State Administrative Law*, 72 Va. L. Rev. 297 (1986).

17. See Occupational Health and Safety Act of 1970 § 6, 29 U.S.C. § 655.18. Corwin ES. *The President: Office and Powers, 1787–1957.* New York, NY: New York University Press; 1957.

18. Corwin ES. *The President: Office and Powers, 1787–1957.* New York: New York University Press; 1957.

19. de Tocqueville A. *Democracy in America.* New York, NY: Vintage Books; 1990.

20. For a full discussion of each of the government branches' role in health policy making, see Lawrence Gostin, "The Formulation of Health Policy by the Three Branches of Government," in *Society's Choices: Social and Ethical Decision Making in Biomedicine*, eds. Ruth Ellen Bulger, Elizabeth Meyer Bobby, and Harvey V. Fineberg (Washington, D.C.: National Academy Press, 1995).

21. U.S. Const. amend. X.

22. American Bar Association, Governmental Affairs Office. An independent judiciary: report of the ABA Commission on Separation of Powers and Judicial Independence. Available at http://www.abanet.org/govaffairs /judiciary/r5.html. Accessed August 1, 2006.

23. U.S. Const. article VI, paragraph 2.

24. 17 U.S. (4 Wheat.) 316 (1819).

25. U.S. (9 Wheat.) 1 (1824).

26. 347 U.S. 483 (1954).

27. Lazarus E. *Closed Chambers: The Rise, Fall, and Future of the Modern Supreme Court.* New York, NY: Penguin Books; 1999.

28. 1 Cranch (5 U.S.) 137 (1803).

29. *Marbury*, 1 Cranch (5 U.S.) at 162.

30. U.S. Const. art. III, § 2, Clause 2.

31. *Mayor v. Cooper*, 73 U.S. 247, 251 (1867).

32. Gewirtz P, Golder C. So who are the activists? *The New York Times.* July 6, 2005: A19.

33. U.S. Const. amend. XIV, § 1.

34. *Korematsu v. United States*, 323 U.S. 214 (1944).

35. For a fuller discussion of how the equal protection standards of review operate, see Lazarus, *Closed Chambers*, 293–294.

36. 163 U.S. 537 (1896).

37. *Mapp v. Ohio*, 367 U.S. 643, 677 (1961) (Harlan, J., dissenting).

ENDNOTES

a. Although the important role that language plays in law is not a topic we delve into in this chapter, it is, particularly for students new to the study of law, one worth thinking about. Words are the basic and most important tool of the law and of lawyers. Without them, how could one draft a law, legal brief, contract, or judicial opinion? Or engage in oral advocacy on behalf of a client, or conduct a negotiation? Or make one's wishes known with respect to personal matters near the end of life? As one renowned legal scholar puts it, "law is primarily a verbal art, its skills verbal skills."[2]

Of course, one problem with the language of law is that it is full of legal jargon, making it difficult sometimes for lay people to understand and apply to their own particular situation. For example, if government regulation is to be effective, the language used to do the regulating must be understandable to those being regulated. Another problem relates to the interpretation of words and terms used in the law, because both ambiguity (where language is reasonably capable of being understood in two or more ways) and vagueness (where language is not fairly capable of being understood) are common to laws, leaving those subject to them and those responsible for applying them unclear about their true meaning. Furthermore, as the Preface to *Black's Law Dictionary*, under the heading "A Final Word of Caution," states: "The language of the law is ever-changing as the courts, Congress, state legislatures, and administrative agencies continue to define, redefine and expand legal words and terms. Furthermore, many legal terms are subject to variations from state to state and again can differ under federal laws."[3(p iv)]

b. However, since the 1980s, the selection (by the president) and approval (by the U.S. Senate) process for federal judges has become highly politicized. There is an extensive body of literature on this topic, as evidenced by a simple Internet search.

c. The potential implications of increasingly injecting politics into the court system are very troubling, and there is likewise extensive literature on this topic.

d. The decision was written, as it turned out, by Chief Justice John Marshall—the very same person who, as Secretary of State, signed Marbury's commission. Marshall was sworn in as Chief Justice of the United States just before Jefferson took office.

e. This understanding is often put to the test, however, as seen in the national discussion of the right to abortion that takes place each time a new U.S. Supreme Court nominee is announced whose political stripes seem to clash with the prevailing law that abortion is a constitutionally protected right.

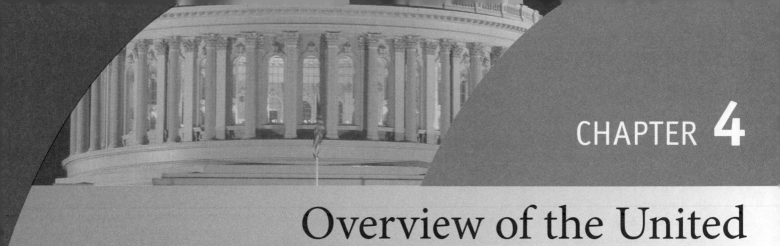

CHAPTER 4

Overview of the United States Healthcare System

LEARNING OBJECTIVES

By the end of this chapter, you will be able to:

- Identify the key players who provide and finance health care in the United States
- Identify common characteristics of the uninsured
- Understand the effect of insurance on access to care and on health status
- Identify barriers to accessing health care
- Understand concerns regarding the quality of health care provided in the United States
- Describe differences in how health care is delivered in various countries

INTRODUCTION

Coordinated. Efficient. Cost-effective. Goal-oriented. These are words one might use to describe a well-functioning system. Unfortunately, they are not words that are often used when discussing how healthcare services are delivered in the United States. Unlike most other developed nations, the United States does not have a unified healthcare system. Even with the passage of the 2010 Patient Protection and Affordable Care Act (ACA), the first major health reform law passed in this country in nearly 50 years, the United States will continue to provide healthcare services through a patchwork of public and private insurance plans; federal, state, and local governments; and institutions and individual providers who are often unconnected to one other.[1]

The United States has never been accused of providing healthcare services in an efficient or cost-effective manner.

This country spends over twice as much on health care per person as other developed countries. While the U.S. healthcare system does some things well, it ranks at or near the bottom on important health outcome measures such as life expectancy, infant mortality, and adult obesity rates.[2] Even though the federal government establishes the nation's healthcare goals through initiatives such as *Healthy People 2020*, the lack of coordination within the healthcare system means that all parts of the system are not working together to achieve these goals.[3]

The lack of a unified healthcare system makes it difficult to provide a straightforward overview of how healthcare services are delivered and financed. For example, the various players in the provision and delivery of health care include:

- Educational institutions such as medical, dental, nursing, and physician assistant programs.
- Research organizations including private entities, public agencies, and non-profit foundations.
- Private suppliers of goods and services such as hospital equipment manufacturers, home health agencies, and uniform suppliers.
- Private health insurance provided through employers, on the individual market, and, in the future, through state health exchanges.
- Public health insurance programs such as Medicaid, Medicare, and Tri-Care (the Department of Defense healthcare program for members of the uniformed services and their families).

- Individual providers such as physicians, dentists, pharmacists, and physical therapists.
- Institutional providers such as hospitals, community health centers, and skilled nursing facilities.
- Private trade associations representing providers (e.g., the American Medical Association, which represents physicians), institutions (e.g., the National Association of Community Health Centers), and industries (e.g., PhARMA, which represents the pharmaceutical industry).
- Private accreditation agencies that provide quality certifications to healthcare institutions.
- Consumers of healthcare goods and services.
- Local, state, and federal government agencies that have roles in delivering care, financing care, setting health policy, developing laws and regulations, and conducting and funding research.

In the absence of a unified system or single government program to describe, it is easiest to understand the provision of U.S. health care through the concepts of finance (how do individuals pay for health care and how are providers reimbursed for their services?), access (how do individuals access healthcare services and what barriers to access exist?), and quality (what is the quality of healthcare services that are provided and what can be done to improve the quality of care?). It is also helpful to consider the health system choices made by this country against those made by other developed countries. This chapter begins with a discussion of the concepts of finance, access, and quality and then turns to a comparative overview of how other countries have designed their healthcare systems.

HEALTHCARE FINANCE

In 2009, the United States spent $2.5 trillion on aggregate healthcare spending, the equivalent of $8,086 per person and 17.6% of the nation's Gross Domestic Product (GDP). Figure 4-1 shows present and projected national health expenditures as a percentage of GDP. This represents a 4% increase over 2008 spending, a relatively modest increase as compared to recent years.[4] Although there has been a slowdown in spending growth, national health expenditures are expected to average 6.3% growth from 2009–2019 and reach 19.6% of the GDP by 2019.[5] Put differently, come 2019, one-fifth of the nation's economy will be consumed by healthcare spending. This is nothing short of staggering.

As shown in Figure 4-2, the largest portion of national healthcare spending in 2009 was on hospital services, followed by physician and clinical services. While experts disagree about the exact cause of healthcare spending growth,

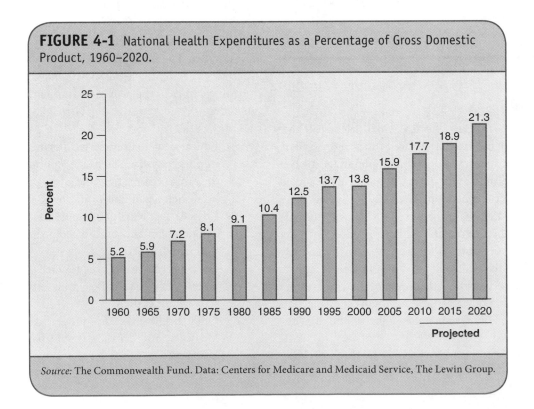

FIGURE 4-1 National Health Expenditures as a Percentage of Gross Domestic Product, 1960–2020.

Source: The Commonwealth Fund. Data: Centers for Medicare and Medicaid Service, The Lewin Group.

commonly discussed factors include spending on state-of-the-art technology and new prescription drugs, the cost of providing care for an increasing number of patients with chronic diseases, an aging population, and high administrative costs (while there is not one set definition of administrative costs, it could cover costs for marketing, billing, and medical underwriting).[6]

With many ACA provisions taking effect in 2014, healthcare spending is projected to grow by 9.2% that year. Private health expenditures are expected to increase by 12.8% in 2014, as an estimated 16 million previously uninsured people will sign up for health insurance through the new state health insurance exchanges. In addition, 22 million people are expected to enroll for the first time in Medicaid or the Children's Health Insurance Program (CHIP), resulting in projected spending growth of 17.4% for these two public programs in 2014. Medicare's annual projected growth rate is 6.2% from 2009–2019, which is lower than the other growth rates due to cost reductions brought about by the ACA. Private out-of-pocket spending is expected to decline in 2014 and then increase to 9.6% by 2018, reflecting a likely increase in patient cost-sharing as employers scale back their health plans to avoid paying taxes on high-cost insurance plans.[5]

Health Insurance

While most people in the United States have health insurance, one of the main goals of the ACA was to decrease the number of uninsured people. By 2019, it is projected that 92.7% of the population will be insured, up from the 83.3% that were insured prior to passage of the ACA.[5] Having health insurance reduces the risk of financial ruin when expensive health services are needed and often provides coverage for preventive services at low or no cost. As discussed below in the section on healthcare access, individuals without health insurance must pay for services themselves, find services provided at no cost, or go without care.

As shown in Figure 4-3, most people in the United States are privately insured and obtain their health insurance through their employer. Employer-sponsored insurance plans may be self-funded (meaning employers set aside funds to pay for their employees' health insurance claims instead of paying a premium to a health insurance carrier) or fully insured (meaning employers pay a premium to a private health insurance company to administer their plans and pay the healthcare claims of the employees). Another significant portion of the population is publically insured through Medicaid,

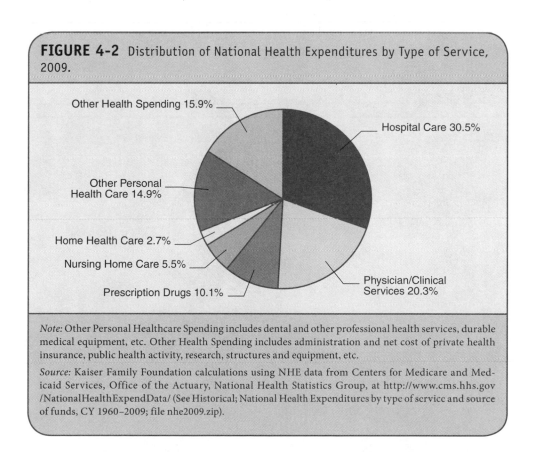

FIGURE 4-2 Distribution of National Health Expenditures by Type of Service, 2009.

Other Health Spending 15.9%

Hospital Care 30.5%

Other Personal Health Care 14.9%

Home Health Care 2.7%

Nursing Home Care 5.5%

Prescription Drugs 10.1%

Physician/Clinical Services 20.3%

Note: Other Personal Healthcare Spending includes dental and other professional health services, durable medical equipment, etc. Other Health Spending includes administration and net cost of private health insurance, public health activity, research, structures and equipment, etc.

Source: Kaiser Family Foundation calculations using NHE data from Centers for Medicare and Medicaid Services, Office of the Actuary, National Health Statistics Group, at http://www.cms.hhs.gov /NationalHealthExpendData/ (See Historical; National Health Expenditures by type of service and source of funds, CY 1960–2009; file nhe2009.zip).

CHIP, Medicare, the Veteran's Administration, and the Department of Defense. Public programs are funded and run by federal and/or state government agencies, depending on the program.

As shown in Figure 4-4, health insurers act as an intermediary between consumers (sometimes referred to as "insureds") and providers (which refers to both individual providers, such as physicians or nurses, as well as institutions, such as hospitals and community health centers). The specifics regarding eligibility for a particular insurance plan, choice of plans, how much a plan costs to enroll in or use, what benefits are covered, and how and how much providers are reimbursed varies by plan or government program. In some circumstances, providers may only accept insurance from a single plan, but often providers will accept patients from a variety of plans.

Consumers interact with health insurance companies or government programs by enrolling into an insurance plan by which they are accepted (in the case of private plans) or for which they are eligible (in the case of public programs), providing payments to the insurance plan for being enrolled (either directly or through a payroll deduction), choosing which provider to see based on plan restrictions or incentives, and working with the plan if they have questions or complaints. Providers that agree to be part of a plan's "network" (i.e., the group of providers who will see patients insured by the plan) are reimbursed a contractually agreed upon amount from the insurance company and/or the patient for providing services covered under the plan, may accept consumers who are enrolled in the plan, may be subject to plan quality-control measures, and will participate as necessary in plan appeals processes.

Direct Services Programs

In addition to providing publically funded health insurance to certain populations through programs such as Medicare and Medicaid, federal, state, and local governments also fund numerous programs that directly provide healthcare services to vulnerable populations. Many of these programs also receive private funding and donations to support their operations. Direct service programs generally exist to fill gaps in the private healthcare delivery system. Examples of these types of programs include:

- Federally Qualified Health Centers: Also known as FQHCs, these centers are located in medically underserved areas and provide primary care services to individuals on a sliding fee scale (meaning that how much one pays for services depends on the individual's income level). While anyone may use an FQHC, the health center patient population is made up of mostly uninsured and publically insured patients. Funding for health centers usually comes from the federal and state governments, and sometimes from local governments and private donations.

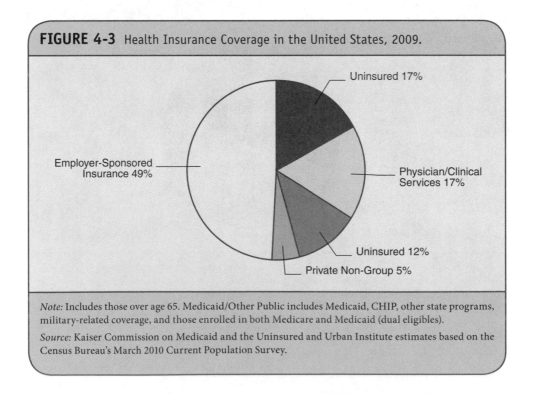

FIGURE 4-3 Health Insurance Coverage in the United States, 2009.

Uninsured 17%

Physician/Clinical Services 17%

Uninsured 12%

Private Non-Group 5%

Employer-Sponsored Insurance 49%

Note: Includes those over age 65. Medicaid/Other Public includes Medicaid, CHIP, other state programs, military-related coverage, and those enrolled in both Medicare and Medicaid (dual eligibles).

Source: Kaiser Commission on Medicaid and the Uninsured and Urban Institute estimates based on the Census Bureau's March 2010 Current Population Survey.

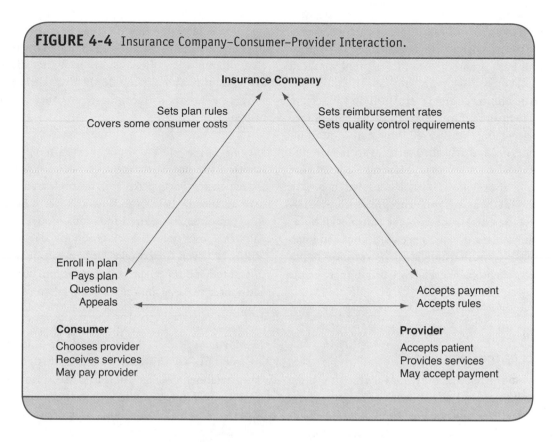

FIGURE 4-4 Insurance Company–Consumer–Provider Interaction.

- HIV/AIDS Services: The Ryan White HIV/AIDS Program works with states, cities, and local organizations to provide services to patients with HIV or AIDS who do not have health insurance coverage or the financial resources to pay for needed care. The program is federally funded and provides grants to state agencies that deliver care to patients. The Ryan White program also includes the state AIDS Drug Assistance Program (ADAP), which provides medications to low-income individuals with HIV. A supplementary ADAP for high-need states includes federal funding and a state matching requirement. In addition, states often supplement federal funding with state-funded HIV prevention and treatment programs. Some local public health departments also provide HIV testing and counseling services and help individuals' access treatment. Many programs also accept private donations.

- Family Planning Services: Title X of the Public Health Service Act provides federal funding for family planning services offered to women who do not qualify for Medicaid, maintains family planning centers, and establishes standards for providing family planning services (although federal dollars may not be used to support abortion services except in the case of rape, incest, or danger to the life of the pregnant woman).

In addition, states also fund family planning services. Services provided vary by state, but may include contraception, cervical cancer screening, tubal sterilization, STD screening, HIV testing, and abstinence counseling. State laws vary on the use of state funds for abortion services. Local health departments may also offer some of these services as well as help people access family planning services from private providers. Private donations provide revenue to many family planning clinics.

HEALTHCARE ACCESS

Access to care refers to the ability to obtain needed health services. There are a variety of factors that can hinder access to care. One important factor is lack of health insurance. Individuals without health insurance have to pay more for comparable services because they do not have the advantage of sharing costs as part of a pool of consumers. Since many individuals without health insurance are low-income, they may be unable to pay for the cost of needed care, and providers are often unwilling to accept uninsured patients because of the risk of not being paid for their services. Some providers, referred to as "safety net" providers, focus on providing care to uninsured patients, but gaining access to needed care remains a significant issue for this population. Many changes taking place in 2014 as part of ACA implementation are intended to reduce the number of uninsured people, but even so it is important to understand the healthcare problems faced by the uninsured; before 2014, many millions of individuals will continue to be uninsured and several million will remain uninsured despite health reform. Even those with insurance face barriers to accessing care, as well. This may occur if individuals are underinsured, if needed services are not covered by health insurance, if providers will not take a particular insurance plan, or if providers are not available in certain geographic area. Finally, access problems are exacerbated by provider shortages, especially in primary care fields. Many areas of the country already experience workforce shortages and the influx of newly insured individuals as a result of health reform will make this problem even more pronounced in the years to come.

The Uninsured

Characteristics of the Uninsured

There are many myths relating to the uninsured. It is often assumed that the uninsured do not work or simply choose not to purchase health insurance even though it is available

and affordable. Although this may be true in some cases, in most instances it is not. Furthermore, many people believe that all employers offer insurance or that those individuals without private insurance are always eligible for public programs. As you will see, these and other assumptions are also false.

Income Level The primary reason people do not have health insurance is financial—available coverage is simply too expensive. Forty percent of the uninsured are people who earn an income below the Federal Poverty Level (FPL) and nine out of ten uninsured individuals earn less than 400% FPL (the poverty level for a family of four was $22,050 in 2010).[7(p5)] Given the correlation between income and being uninsured, it is not surprising that the uninsured rate among the poor is twice as high as the national average, as shown in Figure 4-5.

Employment Status Over 70% of the uninsured work or are in families with workers. Among this population, most of them (about 60%) have at least one full-time worker in the family, and a much smaller proportion have only part-time workers.[7(p5)] This pattern holds true even for the very poor.

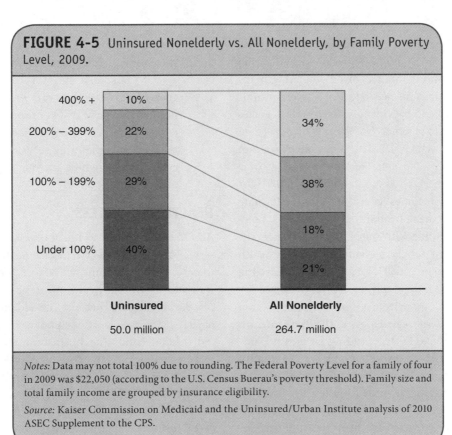

FIGURE 4-5 Uninsured Nonelderly vs. All Nonelderly, by Family Poverty Level, 2009.

	Uninsured	All Nonelderly
400% +	10%	34%
200% – 399%	22%	34%
100% – 199%	29%	38%
		18%
Under 100%	40%	21%
	50.0 million	264.7 million

Notes: Data may not total 100% due to rounding. The Federal Poverty Level for a family of four in 2009 was $22,050 (according to the U.S. Census Buerau's poverty threshold). Family size and total family income are grouped by insurance eligibility.

Source: Kaiser Commission on Medicaid and the Uninsured/Urban Institute analysis of 2010 ASEC Supplement to the CPS.

Forty percent of the poor uninsured has at least one worker in their family.[7(p1)] Workers are often uninsured because they cannot afford the cost-sharing associated with the insurance coverage offered by their employers or because they work in jobs that do not offer coverage.

From 1999 to 2009, the percentage of all companies offering health insurance declined from 66% to 60%.[8(p38)] Most employers who stop offering health insurance coverage do so because of cost, and the economic downturn between 2008 and 2010 played a major role in the decisions of many firms to drop coverage.[8(p37)] Furthermore, the unemployment rate jumped from 4.6% in 2007 to 10% in 2009, and job losses since 2008 have resulted in 6.9 million people losing their employer-sponsored coverage.[7(pp8–9),9]

Workers are more likely to be uninsured if they are employed by small firms, low-paying firms, non-unionized firms, retail/sales firms, or in the agricultural, forestry, fishing, mining, and construction sectors. In addition, self-employed individuals are often uninsured. Finally, families whose primary wage earner is a blue-collar worker are more likely to be uninsured than families whose primary wage earner is a white-collar worker.[7(p17)]

Age   Because Medicaid and CHIP provide extensive coverage to low-income children, adults are more likely to be uninsured than children. In 2009, 7.5 million children were uninsured, compared to 43.2 million adults.[10(p22–23)] Approximately 30% of young adults (ages 18–24) are uninsured, which is nearly twice the rate of the general population[10(p23)] and which represents a trend that has remained in place since the mid-1980s.[11]

As young adults transition from school to the workforce, they may become ineligible for their family's coverage for the first time, may have entry-level jobs earning too little income to afford a policy, or may work for an employer that does not offer health insurance. The ACA addresses part of this problem by requiring insurers to cover dependents (someone who relies on the primary insured for support) until age 26. Although some young adults do not consider health insurance

---

FIGURE 4-6 Characteristics of the Uninsured, 2009.

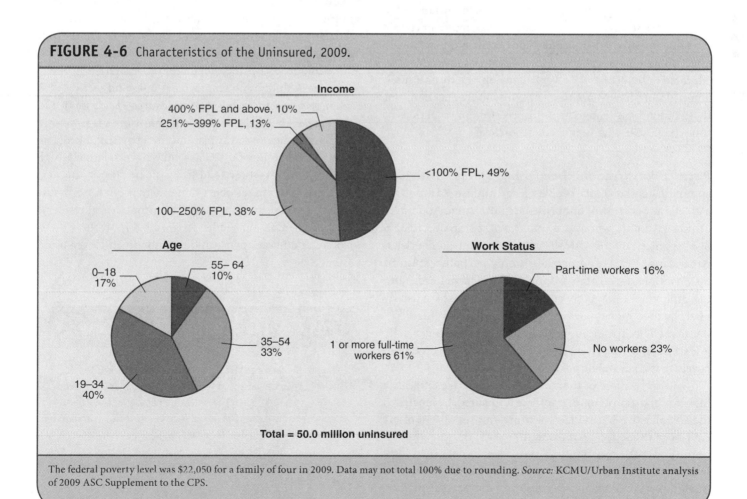

Total = 50.0 million uninsured

The federal poverty level was $22,050 for a family of four in 2009. Data may not total 100% due to rounding. *Source:* KCMU/Urban Institute analysis of 2009 ASC Supplement to the CPS.

a priority expense because they are relatively healthy, studies have shown that cost is the primary factor in whether people in this age bracket decide to obtain coverage.[11(pp73–74)]

Although adults ages 55–64 are more likely to be insured than the overall population, the 10% of uninsured who fall into this age group are a cause for concern because they are medically high-risk and often have declining incomes.[11(p72)] These adults account for two-thirds of all deaths and one-third of all hospital stays among non-elderly adults. In addition, they are more likely to report being in fair or poor health, having a chronic disease, or experiencing a disabling condition.[11(p74)] The disability provisions of Medicaid and Medicare and the availability of employer-based insurance keep the number of uninsured in this group relatively small, which is important because it would be very expensive for individuals in this demographic to purchase individual insurance policies in the private market. Figure 4-6 illustrates the characteristics of the uninsured by income, age, and work status.

Education Level   Education level is also an important factor in insurance status because it is easier, for example, for college graduates to earn higher incomes and obtain jobs that provide affordable employment-based insurance as compared to less-educated individuals.[11(p74)] Over half of non-elderly uninsured adults do not have more than a high school education, and these individuals tend to be uninsured for longer periods of time than those with higher education levels.[7(p6)]

Race, Ethnicity, and Immigrant Status   Although approximately half of the people who are uninsured are white, a greater proportion of minorities are uninsured. About 12% of non-Hispanic whites are uninsured, compared to 32% of Hispanics, 21% of African Americans, and 17% of Asian Americans.[10(p23)] This difference is only partially explained by variations in income. Minorities also have lower rates of employment-based coverage, although this is partially offset by their higher rates of public insurance coverage.[11(p83)] Because eligibility for public insurance coverage is generally less stable than for private coverage, this difference in type of coverage is a key public policy issue.[11(p89)]

Although most of the uninsured are native citizens, a higher proportion of immigrants are uninsured. Compared to the 14% of native-born citizens who are uninsured, 34% of foreign-born residents are uninsured.[10(p27)] Of the foreign-born uninsured, 19% are naturalized and 46% are noncitizens.[10(p27)] Some of the disparity in coverage rates among U.S. native and foreign-born individuals is because non-native residents have lower rates of employer-based coverage, higher rates of low-wage jobs, and higher rates of employment in sectors that are less likely to provide insurance.[7(p6)] Restrictive eligibility rules pertaining to immigrants in public programs make it difficult for non-natives to obtain public coverage and, under the ACA, undocumented immigrants are not eligible for federal subsidies to assist with purchasing health insurance through the new state exchanges.

Gender   Gender variations exist in both the rate and type of insurance coverage. In general, non-elderly men are more likely to be uninsured than non-elderly women. Yet, of those with insurance, men are more likely to have employer-based coverage and women are more likely to have public coverage, due to their lower average income level. This difference in public coverage rates is due, in large part, to the extensive coverage for low-income pregnant women under Medicaid.

Geography   Residents of the South and West are more likely to be uninsured than residents of the North and Midwest, although in 2009, the greatest increase in the number of uninsured occurred in the Midwest.[7(p7)] Similarly, there are variations in the uninsured rate from state to state. These differences are based on numerous factors including racial/ethnic composition, other population characteristics, public program eligibility, and employment rates and sectors.[11(p90)] Although a greater number of uninsured residents live in urban areas, the likelihood of being uninsured is similar in urban and rural areas. Uninsurance is a particular problem among rural residents because they have relatively high healthcare needs—they tend to be older, poorer, and less healthy than urban residents—and there is often a provider shortage in these areas. Among the insured, rural residents rely more heavily on public programs due to their lower incomes and fewer opportunities to obtain employer-based coverage.

BOX 4-1 Discussion Questions

Are the characteristics just described interrelated, or should they be addressed separately from a policy perspective? If you are trying to reduce the number of uninsured, do you believe the focus should be on altering insurance programs or changing the effect of having one or more of these characteristics? Whose responsibility is it to reduce the number of uninsured? Government? The private sector? Individuals?

BOX 4-2 Discussion Questions

The Affordable Care Act, the 2010 health reform law, made it a priority to reduce the number of uninsured. At what point, if any, should the government step in to provide individuals with assistance to purchase insurance coverage? Do you think such assistance should be a federal or state responsibility?

The Importance of Health Insurance Coverage to Health Status

Having health insurance provides tangible health benefits. For a variety of reasons discussed in this section, having health insurance increases access to care and positively affects health outcomes. Conversely, the uninsured, who do not enjoy the benefits of health insurance, are more likely to experience adverse health events and a diminished health-related quality of life, and are less likely to receive care in appropriate settings or receive the professionally accepted standard of care.[7(pp10–11)]

Health insurance is an important factor in whether someone has a "medical home," or consistent source of care. Having a consistent source of care is positively associated with better and timelier access to care, better chronic disease management, fewer emergency room visits, fewer lawsuits against emergency rooms, and increased cancer screenings for women.[12,13] Unfortunately, the uninsured are much less likely to have a usual source of care than insured individuals. Approximately 55% of the uninsured do not have a usual source of care, compared to 11% of publicly insured people and 10% of privately insured individuals.[7(p10)]

The uninsured are also less likely to follow treatment recommendations and more likely to forgo care due to concerns about cost[7(p10)] (see Figure 4-7). In addition, the uninsured are less likely to receive preventive care and appropriate routine care for chronic conditions.[7,9(p11)] One result of this is that children without insurance are more likely to have developmental delays, often leading to difficulties in education and employment. Also, quality of life may be lower for the uninsured due to their lower health status and anxiety about both monetary and medical problems.

Since the uninsured are less likely to obtain preventive care or treatment for specific conditions, they have a higher mortality rate overall, have a higher in-hospital mortality rate, and are more likely to be hospitalized for avoidable health problems.[7(p11)] Of course, without regular access to care, it is less likely that a disease will be detected early when treatment may be cheaper and more effective. For example, uninsured

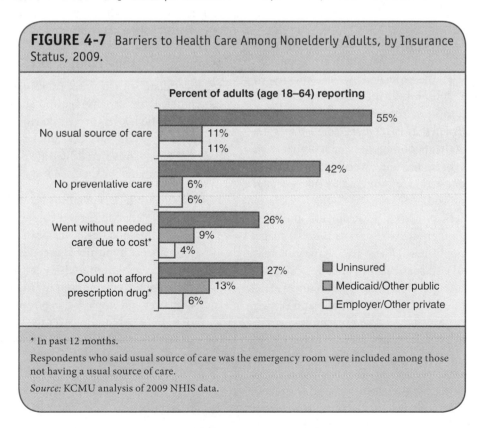

FIGURE 4-7 Barriers to Health Care Among Nonelderly Adults, by Insurance Status, 2009.

* In past 12 months.

Respondents who said usual source of care was the emergency room were included among those not having a usual source of care.

Source: KCMU analysis of 2009 NHIS data.

cancer patients are diagnosed at later stages of the disease and die earlier than insured cancer patients.[14(p3)] Studies have estimated that overall, having health insurance could reduce mortality rates for the uninsured by 10–15%, resulting in 18,000 fewer deaths per year.[14(p3)]

Ways to Assess the Cost of Being Uninsured

There are several ways to think about the costs of being uninsured. These costs include the health status costs to the uninsured individual, as discussed above; financial cost to the uninsured individual; financial cost to state and federal governments and to private insurers; financial cost to providers; productivity costs from lost work time due to illness; and costs to other public priorities that cannot be funded because of the resources spent on providing care to the uninsured.

The financial burden of being uninsured is significant. Although on average the uninsured spend fewer dollars on health care than the insured, those without insurance spend a greater proportion of their overall income on medical needs. Furthermore, when the uninsured receive care, it is often more expensive because the uninsured are not receiving care as part of an insurance pool with leverage to negotiate lower rates from providers. Given their lower income, relatively high healthcare expenses, and competing needs, those without insurance are three times as likely as the insured to find basic necessities unaffordable due to medical bills they have accumulated.[7(p12)]

Costs of medical care provided by, but not fully reimbursed to, health professionals are referred to as uncompensated care costs. In 2008, it was estimated that uncompensated care costs reached $57 billion in this country, with federal, state, and local spending covering 75% of the tab, mostly through "disproportionate share payments" to hospitals. Although hospitals provide about 60% of all uncompensated care services and receive significant government assistance, most of the uncompensated care provided by non-hospital physicians is not subsidized.[7(p14)]

Every dollar spent by providers, governments, and communities to cover uncompensated care costs is a dollar that is not spent on another public need. There are a variety of high-cost public health needs, such as battling infectious diseases like tuberculosis, engaging in emergency preparedness planning, and promoting healthy behaviors. Public and private funds used to cover uncompensated care, especially when the care is more expensive than necessary because of the lack of preventive care or early interventions, are resources that are no longer available to meet the country's other health needs.

One final cost associated with the uninsured is the cost of lower productivity. This refers to the reduced productivity

in the workforce stemming from the lower health status associated with being uninsured. Productivity may be reduced when workers are absent or when they are not functioning at their highest level due to illness. In addition, several studies show that providing health insurance helps employers recruit better employees and that workers with health insurance are less likely to change jobs, reducing the costs of hiring and training new employees.[15]

The Underinsured

An estimated 25 million individuals have insurance but are considered "underinsured," a figure that increased 60% from 2003 to 2007.[16] While there are disagreements about how to measure the underinsured, in general being underinsured means individuals do not have the financial means to cover the gap between what their insurance coverage pays for and the total cost of their medical bills. This problem is exacerbated during a recession when more individuals cannot afford to pay their deductibles and co-payments. Like the uninsured, the underinsured may delay care or forgo treatment due to cost. Everyone ends up paying for the underinsured. Providers attempt to shift the cost associated with the underinsured and uninsured to others who can afford to pay, including the government and insured individuals. Institutions such as hospitals may try to negotiate higher reimbursement for their services, which leads insurers to charge higher premiums to their clients to cover the additional costs.

Insurance Coverage Limitations

Even individuals with insurance coverage may face healthcare access problems due to coverage limitations. These limitations could include high levels of cost-sharing, reimbursement and visit caps for specific services, and service exclusions. (Another problem—annual and lifetime dollar limits on coverage—was eliminated by the ACA).

Cost-Sharing: A typical insurance plan includes premiums, deductibles, and co-payments (the latter can also be designed as co-insurance). A premium is an annual cost, typically charged monthly, for enrolling in a plan. For those with health insurance through their employer, the premium is often split between employer and employee. Figure 4-8 shows the increase in monthly premiums over the last decade. A deductible is an amount the insured pays out-of-pocket before the insurance plan assists with the costs of healthcare services. There may be an annual deductible for the plan overall or separate deductibles for different types of services covered by the plan, such as in-patient care, out-patient care, and prescription drug coverage. Co-payments refer to a specific dollar amount that patients pay when they receive services or drugs. For example, one might have a $15 co-payment to see a primary care provider for an office visit. Co-insurance refers to a percentage of service cost that patients pay when they receive services or drugs. For example, an insured might have a 20% co-insurance requirement to see a primary care provider for an office visit. If the visit cost $150, a 20% co-insurance requirement would cost $30. Co-payment and co-insurance amounts may vary depending on the service received.

Cost-sharing requirements can vary widely by plan and plan type. Some plans do not have general deductibles, and for those with general deductibles the amount varies significantly. For example, in 2010 the average deductible for a single worker in a high-deductible health plan was $1,093, while the average for a single worker in a Health Maintenance Organization plan was $610.[8(p98)] An increasing number of plans have deductibles of $1,000 or more (see Figure 4-9).

Variation also exists for service-specific deductibles. For the few private plans with an in-patient hospital deductible, the average amount is $723.[8(p.101)] Medicare, on

the other hand, charged a $1,132 deductible for the first 60 days of hospitalization in 2011. Most private insurance plans have a cost-sharing arrangement for hospital admissions—either a co-payment, co-insurance, or a per day fee. On average, private plans charge 18% for co-insurance, a $232 co-payment per admission, or $228 per day for hospital admissions.[8(p.101)] Medicare beneficiaries do not pay a per diem for the first 60 days in a hospital, but then pay $283 per day for the next three months.[17] This fee increases for longer stays.

Reimbursement and Visit Caps: Insurance plans may limit the amount they will reimburse for a specific service during the year, with patients responsible for costs that exceed dollar amount limits. In addition, plans may limit the number of times a patient may see a certain type of provider during the year. Visit caps vary by insurance plan. For example, the Blue Cross Blue Shield Standard PPO option for the Federal Employee Health Benefit Plan (FEHBP) limits physical, occupational, and speech therapy to 75 visits per year and chiropractic services to one office visit and 12 spinal manipulations per year.[18] The Kaiser Permanente Standard HMO option for the FEHBP limits annual outpatient physical therapy to 30 office

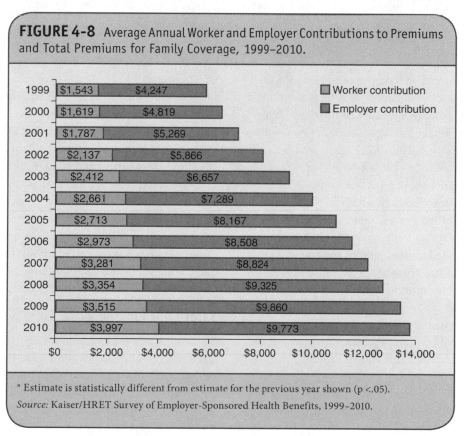

FIGURE 4-8 Average Annual Worker and Employer Contributions to Premiums and Total Premiums for Family Coverage, 1999–2010.

* Estimate is statistically different from estimate for the previous year shown (p <.05).
Source: Kaiser/HRET Survey of Employer-Sponsored Health Benefits, 1999–2010.

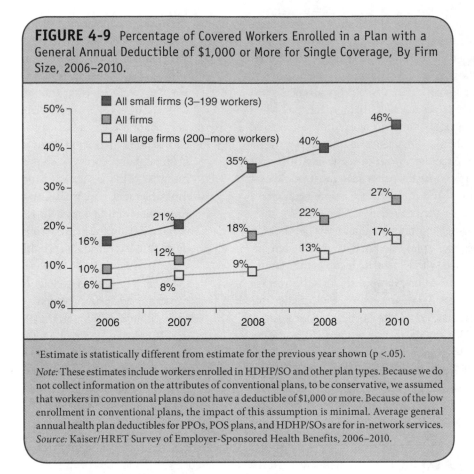

FIGURE 4-9 Percentage of Covered Workers Enrolled in a Plan with a General Annual Deductible of $1,000 or More for Single Coverage, By Firm Size, 2006–2010.

*Estimate is statistically different from estimate for the previous year shown (p <.05).

Note: These estimates include workers enrolled in HDHP/SO and other plan types. Because we do not collect information on the attributes of conventional plans, to be conservative, we assumed that workers in conventional plans do not have a deductible of $1,000 or more. Because of the low enrollment in conventional plans, the impact of this assumption is minimal. Average general annual health plan deductibles for PPOs, POS plans, and HDHP/SOs are for in-network services.
Source: Kaiser/HRET Survey of Employer-Sponsored Health Benefits, 2006–2010.

visits or 60 consecutive days per condition, outpatient speech therapy to 90 consecutive days per condition, and skilled nursing facility care to 100 days.[19] Once a patient reaches these limits, the insurance plan will not cover additional visits and the patient would have to pay the entire cost of a visit out-of-pocket.

Service Exclusions: Health insurance plans may also partially or fully exclude certain types of services from coverage altogether. For example, the Kaiser FEHBP Standard HMO plan only covers high-dose chemotherapy associated with bone marrow transplants for specified organ and tissue transplants and covers surgical treatment for morbid obesity only if certain conditions are met. Examples of services not covered at all by the plan include: long-term, cognitive, or vocational rehabilitative therapy; cosmetic surgery; private duty hospice nursing; and transportation other than by ambulance.[19]

Coverage for abortion and family planning services is also limited in many instances. Federal funds may be used for

abortion services only in cases of rape, incest, or to save the life of the pregnant woman, and four states limit private plan abortion coverage to cases when the woman's life would be in danger if the pregnancy were carried to term.[20] As of January 2011, 28 states required insurance plans to cover the full range of contraceptive drugs, but 20 of those states exempted select employers and insurers and two states excluded emergency contraception from the mandate.[21] Since the ACA was passed, 15 states have enacted legislation barring abortion coverage by plans in their state exchange.[22] As discussed in more detail elsewhere, abortion coverage remains limited under the ACA and it is not yet clear what requirements, if any, plans will have to follow regarding contraceptive coverage.

Safety Net Providers

Securing access to care can be difficult for those without comprehensive private insurance. For the uninsured, the high cost of care is often a deterrent to seeking care. For those with public coverage, it is often difficult to find a provider willing to accept their insurance due to the low reimbursement rates and administrative burdens associated with participating in these programs. For these patients and the underinsured, the "healthcare safety net" exists.

The healthcare safety net refers to providers who serve disproportionately high numbers of uninsured, underinsured, and publicly insured patients. Although there is no formal designation indicating that one is a safety net provider, the Institute of Medicine (IOM) defines the healthcare safety net as "[t]hose providers that organize and deliver a significant level of health care and other related services to uninsured, Medicaid, and other vulnerable populations."[23(p21)] According to the IOM, "core" safety net providers are those who serve vulnerable populations and have a policy of providing services regardless of patients' ability to pay.[23(p21)] Some safety net providers have a legal requirement to provide care to the underserved, while others do so as a matter of principle.

Who are safety net providers? It is a difficult question to answer because there is no true safety net "system." Safety net providers can be anyone or any entity providing health care to the uninsured and other vulnerable populations, whether community or teaching hospitals, private health professionals, school-based health clinics, or others. Those providers that fit the narrower definition of "core" safety net providers include some public and private hospitals, community health centers, family planning clinics, and public health agencies that have a mission to provide access to care for vulnerable populations. Safety net provider patient loads are mostly composed of people who are poor, on Medicaid, or uninsured, and are members of racial and ethnic minority groups. For example, in 2009, 92% of health center patients had incomes at or below 200% FPL, 75% were on Medicaid or uninsured, and 60% were racial or ethnic minorities.[24,25] Of the National Association of Public Hospital (NAPH) member hospital patients, in 2009, 57% were on Medicaid or uninsured and 58% were racial or ethnic minorities.[26]

Community health centers provide comprehensive primary medical care services, culturally sensitive care, and enabling services such as transportation, outreach, and translation that make it easier for patients to access services. Many health centers also provide dental, mental health, and pharmacy services. Because health centers are not focused on specialty care, public hospitals are often the sole source of specialty care for uninsured and underserved populations.[25(p4)] In addition, public hospitals provide traditional healthcare services, diagnostic services, outpatient pharmacies, and highly specialized trauma care, burn care, and emergency services.[25(p2)] Although not all local government health departments provide direct care, many do. Local health departments often specialize in caring for specific populations, such as individuals with HIV or drug dependency, as compared

to public hospitals and health centers, which provide a wider range of services.[23(pp63-65)]

Safety net providers receive funding from a variety of sources, but they often struggle financially. Medicaid is the single largest funding stream for both public hospitals and health centers, accounting for over one-third of their revenue.[24,25] Federal grants to health centers are intended to cover the cost of caring for the uninsured; however, this grant funding has not kept pace with the cost of provided care. In 2007, federal dollars paid for only 48% of the cost of treating the uninsured, a decrease of 10% since 2001.[7(p15)] In addition, payment from private insurance is unreliable due to the high-cost-sharing plans held by many privately insured, low-income individuals. Furthermore, Medicare payments to health centers are capped under federal law at an amount that does not match the growth in healthcare spending.

Public hospitals face a similarly difficult economic picture. Many public hospital services are not fully reimbursed because payments made by individuals or insurers do not match the cost of care. Even though NAPH members accounted for only 2% of the nation's acute care hospitals in 2009, they delivered 20% of the uncompensated care provided by hospitals that year.[26(pxi)] Like health centers, public hospitals receive funds to cover low-income patients, including Medicaid disproportionate share payments (DSH), state and local subsidies, and other revenues such as sales tax and tobacco settlement funds.[25] In 2009, DSH payments accounted for 22% of NAPH members' uncompensated care costs, but these payments were reduced under health reform.[26(pxi)] State and local payments covered 33% of their uncompensated care costs, but the budget deficits faced by many states are likely to result in fewer funds provided to public hospitals.[26(pxi)]

For all the positive work accomplished by safety net providers, they cannot solve all healthcare problems for vulnerable populations. Safety net patients may lack continuity of care, whether because they cannot see the same provider at each visit or because they have to go to numerous sites or through various programs to receive all the care they need. Even though safety net providers serve millions of patients every year, there are not enough providers in enough places to satisfy the need for their services. While the ACA included an infusion of funds to safety net providers, they also will serve an influx of newly insured patients. Health centers received $11 billion under the ACA and expect to double their patient load to 40 million people by 2015.[27] And, as noted earlier, many safety net providers are underfunded and constantly struggling to meet the complex needs of their patient population.

The problems facing the uninsured and the stressors on the healthcare safety net highlight the inadequacies of the current "system" of providing health care, and many of these problems will remain even after the ACA is implemented. Given the country's patchwork of programs and plans, decisions made in one area can significantly affect another. For example, if Medicaid reimbursement rates are cut or program eligibility is reduced, safety net providers will have a difficult time keeping their doors open while, simultaneously, more patients will become uninsured and seek care from safety net providers. If more people choose high-deductible private insurance plans that they cannot easily afford, individuals may go without needed services or safety net providers will end up providing an increasing amount of uncompensated care. If employers decide to reduce or end coverage or increase employee cost-sharing, previously insured people may fall into the ranks of the uninsured. As a result, safety net providers and their patients are affected by many policies that are not directed at them, but still greatly impact their ability to provide or access care.

Workforce Issues

Problems accessing care may also occur due to provider shortages and an uneven distribution of providers throughout the country. This problem affects both the uninsured and the insured alike. If a provider is not available to take you as a patient, it matters little if you have an insurance plan that would cover the cost of your care. Of course, if a provider shortage is so great that those with insurance are turned away, the uninsured will have an even harder time accessing care.

Overall, it is estimated that this country will have 200,000 fewer physicians and 1 million fewer nurses than necessary by 2020. Already the nursing shortage has reached 400,000, with many unfilled jobs in nursing homes and hospitals. Reducing

BOX 4-3 Discussion Questions

Safety net providers mostly serve uninsured and publicly insured low-income patients. Many of the safety net provider features you just read about are in place to assist these patients in accessing health care. Instead of pursuing universal coverage, would it be an equally good strategy to expand the number of safety net providers? Are there reasons for both safety net providers and health insurance to exist? How does having insurance relate to accessing care?

the number of uninsured will exacerbate the provider shortage because people are more likely to seek care when they have insurance. For example, demand for physician services would be expected to rise by 25% if universal coverage were achieved.[28]

One of the main concerns with the healthcare workforce is a shortage of primary care providers. Sixty million people are already "medically disenfranchised," meaning they lack adequate access to primary care due to a provider shortages.[29] In 2008, only 35% of physicians and 37% of physician assistants practiced primary care. Only half of the advanced nurse practitioners work in an ambulatory care setting, and not all of them are in the primary care field.[30] These shortages reflect a waning desire among medical and nursing students to become primary care providers; between 1997 and 2005, graduates of programs in the United States choosing a primary care residency dropped by 50%.[31] The long work hours, increased demands (particularly administrative demands associated with insurance companies), and comparatively low pay for primary care providers are sending future practitioners to other fields (see Figure 4-10). For example, one study showed that, over a lifetime, a cardiologist will make $2.7 million more than a primary care physician.[32] An increasing number of graduates are going into specialty fields, accounting for three-quarters of the growth in total per capita physicians from 1980–1999.[33(p15)]

While fewer graduates are turning to primary care, demand for primary care services is expected to increase in the next several years. Prior to the passage of the ACA, it was estimated that the United States would already have 21,000 fewer primary care physicians than necessary by 2015.[34] The primary care shortage is expected to increase after the ACA is implemented, as it is estimated to add 32 million newly insured individuals who are likely to seek care.

Furthermore, the population is aging, with the population over age 65 projected to increase from 13% in 2010 to 20% in 2020.[35] Elderly patients are heavy users of healthcare services. Even though older patients made up about 12% of the population in 2008, they accounted for over 45% of all primary care office visits that year.[36] Furthermore, geriatric training is lacking among primary care providers. Only 3 of the top 145 medical schools have a full geriatric department and less than 3% of all medical students take at least one class in geriatrics.[37]

In addition to provider shortages, access problems may exist because providers are not distributed evenly throughout the country. For example, many states have a poor distribution of children's doctors. Nearly one million children live in areas without local doctors, with Mississippi having the

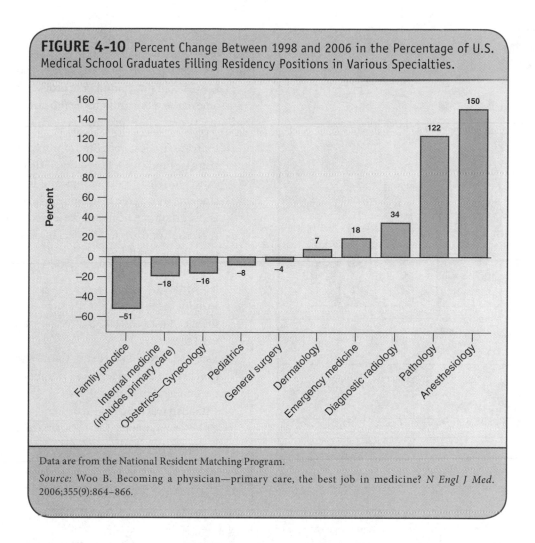

FIGURE 4-10 Percent Change Between 1998 and 2006 in the Percentage of U.S. Medical School Graduates Filling Residency Positions in Various Specialties.

Data are from the National Resident Matching Program.

Source: Woo B. Becoming a physician—primary care, the best job in medicine? *N Engl J Med.* 2006;355(9):864–866.

highest percentage of children (42%) in low-supply areas. States as diverse as Arkansas, Oklahoma, Maine, and Idaho also have many children without adequate access to primary care. Conversely, Washington, DC and Delaware have no children in low-supply areas and Maryland, Wisconsin, and Washington state generally have very few children who could not gain access to a pediatrician.[38]

As shown in Figures 4-11 and 4-12, rural areas are particularly susceptible to provider shortages, which is a pressing problem because individuals who live in rural areas are more likely to be sicker, older, and poorer than their urban counterparts. While 19% of the population lives in rural areas, only 11% of physicians practice in those parts of the country. Family practice doctors are the ones most likely to practice in rural areas, accounting for two-thirds of the physicians in smaller rural locales.[39] Rural areas also have a shortage of other types of providers such as dentists, registered nurses,

nurse practitioners, and physician assistants, who are key to providing primary care services.[40,41] The high vacancy rates for various positions in community health centers, which are located in medically underserved areas, illustrate the workforce problem facing many communities.

Shortages also exist within the public health workforce. The public health workforce has been defined to include anyone who is providing one of the 10 essential public health functions, regardless of whether their employer is a government agency, not-for-profit organization, private for-profit entity, or some other type of organization.[42] The public health workforce includes professions such as public health physicians and nurses, epidemiologists, health educators, and administrators. This workforce has been shrinking and about one-quarter of the public health workforce employed by the government is eligible to retire in 2012. It is estimated that by 2020, the United States will have a shortfall of 250,000 public

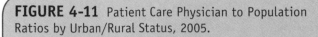

FIGURE 4-11 Patient Care Physician to Population Ratios by Urban/Rural Status, 2005.

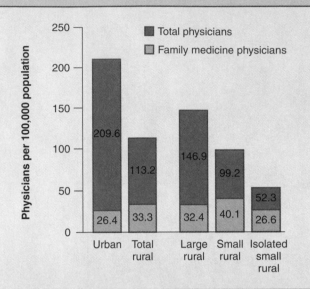

Source: Rosenblatt RA, Frederick MC, Lishner DM, Doescher MP. *The future of family medicine and implications for rural primary care physician supply.* 2010. WWAMI Rural Health Research Center. Available at http://depts.washington.edu/uwrhrc/uploads/RHRC%20FR125%20Rosenblatt.pdf.

health workers, and schools of public health would have to train three times as many public health students as normal from 2008–2019 to prevent a shortage of this magnitude.[43]

The ACA contains a number of provisions intended to address some of the more pressing healthcare and public health workforce issues. These provisions:

- Increase funding for community health centers.
- Increase funding for the National Health Service Corps, which provides scholarships and loan repayments to students who agree to become primary care providers and work in medically underserved communities.
- Increase funding for physician assistant and nurse practitioner training.
- Provide new funding to establish nurse-practitioner-led clinics.
- Provide new funding for states to plan and implement innovative strategies to boost their primary care workforce.
- Establish a National Health Care Workforce Commission to coordinate federal workforce efforts and bolster data collection and analysis.
- Establish teaching health centers.
- Provide payments for primary care residencies in community-based ambulatory care centers.

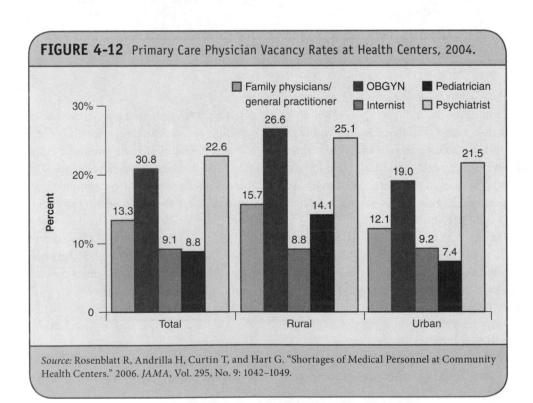

FIGURE 4-12 Primary Care Physician Vacancy Rates at Health Centers, 2004.

Source: Rosenblatt R, Andrilla H, Curtin T, and Hart G. "Shortages of Medical Personnel at Community Health Centers." 2006. *JAMA*, Vol. 295, No. 9: 1042–1049.

- increase the number of Graduate Medical Education slots available to primary providers by redistributing unused slots.
- promote residency training in outpatient settings;
- provide grants to training institutions to promote careers in the healthcare sector; and
- increase reimbursement for primary care providers under Medicare and Medicaid.

HEALTHCARE QUALITY

It is well documented that the United States spends more on health care than most other developed countries (the $8,086 per person spending in the United States is more than two-and-a-half times the average of other developed countries),[44] yet frequently the care provided does not result in good health outcomes. While the United States does some things very well, such as screening for and treating cancer, the country lags on measures relating to primary care services. For example, the United States ranked 30th in infant mortality in 2005, the last year such rankings were available, and has much higher hospital admission rates for complications due to asthma and diabetes as compared to other developed countries.[44,45]

Researchers and policymakers have highlighted the need to improve the quality of care provided in this country. A 2003 landmark study raised many quality concerns, including findings that patients only received the appropriate medical care 55% of the time and that patients were much more likely not to receive appropriate services than to receive potentially harmful care.[46] The lack of appropriate care was seen across medical conditions, similarly affecting treatments relating to preventive care, acute care, and for chronic diseases.[46(p2641)] The degree to which patients received appropriate care varied greatly. For example, only 10% of patients with alcohol dependence received the standard of care, as opposed to 78% of those with senile cataracts.[46(2641)]

In 2001, the Institute of Medicine (IOM) released *Crossing the Quality Chasm: A New Health System for the 21st Century*, which represented nothing less than an urgent call to redesign the healthcare system to improve the quality of care provided.[47] The IOM attributes our inability to provide consistent, high-quality health care to a number of factors, including: the growing complexity of health care, including quickly developing technological advancements; an inability to meet rapid changes; shortcomings in safely using new technology and applying new knowledge to practice; increased longevity among the population, which carries concerns relating to treating chronic conditions in a system better designed to address episodic, acute care needs; and a fragmented delivery system that lacks coordination, leading to poor use of information and gaps in care.[47(pp2–4)] In its call to redesign the healthcare system to improve quality, the IOM focuses on six areas of improvement: safety, efficacy, patient-centeredness, timeliness, efficiency, and equity.[47(p43)]

Safety. In a safe healthcare system, patients should not be endangered when receiving care that is intended to help them, and healthcare workers should not be harmed by their chosen profession.[47(p44)] In an earlier report, *To Err is Human*, the IOM found that deaths due to medical errors in hospitals could be as high as 98,000 annually and cost up to $29 billion, over half of which is attributable to healthcare costs.[48(pp1–2)] A safe healthcare system also means that standards of care should not decline at different times of the day or week or when a patient is transferred from one provider to another. In addition, safety requires that patients and their families are fully informed and participate in their care to the extent they wish to do so.[47(p45)]

Efficacy. While scientific evidence regarding a particular treatment's effectiveness is not always available, an effective healthcare system should use evidence-based treatments whenever possible. This includes avoiding the underuse of effective care and the overuse of ineffective care.[47(p47)] Evidence-based medicine is not limited to findings from randomized clinical trials, but may use results from a variety of research designs. To promote the use of evidenced-based medicine, healthcare providers and institutions should improve their data collection and analysis capabilities so it is possible to monitor results of care provided.[47(p48)]

Patient-Centeredness. A patient-centered healthcare system is sensitive to the needs, values, and preferences of each patient, includes smooth transitions and close coordination among providers, provides complete information and education at a level and in a language patients can understand, involves the patient's family and friends according to the patient's wishes and, to the extent possible, reduces physical discomfort experienced by patients during care.[47(pp49–50)] A language or cultural barrier may be a significant hurdle to receiving high quality and patient-centered care. One in six Americans speak a language other than English at home.[49] Individuals with language barriers are less likely to adhere to medication regimes, have a usual source of care, and understand their diagnosis and treatment, and are more likely to leave a hospital against a provider's advice and miss follow-up appointments. While use of interpreters can improve a patient's quality of care, when friends or family members serve as interpreters, there is greater risk that the interpreter will misunderstand or omit a provider's questions, and that embarrassing symptoms will be omitted by the patient.[49(p2)] Similarly, cultural differences between provider and patient can result in patients receiving less than optimal care. Cultural differences can define how healthcare information is received, whether a problem is perceived as a healthcare issue, how patients express symptoms and concerns, and what type of treatment is most appropriate. As a result, healthcare organizations should ensure that patients receive care that is both linguistically and culturally appropriate.[50]

Timeliness. A high-quality healthcare system will provide care in a timely manner. Currently, U.S. patients experience long waits when making appointments, sitting in doctors' offices, standing in hallways before receiving procedures, waiting for test results, seeking care at Emergency Departments, and appealing billing errors.[47(p51)] These can take an emotional as well as physical toll if medical problems would have been caught earlier with more timely care. Timeliness problems also affect providers because of difficulties in obtaining vital information and delays that result when consulting specialists. In addition, lengthy waits are the result of a system that is not efficient and does not respect the needs of its consumers.[47(p51)]

Efficiency. An efficient healthcare system makes the best use of its resources and obtains the most value per dollar spent on healthcare goods and services. The uncoordinated and fragmented U.S. system is wasteful when it provides low quality care and creates higher than necessary administrative and production costs.[47(p52)] As indicated previously, the high level of spending and poor outcomes relating to preventable conditions,

---

BOX 4-5 Discussion Questions

Unfortunately, evidence is not available to support the effectiveness or cost–benefit of every procedure or drug. How should policymakers and providers make decisions when faced with a dearth of evidence? Do you prefer a more cautious approach that does not approve procedures or drugs until evidence is available or a more aggressive approach that encourages experimentation and use of treatments that appear to be effective? What about medical care for children, who are generally excluded from clinical and research trials for ethical reasons? When, if ever, is it appropriate for insurers to cover or the government to pay for treatments that are not proven effective?

---

the number of patients who do not receive appropriate care, and the high number of medical errors make it clear that the quality of healthcare services provided can be improved.

In addition, significant geographic variations in the provision of healthcare services suggest a lack of efficiency in the system; however, this is a complicated issue to understand and solve. For example, the Dartmouth Atlas Project has studied regional variations in healthcare practices and spending for several decades. Even after controlling for level of illness and prices paid for services, researchers have found a two-fold difference in Medicare spending in the country.

Furthermore, higher spending areas are not associated with better quality of care, more patient satisfaction, better access to care, more effective care, or improved outcomes.[51] Instead, both health system capacity and local practice styles appear to be key factors in geographic variations in cost. In one study, other researchers found that expenses associated with high-cost beneficiaries were related to their health needs, rather than physician-, practice-, or market-related factors.[52] Even so, there was a modest association between less fragmented markets and lower costs, and between a higher concentration of for-profit providers and higher costs.[52(p21)] In addition, geographic variation was difficult to assess because 20% of Medicare beneficiaries receive care across census divisions and those patients were often high-cost beneficiaries.[52(p20)] As policymakers try to improve quality of care in the United States, they will have to untangle difficult questions of why some parts of the country spend more on services than others.

The nation also spends close to one-third of healthcare expenditures on administration.[53] As shown in Figure 4-13, this high level of administrative spending dwarfs that of other countries.[54(p934)] Extensive use of private insurers, who often have high administrative costs relative to public insurance programs, as well as the use of multiple insurers instead of a single-payer system, result in high administrative costs in the United States.

Equity. An equitable healthcare system provides essential health benefits to all people and includes universal access to care. Equity can be considered on an individual level and on a population level.[47(p53)] While the ACA should improve individual access to services by reducing the number of uninsured, insurance alone is not sufficient to ensure access to care. The care itself still must be accessible (providers are willing to accept you as a patient), affordable, and available (sufficient providers are available). Population-level equity refers to reducing healthcare disparities among subgroups. In the United States, racial and ethnic minority groups generally receive lower quality care and fewer routine preventive procedures than white people. African-Americans are less likely than whites to receive appropriate cardiac medication, undergo necessary artery bypass surgery, and use dialysis or receive a kidney transplant even when controlling for factors such as age, insurance status, income level, and co-morbidities. Not surprisingly, African-Americans also have higher mortality rates than their white counterparts.[55(pp2–3)] Hispanics experience similar disparities. As compared to white Americans, Hispanics are more likely to be uninsured, have late or no prenatal care, and suffer from stroke, obesity, chronic liver disease, diabetes, asthma, and certain cancers.[56,57]

The IOM has called for sweeping changes to the healthcare system to address the numerous ways in which the quality of care could be improved. While the ACA makes significant changes to the healthcare system, the law is focused more on improving access than quality or the delivery system. Many of the law's quality improvement provisions are pilot programs and demonstration projects that may eventually result in significant changes—or fall to the wayside once they expire. None of the quality improvements tasks the IOM calls for will be simple to achieve and, at times, they seem to have conflicting goals. For example, making the healthcare system patient-centered may not always result in enhanced efficiency. Furthermore, the IOM's proposed changes would require increased resources at a time when the United States is

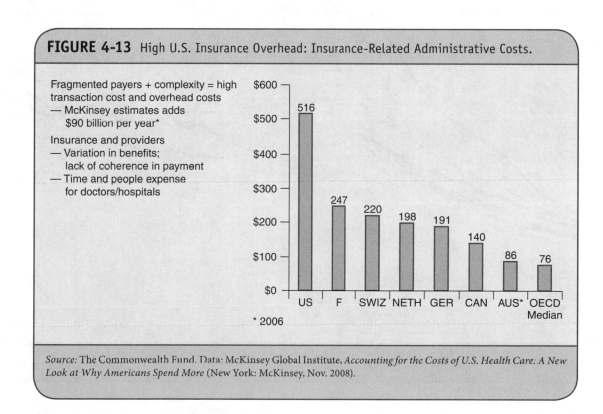

FIGURE 4-13 High U.S. Insurance Overhead: Insurance-Related Administrative Costs.

Fragmented payers + complexity = high transaction cost and overhead costs
— McKinsey estimates adds $90 billion per year*

Insurance and providers
— Variation in benefits; lack of coherence in payment
— Time and people expense for doctors/hospitals

US 516
F 247
SWIZ 220
NETH 198
GER 191
CAN 140
AUS* 86
OECD Median 76

* 2006

Source: The Commonwealth Fund. Data: McKinsey Global Institute, *Accounting for the Costs of U.S. Health Care: A New Look at Why Americans Spend More* (New York: McKinsey, Nov. 2008).

facing record deficits and unsustainable healthcare spending levels. Improving the quality of the healthcare system is an enormous challenge and one that is likely to be on the nation's agenda for years to come.

COMPARATIVE HEALTH SYSTEMS

A review of the U.S. healthcare system and a discussion of its flaws often leads one to ask: How do other countries deliver health care and do they do a better job? Since the United States spends more overall and more per person on health care comparatively speaking, perhaps there are lessons to learn from other countries (see Figure 4-14). While there are many problems with healthcare delivery in the United States, it is also true that each type of healthcare system has its advantages and drawbacks.

There are three types of healthcare systems often found in other countries: (1) a national health insurance system which is publically financed, but in which care is provided by private practitioners (e.g., Canada); (2) a national health system which is publically financed and where care is provided by government employees or contractors (e.g., Great Britain); and (3) a socialized insurance system that is financed through mandatory contributions by employers and employees and in which care is delivered by private practitioners (e.g., Germany).[58(p22)] Of course, variations exist within these types of systems in terms of the role of the central government, the presence of private insurance, the way the healthcare system is financed, and how care is administered by providers and accessed by patients. While comparing the systems in the three countries used as examples above does not cover all

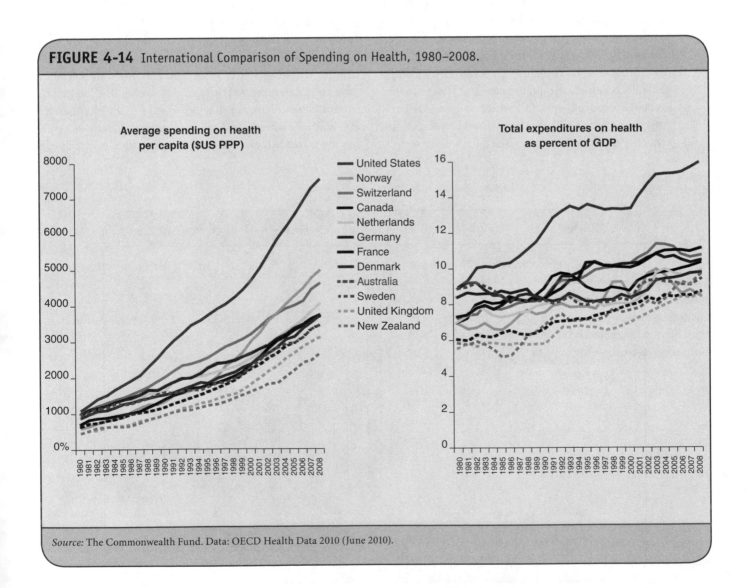

FIGURE 4-14 International Comparison of Spending on Health, 1980–2008.

Source: The Commonwealth Fund. Data: OECD Health Data 2010 (June 2010).

TABLE 4-1 A Comparison of Health Systems Across Four Countries

	United States	Canada	Great Britain	Germany
System Type	No unified system	National health insurance	National health system	Socialized health insurance
Universal Coverage	Near universal after ACA implemented	Yes	Yes	Yes
Role of Private Insurance	Significant	Supplemental to Medicare	Minimal	Minimal
Financing	Private payments and tax revenue	Mostly tax revenue (federal, provincial, territorial)	All federal income tax revenue	Mandatory employer and employee contributions to national health fund
Hospital Reimbursement	Varies by payor (DRG[a], FFS[b], capitation, per diem)	Global budget	Global budget	DRG
Physician Reimbursement	Fee schedule or capitation	Negotiated fees with provinces/territories	Salary or capitation	Negotiated fees with funds

a = Diagnostic Related Group (payment based on bundle of services needed for diagnosis)
b = Fee For Service (payment per service rendered)

possible permutations of how healthcare systems are designed, it provides an overview of the choices made by policy makers in different countries (see Table 4-1).

A National Health Insurance System: Canada

Canada's healthcare system is called Medicare. Prior to establishing the Medicare program in 1968, Canada provided insurance in a manner that was similar to the United States, with private plans offering coverage to many, even while millions remained uninsured. Incremental changes were made to the Canadian healthcare system until the Medical Care Act of 1968 established Medicare's framework. The act included three primary changes to the healthcare system: (1) universal insurance coverage with medically necessary services provided free of charge; (2) a central regulatory authority overseeing hospitals; and (3) governmental power to negotiate reimbursement rates for physicians.

Canada's healthcare system is largely decentralized, with Canada's provinces and territories responsible for setting up their own delivery system. As such, Canada's Medicare system is a collection of single-payer systems governed by the provinces and territories, with the central government

taking a more limited role. The provinces and territories set their own policies regarding many healthcare and other social issues, administer their own individual single-payer systems, reimburse hospitals directly or through regional health authorities, and negotiate physician fees schedules with provincial medical associations. Provinces and territories use regional health authorities as their primary payor of healthcare services. While funding methods vary by location, regional health authorities have the ability to tailor funds in a way that best serves the needs of their population. The federal government has responsibility for specific health areas such as prescription drugs, public health, and health research, as well as for providing care to certain populations (e.g., veterans and indigenous peoples).[59(p2)]

Financing for health benefits varies by benefit type. Hospital services, physician services, and public health services are financed through public taxation. Certain services, including prescription drugs, home care, and institutional care, are financed through a combination of public taxation and private insurance coverage. Other goods and services, such as dental and vision care, over-the-counter drugs, and alternative medicines are only covered through private insurance. In general, private insurance is used to cover goods and services not provided by Medicare; six provinces go so far as to prohibit private insurance companies from competing based on price or access time for Medicare-covered benefits.[59(p3)]

Tax revenue from the provincial, territorial, and federal governments pay for 70% of total Medicare expenditures, while private insurance reimbursement accounts for 12% of costs, patient out-of-pocket payments cover 15%, and various sources account for the final 3%.[59(p3)] Healthcare spending is expected to reach C$192 billion in 2010, with the government paying C$135 billion and private insurance and out-of-pocket payments responsible for most of the remaining expenditures. The provinces and territories spend an average of 39% of their budgets on healthcare services, but healthcare spending varies considerably across the country. For example, Alberta spends C$6,266 per person, compared to Quebec's C$5,096 per person costs.[60]

In addition to paying for care, regional health authorities also organize the delivery of care. They hire staff at most acute care facilities and contract for some ambulatory care services. General practitioners and specialists work on a fee-for-service arrangement and generally work in either the public program or private practice, but not both.[59(p4)] While fee-for-service payments account for most of physicians' income, hospitals rely on global budgets allocated by the regional health authorities.

A National Health System: Great Britain

Great Britain's healthcare system was designed by Sir William Beveridge as part of a social reconstruction plan after World War II. The National Health Services Act of 1946 created the National Health Service (NHS), a centrally run healthcare system that provides universal insurance coverage to all residents of Great Britain. It was designed based on the principle that the government is responsible for providing equal access to comprehensive health care that is generally free at the point of service.[59(p31)]

The central government has a significant role in the NHS. It sets national health policies and priorities, establishes which benefits are covered, and controls an overall pool of funds that is distributed to 10 regional health authorities to manage healthcare services and disburse funds in their service area.[59(p31)] Health care is delivered through a variety of trusts that cover services such as primary care, mental healthcare, acute care, and ambulance services. Primary care trusts work with local health and social services agencies to assure the community's needs are being met, and these trusts account for over 80% of the NHS budget. Acute care trusts manage the

delivery of hospital care and are also responsible for monitoring quality of care and using resources efficiently. They also employ a large proportion of NHS workers, including nurses, doctors, midwives, pharmacists, and others.[61]

NHS is the largest publically financed national health system in the world. The 2010–2011 budget of £102 billion is financed primarily through general tax revenues, with most of the rest of the funds coming through Social Security contributions.[61(p9)] While most residents receive their care through NHS, private insurance is also available. Approximately 10% of residents have private health insurance, which provides the same benefits as the NHS but allows for reduced waiting times and access to higher quality care in some cases.[59(p33),62] Those with private insurance tend to have a higher socioeconomic status than individuals covered by NHS.[59(p33)]

Most physicians and nurses are private practitioners who work for NHS as independent contractors, not salaried employees, while NHS owns the hospitals and hospital staff are salaried employees. Patients select a general practitioner (GP) in their service area and this provider is the gateway to NHS services. Almost everyone (99%) has a registered GP and 90% of all patient contact is with this provider.[59(p33)] Services are provided free of charge, except for specific services designated by law.

A Socialized Insurance System: Germany

In 1883, Germany's Otto von Bismarck created the first healthcare system in the world. He viewed a strong health and pension system as a way to build a superior nation, earn support from Germany's working class, and undermine any attempts by Germany's socialist party to gain power. The central government is responsible for setting health policy and regulating the Social Health Insurance System (SHIS). German healthcare policy emphasizes solidarity, the idea that all should have equal access to health care regardless of ability to pay.[59(p12)] Germany's legislature has passed two major health reform bills in recent years. In 2007, the goals of health reform were to mandate universal coverage, improve medical care, modernize sickness funds, and reform the health fund. Germany's 2010 health reform law adjusted insurance levies, reduced the power of pharmaceutical companies to set prices, and cut costs.[59(p11), 63]

SHIS is composed of a collection of non-profit regional sickness funds with a standard benefit package that includes inpatient services, outpatient services, medications, rehabilitation therapy, and dental benefits.[59(p15)] The funds are organized around industry or geography and are responsible for managing healthcare services. Germans must enroll in sickness funds or obtain coverage through private insurance. Some populations are required to be under SHIS, including individuals who earn less than $60,000 per year or are pensioners, students, unemployed, disabled, poor, and homeless, and funds may not refuse to cover them and physicians may not refuse to treat them.[59(p15)] Germans who earn over $60,000 per year for three consecutive years or who are self-employed may choose to opt out of SHIS and purchase private coverage. About 10% of the population opts out of SHIS. In addition, approximately 20% of Germans choose to purchase private insurance to supplement their SHIS benefit plan.[54(p2325)]

Health care is provided in the public and private sectors. Both public and private providers deliver inpatient hospital care. Sickness funds finance most inpatient hospital care, with state governments covering a small percentage of those costs. Hospitals are reimbursed based on a diagnostic-related group methodology.[59(p14)] Physicians and other ambulatory care providers deliver care through the private sector, although most physicians are authorized SHIS providers. Regional associations negotiate contracts on behalf of their members and the resources are split into primary care and specialty care funds, with individual providers reimbursed per services provided based on a relative value scale.[59(p14)]

Sickness funds are financed through employer and employee contributions as well as federal subsidies. Under the 2007 health reform law, individuals and employers each pay a flat rate to the funds and are responsible for cost-sharing when receiving care. If patients are unable to pay their premiums, the welfare system covers the costs. Sickness funds distribute money to insurance plans on a capitated basis with rates risk-adjusted based on age, sex, and disease status.[59(p13)] Well-run funds with excess resources have the choice of remitting money to insureds or providing additional benefits not covered by the standard package. Funds that run a deficit

BOX 4-6 Discussion Questions

Do you prefer one of these health systems to the others? Why or why not? Are there features that you think should be incorporated into the U.S. healthcare system? Are there reasons why certain features might be difficult to incorporate into the U.S. healthcare system?

may levy an additional premium capped at 1% of individual gross income, but if the plan imposes the additional premium, individuals are immediately free to change plans.[59(p14)]

The Importance of Health Insurance Design

Reviewing the healthcare systems of four countries—the United States, Canada, Great Britain, and Germany—shows how varied healthcare systems are around the world. Differences exist regarding the role of government, the ability to purchase private insurance, cost-sharing requirements, and how the system is financed. Even countries that share the same general type of system have variations based on their specific culture, politics, and needs. How a system is designed matters in terms of access to care, financing, and patient satisfaction. A survey in 11 countries asked residents about their experience with their country's healthcare system.[64] What issues were primary concerns and how different residents fared within a system varied by country (see Figures 4-15 to 4-18).

Affordability was a key issue in the United States. Of those surveyed, U.S. residents were the most concerned about being able to afford health care in the event of an illness, most likely to have not received care due to cost, most likely to have spent at least $1,000 out-of-pocket on health care, and most likely to have had serious problems paying for care.[64(pp2326–2327)] Residents of Great Britain were least likely to be worried about costs and German residents rarely spent $1,000 on health care.[64(p2327)] On the other hand, access to care was generally quicker for Americans and Germans compared to Canadians and the British. While residents of Great Britain indicated quick access to primary care providers, they experienced longer waits for specialty care and elective surgery, although their wait times have decreased in recent years.[64(p2328)] Variations also exist regarding the complexity of dealing with the insurance system and with patient satisfaction. Residents of the United States and Germany were more likely to spend time on insurance paperwork and disputes with insurance companies, while it was rare for British residents to make similar complaints.[64(p2330)]

Even though most countries in the survey have universal or near-universal coverage, low-income individuals still report more problems with health care than their wealthier counterparts. In every country, low-income residents were more likely to be in poor health and more concerned about affording health care than higher income residents, with the United States showing the widest gap in experience by income level.[64(p2331)] Residents of Great Britain were the only ones who did not report access-related barriers by income level. Also, low-income residents in the United States and Canada

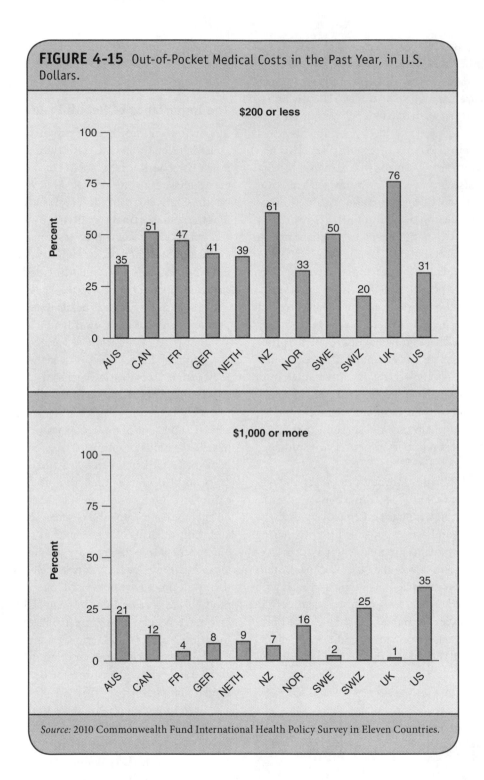

FIGURE 4-15 Out-of-Pocket Medical Costs in the Past Year, in U.S. Dollars.

Source: 2010 Commonwealth Fund International Health Policy Survey in Eleven Countries.

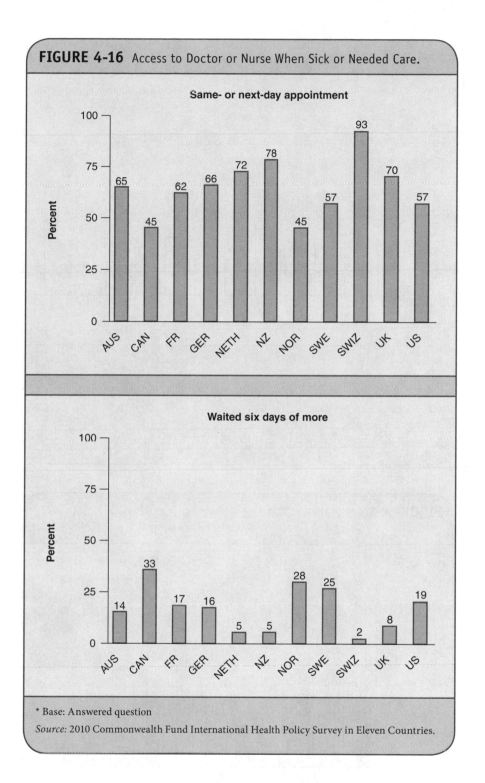

FIGURE 4-16 Access to Doctor or Nurse When Sick or Needed Care.

* Base: Answered question

Source: 2010 Commonwealth Fund International Health Policy Survey in Eleven Countries.

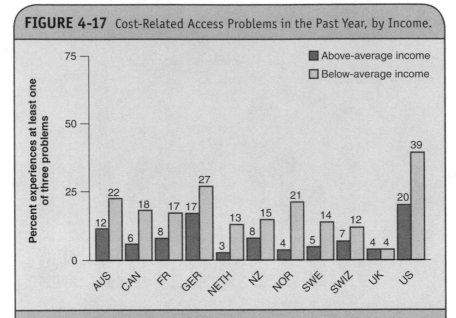

FIGURE 4-17 Cost-Related Access Problems in the Past Year, by Income.

Note: Percentages adjusted based on logistic regression to control for health status, age, and—in the U.S.—insurance status.

* Indicates significant within-country differences with below-average income (p <0.05).

** Did not fill/skipped prescription, did not visit doctor with medical problem, and/or did not get recommended care.

Source: 2010 Commonwealth Fund International Health Policy Survey in Eleven Countries.

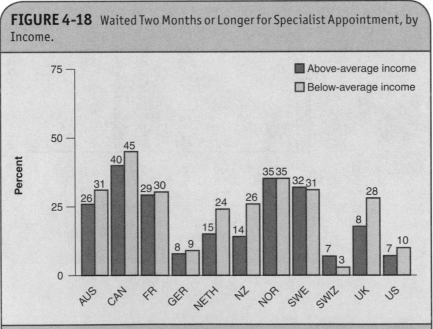

FIGURE 4-18 Waited Two Months or Longer for Specialist Appointment, by Income.

Note: Percentages adjusted based on logistic regression to control for health status, age, and—in the U.S.—insurance status.

* Indicates significant within-country differences with below-average income (p <0.05).

Source: 2010 Commonwealth Fund International Health Policy Survey in Eleven Countries.

were more likely to experience longer waiting times than low-income residents in Germany and Great Britain.

CONCLUSION

This wide-ranging review of the U.S. healthcare system was intended to provide readers with a general sense of how health care is accessed, financed, and administered in this country. Understanding the various players in the healthcare system, from providers to researchers to policymakers, is crucial to being able to participate in debates over current issues in health policy and law. While the U.S. system excels on many fronts, it falls short in many areas relating to access, quality, and efficiency. Perhaps policymakers in this country could learn lessons from successes abroad, but the United States has a unique political environment and it is clear there is no silver bullet that will solve all the problems we face. Specific health policy and law concerns will be described in much greater detail elsewhere, providing a foundation to tackle the many problems that will confront the country in the years ahead.

REFERENCES

1. Pub L No. 111-148, the Patient Protection and Affordable Care Act.

2. Chartset for Health at a Glance 2009. *OECD Web site.* Available at http://www.oecd.org/document/11/0,3746,en_2649_37407_16502667_1_1_1_37407,00.html. Accessed January 25, 2011.

3. HealthyPeople.gov home page. Available at http://www.healthypeople.gov/2020/default.aspx. Accessed January 25, 2011.

4. Centers for Medicare and Medicaid Services. *National health expenditures 2009 highlights.* Available at https://www.cms.gov/NationalHealthExpendData/downloads/highlights.pdf. Accessed January 25, 2011.

5. Centers for Medicare and Medicaid Services. *National health expenditure projections 2009–2019.* Available at https://www.cms.gov/NationalHealthExpendData/downloads/NHEProjections2009to2019.pdf. Accessed January 25, 2011.

6. Kaiser Family Foundation. *US health care costs background brief.* 2010. Available at http://www.kaiseredu.org/Issue-Modules/US-Health-Care-Costs/Background-Brief.aspx. Accessed January 25, 2011.

7. Kaiser Family Foundation. *The uninsured: a primer—key facts about Americans without insurance.* 2010. Available at: http://www.kff.org/uninsured/upload/7451-06.pdf. Accessed January 6, 2011.

8. Kaiser Family Foundation and Health Research and Educational Trust. *Employer health benefits.* 2010. Available at: http://ehbs.kff.org/pdf/2010/8085.pdf. Accessed February 1, 2011.

9. Holahan J, Garrett B. *Rising unemployment, Medicaid, and the uninsured.* 2009. Available at http://www.kff.org/uninsured/7850.cfm. Accessed February 1, 2011.

10. U.S. Bureau of the Census. *Income, Poverty, and Health Insurance Coverage in the United States: 2009.* Washington, DC: Bureau of the U.S. Census; 2010.

11. Institute of Medicine. *Coverage Matters: Insurance and Health Care.* Washington, DC: National Academy Press; 2001.

12. Starfield B, Shi L. The medical home, access to care, and insurance: a review of evidence. *Pediatrics.* 2004;113:1493–1498.

13. Lambrew J, DeFriese G, Carey, T et al. The effects of having a regular doctor on access to primary care. *Med Care.* 1996;34:1493–1498.

14. Institute of Medicine. *Hidden Costs, Value Lost: Uninsurance in America.* Washington, DC: National Academy Press; 2003.

15. Families USA. *Paying a premium: the added cost of care for the uninsured.* 2005. Available at http://www.familiesusa.org/resources/publications/reports/paying-a-premium.html. Accessed July 18, 2011.

16. Kavilanz, PB. *Uninsured Americans: cost to you.* March 5, 2009. CNN Money. Available at http://money.cnn.com/2009/03/05/news/economy/healthcare_underinsured/. Accessed July 18, 2011.

17. Medicare.gov. *Medicare premium and co-insurance rates for 2011.* Available at https://questions.medicare.gov/app/answers/detail/a_id/2305/~/medicare-premiums-and-coinsurance-rates-for-2011. Accessed February 8, 2011.

18. Blue Cross Blue Shield Federal Employee Program. *Standard option medical benefits.* Available at http://www.fepblue.org/benefitplans/standard-option/medical-benefits.jsp. Accessed February 8, 2011.

19. US Office of Personnel Management. *Plan Brochure—Kaiser Foundation Health Plan of the Mid-Atlantic States.* Available at http://www.opm.gov/insure/health/planinfo/2011/brochures/73-047.pdf. Accessed February 8, 2011.

20. Guttmacher Institute. *An Overview of Abortion Laws.* Washington, DC: Guttmacher Institute. Available at http://www.guttmacher.org/statecenter/spibs/spib_OAL.pdf. Accessed February 8, 2011.

21. Guttmacher Institute. *Insurance Coverage of Contraceptives.* Washington, DC: Guttmacher Institute. Available at http://www.guttmacher.org/statecenter/spibs/spib_ICC.pdf. Accessed February 8, 2011.

22. Cartwright-Smith L. *Update: abortion coverage. Health Reform GPS.* Available at http://www.healthreformgps.org/resources/update-abortion-coverage/. Accessed July 19, 2011.

23. Institute of Medicine. *America's Health Care Safety Net: Intact but Endangered.* Washington, DC: National Academy Press; 2000.

24. National Association of Community Health Centers. *America's health centers—fact sheet.* 2010. Available at http://www.nachc.com/client/America's%20Health%20Centers%20updated%2009%2010.pdf. Accessed February 1, 2011.

25. Regenstein M, Huang J. *Stresses to the safety net: the public hospital perspective.* Kaiser Family Foundation; 2005. Available at http://www.kff.org/medicaid/7329.cfm. Accessed July 19, 2011.

26. National Association of Public Hospitals and Health Systems. *America's public hospitals and health systems, 2009: Results of NAPH annual hospital characteristics survey.* Available at http://www.naph.org/Main-Menu-Category/Our-Work/Safety-Net-Financing/Characteristics-Report/2009-Public-Hospital-Financial-Characteristics-.aspx?FT=.pdf. Accessed February 22, 2011.

27. National Association of Community Health Centers. *Expanding health centers under health reform: doubling patient capacity and bringing down costs.* Available at http://www.nachc.com/client/HCR_New_Patients_Final.pdf. Accessed June 28, 2011.

28. Center for American Progress. *Closing the health care workforce gap.* Available at http://www.americanprogress.org/issues/2010/01/health_workforce.html. Accessed February 11, 2011.

29. National Association of Community Health Centers. *Primary care access: An essential building block of health reform.* 2009. Available at http://www.nachc.com/client/documents/pressreleases/PrimaryCareAccessRPT.pdf. Accessed February 11, 2011.

30. Iglehart JK. Despite tight budgets, boosting US health workforce may be policy that is 'just right.' *Health Affairs.* 2011;30(2):191–192.

31. Bodenheimer T. Primary care—will it survive? *New Eng J Med.* 2006;355(9):861–864. Available at http://www.nejm.org/doi/full/10.1056/NEJMp068155. Accessed July 19, 2011.

32. Vaughn BT, DeVrieze SR, Reed SD, Schulman KA. Can we close the income and wealth gap between specialists and primary care physicians? *Health Affairs.* 2010;933–940,936.

33. National Association of Community Health Centers. *Access denied: A look at America's medically disenfranchised*. 2007. Available at http://www.nachc.com/access-reports.cfm. Accessed July 19, 2011.

34. National Conference of State Legislatures. *Primary care workforce*. Available at http://www.ncsl.org/default.aspx?tabid=21702. Accessed February 11, 2011.

35. U.S. Census. *National population projections, 2008*. Available at http://www.census.gov/population/www/projections/summarytables.html. Accessed February 11, 2011.

36. Centers for Disease Control and Prevention. *NCHS data brief: Population aging and the use of office-based physician services*. Available at http://www.cdc.gov/nchs/data/databriefs/db41.htm#ref1. Accessed February 11, 2011.

37. O'Neill G, Barry PP. Training physicians in geriatric care: Responding to critical need. *Public Policy and Aging Report*. 2000;13(2):17–21. Available at http://www.agingsociety.org/agingsociety/pdf/trainging.pdf. Accessed February 11, 2011.

38. Many children lack doctor, study finds. *New York Times*. December 19, 2010. Available at http://www.nytimes.com/2010/12/20/us/20doctors.html. Accessed February 15, 2011.

39. Rosenblatt RA, Chen FM, Lishner DM, Doescher MP. *The future of family medicine and implications of future rural primary care physician supply*. Rural Health Research Center. 2010. Available at http://depts.washington.edu/uwrhrc/uploads/RHRC_FR125_Rosenblatt.pdf. Accessed February 15, 2011.

40. Florell ML. *Rural health care workforce: opportunities to improve care delivery*. Center for Rural Affairs. 2009. Available at http://files.cfra.org/pdf/Health care_Workforce.pdf. Accessed February 15, 2011.

41. United States faces dentist shortage. *Canadian Med Assoc J*. 2009;181(11):E253–E254.

42. US Department of Health and Human Services. *The public health workforce: an agenda for the 21st century*. Available at http://www.health.gov/phfunctions/pubhlth.pdf. Accessed February 15, 2011.

43. Association of Schools of Public Health. *Confronting the public health workforce crisis*. 2008. Available at http://www.asph.org/UserFiles/WorkforceShortage2008Final.pdf. Accessed February 15, 2011.

44. Organisation for Economic Co-operation and Development. *OECD health at a glance, 2009: key findings for the United States*. Available at http://www.oecd.org/document/21/0,3746,en_2649_37407_44219221_1_1_1_37407,00.html. Accessed February 15, 2011.

45. Centers for Disease Control and Prevention. *NCHS Data Brief. Behind international rankings of infant mortality: how the United States compares with Europe*. 2009. Available at http://www.cdc.gov/nchs/data/databriefs/db23.htm. Accessed February 15, 2011.

46. McGlynn EA, Asch SM, Adams J. The quality of health care delivered to adults in the United States. *New Engl J Med*. 2003;348:2635–2645.

47. Institute of Medicine. *Crossing the Quality Chasm: A New Health System for the 21st Century*. Washington, DC: National Academy of Sciences; 2001.

48. Institute of Medicine. *To Err is Human: Building a Safer Health Care System*. Washington, DC: National Academy of Sciences; 2000.

49. Speaking Together. *Addressing language barriers in health care: what's at stake*. 2007. Available at http://www.rwjf.org/files/research/stissuebriefmarch07.pdf. Accessed February 18, 2011.

50. Office of Minority Health. *National standards for culturally and linguistically appropriate services in health care*. 2001. Available at http://minorityhealth.hhs.gov/assets/pdf/checked/finalreport.pdf. Accessed February 18, 2011.

51. Dartmouth Atlas Project. *Health care spending, quality, and outcomes: more isn't always better*. 2009. Available at http://www.dartmouthatlas.org/downloads/reports/Spending_Brief_022709.pdf. Accessed February 18, 2011.

52. Reschovsky JD, Hadley J, Saiontz-Martinez CB, Boukus ER. Following the money: factors associated with the cost of treating high-cost Medicare beneficiaries. *Health Serv Res*. 2010;1–25. Available at http://www.hschange.com/CONTENT/1185/1185.pdf. Accessed February 22, 2011.

53. Woolhandler S, Campbell T, Himmelstein DU. Costs of health care administration in the US and Canada. *New Engl J Med*. 2003;349:768–775.

54. Bodenheimer T. High and rising health care costs, Part 2: technological innovation. *Ann Internal Med*. 2005;142:932–937.

55. Institute of Medicine. *Unequal Treatment: Confronting Racial and Ethnic Disparities in Health Care*. Washington, DC: National Academics of Sciences; 2003, 2–3.

56. Centers for Disease Control and Prevention. *Highlights in minority health and health disparities*. 2010. Available at http://www.cdc.gov/omhd/Highlights/2010/HSeptOct10.html. Accessed February 18, 2011.

57. Centers for Disease Control and Prevention. *MMR Weekly Report—Health disparities experienced by Hispanics, United States*. 2004. Available at http://www.cdc.gov/mmwr/preview/mmwrhtml/mm5340a1.htm. Accessed February 18, 2011.

58. Shi L, Singh DA. *Delivering Health Care in America: A Systems Approach*. 4th ed. Boston, MA: Jones and Bartlett Publishers; 2008.

59. Schabloski AK. *Health care systems around the world. Insure the uninsured project*. 2008. Available at http://www.itup.org/Reports/Fresh%20Thinking/Health_Care_Systems_Around_World.pdf. Accessed July 19, 2011.

60. Canadian Institute for Health Information. *Health care spending to reach $192 billion this year*. Available at http://www.cihi.ca/CIHI-ext-portal/internet/en/Document/spending+and+health+workforce/spending/RELEASE_28OCT10. Accessed March 2, 2011.

61. National Audit Office. *Briefing for the House of Commons Health Select Committee—Health Resource Allocation*. London, England: 2010. Available at http://www.nao.org.uk/publications/1011/health_resource_allocation.aspx. Accessed March 2, 2011.

62. *HealthCare Economist*. April 23, 2008. Available at http://healthcare-economist.com/2008/04/23/health-care-around-the-world-great-britain/. Accessed March 2, 2011.

63. Kirschbaum E. Germany passes unpopular health reform. *Reuters*. November 12, 2010. Available at http://www.reuters.com/article/2010/11/12/us-germany-health care-reform-idUSTRE6AB3TL20101112. Accessed March 4, 2011.

64. Schoen C, Osborne R, Doty MM, Pierson R, Applebaum S. How health insurance design affects access to care and costs, by income, in eleven countries. *Health Affairs*. 2010;29(12):2323–2334.

CHAPTER 5

Public Health Institutions and Systems

LEARNING OBJECTIVES

By the end of this chapter, the student will be able to:

- Identify goals of governmental public health.
- Identify the ten essential services of public health.
- Describe basic features of local, state, and federal public health agencies in the United States.
- Identify global public health organizations and agencies and describe their basic roles.
- Identify roles in public health for federal agencies not identified as health agencies.
- Illustrate the need for collaboration by governmental public health agencies with other governmental and nongovernmental organizations.
- Describe approaches to connecting public health and the healthcare system.

A young man in your dormitory is diagnosed with tuberculosis. The health department works with the student health service to test everyone in the dorm, as well as in his classes, with a TB skin test. Those who are positive for the first time are advised to take a course of a medicine called INH. You ask: is this standard operating procedure?

You go to a public health meeting and learn that many of the speakers are not from public health agencies, but from the Departments of Labor, Commerce, Housing, and Education. You ask: what do these departments have to do with health?

You hear that a new childhood vaccine was developed by the NIH, approved by the FDA, endorsed for

federal payment by the CDC and recommended for use by the American Academy of Pediatrics. You ask: do all these agencies and organizations always work so well together?

A major flood in Asia leads to disease and starvation. Some say it is due to global warming, others to bad luck. Coordinated efforts by global health agencies, assisted by nongovernmental organizations (NGOs) and outside governmental donors, help get the country back on its feet. You ask: what types of cooperation are needed to make all of this happen?

A local community health center identifies childhood obesity as a problem in their community. They collect data demonstrating that the problem begins as early as elementary school. They develop a plan that includes clinical interventions at the health center and also at the elementary school. They ask the health department to help them organize an educational campaign and assist in evaluating the results. rking together, they are able to reduce the obesity rate among elementary school children by one-half. This seems like a new way to practice public health, you conclude. What type of approach is this?

These cases all reflect the responsibilities of public health agencies at the local, federal, and global levels. They illustrate public health working the way it is supposed to work. Of course, this is not always the case. Let us start by taking a look at the goals and roles of public health agencies.

WHAT ARE THE GOALS AND ROLES OF GOVERNMENTAL PUBLIC HEALTH AGENCIES?

Public health is often equated with the work of governmental agencies. The role of government is only a portion of what we mean by public health, but it is an important component. So important, in fact, that we often define the roles of other components in terms of how they relate to the work of governmental public health agencies.

In 1994, the United States Public Health Service put forth the "Public Health in America Statement," which provided the framework that continues to define the goals and services of governmental public health agencies.[1] These goals should already be familiar to you. They are:

- to prevent epidemics and the spread of disease
- to protect against environmental hazards
- to prevent injuries
- to promote and encourage healthy behaviors
- to respond to disasters and assist communities in recovery
- to ensure the quality and accessibility of health services

These are ambitious and complicated goals to achieve. To be able to successfully achieve them, it is important to further define the roles that governmental public health agencies themselves play, and by implication, the roles that other governmental agencies and nongovernmental organizations need to play.

The Public Health in America Statement built upon the Institute of Medicine's (IOM) 1988 report called The Future of Public Health.[2] The IOM defined three **core public health functions** that governmental public health agencies need to perform. The concept of "core function" implies that the job cannot be delegated to other agencies or to nongovernmental organizations. It also implies that the governmental public health agencies will work together to accomplish these functions because as a group they are responsible for public health as a whole—no one agency at the local, state, or federal level is specifically or exclusively responsible for accomplishing the essential public health services.[a]

The core functions defined by the IOM are: 1) assessment, 2) policy development, and 3) assurance.[2]

- **Assessment** includes obtaining data that defines the health of the overall population and specific groups within the population, including defining the nature of new and persisting health problems.

- **Assurance** includes governmental public health's oversight responsibility for ensuring that key components of an effective health system, including health care and public health, are in place even though the implementation will often be performed by others.
- **Policy development** includes developing evidence-based recommendations and other analyses of options, such as health policy analysis, to guide implementation including efforts to educate and mobilize community partnerships.

The three core functions, while useful in providing a delineation of responsibilities and an intellectual framework for the work of governmental public health agencies, were not tangible enough to provide a clear understanding or definition of the work of public health agencies. Thus, in addition to the goals of public health, the Public Health in America Statement defined a series of **ten essential public health services** that build upon the IOM's core functions, guide day-to-day responsibilities, and provide a mechanism for evaluating whether the core functions are fulfilled. These ten services have come to define the responsibilities of the combined local, state, and federal governmental public health system.

WHAT ARE THE TEN ESSENTIAL PUBLIC HEALTH SERVICES?

Table 5-1 outlines the ten essential public health services and organizes them according to which IOM core function they aim to fulfill.[1] A description of each service is presented in column two and examples of these essential services are listed in column three.

We have now looked at the core public health functions and the ten essential services of public health agencies. Figure 5-1 puts these together to allow you to see the connections.

These public health services are delivered through a complex web of local and federal agencies, as well as via increasing involvement of global organizations. Let us take a look at the work of public health agencies at each of these levels.

Figure 5-2 provides a framework to guide our review of the delivery of public health services. It diagrams the central role of governmental public health agencies and the complicated connections required to accomplish their responsibilities. We will begin by taking at look at the structure and function of governmental public health agencies at the local/state, federal, and global levels. Then, we will examine the key connections with other governmental agencies, community, and private organizations, and finally with the healthcare delivery system as a whole.

TABLE 5-1 Ten Essential Public Health Services

Essential Service	Meaning of Essential Service	Example
ASSESSMENT—Core function		
1. Monitor health status to identify and solve community health problems	This service includes accurate diagnosis of the community's health status; identification of threats to health and assessment of health service needs; timely collection, analysis, and publication of information on access, utilization, costs, and outcomes of personal health services; attention to the vital statistics and health status of specific groups that are at a higher risk than the total population; and collaboration to manage integrated information systems with private providers and health benefit plans.	Vital Statistics Health Surveys Surveillance, including reportable diseases
2. Diagnose and investigate health problems and health hazards in the community	This service includes epidemiologic identification of emerging health threats; public health laboratory capability using modern technology to conduct rapid screening and high-volume testing; active infectious disease epidemiology programs; and technical capacity for epidemiologic investigation of disease outbreaks and patterns of chronic disease and injury.	Epidemic investigations CDC–Epidemiology Intelligence Service State Public Health Laboratories
POLICY DEVELOPMENT—Core function		
3. Inform, educate, and empower people about health issues	This service includes social marketing and media communications; providing accessible health information resources at community levels; active collaboration with personal healthcare providers to reinforce health promotion messages and programs; and joint health education programs with schools, churches, and worksites.	Health education campaigns, such as comprehensive state tobacco programs
4. Mobilize community partnerships and action to identify and solve health problems	This service includes convening and facilitating community groups and associations, including those not typically considered to be health-related, in undertaking defined preventive, screening, rehabilitation, and support programs; and skilled coalition-building to draw upon the full range of potential human and material resources in the case of community health.	Lead control programs: testing and follow-up of children, reduction of lead exposure, educational follow-up, and addressing underlying causes
5. Develop policies and plans that support individual and community health efforts	This service requires leadership development at all levels of public health; systematic community and state-level planning for health improvement in all jurisdictions; tracking of measurable health objectives as a part of continuous quality improvement strategies; joint evaluation with the medical healthcare system to define consistent policy regarding prevention and treatment services; and development of codes, regulations, and legislation to guide public health practice.	Newborn screening program for PKU and other genetic and congenital diseases
ASSURANCE—Core function		
6. Enforce laws and regulations that protect health and ensure safety	This service involves full enforcement of sanitary codes, especially in the food industry; full protection of drinking water supplies; enforcement of clean air standards; timely follow-up of hazards, preventable injuries, and exposure-related diseases identified in occupational and community settings; monitoring quality of medical services (e.g., laboratory, nursing home, and home health care); and timely review of new drug, biological, and medical device applications.	Local: Fluoridation and chlorination of water State: Regulation of nursing homes Federal: FDA drug approval and food safety

(Continues)

TABLE 5-1 Ten Essential Public Health Services *(Continued)*

Essential Service	Meaning of Essential Service	Example
7. Link people to needed personal health services and ensure the provision of health care when otherwise unavailable	This service (often referred to as "outreach" or "enabling" service) includes ensuring effective entry for socially disadvantaged people into a coordinated system of clinical care; culturally and linguistically appropriate materials and staff to ensure linkage to services for special population groups; ongoing "care management"; and transportation.	Community Health Centers
8. Ensure the provision of a competent public and personal healthcare workforce	This service includes education and training for personnel to meet the needs for public and personal health services; efficient processes for licensure of professionals and certification of facilities with regular verification and inspection follow-up; adoption of continuous quality improvement and lifelong learning within all licensure and certification programs; active partnerships with professional training programs to ensure community-relevant learning experiences for all students; and continuing education in management and leadership development programs for those charged with administrative/executive roles.	Licensure of physicians, nurses, and other health professionals
9. Evaluate effectiveness, accessibility, and quality of personal and population-based health services	This service calls for ongoing evaluation of health programs, based on analysis of health status and service utilization data, to assess program effectiveness and to provide information necessary for allocating resources and reshaping programs.	Development of evidence-based recommendations
ALL THREE IOM—Core function		
10. Research for new insights and innovative solutions to health problems	This service includes continuous linkage with appropriate institutions of higher learning and research and an internal capacity to mount timely epidemiologic and economic analyses and conduct needed health services research.	NIH, CDC, AHRQ other federal agencies

Source: Data from Public Health in America. Essential Public Health Services. Available at http://www.health.gov/phfunctions/public.htm. Accessed November 8, 2008.

WHAT ARE THE ROLES OF LOCAL AND STATE PUBLIC HEALTH AGENCIES?

The United States Constitution does not mention public health. Thus, public health is first and foremost a state responsibility. States may retain the authority, voluntarily request or accept help from the federal government, or delegate their responsibility and/or authority to local agencies at the city, county, or other local levels.[b]

Box 5-1 describes a brief history of public health agencies in the United States. It is a complex history and has resulted in more structures than there are states—more because large cities often have their own public health systems.[3] In addition, the District of Columbia and several U.S. territories have their own systems and often have authority to make public health system decisions as if they were states.

To understand the role of local health departments, it is useful to think of two models.[4] In the first model, which we will call the home rule or local autonomy model, authority is delegated from the state to the local health department. The local health department, or the local government, has a great deal of autonomy in setting its own structure and function and often raising its own funding.

In the second model, which we will call the branch office model, the local health department can be viewed as a branch office of the state agency with little or no independent authority or funding. Most health departments lie somewhere in between these two extreme models, however these models

FIGURE 5-1 Essential Public Health Services and IOM Core Functions.

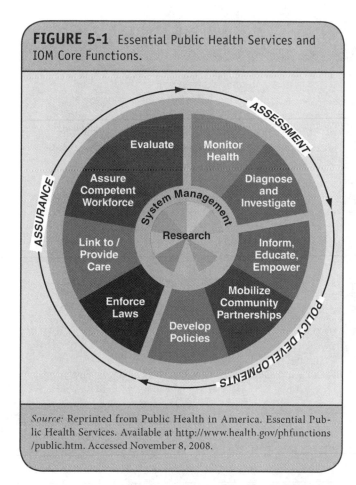

Source: Reprinted from Public Health in America. Essential Public Health Services. Available at http://www.health.gov/phfunctions /public.htm. Accessed November 8, 2008.

FIGURE 5-2 Framework for Viewing Governmental Public Health Agencies and Their Complicated Connections.

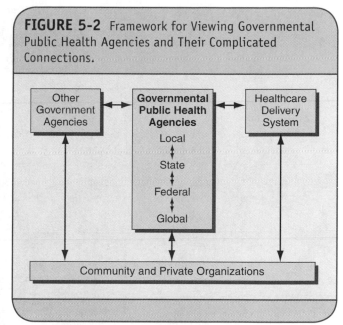

- tobacco control programs
- public health preparedness and response to disasters

Health departments in many parts of the United States have also served as the healthcare provider for those without other sources of health care. This has been called the **healthcare safety net**. In recent years, many health departments have reduced or discontinued these services often transferring them to the healthcare system or integrating their efforts into community health centers. The concept of core functions holds that while these activities can be performed by other organizations or agencies, the public health agencies still retain responsibility for ensuring access to and the quality of these services.

The work of local public health agencies cannot be viewed in isolation. The State Health Department usually retains important roles even in those states where the local departments have home rule authority. These responsibilities often include: collecting vital statistics, running a public health laboratory, licensing of health professionals, administering nutrition programs, and regulation of health facilities, such as nursing homes. In addition, drinking water regulation, administration of the state Medicaid program, and the office of the medical examiner may also fall under the authority of the State Health Department.

Today, the federal government has a great deal of involvement in national and global issues of public health and often works closely with local agencies. Let us take a look at

provide a framework for understanding the many varieties of department structures. Thus, when we speak of local public health, we may be speaking of a state agency with branch offices or a relatively independent local agency. Regardless of which model a state uses, many public health responsibilities of local public health departments are quite similar and they usually have authority and responsibility for at least the following:[4]

- immunizations for those not covered by the private system
- communicable disease surveillance and initial investigation of outbreaks
- communicable disease control, often including at a minimum tuberculosis and syphilis case finding and treatment
- inspection and licensing of restaurants
- environmental health surveillance
- coordinating public health screening programs, including newborn and lead screenings

BOX 5-1 Brief History of American Public Health Agencies

An understanding of the history of American public health institutions requires an understanding of the response of local, state, and federal governments to public health crises and the complex interactions between these levels of government.

The colonial period in America saw repeated epidemics of smallpox, cholera, and yellow fever focused in the port cities. These epidemics brought fear and disruption of commerce, along with accompanying disease and death. One epidemic in Philadelphia in 1793 in what was then the nation's capital nearly shut down the federal government. These early public health crises brought about the first municipal Boards of Health, made up of respected citizens authorized to act in the community's interest to implement quarantine, evacuation, and other public health interventions of the day. The federal government's early role in combating epidemics led to the establishment in 1798 of what later became known as the U.S. Public Health Service.

Major changes in public health awaited the last half of the 19th century with the great expansion of understanding of disease and the ability to control it through community actions. The Shattuck Commission in Massachusetts in 1850 outlined the roles of state health departments as responsible for: sanitary inspections, communicable disease control, food sanitation, vital statistics, and services for infants and children. Over the next 50 years, the states gradually took the lead in developing public health institutions based upon delivery of these services.

Local health departments outside of the largest cities did not exist until the 20th century. The Rockefeller Foundation stimulated and helped fund early local health departments and campaigns in part to combat specific diseases, such as hookworm. There was no standard model for local health departments. Local health departments developed in at least 50 different ways in the 50 states and were chronically underfunded.

The federal government played a very small role in public health throughout the 1800s and well into the 20th century. An occasional public health crisis stimulated in part by media attention did bring about federal action. The founding of the Food and Drug Administration in 1906 resulted in large part from the journalistic activity known as "muckraking," which exposed the status of food and drug safety. The early years of the 20th century set the stage for expansion of the federal government's role in public health through the passage of the 16th Amendment to the Constitution authorizing federal income tax as a major source of federal government funding.

The Great Depression, in general, and the Social Security Act of 1935, in particular, brought about a new era in which federal funding became a major source of financial resources for state and local public health departments and nongovernmental organizations. The founding of the what was then called the Communicable Disease Centers (CDC) in 1946 led to a national and eventually international leadership role for the CDC which attempts to connect and hold together the complex local, state, and federal public health efforts and integrate them into global public health efforts.

The Johnson Administration's War on Poverty, as well as the Medicare and Medicaid programs, brought about greatly expanded funding for healthcare services and led many health departments to provide direct healthcare services especially for those without other sources of care. The late 1980s and 1990s saw a redefinition of the roles of governmental public health including the Institute of Medicine's definition of core functions and the development of the 10 Essential Public Health Services. These documents have guided the development of a broad population focus for public health and a move away from the direct provision of healthcare services.

As we will explore in Chapter 12, the terrorism of 9/11 and the subsequent anthrax scare moved public health institutions to the center of efforts to protect the public's health through emergency and disaster preparedness. The development of flexible efforts to respond to expected and unexpected hazards is now a central feature of public health institutions' roles and funding. The success of these efforts requires new levels of coordination of local, state, federal, and global public health agencies utilizing state-of-the-art surveillance, laboratory technology, and communications systems.

the structure and role of the federal government in public health.

WHAT ARE THE ROLES OF FEDERAL PUBLIC HEALTH AGENCIES?

As we saw in Chapter 3, the federal government's role in public health does not explicitly appear in the United States Constitution. It has been justified largely by the Interstate Commerce clause, which provides federal government authority to regulate commerce between the states. Federal public health authority often rests on the voluntary acceptance by the states of funding provided by the federal government. This funding may come with requirements for state action in order to qualify for the funding.

The Department of Health and Human Services (HHS) is the central public health agency of the federal government. It includes operating agencies each of which report directly to the cabinet-level Secretary of HHS. Table 5-2 outlines most of these agencies, their roles and authority, and their basic public health structure and activities.[5]

The National Institutes of Health (NIH) is far and away the largest agency within HHS with a budget of over $30 billion—as much as all the other six agencies' budgets combined. However, most of its efforts are devoted to basic science research and the translation of research into clinical practice.

Some of the federal agencies, such as the Health Services and Resources Administration (HRSA), Substance Abuse and Mental Health Services Administration (SAMHSA), and the Indian Health Service, provide or fund individually oriented health services in addition to population-oriented preventive services. The Indian Health Service is unique because it is responsible for both public health and healthcare services for a defined population.

The Centers for Disease Control and Prevention (CDC) is perhaps the agency most closely identified with public health at the federal level. Box 5-2 describes its first 50 years from

TABLE 5-2 Key Federal Health Agencies of the Department of Health and Human Services

Agency	Roles/Authority	Examples of Structures/Activities
Centers for Disease Control and Prevention (CDC) and Agency for Toxic Substances and Disease Registry (ATSDR)	CDC is the lead agency for prevention, health data, epidemic investigation, and public health measures aimed at disease control and prevention. The CDC administers ATSDR, which works with the Environmental Protection Agency to provide guidance on health hazards of toxic exposures.	The CDC and ATSDR work extensively with state and local health departments. The CDC's Epidemiology Intelligence Service (EIS) functions domestically and internationally at the request of governments.
National Institutes of Health (NIH)	Lead research agency. Also funds training programs and communication of health information to the professional community and the public.	17 institutes in all—the largest being the National Cancer Institute. The National Library of Medicine is part of NIH Centers. The Centers include the John E. Fogarty International Center for Advanced Study in the Health Sciences. NIH is the world's largest biomedical research enterprise with intramural research at NIH and extramural research grants throughout the world.
Food and Drug Administration (FDA)	Consumer protection agency with authority for safety of foods and safety and efficacy of drugs, vaccines and other medical and public health interventions.	Divisions responsible for food safety, medical devices, drug efficacy and safety pre- and post-approval.
Health Resources and Services Administration (HRSA)	Seeks to ensure equitable access to comprehensive quality health care.	Funds community health centers, HIV/AIDS services, scholarships for health professional students.
Agency for Healthcare Research and Quality (AHRQ)	Research agenda to improve the outcomes and quality of health care, including patient safety and access to services.	Supports U.S. Preventive Services Task Force, Evidence-based medicine research, and Guidelines Clearinghouse.
Substance Abuse and Mental Health Services Administration (SAMHSA)	Works to improve quality and availability of prevention, treatment, and rehabilitation for substance abuse and mental illness.	Research, data collection and funding of local services.
Indian Health Service (IHS)	Provides direct health care and public health services to federally recognized tribes.	Services provided to 550 federally-recognized tribes in 35 states. Only comprehensive federal responsibility for health care, plus public health services.

BOX 5-2 History of the CDC

The Communicable Disease Center was organized in Atlanta, Georgia on July 1, 1946; its founder, Dr. Joseph W. Mountin, was a visionary public health leader who had high hopes for this small and comparatively insignificant branch of the Public Health Service (PHS). It occupied only one floor of the Volunteer Building on Peachtree Street and had fewer than 400 employees, most of whom were engineers and entomologists. Until the previous day, they had worked for Malaria Control in War Areas, the predecessor of CDC, which had successfully kept the southeastern states malaria-free during World War II and, for approximately 1 year, from murine typhus fever. The new institution would expand its interests to include all communicable diseases and would be the servant of the states, providing practical help whenever called.

Distinguished scientists soon filled CDC's laboratories, and many states and foreign countries sent their public health staffs to Atlanta for training . . . . Medical epidemiologists were scarce, and it was not until 1949 that Dr. Alexander Langmuir arrived to head the epidemiology branch. Within months, he launched the first-ever disease surveillance program, which confirmed his suspicion that malaria, on which CDC spent the largest portion of its budget, had long since disappeared. Subsequently, disease surveillance became the cornerstone on which CDC's mission of service to the states was built and, in time, changed the practice of public health.

The outbreak of the Korean War in 1950 was the impetus for creating CDC's Epidemiological Intelligence Service (EIS). The threat of biological warfare loomed, and Dr. Langmuir, the most knowledgeable person in PHS about this arcane subject, saw an opportunity to train epidemiologists who would guard against ordinary threats to public health while watching out for alien germs. The first class of EIS officers arrived in Atlanta for training in 1951 and pledged to go wherever they were called for the next 2 years. These "disease detectives" quickly gained fame for "shoe-leather epidemiology" through which they ferreted out the cause of disease outbreaks.

The survival of CDC as an institution was not at all certain in the 1950s. In 1947, Emory University gave land on Clifton Road for a headquarters, but construction did not begin for more than a decade. PHS was so intent on research and the rapid growth of the National Institutes of Health that it showed little interest in what happened in Atlanta. Congress, despite the long delay in appropriating money for new buildings, was much more receptive to CDC's pleas for support than either PHS or the Bureau of the Budget.

Two major health crises in the mid-1950s established CDC's credibility and ensured its survival. In 1955, when poliomyelitis appeared in children who had received the recently approved Salk vaccine, the national inoculation program was stopped. The cases were traced to contaminated vaccine from a laboratory in California; the problem was corrected, and the inoculation program, at least for first and second graders, was resumed. The resistance of these 6- and 7-year-olds to polio, compared with that of older children, proved the effectiveness of the vaccine. Two years later, surveillance was used again to trace the course of a massive influenza epidemic. From the data gathered in 1957 and subsequent years, the national guidelines for influenza vaccine were developed.

CDC grew by acquisition . . . . When CDC joined the international malaria-eradication program and accepted responsibility for protecting the earth from moon germs and vice versa, CDC's mission stretched overseas and into space.

CDC played a key role in one of the greatest triumphs of public health, the eradication of smallpox. In 1962 it established a smallpox surveillance unit, and a year later tested a newly developed jet gun and vaccine in the Pacific island nation of Tonga . . . . CDC also achieved notable success at home tracking new and mysterious disease outbreaks. In the mid-1970s and early 1980s, it found the cause of Legionnaires disease and toxic-shock syndrome. A fatal disease, subsequently named acquired immunodeficiency syndrome (AIDS), was first mentioned in the June 5, 1981, issue of *MMWR*.

Although CDC succeeded more often than it failed, it did not escape criticism. For example, television and press reports about the Tuskegee study on long-term effects of untreated syphilis in black men created a storm of protest in 1972. This study had been initiated by PHS and other organizations in 1932 and was transferred to CDC in 1957. Although the effectiveness of penicillin as a therapy for syphilis had been established during the late 1940s, participants in this study remained untreated until the study was brought to public attention. CDC was also criticized because of the 1976 effort to vaccinate the U.S. population against swine flu, the infamous killer of 1918–1919. When some vaccinees developed Guillain-Barre syndrome, the campaign was stopped immediately; the epidemic never occurred.

As the scope of CDC's activities expanded far beyond communicable diseases, its name had to be changed. In 1970 it became the Center for Disease Control and in 1981, after extensive reorganization, Center became Centers. The words "and

Prevention" were added in 1992, but, by law, the well-known three-letter acronym was retained. In health emergencies CDC means an answer to SOS calls from anywhere in the world, such as the recent one from Zaire where Ebola fever raged.

Fifty years ago CDC's agenda was non-controversial (hardly anyone objected to the pursuit of germs), and Atlanta was a backwater. In 1996, CDC's programs are often tied to economic, political, and social issues, and Atlanta is as near Washington as the tap of a keyboard.

Source: Reprinted from Centers for Disease Control and Prevention, *MMWR* 1996;45: 526–528.

1946 to 1996 in a reprint of its official history first published in the *Morbidity and Mortality Weekly Report* (MMWR), a weekly publication of agency.[6]

Today, the CDC's role in connecting federal, state, and local governmental public health efforts is central to the success of the system. Approximately half of the CDC's current approximately $10 billion budget is channeled to state and local health departments. A key function of the CDC is to provide national leadership and to coordinate the efforts of local/state and federal public health agencies.

To understand the local/state and federal public health system, it is important to appreciate that only five percent of all health-related funding goes to public health and of that, less than half goes to population-based prevention as opposed to providing healthcare services as a safety net for individuals. In addition, the role of governmental public health is limited by social attitudes toward government. For instance, we have seen that there are constitutional limitations on the authority of public health and other government agencies to impose actions on individuals. These may limit public health agencies' abilities to address issues ranging from tuberculosis and HIV control to responses to emergencies. The social attitudes of Americans may also limit the authority and resources provided to public health agencies. Americans often favor individual or private efforts over governmental interventions when they believe that individuals and private organizations are capable of success. For instance, some Americans resist active efforts in the schools to provide information and access to contraceptives, while others resist the type of case-finding efforts for HIV/AIDS that have been used successfully in investigating and controlling other communicable diseases.

Today, governmental public health is a global enterprise. Let us take a look at the roles of global health organizations and agencies.

WHAT ARE THE ROLES OF GLOBAL HEALTH ORGANIZATIONS AND AGENCIES?

Public health is increasingly becoming a global enterprise. Global governmental efforts have grown dramatically in recent years. The World Health Organization (WHO) was created in 1948. Its impact has become more prominent in the 21st century with the increasing importance of global health issues. The WHO is a part of the United Nations organizations, which also include the United Nations Infant and Child Emergency Fund (UNICEF) and the Joint United Nations Programme on AIDS/HIV (UNAIDS).[7]

Today, the World Bank and other multilateral financial institutions are the largest funding source for global health efforts.[8] National governmental aid programs, including the United States Agency for International Development (USAID), also play an important role in public health. Table 5-3 outlines the structure/governance, roles, and limitations of global public health agencies.

The complexity of local, state, federal, and global public health agencies raises the question of whether or not these agencies can and do work together. It should not surprise you that close collaboration, while the goal, is often difficult to achieve with so many organizations involved. Thus, it is important to ask: how can public health agencies work together?

HOW CAN PUBLIC HEALTH AGENCIES WORK TOGETHER?

Coordination among public health agencies has been a major challenge that is built into our local, state, and federal system of governance. Increasingly, coordination also requires a global aspect as well. Efforts on all levels have a long way to go. There are signs of hope with the recent progress in such

TABLE 5-3 Global Public Health Organizations

Type of agency	Structure/Governance	Role(s)	Limitations
World Health Organization	United Nations Organization/Seven "regional" semi-independent components, e.g., Pan American Health Organization covers North and South America	Policy development, e.g., tobacco treaty, epidemic control policies/ Coordination of services, e.g., SARS control, vaccine development/Data collection and standardization, e.g., measures of healthcare quality, measures of health status	Limited ability to enforce global recommendations, limited funding and complex international administration
International organizations with focused agenda	UNICEF/UNAIDS	Focus on childhood vaccinations/Focus on AIDS	Limited agendas and limited financing
International financing organizations	The World Bank/Other multilateral regional banks, e.g., InterAmerican and Asian Development Banks	World Bank is largest international funder. Increasingly supports "human capital" projects and reform of healthcare delivery systems and population and nutrition efforts/ Provides funding and technical assistance primarily as loans	Criticized for standardized approach with few local modifications
Bilateral governmental aid organizations	USAID/Many other developed countries have their own organizations and contribute a higher percentage of their gross domestic product to those agencies than does the United States	Often focused on specific countries and specific types of programs, such as the United States' focus on HIV/ AIDS, and maternal and child health	May be tied to domestic politics and global economic, political, or military agendas

fields as tobacco control, food safety, and most notably, the response to SARS. Box 5-3 discusses the dramatic events of the 2003 SARS epidemic, providing an example of what can be done and what needs to be done to address future public health emergencies.[9]

Collaboration needs to be an everyday effort, and not just a requirement for emergencies or epidemics. Let us look at the relationships and needed collaboration among governmental public health and other governmental agencies, nongovernmental organizations, and the healthcare delivery system.

WHAT OTHER GOVERNMENT AGENCIES ARE INVOLVED IN HEALTH ISSUES?

To address health issues, it is important to recognize the important roles that government agencies not designated as health agencies play in public health. Such agencies exist at the local/state, federal, and global levels. To illustrate the involvement of these agencies in health issues, let's begin with the roles of nonhealth agencies at the federal level.

A number of federal agencies serve public health functions even though they are not defined as health agencies. The roles they play are important especially when we take the population health perspective that includes the totality of efforts to promote and protect health and prevent disease, disability, and death.

Environmental health issues are an important part of the role of the Environmental Protection Agency (EPA). Reducing injury and hazardous exposures in the workplace are key goals of the Occupational Safety and Health Administration (OSHA), which is part of the Department of Labor.

Protecting health as part of preparation and response to disasters and terrorism is central to the role of the Department of Homeland Security. The Department of Agriculture shares with the U.S. Food and Drug Administration (FDA) the role of protecting the nation's food supply. The Department of Housing and Urban Development influences the built environment and its impacts on health. The Department of Energy plays important roles in setting radiation safety standards for nuclear power plants and other sources of energy.

The multiple federal agencies involved in health-related matters often means that coordination and collaboration are required across agencies. This is certainly the case with food safety and disaster planning and response. It is true as well for efforts to address problems that cut across agencies,

BOX 5-3 SARS and the Public Health Response

The SARS epidemic of 2003 began with little notice, most likely somewhere in the heartland of China and then spread to other areas of Asia. The world took notice after television screens filled with reports of public health researchers sent to Asia to investigate the illness subsequently contracting and dying from the disease. Not an easily transmissible disease except for those in very close contact, such as investigators, family members, and healthcare providers, the disease spread slowly but steadily through areas of China. Among those infected, the case-fatality rate was very high especially without the benefits of modern intensive care facilities.

The disease did not respond to antibiotics and was thought to be a viral disease by its epidemiological pattern of spread and transmission, but at first no cause was known. The outside world soon felt the impact of the brewing epidemic when cases appeared in Hong Kong that could be traced to a traveler from mainland China. Fear spread when cases were recognized that could not be explained by close personal contact with a SARS victim.

The epidemic continued to spread jumping thousands of miles to Toronto, Canada, where the second greatest concentration of disease appeared. Soon, the whole world was on high alert, if not quite on the verge of panic. At least 8000 people worldwide became sick and almost 10 percent of them died. Fortunately, progress came quite quickly. Researchers coordinated by the World Health Organization (WHO) were able to put together the epidemiological information and laboratory data and establish a presumed cause, a new form of the coronavirus never before seen in humans leading to the rapid introduction of testing.

The WHO and the CDC put forth recommendations for isolation, travel restrictions, and intensive monitoring that rapidly controlled the disease even in the absence of an effective treatment aimed at a cure. SARS disappeared as rapidly as it emerged, especially after systematic efforts to control spread were put in place in China. Not eliminated, but no longer a worldwide threat, SARS left a lasting global impact. The WHO established new approaches for reporting and responding to epidemics—these now have the widespread formal acceptance of most governments.

Once the world could step back and evaluate what happened, it was recognized that the potential burden of disease posed by the SARS epidemic had worldwide implications and raised the threat of interruption of travel and trade. Local, national, and global public health agencies collaborated quickly and effectively. Infection control recommendations made at the global level were rapidly translated into efforts to identify disease at the local level and manage individual patients in hospitals throughout the world. It is a model of communicable disease control that will be needed in the future.

---

such as lead exposure or efforts to reduce the environmental causes of asthma.

WHAT ROLES DO NONGOVERNMENTAL ORGANIZATIONS PLAY IN PUBLIC HEALTH?

Nongovernmental organizations play increasingly important roles in public health in the United States and around the world. The United States has a long tradition of private groups organizing to advocate for public health causes, delivering public health services, and providing funding to support public health efforts. In recent years, these efforts have been expanding globally as well.

The American Red Cross and its network of international affiliates represent a major international effort to provide public health services. The organization plays a central role in obtaining volunteers for blood donations and ensuring the safety and effectiveness of the U.S. and world supply of blood products in collaboration with the FDA.

The ability of the Red Cross to obtain donations, mobilize volunteers, and publicize the need for disaster assistance has allowed it to play a central role in providing lifesaving public health services.

Many private organizations provide public health education, support research, develop evidence-based recommendations, and provide other public health services. Many of these are organized around specific diseases or types of disease, such as the American Cancer Association, the American Heart Association, the American Lung Association and the March of Dimes, which focuses on birth defects. Other private organizations focus primarily on advocacy for individuals with specific diseases, but these organizations also may advocate for specific public health interventions. For instance, Mothers Against Drunk Driving (MADD) has had a major impact on the passage and enforcement of drunk driving laws. HIV/AIDS advocacy groups have influenced policies on confidentiality, funding, and public education.

Globally, nongovernmental organizations (NGOs) increasingly play a key role in providing services and advocating for public health policies. CARE and OXFAM are examples of the types of organizations involved in global health-related crises. Physician groups, including Physicians for Social Responsibility and Doctors Without Borders, have been active in advocating for public health efforts, seeking funding for public health needs, and addressing the ethical implementation of public health programs.

New combinations of governmental and nongovernmental organizations are increasingly developing to fill in the gaps. At the global level, the Global Fund to Fight AIDS, Tuberculosis and Malaria, a public-private effort, provides funding for evidence-based interventions to address these diseases. It is funded not only by governments, but also by private foundations, such as the Bill and Melinda Gates Foundation.

Private foundations have played major roles in funding public health efforts and also stimulating governmental funding. The Rockefeller Foundation's efforts were instrumental in developing local health departments and initiating Schools of Public Health in the United States during the early years of the 20th century. The Kellogg Foundation, the Robert Wood Johnson Foundation, and most recently the Gates Foundation have all played key roles in advancing public health efforts in areas ranging from nutrition to tobacco control to advancing new public health technologies.

Foundation funding has been the catalyst in initiating new funding efforts and sustaining those that are not adequately funded by governments. They cannot be expected, however, to provide long-term support for basic public health services. Thus, additional strategies are required. One key strategy is to link public health efforts with the efforts of healthcare professionals and the healthcare system.

HOW CAN PUBLIC HEALTH AGENCIES PARTNER WITH HEALTH CARE TO IMPROVE THE RESPONSE TO HEALTH PROBLEMS?

We have already seen a number of traditional connections between public health and health care. Clinicians and public health professionals increasingly share a common commitment to evidence-based thinking, cost-effective delivery of services, and computerized and confidential data systems. They also increasingly share a commitment to provide quality services to the entire population and eliminate health disparities. The potential for successful collaboration between public health and health care is illustrated by the National Vaccine Plan, which is discussed in Box 5-4.[10]

In the mid-1990s, a Medicine-Public Health Initiative was initiated to investigate better ways to connect public health with medicine, in particular, and health care, in general. Connecting these two fields has not always had easy or successful results. Additional structures are needed to formalize effective

---

BOX 5-4 National Vaccine Plan

In 1994, a National Vaccine Plan was developed as part of a coordinated effort to accomplish the following goals:

1. Develop new and improved vaccines.

2. Ensure the optimal safety and effectiveness of vaccines and immunizations.

3. Better educate the public and members of the health profession on the benefits and risks of immunizations.

A recent Institute of Medicine (IOM) report evaluated progress since 1994 on achieving the above goals and made recommendations for the development of a revised National Vaccine Plan.[10] The IOM highlighted a number of successes since 1994 in achieving each of the goals of the Plan. These successes illustrate the potential for improved collaboration between public health systems and healthcare systems.

In terms of the development of new and improved vaccines since 1994, over 20 new vaccine products resulting from the collaborative efforts of the National Institutes of Health (NIH), academic, and industry researchers were approved by the Food and Drug Administration (FDA). Novel vaccines introduced include vaccines against pediatric pneumococcal disease, meningococcal disease, and the human papillomavirus (HPV)—a cause of cervical cancer.

In terms of safety, vaccines and vaccination approaches with improved safety have been developed since 1994, including those directed against rotavirus, pertussis (whooping cough), and polio. The FDA Center for Biologics Evaluation and Research (CBER), which regulates vaccines, now has an expanded array of regulatory tools to facilitate the review and approval of safe and efficacious vaccines. The FDA and the Centers for Disease Control and Prevention (CDC) have collaborated on surveillance

---

BOX 5-4 *(Continued)*

for and evaluation of adverse events. Efforts have also been made to increase collaboration with the Centers for Medicare and Medicaid, the Department of Defense, and the Department of Veterans Affairs to improve surveillance and reporting of adverse events following immunization in the adult populations these agencies serve.

In terms of better education of health professionals and the public, progress has also been made. The American Academy of Pediatrics (AAP) collaborates with the CDC for its Childhood Immunization Support. The American Medical Association (AMA) cosponsors the annual National Influenza Vaccine Summit, a group that represents 100 public and private organizations interested in preventing influenza.

Despite the growing collaboration and success in vaccine development and use, new issues have appeared in recent years. Vaccines are now correctly viewed by the health professionals and the public as having both benefits and harms. In recent years, the public has grown more concerned about the safety of vaccines, including the issue of the use of large numbers of vaccines in children. The limitations of vaccines to address problems, such as HIV/AIDS, have also been increasingly recognized. Hopefully, the new National Vaccine Plan will build upon these recent successes and address the new realities and opportunities.

---

and efficient bonds. Models do exist and new ideas are being put forth to connect clinical care and public health. Box 5-5 discusses one such model called **community-oriented primary care (COPC)**.[11]

Despite efforts in the healthcare system to reach out to the community and address public health issues (such as COPC), it remains the primary responsibility of public health to organize and mobilize community-based efforts. Working with nongovernmental organizations and healthcare professionals and organizations is imperative to effectively and efficiently

accomplish the goals of public health. But, how exactly can public health agencies accomplish these goals?

HOW CAN PUBLIC HEALTH TAKE THE LEAD IN MOBILIZING COMMUNITY PARTNERSHIPS TO IDENTIFY AND SOLVE HEALTH PROBLEMS?

An essential service of public health is the mobilization of community partnerships and action to identify and solve health problems. These efforts by public health agencies are critical to putting the pieces of the health system together

---

BOX 5-5 Community Oriented Primary Care (COPC)

Community-oriented primary care (COPC) is a structured effort to expand the delivery of health services from a focus on the individual to also include an additional focus on the needs of communities. Serving the needs of communities brings healthcare and public health efforts together. COPC can be seen as an effort on the part of healthcare delivery sites, such as community health centers, to reach out to their community and to governmental public health institutions.

Table 12–4 outlines the six steps in the COPC process and presents a question to ask when addressing each of these steps. Notice the parallels between COPC and the evidence-based approach that we have outlined. In both cases, the process is actually circular because evaluation efforts often lead to recycling to move the process ahead.

A series of principles underlies COPC including:

- Healthcare needs are defined by examining the community as a whole, not just those who seek care.
- Needed healthcare services are provided to everyone within a defined population or community.
- Preventive, curative, and rehabilitative care are integrated within a coordinated delivery system.
- Members of the community directly participate in all stages of the COPC process.

The concept of COPC, if not the specific structure, has been widely accepted as an approach for connecting the organized delivery of primary health care with public health. It implies that public health issues can and should be addressed when possible at the level of the community with the involvement of healthcare providers and the community members themselves.

TABLE 5-4 The Six Sequential Steps of Community-Oriented Primary Care (COPC).

Steps in the COPC Process	Questions to Ask
1. Community definition	How is the community defined based upon geography, institutional affiliation, or other common characteristics, e.g., use of an Internet site?
2. Community characterization	What are the demographic and health characteristics of the community and what are its health issues?
3. Prioritization	What are the most important health issues facing the community and how should they be prioritized based upon objective data and perceived need?
4. Detailed assessment of the selected health problem	What are the most effective and efficient interventions for addressing the selected health problem based upon an evidence-based assessment?
5. Intervention	What strategies will be used to implement the intervention?
6. Evaluation	How can the success of the intervention be evaluated?

Source: Data from District of Columbia Area Health Education Center. The Conceptual Framework for COPC. Available at http://dcahec.gwumc.edu/education/session4/index.html. Accessed November 8, 2008.

to protect and promote health and prevent disability and death.

Examples of successful collaboration include state tobacco control programs that have been led by public health agencies, but rely heavily on nongovernmental organizations, healthcare professionals and other governmental agencies. These efforts have been able to substantially reduce statewide cigarette smoking rates.

BOX 5-6 Child Oral Health and Community Oriented Public Health (COPH)

The problem of childhood dental disease illustrates the potential for community-oriented public health (COPH). A lack of regular dental care remains a major problem for children in developed, as well as developing countries. The need for this type of care is often high on the agenda of parents, teachers, and even the children themselves.

Public health efforts to improve oral health go back to the late 19th- and early 20th centuries when toothbrushing and toothpaste were new and improved technologies. The public health campaigns of the early 20th century were very instrumental in making toothbrushing a routine part of American life. The history of public health interventions in childhood oral health is a story of great hope and partial success. The benefits of the fluoridation of drinking water were well grounded in evidence. The American Dental Association and the American Medical Association have supported this intervention for over half a century. Resistance from those who view it as an intrusion of governmental authority, however, has prevented universal use of fluoridation in the United States. After over a half century of effort, fluoridation has reached less than two-thirds of Americans through the water supply.

Today, new technologies from dental sealants to more cost-effective methods for treating cavities have again made oral health a public health priority. However, the number of dentists has not grown in recent years to keep up with the growing population. In addition, dental care for those without the resources to pay for it is often inadequate and inaccessible. Thus, a new approach is needed to bring dental care to those in need. Perhaps a new strategy of COPH can make this happen.

Community-oriented public health can reach beyond the institutional and geographical constraints that COPC faces when based in a community health center or other institutions serving a geographically defined population or community. COPH as a governmentally led effort allows a greater range of options for intervention, including those that require changes in laws, incentives and governmental procedures. These might include: authorizing new types of clinicians, providing services in nontraditional settings such as schools, funding innovations to put new technologies into practice, and addressing the regulatory barriers to rapid and cost-effective delivery of services.

Efforts to organize coordinated programs for lead control have also met with some success. Collaborative efforts between public health and health care have identified and treated children with elevated lead levels. Cooperation with other agencies has provided for the removal of lead paint from homes and testing and control of lead in playgrounds, water, and most recently, toys.

It is possible to view the coordinated mobilization of public and private efforts as **community-oriented public health (COPH)**. We can see this as a parallel to COPC. In COPC, healthcare efforts are expanded to take on additional public health roles. In COPH, public health efforts are expanded to collaborate with healthcare delivery institutions, as well as other community and governmental efforts. Child oral health, an example of COPH, is illustrated in Box 5-6.[12]

Developing community partnerships is a time-consuming and highly political process that requires great leadership and diplomatic skills. Central authority and command and control approaches are generally not effective in the complex organizational structures of the United States. New approaches and new strategies are needed to bring together the organizations and individuals who can get the job done.

We have now looked at the organization of the public health system and the challenges it faces in accomplishing its core functions and providing its essential services. The role of public health cannot be viewed only in its current form. Understanding public health also requires considering its future and how we can plan for the expected and the unexpected.

Discussion Questions

Take a look at the questions posed in the following scenarios which were presented at the beginning of this chapter. See now whether you can answer them.

1. A young man in your dormitory is diagnosed with tuberculosis. The health department works with the student health service to test everyone in the dorm, as well as in his classes, with a TB skin test. Those who are positive for the first time are advised to take a course of a medicine called INH. You ask: is this standard operating procedure?

2. You go to a public health meeting and learn that many of the speakers are not from public health agencies, but from the Departments of Labor, Commerce, Housing, and Education. You ask: what do these departments have to do with health?

3. You hear that a new childhood vaccine was developed by the NIH, approved by the FDA, endorsed for federal payment by the CDC and recommended for use by the American Academy of Pediatrics. You ask: do all these agencies and organizations always work so well together?

4. A major flood in Asia leads to disease and starvation. Some say it is due to global warming, others to bad luck. Coordinated efforts by global health agencies, assisted by nongovernmental organizations (NGOs) and outside governmental donors, help get the country back on its feet. You ask: what types of cooperation are needed to make all of this happen?

5. A local community health center identifies childhood obesity as a problem in their community. They collect data demonstrating that the problem begins as early as elementary school. They develop a plan that includes clinical interventions at the health center and also at the elementary school. They ask the health department to help them organize an educational campaign and assist in evaluating the results. Working together, they are able to reduce the obesity rate among elementary school children by one-half. This seems like a new way to practice public health, you conclude. What type of approach is this?

REFERENCES

1. Public Health in America. Essential Public Health Services. Available at http://www.health.gov/phfunctions/public.htm. Accessed April 3, 2009.

2. Institute of Medicine. *The Future of Public Health*. Washington, DC: National Academies Press; 1988.

3. Turnock BJ. *Public Health: What It Is and How It Works*. 4th ed. Sudbury, MA: Jones and Bartlett Publishers; 2009.

4. Turnock BJ. *Essentials of Public Health*. Sudbury, MA: Jones and Bartlett Publishers; 2007.

5. United States Department of Health and Human Services. Organizational Chart. Available at http://www.hhs.gov/about/orgchart/. Accessed April 3, 2009.

6. Centers for Disease Control and Prevention. History of CDC. *Morbidity and Mortality Weekly Report*. 1996;45: 526–528.

7. World Health Organization. About WHO. Available at http://www.who.int/about/en/. Accessed April 3, 2009.

8. The World Bank. Health, Nutrition and Population. Available at http://web.worldbank.org/WBSITE/EXTERNAL/TOPICS/EXTHEALTH NUTRITIONANDPOPULATION/0,,menuPK:282516~pagePK:149018~p iPK:149093~theSitePK:282511,00.html. Accessed April 3, 2009.

9. Duffin J, Sweetman A. *SARS in Context: Memory, History, Policy*. Montreal: McGill-Queen's University Press; 2006.

10. Institute of Medicine. Initial Guidance for an Update of the National Vaccine Plan: A Letter Report to the National Vaccine Program Office. Available at http://www.nap.edu/catalog/12257.html. Accessed April 3, 2009.

11. District of Columbia Area Health Education Center. The Conceptual Framework for COPC. Available at http://dcahec.gwumc.edu/education/session4/index.html. Accessed April 3, 2009.

12. Pfizer Global Pharmaceuticals. *Milestones in Public Health: Accomplishments in Public Health over the Last 100 Years*. New York: Pfizer Global Pharmaceuticals; 2006.

ENDNOTES

a. This does not imply that components of the work cannot be contracted to nongovernmental organizations. This activity is increasingly occurring. The concept of core function, however, implies that public health agencies remain responsible for these functions even when the day-to-day work is conducted through contracts with an outside organization.

b. This delegation may occur at the discretion of the state government or it may be included in the state's constitution providing what is called **home rule authority** to local jurisdictions. In general, jurisdictions with home rule authority exercise substantially more autonomy.

PART I ADDENDUM: Historical Contextual Timeline of Important Events in Health Policy and Law

	1800	1820	1830
Political Party in Power—Federal Government	Federalist (1789–1801);	Democrat–Republican (1801–1829); Democrat (1829–1841)	
President	George Washington (1789–1797); John Adams (1797–1801)	Thomas Jefferson (1801–1809); James Madison (1809–1817); James Monroe (1817–1825); John Quincy Adams (1825–1829); Andrew Jackson (1829–1837); Martin Van Buren (1837–1841)	
U.S. House of Representatives	Pro-Administration (1789–1793); Anti-Administration (1793–1795); Jeffersonian Republican (1795–1797); Federalist (1797–1801)	Jeffersonian Republican (1801–1823)	Adams–Clay Republican (1823–1825); Adams (1825–1827); Jacksons (1827–1829) · Jacksons (1829–1837); Democrat (1837–1841)
U.S. Senate	Pro-Administration (1789–1795); Federalist (1795–1801)	Republican (1801–1823)	Jackson–Crawford Republican (1823–1825); Jacksonian (1825–1833) · Anti-Jacksonian (1833–1835); Jacksonian (1835–1837); Democrat (1837–1841)
Major Social and Political Events	Industrial Revolution (~ 1790–1860) and increased urbanization	War of 1812 (1812–1814) and post-war economic growth	
Key Federal Legislative Proposals/Laws and Key Legal Decisions	1798 U.S. Public Health Service Act: Creates the **Marine Hospital Service**, predecessor to the Public Health Service, to provide medical care to merchant seamen.	*Marbury v. Madison,* 5 U.S. 137 (1803): Established the Supreme Court's power of judicial review; **1818 Office of the Surgeon General** established.	
Important Developments in Health and Medicine	State Poor Laws require communities to care for residents who are physically or mentally incapable of caring for themselves; States begin building dispensaries in the late 1700s to provide medication to the poor; Almhouses serve as primitive hospitals, providing limited care to the indigent; Public health focuses on fighting plague, cholera, and smallpox epidemics, often through quarantine.		

PART I ADDENDUM: Historical Contextual Timeline of Important Events in Health Policy and Law

		1840	1850	1860
Political Party in Power—Federal Government	President	Whig (1841–1845); Democrat (1849–1853); Democrat (1853–1861)	Millard Fillmore (1850–1853); Franklin Pierce (1853–1857); James Buchanan (1857–1861)	Republican; Democrat
		William Henry Harrison (1841); John Tyler (1841–1845); James K. Polk (1845–1849); Zachary Taylor (1849–1850)		Abraham Lincoln (1861–1865); Andrew Johnson (1865–1869)
	U.S. House of Representatives			Republican 1859–1875
	U.S. Senate	Whig 1841–1845 (27th–28th); Democrat 1845–1861 (29th–36th)		Republican 1861–1879 (37th–45th)
Major Social and Political Events		Industrial Revolution (~ 1790–1860) and increased urbanization		U.S. Civil War (1861–1865) and postwar expansion in interstate commerce.
		U.S.-Mexican War 1846–1848	Crimean War 1853–1856	
Key Federal Legislative Proposals/Laws and Key Legal Decisions		1848 Import Drug Act: Initiates drug regulation; U.S. Customs Service is required to enforce purity standards for imported medications.		1862 Bureau of Chemistry (forerunner of the FDA) is established as a scientific laboratory in the Department of Agriculture.
Important Developments in Health and Medicine		1846 First publicized use of general anesthetic; use of anesthetics increases the number of surgeries performed; 1847 American Medical Association is founded.	Studies by Edwin Chadwick in England, Lemuel Shattuck in Massachusetts, and others reveal that overcrowded and unsanitary conditions breed disease, and advocate establishment of local health boards; By the end of the 1800s, 40 states and several localities establish health departments.	1861 First nursing school is founded and the role of nursing is established during the Civil War; 1860s Louis Pasteur develops the germ theory of disease; 1865 Antiseptic surgery is introduced by Joseph Lister, decreasing death rates from surgical operations; with the advent of licensing, the practice of medicine begins to become a more exclusive realm.

PART I ADDENDUM: Historical Contextual Timeline of Important Events in Health Policy and Law

		1870	1880	1890
Political Party in Power—Federal Government	President	Republican Ulysses S. Grant (1869–1877); Rutherford B. Hayes (1877–1881)	Republican (1881–1885); Democrat (1885–1889) James A. Garfield (1881); Chester A. Arthur (1881–1885); Grover Cleveland (1885–1889)	Republican (1889–1893); Democrat (1893–1897); Republican (1897–1901) Benjamin Harrison (1889–1893); Grover Cleveland (1893–1897); William McKinley (1897–1901)
	U.S. House of Representatives	Democrat 1875–1881	Republican 1881–1883; Democrat 1883–1889	Republican 1889–1891; Democrat 1891–1895; Republican 1895–1911
	U.S. Senate	Democrat 1879–1881 (46th)	Republican 1881–1893 (47th–52nd)	Democrat 1893–1895 (53rd); Republican 1895–1913 (54th–62nd)
Major Social and Political Events				
Key Federal Legislative Proposals/Laws and Key Legal Decisions		**1870s Medical Practice Acts:** Establish state regulation of physician licensing; **1870 Marine Hospital Service** is centralized as a separate bureau of the Treasury Department; **1878 National Quarantine Act:** Grants the Marine Hospital Service quarantine authority, due to its assistance with yellow fever outbreak.	**1887** National Hygienic Laboratory, predecessor lab to the National Institutes of Health, is established in Staten Island, New York, by the National Marine Health Service.	**1890 Sherman Antitrust Act:** Prohibits interstate trusts so economic power would not be concentrated in a few corporations.
Important Developments in Health and Medicine		**1877** Louis Pasteur discovers that anthrax is caused by bacteria; scientists find bacteriologic agents causing tuberculosis, diphtheria, typhoid, and yellow fever; immunizations and water purification interventions follow recent discoveries; state and local health departments create laboratories; states begin passing laws requiring disease reporting and establishing disease registries.	**1880s** First hospitals established and the importance of hospitals in the provision of medical care increases; **1882** First major employee-sponsored mutual benefit association was created by Northern Pacific Railway, includes health care benefit; Social Insurance movement results in the creation of "sickness" insurance throughout many countries in Europe; **1895** X-rays discovered.	

PART I ADDENDUM: Historical Contextual Timeline of Important Events in Health Policy and Law

		1900	1910
Political Party in Power—Federal Government		Republican/Progressive	Republican
	President	Theodore Roosevelt (1901–1909)	William H. Taft (1909–1913)
	U.S. House of Representatives	Republican 1895–1911	Democrat 1911–1919 (62nd–65th)
	U.S. Senate	Republican	Republican
Major Social and Political Events		**Progressive Era** 1900–1920: Characterized by popular support for social reform, part of which included compulsory health insurance. Roosevelt campaigned on a social insurance platform in 1912.	
Key Federal Legislative Proposals/Laws and Key Legal Decisions		*Hurley v. Eddingfield*, 59 N.E. 1058 (Ind. 1901): Physicians are under no duty to treat; a physician is not liable for arbitrarily refusing to render medical assistance; **1902 Marine Health Service** renamed the **Public Health and Marine Hospital Service (PHMHS)** as its role in disease control activities expands; **1902 Biologics Control Act:** Regulates safety and effectiveness of vaccines, serums, etc.; *Jacobson v. Massachusetts*, 197 U.S. 11 (1905): State statute requiring compulsory vaccination against smallpox is a constitutional exercise of police power; **1906 Food and Drug Act** (Wiley Act): Gives regulatory power to monitor food manufacturing, labeling, and sales to FDA predecessor; **1908** Federal Employers Liability Act: Creates workers compensation program for select federal employees.	**1912 Children's Bureau of Health** established in Department of Commerce (later moved to Department of Labor); **1912 Public Health and Marine Hospital Service** is renamed the **Public Health Service** and is authorized to investigate human disease and sanitation; **1914 Clayton Antitrust Act:** Clarifies the Sherman Antitrust Act and includes additional prohibitions.
Important Developments in Health and Medicine		**1901** AMA reorganizes at local/state level and gains strength, beginning era of "organized medicine" as physicians as a group become a more cohesive and increasingly professional authority;	**1910** Flexner Report on Medical Education creates medical school standards; "Sickness" insurance established by Britain in 1911 and Russia in 1912; Socialist and Progressive parties in the United States support similar "sickness" insurance.

PART I ADDENDUM: Historical Contextual Timeline of Important Events in Health Policy and Law

	1910 (continued)	1920
Political Party in Power—Federal Government	Democrat	Republican
President	Woodrow Wilson (1913–1921)	Warren G. Harding (1921–1923); Calvin Coolidge (1923–1929)
U.S. House of Representatives	Democrat 1913–1919 (63rd–65th); Republican 1919–1933 (66th–72nd)	Republican 1919–1931 (66th–71st)
U.S. Senate	Democrat 1913–1919 (63rd–65th); Republican 1919–1933 (66th–72nd)	Republican
Major Social and Political Events	World War I (1914–1919; U.S. enters in 1917)	
Key Federal Legislative Proposals/Laws and Key Legal Decisions	**1911:** First state workers compensation law enacted; **1918 Chamberlain-Kahn Act:** Provides first federal grants to states for public health services.	**1921 Sweet Act:** Establishes the Veterans Administration; **1922 Shepherd-Towner Act:** Provides grants for the Children's Bureau and state maternal and child health programs; it is the first direct federal funding of health services for individuals.
Important Developments in Health and Medicine	**1913 American College of Surgeons (ACS)** is founded; 1918 ACS begins accreditation of hospitals; **1918–1919 pandemic flu** kills over 600,000 people in the U.S.	**1920 AMA** passes resolution against compulsory health insurance; AMA opposition combined with entry into World War I (and the anti-German sentiments aroused), undermines support for national health reform and government insurance; **1929 Blue Cross** establishes its first hospital insurance plan at Baylor University; chronic illnesses begin to replace infectious diseases as most significant health threat; with innovations in medical care, health care costs begin to rise.

PART I ADDENDUM: Historical Contextual Timeline of Important Events in Health Policy and Law

	1930
Political Party in Power—Federal Government	Republican
President	Herbert Hoover (1929–1933)
U.S. House of Representatives	Democrat 1931–1947 (72nd–79th)
U.S. Senate	Democrat 1933–1947 (73rd–79th)
Major Social and Political Events	**Great Depression** (1929 through 1930s); **New Deal** 1933–1939
Key Federal Legislative Proposals/Laws and Key Legal Decisions	**1930 National Institutes of Health** established; **1933 Federal Emergency Relief Administration:** Provides limited medical services for the medically indigent; **1935 Social Security Act:** Provides federal grant-in-aid funding for states to create and maintain public health services and training, expands responsibilities for the Children's Health Bureau, and establishes Aid to Families with Dependent Children (AFDC) wefare program; **1935 Works Project Administration** is created, including projects to build and improve hospitals; **1938 Food, Drug and Cosmetic Act:** Expands regulatory scope of FDA to require premarket approval (in response to deaths from an untested product); **1939** Public Health Service is transferred from the Treasury Department to the new Federal Security Agency.
Important Developments in Health and Medicine	The Great Depression threatens financial security of physicians, hospitals, and individuals; commercial insurance industry rises in the absence of government-sponsored insurance plans; In the **late 1930s** the Blue Cross (hospital services) and Blue Shield (physician services) health insurance plan created; prepaid group health plans/medical cooperatives gain popularity with some providers and consumers, but are opposed by AMA; 1932–1972 Tuskegee syphillis study.

PART I ADDENDUM: Historical Contextual Timeline of Important Events in Health Policy and Law

	1940	1950
Political Party in Power—Federal Government	Democrat	Democrat
President	Franklin D. Roosevelt (1933–1945)	Harry S Truman (1945–1953)
U.S. House of Representatives	Democrat	Republican 1947–1949 (80th); Democrat 1949–1953 (81st–82nd)
U.S. Senate	Democrat	Republican 1947–1949 (80th); Democrat 1949–1953 (81st–82nd)
Major Social and Political Events	**World War II** (1939–1945, Pearl Harbor 1941)	Cold War ideology and McCarthyism (1950–1954); **Korean War** 1950–1953
Key Federal Legislative Proposals/Laws and Key Legal Decisions	**1941 Manham Act:** Funds wartime emergency building of hospitals; **1942 National War Labor Board** rules that the provision of benefits, including health insurance, does not violate wage freeze; **1944 PublicHealth Service Act:** Consolidates the laws related to the functions of the PHS; **1946 Hill-Burton Act:** Funds hospital construction to improve access to hospital-based medical care; **1946 The 'Communicable Disease Center'** (CDC) opens as part of the Public Health Service; **1949** Truman's national health insurance proposal is defeated.	**1953 Department of Health, Education, and Welfare (HEW)** is created from the Federal Security Agency, and the Public Health Service is transferred to HEW.
Important Developments in Health and Medicine	**1945** Nobel Prize in Medicine awarded for development of penicillin treatment for humans, which is used extensively in the war; **1945** Kaiser Permanente, a large prepaid, integrated health plan is opened to the public; **1946** the Emerson Report released proposing overall plan for public health in the U.S.; **1948** AMA opposes Truman's plan for national health insurance and sentiments against national health reform also fueled by the Cold War; employer-based health insurance grows rapidly with no national health insurance program and as employers compete for a short supply of employees due to the war and because health benefits are exempted from the wage freeze; after WWII, labor unions gained the right to bargain collectively, leading to another expansion in employee health plans; commercial insurance has taken over 40% of the market from Blue Cross.	**1951 Joint Commission on Accreditation of Hospitals (JCAH)** is created to provide voluntary accreditation.

PART I ADDENDUM: Historical Contextual Timeline of Important Events in Health Policy and Law

	1950 (continued)	1960
Political Party in Power—Federal Government	Republican	Democrat
President	Dwight D. Eisenhower (1953–1961)	John F. Kennedy (1961–1963)
U.S. House of Representatives	Republican 1952–1955 (83rd); Democrat 1955–1994 (84th–103rd)	Democrat
U.S. Senate	Republican 1953–1955 (83rd); Democrat 1955–1981 (84th–96th)	Democrat
Major Social and Political Events		Economic downturn
Key Federal Legislative Proposals/Laws and Key Legal Decisions	**1954** IRS declares that employers can pay health insurance premiums for their employees with pretax dollars; *Brown v. Board of Education,* 347 U.S. 483 (1954): racial segregation in public education violates the Equal Protection Clause of 14th Amendment;. **1956 Dependents Medical Care Act:** Creates government medical care program for military and dependents outside VA system; **1956 Social Security Act** is amended to provide Social Security Disability Insurance.	**1962 Amendments to Food, Drug and Cosmetic Acts** require that new drugs be "effective."
Important Developments in Health and Medicine	**1953** Salk creates polio vaccine; **1954** first organ transplant is performed; continued progression in medical science and technology leads to increased costs; political focus turns to Korean War and away from medical care reform.	

PART I ADDENDUM: Historical Contextual Timeline of Important Events in Health Policy and Law

		1960s (continued)	1970s
Political Party in Power—Federal Government		Democrat	Republican
	President	Lyndon B. Johnson (1963–1969)	Richard M. Nixon (1969–1974)
	U.S. House of Representatives	Democrat	Democrat
	U.S. Senate	Democrat	Democrat
Major Social and Political Events			
Key Federal Legislative Proposals/Laws and Key Legal Decisions		**1960 Kerr-Mills program** provides federal funding through vendor payments to states for medically indigent elderly; *Simkins v. Moses H. Cone Memorial Hospital*, 323 F.2d 959 (4th Cir. 1963): Racial segregation in private hospitals receiving federal Hill-Burton funds violates the Equal Protection Clause of the 14th Amendment; **1964: Civil Rights Act** passed; **1965 Medicare and Medicaid** programs created through Social Security Amendments; *Griswold v. Connecticut*, 381 U.S. 479 (1965): The Constitution protects a right to privacy; state law forbidding the use of contraceptives or provision of them to married couples violates a constitutional right to marital privacy; **1966 Civilian Health and Medical Program for the Uniformed Services (CHAMPUS)** created.	President Nixon's proposed comprehensive health insurance plan fails; **1971** proposed Health Security Act from Senator Edward Kennedy (D-MA) fails. **1970** Communicable Disease Center is renamed the **Centers for Disease Control; 1972 Social Security Amendments** extend Medicare eligibility and create Supplemental Security Income (SSI) program; *Canterbury v. Spence*, 464 F.2d 772 (D.C. Cir. 1972): Established modern law of informed consent based on a reasonable patient standard; *Roe v. Wade*, 410 U.S. 113 (1973): Constitutional right to privacy encompasses a woman's decision to terminate her pregnancy; **1973 Health Maintenance Organization Act:** Supports growth of HMOs.
Important Developments in Health and Medicine		**1965** Medicare and Medicaid created; **1967** first human heart transplant.	Health care costs continue to rise dramatically, due to advances in medical technology, high-tech hospital care, the new pool of paying patients from Medicaid and Medicare, increased utilization of services, and increased physician specialization; **1972** computed tomography (CT) scan first used.

PART I ADDENDUM: Historical Contextual Timeline of Important Events in Health Policy and Law

	1970s (continued)		1980s
Political Party in Power—Federal Government	Republican	Democrat	Republican
President	Gerald R. Ford (1974–1977)	Jimmy Carter (1977–1981)	Ronald Reagan (1981–1989)
U.S. House of Representatives	Democrat	Democrat	Democrat
U.S. Senate	Democrat	Democrat	Republican 1981–1987 (97th–99th); Democrat 1987–1995 (100th–103rd)
Major Social and Political Events			**1989** "New Federalism" of the Reagan administration; Berlin Wall falls
Key Federal Legislative Proposals/Laws and Key Legal Decisions	**1974 Employment Retirement Income Security Act (ERISA)** passed; **1977 Health Care Financing Administration (HCFA)** is created to administer the Medicare and Medicaid programs.	**1979** President Carter introduces a National Health Plan to Congress; **1979 Department of Health and Human Services (HHS)** is created from a reorganized HEW.	**1983** Medicare implements prospective payment system for reimbursing hospitals; **1986 Emergency Medical Treatment and Active Labor Act (EMTALA):** Ensures access to emergency services in Medicare-participating hospitals regardless of ability to pay; **1986 Health Care Quality Improvement Act:** Creates the National Practitioner Databank; **1986 Consolidated Omnibus Budget Reconciliation Act (COBRA):** Includes health benefit provisions that establish continuation of employer-sponsored group health coverage; **1989 Medicare Catastrophic Coverage Act of 1988:** Includes outpatient prescription drug benefit and other changes in Medicare (repealed 1989).
Important Developments in Health and Medicine		**1978** First baby conceived through in vitro fertilization is born.	**1981** Scientists identify AIDS; **1987** JAHC changes name to the **Joint Commission on Accreditation of Healthcare Organizations Medicine** (JCAHO); **1980** World Health Assembly declares smallpox eradicated; shift away from traditional fee-for-service insurance plans and toward managed care.

PART I ADDENDUM: Historical Contextual Timeline of Important Events in Health Policy and Law

	1990
Political Party in Power—Federal Government	Republican
President	George Bush (1989–1993)
	Democrat
	William J. Clinton (1993–2001)
U.S. House of Representatives	Democrat
	*First time since 1955 that both houses are Republican; Republican 1995–Present (104th–108th)
U.S. Senate	Democrat
	Republican 1995–Present (104th–108th (Jan 3–20, 2001 and June 6, 2001–Nov 12, 2002 Democrat))
Major Social and Political Events	1990–1991 Gulf War
	Foreign crises in Haiti and Bosnia; 1993 North American Free Trade Agreement (NAFTA); Whitewater investigation; 1995 Oklahoma City bombing; 1998 President Clinton impeached.
Key Federal Legislative Proposals/Laws and Key Legal Decisions	**1989 Agency for Healthcare Policy and Research** created; **1990 Americans with Disabilities Act (ADA):** provides protection against disability discrimination; **1990 Ryan White CARE Act:** Creates federal support for AIDS-related services; *Cruzan v. Director, Missouri. Dep't of Health*, 497 U.S. 261 (1990): First "right to die" case before Supreme Court, in which the Court held that a competent person has a constitutionally-protected liberty interest in refusing medical treatment.
	1993 President Clinton's proposed **Health Security Act** is defeated; **1995** PHS reorganized to report directly to the Secretary of HHS; **1996 Health Insurance Portability & Accountability Act (HIPAA):** Includes privacy rules to protect personal health information, attempts to simplify coding for health bills, makes it difficult to exclude patients from insurance plans due to preexisting conditions; **Personal Responsibility and Work Opportunity Reconciliation Act of 1996** replaces AFDC with the Temporary Assistance for Needy Families program (TANF); **1996 Mental Health Parity Act:** Requires insurance carriers that offer mental health benefits to provide the same annual and lifetime dollar limits for mental and physical health benefits; **1997 Food and Drug Administration Modernization Act:** Relaxes restrictions on direct-to-consumer advertisements of prescription drugs; **1997 Balanced Budget Act:** adds Medicare Part C, the Medicare managed care program, and creates the State Children's Health Insurance Program which allows states to extend health insurance coverage to additional low-income children; **The Ticket to Work and Work Incentives Improvement Act of 1999:** Creates a new state option to help individuals with disabilities stay enrolled in Medicaid or Medicare coverage while returning to work.
Important Developments in Health and Medicine	Enrollment in managed care doubles; greater use of outpatient services; rate of health spending is relatively stable at roughly 12% to 13% of GDP; direct-to-consumer advertising of pharmaceuticals increases dramatically and the Internet is used as a source of medical information; **1997** Ian Wilmut clones a sheep from adult human cells; **1994** Oregon Health Plan rations Medicaid services through a prioritized list of medical treatments and conditions. After the September 11 attacks, public health becomes focused on emergency preparedness.

PART I ADDENDUM: Historical Contextual Timeline of Important Events in Health Policy and Law

		2000
Political Party in Power—Federal Government	President	Republican George W. Bush (2001–2009)	Democrat Barrak Obama (2009–)
	U.S. House of Representatives	Republican 2005–2007 (109th); Democrat 2007–2009 (110th)	Democrat 2009–2011 (111th); Republican 2011– (112th)
	U.S. Senate	Republican	Democrat
Major Social and Political Events		9/11/2001 terrorist attacks on World Trade Center in New York and on the Pentagon; 2001 U.S. military action in Afghanistan; Iraq War 2003 begins.	Great Recession (began in December 2007), including financial crisis and collapse of housing market; Passage of the 2010 Patient Protection and Affordable Care Act.
Key Federal Legislative Proposals/Laws and Key Legal Decisions		Congressional attention and spending turns to international and security concerns, little discussion of health reform; **2002 Homeland Security Act** Transfers some HHS functions, including the Strategic National Stockpile of emergency pharmaceutical supplies and the National Disaster Medical Service, to the new Department of Homeland Security; **2003 Medicare Modernization Act:** Adds a prescription drug benefit to Medicare beginning in 2006; **2004 Project BioShield Act:** Provides funding for vaccines and medications for biodefense and allows expedited FDA review of treatments in response to attacks; **2005 Deficit Reduction Act** makes significant changes to Medicaid, including state options to reduce benefits, increase cost-sharing, and impose new documentation requirements; **2006 Medicare Part D Prescription Drug Plan** goes into effect; **2008 Mental Health Parity Act amended** to require insurers to treat mental health conditions on the same basis as physical conditions.	Congressional focus on health reform, spending cuts; President Obama establishes the Office of Health Reform; **2009 American Reinvestment and Recovery Act (ARRA)** creates incentives to help develop health information technology and expand the primary care workforce, among other things; **2009 Children's Health Insurance Program Reauthorization Act** extending (for 4.5 years) and expanding the program; **2010 Patient Protection and Affordable Care Act (ACA):** Comprehensive health reform including an "individual mandate" to purchase insurance coverage, Medicaid expansion, creation of state health insurance "exchanges," and much more.
Important Developments in Health and Medicine		After the September 11 attacks, public health becomes focused on emergency preparedness; **2003** Sequencing of human genome completed; **2003 SARS** epidemic and **2004** flu vaccine shortage raises concerns about public health readiness; worldwide concern about a possible Avian flu epidemic; high level of concern in the U.S. about the rising rate of obesity; **2006** Guardasil vaccine protecting against two strains of the human papilloma virus (HPV), which is associated with cervical cancer, approved by the FDA; **2007** International Health Regulations, passed by WHO in 2005, are implemented by member states.	Rate of health spending continues to skyrocket, accounting in 2009 for 17% of the Gross Domestic Product; **2009** H1N1 swine flu virus pandemic.

PART I ADDENDUM REFERENCES

1. Birn A-E. Struggles for national health reform in the United States. *Am J Pub Health*. 2003;93(1):86–94.

2. Sultz HA, Young KM. *Health Care USA: Understanding Its Organization and Delivery*, 4th ed. Sudbury, Mass.: Jones and Bartlett; 2004.

3. Shi L, Singh DA. *Delivering Health Care Services in America: A Systems Approach*, 3rd ed. Sudbury, Mass.: Jones and Bartlett; 2004.

4. National Library of Medicine. Exhibitions in the history of medicine: images from the history of the Public Health Service. http://www.nlm.nih.gov/exhibition/phs_history/contents.html. Accessed August 15, 2011.

5. Food and Drug Administration, Center for Drug Evaluation and Research. Time line: chronology of drug regulation in the United States. Available at: http://www.fda.gov/cder/about/history/time1.htm. Accessed August 15, 2011.

6. American Medical Association. Chronology of AMA history. Available at: http://www.ama-assn.org/ama/pub/category/1922.html. Accessed August 15, 2011.

7. U.S. Senate. People. Party leadership. Available at: http://www.senate.gov/pagelayout/history/one_item_and_teasers/partydiv.htm. Accessed August 15, 2011.

8. U.S. House of Representatives. Historical highlights. Party divisions. Available at: http://clerk.house.gov/histHigh/Congressional_History/partyDiv.html. Accessed August 15, 2011.

9. Kaiser Family Foundation. History of Health Reform Efforts in the U.S. http://healthreform.kff.org/flash/health-reform-new.html. Accessed August 15, 2011.

10. Centers for Medicare and Medicaid, National Health Expenditure Data, 2009. https://cms.gov/NationalHealthExpendData/25_NHE_Fact_Sheet.asp. Accessed August 15, 2011.

11. World Health Organization, Global Alert Response Pandemic (H1N1) 2009. http://www.who.int/csr/disease/swineflu/en/index.html. Accessed August 15, 2011.

PART II

Essential Issues in Health Policy and Law

Part I of this book introduced frameworks for conceptualizing health policy and law and described basic aspects of policy, the policymaking process, law, the legal system, and the healthcare and public health systems. Part II covers many of the essential issues in health policy and law. Chapter 6 addresses individual rights in health care and public health, followed by discussions of the fundamentals of health insurance and health economics in Chapters 7 and 8, respectively. Chapter 9 provides an overview of national health reform.   Chapters 10–12 cover government insurance programs, healthcare quality, and public health preparedness, respectively. After completing Part II, you will understand, among other things, how health insurance functions, why private employer-based coverage dominates the health insurance market, why gaps in health insurance coverage remain, the importance of health economics to health policymaking, key provisions in the Affordable Care Act, various policy and legal dimensions to healthcare quality, and the role of public health in preparing for and responding to national and global emergencies.

CHAPTER 6

Individual Rights in Health Care and Public Health

LEARNING OBJECTIVES

By the end of this chapter, you will be able to:

- Describe the meaning and importance of the "no-duty" principle
- Explain generally how the U.S. approach to health rights differs from that of other high-income countries
- Describe the types and limitations of individual legal rights associated with health care
- Describe the balancing approach taken when weighing individual rights against the public's health

Around the same time as the scenario just described, the Cambridge, Massachusetts, Board of Health ordered everyone within city limits to be vaccinated against the smallpox disease under a state law granting local boards of health the power, under certain circumstances, to require the vaccination of individuals. After refusing to abide by the Cambridge Board's order, Henning Jacobson was convicted by a state trial court and sentenced to pay a $5 fine. Remarkably, Mr. Jacobson's case not only made its way to the United States Supreme Court, it resulted in one of the Court's most important public health rulings and a sweeping statement about limitations to fundamental individual rights in the face of threats to the public's health.

BOX 6-1 **Vignette**

At the turn of the 20th century, an Indiana physician named George Eddingfield repeatedly refused to come to the aid of Charlotte Burk, who was in labor, even though he was Mrs. Burk's family physician. Doctor Eddingfield conceded at trial that he made this decision for no particular reason, and despite the facts that he had been offered monetary compensation in advance of his performing any medical services and that he was aware that no other physician was available to provide care to Mrs. Burk. Unattended by any medical providers, Mrs. Burk eventually fell gravely ill, and both she and her unborn child died. After a trial and subsequent appeals, Dr. Eddingfield was found to not have wrongfully caused either death.

INTRODUCTION

The real-life scenarios in the vignette touch upon the key issues you will confront in this chapter: namely, the ways in which the law creates, protects, and restricts individual rights in the contexts of health care and public health. Individuals in society are deeply impacted by law on a daily basis, and this fact is no less true when individuals navigate the healthcare system, or when an individual's actions are measured against the broader interests of the public's health. Over many decades, legal principles have been rejected, developed, and refined as the law continually struggles to define the appropriate relationship between individuals and the physicians, hospitals, managed care companies, and others they encounter in the healthcare delivery system, and between individuals and governmental sectors charged with protecting public health and welfare. These balancing acts are made all the more difficult as the legal system bumps up against the quick pace of technological advancements in medicine and against amorphous, potentially deadly risks to the public's health, such as bioterrorism and fast-spreading influenzas.

After a background section, this chapter considers individual legal rights in health care, beginning with a brief overview of health rights under international and foreign law. This sets up a much lengthier discussion of healthcare rights in the United States, which for purposes of this chapter are classified according to an important distinction: legal rights *to* health care, and rights that individuals can claim only *within* the context of the healthcare system—that is, only once they have found a way to access needed care.[a] Examples of the latter type of rights include the right to refuse unwanted treatment, the right to autonomy in making personal healthcare decisions, and the right to be free from wrongful discrimination when receiving care. Finally, the chapter turns to a discussion of individual rights in the context of government-initiated public health efforts. This topic is dominated by the role and scope of government "police powers," which permit governments, when acting to promote or protect public health, to curtail individual freedoms and liberties.

BACKGROUND

Lurking behind any discussion of individual rights in a health context is one of the most basic principles in U.S. health law: Generally speaking, individuals have no legal right to healthcare services (or to public health insurance) and, correspondingly, there exists on the part of healthcare providers no general, legal duty to provide care. This is referred to as the "no-duty" or "no-duty-to-treat" principle, which is aptly described by the Indiana Supreme Court in the well-known case of *Hurley v. Eddingfield*,[1] the facts of which we referred to in the first vignette at the opening of this chapter. In its decision, the court wrote that the state law permitting the granting of a medical license

> provides for . . . standards of qualification . . . and penalties for practicing without a license. The [state licensing] act is preventive, not a compulsive, measure. In obtaining the state's license (permission) to practice medicine, the state does not require, and the licensee does not engage, that he will practice at all or on other terms than he may choose to accept.[2]

In other words, obtaining a license to practice medicine does not obligate an individual to actually practice, or to practice in a particular fashion or with a particular clientele; the

licensure requirement exists instead to filter out individuals who may not have the requisite knowledge or skills to practice medicine. The same can be said for obtaining a law license, or even a driver's license: the former does not obligate a lawyer to practice, or to choose certain types of clients or cases; the latter does not require that a person actually drive, or drive a certain make of car. As with a medical license, the point of a law or driver's license is to guarantee that should the licensee *choose* to practice law or operate a motor vehicle, she is qualified to do so. Furthermore, you will recall from the facts provided in the vignette that Dr. Eddingfield was Mrs. Burk's family physician, and may believe that this fact is enough to establish a sufficient legal relationship between the two to hold Dr. Eddingfield accountable for the death of Mrs. Burk. However, the general legal rule is that physician–patient relationships are specific to "spells of illness" and that past treatment is not tantamount to an *existing* physician–patient relationship. Put another way, under the law a physician–patient relationship does not exist as a general, continuous matter—even with one's family physician, internist, primary care physician, etc.—but rather it exists for a specific period of time and must be established (or renewed) accordingly.

Note that this basic premise—that there is no fundamental right to healthcare services in the United States—was not altered by the passage in 2010 of the Patient Protection and Affordable Care Act (ACA). While it is arguable that the ACA moves the country in a direction that makes a legal right to health care more plausible down the road,[3] and there can be no arguing that it makes health care more accessible to millions of people by virtue of its health insurance reforms (as discussed later in this chapter and in greater detail elsewhere), it does not create a right to care.

As you begin to think through the significance and implications of the no-duty principle, it is important to understand that there are many other legal principles and health laws that define the relationship between an individual and another health system stakeholder (e.g., a physician, hospital, or government program). In fact, there are several federal and state laws that narrow the scope of the no-duty principle. For example, a federal law called the Examination and Treatment for Emergency Medical Conditions and Women in Labor Act enables all individuals to access needed hospital care in medical emergencies, irrespective of the individual's ability to pay for that care or a hospital's willingness to treat the individual. Also, both federal and state laws that generally prohibit certain forms of discrimination (say, based on race or disability) apply with equal force in the context of health care, and might force an accessibility to health services that otherwise would not exist. Furthermore, some public health insurance programs—Medicaid and Medicare, most prominently—create entitlements (a legal concept denoting a legal claim to something) to services for individuals who meet the programs' eligibility criteria,[4] and some health insurance products obligate physicians participating in the plan's networks to extend care to plan members. Finally, some states have implemented universal healthcare coverage programs, such as Maine's Dirigo Health Reform Act, which is designed to provide access to health coverage to every person in Maine.

When thinking about the law's no-duty principle, you must also take into account the role of medical ethics, which might require more of a healthcare professional than does the law. For example, no law mandates that licensed physicians aid a stranger in medical distress, but many believe an ethical obligation exists in this instance. And although legally the no-duty principle would dictate otherwise, many healthcare providers consider themselves ethically obligated to furnish at least some level of care to those who cannot pay for it. In short, although there is no universal legal right to health care in the United States, certain situations give rise to healthcare rights, and specific populations may be entitled to health care or receive it purely through the magnanimity of ethics-conscious providers.

Perhaps because of the federal and state laws that chip away at the no-duty-to-treat principle, many students new to the study of health law erroneously assume that the principle is a legal anomaly, borne solely of the incredible historical power and autonomy of the medical profession and without modern precedent. In this case, it is instructive to place the principle in a broader "welfare rights" context. During the 1960s, public interest lawyers, social reform activists, and others pressed for an interpretation of the federal Constitution that would have created an individual right to welfare. Under this view, the government must provide individuals with minimally adequate levels of education, food, housing, health care, and so on.[5] But in a series of cases, the Supreme Court rejected the notion of a constitutional right to welfare.

Consider the right to education. Even though every state provides free public schools and makes education for minors compulsory, there is no national, generalized legal right to education. In the case of *San Antonio Independent School District v. Rodriguez*,[6] the Supreme Court ruled that education is not a fundamental right under the federal Constitution's Equal Protection Clause. The plaintiffs in the *Rodriguez* case were Mexican-American parents whose children attended elementary and secondary schools in an urban San Antonio school district. They had attacked as unconstitutional Texas' system of financing public education and filed the suit on behalf of schoolchildren throughout the state who were members of minority groups or who resided in relatively poor school districts. But the Court turned the plaintiffs' argument away, noting that although education is one of the most important services states perform, "it is not among the rights afforded explicit protection under our Federal Constitution. Nor do we find any basis for saying it is implicitly so protected. . . . [T]he undisputed importance of education will not alone cause this Court to depart from the usual standard for reviewing a State's social and economic legislation."[7]

In the wake of the *Rodriguez* decision, several states interpreted their own constitutions as prohibiting inequitable methods of financing public education, thereby recognizing on some level a right to a minimally "meaningful" education. Subsequently, lawyers and social activists seeking to promote equal access to all manner of critical services seized on these state determinations, arguing that an egalitarian approach to constitutional interpretation should not be limited to education.[8] Note, for example, how easily one author's writings about the right to education could just as well have been written with respect to health care:

> Requiring an adequate education will help to fulfill our nation's promise, articulated in *Brown [v. Board of Education]*, that an individual be free to achieve her full potential. Ensuring educational adequacy will promote children's emotional and intellectual development, their career path and earning potential and thus their success throughout life. A meaningful education offers the hope that children can escape the degradation of poverty and its lack of opportunity, and attain pride, participation in this country's economic and political life, and financial and emotional success.[9(p825)]

However, efforts around ensuring adequate education have not been emulated in other social policy areas, such as health care. In fact, health care is treated not as a right, but as a commodity (like televisions or vacuum cleaners) subject to private market forces and socioeconomic status. During the public debate in 1993 over President Bill Clinton's failed attempt at national health reform, U.S. Representative Dick Armey (R-TX) stated that "health care is just a commodity, just like bread, and just like housing and everything else."[10(p102)] But why should this be the case, particularly when the private health insurance market has presumably found equilibrium at a point that continually leaves tens of millions of Americans uninsured, and particularly because health care (like education) is different from vacuum cleaners and other everyday goods in that it has "a fundamental bearing on the range of one's opportunities to realize one's life plans"?[8(p80)]

There is no single answer to the question of why health care is generally treated in this country as something less than an individual legal right. Many factors beyond the scope of this chapter are implicated: the nature and interpretation of the federal Constitution, politics, a weak labor movement, powerful interest groups, the nation's free market philosophies, the public's often negative view of the government, and more.[11] In this chapter, we limit the discussion to describing the kinds of health rights that do exist, how they operate in the context of the healthcare delivery system and when considered against government-initiated public health efforts. Before we explore in depth the scope of individual health-related rights under U.S. law, however, we briefly describe these same types of rights under international law and under the law of other countries. Through this examination, we provide a backdrop for understanding this country's approach to legal rights in the context of health.

INDIVIDUAL RIGHTS AND HEALTH CARE: A GLOBAL PERSPECTIVE

Despite being the world leader in terms of the development of medical technologies and the quantity of medical services, the United States is one of the only high-income nations that does not guarantee health care as a fundamental right, and it is the only developed nation that has not implemented a system for insuring at least all but the wealthiest segment of its population against healthcare costs.[4(p3)] In essence, other high-income nations with social democracies treat the provision of health care as a social good[b] (i.e., something that could be supported through private enterprise but is instead supported by the government and financed from public funds). And, it is worth noting that nations that provide universal healthcare entitlements have not been bankrupted as a result. In fact, according to Professor Timothy Jost, "all of the other developed nations spend less on health care than does the U.S., in terms of both dollars per capita and proportion of gross domestic product."[4(p3)]

A foreign nation's universal healthcare rights—whether an unlimited right to health, a right to medical care generally or to a basic package of services, a right to healthcare insurance, or something else—exist under international human rights principles or under its national constitution. When recognized by governments, human rights accrue to all individuals because the rights are based upon the dignity and worth of the human being; thus, technically, a human right exists regardless of whether positive law (a constitution, a statute) has given it expression.[12] Examples of positive expressions of health as a human right include Article 25 of the 1948 Universal Declaration of Human Rights, which states that "[e]

veryone has the right to a standard of living adequate for the health and well-being of himself and of his family, including . . . medical care . . . and the right to security in the event of . . . sickness, disability," and the Constitution of the World Health Organization, which says that "The enjoyment of the highest attainable standard of health is one of the fundamental rights of every human being without distinction of race, religion, political belief, economic or social condition."

In terms of national constitutions, a 2004 survey reported that some two-thirds of constitutions worldwide address health or health care, and that almost all of these do so in universal terms, rather than being limited to certain populations.[13] For example, consider the health-related constitutional aspects of four politically and culturally diverse countries—Italy, the Netherlands, South Africa, and Poland—that have some type of "right to health": Italy's Constitution guarantees a right to health; under the Dutch Constitution, the government is mandated "to promote the health of the population"; the Constitution of South Africa imposes on government the obligation to provide access to health services; and under Polish constitutional law, citizens are guaranteed "the right to health protection" and access to publicly financed healthcare services.[14]

Of course, including language respecting health rights in a legal document—even one as profound as a national constitution—does not guarantee that the right will be recognized or enforced. As in the United States, multiple factors might lead a foreign court or other tribunal to construe rights-creating language narrowly or to refuse to force implementation of what is properly considered a right. Examples of these factors include the relative strength of a country's judicial branch vis-a-vis other branches in its national governance structure and a foreign court's view of its country's ability to provide services and benefits inherent in the health right.

BOX 6-2 Discussion Question

Depending on one's personal experience in obtaining health care, or one's view of the role of physicians in society, of law as a tool for social change, of the scope of medical ethics, or of the United States' place in the broader global community, the no-duty principle might seem appropriate, irresponsible, or downright wrong. Imagine you are traveling in a country where socialized medicine is the legal norm, and your discussion with a citizen of that country turns to the topic of your countries' respective health systems. When asked, how will you account for the fact that health care is far from being a fundamental right rooted in American law?

INDIVIDUAL RIGHTS AND THE HEALTHCARE SYSTEM

The "global perspective" you just read was brief for two reasons. First, a full treatment of international and foreign health rights is well beyond the scope of this chapter, and second, historically speaking, international law has played a limited role in influencing this nation's domestic legal principles. As one author commented, "Historically the United States has been uniquely averse to accepting international human rights standards and conforming national laws to meet them."[15(p1156)] This fact is no less true in the area of health rights than in any other major area of law. As described earlier in this chapter, universal rights to health care are virtually nonexistent in the United States, even though this stance renders it almost solitary among industrialized nations of the world.

This is not to say that this country has not contemplated health care as a universal, basic right. For instance, in 1952, a presidential commission stated that "access to the means for attainment and preservation of health is a basic human right."[16(p4)] Medicaid and Medicare were the fruits of a nationwide debate about universal healthcare coverage. And during the 1960s and 1970s, the claim that health care was not a matter of privilege, but rather of right, was "so widely acknowledged as almost to be uncontroversial."[17(p389)] Nor is it to say that certain populations do not enjoy healthcare rights beyond those of the general public. Prisoners and others under the control of state governments have a right to minimal health care,[18] some state constitutions expressly recognize a right to health or healthcare benefits (for example, Montana includes an affirmative right to health in its constitution's section on inalienable rights), and individuals covered by Medicaid have unique legal entitlements. Finally, it would be inaccurate in describing healthcare rights to only cover rights to obtain health care in the first instance, because many important healthcare rights attach to individuals once they manage to gain access to needed healthcare services.

The remainder of this section describes more fully the various types of individual rights associated with the healthcare system. We categorize these rights as follows:

1. Rights related to receiving services explicitly provided under healthcare, health financing, or health insurance laws; for example, the Examination and Treatment for Emergency Medical Conditions and Women in Labor Act, Medicaid, and the Affordable Care Act.
2. Rights concerning freedom of choice and freedom from government interference when making healthcare decisions; for example, choosing to have an abortion.
3. The right to be free from unlawful discrimination when accessing or receiving health care; for example, Title VI of the federal Civil Rights Act of 1964, which prohibits discrimination on the basis of race, color, or national origin by entities that receive federal funding.[12(p12),19]

Rights Under Healthcare and Health Financing Laws

We begin this discussion of rights-creating health laws with the Examination and Treatment for Emergency Medical Conditions and Women in Labor Act (also referred to as EMTALA, which is the acronym for the law's original name—the Emergency Medical Treatment and Active Labor Act—or, for reasons soon to become clear, the "patient anti-dumping statute"). We then briefly discuss the federal Medicaid program in a rights-creating context and wrap up this section with a brief discussion of the ACA.

Rights Under Health Care Laws: Examination and Treatment for Emergency Medical Conditions and Women in Labor Act

Because EMTALA represents the only truly universal legal right to health care in this country—the right to access emergency hospital services—it is often described as one of the building blocks of health rights. EMTALA was enacted by Congress in 1986 to prevent the practice of "patient dumping"—that is, the turning away of poor or uninsured persons in need of hospital care. Patient dumping was a common strategy among private hospitals aiming to shield themselves from the potentially uncompensated costs associated with treating poor and/or uninsured patients. By refusing to treat these individuals and instead "dumping" them on public hospitals, private institutions were effectively limiting their patients to those whose treatment costs would likely be covered out-of-pocket or by insurers. Note that the no-duty principle made this type of strategy possible.

EMTALA was a conscious effort on the part of elected federal officials to chip away at the no-duty principle: By creating legally enforceable rights to emergency hospital care for all individuals regardless of their income or health insurance status, Congress created a corresponding legal *duty* of care on the part of hospitals. At its core, EMTALA includes two related duties, which technically attach only to hospitals that participate in the Medicare program (but then again, nearly every hospital in the country participates). The first duty requires covered hospitals to provide an "appropriate" screening examination to all individuals who present at a hospital's emergency department seeking care for an "emergency medical condition." Under the law, an appropriate medical screening is one that is nondiscriminatory and that adheres to a hospital's established emergency care guidelines. EMTALA defines an emergency medical condition as a

> medical condition manifesting itself by acute symptoms of sufficient severity (including severe pain) such that the absence of immediate medical attention could reasonably be expected to result in (i) placing the health of the individual (or, with respect to a pregnant woman, the health of the woman or her unborn child) in serious jeopardy, (ii) serious impairment to bodily functions, or (iii) serious dysfunction of any bodily organ or part; or with respect to a pregnant woman who is having contractions, that there is inadequate time to effect a safe transfer to another hospital before delivery, or that transfer may pose a threat to the health or safety of the woman or the unborn child.[20]

The second key duty required of hospitals under EMTALA is to either stabilize any condition that meets the above definition or, in the case of a hospital without the capability to treat the emergency condition, undertake to transfer the patient to another facility in a medically appropriate fashion. A proper transfer is effectuated when, among other things, the transferring hospital minimizes the risks to the patient's health by providing as much treatment as is within its capability, when a receiving medical facility has agreed to accept the transferred patient, and when the transferring hospital provides the receiving facility all relevant medical records.

The legal rights established under EMTALA are accompanied by heavy penalties for their violation. The federal government, individual patients, and "dumped on" hospitals can all initiate actions against a hospital alleged to have violated EMTALA, and the federal government can also file a claim for civil money penalties against individual physicians who negligently violate an EMTALA requirement.

Rights Under Healthcare Financing Laws: Medicaid

Many laws fund programs that aim to expand access to health care, such as state laws authorizing the establishment of public hospitals or health agencies, and the federal law establishing the vast network of community health clinics that serve medically underserved communities and populations. However, the legal obligations created by these financing laws are generally enforceable only by public agencies, not by individuals.

The Medicaid program is different in this respect. (Medicaid has been covered elsewhere in greater depth, but because

of its importance in the area of individual healthcare rights, we mention it also in this context.) Although most certainly a law concerning healthcare financing, Medicaid is unlike most other health financing laws in that it confers the right to individually enforce program obligations through the courts.[21(pp419–424)] This right of individual enforcement is one of the reasons why Medicaid, nearly 50 years after its creation, remains a hotly debated public program. This is because the legal entitlements to benefits under Medicaid are viewed as a key contributor to the program's high cost. Yet whether Medicaid's legal entitlements are any more of a factor in the program's overall costs than, say, the generally high cost of health care, is not clearly established.

Rights Under Health Insurance Laws: The Affordable Care Act

As you will learn in subsequent chapters, the ACA is far more than a law that just concerns health insurance; in fact, it is a sweeping set of reforms that touch on healthcare quality, public health practice, health disparities, community health centers, healthcare fraud and abuse, comparative effectiveness research, the health workforce, health information technology, long-term care, and more. However, for purposes of this chapter, we mention it briefly it in terms of its impact on the rights of individuals to access health insurance and to equitable treatment by their insurer. Details concerning the ACA's effect on the public and private insurance markets are discussed elsewhere.

Through a series of major reforms to existing policies, the ACA reshapes the private health insurance market, transforming private health insurance from a commodity that regularly classified (and rejected) individuals based on their health status, age, disability status, and more into a social good whose availability is essential to individual and population health.[22] The key elements of this shift include: a ban on exclusion and discrimination based on health status or pre-existing health conditions; new protections that ensure that, once covered by insurance, individuals will have access to necessary care without regard to artificial annual or lifetime expenditure caps; a guarantee that once insurance coverage is in place, it cannot be rescinded except in cases of applicant fraud; a ban on additional fees for out-of-network emergency services; the provision (by 2019) of financial subsidies for an estimated 19 million low- and moderate-income individuals and for some 4 million small businesses; the inclusion, in the individual and small group insurance markets, of a package of "essential health benefits" that must be covered; and the creation of state health insurance "exchanges" through which individuals and small employer groups can purchase high-quality health insurance in a virtual marketplace that is substantially regulated and that simplifies the job of learning about, selecting, and enrolling in insurance plans.

The ACA also reforms the public health insurance market, primarily through an expansion of Medicaid eligibility to cover all non-elderly low-income persons who are legal residents or citizens. This reform essentially closes Medicaid's last remaining coverage gap for the poor—namely, the program's historical denial of coverage for non-pregnant, working-age adults without minor children—and in so doing promises insurance coverage (and the resulting access to health care that often follows coverage) to an additional 16 million people.

Rights Related to Freedom of Choice and Freedom from Government Interference

EMTALA and Medicaid are remarkable in terms of the rights *to* health care that they each provide, though as mentioned earlier in this chapter, individual rights that attach *within* the context of healthcare provision can be equally important. Important individual rights within health care include the right to make informed healthcare decisions and the right to personal privacy and autonomy.

The Right to Make Informed Healthcare Decisions

One of the most important healthcare rights is the right of individual patients to make informed decisions about the scope and course of their own care. This includes the right to *refuse* treatment, regardless of the treatment's nature or urgency: The right to refuse treatment exists whether the patient is considering ingesting prescribed medication for minor pain, to undergo a minimally invasive test or procedure, or to consent to a major, potentially life-sustaining operation like the removal of a brain tumor. However, the right pertaining to informed decision making does not come without qualifiers and exceptions, as described below.

Modern notions of informed consent have their roots in the Nuremberg Code, which derived from the Nuremberg trials in the late 1940s of German physicians who performed horrendous experiments on prisoners in Nazi concentration camps during the Second World War. The code spells out principles of research ethics, including the need to secure in advance the voluntary consent of the research subject. These principles have been codified and expanded in American federal statutory and regulatory law concerning federally funded biomedical research.[23] But if the Nuremberg Code can be thought of as the roots of U.S. informed consent law, then the decision in *Canterbury v. Spence*[24] can be thought of as the trunk.

In 1959, Jerry Canterbury was a 19-year old suffering from severe back pain. His neurosurgeon, Dr. William Spence, informed him that he would need a laminectomy—a surgical procedure where the roof of spinal vertebrae are removed or trimmed to relieve pressure on the spinal cord—to correct what the doctor believed was a herniated disc. However, Dr. Spence did not inform Canterbury of any risks associated with the surgery. The day after the operation, while appearing to recuperate normally, Canterbury fell from his hospital bed while no attendant was on hand and a few hours later began suffering paralysis from the waist down. This led to a second spinal surgery, but Canterbury never fully recovered; years later, he needed crutches to walk and he suffered from paralysis of the bowels.

Canterbury sued Dr. Spence, alleging negligence in both the performance of the laminectomy and the doctor's failure to disclose risks inherent in the operation. The federal trial judge ruled in Dr. Spence's favor and Canterbury appealed, setting the stage for the now-famous decision in 1972 by the federal Court of Appeals for the District of Columbia Circuit (considered second in national importance to the Supreme Court).[c] The decision includes two important determinations pertinent to this chapter. The first is that "as a part of the physician's overall obligation to the patient, [there exists a] duty of reasonable disclosure of the choices with respect to proposed therapy and the dangers inherently and potentially involved."[25] The court viewed this duty as a logical and modest extension of a physician's existing general duty to his patients. Importantly, the court discarded the notion that "the patient should ask for information before the physician is required to disclose."[26] In other words, the duty to disclose requires more than just answering patient questions; it demands voluntary disclosure on the part of the physician of pertinent medical information.

The *Canterbury* court's second key determination concerns the actual scope of the disclosure required—in other words, once the physician's duty to disclose is triggered, what information satisfies the legal requirement? On this matter the court made several observations: that the patient's right of "self-decision" is paramount, that the right to consent can be properly exercised only if the patient has sufficient information to make an "intelligent choice," that the sufficiency test is met when all information "material to the decision" is disclosed, and that the disclosure's legality should be measured objectively, not subjectively from the perspective of a particular physician or patient. From these observations, the court settled on three required pieces of disclosed information: a proposed treatment's inherent and potential risks, any alternatives to a proposed treatment, and the likely outcome of not being treated at all. Applying these criteria, the court ruled that Dr. Spence's failure to disclose even the tiniest risk of paralysis resulting from the laminectomy entitled Canterbury to a new trial.

As mentioned earlier, the right to make informed healthcare decisions is not boundless. For example, the court in *Canterbury* wrote that where disclosure of a treatment's risks would pose a threat of harm to the patient (for example, because it would severely complicate treatment or psychologically damage the patient) as to become "unfeasible or contraindicated from a medical point of view," the physician's duty to disclose could be set aside. Furthermore, a patient's competency from a legal vantage point plays a major role in her ability to consent to treatment.

The *Canterbury* decision, and subsequent decisions based on it, have over the years been interpreted expansively, and today the right to make informed healthcare decisions has many facets beyond a clear explanation of proposed treatments, potential risks and complications, and the like. For example, patients have the right to know whether outside factors, like research interests or financial considerations, are coloring a physician's thinking about a proposed course of treatment; patients whose first language is not English have the right to an interpreter; and patients have the right to designate in advance their treatment wishes, whether through written advance directives or another individual.

The Right to Personal Privacy

Another right related to freedom of choice/freedom from government interference is the constitutional right to personal privacy. Although the federal Constitution makes no explicit mention of the right to privacy, the Supreme Court has recognized some form of it since the 1890s.[d] The Court has taken a more or less two-pronged approach to the right. The first defines the protected personal interest as "informational privacy," meaning the limiting of others' access to and use of an individual's private information.[e] The second approach is concerned with individual autonomy and freedom from governmental interference in making basic personal decisions, and is the type of privacy right focused on in this section. This right is one of the most debated in law, both because of its implicit nature (constitutionally speaking) and because it has served as the legal underpinning of several divisive social issues, including abortion, intimate associations, and the decisions as to whether, when, and how to end one's life.

The right to privacy achieved prominence beginning with the Supreme Court's landmark 1965 decision in *Griswold v. Connecticut*,[27] in which the Court considered the constitutionality of a state law criminalizing the provision of contraception to married couples. In the early 1960s, Estelle Griswold, the Executive Director of the Planned Parenthood League of Connecticut, and one of her colleagues were convicted of aiding and abetting "the use of a drug, medicinal article, or instrument for the purpose of preventing conception" by providing contraceptives to a married couple in violation of Connecticut law. The Court determined that although the Constitution does not explicitly protect a general right to privacy, certain provisions in the Bill of Rights create "penumbras," or zones, of guaranteed privacy, and that Connecticut's law constituted an undue intrusion into one of these zones (i.e., marriage).[28]

After the *Griswold* decision, advocates of the constitutional right to privacy flooded the federal courts with cases designed to expand the scope of the right. Quickly, laws banning interracial marriage were struck down,[29] as were laws prohibiting unmarried individuals from using contraception.[30] At the same time, federal courts were confronted with cases asking them to determine how the right to privacy applied in the context of abortion. The remainder of this section analyzes the courts' response to this particular issue. We selected the constitutional right to abortion as the focal point of the right to privacy discussion because it is not only one of the most contested rights in a health context, but also one of the most contested areas of public policy generally.

The Roe v. Wade Decision   Few judicial decisions have affected this country's legal, political, and social landscape as much as *Roe v. Wade*.[31] In 1970, an unmarried pregnant woman filed a lawsuit under the pseudonym "Roe" challenging the constitutionality of a Texas criminal law that prohibited procuring or attempting an abortion at any stage of pregnancy,

---

BOX 6-3 Discussion Questions

Go back to the first legal principle drawn from the *Canterbury* decision: namely, that physicians have a duty of reasonable disclosure to include therapy options and the dangers potentially involved with each. Do you agree with the court that this duty is both a logical and modest extension of physicians' "traditional" obligation to their patients? Why or why not? Depending on your answer, are you surprised to learn that some states have opted not to follow the *Canterbury* court's patient-oriented standard of informed consent, relying instead on the more conventional approach of measuring the legality of physician disclosure based on what a reasonable physician would have disclosed?

except for the purpose of saving the pregnant woman's life. Roe was joined in the lawsuit by a doctor who performed abortions in violation of the law. They argued that the constitutional right to privacy articulated in *Griswold* and its progeny included a woman's right to choose to obtain an abortion. Texas, through district attorney Henry Wade, claimed that the law was permissible because the state had a compelling interest in protecting women from an unsafe medical procedure and in protecting prenatal life. The federal trial court agreed with Roe and declared the law unconstitutional, and Texas immediately appealed to the U.S. Supreme Court, which agreed to hear the case (in rare circumstances, the Supreme Court will hear a case without an intermediate appellate court ruling.).

At the Supreme Court, the work of drafting the majority opinion in *Roe v. Wade* fell to Justice Harry Blackmun, who earlier in his legal career had been counsel to a well-known and highly regarded medical clinic. By a 7–2 margin, the Court ruled that the constitutional right to privacy, which in its view most strongly emanates from the Fourteenth Amendment's due process protections, is broad enough to encompass a woman's decision to terminate her pregnancy.

Once the Court established that a woman has a constitutional right to obtain an abortion, it went on to discuss the limits of that right. Roe had argued that the right to obtain an abortion is absolute, and that no state or federal law abridging the right could be enacted. The Court did not agree. Justice Blackmun wrote that states have both an interest in protecting the welfare of its citizens and a duty to protect them, and that the duty extends to the unborn. According to the Court, "a State may properly assert important interests in safeguarding health, in maintaining medical standards, and in protecting potential life. At some point in pregnancy, these respective interests become sufficiently compelling to sustain regulation of the factors that govern the abortion decision."[32] The Court then linked both a woman's "right to choose" and states' interest in protecting potential life to the viability of the fetus, setting forth the following "trimester framework" that enhances state power to regulate the abortion decision and restricts a pregnant woman's right as the fetus grows older:

a. For the stage prior to approximately the end of the first trimester, the abortion decision and its effectuation must be left to the medical judgment of the pregnant woman's attending physician.

b. For the stage subsequent to approximately the end of the first trimester, the State, in promoting its interest in the health of the mother, may, if it chooses, regulate the abortion procedure in ways that are reasonably related to maternal health.

c. For the stage subsequent to viability, the State, in promoting its interest in the potentiality of human life may, if it chooses, regulate, and even proscribe, abortion except where it is necessary, in appropriate medical judgment, for the preservation of the life or health of the mother.[33]

As a matter of both policy and law, the *Roe* decision has been vigorously criticized.[34–37] For example, detractors claim that the Court improperly made social policy by "finding" an expansive constitutional right to privacy (one broad enough to include the right to terminate a pregnancy) where one did not expressly exist. As a legal matter, many have argued that the decision relied too heavily on medical concepts that would be rendered obsolete as medical technology advanced and that would, in turn, result in a narrowing of the constitutional right advanced in the decision.[f]

Regardless of these and other criticisms, the *Roe* decision was monumental beyond its legal implications. It galvanized political forces opposed to abortion and prompted a movement to create ways to discourage the practice through state policies designed to regulate the factors involved in the abortion decision. For example, as described next, Pennsylvania enacted a law that imposed a series of requirements on women seeking abortion services, and it was this law that nearly 20 years after *Roe* set the stage for another battle at the Supreme Court over abortion and the right to privacy.

The* Planned Parenthood of Southeastern Pennsylvania v. Casey *Decision At issue in the 1992 case of *Planned Parenthood of Southeastern Pennsylvania v. Casey*[38] were several amendments to Pennsylvania's Abortion Control Act that made it more difficult for a pregnant woman to obtain an abortion: one provision required that a woman seeking an abortion be provided with certain information at least 24 hours in advance of the abortion; a second stated that a minor seeking an abortion had to secure the informed consent of one of her parents, but included a "judicial bypass" option if the minor did not wish to or could not obtain parental consent; a third amendment required that a married woman seeking an abortion had to submit a signed statement indicating that she had notified her husband of her intent to have an abortion, though certain exceptions were included; and a final provision imposed new reporting requirements on facilities that offered abortion services. The revised law exempted compliance with these requirements in the event of a "medical emergency."

Before any of the new provisions took effect, they were challenged by five Pennsylvania abortion clinics and a group of physicians who performed abortions. The federal trial court struck down all of the provisions as unconstitutional violations under *Roe*. On appeal, the Third Circuit Court of Appeals reversed and upheld all of the provisions, except for the husband notification requirement, as constitutional. The plaintiffs appealed to the Supreme Court, which agreed to hear the case.

The Court's 5–4 decision in favor of the plaintiffs in *Casey* expressly acknowledged the widespread confusion over the meaning and reach of *Roe*, and it used its opinion in *Casey* to provide better guidance to legislatures seeking to regulate abortion as a constitutionally protected right. Specifically, the Court in *Casey* sought to define more precisely both the constitutional rights of pregnant women and the legitimate authority of states to regulate some aspects of the abortion decision. The deeply divided Court wrote:

> It must be stated at the outset and with clarity that *Roe*'s essential holding, the holding we reaffirm, has three parts. First is a recognition of the right of the woman to choose to have an abortion before viability and to obtain it without undue interference from the State. Before viability, the State's interests are not strong enough to support a prohibition of abortion or the imposition of a substantial obstacle to the woman's effective right to elect the procedure. Second is a confirmation of the State's power to restrict abortions after fetal viability, if the law contains exceptions for pregnancies which endanger the woman's life or health. And third is the principle that the State has legitimate interests from the outset of the pregnancy in protecting the health of the woman and the life of the fetus that may become a child. These principles do not contradict one another; and we adhere to each.[39]

Notice how, in interpreting *Roe*, the Court in *Casey* makes some remarkable alterations to the contours of the right to choose to have an abortion. First, trimesters were replaced by fetal viability as the regulatory touchstone. Second, the pregnant woman, not her attending physician, effectuates the abortion decision. Third, a state's interest in protecting pregnant women and fetuses now attaches "from the outset of the pregnancy," not at the beginning of the second trimester. Fourth, and perhaps most important, the Court's invalidation of the trimester framework enabled the establishment of a new "undue burden" standard for assessing the constitutionality of state abortion regulations. Under this new standard, a state may not prohibit abortion prior to fetal viability, but it may promulgate abortion regulations as long as they do not pose a "substantial obstacle" to a woman seeking to terminate a

pregnancy. The Court did not, however, alter its decision in *Roe* that, post-viability, a state may proscribe abortion except when pregnancies endanger a woman's life or health. Taken together, these alterations both maintain a pregnant woman's basic constitutional right to obtain an abortion pre-viability, and enhance state interest in protecting the potentiality for human life.

Once the Court established the undue burden standard for assessing the constitutionality of state abortion regulations, it applied the standard to each constitutionally questionable amendment to Pennsylvania's Abortion Control Act. In the end, only the spousal notification provision was struck down as an unconstitutional burden; the Court determined that some pregnant women may have sound reasons for not wishing to inform their husbands of their decision to obtain an abortion, including fear of abuse, threats of future violence, and withdrawal of financial support. As a result, the Court equated the spousal notification requirement to a substantial obstacle because it was likely to prevent women from obtaining abortions.

The Court majority in *Casey* provided a new template for lower courts to use in deciding the constitutionality of state abortion regulations. Likewise, the opinion offered guidance to state legislatures as to what kinds of abortion restrictions were likely to withstand a constitutional attack. Nonetheless, some state legislatures have tested the boundaries of *Casey* by enacting bans on a procedure known as "partial birth" abortion, an issue to which we now turn.

The Stenberg v. Carhart *Decision*   The undue burden standard articulated in *Casey* for assessing the constitutionality of abortion regulations was put to the test in *Stenberg v. Carhart*.[40] At issue in the case was a Nebraska criminal law banning "an abortion procedure in which the person performing the abortion partially delivers vaginally a living unborn child before killing the unborn child and completing the delivery." It further defined "partially delivers vaginally a living unborn child before killing the unborn child" to mean "deliberately and intentionally delivering into the vagina a living unborn child, or a substantial portion thereof, for the purpose of performing a procedure that the person performing such procedure knows will kill the unborn child and does kill the unborn child." The Nebraska law penalized physicians who performed a banned abortion procedure with a prison term of up to 20 years, a fine of up to $25,000, and the automatic revocation of the doctor's license to practice medicine in Nebraska.

Dr. Leroy Carhart, a Nebraska physician who performed abortions, filed a lawsuit seeking a declaration that the Nebraska law violated the constitutional principles set forth in *Roe* and *Casey*. After a lengthy trial, a federal district court agreed with Dr. Carhart and declared the Nebraska law unconstitutional. The Court of Appeals for the Eighth Circuit agreed, concluding that Nebraska's statute violated the Constitution as interpreted by the Supreme Court in *Casey*. The Supreme Court then granted review.

The Court was unequivocal in its opinion in *Stenberg* that the case was not a forum for a discussion on the propriety of *Roe* and *Casey*, but rather an application of the rules stated in those cases. In applying the undue burden standard to pre-viability abortions, the Court considered trial court testimony from expert witnesses regarding several different abortion procedures then-current in medical practice to flesh out the procedures' technical distinctions and to determine whether the procedures fell within Nebraska's definition of "partial birth" abortion. The Court determined that two distinct abortion procedures were relevant—dilation and evacuation (D&E), and dilation and extraction (D&X)—and that the Nebraska law's vague definition of "partial birth" abortion effectively banned both procedures.

Again by a 5–4 majority, the Supreme Court struck down the Nebraska law as unconstitutional on two separate grounds. First, the Court concluded that the statute created an undue burden on women seeking pre-viability abortions. The Court reasoned that banning the most commonly used method for pre-viability second trimester abortions—the D&E procedure—unconstitutionally burdened a woman's ability to choose to have an abortion. Second, the Court invalidated the state law because it lacked an exception for the preservation of the health of the pregnant woman. The Court rejected Nebraska's claim that the banned procedures were never necessary to maintain the health of the pregnant woman and held that "significant medical authority" indicated that the D&X procedure is in some cases the safest abortion procedure available.[41]

At the time *Stenberg* was decided, nearly 30 states had laws restricting D&E- and D&X-type abortions in some manner. Attempts to enact bans on these abortion procedures, however, have not been made only by state legislatures. Congress has tried numerous times to promulgate a federal ban, and after *Stenberg* was handed down, congressional opponents to abortion vowed to craft a ban that would pass constitutional muster. This effort culminated in the Partial Birth Abortion Ban Act of 2003 (PBABA).

Partial Birth Abortion Ban Act of 2003   PBABA represents Congress's third attempt since 1996 to ban "partial birth" abortions. Previous bills were vetoed by President Bill Clinton

in 1996 and 1997, but in late 2003, PBABA easily passed both houses of Congress and was signed into law by President George W. Bush. Immediately, the constitutionality of PBABA was challenged in federal court, and the Supreme Court ultimately decided the law's fate in 2007, as described below.

PBABA establishes criminal penalties for "[a]ny physician who . . . knowingly performs a partial birth abortion and thereby kills a human fetus."[42] Attempting to avoid the definitional vagueness that affected the Nebraska law's constitutionality, the drafters of the federal law used more precise language in an effort to ban only D&X procedures, although PBABA does not specifically refer to any medical procedure by name. Instead, the law defines a "partial birth" abortion as:

> An abortion in which the person performing the abortion deliberately and intentionally vaginally delivers a living fetus until, in the case of a headfirst presentation, the entire fetal head is outside the body of the mother, or, in the case of a breech presentation, any part of the fetal trunk past the navel is outside the body of the mother, for the purpose of performing an overt act that the person knows will kill the partially delivered living fetus.[43]

Furthermore, PBABA contains an exception allowing for these otherwise illegal abortions when necessary to protect a pregnant woman's life, but not health. The law's authors claim that the banned procedure is never necessary to protect the health of a pregnant woman and thus that an exception is not required.

Separate lawsuits challenging PBABA were filed in federal courts in California, Nebraska, and New York. All three federal trial courts concluded that the lack of a health exception necessarily rendered the law unconstitutional under Supreme Court precedent. With enforcement of PBABA halted, the federal government appealed all three cases. The appellate courts that examined PBABA all found that substantial medical authority exists supporting the necessity of the banned procedure and declared PBABA unconstitutional because of its lack of a health exception. As noted, the fate of PBABA was then decided by the Supreme Court.

The Gonzales v. Carhart Decision   The Supreme Court upheld the constitutionality of the PBABA in *Gonzales v. Carhart*, another 5–4 decision. The Court rejected the reasoning of the appellate courts and found that the PBABA was not on its face void for vagueness and did not pose an undue burden on the right to receive an abortion under *Casey*. Although the Court reaffirmed again the various basic principles of

Roe and *Casey*—that women have an unfettered right to an abortion pre-viability, that the government has the power to restrict abortions post-viability, and that the government has an interest from the outset of pregnancy in protecting the health of the woman and the fetus—the Court in *Carhart* focused on the latter and held that the government's legitimate interest in promoting fetal life would be hindered if the act was invalidated.

The Court first ruled that the PBABA was not void for vagueness simply because the law prohibits performing intact D&Es. According to the Court, the law puts doctors on notice of the prohibited conduct by adequately describing the intact D&E procedure and requiring that the doctor have knowledge that he is performing the intact D&E for the purpose of destroying the fetus. The Court also found that the PBABA did not impose an undue burden for being overly broad. To distinguish it from the Nebraska law in *Stenberg*, the Court majority stated that the PBABA targets extraction of the entire fetus, as opposed to the removal of fetal pieces beyond a specific anatomical point in the pregnant woman.

The Court then held that the PBABA did not pose a "substantial obstacle" to obtaining an abortion under *Casey*'s undue burden test. According to the Court, the ban on partial birth abortions furthers the government's interest in protecting fetal life and the government has the ability to prohibit practices ending fetal life that are similar to condemned practices. Finally, in a major shift that received relatively little attention by the Court majority, the Court ruled that the fact that the PBABA did not contain language protecting the health of the woman did not render the law unconstitutional. Deferring to Congress because there are other safe procedures besides intact D&E that a doctor may use to perform an abortion and because according to the Court the PBABA promotes fetal life, the Court simply declared the law constitutional notwithstanding the missing language.

The Right to Be Free from Wrongful Discrimination

We now transition to the final topic in the discussion of individual legal rights to and within health care, namely, the topic of healthcare discrimination.[g] Like discrimination generally, healthcare discrimination has a lurid and lengthy history in this country. Prior to the *Brown v. Board of Education* decision in 1954 and the Civil Rights Movement of the 1960s, healthcare injustice and exclusion based on race and other factors were commonplace, dating to slavery times and plantation-based racially segregated health care. After the end of the First Reconstruction, states passed so-called Jim Crow laws, cementing in place legally segregated health care. As a result, hospitals, physician practices, medical/nursing/dental schools, and professional medical societies were all separated based on race. In places where Jim Crow laws had not been passed, corporate bylaws and contracts between private parties often had the same discriminatory effect, and these "Jim Crow substitutes" were generally honored and enforced by the courts that interpreted them.

Federal law also played a role in perpetuating racially segregated health care. For example, the Hospital Survey and Construction Act of 1946 (more commonly known as the Hill–Burton Act, after the key congressional sponsors of the measure) provided federal money to states to build and refurbish hospitals after World War II, but explicitly sanctioned the construction of segregated facilities:

> A hospital will be made available to all persons residing in [its] territorial area . . . without discrimination on account of race, creed, or color, but an exception shall be made in cases where separate hospital facilities are provided for separate population groups, if the plan makes equitable provision on the basis of need for facilities and services of like quality for each such group.[44]

This provision was not ruled unconstitutional until the 1963 case of *Simkins v. Moses H. Cone Memorial Hospital*, which has been referred to as the "*Brown v. Board of Education* of health care."[45] *Simkins* also helped fuel the passage of the Civil Rights Act of 1964, this country's most important civil rights legislation of the 20th century. For purposes of health care, Title VI of the 1964 Act was of specific importance. Title VI is discussed in more depth later in this chapter; in sum, this portion of the Civil Rights Act makes it illegal for programs and activities that receive federal funding to discriminate on the basis of race, color, or national origin.

Notwithstanding the healthcare rewards brought about by the civil rights movement—Title VI, the passage of Medicaid and Medicare, the establishment of federally financed community health centers—the focus on healthcare civil

---

BOX 6-4 Discussion Question

If you were asked to distill, down to their most essential parts, the constitutional right to privacy and the right to privacy as it applies to abortion, what elements would you include?

rights was waning as early as 1968. Several factors led to this decline, but what is most striking is that compared to the progress made by public and private civil rights efforts over the past 45 years in education, employment, and housing, civil rights enforcement in the healthcare field has been anything but sustained.

Of course, even an enduring and well-funded enforcement effort is no guarantee of wiping out discrimination, regardless of its social context. There are, unfortunately, vestiges of discrimination in many important aspects of American society, including the healthcare system. Moreover, although historically healthcare discrimination on the basis of race and ethnicity has received the most attention, the existence of discrimination in health care on the basis of socioeconomic status, disability, age, and gender also raise troubling questions. The remainder of this section touches briefly on each of these areas, describing laws (where applicable) or legal theories used to combat the particular healthcare discrimination at issue.

Race/Ethnicity Discrimination

The fact that healthcare discrimination premised on race or ethnicity has dominated the healthcare civil rights landscape should not be surprising, because racist beliefs and customs have infected health care no less so than other areas of life, such as education, employment, and housing. This fact is chronicled to a staggering degree by W. Michael Byrd and Linda A. Clayton,[46,47] two physician-researchers at the Harvard School of Public Health. Byrd and Clayton paint a complex and disturbing picture of a healthcare system that itself perpetuates racism in health care in three distinct ways: by not destroying the myth that minority Americans should be expected to experience poorer health relative to Caucasians; by organizing itself as a private, for-profit system that marginalizes the indigent and minorities; and by refusing to acknowledge the historical and ongoing problem of racial exclusion in health care.

One key problem that in part results from the design of the healthcare system is that of racial and ethnic health disparities—differences in healthcare access, treatment, and outcomes between populations of color and Caucasians. In 2003, the Institute of Medicine (IOM) released an influential report that included overwhelming evidence of racial and ethnic health disparities and documented that these disparities could not be explained solely by the relative amount of health care needed by populations of color and nonminority populations.[48] For example, the report concluded that African Americans are relatively less likely to receive treatment for early-stage lung cancer, publicly insured Latinos and African Americans do not receive coronary artery bypass surgery at rates comparable to publicly-insured nonminorities, and Latino and African-American children on Medicaid experience relatively higher rates of hospitalization.

Furthermore, the IOM study revealed that even when relevant patient characteristics are controlled for, racial and ethnic differences arise not only in terms of accessing care initially, but also after individuals have entered the healthcare system, a finding that supports the notion that both the system itself and physician practice style contribute to disparities. This notion is, of course, quite controversial, because it suggests that physician decision making and clinical practice can increase the likelihood of racially disparate outcomes.

The key law used to combat race and ethnicity discrimination in health care is Title VI of the 1964 Civil Rights Act,[49] which states that "[n]o person in the United States shall, on the ground of race, color, or national origin, be excluded from participation in, be denied the benefits of, or be subjected to discrimination under any program or activity receiving federal financial assistance."[50] Because it only attaches to recipients of federal funding, Title VI does not reach, for example, health professionals who do not directly participate in government-sponsored health programs (nor does it reach physicians whose only participation in federal assistance programs is under Medicare Part B; the basis for this exemption is historical and purely political, and the exemption is not codified in Title VI statutory or regulatory law[45(pp115–128)]). Nonetheless, Title VI has long had the potential to greatly impact the field of health care, because an enormous amount of federal funding has been poured into the healthcare enterprise over the past 40-plus years.

The concept of "discrimination" under Title VI applies both to *intentional* acts and to actions or policies that unintentionally have the *effect* of discriminating against racial and ethnic minorities. This is so because federal regulations implementing the Title VI statute (which explicitly only prohibits intentional discrimination) reach actions that, even if neutral on their face, have a disproportionate adverse impact (or effect) on members of minority groups. In the case of healthcare access and delivery, you can imagine several types of conduct that might potentially violate the Title VI disproportionate impact regulations. For example, were a hospital to segregate patients by source of payment—say, by maintaining a ward or floor that only treated patients covered under Medicaid—this might have the effect of adversely impacting racial and ethnic minorities, given the overall makeup of the Medicaid population. Similarly, the Title VI regulations could be violated if a managed care organization enrolled both privately and publicly insured persons, but allowed participating providers to refuse to accept as patients those individuals covered by Medicaid.

The disproportionate impact regulations are critically important to realizing Title VI's full force, because much of the racism in post-1954 America does not take the form of overt, intentional acts. However, as a result of the 2001 Supreme Court decision in *Alexander v. Sandoval*,[51] these regulations were severely undercut. Under *Sandoval*, private individuals were barred from bringing a lawsuit under the disparate impact regulations, leaving the federal government as the sole enforcer when racial or ethnic minorities allege a violation of the regulations.[h]

Physical and Mental Disability Discrimination

Like discrimination based on race or ethnicity, healthcare discrimination premised on disability has a long, sad history in this country and, as with race, the health system itself is partly to blame for its perpetuation. For instance, historically, persons with mental disabilities were viewed from a medical standpoint as having little to offer to society, and they were, as a matter of practice, shipped to mental asylums isolated from communities. Those with physical disabilities were not spared discriminatory practices, either; because individuals with Down syndrome were viewed by medical practitioners as "Mongoloid idiots" and children with cerebral palsy or other serious physical limitations were regularly viewed as unable to contribute to society, they were all simply institutionalized. These historical practices and perspectives resonate even in the modern healthcare system, in which treatment opportunities for the disabled are skewed toward institutional, rather than community, settings, and disease-specific limitations in health insurance are commonplace.

However, passage of the Americans with Disabilities Act (ADA)[52] in 1990 alleviated at least some of the problems associated with disability discrimination in health care. Like Title VI, the ADA is not specifically a "health law"—its intent is to extend to the disabled the maximum opportunity for community integration in many sectors of society, including employment, public services, public accommodations (i.e., privately owned entities open to the public), telecommunications, and more. For this reason, it prohibits discrimination generally against disabled individuals who satisfy the essential requirements of a particular job, or who meet the qualification standards for a program, service, or benefit.

But the ADA's impact on health care for disabled individuals is notable, in large part because the law defines "places of public accommodation" to include private hospitals and other private healthcare providers. So, for example, a dentist in private practice who does not receive any federal funds for his services is nonetheless prohibited from discriminating against a person who is HIV-positive, as the well-known case of *Bragdon v. Abbott*[53] makes clear. This represents an important expansion of federal disability law, because prior to the ADA, only recipients of federal funds were proscribed from discriminating on the basis of disability. Note also how this expanded concept of public accommodations differs from Title VI of the Civil Rights Act, which still requires the receipt of federal money on the part of the offending entity to trigger protections for racial and ethnic minorities.

Although the ADA has dramatically altered the disability law landscape, it is not without limitations. For example, the regulations implementing the ADA's statutory text only require entities that implement public programs and services to make "reasonable modifications"—but not "fundamental alterations"—to those programs and services. Under the ADA, a fundamental alteration is one that would change the essential nature of a public program or service. Whether a requested change to a public program or service by a disabled individual amounts to a "reasonable" or "fundamental" one is potentially determinative to the outcome of the request. Why? Because if a court determines that the request would alter the essential nature of the program or service at issue, it is powerless under the ADA to order the change. Another way of understanding this reasonable modification/fundamental alteration dichotomy is to recognize that fundamental alterations to public services—alterations that might actually be necessary to achieve at least the spirit of the ADA's loftiest goals and meet the expectations of a modern, enlightened society—could only be made by the political branches of government, not by the courts.

Another important limitation of the ADA (at least as it has been interpreted by most courts) is that it does not prohibit arbitrary insurance coverage limits attached to certain medical conditions. A stark example of this is found in the case of *Doe v. Mutual of Omaha Insurance Company*,[54] in which a federal appellate court ruled that a lifetime benefit limitation in a health insurance policy of $25,000 for AIDS or AIDS-related conditions did not violate the ADA, even though the very same policy set a $1 million lifetime limit for other conditions.

Socioeconomic Status Discrimination

Compared to race or disability discrimination in healthcare access and treatment, healthcare discrimination based on class gains little attention—even though socioeconomic status is independently associated with health status, and the negative effects of poverty on health and healthcare access are incontrovertible. Class-related healthcare discrimination can take many forms. For example, healthcare providers might refuse to accept as patients individuals who are covered under Medicaid, or low-income individuals might fall victim to the practice of redlining, which refers to discrimination based on geographic location when companies offer goods and services to consumers. (Although insufficient data exist to know the extent of redlining in healthcare-related goods and services, industries such as home health care, pharmaceuticals, and managed care have come under particular scrutiny.[55]) Another example stems from the fact that healthcare providers (physician and dental practices, hospitals, etc.) sometimes elect to not operate in relatively poor communities, leaving residents of these communities at heightened risk for experiencing a shortage of adequate healthcare resources.

Gender Discrimination

Gender discrimination against women is also a problem in health care. This bias appears to be of particular concern in the area of coronary heart disease,[56] in which delayed or disparate care could have severe consequences. At least, in theory, gender discrimination in health care could be remedied under the Equal Protection Clause of the federal Constitution; however, Equal Protection claims are difficult to win, because they require proof of both state action (a sufficient government connection to the discriminatory acts) and proximate causation (a cause-and-effect link between the discrimination and the harm suffered). Also, consider the fact that healthcare practitioners who receive federal funds cannot face suit under Title VI for even obvious gender discrimination, because Title VI's prohibitions relate only to race, color, and national origin discrimination.

Age Discrimination

Finally, the medical care system also seems to be biased against the elderly. Just one of several disturbing facts on the treatment front is that the elderly sometimes do not receive needed surgical care because health professionals wrongly assume that the chances of recovery are not good.[57] Another concern pertains to insurance coverage, in that many employers are attempting to rescind lifetime health coverage benefits to retired workers, even where the benefits had been promised as part of negotiated labor contracts. At first blush, this may not seem like a critical issue, because many retirees are at or beyond the age required for Medicare eligibility. But some retirees are not yet 65-years old, a retiree's employer-sponsored benefits might provide more or different coverage than Medicare, and employer benefits might cover a retiree's dependents, which Medicare does not do.

INDIVIDUAL RIGHTS IN A PUBLIC HEALTH CONTEXT

The discussion thus far has focused on healthcare legal rights that individuals can claim in the context of access, receipt of services, freedom of choice, and anti-discrimination. In each of these areas, however, the right claimed is not absolute. For example, EMTALA does not make illegal all transfers of indigent patients from private hospitals to public ones; rather, it requires that patients be medically stabilized before a transfer can occur. Even eminent civil rights laws do not provide blanket protections, because they might only be triggered where federal funding is present, or where the assistance requested would not fundamentally alter a government health program.

In this section, we consider restrictions on individual rights and liberties of a different sort: These derive not from the limitations of specific laws, but rather from governmental police powers used to protect the general public's health and welfare. One simple way to think about individual rights in a public health context is to use a balancing approach—what might the appropriate legal trade-offs be between private rights and public welfare? Public discussion of this trade-off intensified after the terrorist attacks of September 11, 2001, because many government actions taken in their wake—the passage of new laws, the tightening of existing regulations, the detainment of alleged terrorists—starkly raised the question of where to draw the line between individual autonomy and government authority to restrain that autonomy in the name of public welfare and national security. The attacks raised new public health law-related questions as well, including whether the potential for a bioterrorist attack utilizing smallpox should compel the federal government to vaccinate individuals—even against their will—against the virus in order to protect the public at large in the event of an attack.

Overview of Police Powers

Police powers represent state and local government authority to require individual conformance with established standards of conduct. These standards are designed to promote and protect the public's health, safety, and welfare, and to permit government control of personal, corporate, and other private interests. The government's police powers are broad and take many forms. Healthcare professionals are required to obtain licenses from government agencies. Healthcare facilities face accreditation standards. Food establishments are heavily regulated. Employers are bound by numerous occupational health and safety rules. Businesses are constrained by pollution control measures. Tobacco products can only be marketed in certain ways. The purchase of guns is controlled, buildings have to abide by certain codes, motorcyclists must wear helmets. The list goes on and on.

The government's police powers are oftentimes invasive, a result that stems in part from the fact that the American colonies were battling multiple communicable diseases during the time of the writing of the Constitution, and its drafters were thus well aware of the need for pervasive governmental public health powers. At the same time, the government may not overreach when restricting private autonomy in the name of public health promotion and protection. For example, police powers cannot be used as a form of punishment, they cannot be used arbitrarily and capriciously, and they cannot be used for purposes unrelated to public health and welfare.

A key principle inherent to the use of police powers is that of coercion.[58] This is so because, in a country founded upon the twin ideals of individualism and a limited government, many individuals and businesses do not respond kindly to being told to conform with public health regulations that limit their actions. For example, sometimes a public health concern (e.g., pollution) requires a response (enhanced governmental regulation) that may not be in the best economic interests of an implicated party (a refinery). This is not to say that individuals and businesses do not voluntarily assume responsibilities and measures that are in the public's interest. For instance, one effect of poor exercise habits—obesity—has enormous implications for the public's health and for national healthcare costs. As a result, the government would prefer that all individuals exercise for a minimum amount of time each week, but there is of course no law requiring this; rather, voluntarism is the guiding principle when it comes to personal exercise. Nonetheless, personal coercion and industrial regulation have long been adopted (and accepted) practices of public health officials, and all of the major communicable disease outbreaks have been combated with some combination of compulsory screening, examination, treatment, isolation, and quarantine programs.

The *Jacobson v. Massachusetts* Decision

The fact that government coercion can be justified by important public health goals does not answer the question of where to draw the line between personal/economic freedom on the one hand, and the public welfare on the other. This question was taken up by the Supreme Court in *Jacobson v. Massachusetts*,[59] perhaps the most famous public health law decision in the Court's history and the one to which we alluded in the second factual scenario at the opening of this chapter.

The facts in *Jacobson* are straightforward enough. At the turn of the 20th century, the state of Massachusetts enacted a law granting local health boards the power to require vaccination when necessary to protect the public's health or safety. In 1902, the Cambridge Board of Health, in the throes of attempting to contain a smallpox outbreak, took the state up on its offer and issued an order requiring all adults in the city to be vaccinated against the disease. Henning Jacobson refused vaccination on the ground that he previously suffered negative reactions to vaccinations. Jacobson was fined $5 for his refusal, a penalty upheld by the state's highest court. Jacobson appealed to the U.S. Supreme Court, setting the stage for a decision that, more than 100 years later, remains both controversial and at least symbolically forceful.[60,61]

Like the enduring private interest/public welfare tension underpinning public health law generally, the *Jacobson* decision amounts to "a classic case of reconciling individual interests in bodily integrity with collective interests in health and safety."[60(p577)] The 7–2 decision went the state's way, with the Supreme Court recognizing that police powers were generally broad enough to encompass forced vaccination. Responding to Jacobson's argument that the Massachusetts law impermissibly infringed on his constitutional right to liberty, the Court wrote:

> [T]he liberty secured by the Constitution of the United States to every person within its jurisdiction does not import an absolute right in each person to be, at all times and in all circumstances, wholly freed from restraint. There are manifold restraints to which every person is necessarily subject for the common good. On any other basis organized society could not exist with safety to its members. Society based on the rule that each one is a law unto himself would soon be confronted with disorder and anarchy.[62]

Due to this and other language used by the Court in the decision, *Jacobson* is often described as sweepingly deferential to public health officials and their use of police powers. And without question, social compact theory (the idea that citizens have duties to one another and to society as a whole) animates the Court's decision. However, the *Jacobson* decision also recognizes the individual liberties protected by the Constitution, and in fact requires a deliberative governmental process to safeguard these interests.

According to the *Jacobson* Court, public health powers must be exercised in conformity with four standards in order to pass constitutional muster:

- The first standard, that of "public health necessity," requires that government use its police powers only in the face of a demonstrable public health threat.
- The second standard, termed "reasonable means," dictates that the methods used when exercising police powers must be designed in such a way as to prevent or ameliorate the public health threat found to exist under the first standard.
- "Proportionality" is the third *Jacobson* standard; it is violated when a particular public health measure imposes a burden on individuals totally disproportionate to the benefit to be expected from the measure.
- Finally, and axiomatically, the public health regulation itself should not pose a significant health risk to individuals subject to it. This is the standard of "harm avoidance."

These standards have never been explicitly overturned, but it can be argued that they have at the very least been implicitly replaced, given that in the 100-plus years since *Jacobson* was decided, the Supreme Court has developed a much more complex approach to applying constitutional provisions to cases implicating individual autonomy and liberty.

The "Negative Constitution"

The discussion of police powers up to this point might reasonably lead you to believe that the Constitution *obligates* the government to protect the public's health and welfare through affirmative use of its powers. This view, however, has never been adopted by the Supreme Court. Instead, the prevailing view is that the Constitution *empowers* government to act in the name of public health, but does not require it to do so. This interpretation of the Constitution refers to what is known as the "negative constitution," that is, the idea that the Constitution does not require government to provide any services, public health or otherwise. This approach to constitutional law derives from the fact that the Constitution is phrased mainly in negative terms (e.g., the First Amendment prohibits government abridgment of free speech). Professor Wendy Parmet describes the "negative constitution" this way:

> In the century that has witnessed Auschwitz and Chernobyl, it is easy to see the dangers posed by state power. This recognition tempers enthusiasm for public authority and leads us to use law as a limiting device. In our legal tradition, this view of law is integral to constitutional structure, with its emphasis on separation of powers, checks and balances, procedural protections, and individual rights. We rely on the Constitution to limit the power of the government to restrain our freedoms and cause us harm. In this sense, law is a negative force that prevents the state from intruding upon the individual. This negative conception of law, which sees legal rights as a restraint upon the state, has played a dominant role in the formulation of contemporary American public health law. It explains the central pillars of constitutional public health law: the search for limits on governmental authority to restrain individual freedoms in the name of public health, and the concomitant assumption that government has no obligation to promote public health.[63(pp267,271)]

In two important decisions, *DeShaney v. Winnebago County Department of Social Services*[64] and *Town of Castle Rock, Colorado v. Gonzales*,[65] the Supreme Court has advanced this view of the negative constitution. In the former case, one-year-old Joshua DeShaney was placed in his father's custody after his parents divorced. Two years later, the father's second wife complained to county officials in Wisconsin that the father had been abusing Joshua physically. Social service workers opened a file on the case and interviewed Joshua's father, but the county did not pursue the matter further after the father denied the charges. One year after that, an emergency room physician treating Joshua alerted social services of his suspicion that Joshua's injuries were the result of abuse. The county again investigated but decided that insufficient evidence of child abuse existed to remove Joshua from his father's custody. This emergency room scenario played out two additional times over the next several months, but Joshua's

---

BOX 6-5 Discussion Question

Jacobson v. Massachusetts is a product of the early 20th century, and the public health law principles supporting it are vestiges of an even earlier time. This, coupled with a century of subsequent civil liberties jurisprudence and societal advancement, has led some commentators to question whether *Jacobson* should continue to retain its paradigmatic role in terms of the scope of government police powers. At the same time, other public health law experts call for *Jacobson*'s continued vitality, arguing that it is settled doctrine and a still-appropriate answer to the private interest/collective good question. What do you think?

caseworkers still believed that they had no basis on which to place Joshua in court custody. Some months later, when Joshua was four years old, he suffered a beating so severe that he fell into a life-threatening coma. He survived but was left with permanent, severe brain damage, and he was expected to live his life in an institution for the profoundly mentally retarded. Joshua's father was subsequently convicted of child abuse.

Joshua's mother filed a civil rights claim on Joshua's behalf against the county officials who failed to take the boy into their custody. The lawsuit was based on the Due Process Clause of the federal Constitution, which prohibits states from depriving any person of property without due process of law. However, the Supreme Court in *DeShaney* concluded that the "substantive" component of the Due Process Clause—which focuses on challenges to government conduct—could not be read to provide Joshua with a property interest in having state child welfare officials protect him from beatings by his father. For a 6–3 majority, Chief Justice Rehnquist held that state officials had no affirmative constitutional duty to protect Joshua:

> [N]othing in the language of the Due Process Clause itself requires the State to protect the life, liberty, and property of its citizens against invasion by private actors. The Clause is phrased as a limitation on the State's power to act, not as a guarantee of certain minimal levels of safety and security. It forbids the State itself to deprive individuals of life, liberty, or property without "due process of law," but its language cannot fairly be extended to impose an affirmative obligation on the State to ensure that those interests do not come to harm through other means.[66]

The majority further rejected the argument that the state's knowledge of the danger Joshua faced, and its expression of willingness to protect him against that danger, established a "special relationship" that gave rise to an affirmative constitutional duty to protect.

In dissent, three justices in *DeShaney* argued that through the establishment of its child protection program, the state of Wisconsin undertook a vital duty and effectively intervened in Joshua's life, and its failure to live up to its child protection duty amounted to a constitutional violation. According to the dissenters, the majority opinion "construes the Due Process Clause to permit a State to displace private sources of protection and then, at the critical moment, to shrug its shoulders and turn away from the harm that it has promised to try to prevent."[67]

Sixteen years after *DeShaney*, the Supreme Court in *Castle Rock v. Gonzales* had an opportunity to again consider whether the government has a duty to affirmatively protect its citizens. This time, however, the Court was concerned not with substantive due process, but rather with procedural due process, which mandates that when a state establishes a benefit or right for its citizens, it is not entitled to deny individuals the benefit or right in an arbitrary or unfair way.

Unfortunately, the facts in *Gonzales* are as tragic as those in *DeShaney*. In May 1999, Jessica Gonzales received a court order protecting her and her three young daughters from her husband, who was also the girls' father. On June 22nd, all three girls disappeared in the late afternoon from in front of the Gonzales home, and Jessica suspected that her husband had taken them in violation of the restraining order. This suspicion was confirmed in a phone conversation she had with her husband. In two initial phone conversations with the Castle Rock Police Department, she was told there was nothing the police could do and to wait until 10:00 p.m. to see if her husband brought the girls home.

Shortly after 10:00 p.m., Jessica called the police to report that her children were still missing, but this time she was told to wait until midnight to see what transpired. She called the police again at midnight, reported that her children were still missing, and left her home to go to her husband's apartment. Finding nobody there, she called the police again at 12:10 a.m. and was told to wait for an officer to arrive. Thirty minutes later, after no officer showed up, she went to the police station to submit a report. According to the Supreme Court decision, the officer who wrote up the report "made no reasonable effort to enforce the [restraining order] or locate the three children. Instead, he went to dinner." A couple of hours later, Jessica's husband pulled his truck up to, and began shooting at, the Castle Rock Police Department. After he was killed by police during the gunfight, the three Gonzales daughters were found dead in the back of the truck; they had been murdered by their father hours earlier.

Jessica sued the police department, claiming that her constitutional right to procedural due process was violated by the department's inaction. She argued that the restraining order she received was her "property" under the Constitution's Due Process Clause and that it was effectively "taken" from her without due process. Overturning the federal appellate court that ruled in her favor, the Supreme Court decided by a 7–2 margin that Jessica did not have a property interest in police enforcement of the restraining order against her husband.

The Court said it was not clear that *even if* it had found an individual entitlement to enforcement of a restraining order under a Colorado state statute requiring officers to use every reasonable means to enforce restraining orders, that this entitlement would constitute a protected "property" interest that triggers due process protections under the federal Constitution. Justice Antonin Scalia wrote that the Due Process Clause does not protect all government "benefits," including those things that government officials have discretion to grant or deny. Applying this standard, the Court ruled that Colorado's protection order law did not create an individual entitlement to police enforcement of restraining orders, explaining that police have discretion to act or not act under many circumstances, including when to enforce a restraining order (e.g., police officers have discretion to consider whether a violation of a protection order is too "technical" or minor to justify enforcement). Furthermore, the Court noted that if the Colorado legislature included statutory language making police enforcement of a restraining order "mandatory," even that would not necessarily mean that Mrs. Gonzales had a personal entitlement to its enforcement, given that the statute makes no mention of an individual's power to demand—or even request—enforcement.

In dissent, two justices in *Gonzales* argued that restraining orders amount to a personal, enforceable property interest. They asserted that the majority opinion wrongly ruled that

a citizen's interest in government-provided police protection does not resemble a "traditional conception" of property. Looking to the legislative history and text of Colorado's own protection order law and to the purpose of the state's domestic violence legislation, the dissent concluded that a particular class of individuals was indeed entitled beneficiaries of domestic restraining orders.

CONCLUSION

This chapter offered a snapshot of the current state of health-related legal rights. But, as alluded to early on in the chapter, there were times in its relatively short history that this country was closer to recognizing broader individual healthcare rights than is currently the case, just as there have been times (as the aftermath of September 11, 2001, proved) when concerns for the public's health and safety have eclipsed the nation's more natural inclinations toward individualism and a deregulated marketplace. That this is so is of no surprise: Legal rights are, by nature, subject to shifts in the political terrain. For example, the Aid for Families with Dependent Children program (commonly known as AFDC), the federal welfare entitlement program for low-income populations, was dismantled in 1996 after more than 60 years in existence. Originally enacted under a slightly different name as part of the New Deal in 1935, AFDC was replaced with the Temporary Assistance for Needy Families (TANF) program by a moderate Democrat (President Bill Clinton) and a conservative, Republican-controlled Congress. Compared to AFDC, TANF dramatically limited the receipt of individual benefits and focused much more heavily on creating work opportunities for needy families. Like legal rights generally, health-related legal rights are similarly subject to changing political currents. For example, at the time of this writing, several state legislatures continue to pass bills that protect health professionals from providing care that conflicts with their personal beliefs, reflecting the current political power of social conservatives.[i]

Of course, changes to legal rights are not always represented by restrictions of those rights. The enactment of Medicaid and Medicare, which created new health-related rights, is an obvious example. Other major examples include EMTALA and expanded state consumer rights for persons in managed care. On a less noticed scale, legal rights for persons with HIV/AIDS have expanded since the 1980s,[68] and federal courts now review the constitutionality of the treatment provided in, and conditions of, psychiatric hospitals.[69] These are just a few of many examples.

Nonetheless, vast challenges remain. After all, many scholars, politicians, and consumers point to the millions of uninsured Americans as just one example of not only a failing

BOX 6-6 Discussion Questions

The "negative constitution" is a concept over which reasonable people can easily disagree. Notwithstanding the "defensive" manner of some of the Constitution's key provisions, there are several arguments in support of more affirmative action on the part of government health and welfare officials than current Supreme Court jurisprudence requires. For example, the dissent in *DeShaney* argues persuasively that Wisconsin's implementation of a child protection program effectively created a constitutional duty to actually protect children from seemingly obvious danger. As one leading scholar put it, "If an agency represents itself to the public as a defender of health, and citizens justifiably rely on that protection, is government 'responsible' when it knows that a substantial risk exists, fails to inform citizens so they might initiate action, and passively avoids a state response to that risk?"[58(p34)] What do you think of this argument? And can you think of others that call into question the soundness of the negative theory of constitutional law?

healthcare financing and delivery system, but also a failing of the legal system. To reduce this nation's huge uninsured population takes not just political will, but also an enormous undertaking to change the law, as witnessed with the ACA. A "rights revolution" in a health context, like other major legal upheavals, requires something else, too: a substantial amount of general economic and social unrest.[70] As historian Brooks Adams once noted, "Law is merely the expression of the will of the strongest for the time being, and therefore laws have no fixity, but shift from generation to generation."[71(p197)]

REFERENCES

1. 59 N.E. 1058 (Ind. 1901).
2. Ibid.
3. Friedman EA, Adashi EY. The right to health as the unheralded narrative of health care reform. *JAMA*. 2010;304(23):2639–2640.
4. Jost TS. *Disentitlement? The Threats Facing Our Public Health-Care Programs and a Rights-Based Response*. New York, NY: Oxford University Press; 2003.
5. Davis MF. *Brutal Need: Lawyers and the Welfare Rights Movement, 1960–1973*. New Haven, CT: Yale University Press; 1993.
6. 411 U.S. 1 (1973).
7. Ibid., 35.
8. Stacy T. The courts, the constitution, and a just distribution of health care. *Kans J Law Public Policy*. 1993/1994;3:77–94.
9. Smith PS. Addressing the plight of inner-city schools: the federal right to education after *Kadrmas v. Dickinson Public Schools*. *Whittier Law Rev*. 1997;18:825.
10. Reinhardt U. The debate that wasn't: the public and the Clinton health care plan. In; Aaron H., ed. *The Problem That Won't Go Away: Reforming U.S. Health Care Financing*. Washington, D.C.: Brookings Institution; 1996: 70–109.
11. Vladeck B. Universal health insurance in the United States: reflections on the past, the present, and the future [editorial]. *Am J Pub Health*. 2003;93:16. Blum JD, Talib N, Carstens P, et al. Rights of patients: comparative perspectives from five countries. *Med Law*. 2003;22:451. Rich RF. Health policy, health insurance and the social contract. *Comp Labor Law Policy J*. 2000;21:397.
12. Barnes A, McChrystal M. The various human rights in health care. *Human Rights*. 1998;25:12.
13. Kinney ED, Clark BA. Provisions for health and health care in the constitutions of the countries of the world. *Cornell Int Law J*. 2004;37:2.
14. Littell A. Can a constitutional right to health guarantee universal health care coverage or improved health outcomes?: A survey of selected states. *Conn Law Rev*. 2002;35:289.
15. Yamin AE. The right to health under international law and its relevance to the United States. *Am J Public Health*. 2005;95(7):1156.
16. President's Commission for the Study of Ethical Problems in Medicine and Biomedical and Behavioral Research. *Securing Access to Health Care: A Report on the Ethical Implications of Differences in the Availability of Health Services*. Washington, DC: The National Academies Press; 1983.
17. Starr P. *The Social Transformation of American Medicine: The Rise of a Sovereign Profession and the Making of a Vast Industry*. New York, NY: Basic Books; 1982.
18. Wing KR. The right to health care in the United States. *Ann Health Law*. 1993;2:163.
19. Annas GJ. *The Rights of Patients*. 3rd ed. Carbondale, IL: Southern Illinois University Press; 2004.
20. 42 U.S.C. § 1395dd(e)(1).
21. Rosenblatt RE, Law SA, Rosenbaum S. *Law and the American Health Care System*. New York, NY: The Foundation Press; 1997.
22. Rosenbaum S. Realigning the social order: the patient protection and affordable care act and the U.S. health insurance system," *Suffolk Journal of Health and Biomedical Law* (winter 2011).
23. 45 C.F.R. Part 46.
24. 464 F.2d 772 (D.C. Cir. 1972).
25. Ibid., 782.
26. Ibid., 783 fn. 36.
27. 381 U.S. 479 (1965).
28. Ibid., 484–486.
29. *Loving v. Virginia*, 388 U.S. 1 (1967).
30. *Eisenstadt v. Baird*, 405 U.S. 438 (1972).
31. 410 U.S. 113 (1973). For a compelling look at what the case has meant to society, see David J. Garrow, *Liberty and Sexuality: The Right to Privacy and the Making of Roe v. Wade* (California: University of California Press, 1994).
32. 410 U.S., 154.
33. Ibid., 164–165.
34. Barzelay DE, Heymann PB. The forest and the trees: Roe v. Wade and its critics. *Boston Univ Law Rev*. 1973;53:765.
35. Ely JH. The wages of crying wolf: a comment on Roe v. Wade. *Yale Law J*. 1973;82:920.
36. Regan DH. Rewriting Roe v. Wade. *Mich Law Rev*. 1979;77:269.
37. Bopp J, Coleson R. The right to abortion: anomalous, absolute, and ripe for reversal. *Brigham Young Univ J Public Law*. 1989;3:181.
38. 505 U.S. 833 (1992).
39. Ibid., 847.
40. 530 U.S. 914 (2000).
41. Ibid., 932.
42. 18 U.S.C.A. § 1531 (a) (2004).
43. Ibid., (b).
44. 42 U.S.C. § 291e(f).
45. Smith DB. *Health Care Divided: Race and Healing a Nation*. Ann Arbor, MI: The University of Michigan Press; 1999.
46. Byrd WM, Clayton LA. *An American Health Dilemma: A Medical History of African Americans and the Problem of Race, Beginnings to 1900*. New York, NY: Routledge; 2000.
47. Byrd WM, Clayton LA. *An American Health Dilemma: Race, Medicine, and Health Care in the United States, 1900–2000*. New York, NY: Routledge; 2002.
48. Smedley BD, Stith AY, Nelson AR, eds. *Unequal Treatment: Confronting Racial and Ethnic Disparities in Health Care*. Washington, DC: The National Academies Press; 2003.
49. 42 U.S.C. §§ 2000a *et seq.*
50. 42 U.S.C. § 2000d.
51. 532 U.S. 275 (2001).
52. 42 U.S.C. §§ 12101 *et seq.*
53. 524 U.S. 624 (1998).
54. 179 F.3d 557 (7th Cir.1999), cert. denied, 528 U.S. 1106 (2000).
55. Perez TE. The civil rights dimension of racial and ethnic disparities in health status. In: Smedley BD, Stith AY, Nelson AR, eds. *Unequal Treatment: Confronting Racial and Ethnic Disparities in Health Care*. Washington, DC: The National Academies Press; 2003; 626–663.
56. Bess CJ. Gender bias in health care: a life or death issue for women with coronary heart disease. *Hastings Women's Law J*. 1995;6:41.
57. Smith GP, II. Our hearts were once young and gay: health care rationing and the elderly. *Univ Fla J Law Public Policy*. 1996;8:1.
58. Gostin LO. *Public Health Law: Power, Duty, Restraint*. Berkeley, CA: University of California Press/New York, NY: The Milbank Memorial Fund; 2000.
59. 197 U.S. 11 (1905).

60. Gostin LO. *Jacobson v. Massachusetts* at 100 years: police powers and civil liberties in tension. *Am J Public Health.* 2005;95(4):576.

61. Mariner WK, Annas GJ, Glantz LH. *Jacobson v. Massachusetts*: it's not your great-great-grandfather's public health law. *Am J Public Health.* 2005;95(4):581.

62. 197 U.S. at 26.

63. Parmet W. Health care and the constitution: public health and the role of the state in the framing era. *Hastings Constitutional Law Q.* 1992;20:267, 271.

64. 489 U.S. 189 (1989).

65. 125 S.Ct. 2796 (2005).

66. 489 U.S. at 195.

67. Ibid., 212.

68. Halpern SA. Medical authority and the culture of rights. *J Health Politics Policy Law.* 2004;29(4–5):835.

69. *Wyatt v. Stickney*, 344 F. Supp. 373 (M.D. Ala. 1972).

70. Friedman LM. The idea of right as a social and legal concept. *J Social Issues.* 1971;27(2):189–198.

71. Nash B, Zullo A, eds. *Lawyer's Wit and Wisdom: Quotations on the Legal Profession, In Brief.* Philadelphia, PA: Running Press; 1995.

ENDNOTES

a. These competing concepts were given life in Paul Starr's influential book, *The Social Transformation of American Medicine: The Rise of a Sovereign Profession and the Making of a Vast Industry* (New York, NY: Basic Books, Inc., 1982). Incidentally, *The Social Transformation of American Medicine* should be read by all students with an interest in the history of medicine; the book's significance across a range of disciplines is hard to overstate. See "Special Issue: Transforming American Medicine: A Twenty-Year Retrospective on *The Social Transformation of American Medicine*," *Journal of Health Politics, Policy, and Law* 29, nos. 4–5 (August–October 2004).

b. For an interesting article describing the importance of political structures in determining the level of equalities/inequalities in a society, including the level of government-provided health care coverage, see Vicente Navarro and Leiyu Shi, "The Political Context of Social Inequalities and Health," in *Health and Social Justice: Politics, Ideology, and Inequity in the Distribution of Disease*, ed. Richard Hofrichter (San Francisco, CA: Jossey-Bass, 2003).

c. Incidentally, the *Canterbury* decision was authored by Spottswood Robinson, III who, prior to becoming a highly regarded federal judge, was instrumental in the fight for civil rights, in part as one of the National Association for the Advancement of Colored People (NAACP) lawyers who initially brought suit in one of the cases that eventually morphed into *Brown v. Board of Education*.

d. A now-famous 1890 Harvard Law Review article titled "The Right to Privacy," written by Samuel Warren and Louis Brandeis, is often credited with introducing the constitutional "right to be let alone."

e. In a health context, this type of privacy is embodied by the Health Insurance Portability and Accountability Act (HIPAA), found in large part at 29 U.S.C. §§ 1181–1187, 42 U.S.C. §§ 300gg *et seq.* and 42 U.S.C. §§ 1320a *et seq.*, which creates a federal right to maintain the confidentiality of one's personal health information.

f. For example, notice how the Supreme Court linked states' power to ban abortions (with certain exceptions) to fetal viability, even though the progression of medical knowledge and technology could push back the point of viability earlier into pregnancy. Also, who appears to hold the power, under "(a)" above, to decide whether an abortion should occur? The *physician*, a fact often overlooked by those who hail *Roe* as a seminal women's rights case and one that calls into question how the pregnant woman's constitutional right to privacy could be effectuated by her treating physician.

g. This section was adapted from Joel B. Teitelbaum, "Health Care and Civil Rights: An Introduction," *Ethnicity and Disease* 15, no. 2, Supp. 2, (2005): 27–30.

h. For a discussion of the implications of the *Sandoval* decision in a health care context, see Sara Rosenbaum and Joel Teitelbaum, "Civil Rights Enforcement in the Modern Healthcare System: Reinvigorating the Role of the Federal Government in the Aftermath of *Alexander v. Sandoval*," *Yale Journal of Health Policy, Law, and Ethics* III:2 (2003): 1.

i. These bills represent a "surge of legislation that reflects the intensifying tension between asserting individual religious values and defending patients' rights . . . .The flurry of political activity is being welcomed by conservative groups that consider it crucial to prevent health workers from being coerced into participating in care they find morally repugnant—protecting their 'right of conscience' or 'right of refusal.' . . . The swell of propositions is raising alarm among advocates for abortion rights, family planning, AIDS prevention, the right to die, gays and lesbians, and others who see the push as the latest manifestation of the growing political power of social conservatives." Stein R. Health workers' choice debated: proposals back right not to treat. *Washington Post.* January 30, 2006:A01.

Understanding Health Insurance

INTRODUCTION

Unlike many other countries, the United States does not have a national healthcare delivery system; whether individuals have access to healthcare services—and whether they receive health care of appropriate quantity and quality—often depends on whether they are insured. Even if an individual is insured, the kind of coverage she has can affect her ability to obtain care. Understanding health insurance, however, requires more than understanding its importance to healthcare access.

Policymakers must also know how providers, suppliers, employers, states, and others respond to changes in the health insurance market. For example, if policymakers decide to reduce the number of uninsured by creating a new government-sponsored health insurance program, they must know whether providers will participate in the program and what features will make it more or less attractive to providers. Or, if policymakers want to reduce the number of uninsured by increasing access to employer-sponsored health insurance plans, they must know which policy changes will make it more

or less likely that employers will offer (or expand) insurance coverage to their employees. In either case, policymakers might also want to know whether an initiative will affect the financial viability of public hospitals or health centers.

Several themes emerge when considering these types of health insurance-related policy questions. First, insurance is rooted in the concepts of uncertainty and risk; reducing uncertainty and risk by, for example, offering a health insurance product, participating as a provider in a health insurance plan, or purchasing health insurance coverage as a consumer creates various incentives for insurers, the insured, providers, and governments to act or refrain from acting in certain ways. As noted in the vignette, one goal of the Patient Protection and Affordable Care Act (ACA) is to reduce the risk of insuring small businesses and individuals by creating a large purchasing pool through state health insurance exchanges.[1] Second, to a large extent, insurance carriers choose the design of their health insurance products, and employers and individuals choose whether to (and what type of) health insurance to purchase. Indeed, insurance carriers have had wide latitude to determine the individuals or groups that may join a plan, employers have had broad discretion to determine whether to offer coverage and what type to offer, and individuals have had the choice whether to purchase health insurance coverage, although this choice was often illusory due to the high cost of health care. Once again, the ACA attempts to change these choices and incentives. For example, many insurance plans will have to meet new requirements, such as offering a package of "essential health benefits"; most employers will have to provide health insurance coverage or pay a penalty;

BOX 7-1 Vignette

Bob owns a small business that sells eponymous novelties. He has nine employees and has always made it a priority to offer competitive benefits, including health insurance. Unfortunately, last year one of his employees was diagnosed with cancer, which he continues to fight. Due to the sharp increase in use of health services by his employee group, the insurance company doubled his group premiums for the upcoming year. When Bob contacted other carriers, several of them would not consider insuring his group, and most of the others gave him quotes as expensive as his current carrier. One company gave him a lower quote, but it covered only catastrophic care; his employees would have to pay for the first $5,000 of care out of their own pockets. After reviewing his company's finances, Bob is left with several unattractive options: stop offering health insurance; offer comprehensive health insurance but pass on the cost increase to his employees, which would make it unaffordable for most of them; offer the bare-bones catastrophic plan only; or significantly lower wages and other benefits to defray the rising health insurance costs. In addition to wanting to offer competitive benefits, Bob is concerned that adopting any of these options will cause his employees to leave and make it hard to attract others, threatening the sustainability of his company. The 2010 health reform law, the Patient Protection and Affordable Care Act, attempts to help small businesses like Bob's by creating state health insurance exchanges. Starting in 2014, these exchanges are intended to offer a variety of plans to individuals and small businesses that otherwise might not be able to afford health insurance coverage. By creating large groups of purchasers though the exchanges, it is possible to pool risk and keep prices lower than if individuals or small businesses were attempting to purchase insurance coverage on their own.

and most individuals will have to purchase health insurance or pay a penalty. For each choice, the question is: What policy goal (e.g., equity, universal coverage, fiscal restraint, market efficiency) should drive the design and regulation of health insurance?

This chapter begins with a short history of health insurance in this country and then reviews the health insurance concepts key to understanding the structure and operation of health insurance. It concludes with an overview of man-

aged care, a particular form of health insurance dominant in today's market.

A BRIEF HISTORY OF THE RISE OF HEALTH INSURANCE IN THE UNITED STATES

Although 83% of people in this country are insured today, health insurance was not always an integral part of our society.[2(p22)] The initial movement to bring health insurance to the United States was modeled after activities in Europe. In the late 1800s and early 1900s, the European social insurance movement resulted in the creation of "sickness" insurance throughout many countries: Germany in 1883, Austria in 1888, Hungary in 1891, Britain in 1911, and Russia in 1912, to name just a few examples. These programs varied in scope and structure, from a compulsory national system in Germany, to industry-based requirements in France and Italy, to extensive state aid in Sweden and Switzerland. Although the Socialist and Progressive parties advocated for the adoption of similar social insurance systems in the United States in the early 1900s, their efforts were unsuccessful.[3]

In the absence of government-sponsored health insurance plans, the private sector insurance industry flourished with the growth of Blue Cross, Blue Shield, and commercial insurance carriers. Blue Cross established its first hospital insurance plan at Baylor University in 1929 by agreeing to provide 1,500 teachers with 21 days of hospital care per year for the price of $6 per person.[3(p295)] The hospital industry supported the growth of private insurance as a way to secure payment for services during the Depression. Blue Shield, the physician-based insurance plan, began in 1939 as a way to forestall renewed efforts to enact compulsory national health insurance and to avoid growth in consumer-controlled prepaid health plans, both of which would have reduced the type of physician autonomy endemic at that time.[3(p307)]

World War II led to rapid growth in employer-sponsored health insurance. With employees scarce and a general wage freeze in effect, a 1942 War Labor Board ruling that employee fringe benefits of up to 5% of wages did not violate the wage freeze created a strong incentive for employers to provide health benefits to attract new workers and keep their current ones. After the war, labor unions gained the right to bargain collectively, leading to another expansion of employee health plans. In 1954, the Internal Revenue Service declared that employers could pay health insurance premiums for their employees with pre-tax dollars, further increasing the value of the fringe benefit to employers.[a] By 1949, 28 million people had commercial hospital insurance, 22 million had commercial physician insurance, and 4 million had independent hospital plans. At that time, over 31 million had Blue Cross hospital coverage and 12 million had Blue Shield coverage.[3(p327)] Employer-sponsored health insurance, not national health insurance, was well on its way to becoming entrenched as the primary form of health insurance.

The federal government first became a major player in health insurance with the passage of Medicaid and Medicare in 1965. These programs were created, in part, to fill in coverage gaps left by the private insurance market—namely, coverage for the elderly, disabled, and low-income populations who had too little income and too high health risks to be viable candidates for insurance coverage from the insurance carriers' point of view. Like many major policy changes, the passage of these programs was a multi-layered compromise. Before the final design of these programs was established, several proposals were considered. The American Medical Association (AMA) supported a combination federal–state program to subsidize private insurance policies for the elderly to cover hospital care, physician care, and prescription drugs; Representative John Byrnes (R-WI), ranking Republican on the House Ways and Means Committee, endorsed an AMA-like proposal but with federal, instead of federal–state, administration; the Johnson Administration supported hospital insurance for the elderly through Social Security; and Senator Jacob Javitz (R-NY) supported federal payments to state programs to provide health care to poor, elderly individuals.[4(pp46–48)] In the end, the Medicare and Medicaid programs were passed in one bill with features from all of these proposals. For example, Medicare was established as a federally funded program with

BOX 7-2 Discussion Questions

Most people in this country obtain health insurance through employer-sponsored plans. Although the historical background you just read explains *why* this occurred, it does not discuss whether this is a good or bad thing. Is our reliance on employer-sponsored health insurance ideal for individuals? Providers? Employers? Society? What are the benefits and drawbacks to having employers as the primary source of health insurance? How different are the benefits and drawbacks when considered from various stakeholder perspectives? Would it be better to have more federal government involvement in providing health insurance? What primary policy goal would you use to decide how to answer these questions?

two parts, one for hospital insurance and one for physician insurance, and Medicaid as a state–federal program for the poor.

By the 1970s a number of factors converged to place rising healthcare costs on the national agenda: advances had been made in medical technology, hospitals expanded and became more involved in high-tech care, physician specialties became more common, hospitals and physicians had a large new pool of paying patients due to Medicaid and Medicare, wages for medical staff increased, and an aging population required an increasing amount of services.[3(pp383–384)] In addition, the prevailing fee-for-service (FFS) insurance system rewarded healthcare professionals for providing a high quantity of services. As the name suggests, fee-for-service reimbursement means the providers are paid for each service they provide—the more services (and more expensive services) rendered, the more reimbursement the provider receives. From 1960 to 1970, hospital care expenditures tripled from $9.3 billion to $28 billion and physician service expenditures almost matched that growth rate, increasing from $5.3 billion to $13.6 billion.[6(pp257–258)] Federal and state governments were also feeling the burden of high healthcare costs. From 1965 to 1970, federal and state governments collectively experienced a 21% annual rate of increase in their healthcare expenditures.[3(p384)]

As is discussed in more detail later in this chapter, managed care moves away from the FFS system by integrating the payment for services and the delivery of services into one place in an attempt to rein in healthcare costs and utilization. The federal Health Maintenance Organization Act of 1973 was intended to spur the growth of managed care by providing incentives to increase the use of health maintenance organizations (HMOs). The act relied on federal loans and grants and a mandate that employers with 25 or more employees offer an HMO option if one was available in their area.[6(pp262–263)] Even so, managed care did not flourish due to opposition by patients who did not want their provider and service choices restricted, and by providers who did not want to lose control over their practices.

As healthcare cost and quality concerns remained a national priority, the managed care industry eventually found a foothold in the health insurance market. Indeed, enrollment in managed care doubled during the 1990s, with almost 80 million enrollees by 1998. In 2010, only 1% of workers were in conventional, non-managed care arrangements.[7] Although only about 24% of Medicare enrollees choose managed care arrangements, some 70% of Medicaid beneficiaries receive some or all of their services through managed care, though for many of them it is mandatory that they receive services through a managed care arrangement.[8,9]

HOW HEALTH INSURANCE OPERATES

This section provides an overview of the purpose and structure of health insurance. It begins with a review of basic health insurance terminology, considers the role of uncertainty and risk in insurance, and concludes with a discussion of how insurance companies set their premium rates.

Basic Terminology

As you read earlier, the health insurance industry first developed when the FFS system was standard. Under this system, not only do providers have incentive to conduct more and more expensive services, but patients are unbridled in their use of the healthcare system because FFS does not limit the use of services or accessibility to providers. As we will discuss later in this chapter, managed care developed as a response to the incentives created by the FFS system. However, even though there are numerous differences between FFS and managed care, many of the fundamental principles of how insurance operates are applicable to any type of health insurance contract. The following discussion reviews how health insurance works generally, regardless of the type of insurance arrangement.

The health insurance consumer (also known as the *beneficiary* or *insured*) buys health insurance in advance for an annual fee, usually paid in monthly installments, called a *premium*. In return, the health insurance carrier (or company) pays for all or part of the beneficiary's healthcare costs if she or he becomes ill or injured and has a covered medical need. (A covered need is a medical good or service that the insurer is obligated to pay for because it is covered based on the terms of the insurance contract or policy. As discussed in detail elsewhere, the ACA requires many plans to cover all "essential health benefits," which at the time of this writing have not yet been defined by the Obama Administration through the regulatory process.) Insurance contracts cannot identify every conceivable healthcare need of beneficiaries, so they are generally structured to include categories of care (outpatient, inpatient, vision, maternity, etc.) to be provided if deemed medically necessary. Definitions of the term *medically necessary* vary by contract and are important when determining whether a procedure is covered.

Even if the beneficiary never needs healthcare services covered by the insurance policy, she still pays for the policy through premiums. The consumer benefits by having financial security in case of illness or injury, and the insurance company benefits by making money selling health insurance.

In addition to premiums, the beneficiary typically pays other costs under most health insurance policies. Many policies have *deductibles*, which is the amount of money the beneficiary must pay on her own for her healthcare needs each year before the insurance carrier starts to help with the costs. For example, if a policyholder has a $500 deductible, the beneficiary must pay 100% of the first $500 of healthcare costs each year. The insurance carrier is not liable to cover any costs until the individual's healthcare bill reaches $501 in a given year. If the individual does not need more than $500 worth of health care in a specific year, the insurance carrier generally will not help that individual pay her healthcare costs.

Furthermore, a beneficiary generally continues to incur some costs in addition to the premiums even after the deductible has been met. Insurance carriers often impose cost sharing on the beneficiary through *co-payment* or *co-insurance* requirements. A co-payment is a set dollar amount the beneficiary pays when receiving a service from a provider. For example, many HMOs charge their beneficiaries $10 every time

---

BOX 7-3 Discussion Questions

As a general matter, all types of insurance under traditional economic models cover expensive and unforeseen events, not events that have small financial risk or little uncertainty.[5(p195)] For example, auto insurance does not cover regular maintenance such as an oil change, and home insurance does not protect against normal wear and tear, such as the need to replace an old carpet. Accordingly, many economists argue that health insurance should not cover regular, foreseeable events such as physical exams or low-cost occurrences such as vaccinations. Other economists support a different school of thought. An alternative economic view is that health insurance should insure one's health, not just offer protection against the financial consequences of major adverse health events. Because people without health insurance are less likely to obtain preventive care such as physical exams or vaccinations, these economists believe it is in everyone's best interest, ethically and financially, to promote preventive care. Therefore, it is appropriate for insurance to cover both unpredictable and expensive events as well as predictable and less expensive events. Which theory do you support? What do you think is the best use of insurance? If insurance does not cover low-cost and predictable events, should another resource be available to assist individuals, or should people pay out of their own pockets for these healthcare needs?

a beneficiary sees a primary care provider. Co-insurance refers to a percentage of the healthcare cost the individual must cover. For example, 20% is a common co-insurance amount. This means the beneficiary pays 20% of all healthcare costs after the deductible has been met, with the insurance carrier paying the other 80%.

Uncertainty

From a traditional economic perspective, insurance exists because of two basic concepts—risk and uncertainty. The world is full of risks—auto theft, house fires, physical disabilities—and uncertainty about whether any such events might affect a particular individual. As a result, people buy a variety of forms of insurance (e.g., automobile insurance, home insurance, life or disability insurance) to protect themselves and their families against the financial consequences of these unfortunate and unforeseen events.

Although genetic predisposition or behavioral choices such as smoking or working a high-risk job may increase the chances that an individual will suffer from a health-related problem, in general there is a high level of uncertainty as

to whether a particular person will become sick or injured and need medical assistance. Health insurance protects the consumer from medical costs associated with both expensive and unforeseen events. Even if the consumer does not experience a negative event, a benefit exists from the peace of mind and reduced uncertainty of financial exposure that insurance provides.

In terms of health status and wise use of resources, when insurance allows consumers to purchase necessary services they would not otherwise be able to afford, it functions in a positive manner. Conversely, when insurance leads consumers to purchase unnecessary healthcare goods or services of low value because the consumer is not paying full cost, it works in a negative manner. The difficult task is trying to figure out how to set the consumer's share of the burden at just the right point to encourage and make available the proper use of health care, while discouraging improper usage.

Risk

Risk is a central concern in insurance. Consumers buy insurance to protect themselves against the risk of unforeseen and costly events. But health insurers are also concerned about risk—the risk that their beneficiaries will experience a covered medical event.

Individuals purchase health insurance to protect themselves against the risk of financial consequences of healthcare needs. Because of differences in risk level, individuals who are generally healthy or otherwise do not anticipate having health expenses may place a lower value on insurance than individuals who are unhealthy or those who are healthy but expect to have medical expenses, such as pregnant women. Therefore, healthy individuals tend to seek out lower-cost insurance plans or refrain from obtaining insurance altogether if it is not, in their view, cost effective. Unhealthy individuals or healthy individuals who often use the healthcare system would obviously prefer a low-cost insurance plan (with comprehensive benefits) but are generally more willing to pay higher premiums because of the value they place on having insurance.

Health insurance carriers are businesses that need to cover their expenditures, including the cost of accessing capital needed to run their company, to stay in the market.[b] They earn money by collecting premiums from their beneficiaries, and they pay out money to cover their beneficiaries' healthcare costs above the deductible amount and to cover the costs of running a business (overhead, marketing, taxes, etc.). One way health insurance companies survive is to make sure the premiums charged to beneficiaries cover these costs. From the insurance carrier's perspective, it would be ideal to be

---

BOX 7-4 Discussion Questions

As discussed earlier, risk and uncertainty are important concepts in health insurance. Individuals purchase health insurance policies to protect themselves financially against healthcare costs, and insurance carriers try to set premiums that will cover the cost of the services used by their beneficiaries. Currently (when allowed by law), insurance carriers may consider factors such as medical history, demographics, type of occupation, size of the beneficiary pool, and similar criteria when setting the terms of an insurance policy. Should health insurance carriers also have access to and be able to use genetic testing results when carriers decide whether to insure an individual, what premiums to charge, or which services to cover? If you think the answer to that question should be "no," why is genetic information different from all of the other kinds of information insurance carriers may take into account when making those decisions? Conversely, what is the strongest argument you can make in favor of allowing insurance carriers to consider an applicant's genetic information? How would allowing genetic testing alter an individual's or a provider's diagnosis and treatment decisions? What is the primary policy goal that affects your view?

able to charge lower premiums to attract healthy individuals who are less likely to use their benefits, and higher premiums to unhealthy individuals who are more likely to need medical care.

However, insurance companies have difficulty matching healthy people with low-cost plans and unhealthy people with high-cost plans because of the problem of *asymmetric information*. This is the term used by economists when one party to a transaction has more information than the other party. In the case of insurance, the imbalance often favors the consumer because insurance carriers generally do not know as much as the individual does about the individual's healthcare needs and personal habits. Although relatively healthy low-cost individuals want to make their status known because insurance carriers might be willing to sell them an insurance product for a lower price, relatively unhealthy individuals do not want their status known because insurance companies might charge them higher premiums. For this reason, when an insurance carrier lacks complete information, it is more beneficial to unhealthy beneficiaries than to healthy ones.

Together, uncertainty about risk and the presence of asymmetric information lead to the problem of *adverse selection*. In terms of health insurance, adverse selection is when unhealthy people over-select (that is, select beyond a random distribution) a particular plan. This occurs because people at risk for having high healthcare costs choose a particular plan because of that plan's attractive coverage rules.[10(pp12–13)] The consumer who knows he is a high risk for needing services will be more likely to choose a more comprehensive plan because it covers more services, even though it is probably a more expensive option. This leaves the insurer that offers the comprehensive plan with a disproportionate number of high-risk beneficiaries. As a result of the relatively high-risk pool, beneficiaries will have high service utilization rates and, in turn, the insurance carrier would need to raise premiums to be able to pay for the increased cost of covering services for beneficiaries. In turn, some of the healthier individuals might choose to leave the plan because of the higher premiums, resulting in an even riskier beneficiary pool and even higher premiums, and the cycle continues. The healthier consumers may find a lower-cost plan or may choose to go without health insurance and pay the penalty under the ACA, while the insurance plan is left with an increasingly higher percentage of relatively unhealthy people. This is the problem of adverse selection.

One instance where adverse selection is a key concern is with an increasingly popular type of health plan, the high deductible health plan (HDHP). As the name suggests, these plans have very high deductibles (usually defined as at least

$1,000 for an individual or $2,000 for a family). In 2010, annual premiums for the average HDHP were $4,702 for individuals and $11,683 for families.[7(p141)] As with other insurance plans, consumers pay most of their healthcare expenses out-of-pocket until they reach the deductible.[g] HDHPs are often used in conjunction with health reimbursement arrangements (HRAs) or health savings accounts (HSAs), which allow individuals to set aside money for future healthcare needs. Health reimbursement arrangements are funded solely by employers, who usually commit to making a specified amount of money available for healthcare expenses incurred by employees or their dependents, while HSAs are created by individuals, but employers may also contribute to HSAs if the employers offer a qualified HDHP. Individual contributions to HSAs are made with pre-income tax dollars, and withdrawals to pay for qualified healthcare expenses are also not taxed. As shown in Figures 7-1 and 7-2, high-deductible plans are increasingly popular with employers and employees.

Those who support HDHPs assert that high deductible plans promote personal responsibility because enrollees have a financial incentive to avoid overutilizing the healthcare system and to choose cost-effective treatment options. As a result, HDHPs are favored by employers and others as a cost-cutting strategy. Others are concerned that HDHPs will result in adverse selection, harming low-income and unhealthy individuals. Critics argue that enrollees of high deductible plans are more likely to be wealthier and healthier individuals who can afford high out-of-pocket expenses and are less likely to use the healthcare system.[11] As a result, relatively poorer and sicker individuals will choose a comprehensive group health insurance plan (assuming one is available and affordable), resulting in plans facing the possibility of adverse selection due to having a relatively high-risk insurance pool. In addition, there are concerns that employers will replace their more expensive comprehensive plan options with HDHPs, potentially resulting in less affordable health care for poorer and sicker individuals. Finally, critics also contend that the lower service utilization associated with HDHP enrollees is due to their better health status, not price sensitivity, undermining one of the main arguments in support of these plans.[11]

Setting Premiums

Assuming that insurance companies make their decisions in the context of asymmetric information, they cannot determine with certainty the appropriate amount of premium to charge each individual. Instead, insurance companies rely on making educated guesses about the risk each individual or group of individuals has of needing healthcare services. The

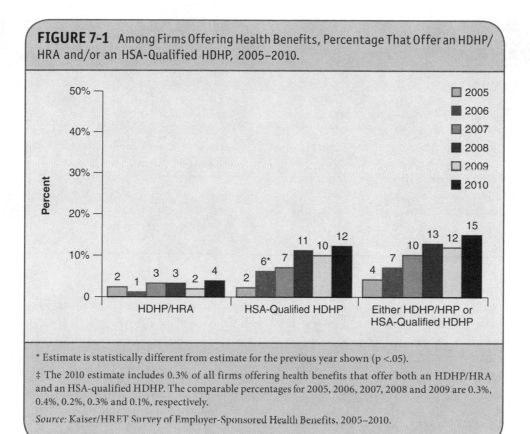

FIGURE 7-1 Among Firms Offering Health Benefits, Percentage That Offer an HDHP/HRA and/or an HSA-Qualified HDHP, 2005–2010.

* Estimate is statistically different from estimate for the previous year shown (p <.05).

‡ The 2010 estimate includes 0.3% of all firms offering health benefits that offer both an HDHP/HRA and an HSA-qualified HDHP. The comparable percentages for 2005, 2006, 2007, 2008 and 2009 are 0.3%, 0.4%, 0.2%, 0.3% and 0.1%, respectively.

Source: Kaiser/HRET Survey of Employer-Sponsored Health Benefits, 2005–2010.

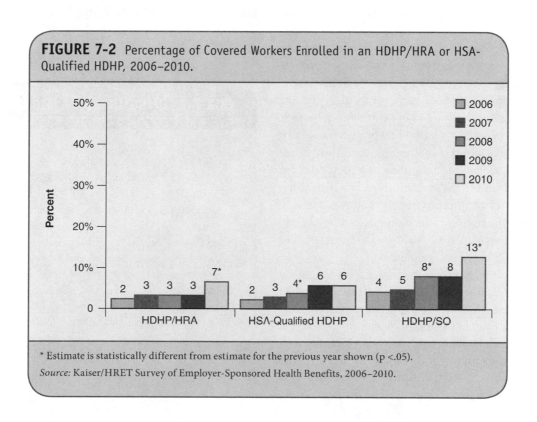

FIGURE 7-2 Percentage of Covered Workers Enrolled in an HDHP/HRA or HSA-Qualified HDHP, 2006–2010.

* Estimate is statistically different from estimate for the previous year shown (p <.05).

Source: Kaiser/HRET Survey of Employer-Sponsored Health Benefits, 2006–2010.

BOX 7-5 Discussion Questions

In general, people with low incomes or no health insurance (or both) tend to be less healthy than those who are financially better off or insured (or both). As a result, policy proposals that suggest including poor, uninsured individuals in already-existing insurance plans are met with resistance by individuals in those plans and by carriers or employers who operate them. Yet, if an insurance plan is created that only subscribes a less-healthy, poor, or uninsured population, it is likely to be an unattractive business opportunity because beneficiaries are likely to need a high quantity of health care that will be costly to provide. Given what you know about adverse selection and risk, what, in your opinion, is the best way to provide insurance coverage to the poor and uninsured? Should they be included in current plans? Should the government provide financial incentives for private carriers to insure them? Should a separate plan or program be created to serve them? In these various scenarios, what incentives are created for plans, current plan members, government, and so on? Can high-deductible health plans work for a low-income population?

BOX 7-6 Discussion Questions

What populations or types of people pay more under experience rating? Does experience rating create any incentives for individuals to act in a certain way? What populations or types of people pay more under community rating? Does community rating create any incentives for individuals to act in a certain way? Which rating system seems preferable to you? What trade-offs are most important to you? Should the focus be on the good of the individual or the good of the community? Are these mutually exclusive concerns?

to provide greater coverage for the higher amount, but something in the market prevents this transaction from occurring, then the optimal amount of risk shifting has not occurred. Or, if individuals value a certain level of insurance coverage at a price that is less than the price at which insurers are willing to provide that coverage, but individuals buy coverage anyway at the higher price, the market is not optimally efficient (due to excess coverage).

Conversely, the market may be judged based on equity or fairness. Even the most efficient market may result in some inequities. Some individuals may be uninsured, some may have to pay more than other individuals for the same level of

two main methods of setting premiums are *experience rating* and *community rating*.

When insurance companies use experience rating to make an educated guess about the risk of someone's needing healthcare services, they are relying on how much a beneficiary or group of beneficiaries spent on medical services previously to determine the amount of the premium for each member or group. Thus, if an individual or group had very high medical costs in a given year, premiums are likely to rise the following year. Conversely, community rating does not take into account health status or claims history when setting premiums. In "pure" community rating, insurers use only geography and family composition to set rates; in "modified" community rating, insurers may be allowed to consider other characteristics, such as age and gender.

Which rating system makes more sense from a policy perspective as a basis for setting premiums may depend on whether you evaluate the insurance market based on efficiency or equity (think back to discussions of competing conceptual frameworks). If the market is judged based on efficiency, then the key issue is whether the optimal amount of risk has shifted from consumers to insurers. If there are individuals willing to pay a higher amount for greater coverage and insurers willing

BOX 7-7 Discussion Questions

While it has been more common for insurers to use experience rating than community rating, the ACA requires health plans in the individual and small group markets to use adjusted community rating rules. These rules only allow insurance companies to account for geography, age, tobacco use, and family size when setting premiums. The oldest beneficiaries may be charged three times more than the youngest and tobacco users may be charged 50% more than non-tobacco users. Insurers are prohibited from varying premiums based on health status or indicators of health status, such as claims history. What do you think of this rule? What are the pros and cons? Who is hurt and who is helped by this rule? Are there other factors that insurers should be able to take into account when setting premiums?

insurance, some may not be able to purchase the level of coverage they desire, and some individuals may not be able to join a particular plan. These inequities are often a concern in the context of the uninsured, especially as uninsurance relates to low-income individuals or those with high health needs due to random events, such as an accident or genetic condition.

Regardless of the underwriting methodology used, premiums are cheaper for people purchasing insurance as part of a large group rather than buying health insurance individually or as part of a small group. Due to the law of averages, larger groups of people are more likely to have an average risk rate. When people join a group for reasons unrelated to health status, such as working for the same company, it is also more likely that the group will have an average risk rate. Groups with average risk rates are attractive to insurers because the cost of insuring a few unhealthy people will probably be offset by savings from insuring many healthy ones. Conversely, in smaller groups it is more likely that the group will have a relatively high risk rate and less likely that the cost of insuring an unhealthy person can be offset by the savings of insuring a few other healthy people. This is the problem faced by Bob, the small business owner described at the outset of the chapter who has one high-cost employee. Even though he would like to offer health insurance coverage to his employees, Bob and other small business owners like him often are able to offer only expensive or limited coverage, if they can offer any health insurance benefit at all. In order to help individuals and small business owners like Bob, some states require insurers to use a community rating system to set premiums for these groups and in the state health insurance exchanges that were created by the ACA.

Carriers also prefer to insure large groups because most of the administrative costs associated with insurance are the same whether the carrier is covering a few people or a few thousand.[12(pp342–344)] In fact, group coverage has traditionally required fewer marketing resources than individual coverage, which targets customers one at a time. However, the proliferation of information on the Internet may change this equation.

Medical Underwriting

The prior discussion about rate setting assumed asymmetric information (i.e., where the insurer has little information about the consumer's health status and the consumer has substantial information about his or her own healthcare needs). Of course, there are ways for insurers to gain information about the medical needs of a consumer looking to join a health plan: Physical exams, questionnaires, medical records, occupation, and demographics all provide clues about the health status of the consumer. Although it is much more difficult to accomplish, insurers may also try to predict an individual's future costs through questionnaires that ask, for example, whether an individual engages in risky activities (e.g., riding a motorcycle) or through genetic testing (which is itself an emerging health policy and law issue).

Whether companies are allowed to consider an applicant's medical history or other personal information to help assess risk of healthcare needs in the future—a practice referred to as medical underwriting—is a somewhat complicated legal question that involves both federal and state law. The Health Insurance Portability and Accountability Act of 1996 (HIPAA)[13] includes an important protection for consumers by prohibiting group health plans from excluding or limiting otherwise qualified individuals due to pre-existing conditions (a pre-existing condition is a medical condition, such as cancer or diabetes, that is present at the time an individual applies to enroll in an insurance plan). The ACA expands this protection by requiring all health insurers to sell policies to all applicants, regardless of pre-existing conditions, This requirement is already in effect for children and will take effect for adults in 2014.

Prior to HIPAA, many individuals with pre-existing conditions were denied insurance altogether, denied coverage for particular medical care, or charged very high premiums if they sought to purchase a policy. These practices led to a problem referred to as "job lock." Because most Americans receive insurance coverage through their employers, many employees with pre-existing conditions could not switch jobs for fear that their new company's insurance policy would be denied to them on account of their pre-existing condition. One study estimated that job lock resulted in a 4% reduction in voluntary turnover.[12(p341)]

Although HIPAA and the ACA do not regulate the amount of premiums that may be charged, all members of a group generally pay the same premium due to the laws' nondiscrimination provisions. In HIPAA, these provisions prohibit plans or insurance carriers from requiring any individual to pay a higher premium or contribution than another "similarly situated" individual[14] in the plan based on eight health factors: health status, physical or mental medical conditions, claims experience (i.e., the individual has a history of high health claims), receipt of health care, medical history, genetic information, evidence of insurability, and disability.[15] However, because those who purchase individual health insurance plans are not covered by HIPAA's protections, the ACA protections were needed as well. The ACA also prohibits plans from charging individuals higher premiums due to their pre-existing conditions.

MANAGED CARE

The prior sections reviewed the history, basic structure, and purpose of health insurance generally. In this section, we discuss a specific kind of health insurance structure that has come to dominate the American market: managed care. We will describe why managed care emerged, some of the frequent cost-containment strategies used by managed care organizations, and the most common managed care structures in the market today.

Managed care became the predominant healthcare financing and delivery arrangement in the United States because healthcare costs had risen to alarming levels and there were few mechanisms for containing costs under the FFS system. As mentioned earlier, FFS does not create incentives for providers or patients to utilize healthcare services sparingly. Providers have an incentive under FFS to provide more services and more expensive services (but not necessarily higher-quality services) because their income rises with each procedure or office visit and fees are higher for more expensive services. As long as providers are accessible, insured patients can request services and assume their insurance company will pay most or all of the costs to the extent that the services are covered by the health plan and medically necessary.

In addition, the FFS system does not create incentives for providers or patients to use the lowest-cost quality care available. Many people believe specialists provide higher quality care and turn to them even for minor needs that do not truly require expensive specialty services, and the FFS system does not discourage this behavior. Furthermore, because traditional insurance coverage requires a specific diagnosis for reimbursement, patients are discouraged from seeking preventative services when they are symptom-free under FFS.[16(p332)] At the same time, traditional insurance companies do not have the ability to control costs or quality of care under FFS—their job is limited to determining whether a service is covered and medically necessary and providing the agreed-upon reimbursement. They have little ability to measure or improve the quality of care provided by healthcare professionals and cannot control costs by limiting the amount or type of services received; instead, they can only raise premiums and other rates in the future to cover increasing costs.

To alter the inherent incentives under FFS and to grant insurers some ability to control the quality and utilization of services, managed care integrates the provision of and payment for healthcare services. Through various strategies discussed in the following sections, managed care organizations (MCOs) and managed care plans create incentives to provide fewer services and less expensive care, while still maintaining the appropriate level of healthcare quality. Managed care organizations also attempt to alter patients' decision making through cost-sharing requirements, cost containment tools, utilization restrictions, and free or low-cost coverage for preventive care.

Managed care organizations take various forms, but certain general features apply to all of them to varying degrees. All MCOs provide a comprehensive, defined package of benefits to the purchaser/member for a pre-set fee (including both monthly premium and cost-sharing requirements). Services are offered to members through a network of providers, all of whom have a contractual relationship with the MCO. The MCOs choose which providers to include in their networks and what services are rendered by network providers. Most notably, they also use financial incentives and other mechanisms to control the delivery, use, quality, and cost of services in ways that are not present in FFS insurance systems.[6(p260)]

Cost Containment and Utilization Tools

Managed care introduced a variety of tools in its attempt to contain costs and control healthcare service utilization. The cost containment strategies of *performance-based salary bonuses or withholdings*, *discounted fee schedules*, and *capitated payments* shift financial risk or limit payments to providers who, in turn, have an incentive to choose the least costly, but still effective, treatment option. The utilization control strategies of *gatekeeping* and *utilization review* focus on making sure that only appropriate and necessary care is provided to patients. Another type of strategy, *case management*, is designed to make sure that necessary care is provided in the most coordinated and cost-effective way possible.

Provider Payment Tools

Depending on the structure of the MCO, providers are paid by salary, discounted fee schedule, or capitation rate. Providers in what are called staff-model MCOs are employees of the MCO and are paid an annual salary. The salary structure often includes bonuses or salary withholdings that are paid (or withheld) upon meeting (or not meeting) utilization or performance goals, thus shifting some financial risk from the MCO to the provider. A discounted fee schedule is a service-specific fee system as is used in FFS. However, an MCO-style fee schedule pays lower reimbursement rates than is true in FFS systems; providers agree to accept less than their usual fee in return for the large volume of patients available to them by being a part of the MCO provider network. The MCO retains the financial risk in a discounted fee system, but the costs are lower for the company due to the discounted rate paid to providers. Finally, a capitated payment rate is a fixed monthly sum per member that the provider receives regardless of the number or type of services provided to patients. The physician receiving the capitated rate is responsible for providing all of the care needed by his or her MCO patients, within the provider's scope of practice. As a result, the financial risk in the case of capitated arrangements is shifted entirely from the MCO to the provider. Depending on the contract between the provider and MCO, the insurance company may or may not guarantee the provider a minimum number of patients in exchange for accepting a capitated rate. These provider-focused cost containment strategies are summarized in Table 7-1.

Both the salaried and capitation payment methods have very different incentives for providers than is the case under the FFS system. Instead of being paid more for doing more, MCO providers are paid the same amount regardless of the number or type of services they provide. Given the use of bonuses and withholdings, salaried providers may be paid more if they make treatment decisions deemed favorable by an MCO. By using these incentives, MCOs encourage providers to render the fewest and most cost-effective services necessary.

Critics of managed care payment methodologies argue that MCO plan members will not receive all necessary care if providers are incentivized to provide fewer services and less-costly care. Instead of treating patients using both the most cost-efficient and medically necessary services, critics claim MCOs encourage providers to save money by providing fewer services and less specialized care than necessary; MCOs counter that their own incentive is to keep their members healthy so they do not need expensive services in the future. In addition, MCOs point to their ability to impose quality control measures on providers as a way to ensure that patients are properly treated. In response, critics argue that because members switch health plans relatively frequently, MCOs do not have an incentive to keep their members healthy because

the MCOs will not realize the long-term savings as members come and go.

Which side has the better argument? There is no definitive answer. On the one hand, studies have found that treatment decisions under MCO arrangements are mostly influenced by clinical factors (not economic ones), that there is little or no measurable difference in the health outcomes of patients in FFS versus managed care plans, that the quality of care provided under FFS and managed care plans is basically equal, and that most Americans are satisfied with their health plan, whether it is FFS or through an MCO.[16(pp351–352)] On the other hand, studies have also shown that mental health patients do not fare as well in MCOs as in FFS plans; that nonprofit HMOs (a type of MCO) score better on quality measures than for-profit ones; and that managed care enrollees are less likely than FFS patients to give excellent ratings to their plan overall, the quality of services they receive, access to specialty care, and time spent with physicians.[16(pp351–352)]

Utilization Control Tools

Managed care organizations also employ other techniques, not related to provider payment methods, to control use of healthcare services. Once again, the goal in using these tools is to reduce the use of unnecessary and costly services. We review three common utilization control tools: gatekeeping, utilization review, and case management.

Gatekeepers monitor and control the services a patient receives. Members of managed care plans are often required to select a primary care provider from the MCO network upon enrollment. This provider acts as the member's "gatekeeper" and is responsible for providing primary care, referring patients for additional care, and generally coordinating the patient's care. Having a gatekeeper allows the MCO, not the patient or specialty provider, to determine when a patient needs additional or specialty services, diagnostic tests,

TABLE 7-1 Provider Payment Cost Containment Strategies

Strategy	Provider Payment Method	How Costs Are Controlled	Who Assumes Financial Risk
Salary and bonuses/withholds	Provider receives a salary as an employee of an MCO	Incentive for provider to perform fewer and/or less costly services	MCO and provider
Discounted fee schedule	Provider receives a lower fee than under FFS for each service to members	Pays provider less per service rendered than under FFS	MCO (but also has lower costs)
Capitation	Provider receives a set payment per month for each member regardless of services provided	Incentive for provider to perform fewer and/or less costly services	Provider

hospital admissions, and the like. As with the cost containment strategies discussed earlier, there are critics who contend that utilization-based bonuses or salary withholdings give gatekeepers financial incentive not to provide specialty referrals even when it is in the best interest of the patient.

Utilization review (UR) allows an MCO to evaluate the appropriateness of the services provided and to deny payment for unnecessary services. Managed care organization personnel review and approve or deny the services performed or recommended by network providers. Utilization review specialists are often healthcare professionals, and MCOs generally use existing clinical care guidelines to determine whether services are appropriate.

Utilization review may occur prospectively, concurrently, or retrospectively. Prospective UR means that an MCO reviews the appropriateness of treatment before a service is rendered. A request for a recommended service is sent to a UR panel for approval or denial. A denial does not mean a patient cannot move forward with his preferred treatment plan; however, it does mean that the patient will have to pay for the treatment out of his own pocket. Prospective UR is distinguished from concurrent UR, which is when the MCO review of the appropriateness of treatment occurs while treatment is being rendered. For example, a patient may need a procedure that requires hospitalization. Even though the procedure is performed and covered, a UR specialist might still determine the number of days the patient may remain in the hospital or whether certain services, such as home care or physical therapy, will be covered upon discharge from the hospital. Finally, retrospective review means the MCO reviews the appropriateness of treatment (and therefore its coverage) after a service is rendered. In this case, a patient's medical records are reviewed to determine whether the care provided was appropriate and billed accurately; MCOs will not provide reimbursement for services deemed inappropriate

or unnecessary. This latter type of review may also be used to uncover provider practice patterns and determine incentive compensation.[16(p339)] Regardless of when the review occurs, the use of UR is controversial because it may interfere with the patient–provider relationship and allow for second-guessing of provider treatment decisions by a third party who is not part of the diagnosis and treatment discussions.

Case management is a service utilization approach that uses trained personnel to manage and coordinate patient care. Although gatekeeping serves as a basic form of case management for all members, many patients with complex or chronic conditions, such as HIV/AIDS or spinal cord injuries, may benefit from more intensive case management. These patients may have frequent need for care from various specialists and thus benefit from assistance by personnel who are familiar with the many resources available to care for the patient and who are able to provide information and assistance to patients and their families. A case manager works with providers to determine what care is necessary and to help arrange for patients to receive that care in the most appropriate and cost-effective settings.[16(pp336–337)] Although the general idea of case management is not controversial, some people believe it can be implemented in a manner that acts more as a barrier than an asset to care because additional approval is needed before a patient receives care and because another layer of bureaucracy is placed between the patient and the provider. Table 7-2 summarizes the three service utilization control strategies just discussed.

As you might imagine, managed care's use of service utilization control mechanisms frequently leads to disputes between patients and their managed care company over whether the company is improperly affecting the provider–patient relationship (and negatively impacting the quality of care provided) by making decisions as to the type or quantity of care a patient should receive. This is both a highly charged

TABLE 7-2 Service Utilization Control Strategies

Strategy	Description	Potential Concerns
Gatekeeper	Uses a primary care provider to make sure only necessary and appropriate care is provided.	Gatekeepers may have financial incentive to approve fewer services or less costly care.
Utilization review	Uses MCO personnel to review and approve or deny services requested by a provider to make sure only necessary and appropriate care is provided.	Interferes with patient–provider relationship; someone other than the patient's provider decides whether treatment is appropriate.
Case management	Uses MCO personnel to manage and coordinate patient care to make sure care is provided in the most cost-effective manner.	May act as a barrier to receiving care if the case manager does not approve a desired service or service provider.

health policy issue and a complicated legal issue, and one that is discussed in more detail in a review of individual rights in health care. For purposes of this chapter, it is enough to note that MCOs must have a grievance and appeal process to at least initially handle these sorts of disputes. Although companies' processes differ in their specifics, they generally allow members to appeal a coverage decision, provide evidence to support the appeal, and receive an expedited resolution when medically necessary. The ACA included a number of provisions relating to the appeals process required of insurance plans; these provisions establish a federal standard for state external appeals laws governing products in the individual and group markets and create a new federal appeals process for self-insured plans (the provisions do not affect Medicaid and Medicare, which have their own appeals processes).[17] The need for adequate grievance and appeal procedures can be particularly acute for patients with special healthcare needs, such as those with physical or mental disabilities, and patients who otherwise use the healthcare system more frequently than most.

Common Managed Care Structures

There are three managed care structures common in the market today: health maintenance organizations (HMOs), preferred provider organizations (PPOs), and point-of-service plans (POS). All three provide preventive and specialty care, but the rules relating to accessing care differ for each. In general, HMOs have the most restrictive rules pertaining to patients and providers, PPOs have the least restrictive rules, and POSs fall in the middle.

BOX 7-8 Discussion Questions

Cost containment strategies embraced by MCOs were a direct result of the FFS experience with ever-increasing utilization and healthcare costs. However, many consumers and providers chafe at the restrictions imposed by MCOs and are concerned that someone other than the provider is making treatment decisions. Are these restrictions appropriate and necessary? Do you favor some of the restrictions over others? Is it appropriate for one entity to be responsible for both paying for and providing care? Should someone other than an MCO—say the federal or state governments—have primary responsibility for making determinations about service utilization?

As shown in Figure 7-3, PPOs are the most popular type of managed care plan, while very few people are still insured by a conventional FFS plan. In general, the more control an MCO has over its providers and members, the easier it is to control utilization of services and, therefore, healthcare costs and quality. Conversely, providers and patients prefer to have as much autonomy as possible, so the more restrictive MCO structures may be less desirable in that respect. However, the distinctions among managed care structures have become blurred recently because of the consumer and provider backlash against MCO restrictions.

Health Maintenance Organizations

When managed care first became prominent in the 1970s, HMOs were the most common type of MCO. There are several characteristics shared by all HMOs:

- They pay providers a salary to cover the cost of any and all services that beneficiaries need within a provider's scope of practice;
- They negotiate a capitated rate with plan purchasers (e.g., employers) which prices the plan based on a per member per month amount for each type of provider;
- They coordinate and control receipt of services;
- They arrange for care using only their network providers, and
- They are responsible for providing care according to established quality standards.

Despite these commonalities, HMOs may be structured through a variety of models, including staff-model/closed panel, group model, network model, individual practice associations (IPAs), and direct contract model.[16(pp340–344)] Each model has advantages and disadvantages from the perspective of the HMO, its providers, and its members, as shown in Table 7-3.

Preferred Provider Organizations

As is evident from Table 7-3, every form of HMO is fairly restrictive. In all models, the HMO provides coverage only if members seek care from network providers and providers may or may not be limited to serving only HMO members. As both patients and providers began rebelling over these restrictions, new forms of MCOs emerged, often formed by providers and hospitals themselves.

Like HMOs, PPOs have a provider network, referred to as preferred providers. Unlike HMOs, however, PPOs provide coverage to patients seeking care from any provider, regardless of whether the provider is part of the member's PPO preferred

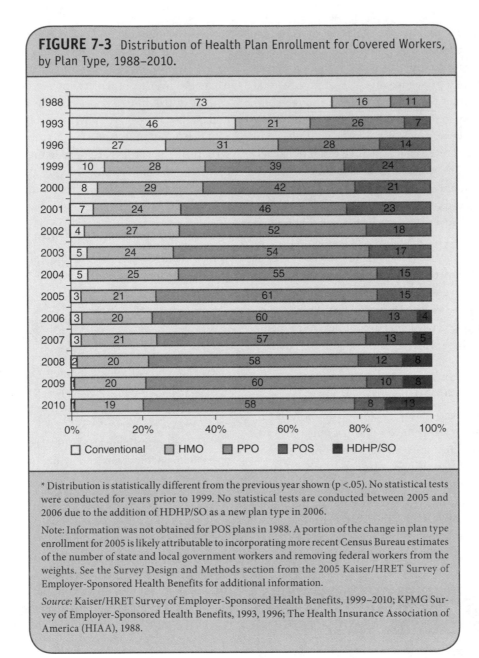

FIGURE 7-3 Distribution of Health Plan Enrollment for Covered Workers, by Plan Type, 1988–2010.

* Distribution is statistically different from the previous year shown (p <.05). No statistical tests were conducted for years prior to 1999. No statistical tests are conducted between 2005 and 2006 due to the addition of HDHP/SO as a new plan type in 2006.

Note: Information was not obtained for POS plans in 1988. A portion of the change in plan type enrollment for 2005 is likely attributable to incorporating more recent Census Bureau estimates of the number of state and local government workers and removing federal workers from the weights. See the Survey Design and Methods section from the 2005 Kaiser/HRET Survey of Employer-Sponsored Health Benefits for additional information.

Source: Kaiser/HRET Survey of Employer-Sponsored Health Benefits, 1999–2010; KPMG Survey of Employer-Sponsored Health Benefits, 1993, 1996; The Health Insurance Association of America (HIAA), 1988.

provider network. However, the amount of the service price that the PPO will cover is greater for an in-network provider than an out-of-network provider. For example, a PPO may agree to cover 80% of the cost for an in-network physician visit, but only 70% of the cost for a similar, but out-of-network, physician visit. PPO patients thus have the option of paying more but choosing among a greater number of providers or paying less but choosing among a more limited number of (in-network) providers. In addition, a PPO member's cost-

sharing responsibilities are often higher than is the case for HMO members.

In exchange for being in the network, providers agree to accept a discounted rate for their services, often 25–35% below their usual rates.[16(p345)] Because PPO members have a financial incentive to seek providers who are in-network, these healthcare professionals find it worthwhile to accept a reduced rate from the PPO in exchange for the higher likelihood that PPO members will select them over non-network

TABLE 7-3 Key Characteristics of Common HMO Models

HMO Model	HMO–Provider Relationship and Payment Type	Provider Employment Arrangement	Must Members Seek Care from Network?	May Providers Care for Nonmembers?	General Comments
Staff-model/closed panel	HMO employs providers, pays a salary, often includes bonuses or withholds.	Employed by HMO.	Yes	No	Provides services only in HMO's office and affiliated hospitals. Relatively speaking, HMO has the most control over providers and service utilization, but has fixed costs of building and staff. HMO may contract with outside providers if necessary. Providers and consumers often do not like restrictions imposed by HMO. Providers do not need to solicit patients. Consumers may find it most cost-effective option.
Group	HMO contracts with one multi-specialty group for a capitated rate.	Employed by own provider group.	Yes	Depends on terms of contract	HMO has less control over utilization. HMO contracts for hospital care on a prepaid or FFS basis. Providers may prefer this model because they remain independent as opposed to becoming an employee of the HMO and because they may serve nonmembers if their contract permits.
Network	HMO contracts with several group practices (often primary care practices) for a capitated rate.	Employed by own provider group.	Yes	Depends on terms of contract	The group practices may make referrals, but are financially responsible for reimbursing outside providers. HMO has less control over utilization due to greater number of contracts and ability of providers to subcontract. Providers may prefer additional autonomy, but also take on financial risk of providing primary and specialty care. Members may have a relatively greater choice of providers.
IPA	HMO contracts with IPA for a capitated rate.	IPA is intermediary between HMO and solo practitioners and groups. IPA pays providers a capitated rate.	Yes	Depends on terms of contract	HMO has reduced control over providers but may have less malpractice liability because IPA is an intermediary.[1] HMO may contract with specialty physicians as needed and for hospital care on a prepaid or FFS basis. Providers may prefer contracting with IPA instead of HMO to retain more autonomy. Members may have greater choice of providers.
Direct contract	HMO contracts directly with individual providers for a capitated rate.	Self-employed.	Yes	Depends on terms of contract	HMO has more leverage over providers because it contracts with them as individuals, but its administrative costs are much higher than having one contract or a few contracts with groups. Providers have less leverage regarding practice restrictions when contracting on an individual basis.

BOX 7-9 Discussion Questions

In terms of containing healthcare costs and improving healthcare quality, do you think healthcare consumers and professionals need even more restrictions than are currently used in managed care? Are there any reasons to revert back to the FFS system, even knowing its inflationary qualities? If you think that managed care is not the answer to our still-rising healthcare costs and quality concerns, what other tools might help lower costs and improve the quality of care? Should any tools be imposed by government regulation or agreed to voluntarily by insurers and the insured?

providers. Furthermore, unlike the capitation system found in HMOs, PPO providers do not assume financial risk for providing services. Depending on the terms of their contract with the PPO, preferred providers may or may not agree to limit their practice to PPO members. Although it is rare, PPOs may choose to guarantee preferred providers a minimum number of patients.

Even though an MCO has much less control over service utilization in the PPO model than the HMO model, PPOs still provide more incentives to use care judiciously than is the case in an FFS system. For example, in-network PPO providers are paid less than their customary rate by the company when they provide care to PPO members and often agree to abide by quality control and utilization review strategies used by the PPO. In addition, PPO patients have an incentive to use certain providers who will cost them less and have cost-sharing requirements unlike anything found under FFS. The PPO model attempts to locate a middle ground between the very restrictive HMO models and the FFS structure that resulted in very high health care utilization and costs.

Point-of-Service Plans

In another effort to contain costs while still providing patients the freedom to choose their provider, POS plans combine features of HMOs and PPOs. Like an HMO, POS plans have a provider network, use a capitated or other payment system that shares financial risk with providers, and requires members to use a gatekeeper to help control service utilization. However, designated services may be obtained from out-of-network providers who are paid on an FFS basis, but use of these providers costs the member more money, as with the PPO model. A POS gatekeeper must approve all in-network care and may also have some control over out-of-network

care, depending on the terms of the plan. The call by many consumers for increased choice in providers has become forceful enough that some HMOs are now offering POS plans, which they may refer to as open-ended (as opposed to closed panel) models.

The Future of Managed Care

Managed care is likely to remain an integral part of the health system despite its drawbacks. Patients chafe at utilization restrictions, as is evident by the increase in PPO popularity and the emergence of the hybrid HMO/POS. Accurate or not, there is a widespread perception that managed care plans deny necessary care and provide lower quality care.[16(p352)] Providers also complain that managed care interferes with their ability to practice medicine in a manner of their choosing, placing them in ethical dilemmas due to the use of financial incentives and possibly lowering the quality of care they provide due to limits on tests and procedures they order. Yet, the key circumstance that led to the creation of managed care—high healthcare expenditures—has not abated. While the country struggles with ever-growing healthcare costs, even under managed care, the willingness to experiment with various cost and utilization containment strategies is likely to remain in place.

CONCLUSION

This introduction to health insurance serves as a building block for additional study, which expands upon many of the key health policy and law themes mentioned here. It should be clear to readers that health policy analysts and decision makers must be particularly attuned to health insurance issues; without knowing both the basic structure of health insurance and how various incentives impact the actions of healthcare consumers, professionals, and insurance carriers, they cannot make informed recommendations and policies addressing the key health issues of the day.

REFERENCES

1. Pub L No. 111-148, The Patient Protection and Affordable Care Act.

2. U.S. Bureau of the Census. *Income, Poverty, and Health Insurance Coverage in the United States: 2009.* Washington, D.C.: Bureau of the U.S. Census; 2010.

3. Starr P. *The Social Transformation of American Medicine: The Rise of a Sovereign Profession and the Making of a Vast Industry.* New York, NY: Basic Books, Inc.; 1982.

4. Stevens R, Stevens R. *Welfare Medicine in America: A Case Study of Medicaid.* New Brunswick, NJ: Transaction Publishers; 2003.

5. Council of Economic Advisors. Health care and insurance. In: *Economic Report of the President.* Washington, D.C.: GPO; 2004.

6. Sultz HA, Young KM. *Health Care USA: Understanding Its Organization and Delivery.* 3rd ed. Gaithersburg, MD: Aspen Publishers; 2001.

7. Kaiser Family Foundation and Health Research and Educational Trust. *Employer health benefits. 2010.* Available at http://ehbs.kff.org /pdf/2010/8085.pdf. Accessed February 1, 2011.

8. Kaiser Family Foundation. *Medicare Advantage—fact sheet. 2010.* Available at http://www.kff.org/medicare/upload/2052-14.pdf. Accessed July 20, 2011.

9. Kaiser Family Foundation. *Medicaid and managed care: key data, trends, and issues. 2010.* Available at http://www.kff.org/medicaid /upload/8046.pdf. Accessed July 20, 2011.

10. Penner S. *Introduction to Health Care Economics and Financial Management: Fundamental Concepts with Practical Application.* Philadelphia, PA: Lippincott Williams and Wilkins; 2004.

11. Davis K. Consumer-directed health care: will it improve system performance? *Health Serv Res.* 2004;39:1219–1233.

12. Phelps CE. *Health Economics.* 3rd ed. Boston, MA: Addison-Wesley; 2003.

13. Pub. L. No. 104-191, 110 Stat. 1936 *codified* in sections 18, 26, 29, and 42 U.S.C.

14. Nondiscrimination in Health Coverage in the Group Market; Interim Final Rules and Proposed Rules, 66 Fed. Reg. 1378, 1382 (January 2001) *codified* in 29 CFR 2590.702.

15. 42 U.S.C. § 300gg-1; Nondiscrimination in Health Coverage in the Group Market; Interim Final Rules and Proposed Rules, 1378–1384, 1396–1403.

16. Shi L, Singh DA. *Delivering Health Care in America: A Systems Approach.* 3rd ed. Gaithersburg, MD: Aspen Publishers; 2004.

17. Rosenbaum S. *Appeals of claims for benefits. 2010.* HealthReformGPS. Available at http://www.healthreformgps.org/resources/appeals-of-claims-for-benefits/. Accessed July 20, 2011.

ENDNOTES

a. Section 106 of the IRS Code of 1954 states that employers who pay a share of premiums for employees' hospital and medical insurance may exclude that amount from the gross income of employees.

b. There are both for-profit and not-for-profit insurance companies. Both types of companies seek to earn enough revenues to cover expenses and the cost of accessing capital. However, for-profit companies return excess revenue to their investors whereas not-for-profit companies put excess revenue back into the company.

Health Economics in a Health Policy Context

INTRODUCTION

There are several disciplines that may be used to assist you in analyzing health policy problems; these include frameworks such as topical domains, historically dominant perspectives, and key stakeholder perspectives, along with political and legal analysis. Furthermore, throughout the text, issues are viewed through a social framework by asking you to consider what policies guide your decision making—in other words, what do you think should happen? This chapter informs you about yet another discipline—economics—that is useful when conducting health policy analysis.

Students just beginning their health policy studies often question why it is necessary to study economics. Most would rather think about and discuss what policies they support and what values should govern decision making, not about competitive markets, equilibriums, and externalities. What may not be clear initially to students is that economic theory provides one of the fundamental building blocks for making policy choices, both generally and in the context of health

care and public health. For instance, economic tools help policymakers predict how consumers and producers will react if they implement certain policies. Knowing this may help policymakers choose the most effective and efficient policy to achieve their goals. The governor's request to Sophie (see Box 8-1) provided one example of how economic knowledge would prove helpful in health policy decision-making. Other examples include:

> When federal officials decide which communities should receive grants to support primary care clinics, they need to know if appropriate providers are available to staff clinics. Economic theory can help explain why some providers prefer to locate in urban or suburban Maryland instead of rural West Virginia, why there is a shortage of qualified nurses but an abundance of cardiologists, and how to change this situation and help a rural primary care clinic remain viable.
>
> In the face of a flu vaccine shortage, the president considers launching an initiative to ensure that every American can be vaccinated against the flu in the case of an epidemic. Economic theory sheds light on why there are so few vaccine producers supplying the United States currently and what could be done to entice manufacturers to participate in the flu vaccine market.

Entire books and courses are devoted to the concept of health economics, and this chapter is not an attempt to distill all the theories and lessons of those texts and courses. Instead, our goal is to introduce you to the basic concepts of health economics, because understanding how economists view health-related problems is one essential component of

BOX 8-1 Vignette

Sophie is the governor's chief health policy analyst. The governor is interested in improving the health status of residents in the state, but is also concerned about the impact any new initiative will have on the state's economy. She asks Sophie to compare the economic consequences of three options: tax incentives for individuals to purchase exercise equipment or gym memberships, tax incentives for employers to offer wellness programs, and a mandate requiring that all stores selling food in the state provide fresh food and other healthy options. Fortunately, Sophie has a background in economics and knows that she needs to be concerned with basic principles of supply, demand, and market functions to help her governor make the best choice. This knowledge will lead her to ask questions such as: How big a tax incentive is necessary to compel individuals or employers to act? Will tax incentives encourage people to join a gym or employers to offer wellness programs that they would not otherwise, or will the government simply be subsidizing transactions that would take place anyway? Is the problem that exercise options and health foods are not available and affordable, or are individuals simply making the choice not to engage in healthy behavior because they prefer to spend their time and money on other goods and activities? Will a mandate lead to the proliferation of healthy food stores or encourage stores to leave the state? The answers to these questions will help you supply the governor with informed policy recommendations.

being a good health policy analyst and decision maker. This chapter begins with an overview of what health economics is, how economists view health care, and how individuals determine whether obtaining health insurance is a priority in their lives. It then moves to a review of the basic economic principles of supply, demand, and market structure. As part of this discussion, you will learn what factors make supply and demand increase or decrease, how the presence of health insurance affects supply and demand, how different market structures function, and what interventions are available when the market fails to achieve desired policy goals.

HEALTH ECONOMICS DEFINED

Economics is concerned with the allocation of scarce resources, as well as the production, distribution, and consumption of goods and services. Macroeconomics studies these areas on a broad level, such as how they relate to national production or national unemployment levels, while microeconomics studies the distribution and production of resources on a smaller level, including individual decisions to purchase a good or a firm's decision to hire an employee. Microeconomics also considers how smaller economic units, such as firms, combine to form larger units, such as industries or markets.[1(p3)] "Health economics," then, is the study of economics as it relates to the health field.

How Economists View Decision Making

Economists assume that people, given adequate information, are rational decision makers. Rational decision making requires that people have the ability to rank their preferences (whichever preferences are relevant when any sort of decision is being made) and assumes that people will never purposely choose to make themselves worse off. Instead, individuals will make the decision that gives them the most satisfaction, by whatever criteria the individual uses to rate his level of satisfaction. This satisfaction, referred to as *utility* by economists, may be achieved in many ways, including volunteering time or giving money to charities. Utility in a health context takes into account that individuals have different needs for and find different value in obtaining healthcare goods and services, and that whether and which health resources are purchased will depend on the individual's preferences and resources.

Utility Analysis

What does utility mean in terms of health care? Most people do not enjoy going to the doctor or taking medicine. It seems strange to think that individuals are happy as a result of or maximize their utility by, for example, receiving weekly allergy shots or getting chemotherapy treatments. However, health care can be discussed in terms of utility because most people enjoy being healthy.

Everyone has a different level of health, some due to their status at birth (e.g., infants born prematurely may have problems with their lungs or mental development) and others due to incidents that occur during their lives (e.g., an individual who is in a serious car accident may suffer from back pain in the future). In addition, people have various tolerance levels for being unhealthy. In other words, the willingness to pay for a particular healthcare good or service will vary among individuals based on their circumstances and preferences.

Furthermore, at some point, obtaining additional "units" of a particular good will bring less satisfaction than the previous units did. For example, although icing a sore knee for 20 minutes may reduce swelling, icing the same knee for 40 minutes will not reduce swelling twice as much, or, although buying one pair of glasses may bring high satisfaction, buying two pairs of glasses will not double the consumer's satisfaction because the second pair of glasses can't do more than the first. This is called *diminishing marginal utility*, and it also affects what goods and services a consumer purchases.

In addition, consumers must consider the *opportunity costs* of their decisions. Opportunity costs refer to the cost associated with the options that are not chosen. For example, if a consumer decides not to purchase any medication to ease her back pain, there is zero accounting or monetary cost; that is, it did not cost the consumer any money because she did not purchase the medication. However, there may be opportunity costs, monetary or otherwise, because she is not pain-free. She may endure a monetary loss if she has to take time off from work due to her injury. Or, she may endure a nonmonetary loss because she cannot enjoy walking or exercising due to her back pain. Opportunity costs are the hidden costs associated with every decision, and in order to fully assess the cost and benefits of any decision, these hidden costs must be included in the calculation.

In terms of healthcare goods only, an individual's utility can be thought of as a function of their health and the healthcare goods and services they desire. Utility maximization in health care is the ideal set of health-related goods and services that an individual purchases. However, people need to purchase a variety of goods and services, not just those relating to health care. Overall, consumers maximize their utility by purchasing what they consider to be an ideal bundle of healthcare goods and services, as well as other goods and services, based on their desire for each good and service and subject to the income they have available to make these purchases.

Scarce Resources

In the healthcare arena, consumers have to make choices about the production, distribution, and consumption of healthcare resources. There are many types of health care resources. Healthcare goods include items such as eyeglasses, prescription drugs, and hospital beds; healthcare personnel include providers such as physicians, nurses, and midwives, as well as lab technicians, home healthcare workers, and countless others; and healthcare capital inputs (resources used in a production process) include items such as nursing homes, hospitals, and diagnostic equipment (such as an X-ray machine). All of these things (and others) are considered healthcare resources.

If there were unlimited healthcare resources and an unlimited ability to pay for goods and services, the questions confronted by health policy analysts about what healthcare items should be produced and who should have access to them would still exist, but the answers would be less dire because

there would be enough health care available for everyone. In reality, however, there is a finite amount of healthcare goods, personnel, and capital inputs. The financial resources are not available to provide all of the health care demanded by the entire population and still provide other goods and services that are demanded. As a result of this scarcity of resources, choices and very apparent trade-offs must be made.

In general, consumer choices are based on individual preference, as discussed earlier, and the concept of efficiency. In economic terms, an efficient distribution of resources occurs when the resource distribution cannot be changed to make someone better off without making someone else worse off. This notion of efficiency in exchange is also referred to as Pareto-efficient, named after the Italian economist Vilfredo Pareto, who developed the concept. There are several types of efficiency, such as *allocative efficiency, production efficiency*, and *technical efficiency*.[2(pp9-10),3(p5)] Allocative efficiency focuses on providing the most value or benefit with goods and services. Production efficiency focuses on reducing the cost of the inputs used to produce goods and services. Technical efficiency focuses on using the least amount of inputs to create goods or services.

The notion of efficiency raises many questions because there are always trade-offs to be made when producing goods and services. For example, should the production be more automated or more labor-intensive? Should the production sites be located in the United States or overseas? Can a service be provided in a less costly setting? Is there any additional or different service or product that will enhance the benefits of the goods or services consumers receive?

Although they may not use this technical economic jargon, public and private policymakers often consider concepts of efficiency when they answer these types of questions. The answers, in turn, help identify which goods and services should be produced overall in society and which of those goods and services should be related to health care. Because there is a finite amount of resources available, the choice to produce more healthcare goods and services would result in the production of fewer non-healthcare goods and services, and vice versa. Similarly, the choice to produce more of one kind of healthcare good or service will lead to the production of fewer healthcare goods and services of other types.

Finally, policymakers must also decide whether equity or fairness concerns should be taken into account, and in response alter their production and distribution decisions in ways that may make some people better off at the expense of others. For example, when a U.S. flu vaccine shortage occurred in 2004, some states required that vaccines be given only to individuals in high-risk groups. Individuals who had access to the vaccine, but were not in those high-risk groups, were made worse off by this decision because they were no longer allowed to receive the inoculation. On the other hand, some individuals in the high-risk group who otherwise would not have been able to obtain the vaccine were made better off under the new policy. The point is not that efficiency is more important than equity or vice versa. However, it is important to understand that these are distinct and not always complementary concerns, and whether and how one decides to influence the market will depend, in part, on how much the decision maker values efficiency and equity. In a world of limited resources, balancing consumer preferences, efficiency, and equity concerns can be a very difficult task for policymakers.

How Economists View Health Care

Health economics helps explain how health-related choices are made, what choices should be made, and the ramifications of those choices. Evaluating the consequences of these choices is referred to as *positive* economics. Positive economics identifies, predicts, and evaluates who receives a benefit and who pays for a public policy choice. Positive economics answers the questions, "What is the current situation?" and "What already happened?" *Normative* economics discusses what public policy should be implemented based on the decision maker's values. It answers the question, "What should be?"[3(p14),4(p5)] For example:

> A *positive statement:* In 2010, approximately 50 million people in the United States did not have health insurance.
> A *normative statement:* All people living in the United States should have health insurance.

As shown by the concepts of positive and normative economics, health economists, like other analysts, cannot avoid discussing how health care *should* be perceived. Is health care a good or service like any other good or service such as food, shelter, or clothing that consumers obtain or refrain from obtaining based on availability, price, resources, and preference? Or is health care a special and unique commodity for reasons such as its importance to individuals' quality of life or how the healthcare market is structured? Bear in mind that health policymakers take their own view of health care's place in the market into account when they argue for or against a policy.

Box 8-2 identifies two theories of how to view health care. Many economists' views fall somewhere in the middle of these two theories or combine aspects of the two theories to create a hybrid theory. These theories were not presented

to be an either/or choice, but to illustrate that even within the field of economics there is a fundamental debate about how to view health care.

ECONOMIC BASICS: DEMAND

Consumers, whether an individual, firm, or country, purchase goods and services. *Demand* is the quantity of goods and services that a consumer is willing and able to purchase over a specified time. In the case of health care, for example, demand equals the total demand for healthcare goods and services by all the consumers in a given market.

Demand Changers

In general, as the price of a good or service increases, demand for that good or service will fall. Conversely, as the price of goods or services decreases, demand for those goods or services will rise.

Various factors in addition to price also increase or decrease the demand for a product. Insurance is an important factor relating to demand that is discussed separately later in this chapter. A few of the other factors that may change the demand for a product include:

> *Consumer's income:* As a consumer's income increases, demand for a product may increase. For example, a consumer may desire a new pair of eyeglasses but cannot afford it. Once the consumer's income increases, the consumer can purchase the eyeglasses.
> *Quality:* Consumers have preferences based on quality, both actual and perceived. In addition, a change in quality will likely result in a change in demand. A decrease in the quality of a product may result in a decrease in demand because consumers decide the product is no longer worth the price charged. For example, a consumer may discover that the eyeglasses he wants fall apart easily, thus he may decide not to buy the product.
> *Price of substitutes:* A substitute is a different product that satisfies the same demand. For example, contact lenses may be a substitute for eyeglasses. As the price of contact lenses drops, a consumer may decide he prefers contact lenses to eyeglasses.
> *Price of complements:* A complement is a product associated with another product. For example, cleaning solution is a complement to contact lenses. The price and quality of cleaning solution (the complement) may be an important factor when a consumer is debating whether to keep wearing glasses (the original product) or switch to contact lenses (the alternative product). If

BOX 8-2 Discussion Questions

Consider each issue below and discuss whether you support Theory X, Theory Y, neither theory, or some combination of them.

Issue	Theory X	Theory Y
Your view about how an individual's health is determined	Whether a person is healthy or sick is determined randomly.	Whether a person is healthy or sick depends on lifestyle choices such as whether a person smokes, drinks, or wears a seatbelt.
Your view of medical practice	Medicine is a science, and experts will ultimately discover the best means for treating every illness.	Medicine is an art and there will never be one best way to treat every illness because illnesses are often patient-specific and because there will always be demand for lower-cost and less painful treatments.
Your view of medical care	Medical care is a unique commodity.	Medical care is similar to any other good or service.
Your view of the government's role in health care	Government regulations are necessary to protect this unique commodity, to control profiteering at the cost of patient care, to control the resources spent on health care, and to improve information sharing.	Government regulations are not necessary, technological advances and more services are desirable, and competition, not regulation, should drive the market.

Source: Gerald L. Musgrave. Health Economics Outlook: Two Theories of Health Economics. *Bus Econ.* 1995;30:7–13.

the price of cleaning solution increases, even though the price of contact lenses stays the same, the consumer may decide to purchase eyeglasses instead of contact lenses. In other words, demand for complements and alternative products shifts in opposite ways, so an increase in the price of a complement will decrease the demand for the alternative product, and vice versa.

The physical profile of a consumer has an impact on demand for healthcare services in some predictable ways. Women generally demand more healthcare services than men before reaching age 65, primarily due to health needs related to childbearing, whereas men over age 65 use more care than do women in the same age group. In addition, many diseases are more prevalent in women than in men, resulting in an expected increase in demand for health services by women. Some of these diseases include cardiovascular disease, osteoporosis, and immunologic diseases.[3(p111),5(pp149–150)] Regardless of gender, an individual who is born with a medical problem, or who develops one at a relatively young age, can be expected

to have a higher than average demand for healthcare services. Aging consumers are more likely to have higher healthcare needs than younger consumers. Of course, any factor that usually leads to increases in demand for healthcare services may be offset by lack of financial resources or lack of access to providers.

In addition to the physical profile of a consumer, interesting research is being conducted in relation to consumers' level of education and their demand for services. Although there is no consensus on the direct impact of general education on demand for health services, some studies show a positive relationship between medical knowledge and demand for healthcare services—that is, the more the consumer knows about medicine, the higher the level of consumption of healthcare services. This association may indicate that consumers without as much medical knowledge underestimate the appropriate amount of health services they need, or it may mean that consumers with more medical education have a greater ability to purchase medical care. Other explanations are possible as well.[3(p127)]

Elasticity

Two of the demand changers discussed previously are shifts in price and shifts in income. *Elasticity* is the term used to describe how responsive the change in demand or supply is when there is either a change in price or a change in income. The concept of elasticity is important to understand as a policy analyst because it is essential to know whether changes in consumers' incomes (say, through a tax credit) or changes in the price of a product (perhaps through incentives given to producers) will result in the desired outcome. The desired outcome may be increased consumption, which might be the case if the service is well-child checkups. Conversely, the desired outcome may be decreased consumption, which might be the case if cigarettes are the product being consumed.

Demand Elasticity

Demand elasticity is based on the percentage change in the quantity demanded resulting from a 1% change in price or income. In other words, does consumer demand for a product, such as a vaccination, increase as the price of a product decreases by 1%? Or, how much does consumer demand for the vaccine decrease as the consumer's income drops 1%? The calculation to determine elasticity is:

$$\text{Demand Elasticity} = \frac{\% \text{ Change in quantity demanded}}{\% \text{ Change in price}}$$

Demand for a product is considered elastic if the sum is greater than 1 or greater than –1; it is inelastic if the calculation results in a sum that is between 0 and 1 or 0 and –1.

For example, suppose a vaccine costs $20 per dose and at that price a family buys four doses, for a total of $80. The next year the price increases 20% to $24 per dose and the family only buys three doses for a total of $72.

$$\text{Elasticity} = \frac{-25\% \text{ change in demand}}{20\% \text{ change in price}}$$
$$\text{Elasticity} = -1.25$$

Because elasticity equals –1.25, the product is considered elastic (because the result of the elasticity calculation is greater than –1). In this example, for every 1% increase in vaccine price, demand decreases by 1.25%. If the price decreases, the quantity demanded would be expected to increase.

Of course, goods may also be inelastic, which means the demand for the good is not as sensitive to a change in price. As a result, when price increases, the quantity demanded will not decrease at the same rate as the price increases. For example, some people will not reduce their consumption of cigarettes even if the price of cigarettes increases. However, at some point the price could become high enough that consumer behavior will change, resulting in a decrease in demand.

However, elasticity works in the opposite way in the case of *inferior goods*. An inferior good, as the name suggests, is less desirable than a *normal good*. As a result, as a consumer's income increases, demand for the inferior good will decrease. Instead of buying more of the inferior good, the consumer will prefer to buy the normal good. For example, suppose a generic over-the-counter pain medication is cheaper than a particular prescription pain medication, but the prescription pain medication is more effective. Consumers with low income may choose to purchase the over-the-counter medicine, the inferior good. If their income increases, they will not buy more of the inferior good, but instead will switch to the prescription pain medicine because it is a better good, for their purposes, than the inferior good.

Supply Elasticity

Supply elasticity works in much the same way as demand elasticity, except it refers to the relationship between the quantity of goods supplied and the price of the goods. Supply elasticity is often defined as the percentage change in quantity supplied resulting from a 1% increase in the price of buying the good. The change is usually positive because producers have an incentive to increase output as the price they will receive for the good rises. However, if supply elasticity refers to variables other than the price of the good, such as the cost of raw materials or wages, then the supply elasticity will be negative; that is, as prices of labor or other inputs rise, the quantity supplied will fall (all other things being equal).

$$\text{Supply Elasticity} = \frac{\% \text{ Change in quantity supplied}}{\% \text{ Change in price}}$$

Supply elasticity (with respect to price) is calculated as the quantity of the good supplied divided by the percentage change in its price. For example, assume a medical device supplier is selling 25 needles for $20. Based on the above formula, the needles have a supply elasticity of 1.25.

$$\text{Elasticity} = 25 / 20$$
$$\text{Elasticity} = 1.25$$

Therefore, if the market price increases 10% to $22, the quantity supplied will increase 12.5% to 28 needles.

Health Insurance and Demand

In addition to the general economic rules of demand for health services, the presence of health insurance affects demand for healthcare goods and services. Health insurance acts as a buffer between consumers and the cost of healthcare goods and services. In an insured consumer's view, healthcare goods or services cost less because instead of paying full price, the consumer may only have to pay, for example, a coinsurance rate of 20% (after satisfying the deductible). For example, if a surgical procedure normally costs $10,000, the insured consumer may only have to consider the cost of paying $2,000 for the benefit of the surgery because his insurance company pays for the remainder. In this way, the presence of health insurance can have an effect on the consumer—to increase demand—in the same way that an increase in the consumer's income can increase demand.

In general, insured consumers are not as sensitive to the cost of healthcare goods and services as uninsured consumers.[2(p38)] Because of this, the presence of health insurance creates the problem of *moral hazard*. Moral hazard can occur in a variety of economic situations when consumers buy more goods or services than necessary because they do not have to pay the full cost of acquiring the good or service. In relation to health insurance, moral hazard results when an insured consumer uses more services than she would otherwise because part of the cost is covered by insurance.

For example, if a consumer has a $500 health insurance deductible, the consumer pays 100% of the first $500 of health care received. If there is a 20% coinsurance charge after that, the consumer pays only $.20 per dollar for every dollar spent after $500. If the consumer values a particular healthcare service, such as a preventive dental exam, at $50 but the service costs $100, the consumer will not purchase the service before meeting the deductible. However, after the deductible has been met, the dental exam (assuming it is a covered benefit) will cost the consumer $20 (20% of $100), so the consumer will purchase the service because it is under the consumer's $50 value threshold.

As the portion of the healthcare cost that a consumer pays based on copayments or coinsurance decreases, the consumer becomes less sensitive to changes in the price of the product. Say a consumer decides he is unwilling to pay more than $2,500 for surgery. If the consumer owes a 10% coinsurance charge, the consumer will be willing to pay for surgery as long as it is not priced at more than $25,000. At $25,000, the consumer would pay $2,500 and the insurance company would pay $22,500. However, if the same consumer has a 20% co-insurance rate, he will not elect surgery once the price rises above $12,500 because the cost to the consumer would be more than the consumer's $2,500 limit; for example, if the surgery cost $15,000, the consumer would owe $3,000 and the insurance company would cover the other $12,000.

The problem of moral hazard is particularly relevant in health care because consumers have an incentive to seek out more medical care—they think it will make them feel better. And, as noted earlier, an insured consumer is more likely to purchase a desirable healthcare good or service because the presence of insurance reduces her cost. The same cannot be said of owning a home or auto insurance; although consumers may be a little less careful because of the protection fire or car insurance affords them, it is unlikely that people will seek out a car accident or intentionally burn down their house just because they are insured.

ECONOMIC BASICS: SUPPLY

Supply is the amount of goods and services that producers are able and willing to sell at a given price over a given period of time. As with demand, the price of a product is a key factor in determining the level of supply. However, unlike demand, where there is often an inverse relationship between price and demand, an increase in the price a good is sold for usually leads to an increase in quantity supplied. Conversely, as the price consumers will pay for a product decreases, supply will often decrease as well. As with demand, there are many factors that affect the quantity of a good or service being supplied.

Costs

Costs are a key factor in determining the level of supply. Costs refer to what inputs are needed to produce a good or service. For example, the price of cotton may impact the cost of producing medical scrubs or bed linens made out of cotton, or the price of steel may affect the cost of producing an autoclave or X-ray machine made with steel. As the cost of these inputs increases, the cost of producing the final good increases as well. If the price for a good or service does not increase as the cost of inputs increases, the quantity supplied is likely to decrease. Thus, if it costs a manufacturer $100 more to build an X-ray machine because the cost of steel has risen, it is likely that the manufacturer will pass that production cost increase on to the consumer by raising the purchase price of the X-ray machine. Alternately, the manufacturer may choose to absorb the $100 cost increase and not raise the purchase price, which will lead the manufacturer to supply fewer X-ray machines, find a way to produce the good more cheaply using the same method, or find a different way to produce the good.

Costs are counted in many different ways. We focus here on *average costs* and *marginal costs*.

> *Average cost* is the cost of producing one product over a specific period of time. For example, if it costs a manufacturer $2 million to produce 2,000 hospital beds in one year, the average cost is $1,000 per bed during that year.

Average Cost (AC) = Total Cost/Quantity
AC = $2,000,000/2,000 hospital beds
AC = $1,000 per hospital bed

Marginal cost refers to the price of producing one more unit of the output, or, in our example, one more hospital bed. Whatever additional labor, equipment, and supplies are needed to produce one more hospital bed is the marginal cost of production. As a general matter, the marginal cost increases as output increases.

Supply Changers

Other factors in addition to sale price and cost can increase or decrease the supply of a product. Two common factors are:

Number of sellers: As the number of sellers of a good increases, the supply of the good will increase as well because there are more companies producing the good. As long as the market is profitable, new sellers will be enticed to enter the market. This occurs until the market reaches equilibrium, where the quantity demanded equals the quantity supplied.

Change in technology: New technology may mean a new way to produce a desired outcome, which may alter the supply of a good or service. For example, fiberglass has replaced plaster in most casts and the production of each material has shifted accordingly (fiberglass up, plaster down). New technology can also make a product more accessible than before. For example, many surgeries once handled on an inpatient basis may now be performed on an outpatient basis or in a physician's office due to new technology, such as arthroscopy. In addition, evolving technology has led to brand new fields, such as robotic surgery. Technological improvements can increase demand for some services and reduce it for others, leading to a change in the production of these goods and services.

Profit Maximization

Although consumers are driven by the desire to maximize their satisfaction, suppliers are driven by their desire to maximize revenues. For-profit companies seek to make profits to pass on to their shareholders, while not-for-profit companies face a variety of requirements regarding disposing of the revenue they generate in excess of expenses and the cost of acquiring capital to run the company. For ease of explanation, the term *profit* will be used here to discuss supplier incentives, even though the healthcare field includes a large share of not-for-profit companies.

Profit is the price per unit sold less the production cost per unit. In a competitive market, profit is maximized at the level of output where the marginal cost equals the price. If a hospital bed costs $1,000 to produce and is sold for $1,500, the profit per bed is $500. If the marginal cost of producing one more bed is $1,400, the producer will make that additional bed because it can be sold for $1,500, a $100 profit; however, if the marginal cost of producing an additional bed is $1,600, the producer has no incentive to produce that additional bed because it can only be sold at a loss of $100. Due to the profit maximization goal, if the price of a product increases and a competitive market exists for the product, manufacturers will increase production of the product until the output level again reaches the point where the marginal cost equals the price.

When a profitable market exists, new producers will be drawn into the market so they can reap financial benefits. The new producer may price its hospital bed for less than $1,500 to attract consumers, or the new producer may think there is a niche for a higher-priced bed that has additional features. Assume the new producer chooses to market a similar bed as the $1,500 bed but sells it for $1,250. If a consumer can purchase the bed from the competing company for $1,250 with no additional opportunity costs, demand for the $1,500 hospital bed is likely to fall. The manufacturer of the $1,500 bed will have to lower its price or improve the product (or the perception of the product) to increase demand for a higher-priced bed. At the point where there is a balance between the quantity supplied and the quantity demanded and the price is set to the marginal cost of production, there is *equilibrium* in the market.

If such a balance does not occur, there is *disequilibrium* in the market. The disequilibrium could represent a surplus of a good or service due to excess supply or sudden drop in demand, or it could result from a product shortage due to inadequate supply or a sharp increase in demand. Surpluses occur when the market price in a competitive market is higher than the marginal cost of production; as a result, producers lower their prices to increase sales of their product. This will keep happening until market equilibrium is reached. For example, there could be a sudden drop in demand for a food product due to a news report that eating the product more than three times a week may put people's health at risk. Due to the sudden drop in demand, excess product will be available. Producers will, in turn, lower the price of the product until equilibrium is reached. Shortages occur when the market price is lower than the marginal cost of production. As a result of the shortage, consumers might be willing to pay more for the product, so producers increase their prices until demand stops increasing and market equilibrium is reached. If an opposite news story appeared, hailing the food product as improving health if eaten at least four times a week, there may be a sudden surge in demand. As a result, consumers will likely be willing to pay more for the product and producers will raise the price until equilibrium is reached. Because producers often cannot make significant changes to their production schedule or products in a short amount of time, market equilibrium positions may take some time to achieve.

Health Insurance and Supply

Just as the presence of health insurance affects a consumer's demand for medical goods and services, it also may impact a healthcare provider's willingness to supply goods and services. This is a complicated issue because, on the one hand, a provider is expected to act as her patient's agent and thus should act in her patient's best interests. If providers encourage only appropriate care, insurance is working in a positive way. On the other hand, providers may have a financial incentive to encourage or discourage the consumption of healthcare goods and services. Providers could recommend against treatment because of financial incentives resulting from the presence or absence of health insurance. For example, financial incentives found in managed care may discourage providers from recommending a particular treatment. Additionally, if a patient is both uninsured and unable to pay for services out-of-pocket, providers have a financial incentive not to provide potentially necessary services due to their inability to receive payment.

On the other hand, a provider may seek to increase her income by encouraging inappropriate or excessive care. This problem—the provider version of moral hazard—is referred to as *supplier-induced demand*. Supplier-induced demand is the level of demand that exists beyond what a well-informed consumer would have chosen. The theory behind supplier-induced demand is that instead of consumer demand leading to an increase in suppliers (healthcare providers), the suppliers create demand in the consumers (patients), often by relying on information only available to the supplier. However, economists debate whether supplier-induced demand actually exists because it is difficult to study empirically and because behavior consistent with supplier-induced demand may also be consistent with appropriate medical treatment.[5(pp237–242)]

ECONOMIC BASICS: MARKETS

To this point, we have reviewed many basic aspects of economic theory—how consumers behave, how suppliers behave, what drives and shifts demand, and what drives and shifts supply. To understand how these theories work in the healthcare industry, it is necessary to explore how health insurance affects markets, what kind of market exists for health care, how market structure relates to the production and distribution of goods and services, and why markets fail and what can be done to alleviate the problems associated with market failure.

Health Insurance and Markets

Before delving into the basics of economic markets, it is necessary to highlight how the presence of health insurance alters the dynamics of a standard economic transaction. In a typical market transaction, such as buying food at the grocery store, there are only two parties involved—the consumer who buys the food and the supplier who sells the food. The cost to the consumer is the cost of the food; the consumer bears full responsibility for paying that cost and pays that cost directly to the supplier, the grocery store.

The typical medical transaction, however, does not follow these rules, both because of the types of events that lead to a medical transaction and the presence of health insurance. In health care, there are both routine and expected events (e.g., an annual physical) and unanticipated needs due to an unpredictable illness or injury. The exact diagnosis and treatment are often unknown initially and the patient's response to treatment is not guaranteed, resulting in an inability to predict exactly what resources will be needed. Without knowing what goods and services are required, it is impossible to estimate the cost to be incurred. This makes it very difficult for the consumer to weigh her preferences for medical care as compared to other goods and services, and makes it difficult for suppliers to know which goods and services will be demanded and at what price they can sell their goods and services.

Another reason healthcare transactions often do not follow the typical market exchange is because the presence of health insurance means that healthcare transactions involve three players, instead of two; these three players are (1) patients (the consumer), (2) healthcare providers (the supplier), and (3) insurers (who are often proxies for employers). Insurers are also known as "third-party payers" because they are the third party involved in addition to the two customary parties. In the public insurance system, the third-party payer is the government, whereas in the private sector the third-party payers are private health insurance companies. Having the health insurance carrier as a third party means that consumers do not pay the full cost of healthcare resources used and therefore may be less likely to choose the most cost-effective treatment option, to reduce the information gap between them and providers, or be as vigilant against supplier-induced demand as they might in other circumstances.

Market Structure

Understanding markets begins with the notion of a *perfectly competitive* market, because in economic theory a perfectly competitive market serves society by efficiently allocating the finite resources available. Due to specific market conditions that make up a perfectly competitive market, a competitive equilibrium is reached once quantities supplied equal the quantities demanded.

There are numerous types of market structures, ranging from perfectly competitive markets with many buyers and sellers to *monopolistic* markets with a single seller controlling the market. Other common market structures include oligopolies, which have a few dominant firms and substantial but not complete barriers to entry, and monopsonies, which have a limited number of consumers who control the price paid to suppliers. Based on the market structure, consumers and producers have varying degrees of power in terms of setting prices, choosing among products, and deciding whether to participate in the market. Table 8-1 reviews the characteristics of three market structures that are most useful to understanding healthcare markets: perfectly competitive markets, monopolistic markets, and monopolistically competitive markets.

You know from the discussion of supply and demand that the healthcare market cannot be perfectly competitive based on the description in Table 8-1. (In fact, no markets are truly perfectly competitive.) Some consumers, such as the federal government, may have extensive market power as well as the ability to set prices. Producers of patent-protected healthcare products are provided with supply power for a limited period of time, which gives them an ability to control prices. Consumers do not have perfect information regarding healthcare needs and healthcare costs, and providers and insurers do not have perfect information regarding patient illnesses. Given the presence of health insurance, consumers do not bear all the cost of using healthcare services. With these characteristics, the healthcare market is monopolistically competitive. In many areas of the healthcare market, there are a few dominant firms with a lot of market power and many smaller firms who participate in the market, but the smaller firms do not have the power to shape market conditions.

Market Failure

A *market failure* means that resources are not produced or allocated efficiently. As you recall, we defined efficiency generally as the state of least cost production where the resource distribution cannot be changed to make someone better off without making someone else worse off, and we also described a few specific types of efficiency. When something about the

---

TABLE 8-1 Characteristics of Key Market Structures

	Perfectly Competitive	**Monopoly**	**Monopolistically Competitive**
Number of Firms	Many.	One (in a pure monopoly).	Many.
Market Share	No dominant firms.	One firm has all of the market share and price and output.	There may be many firms with market share and or a few dominant firms. Firms can set price because of product differentiation.
Barriers to Entry for New Firms into Market	No.	Yes. Absolute barriers, no new firms may enter market.	Some barriers, due to differentiation of product, licensure, etc.
Product Differentiation	No. Products are for each other.	No. Only one product, no substitutes available.	Yes. Many products; they are not substitutes for each other (brand loyalty).
Access to Information and Resources	Consumers and producers have perfect information.	One firm controls all information (asymmetric information).	All firms have equal access to resources and technology unless there are a few dominant firms with more access and resources.
Cost of Transaction	Consumers bear cost of consumption and producers bear cost of production.	Higher price to consumer because firm has ability to reduce quantity, retain excess profits.	Blend of costs in perfectly competitive market and monopoly market.

structure of the market prohibits it from being efficient, it is referred to as market failure; the question then becomes what interventions in the market, if any, should occur in an attempt to alleviate the market failure.

Before we turn to why markets fail, we must address one additional issue: Does an inequitable distribution of resources constitute a market failure? Under the traditional economic school of thought, the answer is no; a market failure refers to inefficiency, and concerns about equity are not part of the efficiency calculation. However, some economists consider equity a valid factor when evaluating the functioning of a market. Regardless, whether an inequitable distribution of resources fits under the economic designation of "market failure" is not as important as whether policymakers choose to intervene in a market based on equity concerns.

Some of the most salient reasons that market failures occur in health care include concentration of market power, imperfect information (producers or consumer not having complete and accurate information), the consumption of *public goods*, and the presence of *externalities*. We have already discussed concentration of market power and imperfect information; the next sections focus on public goods and externalities.

Public Goods

Public goods have two main features. First, public goods are *nonrival*, meaning that more than one person can enjoy the good simultaneously. An example of a rival private good would be a single pen, as two people may not use the same pen at the same time. Second, a public good is *nonexclusive* because it is too costly to try to exclude nonpaying individuals from enjoying public goods.[3(p230)]

Classic examples of public goods are national defense measures and lighthouses. Everyone simultaneously benefits from national defense and it is not economically feasible to exclude nonpaying individuals (e.g., tax evaders) from enjoying the benefits. In the same way, multiple ships may benefit at the same time from a warning provided by a lighthouse and it would be very difficult to exclude a particular ship from enjoying the benefit. In the health field, examples of local public goods include clean water in a public swimming area or a public health awareness campaign on city streets. Everyone enjoys the clean water (at least until it is overcrowded) and it would be costly to exclude nonpayers. Similarly, multiple people can benefit from a public health campaign simultaneously, and exclusion of nonpayers would be impossible or quite costly.

Public goods can be transformed into other types of goods. For example, a public good could be made exclusive by charging a fee; these are called *toll goods*.[6(p81)] The public

swimming water could be fenced off and a fee charged for admission, or the public health campaign could be placed in the subway, which would exclude those who could not afford the fare. Once public goods are transformed into toll goods, concerns arise about whether the price is set at the most efficient level. Toll goods may still lead to market failure if the cost of using the good excludes users who would gain more from enjoying the good than they would cost society by consuming the good.[6(pp81–82)]

In addition, goods provided by local, state, and federal governments may be, but are not necessarily, public goods in the economic sense. For example, if a state funds a free healthcare clinic, it is not funding a public good. Even though nonpayers are, by definition, included, the benefits generally inure to the individual and, in most cases, more than one individual cannot enjoy the same healthcare good or service. It is possible, however, that other people will benefit from a healthcare service they do not receive; for example, if your neighbor receives a service that helps him quit smoking, you will receive the benefit of no longer being exposed to your neighbor's secondhand smoke.

Public goods also create the *free rider* problem, making it unprofitable for private firms to produce and sell goods due to the high cost of excluding non-payers.[3(p230)] The free rider is one who enjoys the benefit of the good without paying for the cost of producing the good. Because it is impossible to exclude users or force consumers to reveal their true demand for the public good, they do not have incentive to pay for the units of the good they use.[6(p86)] For example, an individual cannot be prevented from gaining knowledge from a public health awareness campaign, so if a private company were responsible for providing the education campaign, it could not force a consumer to pay for it. Eventually, even though many people would like to take advantage of clean air or health education, the lack of people paying for it would result in an underproduction of these services unless some action was taken to alter the market dynamics.

Externalities

Externalities are much more common than public goods in the healthcare market. An *externality* is "any valued impact (positive or negative) resulting from any action (whether related to production or consumption) that affects someone who did not fully consent to it through participation in a voluntary exchange."[6(p94)] In a typical economic transaction, the costs and benefits associated with a transaction impact only those involved in the transaction. For example, remember our consumer buying food at the grocery store? The only two people affected by that transaction are the consumer who pays money and receives food, and the grocer who provides food and receives money. Situations with externalities, however, are different. Externalities exist when the action of one party impacts another party *who is not part of the transaction*; in other words, the parties to the transaction will find there is an "unpriced byproduct" of producing or consuming a good or service.[3(p231)]

Externalities may be positive or negative. An example of a positive externality is when one person gets vaccinated against the chicken pox and other people benefit because chicken pox is less likely to be transmitted in that community. If enough people get vaccinated, "herd immunity" will exist in the community.[a] In this case, the positive unpriced byproduct is the additional protection received by others who were not vaccinated. An example of a negative externality is represented by illegal hazardous waste disposal. Say a hospital dumps biological waste such as blood, syringes, gauze with infected material on it, and the like into a public water source. The unpriced byproduct is paid by the general public, who face an increased risk of illness from using the contaminated water source. The costs to the general public may not have been included in the hospital's cost–benefit analysis when it decided to dump the biological waste.

With both positive and negative externalities, the cost and benefits of production or consumption are borne by individuals who do not participate in the transaction. Due to the unpriced byproducts, there are external costs and benefits that are not considered when deciding whether to make the transaction, leading to an under- or over-production of the resource from society's perspective.

Government Intervention

When market failures occur, the government may intervene to promote efficiency or to promote equity (of course, it may also choose not to intervene at all). Some examples of government interventions include financing or directly providing public goods, creating incentives through tax breaks and subsidies, imposing mandates through regulation, prohibiting activities, and redistributing income. We discuss these options in the following sections.

Government Finances or Directly Provides Public Goods.

When market failure occurs, the government may choose to finance or provide a good or service directly instead of attempting to influence the actions of private producers. For example, if the government wanted to increase access to health care, it could create new government-run health centers or provide financing to privately run health centers.

These are two different paths—direct provision or financing—with different sets of issues. The main difference when the government provides or finances care instead of a private sector is the lack of profit motive on the part of the government.[3(p252)] Instead of focusing on the financial bottom line, public providers may focus on other goals, such as equity or assuring the presence of a particular good or service for everyone or for specific populations.

When the government creates or expands a public program, there is concern that *crowd out* may occur. Whenever a program is established or expanded, the program has a particular goal and targets a particular audience. For example, the government may try to reduce the number of people without insurance by expanding an existing public program such as Medicaid. Crowd out occurs when instead of only reaching the target audience (in this case, the uninsured), the public program also creates an incentive for other individuals (in this case, privately insured people) to participate in the public program. Because the program has a finite amount of resources, some of the target audience (the uninsured) may be crowded out from participating in the program by the presence of the other, nontargeted individuals (the privately insured). This prevents programs from maximizing cost-effectiveness because instead of obtaining the largest change (in this case, the reduction in the number of uninsured) for the public dollar, some of the change is simply a result of a cost shift from a private payer (the privately insured) to a public payer (the expanded program). Crowd out may also change incentives for other providers of services. In this example, the presence of the new or expanded government program may reduce the incentive for private employers to provide the same good or service (in this case, health insurance).

Government Increases Taxes, Tax Deductions, or Subsidies.

Taxes and subsidies can be used to alter the price, production, or consumption of goods in an effort to fix a market failure. For example, increasing a tax on a good raises the price of that good and discourages consumption; this strategy is often employed to discourage consumption of harmful products, such as cigarettes. Similarly, the government could choose to tax cigarette producers as a way to encourage them to produce less of the harmful product or leave the market altogether.

Conversely, the government could subsidize a good, directly or through a tax deduction, when it wants to encourage the consumption and production of the good. For example, if the government wanted more low-income individuals to purchase health insurance, it could choose to subsidize their insurance premiums or allow individuals to take a tax deduction or receive a tax rebate to cover the cost of paying the premiums. Similarly, if the government wants to encourage vaccine manufacturers to produce more vaccine doses, it could accomplish this goal through direct subsidies to or tax deductions for the manufacturers.

Note that the government has an economic incentive to tax goods that are price inelastic. This incentive exists because the amount purchased declines by a smaller percentage than the price increase. For example, if cigarettes are price inelastic, a 10% cigarette tax increase will result in less than a 10% decrease in cigarette consumption, meaning the cigarette tax will be a good revenue producer for the government because consumers will continue to purchase cigarettes despite the tax. However, taxing price-inelastic goods is less effective as a public health tool for the same reason. If the government desires a 10% reduction in cigarette consumption, the tax must be much higher than 10% if cigarettes are price inelastic. Of course, the government may choose to impose a higher cigarette tax, but it is likely that, for political reasons, a higher tax increase will be harder to obtain than a smaller one.

Government Issues Regulatory Mandates. Regulations may be used to fix a market failure by controlling the price, quantity, or quality of goods and services, or the entry of new firms into the market.[3(p241)] For example, healthcare consumers often have imperfect information when making their healthcare decisions. As a result, the government may choose to create a requirement that a type of provider, such as nursing homes, supply information to the public about the quality of care in their facilities to aid in consumers' decision making. The government may also promulgate regulations that restrict entry of new firms into a market and regulate prices because it is cheaper for one or a few firms to produce a high level of output. Of course, government regulations could also be used to achieve a policy goal like reducing the number of uninsured by mandating that all employers offer health insurance or that all residents purchase health insurance.

The government could also set a cap on the price of a good and prohibit producers from selling that good above the set price. This will keep the good at a price the government deems socially acceptable. However, if the price is set below the market price, some unfavorable market consequences may occur because it is no longer profitable for the producer to supply the product. Possible consequences include:

- Suppliers exiting the market or reducing the quantity of the good supplied, resulting in a shortage

- Suppliers reducing the quality of the good by making cheaper products or providing less care
- Suppliers shifting cost from one product to another
- Suppliers engaging in unethical behavior because some consumers will be willing to pay more than the government price ceiling

Furthermore, regulations aimed at increasing the quality of a good or service will likely impose additional costs on producers of the good. As the cost of inputs rise, the price charged to consumers is likely to rise as well. As a result, some consumers will be priced out of the market for that good or service.

Government Prohibitions. Prohibiting the production of goods and services often is ineffective and leads to a "black market" for such products. Because the prohibited goods or services are not available legally, consumers are not protected by price or quality controls. This situation may occur with the use of non-FDA-approved drugs or supplements, including unapproved drugs from other countries entering the United States via the Internet or other sources. In addition, because other countries are producing the good or service, the United States may be at a competitive disadvantage. For example, if stem cell research is permitted abroad but not in this country, some scientists may leave the United States to work abroad and domestic companies may not remain competitive in certain fields.

BOX 8-3 Discussion Questions

Some people argue that the government should not intervene in the case of a market failure because the government itself is inefficient and will simply create new problems to replace the ones it is trying to fix. In addition, critics contend that the government is usually less efficient than private sectors. Do you think the government is less efficient than the private sector? Does it depend on the issue involved? If you think it is inefficient in a particular area, does that lead you to recommend against government intervention or is there a reason that you would still support government intervention? If you think the government should intervene, which intervention options do you prefer and why?

Redistribution of Income.   In the case of market failure, the government may also act to redistribute income. Remember, efficient allocation of resources is not the same as equitable allocation of resources. A government may decide that every member of society should obtain a certain minimum level of income or resources or health status. Redistributing income may occur by taxing the wealthier members of society and using the revenue to provide resources to poorer members of society. If the government sought to create more market equity through voluntary donations, it is likely that a free rider problem would exist because some citizens would volunteer to contribute resources while others would not, but the latter would still receive a benefit from the redistribution. For example, wealthier citizens who should be in the "donor group" but do not contribute may benefit from the donations given by other wealthy citizens that lead to increased productivity and welfare of those in the recipient group. Both the notion of income redistribution and the decisions as to who should be providing versus receiving resources is open to debate. In addition, it is important to remember that income redistribution may reduce efficiency or have other undesirable market effects.

CONCLUSION

This introduction to economic concepts illustrates why health policy analysts and decision makers must understand how economists analyze healthcare problems. We have taken a broad look at the issues of supply, demand, and market structure with a focus on concerns that are relevant in the health policy field. In particular, it is essential to understand how health insurance affects both consumer and producer decisions. Although we only scratched the surface of healthcare economics in this chapter, you should now realize that without an understanding the economic ramifications of a policy decision, a health policy analyst cannot know, for example, whether to recommend addressing a problem through a government-run program, subsidy, or the like, or if it would be better to let the free market set the production level and price of a resource.

REFERENCES

1. Pindyck RS, Rubinfeld DL. *Microeconomics.* 5th ed. Upper Saddle River, NJ: Prentice Hall; 2003.

2. Penner SJ. *Introduction to Health Care Economics and Financial Management: Fundamental Concepts with Practical Applications.* Philadelphia, PA: Lippincott Williams & Wilkins; 2004.

3. Santerre RE, Neun SP. *Health Economics: Theories, Insights, and Industry Studies.* 3rd ed. Mason, OH: Thomas South-Western; 2004.

4. Feldstein P. *Health Care Economics.* 6th ed. Clifton Park, NY: Thomson Delmar Learning; 2005.

5. Phelps CE. *Health Economics.* 3d ed. Boston, MA: Addison-Wesley, 2003.

6. Weimer D, Vining A. *Policy Analysis: Concepts and Practice.* 3rd ed. Upper Saddle River, NJ: Prentice-Hall; 1999.

7. Gordis L. *Epidemiology.* 2nd ed. Philadelphia, PA: WB Saunders; 2000.

ENDNOTES

a. *Herd immunity* is "the resistance of a group to an attack by a disease to which a large proportion of the members of the group are immune."[9(p19)] Once a certain portion of the group is immune, there is only a small chance that an infected person will find a susceptible person to whom the disease may be transmitted.

Health Reform in the United States

VIGNETTE

Casey is a recent college graduate with a degree in fine arts. She works in retail to pay the bills until her career as an artist takes off. It is 2011 and her employer does not offer health insurance coverage as an employee benefit; however, even if her employer did offer coverage, Casey would rather spend her limited funds on art supplies than on her portion of the coverage. Despite her low income, Casey makes too much money to qualify for any of the public health insurance programs in her state.

One evening when Casey was up late working on an art project, she cut a tendon in her hand with a sharp knife. She rushed to the emergency room, where she waited for 7 hours before being treated because of the high volume of patients that night. Doctors stitched up her hand, provided her with pain killers, and told her she would need physical therapy to ensure she regained full function in her hand. Casey looked into private physical therapy programs but found them unaffordable. The public clinics in her area that provided free or reduced-cost care did not offer physical therapy services. Casey decided to forgo the physical therapy and rehabilitate

her hand on her own. In addition, she received a $1,500 bill from the hospital, an amount equal to her savings.

If the above scenario took place in 2014, the result may have been very different. By then, it is very likely Casey would have health insurance because most individuals will be required to obtain insurance starting that year (or pay a penalty). Although she would not have had the choice to purchase art supplies instead of health insurance, she would be much more likely to receive the care she needs. There would be a better chance her employer would offer affordable coverage, but even if health coverage wasn't offered, Casey would have better public and private options available to her.

INTRODUCTION

In the United States the persistent rate of uninsurance, concerns about the quality of health care services, and the rising cost of health care have led to numerous attempts to implement national health reform that provides comprehensive and universal health insurance coverage. Most people in the United States have health insurance through a patchwork collection of private plans and public programs. Unfortunately, like Casey, there are also many people who are uninsured. As discussed in Chapter 4, over the last several decades the rate of uninsurance has consistently hovered between 12% and 16% of the population.[1(p. 24)] In 2009, 50.7 million people in this country (16.7% of the population) did not have health insurance,[1(p. 22)] and most of them were without coverage for at least 2 years.[2(p. 7)] U.S. spending on health care has been perpetually high, accounting for 17.6% of the gross domestic product in 2009.[3] Despite the high level of spending on health care, the United States ranks poorly on a variety of quality measures, such as infant mortality rates and life expectancy (see Chapters 4 and 11 for a more detailed discussion of quality).

Although there has been general agreement about the problems facing the U.S. health care system, politicians and voters have disagreed about the best solutions. As a result, numerous attempts to pass national health reform legislation did not succeed. What was different in 2010? Why was the Obama administration successful when so many had failed before? This chapter begins with a discussion of why it has been so difficult to achieve broad health reform in this country. It continues by examining the numerous failed attempts at national health reform over the last century. The chapter then analyzes why health reform was enacted in 2010 and ends with an overview of the health reform law. Throughout this chapter we revisit themes highlighted in previous chapters: choosing between state flexibility and national uniformity; determining the appropriate role for government, the private sector, and individuals in health care financing and delivery; defining a primary decision-making goal (e.g., fiscal restraint, equity/social justice, improved health outcomes, uniformity, etc.); and settling on the appropriate scope of coverage to offer beneficiaries.

DIFFICULTY OF HEALTH REFORM IN THE UNITED STATES

The array of problems facing the health care system has led to numerous health reform proposals and implemented policies. The concept of health reform can have several different meanings. Given the patchwork health care system, health reform often refers to changes that seek to reduce the number of uninsured. Due to the high and increasing cost of health care services, health reform might also include changes that seek to contain costs and control utilization. The notion of health reform could also address other shortcomings, such as trying to reduce medical errors, strengthen patient rights, build the public health infrastructure, or confront the rising cost of medical malpractice insurance. The Patient Protection and Affordable Care Act (ACA), the health reform law passed in 2010, touches on many of these issues.[4]

We begin with a discussion about why health reform is difficult to achieve in the United States and then introduce some of the reforms that have been attempted on a national level with varying degrees of success. Numerous authors have addressed the main factors that deter significant social reform in this country, including health reform.[5-7] Factors that are prominently discussed include the country's culture, the nature of U.S. political institutions, the power of interest groups, and path dependency (i.e., the notion that people are generally opposed to change).

Culture

This country's culture and lack of consensus about health reform have impeded attempts to create universal coverage health plans. The twin concepts of entrepreneurialism and individualism have had a real impact on health policy decisions: Americans generally oppose government solutions to social welfare problems.[7(p. 438)] Opposition is high to health reforms that rely either on a direct government-run program or public funding through tax increases.[7(p. 438)] Far less than half of Americans (24%) strongly favor a single-payer health plan, and even the notion of a "public option," a government health plan to compete with private insurers, was soundly rejected in the 2010 health care debate.[8]

At the same time the country also believes the government has some role to play in health reform. Large majorities favor tax credits to assist the uninsured with purchasing health insurance, expanding government programs for low-income individuals, and government mandates that employers provide insurance.[9] In 2010 almost half of Americans (47%) believed it was the federal government's responsibility to ensure that all Americans have health coverage, down from a high of 69% in 2007.[8] In addition to having different views about how to reduce the number of uninsured, there is no agreement about the overall scope of the health care problems we face.[10] Going into the 2010 presidential election, most Americans believed the extant health system needed major changes, yet 22% believed only minor changes were required and another 17% thought the system should basically stay the same.[11]

U.S. Political System

The country's system of government has also made it difficult to achieve universal coverage. Traditionally, social welfare programs—including the provision of health care—have been the responsibility of the states. Initially, there was almost no federal involvement in the provision of health care, and when the federal government became more heavily involved in 1965, Medicaid continued to keep the locus of decision making on the state level. Of course, there are select populations, such as the elderly (Medicare) and veterans (Veterans Health Administration), who have a federalized health insurance system. However, the country appears to support a Medicaid-type expansion over a new federalized program.[8]

Although states are generally home to social welfare changes, it is very difficult to provide universal health care on a state-by-state basis. If state health reform efforts lead the way, the country could have a patchwork of programs and policies that vary from state to state, with the potential to make health coverage even more complex and inefficient than it currently is. In addition, states must consider whether they are making policy decisions that will give employers an incentive to choose to locate in another state with fewer or less onerous legal requirements. If employers leave the state, it could result in loss of jobs and have downstream effects on the state's economy.

The federal government also has resource advantages over states, making it easier for the federal level to be the engine for health reform. Each state has a much smaller tax and revenue base than the federal government to draw from to implement health reform plans. In addition, once the federal government decides to tax a good or service, a state's ability to tax that same good or service is constrained by the individual's willingness and ability to pay a higher price. Unlike the federal government, all states (except Vermont) have some type of balanced budget requirement.[9] Without the ability to deficit spend, states must make difficult choices about resource allocation that federal policymakers often avoid (and thus generate enormous deficits). These restrictions, however, may also help with reform efforts by forcing states to a crisis point where a decision must be made to avoid an untenable situation. The federal government rarely reaches such a crisis point, meaning tough decisions are often left for the next Congress or administration.

In addition, state reform efforts are also constrained by the Employee Retirement Income Security Act of 1974 (ERISA).[a] As discussed in Chapter 11, ERISA is a federal law that regulates "welfare benefit programs," including health plans, operated by private employers. ERISA limits states' ability to reform because it broadly preempts state laws that "relate to" employer-sponsored plans and because it applies to nearly all individuals who receive health benefits through a private employer.[b] One effect of the law, for example, is that states have little regulatory control over the benefits covered in employer-sponsored health plans because ERISA accords employers near-total discretion over the design of their benefit packages.[12(p. 237)]

Despite these hurdles, it is also important to recognize that a health reform strategy focusing on states has benefits as well. At its best, state-level reform can be accomplished more rapidly and with more innovation than at the federal level. State legislatures may have an easier time convincing a narrower band of constituents important to the state than Congress has in accommodating the varied needs of stakeholders nationwide. Along the same lines, states are able to target reforms to meet the particular needs of their population instead of covering more diverse needs across the entire country. Additionally, through the use of "direct democracy" (referenda, ballot initiatives, etc.), citizens can more easily have an impact on decisions by state-level policymakers than

by federal legislators. Finally, because the health care delivery system is run primarily on the state level, states have the expertise and ability to implement many planks of health care reform.

Other aspects of the U.S. political system also make it difficult to institute sweeping reform. For example, although presidents have significant influence on policy agenda setting and proposing budgets, they have very limited power to make changes without the assistance of Congress (as discussed in detail in Chapter 2). The federal government is often politically divided, with different parties holding power in the executive and legislative branches. This division often results in partisanship and policy inaction due to different policy priorities and views.

Furthermore, although members of Congress may ride the coattails of a popular president from their own party, they are not reliant on the president to keep their jobs. The issues and views their constituents care about most may not align with the president's priorities. In those cases, members of Congress have a strong incentive to adhere to the wishes of those who vote for them instead of simply following the president's lead. Barring an overwhelming wave of discontent, as occurred in the 2010 midterm elections when Democrats suffered historic losses in Congress, it is usually difficult to unseat incumbents. For example, 98% of incumbents successfully defended their seats in 2004.[13] As a result, legislators in Congress may have confidence in focusing on their district's or state's needs before those of the entire nation.

Federal legislative rules also support inaction or incremental reform over sweeping changes. In the Senate 60 (of 100) votes are needed to break a filibuster in most cases. Thus, even the political party in the majority can have difficulty effectuating change. Also, because both the House and Senate have to pass bills containing the same policies and language to have any chance at becoming law, a large political majority in one chamber or the other does not guarantee the ability to enact a policy. As a result, in many cases, members of Congress have to work together, at least to some degree, to devise a consensus policy that satisfies enough members to pass a bill. This need to build consensus makes radical change unlikely.

Interest Groups

As discussed in more detail in Chapter 2, decisions by politicians are often influenced by interest groups. The role of interest groups is to represent their members' interests in policy decisions. These groups can be corporate for-profit entities or nonprofit consumer-oriented organizations. They lobby politicians and the general public about the virtues or vices of specific proposals, work to improve proposals on the policy agenda, and attempt to defeat proposals they believe are not in the best interest of their group. By contributing to political campaigns or by helping to draw supportive voters out on election day, interest groups gain the ear, and often the influence, of politicians who vote on issues important to the group.

In terms of health reform, interest groups representing various providers, businesses, employer groups, insurance companies, and managed care organizations have often been opposed to comprehensive health reform.[7(pp. 438–439)] There are numerous points along the path from developing a policy idea to voting for or against a bill when interest groups can attempt to affect politicians' views. The more radical the policy proposal, the more interest groups are likely to become engaged in the political decision-making process, making it difficult to pass a bill that includes comprehensive reform.

In general, it is easier to oppose a proposal than develop one and pass a bill. Opponents of proposals are not required to show a better alternative to whatever is on the table. Instead, they can simply point to aspects of the policy idea that are unpopular and call for the proposal to be rejected. This was the tactic used by the Health Insurance Association of America in their well-known "Harry and Louise" television ads that opposed the Clinton administration's comprehensive health reform bill in 1993, the Health Security Act. In the ad, Harry and Louise, two "average" Americans, are seen discussing the health care system over breakfast. Although they both agree the system needs to be improved, they highlight certain aspects of the Clinton plan that were particularly controversial, such as an overall cap on funds for health care needs and restrictions on provider choice. The punch line for the ad was "There's got to be a better way."[14] Similarly, before the 2010 midterm elections, many Republicans promised to "repeal and replace" the health reform bill without specifying their favored replacement option. To be effective in opposing health reform, opponents did not have to propose an alternative that was scrutinized and compared with the existing proposal. Simply saying "the country can do better" was enough to help create significant opposition to the plan.

Path Dependency

Finally, the concept of "path dependency" has been a hindrance to major health reform. "The notion of path dependency emphasizes the power of inertia within political institutions."[7(p. 439)] That is, once a certain way of doing things becomes the norm, it is hard to change course. Yet, this theory does not mean that health reform is impossible. Inertia may be overcome at "critical moments or junctures" that open a window for change.[7(p. 439)] For example, the passage of Medicaid and Medicare in 1965 was a radical change from the past pattern of limited federal government involvement in health care. The catalysts for this change were the growing social pressure for improving the health care system and the landslide victory of Democrat Lyndon Johnson as president and of liberal and moderate Democrats in Congress. The 1992 election of Democrat Bill Clinton, who ran on a platform emphasizing broad health reform, coupled with the Democratic majority in Congress (until 1994), also presented a window of opportunity. Although Clinton's plan was not ultimately successful, it appeared the American public and politicians were open to changing the course of the health care "path" that had been taken to date. In 2010 another "critical moment" appeared, and President Obama took advantage of the circumstances to push through the health reform bill. Although path dependency suggests that inertia and fear of change have made broad reform difficult to achieve, it is not impossible to succeed.

Path dependency is also evident on the individual level; that is, once individuals are accustomed to having things a certain way, it is difficult for them to accept change. Currently, about 85% of Americans have health insurance, most through employer-sponsored coverage. Comprehensive health reform would likely change the condition of the insured population to some degree by changing either their source of coverage, the benefits included in coverage, the cost of coverage, or some other factor. During the debate over the ACA, about one-third of people surveyed reported that the bill would probably make them worse off, and another third thought it would not make any difference to them.[10] Professor Judith Feder refers to this problem as the "crowd-out" politics of health reform.[15] "[T]he fundamental barrier to universal coverage is that our success in insuring most of the nation's population has 'crowded out' our political capacity to insure the rest."[15(p. 461)] In other words, many of the insured do not want a change in the health care system that will leave them worse off to make the uninsured better off.

According to Professor Feder, the way to solve the political crowd-out dilemma is by changing the very nature of American culture. The focus on individualism must be replaced with a concern for the community and recognition that all Americans are part of a single community. "[T]he challenge to improving or achieving universal coverage is to decide whether we are a society in which it is every man, woman or child for him/herself or one in which we are all in it together."[15(p. 464)] Even with the passage of the ACA, the country remains divided about the extent that "we are all in it together." Shortly before the ACA passed, over half of people surveyed (54%) said they would not be willing to pay more so others could have access to health insurance.[16]

UNSUCCESSFUL ATTEMPTS TO PASS NATIONAL HEALTH REFORM

Since the early 1900s, when medical knowledge became advanced enough to make health care and health insurance a desirable commodity, there have been periodic attempts to implement universal coverage through national health reform. The Socialist Party was the first U.S. political party to support health insurance in 1904, but the main engine behind early efforts for national reform was the American Association for Labor Legislation (AALL), a "social progressive" group that hoped to reform capitalism, not overthrow it.[17(p. 243)] In 1912 Progressive Party candidate Theodore Roosevelt supported a social insurance platform modeled on the European social insurance tradition that included health insurance, workers' compensation, old-age pensions, and unemployment. With his loss to Woodrow Wilson, the national health insurance movement was without a strong national leader for three decades.

The AALL continued to support a form of health insurance after Roosevelt's defeat and drafted a model bill in 1915. This bill followed the European model, limiting participation to working class employees and their dependents. Benefits included medical aid, sick pay, maternity benefits, and a death benefit. These costs were to be financed by employers, employees, and the state. The AALL believed that health insurance for the working population would reduce poverty and increase society's productivity and well-being through healthier workers and citizens.

Opposition to AALL's bill came from several sources.[17(pp. 247–249)] Although some members of the American Medical Association (AMA) approved of the bill conceptually, physician support rapidly evaporated when details emerged about aspects of the plan that would negatively impact their income and autonomy. The American Federation of Labor (a labor union) opposed compulsory health insurance because it wanted workers to rely on their own economic strength, not the state, to obtain better wages and benefits. In addition, the federation was concerned that it would lose power if the government, not the union, secured benefits for workers. Employers were generally opposed to the bill, contending that supporting public health was a better way to ensure productivity. In addition, they feared that providing health insurance to employees might promote malingering instead of reducing lost workdays. After experiencing the high cost associated with workers' compensation, employers were also not eager to take on an additional expensive benefit. Of course, the part of the insurance industry that had already established a profitable niche in the death benefit business was strongly opposed to a bill that included a death benefit provision.

Employers, providers, and insurers have, in general, remained staunch opponents of national health reform over the years, whereas unions have supported national reform efforts. However, this dynamic has recently changed with more provider groups, employers, and even some insurers calling for a national solution to the problems of rising health care costs and the uninsured.

The country's entry into World War I in 1917 also changed the health reform debate. Many physicians who supported the AALL bill entered the military, shifting their focus away from the domestic health policy debate. Anti-German sentiment was high, so opponents of the bill gained traction by denouncing compulsory health insurance as anti-American. One pamphlet read as follows: "What is Compulsory Social Health Insurance? It is a dangerous device, invented in Germany, announced by the German Emperor from the throne the same year he started plotting and preparing to conquer the world."[17(p. 253)]

The next time national health insurance might have taken hold was from the mid-1930s through the early 1940s because the country was coping with the difficulties of the Depression. During this time, there was a significant increase in government programs, including the creation of Social Security in 1935, which provided old-age assistance, unemployment compensation, and public assistance. Yet, the fourth prong of the social insurance package, health insurance, remained elusive. President Franklin Roosevelt heeded his staff's advice to leave health insurance out of Social Security because of the strong opposition it would create.[17(p. 267)]

Even so, members of Roosevelt's administration continued to push for national health insurance. The Interdepartmental Committee to Coordinate Health and Welfare Activities was created in 1935 and took on the task of studying the nation's health care needs. This job fell to its Technical Committee on Medical Care. Instead of supporting a federal program, the committee proposed subsidies to the states for operating health programs. Components of the proposal included expanding maternal and child health and public health programs under Social Security, expanding hospital construction, increasing aid for medical care for the indigent, studying a general medical care program, and creating a compensation program for those who lost wages due to disability.

Although President Roosevelt established a National Health Conference to discuss the recommendation, he never fully supported the medical care committee's proposal. With the success of conservatives in the 1938 election and the administration's concerns about fighting the powerful physician and state medical society lobbies, national health reform did not have a place on Roosevelt's priority list. Senator Robert

Wagner (D-NY) introduced a bill that followed the committee's recommendations in 1939, and although it passed in the Senate, it did not garner support from the president or in the House.

World War II provided another opportunity for the opposition to label national health insurance as socialized medicine. But once the war ended, President Roosevelt finally called for an "economic bill of rights," which included medical care. President Truman picked up where Roosevelt left off, strongly advocating for national health insurance. President Truman's proposal included expanding hospitals, increasing public health and maternal and child health services, providing federal aid for medical research and education, and, for the first time, a single health insurance program for all.[17(p. 281)] Heeding lessons from earlier reform failures, Truman emphasized that his plan was not socialized medicine and that the delivery system for medical and hospital care would not change.

Again, there was strong opposition to the proposal. The AMA vehemently rejected the proposal, and most other health care groups opposed it as well. Although the public initially approved of it, there was no consensus about how national health insurance should be structured, and more people preferred modest voluntary plans over a national, compulsory, comprehensive health insurance program.[17(p. 282)] Additional opposition came from the American Bar Association, the Chamber of Commerce, and even some federal agencies concerned about losing control over their existing programs. In the end, only the hospital construction portion of the proposal was enacted.

When Truman won reelection on a national health insurance platform in 1948, it appeared the tide had turned. However, the AMA continued its strong opposition and its attempts to link national health insurance to socialism. Congress considered various compromises but never reached a consensus. The public remained uncertain about what kind of plan to favor. Employers maintained their opposition to compulsory insurance. In addition, one large group of potential supporters—veterans—was disinterested in the debate because they had already secured extensive medical coverage through the Veterans Administration. As the Korean War moved forward, Truman's focus shifted away from national health insurance and toward the war effort and other priorities.

National health insurance did not return to the national policy agenda until the 1970s. The landscape was quite different from that during Truman's era. Medicaid and Medicare had been created, health care costs had begun to rise exponentially, and the economy was deteriorating. In 1969 President Nixon declared that a "massive crisis" existed in health care and that unless it was fixed immediately, the country's medical system would collapse.[17(p. 381)] The general public seemed to agree, with 75% of respondents in one survey concurring that the health care system was in crisis.[17(p. 381)] Democrats still controlled Congress by a significant margin, and Senator Edward Kennedy (D-MA) and Representative Martha Griffiths (D-MI), the first woman to serve on the powerful House Ways and Means Committee, proposed a comprehensive, federally operated health insurance system.

At the same time a movement supporting health care and patient rights was gaining momentum. These included rights to informed consent, to refuse treatment, to due process for involuntary commitment, and to equal access to health care.[17(p. 389)] The public was both anxious to obtain care and willing to challenge the authority of health care providers.

The Nixon administration's first attempt at health reform focused on the need to change the financing of the health care system from one dominated by a fee-for-service system, which created incentives to provide more and more expensive services, to one that promoted restraint, efficiency, and the health of the patient. The result was a "health maintenance strategy" intended to stimulate the private industry to create health maintenance organizations (HMOs) through federal planning grants and loan guarantees, with the goal of enrolling 90% of the population in an HMO by the end of the 1970s.[17(pp. 395–396)] Ironically, group health plans, often labeled socialized medicine, had become the centerpiece of a Republican reform strategy.

Nixon's proposal included an employer mandate to provide a minimum package of benefits under a National Health Insurance Standards Act, a federally administered Family Health Insurance Program for low-income families. The program had a less generous benefit package than the one required by the National Health Insurance Standards Act, reductions in Medicare spending to help defray the costs, a call for an increase in the supply of physicians, and a change in how medical schools were subsidized. Opponents were plentiful, and this plan did not come to fruition. Some believed the plan was a gift to private insurance companies. Advocates for the poor were outraged at the second tier of benefits for low-income families. The AMA was concerned about HMOs interfering with physician practices and supported an alternative that provided tax credits for buying private insurance.

After the 1972 election, Nixon proposed a second, more comprehensive plan that covered everyone and offered more comprehensive coverage. Private insurance companies would cover the employed and a government-run program would cover the rest of the population, with both groups receiving the same benefit package. Senator Kennedy and Representative Wilbur Mills (D-AR) supported a similar plan, and it appeared a compromise was close at hand. However, labor unions and liberal organizations preferred the original Kennedy plan and resisted compromising with the hope of gaining power in the 1974 post-Watergate elections. Fearing the same political shift, insurance companies actually supported a catastrophic insurance plan proposed by Senator Russell Long (D-LA), believing it was better than any plan that would come out of a more liberal Congress after the elections. Once again, there was no majority support for any of the bills, and a national health insurance plan was not enacted.

Although President Jimmy Carter gave lip service to national health reform, he never fully supported a proposal. It was not until the election of Bill Clinton in 1992 that the next real attempt at national health insurance was made. The Clinton administration plan, dubbed the Health Security Act, was designed to create national health insurance without spending new federal funds or shifting coverage from private to public insurance. It relied on the concept of "managed competition," which combined elements of managed care and market competition.

Under the Health Security Act, a National Health Board would have established national and regional spending limits and regulated premium increases. "Health alliances" would have included a variety of plans that were competing for the business of employees and unemployed citizens in each geographic area. All plans were to have a guaranteed scope of benefits and uniform cost sharing. Employers were required to provide coverage for their workers at a defined high level of benefits, and those with 5,000 employees or fewer had to purchase plans through the health alliance. Subsidies were provided for low-income individuals and small businesses. Funding was to be provided from cost-containment measures that were reinvested. Forced by the Congressional Budget Office (CBO) to provide an alternative funding strategy should the cost containment not create enough funds, the plan also included the option of capping insurance premium growth and reducing provider payments.

Like the national health insurance plans before it, the Health Security Act had opponents from many directions. The health alliances were attacked as big government, employers resisted mandates and interference with their fringe benefits, some advocates feared that cost containment would lead to care rationing, the insured were concerned about losing some of their existing benefits or cost-sharing arrangements, the elderly feared losing Medicare, and academic health centers were concerned about losing funds based on new graduate medical education provisions.[17(p. 463)] In addition, the usually strong support from unions was missing because of an earlier disagreement with the president on trade matters. It is also generally accepted that the Clinton administration made several political mistakes that made a difficult political chore nearly impossible. The Health Security Act never made it to a vote.

WHY THE PATIENT PROTECTION AND AFFORDABLE CARE ACT PASSED

In many ways, 2010 was a very unlikely year to pass a national health reform plan. The country had been bitterly divided ideologically in recent years. Both the popular and electoral votes were almost evenly split in the 2000 and 2004 presidential elections. George W. Bush beat Al Gore despite losing the popular vote in 2000, and Bush beat John Kerry in 2004 with only 51% of the popular vote.[18] Even though Barack Obama won the electoral vote in a landslide over John McCain (365 to 173), only 53% of the population voted for Obama in 2010.[19]

In addition to the ideological divide, a financial crisis erupted toward the end of the 2008 presidential election. In October 2008, President Bush signed into law the Emergency Economic Stabilization Act, which included the $700 billion Troubled Asset Relief Program (TARP), which allowed the federal government to take over distressed assets, primarily bad mortgage loans, from private financial institutions.[20] It was argued that TARP was necessary to save the financial industry from collapsing, which could have led to another Great Depression. Even with TARP, the United States (and many other countries) entered into a recessionary period. Many individuals lived in homes they could no longer afford, banks limited lending opportunities, and employers laid off millions of workers due to the drop in consumer spending. In an effort to improve the economy, Obama signed into law the American Recovery and Reinvestment Act of 2009, also known as the stimulus bill.[21] This almost $800 billion effort was intended to save existing jobs, create new jobs, and spur long-term growth of the U.S. economy.[22] Although TARP was not popular with politicians or the general public, it was seen as necessary by members of both political parties and signed into law by a Republican president. Unlike TARP, however, the stimulus bill was not a bipartisan effort. Republicans in the House unanimously opposed the stimulus bill and only three Republicans voted for the bill in the Senate.

Not surprising, health care was not the only issue on voters' minds during the election campaign. Shortly before the election, 43% of registered voters ranked the economy as their number one priority. Economic concerns trumped health care, which ranked second, by an almost 2-to-1 margin.[23] Although voters from both political parties ranked the economy as their top priority, differences emerged along party lines regarding the next most important issue. Democratic voters ranked health care second, whereas both Republican and Independent voters were more concerned about the size and power of the federal government. These results were not surprising; Democrats have ranked health care as a higher priority than Republican and Independent voters did in every presidential election from 1988 to 2008.[24(p. 2053)]

Against this backdrop of a faltering economy, partisan differences, and the recent passage of two massive government spending bills, President Obama pursued a national health reform plan. Given the history of failed reform efforts, it would have been an accomplishment to pass health reform in the best of times, and clearly this was not the best of times. How did Obama and the 111th Congress succeed? It was a combination of having commitment, exhibiting leadership, applying lessons from past failures, and being pragmatic that lead to the passage of health reform.

Commitment and Leadership

It is highly unlikely that the 2010 health reform effort would have succeeded without a passionate and committed president willing to make health reform a priority. Health care has long been a priority for Democrats, and President Obama was no exception. Perhaps Obama's dedication to pass health reform stemmed in part from his personal experience. Obama's mother was uninsured when she died of ovarian cancer. As he said in one of his campaign ads: "My mother died of cancer at 53. In those last, painful months she was more worried about paying her medical bills than getting well. I hear stories like hers every day."[25]

Some of Obama's political advisors suggested waiting to tackle health reform until after taking action to address the poor economy and rising unemployment. Even voters who supported Obama were split over what his priorities should be during his first days in office.[26] Just days before the election, Obama suggested that the economy and energy independence were higher priorities than health reform. To Obama, that meant he should tackle several major issues at once, not put health reform on the back burner. "Priority number 3 would be health reform. I think the time is right to do it."[27]

Health reform efforts did not begin smoothly. President Obama initially wanted former Senator Tom Daschle to run both the Department of Health and Human Services (DHHS) and the White House Office on Health Reform. It was thought that his experience with the Senate, relationships with legislators, and confidence of the president were the right combination to take the lead on health reform. When his nomination was derailed due to tax problems, it was not a good omen. As deliberations in Congress lagged, Democrats were not able to present a bill to President Obama before recessing for the summer. During the summer of 2009, members of Congress went home to their constituents and held town hall meetings to discuss health reform. Some of the meetings erupted in vocal opposition to health reform, and the media focused on these town hall meetings throughout the summer. Obama and the Democrats were criticized for losing the momentum for reform by letting the debate linger.

At the same time, there were several instances during the political process when the health reform effort appeared doomed and President Obama's leadership made a difference. Obama attempted to reclaim the upper hand on health reform with a speech to a joint session of Congress in September 2009. He memorably proclaimed, "I am not the first president to take up health reform, but I intend to be the last."[28] Though support for health reform had been on the decline for several months, September 2009 polls showed that 62% still thought it was important to address health reform at that time, and 53% thought the country as a whole would be better off if health reform passed.[29] Less support existed for the Democrats' specific reform proposal, however, with 46% in support of the proposed change and 48% opposed to it.[30]

In January 2010, an event occurred that some assumed was the death knell of health reform. In the 2008 elections, Democrats made significant gains in Congress, earning a 59–41 majority in the Senate and a 257–178 majority in the House. Furthermore, Senator Arlen Specter of Pennsylvania switched parties, giving Democrats the crucial 60th vote needed for a filibuster-proof majority. President Obama, Senate Majority Leader Harry Reid (D-NV), and House Speaker Nancy Pelosi (D-CA) would have to balance the competing interests of conservative Democrats who were concerned with having too much government intervention, progressive Democrats who sought a public insurance option to compete with private companies, Blue Dog Democrats who were most concerned with fiscal discipline, and prolife and prochoice factions who would battle over whether and how abortion services would be included in any health reform bill. Then, in August 2009, Senator Ted Kennedy (D-MA) died. In office for 47 years, Kennedy was not only a lifelong supporter of health reform but also an expert negotiator who could work with Republicans and possibly achieve a bipartisan consensus. The January 2010 special election to fill his seat was won by Republican Scott Brown, who campaigned against the Democrats' health reform plan. In a postelection poll, 42% of voters said they voted for Brown to stop the health reform bill.[31]

Despite this setback and concerns by some that health reform efforts should be abandoned, Obama, along with Reid and Pelosi, remained strong in his conviction to pursue reform. President Obama's senior advisors said it would be a "terrible mistake" to walk away from the process based on Brown's victory, and Pelosi reminded her caucus how detrimental it was when Democrats abandoned the health reform effort during the Clinton administration.[32] In his State of the Union address, just a week after the special election, President Obama tied his health reform efforts to fixing the economy and reiterated his commitment to the issue[33]:

> And it is precisely to relieve the burden on middle class families that we still need health reform. Now let's be clear, I did not choose to tackle this issue to get some legislative victory under my belt. And by now it should be fairly obvious that I didn't take on health reform because it was good politics. . . . Here is what I ask of Congress though: Do not walk away from reform. Not now. Not when we are so close. Let us find a way to come together and finish the job for the American people.

Obama was not alone in providing leadership on health reform. Reid's and Pelosi's determination to see health reform succeed and their skill in mobilizing and controlling their caucuses were essential to the passage of the ACA. It is likely that health reform would not have passed without the skillful efforts of all three leaders working together. Even so, it is clear that the health reform effort would not even have begun without a president who put health reform at the top of the agenda and stuck with it throughout all the pitfalls.

Lessons from Failed Health Reform Efforts

The Obama administration tried to avoid the pitfalls that doomed health reform efforts in the past. Although the most recent failed effort from the Clinton administration probably provided the most relevant lessons, Obama confronted some of the same obstacles that reformers had faced decades earlier. At times, President Obama was accused of learning some of the lessons too well, swinging the pendulum too far to the other side. Although that debate may continue, clearly the way in which the Obama administration applied those lessons brought him success where others before him had failed.

President Clinton was criticized for not moving quickly enough to try to enact health reform after he was elected in 1992. He did not present a plan to Congress until a year into his presidency, having been sidetracked by other issues, such as the economy, including a budget showdown with Republicans, and whether gays should be allowed to serve in the military. Even after he finally sent his health care proposal to Congress, Clinton was preoccupied with other issues that sapped his political capital, such as passing the North American Free Trade Agreement and the fallout from the deaths of 18 American soldiers in Somalia.

President Obama, over the objection of some aides, chose to address health reform as quickly as possible despite also having to tackle the poor economy and possible collapse of the financial sector. Obama was elected into office with a 70% approval rating, and he moved to capitalize on his popularity.[34] It was almost inevitable that his approval rating would decline as he tried to turn the promise of a campaign into the reality of running the country. As Lyndon Johnson said after winning the 1964 election in a landslide, "Everyday while I'm in office, I'm gonna lose votes."[35(p. 172)] In addition, it is almost universally expected that the president's party will lose seats in the midterm elections. In the past 10 midterm elections, the incumbent party lost an average of 18.5 seats in the House and 2.5 seats in the Senate.[36(p. 1097)] Obama was correct to assume his Democratic majorities in Congress would not last long. After the 2010 midterm elections, the Democrats lost control of the House and several seats in the Senate.

President Obama also dealt with interest groups in a different way than his predecessors had done. Previous failed efforts of health reform have shown that those vested interests can be important players in the debate. In general, though not in all instances, provider groups, insurers, and employers have opposed health reform, whereas unions have supported health reform efforts. All these stakeholders have been known to devote significant resources and to lean on their representatives to support their point of view. During their reform effort, the Clinton administration warred with many stakeholder groups, with insurance companies and small businesses taking a leading role.[14]

Obama took a different tact from Clinton's by making deals with various stakeholders at the outset of the health reform debate. The lure of millions of newly insured customers helped convince the Pharmaceutical Research and Manufacturers of America and the American Hospital Association to contribute to health reform financing through reduced Medicare and Medicaid payments. In addition, the health insurance industry supported universal coverage under health reform. After being credited for helping derail the Clinton health plan, the Health Insurance Association of America favored the general idea of health reform though it differed with Obama and the Democrats' plan on some of the specifics. To be fair, Clinton may not have been able to broker deals with these stakeholders in the 1990s no matter how hard he tried. A combination of a changing health care environment, the likelihood that some type of health reform was likely to pass, and the uncertain future of employer-sponsored insurance made it more palatable for interest groups to try to influence instead of oppose the 2010 legislation.[37]

Clinton was also criticized for not mastering the legislative process. The Clinton administration chose to design the health reform plan itself and developed a complicated and secretive process, headlined by the Health Care Task Force, run by Hillary Clinton, to do it. While naming Hillary Clinton as the leader of the task force signaled the administration's commitment to the issue, she became a lightning rod for criticism, and questions about the appropriateness of the First Lady taking on such a significant policy role detracted from the substance of the health reform debate. Instead of negotiating with Congress, the administration debated the specifics of health reform among its own advisors and then asked Congress to pass the bill they had developed. Shutting out members of Congress instead of negotiating with them and taking over Congress' role in developing legislation was not, it turned out, a formula for success.

President Obama learned from Clinton's mistakes, as well as other presidents' legislative achievements. Instead of presenting a detailed plan or written legislation to Congress, success has often been found in outlining ideas and principles and letting Congress work through the details. When President Johnson was trying to get a Medicare bill passed, he told key members of Congress that he would not delve into the details of the bill, but he generally pushed for a larger package. When President George W. Bush was pursuing a new Medicare prescription drug benefit, he outlined his desire for an approach that worked with the private sector and encouraged competition but let Congress find the exact formula that would pass.[36(p. 1097)]

Similarly, Obama set out his principles but left the work of drafting a bill and fleshing out the details to Congress. On June 2, 2009, President Obama sent a letter to Senators Kennedy and Baucus, two leaders in the health reform effort, outlining his "core belief" that Americans deserved better and more affordable health insurance choices and that a health reform bill must not add to the federal deficit.[38] Although he let the negotiators know what his priorities were, Obama stayed above the fray during the legislative process. Whereas he preferred a public option to compete with private insurers, he did not insist on it. Although Obama campaigned against an individual mandate as a presidential candidate, he was open to including it in the bill. The president refused to be drawn into the debate over taxing generous health plans or creating a Medicare cost-containment commission. Instead, he focused his efforts on persuading Congress not to give up on the effort, bringing together various factions of the Democratic caucus and reaching out to the public to garner support for health reform.

The legislative process for completing the bill was long, rocky, and ultimately partisan. The House of Representatives moved more quickly and with less fractious debate than did the Senate. Instead of having multiple House committees work on competing bills, as occurred during the Clinton administration, House Democratic leaders created a "Tri-Committee" bill, jointly sponsored by Charles Rangel (D-NY), Henry Waxman (D-CA), and George Miller (D-CA), the chairmen of the House Ways and Means, Energy and Commerce, and Education and Labor (later renamed the Education and Workforce committee) committees, respectively. On November 7, 2009, the House passed its health reform bill with only two votes to spare, 220–215.[39] Only one Republican voted for it, and 39 conservative Democrats voted against it. The bill from the more liberal House contained several provisions that were likely to be rejected by the Senate: a public health insurance option to compete with private plans, a national health insurance exchange instead of state-based exchanges, more generous subsidies for low-income individuals, a broader expansion of Medicaid, and higher taxes on wealthier Americans.

Finance Committee Chairman Max Baucus (D-MT) led the effort in the Senate. The legislative process he established was lengthy, and some observers believed he compromised on too many issues in an attempt to forge a bipartisan bill. For a time, Senator Charles Grassley (R-IA) actively participated in the health reform deliberations, and a few other Republican senators appeared willing to consider a bipartisan measure. Ultimately, however, a bipartisan agreement could not be reached. In a 2009 Christmas Eve vote, the Baucus bill passed 60–39, with all Democrats and two Independents voting for the measure and all Republicans voting against it.[40]

Shortly after the New Year, members of the House and Senate began meeting to resolve differences between the House- and Senate-passed bills. Before those differences were resolved, however, Scott Brown was elected to fill Kennedy's seat in the Senate, and the Democrats no longer had a filibuster-proof majority. Before the special election that led to Brown's victory, it was assumed that after the Senate passed a health reform measure, House and Senate negotiators would work out their differences in a conference committee, with each chamber then voting to pass the compromise bill. With Brown's election and his opposition to health reform, however, this plan became unworkable. Democratic congressional leaders were left with few options, all of them unpalatable: the House could pass the Senate version of the bill; Democrats could try to use the reconciliation process to pass a new comprehensive bill; the House and Senate could compromise on a much smaller, more incremental health reform bill that focused on areas where a bipartisan agreement could be reached; or Democrats could abandon their efforts to pass a health reform bill. The day after Brown's election, House

Speaker Pelosi appeared to eliminate the easiest (legislatively speaking) of these paths by declaring that the House would not pass the Senate version of the bill: "I don't think it's possible to pass the Senate bill in the House. I don't see the votes for it at this time."[41]

In the end, a compromise was reached. House and Senate leaders agreed to use the budget reconciliation process to amend the Senate bill. The House then passed the Senate version of the bill, along with a companion reconciliation bill that amended certain aspects of the Senate bill. The reconciliation bill included more generous subsidies for individuals to purchase insurance than existed in the stand-alone Senate bill, the closure of the Medicare Part D doughnut hole, a tax on more generous insurance plans, changes to the penalties on individuals who would not buy insurance and for employers who would not offer insurance, and an increase in Medicare and investment taxes for higher earners. The Senate then passed the reconciliation bill, which could not be filibustered and only required a simple majority vote to pass. Once again, the vote to approve the bills was along party lines. The House approved the Senate bill by a vote of 219–212, with all Republicans and 34 Democrats voting against it.[42] President Obama signed the bill into law on March 23, 2010.[4]

Some observers argue that Obama may have "overlearned" the lesson about working with Congress and that in doing so he did not provide enough guidance to legislators and allowed the debate over health reform to linger too long.[36(p. 1097)] On one hand, it is difficult to criticize Obama's approach, because he was ultimately successful. On the other hand, could the problems stemming from the 2009 town halls and Scott Brown's election have been avoided, and would public opinion of the health reform effort be higher if the process had been better managed? Only time will tell whether Obama was successful over the long term (e.g., Is the law effective? Will the public support it over time? Will it be repealed?) and whether the political cost of the lengthy battle hurt the Democrats more than passing the bill helped them.

Political Pragmatism

President Obama is both credited and criticized for being as pragmatic as necessary to help ensure that health reform passed. He was comfortable making deals with industry stakeholders even though those agreements limited the savings and other changes that could have been achieved in the health reform bill. Obama ultimately signed a bill that did not include a public option even though he preferred that one was included, and his liberal base thought health reform without such an option was not true reform. An argument over abortion nearly derailed the bill in its final days, and Obama

supported a compromise on abortion language to keep enough Democrats in the fold. Even his goal of universal coverage was not met in the name of passing health reform. Obama's willingness to be pragmatic instead of staunchly principled, taking some victories instead of an all-or-nothing approach, allowed him to succeed in passing a health reform bill where others had failed.[37(p. 1116)] Some people argued it was worse to pass a flawed bill than not pass a bill at all, but Obama believed the promise of reducing the uninsured rate and gaining numerous health insurance market reforms were worth the compromises he made.

PATIENT PROTECTION AND AFFORDABLE CARE ACT

The ACA's reforms are expected to reduce the number of uninsured by 32 million people, including 16 million new Medicaid enrollees. This would leave approximately 23 million nonelderly residents uninsured. Although the ACA is estimated to cost $940 billion over 10 years, the CBO projects that the health care and revenue provisions in the law will reduce the federal deficit by $124 billion during that span.[43]

Although the ACA does not completely alter the way health insurance is provided by establishing a single-payer system or even a large government-run insurance plan to compete with private insurers, it makes significant philosophical and practical changes in how health insurance is regulated, structured, and administered in this country. The ACA is wide ranging and includes new requirements affecting individuals, employers, and states. Key provisions of the law are discussed in more depth below although most provisions relating to Medicaid and Medicare are detailed in Chapter 10. **Figure 9-1** provides a timeline for when major provisions of the ACA will be implemented.

Many people contend that the ACA falls short in its reform of the health care delivery system. And in many cases, they are correct. The ACA is most notable for the transformation changes it makes to health insurance—both access to it and its content—rather than for structural reforms made to the delivery system. Many provisions that focus on improving the health care delivery system, increasing the quality of care received by patients, reducing health care costs, and incentivizing providers to reconsider traditional methods of delivering care are often in the form of temporary pilot programs that may never be enacted permanently even if they prove to be valuable. Other analysts contend that these provisions were written as strongly as they could be at the time given the political environment and data available to policy makers. According to this view, the ACA provides the secretary of DHHS with unprecedented authority to make the pilot programs permanent, and it would have been irresponsible to implement more permanent wholesale changes without more evidence. In any case, as sweeping as the ACA is, it is far from being the last step that needs to be taken to improve how health care is provided in this country.

Individual Mandate

An individual mandate is a requirement that individuals purchase health insurance. This is not a new idea. President Clinton proposed an individual mandate in 1993 as part of his Health Security Act, and other competing proposals at the time, including those supported by Republicans, also included an individual mandate. Massachusetts, the only state in the country to require that everyone over age 18 have insurance, included an individual mandate as one way to achieve that goal. Switzerland and the Netherlands also included an individual mandate in their health reform plans.[44] During the 2008 election, Obama supported a mandate for children to be covered but suggested waiting to see if a mandate was necessary for adults after implementing other major health reform changes.

Individual mandates can be set up in a variety of ways, but usually individuals who do not comply will be required to pay some sort of penalty. The penalty is intended to both provide an incentive to comply with the law and to raise funds to cover the cost of health care for those individuals who choose not to carry health insurance. Individual mandates are considered to be a cornerstone of health reform efforts because they ensure that everyone covered by the mandate will be in an insurance pool to help cover costs and share risk.

The mandate is considered essential because without it, people who are in poor health or otherwise expect to use more health care services will be more likely to purchase health insurance, whereas healthier people will be more likely to opt out of insurance coverage. This would lead to an insurance pool that is sicker and more expensive, a problem referred to as adverse selection (discussed in more detail in Chapter 8). In addition, healthy individuals who choose not to purchase health insurance but then later need health care will likely receive some care even though they are uninsured. This is especially true if the individuals have the resources to pay for health care services. These individuals are referred to as free riders because they avoid paying premiums for health insurance during their healthy years but then enjoy the benefits of health care services when they are sick (free riders are discussed in more detail in Chapter 8). In 2007, more than 9 million people who earned at least $75,000 were uninsured. Because it is likely that many of these individuals could have afforded to purchase health insurance, some analysts consider

this evidence of the free rider problem.[44] In addition, the individual mandate is essential because it was the carrot that enticed health insurers to support health reform.

Starting in 2014, the ACA's individual mandate requires that almost everyone purchase health insurance or pay a penalty. This penalty is phased in over time, beginning at the greatest of $95 or 1% of taxable income per person in 2014 and growing to the greatest of $695 or 2.5% of taxable income per person in 2016. After 2016, the penalty amount increases through cost of living adjustments. Individuals are exempt from this requirement if their income is below the tax filing threshold (in 2010 this was $9,350 for singles and $18,700 for couples), the lowest-cost plan option exceeds 8% of their income, they qualify for a religious exemption, they are incarcerated, they are undocumented immigrants, they were without coverage for less than 3 months, or they are Native Americans.

The individual mandate is controversial. In addition to believing that the individual mandate represents unwanted government intrusion into private decision making, opponents of the individual mandate argue that Congress does not have the legal authority to impose such a requirement. This argument is grounded in jurisprudence relating to the federal Constitution's Commerce Clause, which gives Congress the power to "regulate commerce with foreign nations, and among the several states, and with the Indian tribes."[45] Since the 1940s, the Supreme Court has interpreted the Commerce Clause to permit Congress to regulate economic activity that carries across state lines or are local concerns that substantially affect interstate commerce. Several Commerce Clause cases have allowed the regulation of individual conduct. For example, the Court has upheld laws that prohibit an individual from refusing to interact with a minority and those that regulate an individual's ability to grow wheat or marijuana for home consumption.[46] In addition, regulating health insurance has also been deemed to be within the scope of the Commerce Clause.[47]

The crux of the argument against the individual mandate is that the Commerce Clause does not permit Congress to require an individual to purchase a good or service, such as health insurance. In other words, the argument goes, an individual's decision not to purchase health insurance cannot be considered "economic activity" that Congress may regulate. Instead, it is argued, Congress is trying to regulate economic *in*activity—the decision not to purchase health insurance—and that this is not covered by the Commerce Clause.[48]

Those who contend the Commerce Clause permits Congress to establish an individual mandate to purchase health insurance argue that everyone uses health care services at some point in their lives. Decisions regarding health insurance are an economic activity because no one can opt out of the health care market—the decision individuals make is not whether to participate but how to participate in it. People will participate by purchasing health insurance now to cover the cost of future services or by paying out of pocket later at the time services are needed. Furthermore, it is argued that the decision to purchase health insurance affects everyone's economic activity because of the nature of pricing health insurance. To date, the Supreme Court has not ruled on a case where Congress compels an individual to buy a good or service, and the lower courts that have considered challenges have split on the issue. As of June 2011, 26 cases have been filed in the courts seeking to overturn the ACA. With so many challenges making their way through the judicial system, this legal question will ultimately be decided by the Supreme Court.

State Health Insurance Exchanges

The ACA establishes a new entity called health insurance exchanges, which are intended to create a more organized and competitive market for purchasing health insurance. These exchanges are state-based and geared toward those who purchase health insurance as individuals (through American Health Benefit Exchanges) or through small businesses (through the Small Business Health Options Program). Starting in 2014, these exchanges will offer a variety of health insurance plans that meet ACA criteria regarding plan benefits, payments, and consumer information. CBO projects that by 2019, 24 million individuals will purchase their own health insurance through an exchange and another 5 million individuals with access to employer-sponsored insurance will pick an exchange option.[49]

The exchanges are a critical component of health reform because it would be untenable to require individuals to purchase health insurance without also making comprehensive and affordable health insurance options available.

BOX 9-1 Discussion Questions

What will happen to ACA if the individual mandate is found to be unconstitutional? Will the whole reform bill unravel? Will it work but not as well? Are there alternatives to the individual mandate that accomplish the same goals without potentially running afoul of the Constitution?

As discussed in Chapter 8, individuals and small businesses often face expensive and less comprehensive health insurance choices because their insurance pools are not so large that the premiums paid by healthy individuals offset the costs associated with sicker ones. The exchanges are intended to create a new market by bringing together large numbers of individuals or small businesses to create bigger insurance pools. Individuals are eligible to purchase health insurance through an exchange if they are U.S. citizens or legal immigrants, are not incarcerated, and do not have access to affordable employer-sponsored insurance.

States are required to establish exchanges for individuals and small businesses by January 1, 2014 (although the federal government will provide a fallback option if any state fails, or chooses not, to offer one). States may choose to establish one exchange for both groups or create separate exchanges. Although the ACA defines a small business as one with fewer than 100 employees, states may choose to limit the small business exchange to organizations with fewer than 50 employees for the first 2 years. As of 2017, states may also choose to allow companies with more than 100 employees to enroll in an exchange. States may form a regional exchange with other states or allow multiple exchanges within one state as long as each exchange covers a distinct geographic area. In addition, the Office of Personnel Management is required to offer at least two multistate plans within each exchange.

All plans that participate in the exchange must offer a standard benefits package called "essential health benefits" (Table 9-1).[50] This represents the first time private health insurance plans are subject to a federal standard regarding which benefits must be offered. The ACA outlines the categories of services that must be provided in the essential health benefits package, but important questions about how the scope of services is defined will be decided through the regulatory process. As part of this process, the ACA requires the secretary of DHHS to ensure the scope of benefits is equal to the benefit level found in a "typical employer plan." If a state requires plans to offer any services beyond the essential health benefits package, the state must defray the cost of the additional service through a payment to the enrollee or the plan. Plans may not design their benefit or reimbursement packages in ways that discriminate based on age, disability, or expected length of life.[51]

One exception to the essential health benefits requirement is the option for plans to offer catastrophic coverage with limited benefits and low premiums. A catastrophic plan may be offered only to individuals under the age of 30 who would be exempt from the individual mandate requirement

TABLE 9-1 Essential Health Benefits

All plans in the state exchanges must offer the following benefits:

- Ambulatory patient services
- Emergency services
- Hospitalization
- Maternity and newborn care
- Mental health services
- Substance abuse services
- Prescription drugs
- Rehabilitative services, habilitative services and devices
- Laboratory services
- Prevention and wellness services
- Chronic disease management services
- Pediatric services, including vision and dental services

because the cost of the lowest priced plan available to them exceeds 8% of their income. The coverage level would be set at the current health savings account coverage level but with preventive benefits and three primary care visits exempt from the deductible.

There was significant debate about whether to allow or require plans in the exchange to offer abortion services. In fact, the debate was so divisive, it almost doomed the entire health reform bill at the 11th hour. A compromise was reached with the intent of keeping the status quo regarding federal funding for abortion services (i.e., limit federal funding for abortion services to cases where the life of the pregnant woman is in danger or the pregnancy is a result of rape or incest). Under the compromise, states may enact a law that prohibits plans that participate in their state exchanges from providing abortion services. If a state does not enact such a law and a plan chooses to offer abortion services in other circumstances, the plan must create separate financial accounts to ensure that federal premium and cost-sharing subsidies are not used toward those abortion services. In addition, at least one of the multistate plans is required not to provide abortion services beyond those that are currently allowed with federal funding. As with most compromises, neither side was entirely pleased with the outcome. Those who want more restrictive abortion policies found the separate accounting process to be a meaningless exercise, whereas those who want more permissive abortion policies were disturbed by the ability of states to prohibit plans from offering abortion services.

Because all exchange plans must offer the same essential health benefits package, one key difference among the plans is the cost to the enrollee. Four levels of plans may be offered, and they are distinguished by their actuarial value. Actuarial value is the share of covered benefits generally paid by the insurer based on the cost-sharing provisions in the plan. The higher the actuarial value, the more the plan pays for a given set of services. For example, in a plan with 70% actuarial value, the plan pays 70% of the cost of services on average across all enrollees, and enrollees pay 30%. Actuarial value is set by average cost, but any single enrollee in that plan may pay more or less than 30% of the cost of services. In general, plans with a higher actuarial value will also have higher premiums to cover the cost of providing services to enrollees. The four ACA-approved plan levels by actuarial value are bronze (60% actuarial value), silver (70% actuarial value), gold (80% actuarial value), and platinum (90% actuarial value). Plans must offer at least one silver- and one gold-level option in each exchange in which they participate.

The ACA also requires the exchanges to ensure that plans are meeting other requirements of participating in the exchange. These requirements relate to marketing practices, provider networks, outreach and enrollment, following insurance market regulations, and providing information in plain language. In addition, the entity running the exchange must provide a call center for customers, maintain a website, rate plans in the exchange, develop uniform applications, provide information regarding eligibility for public programs, assist individuals in calculating their tax credits, and certify individuals who are exempt from the individual mandate requirement.

Premium and Cost-Sharing Subsidies

The ACA includes a host of premium tax credits and cost-sharing subsidies to help make it affordable for people to purchase health insurance in a state exchange. Given the mandate to purchase insurance, it was necessary to include some assistance to make it possible for low-income individuals to comply with the new requirement. The tax credits and subsidies will be available starting in 2014, the same year the individual mandate and the state health insurance exchanges go into effect.

Premium tax credits are available to individuals who purchase health insurance in state exchanges and have incomes between 133% and 400% of the federal poverty level. In 2010, 400% of poverty was $43,200 for an individual and $88,200 for a family of four.[52] The tax credits are advanceable and refundable, meaning they will be available when health insurance is purchased and regardless of whether the individual

BOX 9-2 Discussion Questions

There was a lengthy debate about whether to include a public option in health reform. A public option is some type of government-run health plan that would be available to compete with private plans. A public option could exist within the health exchange model or outside of it. Instead of a public option, Congress voted to require the Office of Personnel Management, which runs the Federal Employee Health Benefit Plans, to contract with at least two multistate plans in every state health insurance exchange.

What are the pros and cons of having a public option? Does the Office of Personnel Management compromise achieve all or some of the goals of having a public option? Why do you believe the Office of Personnel Management compromise was acceptable to legislators but the public option was not?

TABLE 9-2 Premium Tax Credit Schedule

Income Level by Federal Poverty Level (FPL)	Premium as a Percent of Income
Up to 133% FPL	2% of income
133–150% FPL	3–4% of income
150–200% FPL	4–6.3% of income
200–250% FPL	6.3–8.05% of income
250–300% FPL	8.05–9.5% of income
300–400% FPL	9.5% of income

owes any taxes. Cost-sharing subsidies are available to people who earn up to 250% of poverty. Under the ACA, individuals with income less than 133% of poverty will be eligible for Medicaid in 2014.

To qualify for assistance, an individual must be a U.S. citizen or legal resident, must not be eligible for any public health insurance program (including military coverage), and must not have access to employer-sponsored health insurance. Exceptions exist if an available employer plan does not cover at least 60% of covered benefits or if the employee's share of premium contributions exceeds 9.5% of the employee's income.

The amount of the premium tax credit is tiered based on income and set so individuals will not have to pay more than a certain percentage of their income on premiums (Table 9-2). The tax credit amount is based on the cost of the second-lowest-cost silver plan in the exchange and location where the individual is eligible to purchase insurance. Individuals who want to purchase a more expensive plan have to pay the difference in cost between the second-lowest-cost silver plan and the plan they prefer to purchase. Under the ACA, DHHS will adjust the premium people are expected to pay to reflect that premium costs typically grow faster than income levels. For example, assume Bob's income is 250% of poverty (about $27,000) and the cost of the second-lowest-cost silver plan in Bob's area is $5,700. Under the premium tax credit schedule, Bob will pay no more than 8.05% of his income, or $2,173. Bob's tax credit is $3,527, which is $5,700 minus $2,173.[53]

Cost-sharing subsidies are available to help low-income people reduce the amount of out-of-pocket spending on health insurance (Table 9-3). The subsidies are tiered by income level and set so plans pay a higher percentage of service costs. In other words, they are set to increase the actuarial value of the plan for low-income individuals.

In addition to the premium tax credits and cost-sharing subsidies, the ACA limits the overall amount of out-of-pocket costs paid by individuals with incomes up to 400% of poverty (Table 9-4). The limits are based on the maximum out-of-pocket costs for health savings accounts ($5,950 for single coverage, $11,900 for family coverage in 2009) and will be indexed annually.

Employer Mandate

Beginning in 2014, employers with 50 or more employees and at least 1 employee who qualifies for a tax credit are required to offer affordable health insurance or pay a penalty. As a result, covered employers have three options: (1) provide affordable health insurance and not pay a penalty, (2) provide health insurance not considered affordable and pay a penalty, or (3) do not provide health insurance and pay a penalty. The penalties are based on whether an employer offers health insurance and whether any full-time employees take a premium tax credit. The amount of the penalty increases over time based on the

TABLE 9-3 Cost-Sharing Subsidy Schedule

Income Level by Federal Poverty Level (FPL)	Actuarial Value
100–150% FPL	94%
150–200% FPL	87%
200–250% FPL	73%

TABLE 9-4 Out-of-Pocket Spending Limits	
Income Level by Federal Poverty Level (FPL)	Out-of-Pocket Limit
100–200% FPL	⅔ of maximum
200–300% FPL	½ of maximum
300–400% FPL	⅓ of maximum

national increase in premium costs. The employer mandate was put in place to encourage employers to continue offering or start offering health insurance. Without such a mandate, employers may have found it profitable not to offer health insurance and let their employees purchase health care through state exchanges, shifting more of the costs of health reform to the public sector and taxpayers.

For employers who do not offer health insurance and have at least one full-time employee who takes the premium tax credit, the penalty is $2,000 per employee after the first 30 employees. In other words, if such an employer has 50 employees, the employer would pay a $40,000 penalty ($2,000 × 20 employees).

Employers who offer health insurance do not pay a penalty if the insurance is considered affordable. Insurance is affordable if the plan has an actuarial value of at least 60% or if the premiums do not cost more than 9.5% of an employee's income. Employees who would have to pay more than 9.5% of their income on premiums have the option to purchase insurance through an exchange and receive a premium tax credit.

Employers who provide unaffordable insurance have to pay a penalty for each employee who takes a tax credit, not counting the first 30 employees. The penalty is $3,000 per employee who takes a tax credit but may not exceed more than $2,000 times the number of employees over 30. For example, if the employer has 50 employees and offers unaffordable coverage, the employer would pay a maximum penalty of

BOX 9-3 Discussion Questions

Premium and cost-sharing subsidies are estimated to cost $350 billion over 10 years. Is this a good use of resources? Are these subsidies well designed? Are they sufficient to make health insurance affordable? Do they cover people with incomes that are too high? Should they cover more people?

$40,000 ($2,000 × 20). If only 10 employees take a tax credit, the penalty would be $30,000 ($3,000 × 10). If all 50 employees take a tax credit, the penalty would be $40,000, which is the maximum penalty allowed, not $150,000 ($3,000 × 50).

Employers must offer vouchers to employees who earn up to 400% of poverty, would have to pay premiums between 8% and 9.8% of their income, and choose to enroll in a state exchange. The voucher is equal to the amount the employer would have paid for the employee in the employer's plan and is used to offset premium costs in the exchange plan. Employees who receive vouchers are not eligible for subsidies.

Congress was concerned about the impact of the employer mandate on small businesses. Given their smaller pool of employees, small businesses have often found it quite expensive to offer health insurance to their employees. In addition to exempting businesses with fewer than 50 employees from the employer mandate and creating a health insurance exchange for small businesses, Congress also included a small business tax credit to encourage these employers to provide coverage. Employers are eligible for the tax credit if they have fewer than 25 full-time equivalent employees, average annual wages under $50,000, and pay for at least half of the cost of health insurance coverage for their employees. The tax credit covers a portion of the cost of the employer's contribution toward employees' premiums. The credit is capped based on the average premium costs in the employer's geographic area and phases out as firm size and annual wages increase.

Changes to the Private Insurance Market

In addition to creating a new marketplace for private insurance through state exchanges, the ACA includes a variety of changes to private health insurance rules and requirements. These requirements cover everything from rate setting to benefits to who must be covered. Although the overall health reform law is controversial, many of these private market reforms have overwhelming support. Together, these changes filled in gaps left by the private market that many people believed were unfair to consumers.

The following coverage changes took effect in 2010:

- **Preexisting conditions:** Individual and group plans may not exclude children due to their health status or based on preexisting conditions.
- **Dependent coverage:** Individual and group plans must provide dependent coverage up to age 26.
- **Preventive services:** New health plans may not impose cost sharing for certain preventive services, including
  - Preventive services with an A or B rating from the U.S. Preventive Services Task Force

- Immunizations recommended by the Centers for Disease Control and Prevention's Advisory Committee on Immunization Practices.
- Preventive care and screening for women based on guidelines to be issued by the Health Resources and Services Administration.
- **Coverage limits:** Individual and group plans may not impose lifetime dollar limits on coverage (and ability to impose annual limits on the dollar value of coverage is prohibited as of 2014).
- **Rescission:** Individual and group plans may not rescind coverage except in the case of fraud.
- **Appeals:** New health insurance plans must have an effective appeals process that includes an external review option.

Congress also focused on the issue of how insurers determine premium rates and what they spend those resources on within their plans. The ACA charges DHHS with establishing an annual process to review "unreasonable" increases in premiums.[4(§1003)] In 2010, 43 states had some type of rate review law, and the federal process is intended to work with, not preempt, those state laws.[54] As of January 2011, DHHS was in the notice and review process for its proposed rule on this subject. In addition, the ACA requires that plans spend at least 85% (large group plans) or 80% (small group or individual plans) of their premium dollars on medical care and quality improvement services, not administrative or other expenses (e.g., profits). Regulations clarifying this medical loss ratio, as it is called, took effect on January 1, 2011.[55] Insurers must provide enrollees with a rebate if they do not spend the requisite percentage on clinical and quality improvement services.

A number of significant changes will also take place in 2014, when the individual mandate, employer mandate, and state health insurance exchanges begin:

- **Guaranteed issue and renewability:** Individual and group plans may not exclude or charge more to individuals based on preexisting conditions or health status in the individual market, small group market, and exchanges.
- **Rate variation limits:** Premium rates may vary based on only age, geographic area, family composition, and tobacco use in the individual market, small group market, and exchanges.
- **Coverage limits:** Individual and group plans may not place annual dollar limits on coverage.
- **Essential health benefits:** Insurers providing coverage to small businesses, individuals, and in the exchanges have to provide essential health benefits through one of four categories of plans (bronze, silver, gold, platinum) and adhere to annual cost-sharing limits.
- **Wellness plans:** Employers may offer rewards that reduce the cost of coverage to employees for participating in a wellness plan.

These private market changes do not affect all plans equally. Plans in small group or nongroup markets must follow these rules whether or not they are offered in an exchange. On the other hand, the ACA included two significant exceptions to these reforms. First, insurance plans that were in existence when the ACA was signed into law are referred to as "grandfathered plans" and are subject to some, but not all, of the new rules. The grandfathered plans must follow new requirements relating to preexisting conditions, lifetime and annual limits, waiting period limits, and dependent coverage rules. These plans are exempt, however, from having to provide essential health benefits, preventive services without copays, and limited cost sharing, although many of the large employer plans already have some of these features. A plan may retain its grandfathered status as long as it does not make significant changes to plan benefits or cost-sharing rules. If it loses its grandfathered status, the plan will have to meet all applicable requirements.

It is estimated that over the next several years, most people who obtain health insurance through a large employer will remain in a plan that is grandfathered under the ACA. Because small businesses are more likely to make significant changes to their health plans, it is estimated that only about one-third of these plans will remain grandfathered over the next several years. It is likely that most people in the individual health care market will receive care in an ACA-covered plan, not a grandfathered plan, sooner rather than later because these individuals switch plans frequently.[56]

The second major exception is for self-funded plans. These are plans where an employer does not buy insurance from a company but instead takes on the insurance risk itself. Self-funded plans are exempt from state law and subject to federal rules under ERISA (see Chapter 11 for more details on ERISA). Self-funded plans must adhere to ACA rules regarding dependent coverage, cost sharing for preventive services, annual and lifetime limits, and waiting period limits but do not need to comply with essential health benefit requirements.[57]

Financing Health Reform

Congress financed health reform primarily through Medicare and Medicaid savings, excise taxes and fees on the health care industry, changes to the income tax code, and a tax on some health insurance plans. (The provisions that alter Medicaid and Medicare are discussed in more detail in Chapter 10.) In addition, it is estimated that individuals ($17 billion) and employers ($52 billion) will pay $69 billion in penalties over a 10-year period for violating the insurance mandates.[58] Several of these financing changes were made as part of the deals the Obama administration struck with various stakeholders.

The ACA's main financing features are as follows:

- **Medicare provider reimbursement:** Reduces "market basket" or cost updates for inpatient and outpatient hospital reimbursement. Reduces payments for preventable hospital readmissions and hospital-acquired infections. Includes productivity adjustments for certain providers that will result in lower reimbursement rates. Estimated savings: $196 billion.
- **Medicare Advantage payments:** Reduces reimbursement rates and imposes cost-sharing limits for Medicare's managed care plans. Estimated savings: $136 billion.
- **Medicare Part A (Hospital Insurance):** Increases Medicare Part A tax rate for high-income earners. Estimated revenue: $210 billion.
- **Medicare premiums:** Reduces Medicare Part D (prescription drug) premium subsidy for high-income beneficiaries. Estimated savings: $36 billion.
- **Medicare employer subsidy:** Eliminates tax deduction for employers who receive a Medicare Part D (prescription drug coverage) subsidy. Estimated revenue: $4.5 billion.
- **Disproportionate share hospital (DSH) payments:** Reduces Medicare payments to DSH hospitals. Payments may increase over time based on percentage of uninsured served and uncompensated care provided. Reduces Medicaid DSH payments and requires DHHS to develop new funding formula. Estimated savings: $36 billion.
- **Medicaid prescription drugs:** Increases rebates drug manufacturers give to state Medicaid programs. Estimated savings: $38 billion.
- **Income tax code provisions:** Increases the threshold from 7.5% to 10% of adjusted gross income to claim deduction for unreimbursed medical expenses. Prohibits purchasing over-the-counter drugs with tax free savings accounts, increases tax burden on distributions not used for qualified medical expenses, and limits amount individuals may put in to accounts toward medical expenses. Estimated revenue: $29 billion.

- **Health industry fees:** Imposes a 10% tax on indoor tanning services, 2.3% tax on all taxable medical devices, annual fees on the pharmaceutical manufacturing sector, and fees on the health insurance sector. Estimated revenue: $107 billion.
- **Health insurance plans:** Imposes a tax on employer-sponsored health insurance plans with aggregate expenses that exceed $10,200 for individual coverage or $27,500 for family coverage. Estimated revenue: $32 billion.

Although it is the responsibility of the CBO to estimate the cost of legislation as it is written, time-bound cost estimates have their limitations. First, the CBO must assume that all the provisions in the bill will be implemented as written. With Republican gains in Congress in the 2010 midterm elections and the possibility of a new administration after the 2012 presidential election, it is not guaranteed that all these taxes, fees, and other features will remain in place. One of the

---

BOX 9-4 Discussion Questions

The ACA includes a tax on insurers for more generous health plans. Because it is likely insurers will pass on the cost of the tax to consumers, the idea behind the tax is to provide incentives for people to choose lower-cost plans. In theory, the less money employers spend on health care costs (and other fringe benefits), the more they will spend on wages. The income tax paid for by workers on their higher wages will provide revenue that can be used to pay for health reform. In addition, people may be less likely to obtain unnecessary care if fewer services are covered by their plan or if cost sharing is higher.

Is it likely that employers will trade lower benefits for higher wages? Are there times or industries where this trade-off is more or less likely to occur?

In 2010, the average cost of an employer plan was $5,079 for single coverage and $13,770 for family coverage. Beginning in 2018, plans that exceed $10,200 for individual coverage and $27,500 for family coverage are taxed. Congress rejected lower thresholds for the tax ($8,500/$23,000) that would have raised an estimated $149 billion. Did Congress pick the right thresholds for the tax? Should they be higher or lower?

Why did Congress delay implementation of the tax until 2018? What are the pros and cons to having the tax start well after the main provisions of health reform are in place?

most unpopular cost-saving tools—a tax on more generous health insurance plans—is not slated to take effect until 2018. Second, because the 10-year estimate, by design, does not consider costs beyond the first decade, some expected costs are not included in the estimate. For example, the CBO concluded that the new Community Living Assistance Services Supports program to help the elderly remain in their homes will save $70 billion over 10 years. It is also expected, however, that the program will cost more than the premiums bring in after the first decade, meaning the program will add to the federal deficit in the long run if it is not altered. In response to congressional inquiries, the CBO also offered a "rough estimate" for the decade beginning in 2020 and found that the ACA would continue to provide a slight reduction in the federal deficit as compared to the pre-ACA law.[59] Third, cost estimates cannot account for provisions that are left out of a bill. For example, Congress has passed several annual "fixes" to the Medicare physician fee schedule formula to avoid significant reimbursement cuts to doctors. Even though this problem is expected to cost the federal government billions of dollars over the next decade, the health reform bill did not include the cost of a permanent fix to the formula. For these reasons, cost estimates should not be taken as the final word on the cost of any bill, as changes in political will can undermine the best projections.

Public Health, Workforce, Prevention, and Quality

The ACA also includes a variety of programs and pilot projects that focus on improving quality of care and increasing access to preventive care. (The provisions related to Medicaid or Medicare are discussed in Chapter 10.) These provisions show both a commitment to these issues and the limitations of that commitment. Although task forces and pilot programs can be useful tools to try new ideas and gather data to inform future changes, their temporary nature can also mean that progress ends once the experiment is over especially in tight budget times. Whether these steps lead to lasting reform and needed change in the delivery of health care and in public health practice remains to be seen.

The ACA's quality improvement efforts are highlighted by the new National Quality Improvement Strategy and the new comparative effectiveness institute. The priorities of the National Quality Improvement Strategy include improving delivery of health care services, patient outcomes, and population health. A process will be created to develop quality measures, and a community-based collaborative care network will be established to integrate and coordinate services for low-income and uninsured populations. The new comparative effectiveness institute, the Patient Centered Outcomes Research Institute, is designed to consider the clinical effectiveness of medical treatments. The idea behind comparative effectiveness is to determine which procedures, devices, and pharmaceuticals provide the best value for a given outcome. The institute is designed to provide information to help others make decisions, but Congress stipulated that findings from the institute may not be construed as mandates or recommendations for payment, coverage, or treatment decisions.

The health reform law also provides funds to promote public health, wellness, and a stable and high-quality health care workforce. The ACA calls for the creation of a national prevention, health promotion, and public health council to develop a national strategy to improve the nation's health. A new regular corps and ready reserve corps will be established to assist when public health emergencies occur. In addition, a variety of programs and incentives are in place to promote employer wellness programs. Finally, the workforce shortage is addressed through graduate medical education reforms that promote primary care training, increases in scholarships and

BOX 9-5 Discussion Questions

As of 2009, the U.S. Preventive Services Task Force no longer recommends routine screening mammograms for women ages 40 to 49, although they said the decision should be made by the patient and her physician. The U.S. Preventive Services Task Force found that physicians would need to screen 1,000 women to save 1 woman's life and concluded that it was not worth the risks associated with false positives (anxiety, unnecessary biopsies, overtreatment). Others, such as the American Cancer Society, disagree with the U.S. Preventive Services Task Force and conclude that the lifesaving effects of routine mammogram screening outweigh the potential harm.

The idea of comparative effectiveness research is to provide information about the value of different tools. Once that information is available, who should make the decisions about whether to provide coverage and reimbursement for a particular good or service? Can one objectively assess the risks and benefits associated with mammograms or other services or medications? Should decisions be made solely by the patient and treating provider? Does it matter if decisions affect taxpayers (for example, if a patient is covered by a government program such as Medicare or the Veterans Administration)?

FIGURE 9-1

Timeline for Health Reform Implementation: Overview

Reform will unfold incrementally. Although some major elements of reform begin in 2010, others will be implemented over the course of several years.

In 2014, the most substantial changes—including shared responsibility for coverage, expansion of Medicaid, insurance exchanges, and creation of an essential benefits package—will take effect.

Early retirees: A temporary reinsurance program will help offset the costs of expensive premiums for employers providing retiree health benefits.

Access to care: Funding will be increased by $11 billion over five years for community health centers and the National Health Services Corps to serve more low-income and uninsured people.

Small-business tax credits: Small businesses (25 or fewer employees and average wages under $50,000) that offer health care benefits will be eligible for tax credits of up to 35 percent of their premium costs for two years.

Coverage for young adults: Parents will be able to keep their children on their health policies until they turn 26.

"Doughnut hole" rebates: Medicare will provide $250 rebates to beneficiaries who hit the Part D prescription drug coverage gap known as the "doughnut hole."

Benefit disclosure: Employers will be required to disclose the value of benefits provided for each employee's health insurance coverage on the employee's W-2 forms.

New payment and delivery approaches: A new Center fo Medicare and Medicaid Innovation will test reforms tha reward providers for quality of care rather than volume o services. Medicare will increase payment for primary car physicians by 10 percent for primary care services.

CLASS Act: A national, voluntary insurance program fo purchasing community living assistance services and support (CLASS) will be established. All working adult: will automatically enrolled—unless they opt out—thougl payroll deductions that, after five years, will qualify them for monthly payments toward services to help then stay at home should they become disabled.

2010 → **2011** →

High-risk pool: People with preexisting conditions who have been uninsured for at least six months will have access to affordable insurance through a temporary, subsidized high-risk pool. Premiums will be based on the average heath status of a standard population. Annual out-of-pocket costs will be capped at $5,950 for individuals and $11,900 for families.

Protection for children: Insurers can no longer deny health coverage to children with preexisting conditions or exclude their conditions from coverage.

Preventive care: All new group and individual health plans will be required to provide free preventive care for proven preventive services. In 2011, Medicare also will provide free preventive care.

Annual review of premium increases: Health insurers will be required to submit justification for unreasonable premium increases to the federal and relevant state governments before they take effect, and to report the share of premiums spent on nonmedical costs.

New insurance rules: Insurance companies will be banned from rescinding people's coverage when they get sick, and from imposing lifetime caps on coverage. Restrictions will be placed on annual limits.

Pharmaceutical manufacturer fee: An annual, nonde ductible fee will be imposed on pharmaceuticals and importers' branded drugs, based on market share.

OTC drug reimbursement restrictions: Over-the-counter drugs not prescribed by a doctor will no longer be reimbursable through flexible spending ac counts or health reimbursement arrangements, or o1 a tax-free basis in health savings accounts.

Physician quality reporting: Medicare will launch a Phy sician Compare Web site where beneficiaries can compar(measures of physician quality and patient experience.

"Doughnut hole" discounts: Medicare beneficiarie in the Part D prescription drug coverage "doughnut hole" will receive 50 percent discounts on all brand name drugs. By 2020, the "doughnut hole" coverag(gap will be closed.

Premium share spending: Health plans in the large-group market that spend less than 85 percent of their premiums on medical care, and plans in the small-grou| and individual markets that spend less than 80 percen on medical care, will be required to offer rebates to enrollees.

Source: Courtesy of the Commonwealth Fund.

Administrative simpli-fication: Health insurers must follow adminis-trative simplification standards for electronic exchange of health information to reduce paperwork and adminis-trative costs.

Medicare value-based purchasing: Medicare will reward hospitals that provide higher quality or better patient outcomes.

Flexible spending limits: Contributions to flexible spending accounts (FSAs) will be limited to $2,500 a year, indexed to the Consumer Price Index (CPI).

Shared responsibility for coverage: Individuals will be required to carry health insurance, and employ-ers with 50 or more workers will be required to offer health benefits or be subject to a fine of $2,000 per employee (not counting the first 30 employees) if any worker receives governmental assistance with premiums through the insurance exchanges.

Insurance industry fee: Insurers will pay an annual fee, based on market share, to help pay for reform.

New rules for insurers: In-surers will be banned from restricting coverage or basing premiums on health status. Annual, in addition to lifetime, limits on ben-efits are banned.

Premium subsidies: Premium and cost-sharing assistance on a sliding scale will make coverage af-fordable for families with annual incomes between $30,000 and $88,000 that buy plans through the exchanges.

Medicare managed care plans: Four- and five-star Medicare private plans will receive 5 per-cent bonuses as a reward for providing better clinical quality and patient experiences.

High-cost insurance plans: Insurers will face a 40 percent excise tax on policies with premi-ums over $10,2000 for individuals or $27,500 for family coverage.

2012   2013   2014   2018

Insurance exchanges: New state-based market-places will offer small businesses and people with-out employer coverage a choice of affordable health plans that meet new essentials benefit standards.

Essential benefits package: The Department of Health and Human Services will establish an essential standard benefits package for poli-cies sold in the exchanges and individual and small-group markets with a choice among tiers of plans (bronze, silver, gold, and platinum) that have different levels of cost-sharing.

Independent payment advisory board: A new independent payment advisory board within the executive branch will work to identify areas of waste and federal budget savings in Medicare. The board's recommendations must not ration care, raise taxes, or change Medicare benefits, eligibil-ity, or cost-sharing.

Medicaid expansion: Medicaid eligibility will be expanded to all legal residents with incomes up to 133 percent of the federal poverty level. Currently, states have different—an in many cases very low—eligibility thresholds, and most states do not cover adults without children.

Source: Courtesy of the Commonwealth Fund.

loans to support primary care providers and workforce diversity, and education, training, and loan repayment programs to address the primary care nursing shortage.

States and Health Reform

Before the ACA and in the wake of numerous failed attempts at national health reform, states had been an active player in health reform. Filling the gap left by the lack of federal action, states took steps to experiment with individual mandates, employer mandates, small business pools, and programs to reduce the number of uninsured. Although the ACA is a federal law, it is full of state obligations and opportunities for state innovation. Even though governors in many states have expressed opposition to health reform, it is likely that states will expend significant efforts toward implementing the ACA over the next several years. The reform implementation challenges facing the states are compounded by the poor economy, which has forced many states to cut government agency personnel and budgets. States will have their hands full developing and running health insurance exchanges, regulating the private health insurance market, and implementing Medicaid changes.

CONCLUSION

After decades of trying and against the predictions of numerous experts, the United States passed a national health reform law that provides near-universal coverage, includes protections for individuals who have been historically excluded from the insurance market, and shows a concern for improving health care quality and access to preventive care. From a philosophical perspective, the ACA moves America toward a society where (almost) everyone is expected to have insurance. In this way, health insurance is considered both an obligation and a right: individuals are required to obtain insurance, and the government is obligated to make it affordable and accessible.

Yet, this is not the end of the story. The ACA remains a controversial bill with almost half of those polled expressing opposition to it, a number of states pursuing legal challenges to the bill, and newly elected Republicans pushing to repeal it. Implementation challenges will be great, from the need for numerous regulations to be created on the federal and state level in a short amount of time, to the ability of the states' health care delivery systems to handle an influx of newly insured individuals, to the ability of the American people to understand their new responsibilities and rights. As complex as the ACA is, gaps remain. Not everyone will be insured under the new system. The law's cost-containment and health care delivery reform measures are often in the form of temporary programs whose future is unknown. Questions remain whether the subsidies are enough to make insurance affordable for all and whether Congress will implement the unpopular financing measures needed to fund the law when they take effect several years down the line. Although the ACA is a significant step in reforming the U.S. health care system, it is not the last step that needs to be taken.

REFERENCES

1. U.S. Bureau of the Census. *Income, Poverty, and Health Insurance Coverage in the United States: 2009.* Washington, D.C.: Bureau of the United States Census; 2010.

2. Kaiser Family Foundation. *The Uninsured: A Primer—Key Facts About Americans Without Health Insurance.* 2010. Available at: http://www .kff.org/uninsured/upload/7451-06.pdf. Accessed January 6, 2011.

3. Goldstein A. Health-care spending rose less in 2009. *Washington Post.* January 6, 2011: A15.

4. Pub. L. No. 111-148, the Patient Protection and Affordable Care Act.

5. Gordon C. *Dead on Arrival: The Politics of Health Care in Twentieth-Century America.* Princeton, N.J.: Princeton University Press; 2003.

6. Blake CH, Adolino JR. The enactment of national health insurance: A boolean analysis of twenty advanced industrial countries. *J Health Politics Policy Law.* 2001;26:670–708.

7. Jost TS. Why can't we do what they do? National health reform abroad. *J Law Med Ethics.* 2004;32:433–441.

8. Newport F. US still split on whether gov't should ensure health care. Gallup. Nov. 18, 2010. Available at: http://www.gallup.com/poll/144839/ Split-Whether-Gov-Ensure-Healthcare.aspx. Accessed January 6, 2011.

9. National Conference of State Legislatures. *NCSL Fiscal Brief: State Balanced Budget Provisions.* Washington, DC; 2010. Available at http:// www.ncsl.org/documents/fiscal/StateBalancedBudgetProvisions2010.pdf. Accessed January 7, 2011.

10. Kaiser Family Foundation. *Kaiser Health Tracking Poll: August 2009.* Available at: http://www.kff.org/kaiserpolls/upload/7965.pdf. Accessed January 6, 2011.

11. Kaiser Family Foundation. *Kaiser Health Tracking Poll: Election 2008.* Available at: http://www.kff.org/kaiserpolls/upload/7832.pdf. Accessed January 6, 2011.

12. Weissert CS, Weissert WG. *Governing Health: The Politics of Health Policy,* 2nd ed. Baltimore: Johns Hopkins University Press; 2002.

13. Friedman J, Holden R. The gerrymandering myth. *The New Republic Online;* 2006. Available at: https://ssl.tnr.com/p/docsub.mhtml?i= w060529&s= friedmanholden060106. Accessed on October 25, 2006.

14. West DM, Heith D, Goodwin C. Harry and Louise go to Washington: Political advertising and health care reform. *J Health Politics Policy Law.* 1996;21:35–68.

15. Feder J. Crowd-out and the politics of health reform. *J Law Med Ethics.* 2004;32:461–464.

16. Kaiser Family Foundation. *Kaiser Health Tracking Poll: November 2009.* Available at: http://www.kff.org/kaiserpolls/upload/8019.pdf. Accessed January 6, 2011.

17. Starr P. *The Social Transformation of American Medicine: The Rise of a Sovereign Profession and the Making of a Vast Industry.* New York: Basic Books; 1982.

18. Federal Election Commission. *2000 Presidential Popular Vote Summary for All Candidates Listed on at Least One State Ballot.* 2000. Available at: http://www.fec.gov/pubrec/fe2000/prespop.htm. Accessed on October 29, 2010; CNN. *Election results—US president.* 2010. Available at: http:// www.cnn.com/ELECTION/2004/pages/results/president/. Accessed October 29, 2010.

19. CNN. *Election Center 2008*. 2008. Available at: http://www.cnn.com/ELECTION/2008/results/president/. Accessed October 29, 2010.

20. Pub. L. No. 110–343.

21. Pub. L. No. 111-5.

22. Recovery.gov. *The Recovery Act*. Available at: http://www.recovery.gov/About/Pages/The_Act.aspx. Accessed October 29, 2010.

23. Jones JM. Economy top issue for voters; size of government may be more pivotal. Gallup. October 26, 2010. Available at: http://www.gallup.com/poll/144029/Economy-Top-Issue-Voters-Size-Gov-May-Pivotal.aspx. Accessed October 29, 2010.

24. Blendon RJ, Altman DE, Benson JM, et al. Voters and health reform in the 2008 presidential election. *New Engl J of Med*. 2008;359(19):2050–2061.

25. CNN. Obama talks about mother's cancer battle in ad. September 21, 2007. Available at: http://politicalticker.blogs.cnn.com/2007/09/21/obama-talks-about-mothers-cancer-battle-in-ad/. Accessed November 2, 2010.

26. Appleby J. Health reform up in the air as the economy sinks. *USA Today*. December 20, 2008. Available at: http://www.usatoday.com/news/health/2008-12-18-health_N.htm. Accessed November 2, 2010.

27. Pear R. Senator takes initiative on health reform. *New York Times*. November 11, 2008. Available at: http://www.nytimes.com/2008/11/12/washington/12health.html. Accessed November 2, 2010.

28. Obama's health care speech to Congress. *New York Times*. September 9, 2009. Available at: http://www.nytimes.com/2009/09/10/us/politics/10obama.text.html. Accessed November 2, 2010.

29. Kaiser Family Foundation. *Kaiser Health Tracking Poll: September 2009*. Available at: http://www.kff.org/kaiserpolls/upload/7990.pdf. Accessed November 2, 2010.

30. Cohen J, Balz D. Opposition to Obama's health care plan is high, but easing. *Washington Post*. September 14, 2009. Available at: http://www.washingtonpost.com/wp-dyn/content/article/2009/09/13/AR2009091302962.html. Accessed November 2, 2010.

31. Condon S. Scott Brown win shakes up health care fight. *CBS News*. January 20, 2010. Available at: http://www.cbsnews.com/8301-503544_162-6119035-503544.html. Accessed November 2, 2010.

32. Brown CB, O'Connor P. The fallout: Democrats rethinking health care bill. *Politico*. January 21, 2010. Available at: http://www.politico.com/news/stories/0110/31693.html. Accessed November 2, 2010.

33. State of the Union: President Obama's speech. *ABC News*. January 27, 2010. Available at: http://abcnews.go.com/Politics/State_of_the_Union/state-of-the-union-2010-president-obama-speech-transcript/story?id=9678572&page=1. Accessed November 2, 2010.

34. Saad L. Obama and Bush: A contrast in popularity. *Gallup*. November 10, 2008. Available at: http://www.gallup.com/poll/111838/obama-bush-contrast-popularity.aspx. Accessed November 4, 2010.

35. Blumenthal D, Morone JA. *The Heart of Power: Health and Politics in the Oval Office*. Berkeley: University of California Press; 2009.

36. Morone J. Presidents and health reform: From Franklin D. Roosevelt to Barack Obama. *Health Affairs*. 2010; 29(6):1096–1100.

37. Oberlander J. Long time coming: Why health reform finally passed. *Health Affairs*. 2010;29(6):1112–1116.

38. Text of a letter from the president to Senator Edward M. Kennedy and Senator Max Baucus. Washington, DC: The White House Office of the Press Secretary; June 2, 2009. Available at: http://www.whitehouse.gov/the_press_office/Letter-from-President-Obama-to-Chairmen-Edward-M-Kennedy-and-Max-Baucus. Accessed November 5, 2010.

39. Affordable Health Care for America Act, H.R. 3962.

40. Patient Protection and Affordable Care Act, H.R. 3590.

41. Murray S, Kane P. House won't pass Senate bill to save health care reform. *Washington Post*. January 22, 2010. Available at: http://www.washingtonpost.com/wp-dyn/content/article/2010/01/21/AR2010012101604.html?sid=ST2010012005092. Accessed November 5, 2010.

42. Murray S, Montgomery L. House passes health care reform bill without Republican votes. *Washington Post*. March 22, 2010. Available at: http://www.washingtonpost.com/wp-dyn/content/article/2010/03/21/AR2010032100943.html?sid=ST2010032201830. Accessed November 5, 2010.

43. Congressional Budget Office. *Cost Estimate for H.R. 4872, Reconciliation Act of 2010*. Washington, DC: Congressional Budget Office; 2010. Available at: http://www.cbo.gov/ftpdocs/113xx/doc11379/AmendReconProp.pdf. Accessed December 23, 2010.

44. Health Affairs. *Health Policy Brief—Individual Mandate*. Washington, DC: Project Hope; 2010. Available at: http://www.healthaffairs.org/healthpolicybriefs/brief.php?brief_id=14. Accessed December 22, 2010.

45. United States Const. Art. 1, §8.

46. *Heart of Atlanta Motel, Inc. v. United States*, 379 U.S. 241 (1964); *Wickard v. Filburn*, 317 U.S. 111 (1942); *Gonzalez v. Raich*, 545 U.S. (2005).

47. Jost TS. State lawsuits won't succeed in overturning the individual mandate. *Health Affairs*. 2010; 29(6):1225–1228.

48. Shapiro I. State suits against health reform are well grounded in law—and pose serious challenges. *Health Affairs*. 2010;29(6):1229–1233.

49. Kaiser Family Foundation. *Explaining Health Care Reform: Questions About State Health Insurance Exchanges*. 2010. Available at: http://www.kff.org/healthreform/upload/7908-02.pdf. Accessed December 23, 2010.

50. Rosenbaum S, Teitelbaum J, Hayes K. The essential health benefit provisions of the Affordable Care Act: Implications for people with disabilities. *Commonwealth Fund*. Pub. 1485, Vol. 3. Available at: http://www.commonwealthfund.org/~/media/Files/Publications/Issue%20Brief/2011/Mar/1485_Rosenbaum_essential_hlt_benefits_provisions_ACA_disabilities_reform_brief_v2.pdf. Accessed June 24, 2011.

51. Rosenbaum S, Teitelbaum J, Hayes K. Crossing the Rubicon: The impact of the Affordable Care Act on the content of insurance coverage for persons with disabilities. *Notre Dame J of Law, Ethics, and Public Policy*. 2011; 25(2):527–562.

52. Center for Medicare and Medicaid Services. *2010 Federal Poverty Guidelines*. Washington, DC: Center for Medicare and Medicaid Services; 2010. Available at: https://www.cms.gov/MedicaidEligibility/downloads/POV10Combo.pdf. Accessed December 23, 2010.

53. Kaiser Family Foundation. *Explaining Health Reform: Questions About Health Insurance Subsidies*. Available at: http://www.kff.org/healthreform/upload/7962-02.pdf. Accessed December 23, 2010.

54. Proposed Rule for Rate Increase Disclosure and Review, 75 *Federal Register* 81004 (2010).

55. Interim Final Rule, Health Insurance Issuers Implementing Medical Loss Ratio Requirements Under the Patient Protection and Affordable Care Act, 75 *Federal Register* 74864 (2010).

56. HealthReform.gov. *Fact Sheet: Keeping the Health Plan You Have: The Affordable Care Act and "Grandfathered" Plans*. Available at: http://www.healthreform.gov/newsroom/keeping_the_health_plan_you_have.html. Accessed January 3, 2011.

57. Kaiser Family Foundation. *Health Reform Resource. FAQ—How Does the New Law Apply to Companies with Self-Funded Plans*. Menlo, CA: Kaiser Family Foundation. Available at: http://healthreform.kff.org/faq/how-does-new-law-apply-to-companies-with-self-funded-plans.aspx. Accessed January 3, 2011.

58. Water PN. *How Health Reform Helps Reduce the Deficit*. Washington, DC: Center for Budget and Policy Priorities; 2010. Available at: http://www.cbpp.org/cms/index.cfm?fa=view&id=3178. Accessed January 4, 2011.

59. Congressional Budget Office. *Cost Estimate for H.R. 4872, Reconciliation Act of 2010*. Washington, DC: Congressional Budget Office; 2010. Available at: http://www.cbo.gov/ftpdocs/113xx/doc11379/AmendReconProp.pdf. Accessed December 23, 2010.

ENDNOTES

a. 88 Stat. 832.

b. ERISA § 514, 29 USC. § 1144.

CHAPTER 10

Government Health Insurance Programs: Medicaid, CHIP, and Medicare

LEARNING OBJECTIVES

By the end of this chapter, you will be able to:

- Describe the basic structure, administration, financing, and eligibility rules for:
  - Medicaid
  - State Children's Health Insurance Program (CHIP)
  - Medicare
- Understand how the Patient Protection and Affordable Care Act alters Medicaid, CHIP, and Medicare
- Discuss key health policy questions and themes relating to each of these public programs

INTRODUCTION

Elsewhere, the significant role of employer-sponsored health insurance in financing health care, the flexibility that private insurers have in designing health insurance coverage and selecting who they will cover, why private insurers do not have incentive to cover high-risk populations, and how the Patient Protection and Affordable Care Act (ACA) has changed the health insurance and healthcare delivery landscape have been discussed in detail. Medicaid, the State Children's Health Insurance Program (CHIP), and Medicare were established in part because the private health insurance market was not developing affordable, comprehensive health insurance products for society's low-income, elderly, and disabled populations. Federal and state governments chose to fill some of those gaps through Medicaid, CHIP, and Medicare. The gaps were substantial, as shown by the over 100 million beneficiaries served by these three programs today.[1] Due to the needs of vulnerable populations and the requirements necessary to make health

insurance coverage for them viable, these programs are quite different from standard private health insurance plans.

There are numerous other important health insurance and direct service programs funded by federal, state, and local governments. Just a few examples include the Ryan White Care Act, which provides HIV/AIDS services to infected individuals and their families; the Women, Infants and Children Supplemental Nutrition Program, which provides nutritional

BOX 10-1 Vignette

Governor Manha is in a quandary. She believes everyone should have access to health care and would like to support state policies that make care accessible and affordable. While she supported President Obama's goal of reducing the number of uninsured, she is concerned that some of the provisions in the Patient Protection and Affordable Care Act are too burdensome on the states, particularly in a fragile economy. The Governor wonders how her state can afford the mandated Medicaid expansion when the recent trend has been to cut services across the board. How will state agencies cope with their new responsibilities when positions are being defunded and employees are being furloughed? Should she spend her state's time and resources to establish a health insurance exchange when the federal government will step in if she does not act? At the same time, does she want to leave decisions about how the exchange will be operated in her state to bureaucrats in Washington, D.C.?

supplements and education to poor women and their children; and the Indian Health Service, which provides federal health services to American Indians and Alaska Natives. Although these and many other health programs are vital to the health of our population, this chapter focuses only on the three major government health insurance programs in this country, because in addition to providing health insurance to millions, these programs are also influential in terms of setting healthcare policy. For example, when Medicare, a program serving over 47 million people, makes a decision to cover a certain treatment, private insurance companies often follow suit, establishing a new standard for generally accepted practice in the insurance industry.[2] Conversely, states may decide to try healthcare innovations with their Medicaid programs that, if successful, may become commonplace across the country. Thus, understanding these three major programs is essential in terms of both how this country finances and delivers health care and how it makes health policy decisions.

The ACA made wide-ranging changes to Medicaid, CHIP, and Medicare. In general, the ACA included a significant Medicaid eligibility expansion, altered which children are eligible for Medicaid and CHIP, added new benefits to Medicare, and included a host of changes intended to produce savings in the Medicare program. Since many of these provisions do not take place until 2014, this chapter describes these programs as they currently exist and highlights how the new health reform law will change them.

As you learn about specific rules for each program, keep in mind the numerous tensions that are present throughout the healthcare system as policymakers decide how to design and implement public insurance programs. This chapter touches on several recurring themes relating to these tensions, which were evident during the debate that led to passage of the ACA: choosing between state flexibility and national uniformity; determining the appropriate role for government, the private sector, and individuals in healthcare financing and delivery; defining a primary decision-making goal (fiscal restraint, equity/social justice, improved health outcomes, uniformity, etc.); and settling on the appropriate scope of coverage to offer beneficiaries.

Before delving into the details of each program, it is necessary to explain the difference between entitlement and block grant programs. Medicaid and Medicare are *entitlement* programs, whereas CHIP is a *block grant* program. Some of the themes listed earlier, such as the appropriate role of government and primary decision-making goals, are implicated in the decision of whether to establish a program as an entitlement or a block grant.

In an *entitlement* program, everyone who is eligible for and enrolled in the program is legally entitled to receive benefits from the program. In other words, the federal or state governments cannot refuse to provide program beneficiaries all medically necessary and covered services due to lack of funds or for other reasons. Because everyone who is enrolled has a legal right to receive services, there cannot be a cap on spending. The absence of a spending cap has the advantage of allowing funds to be available to meet rising healthcare costs and unexpected needs, such as increased enrollment and use of services during recessions or natural or man-made disasters.

Opponents of entitlement programs focus on the open-ended budget obligation entitlements create. With healthcare costs straining federal and state budgets, critics would prefer to establish a cap on the funds spent on entitlement programs such as Medicaid. It is impossible to determine how many people will enroll in the program or how many and what kind of healthcare services they will use in any given year, so governments cannot establish exact budgets for their Medicaid program. In addition to these fiscal objections, many opponents reject the notion that government should play a large role in providing health insurance, preferring to leave that function to the private market.

Entitlement programs are often contrasted with *block grant* programs such as CHIP. A block grant is a defined sum of money that is allocated for a particular program (often, but not always, from the federal government to the states) over a certain amount of time. If program costs exceed available funds, additional money will not be made available and program changes have to be made. Such changes could include

BOX 10-2 Discussion Questions

Do you think it makes more sense to structure government healthcare programs as entitlements or block grants? What are the economic and healthcare risks and benefits of each approach? Does your answer depend on who is paying for the program? Who the program serves? What kinds of benefits the program provides? Do you think various stakeholders would answer these questions differently? How might the answers change if you ask a member of the federal government, a governor, a state legislator, an advocate, or a tax-paying citizen who is not eligible for benefits under the program?

terminating the program, capping enrollment in the program, reducing program benefits, or finding additional resources. Unlike entitlement programs, individuals who qualify for block grant programs may be denied services or receive reduced services due to lack of funds.

The arguments for and against block grant programs are similar to those found with entitlement programs. Proponents of block grant programs laud the limited and certain fiscal obligation and reduced role of government in providing health insurance. Opponents of block grant programs object to the lack of legal entitlement to services and the finite amount of funds available to provide health insurance.

MEDICAID

Medicaid is the country's federal–state public health insurance program for the indigent. In this section, we discuss fundamental aspects of the Medicaid program, including its structure, eligibility, benefits, and financing, as well as changes to Medicaid made by the ACA. Unlike private health insurance plans, which are based on actuarial risk, the Medicaid program is designed to ensure that funds are available to provide healthcare services to a poorer and generally less-healthy group of beneficiaries; in order to do so, Medicaid has several features not found in private health insurance plans.

Program Administration

Medicaid is jointly designed and operated by the federal and state governments. The Centers for Medicare and Medicaid Services is the federal agency in charge of administering the Medicaid program. Each state, the District of Columbia, and certain U.S. Territories,[a] as defined in the statute,[3] have the option to participate in the Medicaid program, and all have chosen to do so. The federal government sets certain requirements and policies for the Medicaid program though statute,[4] regulations,[5] a *State Medicaid Manual*,[6] and policy guidance such as letters to state Medicaid directors.[7] Each state has its own Medicaid agency that is responsible for implementing the program in the state. States file a Medicaid State Plan with the federal government outlining the state's own eligibility rules, benefits, and other program requirements; this plan is effectively a contract between states and the federal government and between states and program beneficiaries.

The federal and state governments jointly set rules concerning who is covered and which services are provided by Medicaid. The federal government outlines which populations must be covered (*mandatory populations*) and which ones may be covered (*optional populations*), as well as which benefits must be covered (*mandatory benefits*) and which ones may be

BOX 10-3 Discussion Questions

What are the benefits and drawbacks of having a health program that varies by state versus having one that is uniform across the country? Do you find that the positives of state flexibility outweigh the negatives, or vice versa? Does your analysis change depending on what populations are served? Does your analysis change depending on whose point of view you consider? Is it fair that similarly situated individuals may be treated differently in different states? Does this occur in other aspects of society?

covered (*optional benefits*). Between these floors and ceilings, states have significant flexibility to determine how Medicaid will operate in their particular state. In general, states must cover mandatory populations and benefits, and they may choose to cover any combination of optional populations or benefits, including the choice not to offer any optional coverage at all. In addition, states may seek a waiver from federal rules, allowing states to experiment with coverage and benefit design while still drawing down federal funds to operate their program. Given all of these possible permutations, it is often said that "if you have seen one Medicaid program, you have seen one Medicaid program"; in other words, within the broad federal parameters, every state (and territory) has a unique Medicaid structure—no two programs are exactly alike. As a result, similarly situated individuals in different states may have very different experiences in terms of the generosity of benefits they are entitled to or even if they are eligible for the program at all.

Eligibility

Traditionally, Medicaid has covered low-income pregnant women, children, adults in families with dependent children, individuals with disabilities, and the elderly. About one-half of all Medicaid beneficiaries are children, while adults account for another 25% of enrollees and the disabled and elderly make up the remaining one-quarter.[8] Approximately 9 million people are called *dual enrollee* or *dual eligible* elderly, meaning they qualify for both Medicaid and Medicare.[9] Although most dual enrollees are eligible for full Medicaid benefits, a small portion of them receives only premium and/or cost-sharing assistance to help them pay for Medicare, not full Medicaid benefits.

FIGURE 10-1 Medicaid Beneficiaries by Race/Ethnicity, 2009.

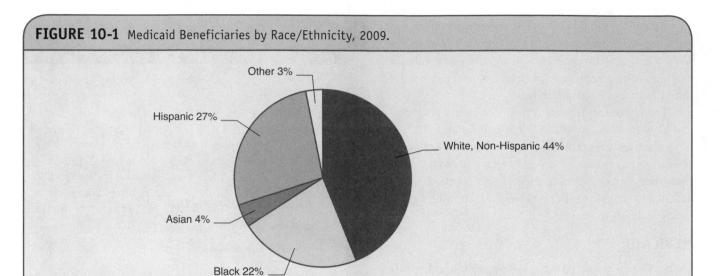

Source: U.S. Bureau of the Census. *Income, Poverty, and Health Insurance Coverage in the United States: 2009.* Washington, DC: Economics and Statistics Administration. Bureau of the U.S. Census: 2010; 72–75.

FIGURE 10-2 Medicaid Enrollees are Sicker and More Disabled than the Privately Insured.

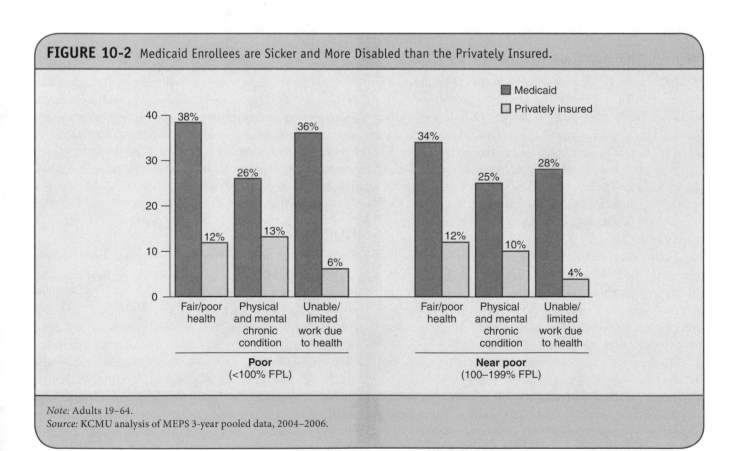

Note: Adults 19–64.
Source: KCMU analysis of MEPS 3-year pooled data, 2004–2006.

BOX 10-4 Federal Poverty Level

Federal poverty guidelines are determined annually and calculated based on the number of individuals in a family. The guidelines are commonly referred to as the Federal Poverty Level (FPL), but U.S. Department of Health and Human Services (HHS) discourages the use of this term because the Census Bureau also calculates, using different methods, a figure referred to as the federal poverty thresholds. However, because the term Federal Poverty Level is still commonly used when discussing eligibility for federal and state programs, we use it here. The poverty guidelines are somewhat higher for Alaska and Hawaii due to administrative procedures adopted by the Office of Economic Opportunity.

Among all people with health insurance, members of ethnic or minority groups are more likely than Caucasians to have coverage through Medicaid. As shown in Figure 10-1, however, Medicaid beneficiaries are split almost evenly between white, non-Hispanic beneficiaries and beneficiaries who are members of ethnic or minority groups. Figure 10-2 indicates that overall, Medicaid beneficiaries are more likely to be in poorer health than privately insured individuals.

Overall, 89% of nonelderly Medicaid enrollees are either poor (meaning they earn less than 100% of the Federal Poverty Level [FPL]) or near-poor (meaning they earn between 100% and 250% of the FPL).[10] Yet, not all low-income individuals have been covered by the program, and over 28 million low-income Americans remain uninsured.[11] Traditionally left out of the program have been low-income adults without disabilities, women who are not pregnant, and the near-poor who earn too much money to qualify for Medicaid. However, the ACA included a significant eligibility expansion that is expected to add 16 million individuals to the program by 2019.[12] As discussed below in more detail, the expansion is designed to include the low-income groups that have been traditionally excluded from Medicaid.

Eligibility Requirements

Under current Medicaid rules, everyone must meet *all five* of the following requirements in order to be eligible:

1. Categorical: An individual must fit within a category (e.g., pregnant women) covered by the program.
2. Income: An individual/family must earn no more than the relevant income limits, which are expressed as an FPL percentage (e.g., 133% of the FPL).
3. Resources: An individual/family must not have nonwage assets (e.g., car, household goods) that exceed eligibility limits.
4. Residency: An individual must be a U.S. resident and a resident of the state in which they are seeking benefits.
5. Immigration status: Immigrants must meet certain requirements, including having been in the country for at least five years (for most immigrants).

As shown in Table 10-1, under current rules it is necessary to consider both categorical eligibility and income limits for all populations to understand who is covered by Medicaid and which populations are mandatory and which are optional. The groups in Table 10-1 represent some of the larger and more frequently mentioned categories of Medicaid beneficiaries, but it is not an exhaustive list. There are approximately 50 categories of mandatory and optional populations in the Medicaid program, with each state picking and choosing which optional populations to include and at what income level.

Medically Needy

Medicaid's *medically needy* category is an option that has been picked up by 32 states and the District of Columbia as of 2009.[13] As its name implies, this category is intended to cover individuals who have extremely high medical expenses. These individuals fit within a covered category, but earn too much money to be otherwise eligible for Medicaid. Medically needy programs have both income and asset requirements. In terms of income requirements, states subtract the costs of individuals' medical expenses from their income level. States have the choice of deducting the medical expenses as they are incurred each month, every six months, or any time in between. As soon as otherwise qualified individuals "spend down" enough money on medical expenses, they are eligible for Medicaid through the medically needy option based on their reduced income level for the remainder of the period.

The following is a simplified example of how the "spend down" process works. Let's say a state calculates incurred medical expenses every three months to determine eligibility for the medically needy option, and in this state an individual (who we'll call Peter) must earn no more than $8,500 a year to qualify as medically needy. Peter earns $11,000 per year and has $6,000 each year in medical expenses, incurred at a rate of $500 per month. After 3 months, Peter has spent $1,500 on medical expenses. Instead of considering the income level to be the annual amount earned ($11,000), the state subtracts Peter's medical expenses as they occur. So, after three months the state considers Peter to earn $9,500 annually ($11,000 − $1,500). Because this amount is still over the $8,500 limit,

TABLE 10-1 Select Medicaid Mandatory and Optional Eligibility Groups and Income Requirements Prior to ACA.

Eligibility Category	Mandatory Coverage	Optional Coverage
Infants under 1	≤133% FPL	≤185% FPL
Children 1–5	≤133% FPL	>133% FPL
Children 6–19	≤100% FPL	>100% FPL
Pregnant women	≤133% FPL	≤185% FPL
Parents	Below state's 1996 AFDCa limit	May use income level above state's 1996 AFDC limit
Parents in welfare-to-work families	≤185% FPL	
Elderly and disabled SSIb beneficiaries	SSI limits	Above SSI limits, below 100% FPL
Certain working disabled	May not exceed specified amount	Variable, SSI level to 250% FPL
Elderly—Medicare assistance onlyc	Variable, up to 175% FPL	Variable up to 175% FPL
Nursing Home Residents		Above SSI limits, below 300% SSI
Medically Needy		"Spend down" medical expenses to state set income level

AFDC = Aid to Families with Dependent Children.

SSI = Supplemental Security Income, a federal program that provides cash assistance to the aged, blind, and disabled who meet certain income and resource requirements.

Medicare Assistance only = payment for Medicare cost-sharing requirements.

Peter is not eligible under the medically needy option. In another three months, Peter will have spent $3,000 in medical expenses over the past 6 months. At that time, the state considers Peter to earn $8,000 annually ($11,000 – $3,000), making him eligible because he earns less than the $8,500 limit. For the rest of this period (i.e., three months), Peter is eligible for Medicaid. After another three months, the state recalculates his earnings and medical expenses. Each year, this entire calculation starts over. In the end, Peter will not be eligible for Medicaid for the first six months of the year, but will be eligible for Medicaid for the second six months of the year.

Immigrants

There are also special Medicaid eligibility rules relating to immigrants. The Personal Responsibility and Work Opportunity Reconciliation Act of 1996 (PRWORA) severely restricted immigrant eligibility for Medicaid (and most of the same rules in PRWORA were later applied to CHIP eligibility in 1997).[14] Prior to PRWORA, legal immigrants followed the same Medicaid eligibility rules as everyone else, but undocumented immigrants were not eligible at all. PRWORA instituted a five-year bar, meaning that most immigrants who come to

BOX 10-5 Discussion Questions

Does the medically needy category make sense to you? Do you think it is a good idea to discount medical expenses of high-need individuals so they can access the healthcare services they need through Medicaid? If so, is the process described above cumbersome and likely to result in people being on and off Medicaid (and therefore likely on and off treatment) because their eligibility is based on their spending patterns? Why should individuals with high medical needs have an avenue to Medicaid eligibility that is not available to other low-income people who have other high expenses, such as child care or transportation costs? Would it make more sense to simply raise the eligibility level for Medicaid so more low-income people are eligible for the program? Politically, which option would likely have more support? Does your view about the medically needy category vary depending on your primary decision-making goal (fiscal restraint, equity, improved health outcomes, etc.)?

the United States after August 22, 1996, are not eligible for Medicaid (or CHIP) for the first five years after their arrival. After five years, legal immigrants are eligible on the same basis as U.S. citizens, while undocumented immigrants remain ineligible for full Medicaid (or CHIP) benefits. However, both legal and undocumented immigrants who are otherwise eligible for Medicaid may receive emergency Medicaid benefits without any temporal restrictions. Immigrant eligibility eased slightly when CHIP was reauthorized in 2009.[15] States now have the option to cover legal immigrant children and/or pregnant women through Medicaid and CHIP in the first five years that they are in the United States.

Proponents of the immigrant restrictions believe they discourage people who cannot support themselves from coming to the United States and prevent immigrants from taking advantage of publicly funded programs they did not support through taxes before their arrival. In addition, some proponents believe that healthcare resources should go first to U.S. citizens, not non-citizens.

Opponents of the restrictions assert that most immigrants pay taxes once they arrive in this country and therefore deserve to receive the full benefits of those taxes.[16(p15)] They also find the restriction ill-suited as a deterrent because immigrants often come to the United States for economic opportunities, not social benefits.[17] Furthermore, restricting immigrants' access to health care may be a public health hazard for all members of the community because contagious diseases do not discriminate by immigration status. Finally, opponents contend that having higher numbers of uninsured individuals in the United States will further strain the ability of providers to care for all vulnerable populations in a community and lead to rising healthcare costs because uninsured immigrants are much less likely to obtain preventive care or early treatment for illnesses or injuries.[16(p15)] As a result, 27 states have decided to use state-only funds to provide Medicaid or CHIP services to some or all individuals who are otherwise ineligible due to their immigration status, and 20 states have implemented the new coverage option available after CHIP reauthorization.[18] Even so, immigrants are still less likely to be insured or have access to care than native citizens.

Medicaid Eligibility Expansion Under the Affordable Care Act

As mentioned earlier, the ACA significantly expanded Medicaid eligibility. Beginning in 2014, all non-Medicare-eligible individuals under age 65, with incomes up to 133% FPL,[b] will be eligible for Medicaid in every state. In addition, children ages 6–19 must be covered up to 133% FPL, instead of at 100% FPL as under current rules. Since 2010, states have had the option of covering low-income childless adults without a waiver. Undocumented immigrants, as well as legal immigrants who have resided in the United States for fewer than five years, will not be eligible for Medicaid under the expansion, although states have the option to cover legal immigrant pregnant women and children who have been in the country fewer than five years (matching the new rules put in place under CHIP).

The eligibility expansion for all non-Medicare-eligible individuals under 65 years of age with incomes up to 133% FPL marks a drastic departure from how Medicaid has generally been structured. Unlike Medicaid's traditional eligibility structure, newly eligible individuals only have to satisfy an income threshold and do not have to meet a resource test or fit within a pre-approved category. In addition, states usually have significant flexibility in determining how individual income and other personal resources are calculated. Under the ACA expansion, however, all states are required to accept newly eligible individuals using the federal income level calculation and without accounting for other assets. As discussed in more detail below, Medicaid has a generous benefit package that must be provided equally to all categorically eligible beneficiaries. While states may choose to offer a variety of benefits, they are only required to offer a benefit package that

BOX 10-6 Discussion Questions

Looking at Medicaid's traditional eligibility rules, you notice numerous value/policy judgments—pregnant women and children are favored over childless adults, the medically needy are favored over other low-income individuals with high costs, non-immigrants are favored over immigrants. Under the ACA expansion, these distinctions mostly disappear and eligibility depends purely on income level in the case of the biggest expansion group. Which approach do you prefer? If the ACA approach were expanded beyond 133% of FPL, the costs of the Medicaid program would soar. Given limited resources, do you think it would be better to cover more people at a higher poverty level across the board or continue to favor some groups over others through the categorical requirement? Should we decide that, for some populations, the government should step in and provide coverage regardless of the cost? In other words, is there a point where equity trumps financial constraints?

BOX 10-7 Discussion Questions

What are the implications of a two-tiered Medicaid system? Is there justification for offering some beneficiaries a less generous benefit package than others? Is it fair to impose additional requirements (categorical, asset test) on only some beneficiaries? Why do you think policymakers created these distinctions? Do you think they will remain in place over time?

is at least as generous as the essential health benefit package offered in the state exchanges. Finally, while Medicaid financing is usually based on a federal–state matching system, the federal government will cover the cost of almost all of the described expansions through 2019. Overall, the ACA expansion has created a two-tier Medicaid program, with newly eligible individuals falling under one set of eligibility, financing, and benefit rules, and the rest of Medicaid beneficiaries adhering to different standards.

Benefits

Medicaid benefits are structured in the same way as Medicaid eligibility—some are mandatory and some are optional, and the newly eligible individuals under the ACA expansion have their own set of rules. Again, this means that no two Medicaid programs are alike, as each state picks its own menu of optional benefits to provide.

Historically, Medicaid programs have offered a rich array of benefits, including preventive services, behavioral health services, long-term care services, supportive services that allow people with disabilities to work, institutional services, family planning services, and more. In fact, the coverage provided by Medicaid generally has been more generous than the typical private insurance plan, particularly in the case of children. While federal Medicaid regulations exclude very few services, there are prohibitions. Since 1977, Congress has prohibited the use of federal funds to pay for the costs of an abortion or Mifepristone (commonly known as RU-486), a drug that induces medical abortions. Also, drug addiction or alcohol dependency may not be used as reasons to qualify an individual as disabled under SSI (and therefore, under Medicaid), though if an individual is eligible for Medicaid for another reason, Medicaid programs may pay for substance abuse treatment.

All states provide the mandatory services listed on the left side of Table 10-2, and may provide the optional services listed on the right side. In addition to requiring a wide array of services, Medicaid also defines many service categories quite broadly. For example, under the category of medical or remedial services, a state may pay for diagnostic, screening, or preventive services provided in any settings that are recommended by a licensed practitioner "for the maximum reduction of physical or mental disability and restoration of an individual to the best possible functional level."[19]

One of the broadest service categories is the early and periodic screening, diagnosis, and treatment (EPSDT) package of services for beneficiaries under age 21. As the *E* in EPSDT indicates, this package of benefits provides preventive care to children to catch problems before they advance, and offers early treatment to promote healthy growth and development. EPSDT benefits include periodic and as-needed screening services, comprehensive health exams (to detect both physical and mental health conditions), immunizations, lab tests, health education, vision services, hearing services, dental services, *and* any other measure to "correct or ameliorate" physical or mental defects found during a screening, *whether or not those services are covered under a state plan*. In addition to these benefits, EPSDT also requires states to inform families about the importance of preventive care, seek out children in need of comprehensive care, and offer families assistance in securing care.

The "correct or ameliorate" standard is very different from the "medical necessity" standard that is used for adults in Medicaid and is commonly found in private health insurance plans. Typically, medically necessary services are those that restore "normal" function after an illness or injury. Not only does this standard generally preclude care before a diagnosis is made, but if recovery is not possible (for example, as a result of blindness), services that improve the quality of life or prevent deterioration of a condition may be denied. By contrast, the EPSDT correct or ameliorate standard means a state must provide coverage for preventive and developmental treatment, as well as for services needed to treat a specific diagnosis. Combined with the requirement to provide services regardless of state plan limitations, the correct or ameliorate standard means that almost any accepted treatment should be covered under EPSDT.

Although Medicaid benefits are quite generous, in 2006 Congress passed, and President Bush signed into law, the Deficit Reduction Act of 2005 (DRA),[20] which contains, among other things, state options for significant changes to Medicaid benefit and cost-sharing rules. As shown in Box 10-8, the DRA gives states the option to choose a "benchmark" or "benchmark-equivalent" package of services for certain population groups instead of following the mandatory and

TABLE 10-2 Medicaid Benefits (Non-Deficit Reduction Act Option)

Mandatory	Optional
Acute Care Benefits	*Acute Care Benefits*
Physician services	Prescription drugs
Laboratory and X-ray services	Medical care or remedial care furnished by non-physician
Inpatient hospital services	licensed practitioners
Outpatient hospital services	Rehabilitation and other therapies
Early and periodic screening, diagnostic, and treatment	Clinic services
services (EPSDT) for beneficiaries under 21	Dental services, including dentures
Family planning services and supplies	Prosthetic devices, eyeglasses, and durable medical equipment
Federally qualified health center (FQHC) services	Primary care case management
Rural health clinic services	Tuberculosis-related services
Nurse midwife services	Other specified medical or remedial care
Certified pediatric and family nurse practitioner services	*Long-Term Care Benefits*
Long-Term Care Benefits	Intermediate care facility services for the mentally retarded (ICF/
Nursing facility services for individuals 21 and over	MR)
Home healthcare services for individuals entitled to nursing	Inpatient/nursing facility services for individuals age 65 years and
facility care	over in an institution for mental disease
New benefits in ACA	Inpatient psychiatric hospital services for individuals under 21
Tobacco cessation program for pregnant women	Home- and community-based waiver services
	Other home health care
	Targeted case management
	Respiratory care services for ventilator-dependent individuals
	Personal care services
	Hospice services
	Services furnished under a Program of All-inclusive Care for the
	Elderly (PACE program)
	New benefits in ACA
	New state option for community-based care
	New state option for home health care
	New state option for family planning services

Source: 42 U.S.C. § 1396d; 42 CFR Parts 430–498.

optional list of services identified in Table 10-2.[21] There are three benchmark packages: (1) the Federal Employee Health Benefits Plan (FEHBP), (2) a state's health plan for its own employees, and (3) the state's largest commercial non-Medicaid health maintenance organization (HMO) plan. In addition, the DRA allows the secretary of HHS to approve a plan as a benchmark.

Benchmarks provide a state with a standard to follow when designing its Medicaid package of benefits—it does not mean that Medicaid beneficiaries are enrolled in the plans identified as benchmarks. Furthermore, a state may instead choose to offer "benchmark-equivalent" coverage that includes certain basic services as shown in Box 10-8. These services must have the same actuarial value as the services provided by one of the three benchmarks listed above (i.e., the value of the services must be similar). States may choose to

supplement their benchmark-equivalent plans with additional services, as listed in Box 10-8. These additional services are required to be worth only 75% of the actuarial value of the same service provided in a benchmark plan. Finally, while the DRA still guarantees the same set of EPSDT services for children under 19, these services may be more difficult to access if they are provided through wrap-around benefits that supplements the benchmark package instead of within the package itself.[22]

The benefit changes allowed by the DRA may only be applied to certain populations, and these groups had to be part of a state plan prior to the law's enactment to receive the new benefits package. DRA-eligible populations include most categorically needy children, as well as parents and caretakers who receive Medicaid but not Temporary Assistance to Needy Families (the new welfare program created by

BOX 10-8 DRA Benefit Options

Benchmark Plans

Federal Employee Health Benefits Plan

State employee health plan

Largest commercial non-Medicaid HMO in the state

HHS secretary-approved plan

Benchmark-Equivalent Plan

Full actuarial value for the following services:

- Inpatient and outpatient hospital
- Physician (surgical and medical)
- Laboratory and X-ray
- Well-baby and well-child
- Other appropriate preventive services (defined by HHS secretary)

Additional Optional Benchmark-Equivalent Services

75% actuarial value for the following services:

- Prescription drugs
- Mental heath
- Vision
- Hearing

Note: States must wrap around EPSDT coverage as necessary.

BOX 10-9 Idaho Implementation of DRA[25]

Idaho took advantage of DRA options to modernize its Medicaid program in response to increasing costs and concerns about the value of its mental health services. The state hoped to reform Medicaid to improve its performance and efficiency, but did not expect to achieve significant cost savings. Idaho made a variety of changes, including separating beneficiaries into basic and enhanced benefit packages based on health needs, increasing assistance to help individuals access preventive services, expanding its premium assistance program, and changing eligibility and co-payments under Medicaid and CHIP. Early indications show improved access to preventive services, a shift to a focus on quality improvement through a pay-for-performance disease management program, and better use of the medical home model. Given the limited time since implementation, the ramifications of the tiered benefit package model are not clear. Furthermore, the state has had less success in changing beneficiary behavior (e.g., in making healthier lifestyle choices), has struggled to translate the pay-for-performance program into cost savings, and has had limited participation in the premium assistance program.

PRWORA). The list of populations excluded from the DRA is quite lengthy and includes beneficiary groups with high expenditures, such as the disabled, dual eligibles, and terminally ill hospice patients.[23]

In states that choose to utilize the options provided in the DRA, the potential exists for Medicaid benefits to be severely curtailed. As of 2008, seven states (Idaho, Kansas, Kentucky, South Carolina, Washington, West Virginia, and Wisconsin) have taken the DRA option to reduce benefits and increase cost-sharing, while 24 states have used the DRA to increase the role of private long-term care insurance.[24]

Amount, Duration, and Scope, and Reasonableness Requirements

Although states have a great deal of flexibility in designing their Medicaid benefit packages, states had to follow several federal requirements prior to the DRA. These rules, collectively referred to as "amount, duration, and scope" and "reasonableness" requirements, were intended to ensure that all Medicaid beneficiaries in a state received adequate, comparable, and nondiscriminatory coverage. As discussed below, some of these rules have changed under the DRA.

Private insurers typically are not drawn to Medicaid's population because of the likelihood that these individuals would have relatively high healthcare needs. In addition, private insurers use a variety of tools (such as limited open-enrollment periods, experience rating, medical condition-based limitations, and narrow medical necessity standards) to limit their financial exposure. Medicaid, on the other hand, was designed as a healthcare entitlement program, with the goal to provide services to a needy population that would otherwise be uninsurable through commercial plans.[26] Table 10-3 identifies some of the requirements that help the Medicaid program achieve this goal, as well as any changes to them found in the DRA.

Medicaid Spending

Health policymakers are concerned with not only how much money Medicaid costs, but also the distribution of program spending. In 2009, Medicaid spent $366 billion, accounting for approximately 16% of total personal healthcare spending in the United States.[27] Understanding which populations utilize

BOX 10-10 Discussion Questions

The DRA also included new rules on citizenship verification. Prior to the DRA, all but four states allowed beneficiaries to self-attest to their citizenship status. Under the DRA, Medicaid and CHIP applicants now have to prove their citizenship status by providing original or certified copies of citizenship documents, such as a U.S. passport, state-issued driver's license, or birth certificate. The exact requirements depend on what type of document is submitted. These rules were intended to ensure that only eligible beneficiaries received Medicaid benefits. Many individuals have had difficulty obtaining access to these documents and as a result were dropped from the program despite being eligible. Do you think these rules are a good idea? Do you think this requirement is a reasonable burden? Does it matter that evidence was not available to support the claim that non-citizens or ineligible immigrants were accessing Medicaid benefits? Or, is the possibility that ineligible immigrants might enroll in Medicaid concerning enough to warrant the new documentation requirements?

BOX 10-11 Discussion Questions

Supporters of the Deficit Reduction Act (DRA) assert that states now have more flexibility to choose benefit packages tailored to the needs of different beneficiaries, provide Medicaid beneficiaries with the same coverage that large private plans provide, and give states additional needed flexibility to control state Medicaid budgets. Are these arguments convincing? Why or why not? If you agree, why do you think so many populations are exempt from DRA changes? Also, the beneficiaries who are excluded are often the most costly groups of patients—does that make sense in terms of budget reduction or equity? What do you think was the primary decision-making goal by those supporting the DRA?

the most services, which services are utilized most frequently, and which services and populations are most costly helps policymakers decide if they need to change the Medicaid program and, if so, what changes should be made.

As you can see from Figure 10-3, not all populations and services are equal when it comes to cost. Generally, children

and adults are fairly inexpensive to cover, whereas elderly and disabled beneficiaries use more, as well as more expensive, services. One of the biggest reasons the elderly and disabled account for a high proportion of Medicaid expenditures is their use of long-term care services, such as nursing homes and home- and community-based services. In addition, they are heavy users of prescription drugs and are relatively more likely to be hospitalized. As is the case with private insurance and Medicare, a relatively small group of individuals account for a large proportion of Medicaid spending. In calendar year 2004, 5% of beneficiaries accounted for over half of all Medicaid spending.[28] Figure 10-4 shows that over one-half

TABLE 10-3 "Reasonableness" and "Amount, Duration, and Scope" Requirements in Medicaid

Requirement	Requirement Purpose	DRA Changes to the Requirement
Reasonableness	State must provide all services to categorically-needy beneficiaries in sufficient amount, duration, and scope to achieve its purpose	States only have to meet amount, duration, and scope requirements found in the named benchmark or benchmark-equivalent plan
Comparability	All categorically needy beneficiaries in the state are entitled to receive the same benefit package in content, amount, duration, and scope	States may apply benchmark or benchmark-equivalent packages to some, but not all, populations
Statewideness	In most cases, states must provide same benefit package in all parts of the state	States may apply benchmark or benchmark-equivalent packages to some, but not all, populations
Non-discrimination	States may not discriminate against a beneficiary based on diagnosis, illness, or type of condition by limiting or denying a mandatory service	DRA does not include language changing Medicaid non-discrimination rules

FIGURE 10-3 Medicaid Enrollees and Expenditures by Enrollment Group, 2007.

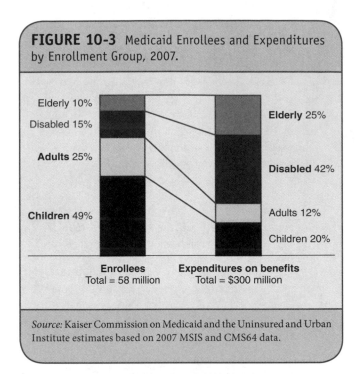

Enrollees
Total = 58 million

Elderly 10%
Disabled 15%
Adults 25%
Children 49%

Expenditures on benefits
Total = $300 million

Elderly 25%
Disabled 42%
Adults 12%
Children 20%

Source: Kaiser Commission on Medicaid and the Uninsured and Urban Institute estimates based on 2007 MSIS and CMS64 data.

of all Medicaid spending is for acute care services, and long-term care services account for over one-third of Medicaid expenditures.

In addition to expanding eligibility, the ACA also included a few changes to Medicaid benefits. States will have new options relating to community-based care, home health care, and family planning. In addition, all states will have to cover tobacco cessation programs for pregnant women. The ACA also includes a variety of demonstration programs that target key health issues such as obesity, high cholesterol, high blood pressure, diabetes, and tobacco use.

Medicaid Financing

The Medicaid program is jointly financed by the federal and state governments, with about 57% of the total program costs paid for by the federal government and the rest by the states. Even with the federal government picking up over half the tab, states have found their share of Medicaid costs to be increasingly burdensome, accounting for 16% of state budgets nationally.[29]

FIGURE 10-4 Medicaid Expenditures by Service, 2009.

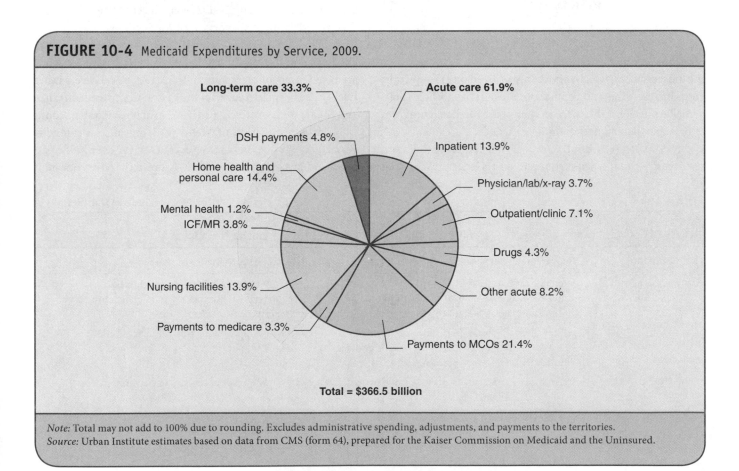

Long-term care 33.3%
Acute care 61.9%
DSH payments 4.8%
Inpatient 13.9%
Home health and personal care 14.4%
Physician/lab/x-ray 3.7%
Mental health 1.2%
Outpatient/clinic 7.1%
ICF/MR 3.8%
Drugs 4.3%
Other acute 8.2%
Nursing facilities 13.9%
Payments to medicare 3.3%
Payments to MCOs 21.4%

Total = $366.5 billion

Note: Total may not add to 100% due to rounding. Excludes administrative spending, adjustments, and payments to the territories.
Source: Urban Institute estimates based on data from CMS (form 64), prepared for the Kaiser Commission on Medicaid and the Uninsured.

BOX 10-12 Discussion Questions

States have enormous flexibility in designing their Medicaid programs. States spend significant resources on optional services or mandatory services for optional populations. Yet, states complain that Medicaid expenditures are unsustainable and that significant reform, such as the DRA, is needed. If states have the ability to reduce Medicaid spending without any reforms, why do you think state politicians are focused on reforming the program? Why might states choose not to reduce their Medicaid program to cover only mandatory services and populations? Politically, what do you think is the most feasible way for states to reduce their Medicaid budgets?

Program financing occurs through a matching payment system that divides the amount paid by the federal and state governments. The matching rate for most medical services, called the Federal Medical Assistance Percentage (FMAP), is determined by a formula that is tied to each state's per capita income. Poorer states—those with lower per capita incomes—receive more federal money for every state dollar spent on Medicaid, while the wealthier states receive less. In addition, the ACA allows for a 1% increase in FMAP for states that cover certain preventive services and immunizations without any cost-sharing requirements. The FMAP rate may not be lower than 50% for any state, meaning that the costliest scenario for a state government is that it splits program costs evenly with the federal government. FMAP rates range from 50% to 76%, although the 2009 stimulus bill included a temporary FMAP increase that expired in 2010.[29(p.27)] Given the variation in matching rates and state programs' size, federal funds are not distributed evenly among the states. In fact, five states (California, New York, Ohio, Pennsylvania, and Texas) account for almost one-third of all federal Medicaid spending.[30]

Medicaid is also partially financed through beneficiary co-payments, co-insurance, and premiums. Prior to the DRA, Medicaid cost-sharing was extremely limited, but the DRA included drastic changes to Medicaid's cost-sharing rules. In most cases, states historically could only charge "nominal" cost sharing, such as $2 per month per family, $.50 to $3.00 per service, or 5% of the state's payment rate.[31] In addition, pre-DRA, states were prohibited from charging any cost-sharing to some beneficiaries and for some services. Furthermore, cost-sharing requirements were "unenforceable," meaning health professionals could not refuse to provide services if a beneficiary did not pay a required cost-share amount.

Under the DRA, however, states have options to impose much higher cost-sharing requirements and to make these requirements enforceable, meaning a provider may refuse service or beneficiaries may be disenrolled from Medicaid if they do not pay the requisite amount. States may now charge Medicaid families earning between 100% and 150% FPL up to 10% of the cost of services, and may charge families earning above 150% FPL both premiums and up to 20% of the cost of services,[32] and the aggregate of these cost-sharing requirements may not exceed 5% of a family's income. Furthermore, the DRA permits higher cost sharing for prescription drugs and the use of emergency departments for nonemergency services. Some beneficiaries are protected from these increased costs. Cost-sharing is generally prohibited for children covered by a mandatory category and is limited to nominal levels for adults with incomes up to 100% FPL. In addition, premium requirements are not enforceable for these groups.[29(p.17)] As with the DRA benefit changes, many groups and services are excluded from the new cost-sharing options.

As noted earlier, the federal government is picking up the bulk of the cost of the ACA Medicaid expansions. From 2014–2016, the federal government will pay 100% of the cost of financing newly eligible enrollees. While the federal government's share will lessen over time, it will still cover 90% of the cost in 2020 and beyond. It is also expected that the Medicaid expansion will reduce the uncompensated care burden of states, since fewer individuals will be uninsured. Even so, many states are concerned about the financial burden of the Medicaid expansion and it is estimated that ACA changes to Medicaid and CHIP will cost states $20 billion over 10 years.[33] While the federal government will provide significant financial help through 2019, the eligibility expansion is intended to be permanent. In addition, the ACA included a maintenance-

BOX 10-13 Discussion Questions

What do you think of the MOE requirements? Is it fair for the federal government to impose new eligibility rules on states when the states are ultimately responsible for the cost of providing services? Does such a requirement violate a fundamental element of Medicaid to permit state flexibility? On the other hand, without an MOE requirement, wouldn't many states simply reduce their eligibility rules, thwarting the intent of Congress to reduce the number of uninsured by expanding Medicaid coverage? Does the budget deficit exception undermine the rule?

of-effort (MOE) rule forbidding states from reducing their own eligibility rules. States must keep the eligibility rules they had in place as of March 2010 (when the law was enacted) for adults until 2014, and for children until 2019. This requirement was included to prevent states from rolling back coverage expansions and from simply replacing state dollars with federal dollars without actually expanding coverage. There is, however, a significant exception to the MOE rule: States with a documented budget deficit may reduce eligibility for non-pregnant, non-disabled adults earning over 133% FPL.

Medicaid Provider Reimbursement

Medicaid's complex design also extends to its provider reimbursement methodology. States have broad discretion in setting provider rates. Not only do reimbursement rates vary by state, but they also vary by whether services are provided in a fee-for-service or managed care setting and by which type of provider (e.g., physicians, hospitals) renders a service.[c]

Fee-for-Service Reimbursement

When reimbursing fee-for-service (FFS) care under Medicaid, states are required to set their payment rates to physicians at levels that are "sufficient" to ensure Medicaid patients have "equal access" to providers compared to the general population.[34] Despite this language, Medicaid reimbursement is much lower than both Medicare and private practice rates. Low reimbursement is one reason that many providers are wary of treating Medicaid patients. In 2008, one study found that approximately 28% of physicians were not accepting *any* new Medicaid patients compared to the 74% of physicians who were accepting *all or most* new Medicare and privately insured patients.[35] The ACA includes a temporary bump in primary care payment rates for services provided in both FFS and managed care settings. For 2013 and 2014, primary care payment rates will equal 100% of Medicare payment rates, with the federal government covering the cost of the increased reimbursement. While this measure is intended to support primary care providers and boost access to primary care services, its temporary nature means it is unlikely to have a lasting effect.

Hospital FFS services are reimbursed at a rate that is "consistent with efficiency, economy, and quality of care."[36] However, there is no specified minimum reimbursement level that states are required to meet, resulting in rates that are lower than what hospitals receive from Medicare and private insurance. Hospitals that serve a high number of low-income patients may receive additional Medicaid payments called dis-

proportionate share hospital (DSH) payments. Under the ACA, however, these payments will be reduced significantly.

Managed Care Reimbursement

As with the rest of the healthcare system, managed care has become an increasingly important part of the Medicaid program. About 36 million patients—71% of all Medicaid patients—were in Medicaid managed care plans in 2009.[37] All states except Alaska and Wyoming enroll some Medicaid beneficiaries in managed care, with 22 states enrolling over 80% of their beneficiaries in managed care plans.[37] States may require managed care enrollment for all beneficiaries except children with special healthcare needs, Native Americans, and Medicare recipients.[38]

Managed care organizations (MCOs) that enroll Medicaid beneficiaries receive a monthly capitated rate per member and assume financial risk for providing services. States and MCOs agree upon a set of services the MCOs will provide for the capitated rate. If there are any Medicaid-covered services that are not included in a state's managed care contract with MCOs, states reimburse them an amount in addition to the capitated rate or reimburse non-MCO providers on a fee-for-service basis to provide those services. In other words, beneficiaries are still entitled to all Medicaid services, even when they are enrolled in a managed care plan.

States are required to pay MCOs on an "actuarially sound basis," a term that is not defined in the Medicaid statute.[39] As with other types of provider rates, capitation rates vary widely among states. However, it is difficult to compare capitation rates across states because of the variation in Medicaid programs generally and in the types of services and populations covered by the managed care contracts.

BOX 10-14 Discussion Questions

Is higher Medicaid cost-sharing a good idea? What are the strongest arguments you can make for and against higher cost-sharing? Should Medicaid beneficiaries have the same cost-sharing responsibilities as privately insured individuals, or should the government bear more of the cost because Medicaid beneficiaries are low-income individuals? What is the primary decision-making goal that led to the exclusion of so many populations and services from the new cost-sharing options?

Medicaid Waivers

Much of the previous discussion about Medicaid highlighted both the numerous requirements placed on states and the enormous amount of flexibility states have in operating their program. Medicaid *waivers* provide still another level of flexibility for states. There are several different types of waivers under Medicaid; here, we focus only on the broadest one—the "section 1115" waiver. Under section 1115 of the Social Security Act, states may apply to the secretary of HHS to waive requirements of health and welfare programs under the Social Security Act, including both Medicaid and CHIP. The secretary may grant section 1115 waivers, also called demonstration projects, as long as the proposal "assists in promoting the objectives" of the federal program.[d] This broad standard has not been defined and leaves the secretary with enormous discretion to approve or reject waiver applications. One of the most important aspects of a waiver is the "budget neutrality" requirement. A state must show that the waiver project will not cost the federal government more money over a five-year period than if the waiver had not been granted. The MOE rule under the ACA also applies to waivers. Although the amount of money spent remains the same, by seeking a waiver, a state is agreeing to use itself as a "policy laboratory" in exchange for being able to operate its Medicaid program with fewer requirements. Ideally, other states and the federal government will learn from these demonstration projects and incorporate their positive aspects, while avoiding negative ones.

In 2001, the Bush administration created a specific type of section 1115 waiver called the Health Insurance Flexibility and Accountability (HIFA) demonstration. These waivers differ from traditional 1115 waivers in that they encourage integration of Medicaid and CHIP with private insurance through premium assistance programs and other means. HIFA waivers also allow states to achieve budget neutrality by reducing the amount, duration, and scope of optional benefits and increasing cost-sharing requirements for optional eligibility groups (changes that may now be possible under the DRA without the need for a formal waiver). Although states may reduce optional benefits and populations under HIFA, mandatory populations must remain covered and mandatory benefits may not be reduced. Given these rules, HIFA waivers often involve a trade-off between covering more people with fewer services or fewer people with more services.

As of June 2011, HHS approved section 1115 waivers in 30 states and the District of Columbia, some of which were HIFA-1115 waivers.[40] States have taken a variety of approaches to changing their Medicaid programs through these waivers. For example, several states have implemented managed care programs, created tiered benefit systems (meaning that not all beneficiaries are entitled to the same benefits) in exchange for covering new populations, altered federal financing, or expanded coverage to low-income adults.

The Future of Medicaid

Due to the high cost of the Medicaid program, the large federal deficit, other pressures on federal and state budgets, and ideological differences among policymakers, Medicaid reform has been a hot topic in recent years. Although the ACA included a significant Medicaid expansion, the battle over Medicaid and other entitlement programs continues. Opponents of the ACA are seeking to overturn the law, and reform of entitlement programs is a central part of the debate about how to reduce the federal deficit. Furthermore, with the newly eligible Medicaid population operating under different rules than traditional Medicaid enrollees, it appears that many policymakers are moving away from viewing Medicaid as a social insurance program that provides a certain set of healthcare benefits and specific legal protections to vulnerable populations. Instead, they are fashioning Medicaid as a program that more closely mirrors private insurance plans in terms of their use of risk, cost-sharing, limited benefits, and lack of extra protections that ensure fairness and access to care. On an ever-larger scale, some policymakers are advocating for ending Medicaid as an entitlement program and transforming it into a block grant program in which the federal government will give states a set amount of funds for a specified period of time to run their Medicaid program as they see fit.

STATE CHILDREN'S HEALTH INSURANCE PROGRAM

Congress created the State Children's Health Insurance Program (CHIP) in 1997 as a $40 billion, 10-year block grant program, codified as Title XXI of the Social Security Act.[41] When the program expired in 2007, Congress tried to extend it by passing two versions of the Children's Health Insurance Program Reauthorization Act (CHIPRA). Despite the bi-partisan support for these bills, then-President George W. Bush vetoed both versions and instead signed a temporary extension of the program. In 2009, Congress again passed CHIPRA and newly elected President Obama signed it into law as one of his first acts in office.[15] CHIPRA included $33 billion in federal funds for children's coverage and extended the program and its funding through 2013.[42] The ACA further extended the program until 2019, but only included funding through fiscal year 2015.

CHIP is designed to provide health insurance to low-income children whose family income is above the eligibility level for Medicaid in their state. The funding and eligibility expansions in CHIPRA are estimated to cover 6.5 million additional children in either Medicaid or CHIP.[42] Overall, CHIP has been successful at insuring low-income children, enrolling more than 7.7 million children by the end of 2010.[43] Nonetheless, over 8 million children remain uninsured as of 2009, and many of them live in low-income families.[44]

CHIP Structure and Financing

CHIP is an optional program for the states, but all 50 have chosen to participate. States have three options regarding how their CHIP program is structured:

1. States may incorporate CHIP into their existing Medicaid program by using CHIP children as an expansion population.
2. States may create an entirely separate CHIP program.
3. States may create a hybrid program with lower-income children part of Medicaid and higher-income children in a separate CHIP program.

In 2010, 17 states had a separate program, 12 states had a Medicaid expansion program, and 21 states had a hybrid program.[45]

As with Medicaid, federal CHIP funds are disbursed on a matching basis, although the federal match is higher for CHIP than for Medicaid; CHIP matching rates range from 65% to 85%, compared to 50% to 76% for Medicaid.[46] The ACA includes a significant increase in the CHIP match for states beginning in 2015, but did not fund the program past 2015.

The matching formula is set by law and was changed when CHIPRA was enacted. Originally, allotments were for three years and were based on state-specific estimates of the number of low-income uninsured children, the number of low-income children generally, and healthcare costs relative to other states. Under CHIPRA, allotments are for two years and fiscal year 2009 allotments were based on prior CHIP spending levels. State allotments will increase annually to account for growth in healthcare spending, increases in the number of children in the state, and state program expansions. Every two years, state allotments will be rebased to reflect actual use of CHIP funds.[47]

The changes to the CHIP allotment formula were intended to allow for more predictable budgeting and to account for state program expansions. In addition, it addresses a recurring problem under the old formula. Previously, if states did not use their full allotment, the unused money reverted to the federal treasury and could be used by the federal government for any purpose. This lead to frequent fights to keep the money in the CHIP and over how the unused funds would be redistributed. Many states became dependent on receiving redistributed funds to keep their CHIP afloat. The new formula and process should help avoid this problem through better budgeting predictability and shorter allotment timeframes. In addition, under CHIPRA, all unused funds are designated to go to Medicaid performance bonuses for increased enrollment and outreach, instead of reverting to the federal treasury.[47]

Table 10-4 highlights a number of differences between Medicaid and CHIP. One very important difference is that whereas Medicaid is an entitlement program, CHIP is a block grant. As mentioned earlier, as a block grant, the federal matching funds are capped (through the allotments). Thus, a state is not entitled to limitless federal money under CHIP, and children, even if eligible, are not legally entitled to services once the allotted money has been spent. If a state runs out of funds and operates its CHIP separate from Medicaid, it will have to cut back its CHIP program by eliminating benefits, lowering provider reimbursement rates, disenrolling beneficiaries, or wait-listing children who want to enroll in the program. A state with a Medicaid expansion CHIP or a hybrid structure would not receive new CHIP money, but would continue to receive federal funds for Medicaid-eligible children as allowed under the Medicaid rules and at the Medicaid matching rate.

CHIP Eligibility

CHIP originally allowed states to cover children up to 200% FPL, but CHIPRA expanded coverage to 300% FPL.[42] All but four states have chosen to cover children up to 200% FPL and 25 states cover children at or above 250% FPL.[48,e]

Since CHIP coverage is built on a state's Medicaid eligibility rules, when CHIP eligibility begins depends on when Medicaid eligibility ends. For example, if a state covers a child up to 150% FPL, CHIP eligibility in that state would start at over 150% FPL. If another state Medicaid program covers children

at 200% FPL, CHIP eligibility would start at over 200% FPL. Under the ACA, states must cover all children aged 6–19 up to 133% FPL in their Medicaid program, and children in families with incomes up to 133% who are currently in CHIP programs must be moved to the state's Medicaid program.[b] Even so, variations may still exist above that level. As a result, children in families with the same income levels could be in CHIP in one state and in Medicaid in another state.

Under the original CHIP, pregnant women were not eligible for coverage without a waiver, although an option to cover unborn children indirectly allowed pregnant women to access the program. CHIPRA explicitly allows for coverage of pregnant women and 6 states have utilized that option as of January 2011. CHIPRA also expanded eligibility by allowing states to cover lawfully residing immigrant pregnant women and children, even if they have not been in the U.S. for five

TABLE 10-4 Comparing Key Features of Medicaid and CHIP		
Feature	**Medicaid**	**CHIP**
Structure	Entitlement	Block grant
Financing	Federal–State match	Federal–State match at higher rate than Medicaid
Funds may be used for premium assistance	No (without a waiver)	Yes
Benefits	Federally defined, with option to use benchmark or benchmark-equivalent benefits package; broad EPSDT services for children	Benefits undefined; use benchmark package; limited "basic" services required
Cost-sharing	Limited or prohibited for some populations and services, higher amounts allowed for some populations and services	Cost-sharing permitted within limits, but prohibited for well-baby and well-child exams
Anti-discrimination provision	Yes	No

years. Prior to CHIPRA, states could only cover these populations with state dollars. As of January 2011, 25 states have picked up this option for immigrant children and 17 states have done so for immigrant pregnant women.[48]

CHIPRA included a number of provisions to streamline enrollment and improve outreach. While states must verify the citizenship status of CHIP enrollees, just as they must for Medicaid enrollees, states may do so through an electronic data match with the Social Security Administration. This option eases the administrative burden of the citizenship verification requirement and makes it much less likely that eligible individuals will be dropped from the program. In addition, CHIPRA allows states to use "express lane eligibility," which permits states to take information provided when individuals apply for other public programs and use that information to assess eligibility for CHIP. Finally, CHIP includes performance bonuses and other financial incentives to states that adopt various enrollment simplification and outreach policies.[48]

CHIP Benefits and Beneficiary Safeguards

States must provide "basic" benefits in their CHIP programs, including inpatient and outpatient hospital care, physician services (surgical and medical), laboratory and X-ray services, well-baby and well-child care, and age-appropriate immunizations. Under CHIPRA, states must now provide dental coverage and may provide dental-only supplemental coverage for otherwise eligible children who have health insurance without dental coverage. States may also choose to provide additional benefits such as prescription drug coverage, mental health services, vision services, hearing services, and other services needed by children. CHIPRA requires that states that choose to provide mental health or substance abuse services to offer the same level of coverage as they do for medical and surgical benefits.[42]

Various standards may be used for a benefit package. The law outlines the following benchmarks that states may use when designing their programs:

- The health insurance plan that is offered by the HMO that has the largest commercial, non-Medicaid enrollment in the state.
- The standard Blue Cross Blue Shield preferred provider plan for federal employees.
- A health plan that is available to state employees.
- A package that is actuarially equivalent to one of the above plans.
- A coverage package that is approved by the HHS secretary.[49]

BOX 10-18 Discussion Questions

When designing CHIP, policymakers chose to follow the private insurance model instead of the Medicaid model. Although states have the choice to create a generous Medicaid expansion program for their CHIP beneficiaries, they also have the choice to implement a more limited insurance program with fewer protections. Similar choices were made when the DRA options were created for Medicaid. These decisions raise essential questions about the role of government in public insurance programs. Does the government (federal or state) have a responsibility to provide additional benefits and protection to its low-income residents? Or, is the government satisfying any responsibility it has by providing insurance coverage that is equivalent to major private insurance plans? What if the standard for private insurance plans becomes lower—does that change your analysis? Is it fair for low-income individuals to receive more comprehensive health insurance coverage than other individuals? Is there a point where fiscal constraints trump equity or the likelihood of improved health outcomes when designing a public insurance program?

(Do these benchmark plans sound familiar? Clearly, the DRA revisions to Medicaid were modeled on the existing CHIP program.) Under a stand-alone CHIP program, the benefit package may be the same as the state's Medicaid package or equal to one of these benchmarks. States with separate CHIP programs commonly create benefit packages that are less generous than the ones available in their Medicaid programs.[47]

In addition to the benefit package options, there are other areas where CHIP provides states with more program flexibility and beneficiaries with less protection than is the case under Medicaid. CHIP does not have the same standards regarding reasonableness, benefit definitions, medical necessity, or nondiscrimination coverage on the basis of illness (though, as noted earlier, states may opt out of or alter some of these protections in Medicaid under the DRA). States, however, may not exclude children based on preexisting conditions. Also, like the new DRA cost-sharing option, states with separate CHIP programs may impose cost-sharing requirements up to 5% of a family's annual income for families with incomes at or above 150% FPL.[47]

CHIP and Private Insurance Coverage

In devising CHIP, Congress was concerned that Medicaid-eligible children would enroll in CHIP instead of Medicaid without reducing the overall number of uninsured children in a state. To avoid this outcome, CHIP requires that all children be assessed for Medicaid eligibility and, if eligible, enrolled in Medicaid instead of CHIP.[50] In addition, Congress wanted to make sure that the government did not start funding health insurance coverage that was previously being paid for in the private sector. In other words, it did not want to give individuals or employers an incentive to move privately insured children to the new public program. To avoid private insurance crowd out, Congress allowed states to institute enrollment-waiting periods and impose cost-sharing requirements as a disincentive to switch to CHIP.

CHIP Waivers

States may apply to the secretary of HHS to waive CHIP program requirements in exchange for experimenting with new ways to increase program eligibility or benefits. Initially, the most common use of CHIP waivers was to expand eligibility for uncovered populations, such as childless adults and parents and pregnant women who are not eligible under a state's Medicaid program. Using CHIP funds to provide coverage for adult populations was controversial because the program was designed to provide health insurance to children. While CHIPRA expands eligibility options for pregnant women, it also prohibits states from obtaining new waivers to cover adults with CHIP funds.[47]

In addition, a few states have used CHIP waivers to create premium assistance programs. Premium assistance means that public subsidies (in this case, CHIP funds) are available to help beneficiaries cover the cost of private health insurance premiums for employer-sponsored coverage or other health insurance plans that are available to them. States favor premium assistance programs as a way to reduce the state's cost of providing a child with health insurance. Premium assistance programs may also reduce crowd out by providing an incentive for people to keep their children in private coverage instead of enrolling them in CHIP. States must abide by numerous rules when creating a premium assistance program and the combination of these rules and the high cost of private insurance has led to low enrollment in CHIP premium assistance programs in the few states that have initiated them. The use of premium assistance programs may increase in the future, as CHIPRA includes provisions to help reduce these barriers.[42]

The Future of CHIP

The future of CHIP is clouded by the ACA. While CHIP has been a very successful (and bi-partisan) program, it is possible that some states will drop the program due to fiscal pressures and the availability of newer insurance options.[51] States will bear increased costs due to the ACA's Medicaid expansion and if CHIP's enhanced match is not extended past 2015, many states may choose to spend their state dollars elsewhere. Given the ACA's individual insurance mandate, most children who are dropped from CHIP would be required to obtain coverage through another source. While other insurance options should be available—employer coverage, Medicaid, or through state health exchanges—many children may be moved to less generous and more expensive coverage if CHIP is not available.

MEDICARE

Medicare is the federally funded health insurance program for the elderly and some persons with disabilities. As a completely federally funded program with uniform national guidelines, Medicare's administration and financing is quite different from that found in Medicaid and CHIP. This section reviews who Medicare serves, what benefits the program provides, how Medicare is financed, and how Medicare providers are reimbursed. As with Medicaid and CHIP, the ACA included several provisions relating to Medicare. These changes include new coverage for preventive services, bonus payments for primary care services, and assistance in paying for prescription drugs. At the same time, a number of changes will result in reduced reimbursement for providers. Taken together, the ACA's Medicare-related provisions are expected to result in $533 billion in savings and $105 billion in new Medicare spending, for a net reduction of $428 billion in Medicare spending over 10 years.[52]

BOX 10-19 Discussion Questions

Although many Medicare beneficiaries are poor, there is no means test (income- or resource-specific eligibility level) to determine eligibility as there is with Medicaid and CHIP. Is there a good public policy reason for this difference? What would be the basis for making this distinction? Does the government have a different role to play in providing health care based on the population involved?

Medicare Eligibility

Medicare covers two main groups of people—the elderly and the disabled. In 2010, there were 39 million elderly and 8 million persons with disabilities or end-stage renal disease[ii] enrolled in Medicare.[2] To qualify for Medicare under the elderly category, individuals must be at least 65 years old and be eligible for Social Security payments by having worked and contributed to Social Security for at least 10 years. Individuals who are 65 but do not meet the work requirements may become eligible for Medicare on the basis of their spouse's eligibility. To qualify for Medicare as a person with disabilities, individuals must be totally and permanently disabled and receive Social Security Disability Insurance (SSDI) for at least 24 months, or have a diagnosis of either end-stage renal disease or amyotrophic lateral sclerosis. The disability categories do not have an age requirement, so these Medicare beneficiaries may be under age 65. Unlike Medicaid and CHIP, Medicare eligibility is not based on an income or asset test—in other words, individuals of any income level are eligible for Medicare if they meet the eligibility requirements.

Even though Medicare does not target low-income elderly and disabled, a significant portion of Medicare beneficiaries are indigent and in poor health. Almost 25% of Medicare beneficiaries are in families with annual incomes of $10,000 or less and just over half have incomes under 200% FPL.[2] These low-income beneficiaries are more likely to be female, in fair or poor health, part of a racial or ethnic minority group, and disabled than other beneficiaries. As shown in Figure 10-5, among all Medicare beneficiaries, many have three or more chronic conditions, are in poor or fair health, or have a cognitive impairment. Even though approximately 78% of Medicare beneficiaries identify as non-Hispanic white, almost twice as many African-American and Hispanic beneficiaries report being in fair or poor health compared to non-Hispanic white beneficiaries.[2(p3)]

Medicare Benefits

Medicare is split into several parts, each covering a specified set of services. Beneficiaries are automatically entitled to Part A, also known as Hospital Insurance (HI). Part B services, also known as Supplemental Medical Insurance (SMI), covers physician, outpatient, and preventive services. (The ACA added coverage for certain preventive services without cost-sharing, including an annual comprehensive risk assessment, provided without cost-sharing when delivered in an outpatient setting.) Part B is voluntary for enrollees, but 95% of Part A beneficiaries also opt to have Part B. Beneficiaries may choose to receive their benefits through Part C, Medicare Advantage, which includes the Medicare managed care program and a few other types of plans. Part D is the new prescription drug benefit. Table 10-5 lists Medicare benefits by part and Figure 10-6 illustrates current and projected spending on Medicare benefits. Significant growth is expected in spending on outpatient prescription drugs over the next 10 years. Although Medicare benefits are quite extensive, the list excludes services that one might expect to be covered in health insurance

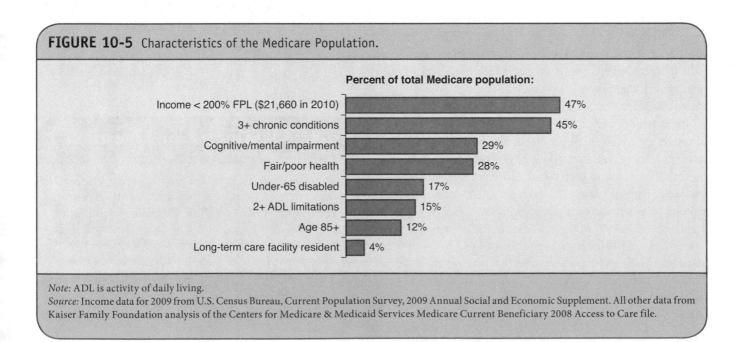

FIGURE 10-5 Characteristics of the Medicare Population.

Percent of total Medicare population:

Income < 200% FPL ($21,660 in 2010) 47%
3+ chronic conditions 45%
Cognitive/mental impairment 29%
Fair/poor health 28%
Under-65 disabled 17%
2+ ADL limitations 15%
Age 85+ 12%
Long-term care facility resident 4%

Note: ADL is activity of daily living.
Source: Income data for 2009 from U.S. Census Bureau, Current Population Survey, 2009 Annual Social and Economic Supplement. All other data from Kaiser Family Foundation analysis of the Centers for Medicare & Medicaid Services Medicare Current Beneficiary 2008 Access to Care file.

FIGURE 10-6 Medicare Benefit Payments, by Type of Service, 2010 and 2020.

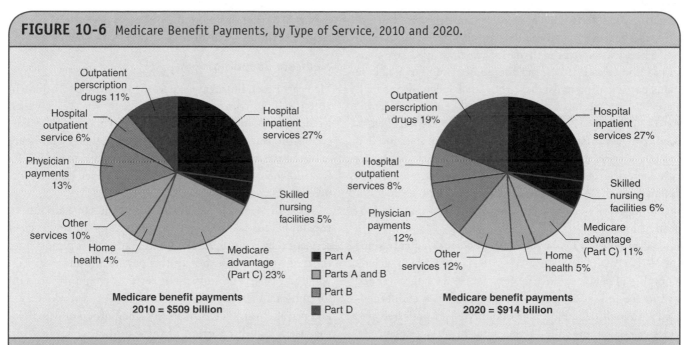

Notes: Totals do not include administrative expenses and are net of recoveries. Other Services include hospice services; durable medical equipment; ambulance services, independent, physician in-office, and hospital outpatient department laboratory services; hospital outpatient services that are not paid for using the prospective payment system (PPS); Part B prescription drugs; rural health clinic services; outpatient dialysis; and benefit payments not allocated to specific services, including adjustments to reflect year-to-date spending (2010), and savings from the Independent Payment Advisory Board (2020).

Source: Congressional Budget Office, Medicare Baseline, August 2010.

TABLE 10-5 Medicare Benefits

Part	Services Covered
A	Inpatient hospital, 100 days at skilled nursing facility (SNF), limited home health following hospital or SNF stay, and hospice care.
B	Physician, outpatient hospital, X-ray, laboratory, emergency room, and other ambulatory services; medical equipment; limited preventive services, including: one preventive physical exam, mammography, pelvic exam, prostrate exam, colorectal cancer screening, glaucoma screening for high-risk patients, prostrate cancer screening, and cardiovascular screening blood test; diabetes screening and outpatient self-management; bone-mass measurement for high-risk patients; hepatitis-B vaccine for high risk patients; pap smear; and pneumococcal and flu vaccinations. New ACA benefits: In 2010, cost-sharing eliminated for select preventive services; coverage for personalized prevention plan, including comprehensive health assessment.
C	Managed care plans, private fee-for-service plans, special needs plans, and medical savings accounts. The plans provide all services in Part A and Part B and generally must offer additional benefits or services as well.
D	Prescription drug benefit.

targeting the elderly, such as nursing home care, routine eye care, and hearing exams and hearing aids.[2(p6)]

There was rapid growth of Medicare managed care plans in the mid-to-late 1990s, but the number of managed care plans participating in Medicare has since fallen by one-half. Future Medicare Advantage enrollment projections vary.[29] As of 2010, over 11 million beneficiaries were enrolled in Medicare Advantage plans, over double the number enrolled in 2005. Even with this growth, only one-quarter of Medicare beneficiaries opt to enroll in managed care plans.[2(p9)] Changes in the ACA to the Medicare Advantage program, including reimbursement cuts, mean the future of the program is uncertain.

Although HMOs have participated in Medicare since the 1970s, Part C has evolved over the last decade to include a number of new insurance options. In 1997, Congress added private fee-for-service plans,[f] medical savings accounts coupled with high-deductible plans, county-based preferred provider organizations (PPOs), and point-of-services plans.[2(p9)] As part of the Medicare Prescription Drug Improvement and Modernization Act of 2003 (MMA),[54] Congress added regional PPOs and "special needs plans" for the institutionalized and for beneficiaries with severe and disabling conditions.[2(p9)]

The MMA also created Part D, Medicare's prescription drug benefit. The drug benefit was made available to recipients beginning in 2006. Medicare contracts with private drug insurance plans in each of 34 regions. If at least two plans are not available in a region, the government contracts with a fallback plan (a private plan that is not an insurer) to serve that area. All plans must cover at least two drugs in each therapeutic class or category of Part D drugs. Dual enrollees (individuals enrolled in both Medicaid and Medicare) are no longer eligible for prescription drug coverage under Medicaid; they must receive their prescription drug benefit through Medicare.

To obtain prescription drugs through Medicare, beneficiaries have the choice of remaining in traditional fee-for-service Medicare under Parts A and B and enrolling in a separate private prescription drug plan, or enrolling in a Part C plan through Medicare Advantage that includes prescription drug coverage. Medicare Advantage plans are required to offer basic prescription drug benefits and may offer supplemental prescription drug benefits for an additional premium. Some beneficiaries may also have access to employer-sponsored health insurance that includes prescription drug benefits. These beneficiaries may keep their employer coverage only, keep their employer coverage and enroll in Part D, or drop their employer coverage. Finally, beneficiaries may also choose not to obtain any prescription drug coverage. However, in certain circumstances, a beneficiary who declines to enroll in Part D during the allotted enrollment period may pay increased premiums if he decides to enroll at a later date.

Medicare Spending

Medicare expenditures are expected to reach $504.3 billion in 2010 (final figures are not yet available for that year), which would account for 12% of the total federal budget.[2(p15)] Medicare is projected to constitute 20.8% of national healthcare expenditures by 2014 and spending is expected to grow 6.2% from 2009–2019. Spending levels would be even higher without savings created by the ACA.[55]

Not all Medicare beneficiaries cost the same amount to care for because of the disparities in the amount and type of services they require. As shown in Figure 10-6, almost one-third of Medicare's expenditures pay for hospital services, while physician and outpatient services combined account for almost a fifth of Medicare payments. As with Medicaid and private insurance, a relatively small group of beneficiaries use a high proportion of these and other services. In 2006, 10% of all beneficiaries accounted for 58% of Medicare expenditures.[2(p16)]

The ACA established an Independent Payment Advisory Board, which has the task of submitting proposals to reduce the rate of Medicare spending if Medicare exceeds specified targets. The Secretary of Health and Human Services is

BOX 10-20 Discussion Questions

Lawmakers were concerned that adding a prescription drug benefit to Medicare would encourage employers to drop prescription drug coverage to the beneficiaries who receive prescription drugs through retiree health plans. In an effort to avoid a shift in elderly people who rely on public insurance instead of private insurance for their prescription drug coverage, Congress included in the MMA a tax-free subsidy to encourage employers to maintain prescription drug coverage. While the ACA eliminates the tax deduction, the subsidy remains in place. The amount of the subsidy is based on the prescription drug costs of individuals who remain with the employer's plan and do not enroll in Part D.

Is this subsidy a good idea? Is the proper role of government to pay private companies to maintain insurance coverage? If so, should it occur for other benefits? Do you have a preference between giving incentives for private entities to provide insurance coverage versus the government financing the coverage directly?

required to implement proposals submitted by the board unless Congress enacts alternative proposals that achieve the same level of savings. Congress limited the board's options by prohibiting consideration of proposals that ration care, increase revenue, change benefits, change eligibility, or change cost-sharing. In addition, hospitals and physicians are exempt from board proposals until 2020.[52]

Medicare Financing

Medicare is a federally funded program. Unlike Medicaid and CHIP, state governments do not generally contribute to Medicare spending, and therefore a matching system is not required. Although Medicare financing is simpler than Medicaid financing in many respects, each Medicare part has its own financing rules, adding some complexity to the program (see Figure 10-7). In addition, beneficiary contributions in the form of premiums, deductibles, and co-payments contribute to financing Medicare expenditures.

Part A (HI) benefits are paid from the HI Trust Fund, funded through a mandatory payroll tax. Employers and employees each pay a tax of 1.45% of a worker's earnings (self-employed persons pay both shares, for a total tax of 2.9%), which is set aside for the Trust Fund. The ACA increases this rate for higher income tax payers. Beginning in 2013, individuals will have to pay a tax of 2.35% on earnings over $200,000 for individuals or $250,000 for couples.[52] In addition, beneficiaries pay a deductible for each inpatient hospital episode, and co-insurance for hospital care beyond 60 days, skilled nursing care beyond 20 days, outpatient drugs, and inpatient respite care.

By relying on payroll taxes, Medicare Part A uses current workers and employers to pay for health benefits for the disabled and those over 65 years old, many of whom are already retired. This formula is problematic in the face of the looming retirement of those from the Baby Boom generation; between 2010 and 2030, it is projected that a 10-million-person increase in the working population will have to support an increase of 30 million new elderly Medicare beneficiaries. To put it another way, in 2003, payroll taxes from almost four workers supported each Medicare beneficiary, but in 2030, it is expected that taxes on only 2.4 workers will be available to support each Medicare beneficiary.[56] Because of this and for other reasons, the 2010 Medicare Board of Trustees estimated that the Part A HI Trust Fund would be exhausted by 2029.[2(p20)]

Part B (SMI) is financed through general federal tax revenues and monthly premiums, deductibles, and cost-sharing paid by beneficiaries. Beneficiaries with incomes over $85,000 (or $170,000 for a couple) will pay a higher income-related monthly premium than other beneficiaries. Instead of increasing each year, this income threshold was frozen from 2009 to 2019 as part of the ACA, meaning more beneficiaries will be subject to the higher premium during those years. In addition to the monthly premium, beneficiaries pay an annual deductible for physician and medical services and have co-insurance requirements for outpatient hospital care, ambulatory surgical care, clinical diagnostic services, outpatient mental health services, and most preventive services.

Despite the federal government's and beneficiaries' investment in Medicare benefits, the program covers less than half of beneficiaries' actual healthcare expenses.[56] As a result, many beneficiaries have some type of supplemental insurance. Figure 10-8 illustrates the most common type of supplemental options: employer-sponsored insurance; Medicare Advantage plans, which offer extra benefits; Medicaid; and Medigap polices. Medigap policies are sold by private insurers and are intended to cover the cost of payments required by Medicare, such as premiums and co-payments. In addition, some Medigap policies offer benefits that are not covered by Medicare.

Part C Medicare Advantage plans provide services from Parts A and B and receive their funding from the sources described above. The federal government contracts with private plans and pays them a capitated rate to provide Medicare

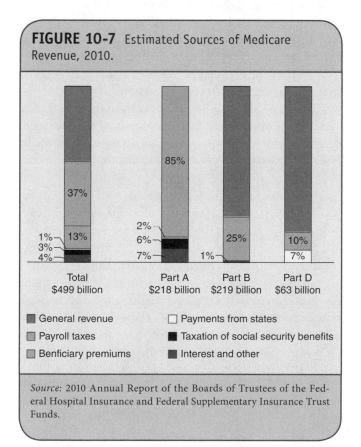

FIGURE 10-7 Estimated Sources of Medicare Revenue, 2010.

Legend:
- General revenue
- Payroll taxes
- Benficiary premiums
- Payments from states
- Taxation of social security benefits
- Interest and other

Total $499 billion: 37%, 1%, 13%, 3%, 4%
Part A $218 billion: 85%, 2%, 6%, 7%
Part B $219 billion: 25%, 1%
Part D $63 billion: 10%, 7%

Source: 2010 Annual Report of the Boards of Trustees of the Federal Hospital Insurance and Federal Supplementary Insurance Trust Funds.

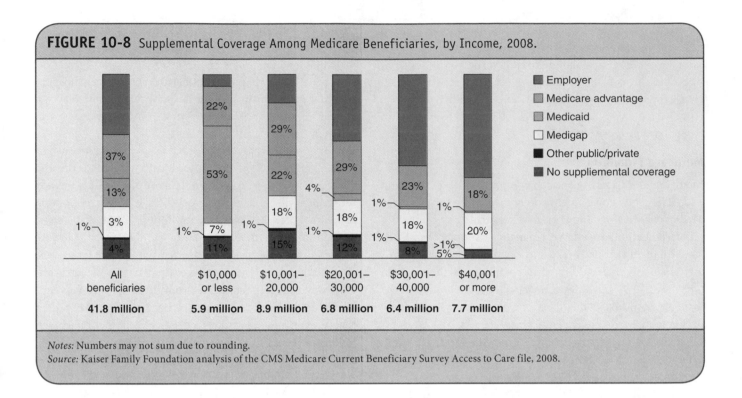

FIGURE 10-8 Supplemental Coverage Among Medicare Beneficiaries, by Income, 2008.

Notes: Numbers may not sum due to rounding.
Source: Kaiser Family Foundation analysis of the CMS Medicare Current Beneficiary Survey Access to Care file, 2008.

benefits to program participants. The plans charge beneficiaries varying premiums and co-payments.

Part D, Medicare's prescription drug benefit, is financed through an annual deductible, monthly premiums, general revenues, and state payments for dual enrollees. As shown in Figure 10-9, beneficiaries pay an annual deductible, 25% of the cost of drugs up to a set amount ($2,840 in 2011), 100% of the cost of drugs above that amount to a catastrophic threshold ($6,448 in 2011), and 5% of the cost above the catastrophic threshold. The gap in Medicare coverage where the beneficiary pays 100% of the cost of drugs is commonly referred to as the "doughnut hole." In 2007, approximately one-quarter of Part D users purchased drugs in the doughnut hole in 2010 and most plans do not offer coverage in this gap. Under Part D, deductibles, premiums, benefit limits, and catastrophic thresholds are not fixed, but indexed to increase with the growth in per capita Medicare spending for Part D. To offset these charges, the MMA included provisions to assist low-income beneficiaries by reducing or eliminating cost-sharing requirements and the doughnut hole. There are three low-income assistance tiers for beneficiaries who earn up to 150% FPL.[2(p8)]

The ACA included provisions to close the doughnut hole such that beneficiaries will only pay 25% cost-sharing in that range of drug spending by 2020. Beneficiaries received a $250 rebate for purchases made in the doughnut hole in 2010. To

close the coverage gap, beneficiaries will receive a phased-in discount for generic and brand name drugs purchased in the doughnut hole going forward. In addition, the amount of out-of-pocket spending needed to reach the catastrophic level was reduced from 2014–2019, but will revert back to its original level in 2020 without further congressional action.[2(p8)]

The MMA also requires that dual enrollees receive their prescription drug benefit through Medicare, not Medicaid. Under the MMA, states are now required to help fund Medicare's prescription drug benefit for dual enrollees through a maintenance-of-effort or "clawback" provision. This provision requires states to pay the federal government a share of expenditures the states would have made to provide prescription drug coverage to dual enrollees. The state share begins at 90% in 2006 and tapers down to 75% in 2015 and beyond. Many states are resisting these requirements and some are threatening not to pay their share. To the extent states adhere to the clawback provision, it represents the first time that states are assisting with Medicare financing. If states choose to provide dual enrollees with prescription drug coverage through Medicaid, states must use 100% of their own dollars to finance the coverage, even if the beneficiary does not enroll in Part D.

Table 10-6 provides a summary of Medicare financing provisions. Because Part C is financed by parts A and B and is an alternative to A and B, it is not included in the table. Whether beneficiaries have cost-sharing and other

FIGURE 10-9 Standard Medicare Prescription Drug Benefit, 2011.

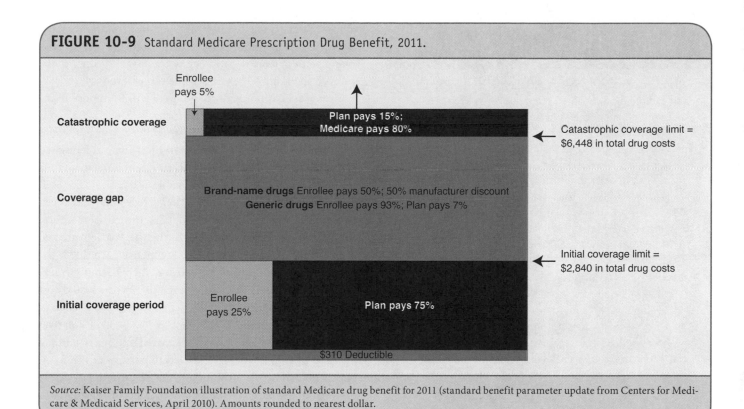

Source: Kaiser Family Foundation illustration of standard Medicare drug benefit for 2011 (standard benefit parameter update from Centers for Medicare & Medicaid Services, April 2010). Amounts rounded to nearest dollar.

requirements under Part C depends on the specifics of each managed care plan.

Medicare Provider Reimbursement

Medicare's reimbursement rules vary by provider type and by whether care is provided through a fee-for-service arrangement or a Medicare Advantage (i.e., managed care) plan. This section reviews physician and hospital reimbursement methodologies under both payment systems.

Physician Reimbursement

Physicians who are paid by a managed care plan to provide Medicare services to beneficiaries follow the same general rules for managed care reimbursement. However, physicians

TABLE 10-6 Medicare Financing by Part

Medicare Part	Government Financing Scheme	Beneficiary Payment Requirements		
		Annual Deductible	Monthly Premium	Cost-Sharing
A	Trust Fund through mandated employer and employee payroll taxes	Yes	No, if Social Security work requirements are met	Yes
B	General federal tax revenue	Yes	Yes	Yes
D	General federal tax revenue and state "clawback" payments for dual enrollees	Yes—except some low-income beneficiaries	Yes—except some low-income beneficiaries	Yes—except some low-income beneficiaries

BOX 10-21 Discussion Questions

The clawback provision is controversial and highlights some of the tensions about state flexibility and national uniformity that policymakers face when designing public programs. The clawback seems to contradict the prior decision to provide states with flexibility and program design responsibilities under Medicaid. In addition, it changes the decision to use only federal funds to pay for Medicare. Given decisions made by states prior to the MMA, there are many variations among state prescription drug benefits that will be "frozen" in place with the clawback provision. At the same time, the MMA creates a uniform rule about how all states finance prescription drug funding in the future, which could impact state-level decisions about dual enrollee coverage.

Is the clawback provision a good idea? Should states help pay for federal prescription drug coverage? Is there a better design? Should states or the federal government control Medicaid prescription drug coverage that is provided to dual enrollees? Should dual enrollees be treated differently than other Medicaid beneficiaries?

providing care on a fee-for-service basis are paid according to the Medicare fee schedule, although the ACA includes a 10% bonus payment from 2011–2015 for primary care providers who operate in Health Professional Shortage Areas. The fee schedule assigns a relative weight to every service to reflect the resources needed to provide the service. These weights are adjusted for geographic differences in costs and multiplied by a conversion factor (a way to convert the relative value that defines all medical services on the fee schedule into a dollar amount) to determine the final payment amount. Payment rates are changed through upward or downward shifts in the conversion factor. Although the ratio of Medicare physician fees to private insurance varies considerably by location, overall, Medicare physician fees are about 81% less than those provided by private insurers,[57(p90)] but about 28% higher than reimbursement rates provided by Medicaid.[58]

The formula for reimbursing physicians, referred to as the Sustainable Growth Rate (SGR), has been a focal point of debate. Congress established the SGR in 1997 as a way to control spending for physician services. The formula sets an overall target amount for spending on physician services (and related services such as laboratory tests) in Part B. Payment rates are adjusted to reflect actual spending as compared to the target level—if actual spending is higher than the target level,

payment rates are cut, but if actual spending is lower than the target level, payment rates are raised. From 1997–2001, physician spending was slightly below the target.[59] Since 2003, however, spending has exceeded the target level.

Congress has not had the political will to impose reimbursement cuts called for by the formula. Since 2003, Congress has suspended the formula annually because it would have resulted in rate reductions, and has instead legislated rate increases for physicians. Deferring reimbursement cuts year after year has led to an untenable situation. If the SGR formula were followed in 2010, physician fees would have been cut 21% that year and an additional 5% annually for several more years.[59(p112)] Unfortunately, fixing the problem created by deferred reimbursement is very expensive. In 2008, the Congressional Budget Office estimated that simply freezing physician rates at their 2009 level for 10 years would cost $318 billion. Replacing the SGR with another index (such as the Medicare Economic Index) would cost $439 billion over 10 years.[59(p113)] While Congress discussed options to address this issue during the debate that led to passage of the ACA, they ultimately left it for another day because the price tag was too high. Some critics complain that it is disingenuous to argue that the ACA reduces the deficit when this multi-billion problem was not addressed in the law.

Hospital Reimbursement

Hospitals are paid for acute inpatient services on a prospective basis using "diagnostic related groups" (DRGs). Diagnostic

BOX 10-22 Discussion Questions

Controlling Medicare spending is a difficult task. Even if provider reimbursement rates are reduced, physicians and hospitals may increase volume and intensity of services to make up for lost revenue. The ACA included a number of pilot programs and demonstration projects to experiment with reforming the way health care is financed and delivered. Some of these projects include bundling payment for acute care services, using value-based purchasing which ties payments to quality outcomes, and creating accountable care organizations that bring together providers across the healthcare spectrum and reward organizations with better outcomes. The ACA created the Centers for Medicare and Medicaid Services (CMS) Innovation Center to oversee these and other reform projects. What approach to reducing costs and improving quality do you prefer? What are the advantages and disadvantages of these ideas?

related groups sort patients into more than 500 groups based on their diagnoses. Various diagnoses are grouped together if they have similar clinical profiles and costs. Each DRG is assigned a relative weight based on charges for cases in that group as compared to the national average for all groups. In addition, the part of the DRG covering hospitals' cost of labor is adjusted by a wage index to account for different geographic costs.[60(p43)] Hospitals may also receive additional payments for providing high-cost outlier cases; incurring costs associated with use of new technology; incurring indirect medical education costs; serving a high proportion of low-income patients; or being a qualified sole community provider, a rural referral center, a small Medicare-dependent hospital, a rural hospital treating fewer than 200 admissions, or a critical access hospital (a qualified rural hospital that provides critical care services).[60(pp43–44)]

For outpatient care, hospitals are reimbursed by Medicare using a different prospective system. Each outpatient service is assigned to one of about 800 ambulatory payment classification (APC) groups. Ambulatory payment classifications have a relative weight based on the median cost of the service as compared to the national average. Again, a conversion factor is used to calculate the specific dollar amount per APC and the labor cost portion is adjusted based on a hospital wage index to account for geographic cost differences. Ambulatory payment classification payments may be adjusted when hospitals use new technologies or biologics, and when they treat unusually high-cost patients.[60(p44)]

The ACA included a number of provisions that reduced reimbursement for hospitals and other Medicare providers, including skilled nursing facilities and hospices. These rate reductions include "market basket" updates, which set the prices for a mix of goods and services, and a lowering of Disproportionate Share Hospital payments, which are given to hospitals that provide services to a relatively high proportion of low-income patients. In addition, hospitals will receive reduced payments for services connected to preventable readmissions and hospital-acquired conditions.

Medicare Advantage Reimbursement

Medicare Advantage plans are paid a capitated rate by the federal government to provide Parts A, B, and D benefits to each enrollee in their plan. Plans submit a bid to the federal government that estimates their cost per enrollee and these bids are compared to benchmarks established by statute and that vary by county. The benchmark is the maximum Medicare will pay for Part A and B services in that county.[61] Once a bid is accepted, a contract between plans and the federal government details the services the plan will provide and the premiums, deductibles, and cost sharing it will charge beneficiaries.

The ACA includes significant reductions in Medicare Advantage payments. On average, Medicare Advantage plans had become 9% to 13% more expensive than fee-for-service providers for comparable services.[61] The ACA phases in reduced payments that bring Medicare Advantage plans closer to the benchmark payment for traditional Medicare services in their county. Additional reductions will occur due to changes in the risk-adjustment formula. On the other hand, plans that provide high-quality care may be eligible for additional payments under the new law.[52]

CONCLUSION

This chapter provided you with an overview of the three main public programs that provide health insurance coverage to millions of people in the United States, and raised a series of policy questions for your consideration. Based on the size of the programs, their costs to the federal and state governments, and their importance to millions of (often low-income) individuals, the role and structure of Medicaid, CHIP, and Medicare are constantly being debated. Some people would like to see coverage expanded to ensure that everyone has adequate access to health insurance, others would like to dismantle the programs in the interest of eliminating government-funded entitlements, and still others suggest incremental changes to the programs. The debate continues even with the passage of the ACA. Some want to repeal the law, while others are discussing cuts to entitlement programs as a way to reduce the federal deficit. Each of these decisions, and many others, reflect the recurring themes that have been discussed throughout this chapter: choosing between state flexibility and national uniformity; determining the appropriate role for government, the private sector, and individuals in healthcare financing and delivery; defining a primary decision-making goal (fiscal restraint, equity/social justice, improved health outcomes, uniformity, etc.); and settling on the appropriate scope of coverage to offer beneficiaries. Given these programs' expected increase in beneficiaries and the complementary increase in their cost, it is likely that the debates over Medicaid, CHIP, and Medicare will continue vigorously in the foreseeable future.

REFERENCES

1. Kaiser Family Foundation. *Health coverage of children: The role of Medicaid and CHIP.* 2011. Available at http://www.kff.org/uninsured/7698.cfm. Accessed July 7, 2011; Kaiser Family Foundation. *Medicaid enrollment: June 2010 Snapshot.* Available at http://www.kff.org/medicaid/enrollmentreports.cfm. Accessed July 7, 2011; Kaiser Family Foundation. *Medicare chartbook.* 2010. Available at http://www.kff.org/medicare/8103.cfm. Accessed July 7, 2011.

2. Kaiser Family Foundation. *Medicare: A primer.* 2010. Available at http://www.kff.org/medicare/upload/7615-03.pdf. Accessed July 7, 2011.

3. Social Security Act §§ 1108(f), (g) & 1905(b), 42 U.S.C. §§ 1308 & 1396d(b).

4. Title XIX of the Social Security Act, §§ 1901–1935; 42 U.S.C. §§ 13961396v.

5. 42 C.F.R. Parts 430–498.

6. Centers for Medicaid and Medicare Services. *The state Medicaid manual.* Available at http://www.cms.gov/Manuals/PBM/itemdetail.asp?itemID=CMS021927. Accessed July 8, 2011.

7. Centers for Medicare and Medicaid Services. *State Medicaid director letters.* Available at https://www.cms.gov/SMDL/SMD/. Accessed July 7, 2011.

8. Kaiser Family Foundation. *The Medicaid program at a glance.* 2010. Available at http://www.kff.org/medicaid/upload/7334-04.pdf. Accessed July 7, 2011.

9. Kaiser Family Foundation. *Dual eligibles: Medicaid's role for low-income Medicare beneficiaries,* Kaiser Family Foundation; 2010. Available at http://www.kff.org/medicaid/upload/4091-07.pdf. Accessed March 10, 2011.

10. Kaiser Family Foundation. *Distribution of the nonelderly with Medicaid by Federal Poverty Level (FPL), states (2008–2009), U.S. (2009). State Health Facts.* Available at http://www.statehealthfacts.org/comparebar.jsp?typ=2&ind=156&cat=3&sub=42&cha=1808&o=a. Accessed March 14, 2011.

11. Kaiser Family Foundation. *Health insurance coverage of low income adults 19–64 (under 200% FPL), states (2008–2009), U.S. (2009).* Available at http://www.statehealthfacts.org/comparetable.jsp?typ=1&ind=878&cat=3&sub=177. Accessed March 14, 2011.

12. Kaiser Family Foundation. *Health reform source—frequently asked questions.* Available at http://healthreform.kff.org/faq/who-will-be-eligible-for-medicaid.aspx. Accessed April 4, 2011.

13. Kaiser Family Foundation. *Medicaid financial eligibility: Primary pathways for the elderly and people with disabilities.* 2010. Available at http://www.kff.org/medicaid/8048.cfm. Accessed March 14, 2011.

14. Pub L No. 104-193.

15. Children's Health Insurance Program Reauthorization Act of 2009. Pub L No. 111-3.

16. Fremstad S, Cox L. Covering new Americans: *A review of federal and state policies related to immigrants' eligibility and access to publicly funded health insurance.* Kaiser Family Foundation. 2004. Available at http://www.kff.org/medicaid/7214.cfm. Accessed July 8, 2011.

17. Passell JS. *Unauthorized migrants: Numbers and characteristics.* Pew Hispanic Center. 2005. Available at http://pewhispanic.org/reports/report.php?ReportID=46. Accessed July 8, 2011.

18. Families USA. *Expanding coverage for recent immigrants: CHIPRA gives states new options.* Available at http://www.policyarchive.org/handle/10207/bitstreams/96110.pdf. Accessed April 4, 2011.

19. 42 U.S.C. § 1396d(a)(13); 42 C.F.R. § 440.130.

20. Pub L No. 109-362.

21. 42 U.S.C. § 1937.

22. 42 U.S.C. § 1937(a).

23. 42 U.S.C. § 1937(a)2.

24. Kaiser Family Foundation. *Medicaid enrollment declines for the first time in nearly a decade, but 42 states are planning to expand coverage for uninsured.* Oct. 10, 2007. http://www.kff.org/medicaid/kcmu101007nr.cfm. Accessed July 8, 2011.

25. Kenny GM, Pelletier JE. *Medicaid policy changes in Idaho under the Deficit Reduction Act of 2005: Implementation issues and remaining challenges.* State Health Access Reform Evaluation. June 2010. Available at http://www.shadac.org/files/shadac/publications/IdahoMedicaidDRACaseStudy.pdf. Accessed April 5, 2010.

26. Rosenbaum S. Health policy report: Medicaid. *N Engl J Med.* 2002;346:635–640.

27. Kaiser Family Foundation. *Urban Institute estimates based on data from CMS (form 64).* Available at http://facts.kff.org/chart.aspx?ch=472. Accessed June 29, 2011.

28. Kaiser Family Foundation. *Federal and state share of Medicaid spending, FY 2009.* Available at http://www.statehealthfacts.org/comparemaptable.jsp?typ=2&ind=636&cat=4&sub=47. Accessed March 18, 2011.

29. Kaiser Family Foundation. *Medicaid primer. 2010.* Available at http://www.kff.org/medicaid/upload/7334-04.pdf. Accessed July 8, 2011.

30. Kaiser Family Foundation. *Total Medicaid spending, FY 2009.* Available at http://www.statehealthfacts.org:/comparemaptable.jsp?typ=7&ind=177&cat=4&sub=47. Accessed July 8, 2011.

31. 42 C.F.R. 447.50-.59.

32. 42 U.S.C. § 1916A.

33. Kaiser Family Foundation. *Medicaid and Children's Health Insurance Program provisions in the new health reform law.* April, 2010. Available at http://www.kff.org/healthreform/upload/7952-03.pdf. Accessed June 30, 2011.

34. 42 U.S.C. 1396a(a)(30)(A).

35. Boukus ER, Cassil A, O'Malley AS. *A snapshot of U.S. physicians: Key findings from the 2008 Health Tracking Study Physician Survey.* 2009. Center for Studying Health System Change. Available at http://www.hschange.com/CONTENT/1078/. Accessed July 8, 2011.

36. 42 U.S.C. § 1916A.

37. Centers for Medicare and Medicaid Services. *Medicaid Managed Care Enrollment as of June 30, 2009.* Available at https://www.cms.gov/MedicaidDataSourcesGenInfo/downloads/09June30f.pdf. Accessed July 8, 2011.

38. 42 U.S.C. § 1936u-2.

39. 42 U.S.C. § 1396b(m)(2)(iii); 42 C.F.R. 438.

40. Kaiser Family Foundation. *Five key questions and answers about Section 1115 waivers.* June 2011. Available at http://www.kff.org/medicaid/upload/8196.pdf. Accessed July 8, 2011.

41. 42 U.S.C. §§ 1397aa-1397jj.

42. Kaiser Family Foundation. *Children's health insurance program reauthorization act of 2009.* 2009. Available at http://www.kff.org/medicaid/upload/7863.pdf. Accessed July 6, 2011.

43. Centers for Medicare and Medicaid Services. *CHIP ever enrolled year graph.* 2011. Available at http://www.cms.gov/NationalCHIPPolicy/downloads/CHIPEverEnrolledYearGraph.pdf. Accessed July 8, 2011.

44. Kaiser Commission on Medicaid and the Uninsured. *Health coverage of children: The role of Medicaid and CHIP.* 2010. Available at http://www.kff.org/uninsured/upload/7698-04.pdf. Accessed July 8, 2011.

45. Kaiser Family Foundation. *CHIP Program Name and Type, 2010.* Available at http://www.statehealthfacts.org/comparetable.jsp?cat=4&ind=238. Accessed July 8, 2011.

46. Kaiser Family Foundation. *Enhanced Federal Medical Assistance Percentage (FMAP) for the Children's Health Insurance Program (CHIP).* Health Facts. Available at http://www.statehealthfacts.org/comparetable.jsp?ind=239&cat=4. Accessed July 8, 2011.

47. Ryan K. *The Children's Health Insurance Program: The fundamentals.* National Health Policy Forum. 2009. Available at http://www.nhpf.org/library/details.cfm/2735. Accessed July 6, 2011.

48. Kaiser Family Foundation. *State adoption of coverage and enrollment options in the Children's Health Insurance Reauthorization Act of 2009.* 2011. Available at http://www.kff.org/medicaid/upload/8146.pdf. Accessed July 6, 2011.

49. 42 U.S.C. § 1397cc.

50. Title XXI, § 2102(a); 42 U.S.C. § 1397bb(a).

51. Alliance for Health Reform. *The future of children's health insurance coverage.* Available at http://www.allhealth.org/publications/Child_health_insurance/The_Future_of_Childrens_Health_Coverage_98.pdf. Accessed July 6, 2011.

52. Kaiser Family Foundation. *Summary of key changes to Medicare in the 2010 health reform law.* 2010. Available at http://www.kff.org/healthreform/upload/7948-02.pdf. Accessed July 8, 2011.

53. Kaiser Family Foundation, "Medicare Enrollment 1966–2010," *Medicare Chartbook, Fourth Edition 2010.* Available at http://facts.kff.org/chart.aspx?cb=58&sctn=162&ch=1714. Accessed July 8, 2011.

54. Pub L No. 108-173.

55. Centers for Medicare and Medicaid Services. *National health expenditure projections 2009–2019.* Available at https://www.cms.gov/NationalHealthExpendData/downloads/NHEProjections2009to2019.pdf. Accessed January 25, 2011.

56. Kaiser Family Foundation. *Medicare Fact Sheet: Medicare Spending and Financing.* 2008. Available at http://www.kff.org/medicare/upload/7305_03.pdf. Accessed July 9, 2011.

57. MedPAC. *Report to the Congress: Medicare payment policy.* 2008. Available at http://www.medpac.gov/documents/Mar08_EntireReport.pdf. Accessed July 9, 2011.

58. Zuckerman S, Williams AF, Stockley KE. Trends in Medicaid physician fees, 2003–2008. *Health Aff.* 2009;28(3/4):W511.

59. Congressional Budget Office. *Budget Options: Volume 1—Health Care.* Washington, DC: Congressional Budget Office. 2008. Publication 3185. Available at http://www.cbo.gov/ftpdocs/99xx/doc9925/12-18-HealthOptions.pdf. Accessed July 7, 2011.

60. Medicare Payment Advisory Committee. *Report to Congress: Medicare Payment Policy.* Washington, D.C.: Medicare Payment Advisory Committee; 2005.

61. Kaiser Family Foundation. *Explaining health reform: key changes in the Medicare Advantage program.* 2010. Available at http://www.kff.org/healthreform/upload/8071.pdf. Accessed July 7, 2011.

ENDNOTES

a. Puerto Rico, the U.S. Virgin Islands, Guam, Northern Mariana Islands, and American Samoa participate in Medicaid. However, financing rules are different in these territories than in the 50 states. Federal spending is capped and appropriated by Congress annually.

b. A special 5% adjustment allowed by law effectively brings the eligibility rate to 138% FPL.

c. Community health centers have their own per-visit prospective payment system for reimbursement under Medicaid.

d. Although federal law does not elaborate on the specifics of section 1115 waivers, other federal guidance does. In 1994, HHS prepared a nonbinding notice, "Demonstration Proposal Pursuant to Section 1115(a) of the Social Security Act," 59 Fed. Reg. 49249 (1994), and then the Health Care Financing Administration (now CMS) published a "Review Guide for Section 1115 Research and Demonstration Waiver Proposals for State Health Care Reform." The *State Medicaid Manual* also contains information relating to Section 1115 waivers.

e. Since New Jersey and New York had already expanded coverage to children beyond 300% FPL prior to CHIPRA, those states are allowed to use their enhanced CHIP match up to their capped allotment.

f. Private fee-for-service plans, usually offered at the county level, provide the standard Medicare coverage, but beneficiaries may see only physicians who participate in the plan and must pay premiums and co-payments or co-insurance to the private plan instead of to individual providers. In return, the private plan may offer additional services not covered by Medicare.

CHAPTER 11

Healthcare Quality Policy and Law

LEARNING OBJECTIVES

By the end of this chapter you will be able to:

- Discuss licensure and accreditation in the context of healthcare quality
- Describe the scope and causes of medical errors
- Describe the meaning and evolution of the medical professional standard of care
- Identify and explain certain state-level legal theories under which healthcare professionals and entities can be held liable for medical negligence
- Explain how federal employee benefits law often preempts medical negligence lawsuits against insurers and managed care organizations
- Describe recent efforts to measure and incentivize high-quality health care

BOX 11-1 Vignette

Michelina Bauman was born on May 16, 1995, in New Jersey. The managed care organization (MCO) through which her parents received healthcare coverage had pre-certified coverage for one day in the hospital post-birth, and both Michelina and her mother were discharged from the hospital 24 hours after Michelina was born. The day after the discharge, Michelina became ill. Her parents telephoned the MCO, but they were neither advised to take Michelina back to the hospital nor provided an in-home visit by a pediatric nurse as promised under the MCO's "L'il Appleseed" infant care program. Michelina died that same day from meningitis stemming from an undiagnosed strep infection.

INTRODUCTION

This chapter steps away from the topics of healthcare access and coverage to focus on healthcare quality. As with access and coverage, healthcare quality has various dimensions, and the topic of healthcare quality has increasingly been a focal point of researchers, analysts, health professionals, and consumers. For instance, in the span of only a couple of years, the influential Institute of Medicine (IOM) of the National Academies of Science has released two major reports pertaining to healthcare quality: *To Err Is Human: Building a Safer Health System,*[1] which focused on the specific quality concern of patient safety, and *Crossing the Quality Chasm: A New Health System for the 21st Century,*[2] which described how the healthcare delivery system should be overhauled to improve care.

Also, like healthcare access and coverage issues, healthcare quality is a key concern in health policy and law. For example, long-standing problems related to the administration of health care—like racial and ethnic health disparities, and the geographic variation in the amount or type of care provided to patients—have drawn responses from policymakers and the legal system. Furthermore, policy and legal responses are often needed as healthcare quality is affected by changes in the marketplace or by advances in medical technology. For instance, institutional payers for healthcare services—traditional insurers, employers, and managed care companies—are more involved in healthcare practice now than was the case historically,[3(p26)] a fact that has spurred policymakers and courts to reconsider traditional notions of healthcare quality and liability.

The role of law as a monitor of the quality of health care was on display in the context of the no-duty-to-treat principle and the case of *Hurley v. Eddingfield*.[4] Recall how Indiana's physician licensure law was described as a filter to weed out individuals without the requisite skills to safely and adequately practice medicine. Licensure in theory permits a second healthcare quality function, as well—it allows state regulators to monitor the conduct of medical practitioners even after they have been licensed, although, as discussed below, this function has not been performed with much vigor over the years.

Holding healthcare professionals and entities liable for substandard care is another (and perhaps the most well-known) legal tool used to promote quality in health care. Physicians have no legal duty to accept a patient into their practice or to provide care upon request, except in limited circumstances. However, a doctor's decision to treat a patient establishes a legally significant physician–patient relationship, under which the physician owes the patient a reasonable duty of care. Failure to meet what is termed the *professional standard of care*—the legal standard used in medical negligence cases to determine whether health professionals and entities have adequately discharged their responsibility to provide reasonable care to their patients—can result in legal liability for reasonably foreseeable injuries.[a]

As you will soon discover, the laws and legal principles that define the circumstances under which aggrieved individuals can successfully sue a managed care organization for substandard care or coverage determinations are complex. This complexity stems from multiple facts. First, the legal framework applied to medical negligence cases was developed long before the advent of managed care. Second, the hybrid nature of managed care (combining as it does the financing and delivery of care) defies easy categorization and makes application of the legal framework challenging. And third, a federal law (the Employee Retirement Income Security Act, or ERISA) pertaining to employee benefit plans preempts (i.e., precludes) many typical state-level legal claims against MCOs.

The next section of this chapter provides a brief overview of healthcare licensure and accreditation in the context of healthcare quality. The chapter then turns to an overview of errors in health care. Although medical errors are only one small component of the broad subject of healthcare quality, they are commonly included in the quality discussion and serve as a jumping-off point for a discussion of healthcare liability. The chapter then turns to a full discussion of the professional standard of care and its evolution, followed by a description of some of the state legal theories under which hospitals, traditional insurers, and MCOs can be held liable for substandard medical professional conduct. It then explores the complex area of how ERISA preempts lawsuits

premised on these same legal theories. Finally, the chapter describes the concepts of measuring and incentivizing health care quality.

QUALITY CONTROL THROUGH LICENSURE AND ACCREDITATION

The licensing of healthcare professionals and institutions is an important function of state law. As noted previously, healthcare licensure is centrally about filtering out those who may not have the requisite knowledge or skills to practice medicine; in other words, states exercise their police powers when applying licensure laws in order to protect residents from being subjected to substandard health care. State licensure laws both define the qualifications required to become licensed and the standards that must be met for purposes of maintaining and renewing licenses.[5]

Important as the licensing function is, however, historically it has been used in the promotion of healthcare quality in only the bluntest sense. This stems from the fact that in most states, the only method by which to promote quality through licensure is, simply, the granting or denial of the license to practice medicine. In other words, there exists no middle ground between being granted a license and not being granted (or renewed for) a license, no ongoing monitoring or application of standards intended to promote quality and ensure competence in the face of evolving medical care practices. In designing licensing laws, most state legislatures assume that medical professional trade associations (e.g., the American Medical Association) and/or accrediting bodies have sufficient ethical and practice standards to effectively regulate healthcare practitioners, and that the "task of quality assurance under licensure is to identify and deal with relatively rare cases of individual provider deviation from those norms."[6] This assumption is correct, to a point—private professional and industry standards do indeed exist, though their effect on day-to-day quality is debatable. Some commentators maintain that accreditation amounts to little more than self-serving indicia of individual or institutional exceptionalism, while others argue that accreditation plays an important and useful role alongside licensure. There are many examples of healthcare accreditation bodies: the Joint Commission (formerly the Joint Commission on Accreditation of Healthcare Organizations), which may be best known for its review and accreditation of hospitals; the National Committee for Quality Assurance, which accredits managed care organizations; the Healthcare Facilities Accreditation Program; the Commission on Accreditation of Rehabilitation Facilities; the Community Health Accreditation Program; the Utilization Review Accreditation Commission; and others.

A second historical fact related to licensure's effect (or lack thereof) on healthcare quality—one that plays into detractors' claims about the self-serving nature of today's industry-designed accreditation processes—is that state licensing schemes were designed not with healthcare quality *per se* in mind, but rather with an eye toward protecting the medical professions from unscrupulous or incompetent providers and bad publicity. For example, "a typical medical licensure act of the early 1960s provided for license suspension or revocation when, for example, a physician: (1) had been adjudicated insane; (2) habitually used intoxicants; (3) had practiced criminal abortion or had been convicted of a crime involving moral turpitude; (4) had advertised fraudulently; (5) had misrepresented his credentials to the licensing board; or (6) had employed unlicensed persons to do work reserved for licensed practitioners."[7] Thus, the laws tended to focus on preventing relatively rare instances of grossly poor-quality care, rather than on long-term promotion of high-quality care.

One final topic pertaining to licensure that bears mentioning is the immensely important role it plays in defining the permissible "scope of practice" of the various types of healthcare providers. It is one thing for state legislators to define the meaning of practice for various broad medical fields (e.g., there is not so much overlap between, say, medicine and dentistry as to cause a huge number of policy and legal disputes), but quite another for legislators to define the lawful activities of doctors as compared to physician assistants as compared to nurses, and even more specifically of advanced practice nurses (APNs) as compared to licensed practical nurses (LPNs) as compared to registered nurses (RNs). It is in delineating permissible scopes of practice within fields and subspecialties that fierce policy disputes take place.

Yet, it is not surprising that these disputes take place. Licensure laws define who has the power to engage in medical practice, who gets to practice specific types of health care, and how and when professional standards of conduct are enforced. In short, licensure laws have the power to determine who is in, as they say, and who is out. Some states are relatively more inclusive in their approach to the licensing of healthcare professionals, while others hew closely to a more traditional approach in which physicians are granted broad scope of practice powers while other professionals (e.g., nurses) have far less ability to diagnose and treat patients. The latter approach is being hotly contested, as nurses[8] and other non-physician healthcare professionals[9] decry their inability to practice to their full education and training, particularly in light of the healthcare workforce shortages that plague the nation[10] and the huge number of individuals who will be newly able to access health insurance (and thus be more likely to seek care) under the Affordable Care Act.

MEDICAL ERRORS AS A PUBLIC HEALTH CONCERN

Notwithstanding licensure laws and accreditation standards, medical errors are bound to, and often do, occur. And while medical errors are obviously not a new problem, framing the issue as a public health problem is a relatively new phenomenon, and healthcare providers, public health professionals, and policymakers have in recent years committed increased attention to the problem of medical errors.

The extent to which medical errors both occur at all and ultimately result in adverse health outcomes and mortalities indicates that the problem is not confined to one ethnic or racial population, socioeconomic group, or geographic area. A study conducted in Colorado and Utah suggests that 44,000 Americans die each year as a result of hospital-related medical error,[1(p1)] while a similar study in New York estimates the number to be as high as 98,000.[1(p1)] Overall, more people die each year from medical errors than from motor vehicle accidents, breast cancer, or AIDS.[1(p1)] The negative effects of medical errors on individual patients and on society as a whole—including associated reductions in work productivity, lost income, and the costs associated with correcting injuries resulting from errors—support the conclusion that medical errors are properly classified as a public health problem requiring a strong response from, among others, policymakers and the legal system.

There are various causes of medical errors. They can be caused by actions that are, relatively speaking, concrete—such as failing to complete an intended medical course of action, implementing the wrong course of action, using faulty equipment or products in effectuating a course of action, failing to stay abreast of one's field of medical practice, or health professional inattentiveness. For example, according to the IOM, errors in the prescribing, administering, and dispensing of medications result in at least 1.5 million injuries or deaths annually in the United States.[11(pA08)] Furthermore, "mistakes in giving drugs are so prevalent in hospitals that, on average, a patient will be subjected to a medication error each day he or she occupies a hospital bed."[11(pA08)] Yet according to the IOM, "at least a quarter of the injuries caused by drug errors are clearly preventable,"[11(pA08)] and some of the errors are spawned by something as simple as name confusion among pharmaceuticals; it is easy to see how physicians, nurses, and pharmacists could easily confuse the arthritis drug Celebrex, the anticonvulsant drug Cerebyx, and the antidepressant drug Celexa when prescribing, administering, and filling medications.[12]

There are more abstract causes of medical errors, as well. For example, they can result from the fact that "[m]uch of medical treatment is still primitive: the etiologies and optimal treatments for many illnesses are not known [and] many treatment techniques, such as cancer chemotherapy, create substantial side effects."[3(p30)] Also, many people argue that the culture of medicine—including its history of elitism, its focus on memorization in both diagnosing and treating illness, and its dedication to secrecy when adverse medical outcomes occur—helps to explain the extent of medical errors.

Just as there are multiple causes of medical errors, so are there various strategies—some broad and systemic, others more incremental—for preventing and reducing their occurrence. For instance, hospitals usually employ two vehicles to minimize medical errors and assure quality care for patients: risk management programs and peer review processes. Risk management programs monitor risks associated with non-physician personnel and with facilities under the direct control of hospital administrators; peer review processes entail a secretive evaluation of hospital-based physician practices by physicians themselves. Most physicians encounter the peer review process when they apply for "staff privileges" at a hospital, which grant doctors the ability to use the hospital for their own private practice, including the ability to admit patients and use the hospital's resources in treating patients. Once a doctor is granted such privileges, he or she is subject to ongoing peer review. Many analysts maintain that the secretive manner in which the peer review process is conducted stifles meaningful improvements to patient safety, and that it is too reactive, responding to errors only after they have occurred.

Recently, public and private policymakers have begun shifting their attention to medical error reforms that are less reactive and more centered on error prevention and patient safety improvements. There are two primary objectives of these reforms: to redesign healthcare delivery methods and structures to limit the likelihood of human error, and to prepare in advance for the inevitable errors that will occur in healthcare delivery regardless of the amount and types of precautions taken. Medical error reform could entail various approaches, including more standardization of medical procedures, mandatory reporting of medical errors, reducing reliance on memory in medical care, increasing and improving medical information technology systems, encouraging patients to be more participatory in their own medical care, and establishing a national focus on the topic of patient safety.[3(pp43–64)] For example, the federal Patient Safety and Quality Improvement Act (PSQIA)[13] was signed into law in 2005 in response to the IOM's *To Err Is Human* report. PSQIA created a system for use by healthcare providers to anonymously report

---

BOX 11-2 Discussion Questions

What do you think of the term *medical error* as a descriptor of adverse medical outcomes? After all, there are many medical procedures (e.g., invasive surgeries) and treatments (e.g., chemotherapy) that not only are inherently risky, but also cause painful and dangerous (and often unpreventable) side effects (i.e., that lead to "adverse" medical results). Given this fact, is it conceivable that the healthcare delivery system could ever operate free of "error"? Can you think of other terms that better (or more fairly) convey the range of adverse outcomes attending healthcare practice?

---

medical error data for systematic analysis. The hope is that by aggregating, analyzing, and disseminating the data analyses to healthcare providers nationwide, healthcare professionals and entities will increase their knowledge about what leads to adverse medical outcomes and alter their practice methods accordingly.

PROMOTING HEALTHCARE QUALITY THROUGH THE STANDARD OF CARE

Not all medical errors rise to the level of being contrary to law. This section details the measure used by the legal system to determine which errors trigger legal protections: the professional standard of care. The standard of care is key both to the provision of high-quality health care and to legal claims that a health professional's, hospital's, or managed care organization's negligence in rendering medical care resulted in injury or death. This type of liability falls under the law of *torts*, a term that derives from the Latin word for "twisted" and which applies to situations where the actions of an individual or entity "twist away" from being reasonable and result in harm to others. Proving tort liability is not easy generally, and this is no less true in the specific context of medical care. A patient seeking to hold a health professional or entity responsible for substandard care or treatment must demonstrate the appropriate standard of care, a breach of that standard by the defendant, measurable damages (for example, physical pain or emotional suffering), and a causal link between the defendant's breach and the patient's injury.[b]

The Origins of the Standard of Care

The professional standard of care has its origins in 18th-century English common law. Courts in England had established that a patient looking to hold a physician legally accountable for substandard care had to prove that the doctor violated the *customs of his own profession*, as determined by *other professionals within the profession*. In other words, no objective standard was utilized by courts to measure the adequacy of physician practice.[c] Furthermore, courts were not in the habit of making searching analyses of whether the customs and standards proffered by the profession as defensible were at all reasonable. This type of physician deference was incorporated into America's legal fabric, as policymakers and courts delegated key decisions about medical practice—including determinations as to whether a specific practice undertaken in the treatment of a particular patient was acceptable or negligent—to the medical profession itself.

The law's reliance on health professionals to determine the appropriate standard of medical care was not without its problems. In effect, this *laissez-faire* approach made it virtually impossible for an injured patient to successfully recover monetary damages from a negligent doctor, because the patient was required to find another health professional willing to testify that the doctor's treatment violated the customary standard of care. (This type of testimony was certainly uncommon, as health professionals rarely openly questioned the practices of other members of the profession.) Moreover, using professional custom as the touchstone for determining legal liability had the effect of thwarting the modernization of medical care, because practicing physicians knew they would be judged, in essence, based on how other physicians customarily practiced.

Furthermore, establishing a violation of professional custom was not the only hurdle injured patients had to clear in their effort to hold their physicians legally accountable for substandard care. English courts also developed what became known as the "locality rule," which held that testimony provided on behalf of a patient as to whether a physician's actions met the standard of care could only come from physicians who practiced *within the same or similar locality* as the physician on trial. Thus, not only did aggrieved patients need to find a physician willing to testify that a fellow member of the profession violated customary practice, they needed to find this expert witness within the (or a similar) locality in which the defendant-doctor actually practiced.[14] As they did with the professional custom rule, U.S. courts gradually adopted the English locality rule. For example, the Supreme Judicial Court of Massachusetts ruled that a small-town physician was bound to possess only the skill that physicians and surgeons of ordinary ability and skill, practicing in similar localities with opportunities for no larger experience, ordinarily possess, and that he was not bound to possess the high degree of art and skill possessed by eminent surgeons practicing in larger cities and making a specialty of the practice of surgery.[15]

Courts' application of the locality rule severely limited patients' ability to bring medical malpractice actions against their physicians. Indeed, some injured patients were prevented from even initially mounting a case, because they were unable to convince a "geographic colleague" of their own physician to serve as an expert witness. (This problem was particularly acute in rural communities where there were fewer doctors to begin with, and where collegiality was the norm.) Furthermore, the locality rule likely resulted in at least a few local medical standards that were set by doctors who were less than completely skilled. The rule had another effect, as well: It led to a gulf among localities and cities in the standard of medical care practiced, and thus to different standards of care for similarly situated patients. Imagine, for example (notwithstanding the fact that the professional custom rule generally discouraged advancements in the standard of medical care), that physicians in a large town or city upgraded their practice techniques to reflect new medical technologies. Small-town practitioners had little incentive to model their big-city colleagues in the improvement of their own practice techniques, because the locality rule limited testimony as to the reasonableness of a physician's care to practitioners in the same or similar locality as the doctor on trial and their own actions would never be measured against the elevated techniques of their big-city counterparts.

By the 1950s, policymakers and the legal system grew wary of a healthcare system effectively in charge of policing itself; not surprisingly, this view was reflective of society more broadly, which during the civil rights era adopted a set of values heavily influenced by social justice and circumspect of concentrated institutional power. It also reflected the fact that no matter how chilling the effects of the professional custom and locality rules, the practice of medicine—particularly the dissemination of medical research findings—had obviously evolved from the 1800s. These facts both vastly altered the law's approach to measuring physician care and promoted higher-quality health care.[14]

The Evolution of the Standard of Care

Under the law's modernized approach to the standard of care, both legal pillars of the physician autonomy era—the professional custom rule and the locality rule—were more or less razed.

The Professional Custom Rule

Courts no longer defer to professional custom as solely determinative of whether a physician's actions reached the accepted standard of care. Instead, courts now analyze whether the custom itself is reasonable in light of existing medical knowledge and technology.[d] Although evidence of professional custom remains probative in determining whether the standard of care has been met, courts consider a range of other relevant evidence as well. Thus, the benchmark courts employ today to determine whether a health professional's treatment of a particular patient rose to the standard of care is whether it was *reasonable given the "totality of circumstances."*

Furthermore, it is no longer the case that evidence as to what is and is not customary medical practice is limited to what medical professionals themselves testify. Although evidence as to medical custom may still be introduced by medical professionals, objective clinical and scientific evidence—such as scientific research and clinical trial results—are now considered relevant in determining medical negligence. For example, the well-known case of *Helling v. Carey*[16] shows how advances in medical knowledge can obliterate long-standing medical customs and replace them with new requirements. In *Helling*, a 32-year-old woman sought treatment from a series of ophthalmologists for glaucoma-type symptoms. The ophthalmologists, however, refrained from screening the patient for glaucoma, on the ground that professional custom only called for the screen in patients beyond the age of 40 because the incidence of glaucoma in younger people was low. The State of Washington's Supreme Court ruled that notwithstanding the fact that the ophthalmologists had properly adhered to accepted custom, the *custom itself* was outdated based on current medical knowledge and was therefore unreasonable. The court effectively determined that a new treatment standard was required of the ophthalmology profession, and held that the defendant-physicians were liable for the patient's blindness.

The key legal principle at work in *Helling* is that courts can (and do, in rare circumstances) determine for an entire industry (medical or otherwise) what is legally required of them, despite long-standing industry practices. This principle is premised on the famous case of *The T.J. Hooper*,[17] in which the U.S. Second Circuit Court of Appeals held that a tugboat company was liable for damages to cargo it was shipping because the company failed to maintain radio-receiving equipment that could have warned the crew of a storm that battered the boat. The company argued that it should not be liable for the damage because at the time it was not typical practice in the tugboat industry to carry radio equipment. In response, the court wrote:

> There are, no doubt, cases where courts seem to make the general practice of the calling the standard of proper diligence . . . . Indeed in

> most cases reasonable prudence is in fact common prudence; but strictly it is never its measure; *a whole calling may have unduly lagged in the adoption of new and available devices.* It never may set its own tests, however persuasive be its usages. *Courts must in the end say what is required*; there are precautions so imperative that even their universal disregard will not excuse their omission.[18]

Essentially, the court determined that the tugboat company was not acting reasonably under the circumstances, but was instead hewing too closely (and foolishly) to what should have been considered an outmoded industry practice. This same view appeared to drive the court in *Helling v. Carey*, as well. Indeed, the idea that the quality of health care provided by a health professional should be measured by an objective standard based on reasonableness under the circumstances—rather than by other professionals cloaked in the protections of outright autonomy—is today considered the norm. Furthermore, this view extends to big cities and small towns alike, and to both well-off and indigent patients.

The Locality Rule

Just as professional custom was transformed by the courts from being conclusive evidence of proper medical practice to being merely one piece of the evidentiary puzzle, so too was the locality rule mostly undone by more modern judicial thinking. Based in part on the fact that medical education and hospital-based care were becoming increasingly standardized under national accreditation efforts, courts stopped restricting evidence regarding the appropriate standard of care to the locality in which a physician practiced. Instead, most states have adopted what could be termed the "reasonably competent physician" standard, described as

> that degree of care and skill which is expected of a reasonably competent practitioner in the same class to which he belongs, acting in the same or similar circumstances. Under this standard, advances in the profession, availability of facilities, specialization or general practice, proximity of specialists and special facilities, together with all relevant considerations, are to be taken into account.[19]

Under this revised standard, the practice of medicine nationally is key, because for purposes of determining medical liability, a physician's actions are now measured objectively against those of a reasonably prudent and competent practitioner under similar circumstances, not against the actions of physicians who practice within a particular defendant's locality. Thus, in the eyes of most state laws, local medical practice customs have properly given way to higher expectations where health quality is concerned.

At the same time, some states still retain the locality rule as the appropriate standard for the admissibility of medical evidence, and some states utilize a modified rule that takes into account local resources and other factors in determining whether a defendant-doctor was able to meet the standard of care. For an example of the latter point, see *Hall v. Hilbun*,[20] in which the Mississippi Supreme Court determined that the locality rule still had relevance to the extent that a physician's imperfect care resulted not from his substandard medical knowledge and skills, but from the fact that he did not have access to needed resources and equipment. In this type of situation, the court reasoned, health professionals who genuinely attempt to meet the requisite standard of care should not be held legally responsible when factors outside their control prevent them from doing so. The court in *Hall* went on to explain that under these circumstances, a physician is required to be aware of extant limitations and to actively demonstrate an effort to assist patients as best he can by, for example, referring them to doctors and facilities better able to care for them.

For purposes of determining legal liability for substandard treatment, the notion of distinguishing between medical knowledge and skills on the one hand and medical resources and outside factors on the other has particular relevance when the treatment involves an indigent patient whose care implicates broad contextual problems, such as poor living conditions or insufficient access to providers. Here, again, many courts look to see whether the treating physician's actions demonstrate an understanding of the proper level of care and a sincere effort to reach that level. However, do not confuse the fact that the law does not generally hold physicians liable for the consequences of resource problems attending the healthcare system, or of poverty, with the idea that different standards of care exist for the well-off and for the poor. As far as the law is concerned, there is a unitary standard of care to be applied regardless of a patient's socioeconomic status, and physicians can certainly be held legally responsible for mistreating an indigent patient.

Together, the revamped legal rules pertaining to medical custom and local practice were combined to create what is called the *national standard of care*. We turn now to a discussion of how this standard is applied to healthcare institutions and insurers.

TORT LIABILITY OF HOSPITALS, INSURERS, AND MANAGED CARE ORGANIZATIONS

Just as physicians are now held to a national standard of care in cases challenging the quality of their care and treatment, so too have courts moved to apply this same standard to hospitals, traditional health insurers, and managed care organizations. The following sections consider each of these in turn.

Hospital Liability

By the early 1900s, the healthcare industry began to rely much more heavily than had been the case previously on hospitals (as opposed to physicians' offices or patients' homes) as a focus of patient care. As with all healthcare settings, hospital-based medical practice created circumstances that led patients to challenge the quality of care provided. Out of necessity, the legal system (specifically, state-level courts) responded to these challenges by applying theories of liability—premised on the national standard of care—meant to hold hospitals accountable for negligence that occurred within their walls. Two theories—one premised on hospitals' relationship with doctors and one based on the actions and decisions of hospitals themselves—dominate the field of hospital liability. The former theory is called vicarious liability; the latter is termed corporate liability.

Vicarious Liability

The concept of vicarious liability, which maintains that one party can be held legally accountable for the actions of another party based solely on the type of relationship existing between the two parties, is premised on the long-standing principles of "agency" law. Under this field of law, where one party to a relationship effectively serves (or is held out to society) as an agent of another party, a court can assign legal responsibility to the other party where the agent's actions negligently result in injury to a person or damage to property. For example, vicarious liability allows a hospital to be held responsible in some situations for the negligent acts of the doctors that practice medicine under its roof—not because the hospital itself somehow acted negligently, but rather because the doctor is (or is viewed as by the law) an agent of the hospital.

One relatively easy way for a plaintiff to win a lawsuit premised on vicarious liability is to establish through evidence that the two parties at issue are engaged in an employer–employee relationship, and that the employee (i.e., the agent) was acting within the normal scope of her professional duties when the act of negligence occurred. In these instances, courts frequently look to the employer to adequately supervise the employee while on the job and hold the employer responsible when an employee's negligent acts occur within the parameters of the employee's job responsibilities.

However, many "agents" of the companies they are hired to work for are not formal employees; rather, they are hired as independent contractors. Indeed, this is true of most hospital–physician relationships. Historically, agency law respected hiring entities' decisions to hire individuals as independent contractors rather than as employees, and the general legal rule is that employers are not accountable for the illegal actions of these contractors. Nonetheless, there are exceptions to this rule, and courts have developed theories of vicarious liability—such as *actual agency*, *apparent agency*, and *nondelegable duty*—that are more concerned with the scope of an employer–independent contractor relationship than with the formal characterization of the relationship as determined by the parties themselves. In other words, employers cannot avoid legal liability simply by labeling a hired worker as an independent contractor, because courts will analyze the relationship to determine whether it operates at the end of the day like a typical employer–employee relationship.

Actual agency exists—and the negligence of an independent contractor can be imputed to his employer—when the employer exercises *de facto* supervision and control over the contractor. Thus, for example, agency can be shown to exist between a healthcare corporation and a health professional when the particular facts pertaining to the relationship reveal that the corporation actually exercises control over the professional, even though the professional is not technically an employee. Similarly, the doctrine of apparent agency (also called ostensible agency) is another exception to the general rule that employers should not be legally exposed for the negligence of their independent contractors. In the context of health care, this type of agency exists, for example, when a patient seeks care from a hospital emergency department (rather than from any particular physician working in that department) and the hospital has led patients to believe that physicians are employees of the hospital (for example, via a billboard extolling the skills of the physicians who practice in its emergency department).[21] Finally, courts have also associated the doctrine of vicarious liability with certain duties considered so important to society as to be legally "nondelegable." For example, the importance of a hospital's obligation to maintain control over the care provided in its emergency department led one court to rule that it would be improper for the hospital to claim immunity from vicarious liability when its independent contractor furnished substandard medical care.[22]

Corporate Liability

As opposed to vicarious hospital liability, which is predicated on the negligence of individual health professionals, corporate liability holds hospitals accountable for their own "institutional" acts or omissions. In other words, a hospital can also be held liable when its own negligent acts as a corporation cause or contribute to a patient's injury. Several general areas give rise to litigation around hospitals' direct quality of care duties to patients: failure to screen out incompetent providers (i.e., negligence in the hiring of clinicians), failure to maintain high-quality practice standards, failure to take adequate action against clinicians whose practices fall below accepted standards, and failure to maintain proper equipment and supplies.[14]

The most famous hospital corporate liability case is *Darling v. Charleston Community Memorial Hospital*.[23] In *Darling*, the Illinois Supreme Court found Memorial Hospital liable for negligent treatment provided to plaintiff Dorrence Darling, an 18-year-old who suffered a broken leg while playing in a college football game. The poor treatment Darling received by the hospital's emergency room staff—his leg cast was not properly constructed and its application cut off blood circulation—ultimately resulted in amputation of Darling's leg below the knee. The court held the hospital liable not for the actions of the emergency room staff, but for *its own* negligence: According to the court, Memorial Hospital did not maintain a sufficient number of qualified nurses for post-emergency room bedside care (when Darling's leg became gangrenous), and it neither reviewed the care provided by the treating physician nor required the physician to consult with other members of the hospital staff.

Insurer Liability

Like hospitals, conventional (i.e., indemnity) health insurers historically were not susceptible to being sued under tort principles; rather, they were subject mainly to breach of contract lawsuits when they failed to reimburse medical claims for services covered under beneficiaries' health insurance policies. This stemmed from two related facts: First, normative insurer practice was to leave medical judgments and treatment decisions in the hands of doctors, meaning that it was rare for an insurer-related action to lead to the type of injury covered by tort law; second, to the extent that an insurer did deny a beneficiary's claim for insurance coverage, it did so retrospectively—in other words, *after* the beneficiary received needed diagnostic tests, treatments, medications, and so on. This effectively meant that when beneficiaries sued their health insurer, they did so not because they had been physically or emotionally injured by the insurer's decision to deny an insurance claim, but because there was a dispute as to whether the insurer was going to pay for the already-received medical care.[24] Thus, although coverage denials had potentially enormous economic implications for affected beneficiaries, they did not tend to raise healthcare access or quality issues.

In the years following the *Darling* decision, however, courts began to apply tort liability principles to traditional indemnity insurers when their coverage decisions were at least partially responsible for an individual's injury or death,[25] which had the effect of opening insurers to a fuller range of potential damages (e.g., pain and suffering) than had been the case previously (when under breach of contract principles insurers were only liable for the actual cost of care they had initially declined to cover). This increased exposure to liability grew out of the fact that insurers were becoming more aggressive in their use of *prospective* coverage decisions, and courts were aware of how these types of coverage determinations could impact access to and the quality of health care. The advent of managed care as the primary mechanism for delivering and financing health care only magnified this concern given managed care's use of techniques such as utilization review, and opened the door to one of the most contentious aspects of health services quality today: the extent to which patients can sue managed care organizations for negligent coverage or treatment decisions.

Managed Care Liability

Just as state courts were important in the extension of tort principles to health professionals, hospitals, and insurers, so too did they inaugurate application of these principles to managed care organizations. Modern managed care organizations are complex structures that heavily regulate the practices of their network physicians. Indeed, perhaps the most defining aspect of managed care is its oversight of physician medical judgment through various mechanisms—utilization review, practice guidelines, physician payment incentives, and so on.

A function of managed care's oversight of physician practice is that there is no longer any doubt that application of the professional standard of care for the purpose of determining negligence extends beyond the literal quality of health care delivered and reaches the very *coverage* of that care. This is because managed care has so altered coverage decision-making practices to focus on prospective decisions; where this type of coverage determination used to be the exception, it is now the rule. Instead of coverage denials leading to disputes over who was going to pay for an already-received medical service, prospective managed care coverage decisions more or less determine whether an individual receives treatment at all.[26]

Needless to say, prospective coverage decisions' negative impact on individuals' ability to access necessary, high-quality care is no small policy matter. At the same time, in one critical legal sense it does not particularly matter whether a dispute between an MCO and one of its beneficiaries is framed as one of negligence in health care *quality* or health care *coverage*—either way, the key issue is whether the medical judgment exercised by the MCO met the professional standard of care. In applying this standard, courts have had little trouble finding MCOs liable under state law both for the negligence of their network physicians and for their own direct negligence. (However, as discussed in the next section, these court decisions presume the nonapplicability of ERISA, a federal law that often precludes individuals from suing their managed care company under state tort laws.)

There have been a number of cases in which courts have determined that MCOs can be held vicariously liable for the negligent actions of their network physicians where a patient can prove an agency relationship under one of the theories (actual agency, apparent agency, or nondelegable duty) described previously. In these cases, courts perform an exhaustive examination of the facts to determine the specific relationship between the treating physician and the MCO or the ways in which the MCO portrays and obligates itself to its beneficiaries. For example, in the leading case of *Boyd v. Albert Einstein Medical Center*,[27] a Pennsylvania court closely analyzed a health maintenance organization's (HMO's) literature for evidence of a contractual relationship to its beneficiaries to determine whether the HMO could be held vicariously liable under a theory of apparent agency for the treatment of a woman who died after physicians negligently treated her for a lump in her breast. Among other things, the court noted that the HMO's contract with its beneficiaries agreed to "provide healthcare services and benefits to members in order to protect and promote their health," and that the patients' contractual relationship was with the HMO, not with any individual physician in the HMO's network. In the end, the court determined that because the patient looked to the HMO itself for care and the HMO held itself out as providing care through its network physicians, the HMO was vicariously liable for the patient's negligent treatment.

Similarly, courts have applied the doctrine of corporate liability to managed care organizations. Courts have given various reasons for subjecting MCOs to this type of liability: At least in their role as arrangers or providers of health care, MCOs are much like hospitals; MCOs have the resources to monitor and improve the quality of healthcare delivery; and MCOs maintain tremendous authority over the makeup of their physician networks. The case of *Jones v. Chicago HMO Ltd. of Illinois*[28] is a good example of the application of corporate liability principles to managed care. In *Jones*, the plaintiff called her MCO-appointed physician (Dr. Jordan) after her three-month-old daughter (Shawndale) fell ill with constipation, fever, and other problems. Both an assistant to Dr. Jordan and, eventually, Dr. Jordan himself, explained that Shawndale should not be brought to the physician's office but should instead be treated at home with castor oil. A day later, Shawndale was still sick and her mother took her to a hospital emergency room, where she was diagnosed with bacterial meningitis secondary to an ear infection. Shawndale was permanently disabled as a result of the meningitis. It emerged through pretrial testimony that the defendant MCO had assigned 4,500–6,000 patients to Dr. Jordan, far more than its own medical director deemed acceptable under the professional standard of care. The Illinois Supreme Court agreed, ruling that MCOs breach a legal duty as a corporate entity by assigning an excessive number of patients to any single network physician, because doing so can affect the quality of care provided to beneficiaries.

This section reviewed generally the application of the professional standard of care to hospitals, insurers, and managed care organizations and described certain state-level theories of liability that are implicated when patients claim that the care they received fell short of this standard. However, as alluded to earlier, the federal Employee Retirement Income Security Act often preempts (i.e., supersedes) these kinds of state law liability claims against insurers and managed

care organizations. This chapter now turns to a discussion of ERISA and its preemptive force.

FEDERAL PREEMPTION OF STATE LIABILITY LAWS UNDER THE EMPLOYEE RETIREMENT INCOME SECURITY ACT

Generally speaking, ERISA prohibits individuals from recovering damages for death and injuries caused by substandard medical professional conduct to the extent that the individual receives her health coverage through a *private employer-sponsored* benefit plan. (Among others, individuals who work for federal, state, and local public employers are not covered by ERISA's rules.) Because approximately 150 million workers and their families in the United States receive this type of health coverage, and because managed care represents the dominant structure of healthcare delivery, the issue of whether individuals with private employer-sponsored managed care coverage can recover damages for substandard medical professional conduct is paramount.

Overview of ERISA

One of the most complex areas of federal civil law, the Employee Retirement Income Security Act[e] was established in 1974 mainly to protect the employee pension system from employer fraud. However, the law was drafted in such a way as to extend to all benefits offered by ERISA-covered employers, including health benefits. Because ERISA does not distinguish among employers based on size, essentially all employees in this country who receive health and other benefits through a private employer can be said to work for an "ERISA-covered" employer.

ERISA employs two main devices to protect employee pensions and other benefits. First, it imposes "fiduciary" responsibilities on those individuals or entities that administer various types of employer-sponsored benefit plans (in the case of health benefits, these are often conventional insurers or MCOs, or the employers themselves). A person or entity with fiduciary responsibilities is analogous to a trustee, who is expected to act primarily for another's benefit in carrying out his or her duties. Put differently, a fiduciary is one who manages money or property (like a pension fund or healthcare benefit) for another person and who is expected to act in good faith in that management. One critical fiduciary responsibility is to act with an eye toward the best interests of the person who has placed his or her trust in the fiduciary, rather than seeking personal enrichment through trustee activities.

The second tool used by Congress in ERISA to regulate employee benefits is a set of uniform, nationwide rules for the administration of employee benefits. However, although

---

BOX 11-4 Discussion Questions

What do you think about the role and success of tort law in promoting high-quality health care? Does it help to deter errors? If not, why?

ERISA closely regulates the structure and operation of pension plans, the law includes few substantive standards governing the design or administration of health (or other) employee benefits. This stems mainly from the fact that Congress's main purpose in passing ERISA was to confront the employer fraud and underfunding evident in the pension system in the early 1970s (after all, the title of the law hints that its purpose is to specifically protect employee *retirement income*), not to regulate all employee benefit plans. However, the language used by ERISA's drafters is both broad and ambiguous, and courts have interpreted the statute as applying well beyond the field of pensions.[29] As a result of the dearth of substantive standards pertaining to employee health benefits, employers enjoy discretion under ERISA to decide whether to offer health benefits at all and, if they do, to offer a benefit package of their choosing. This discretion allows the employer to design the benefit plan itself or buy an "off the shelf" insurance policy from a health insurer. If the employer chooses the latter, it also must decide whether to use a conventional insurer or a managed care company; if using a managed care company, it must decide whether to include physician incentive schemes in its benefit plan.

ERISA's lack of substantive health benefit regulations is compounded by the fact that the law contains few avenues for employees to remedy negligent benefit plan administration, including substandard conduct in the administration of health plan benefits. As mentioned, ERISA precludes the recovery of monetary damages under state law theories of liability when employer-sponsored benefits are improperly denied; Congress was of the opinion in fashioning ERISA that payment of these types of damages would drain employer benefit plans of needed resources. However, one might assume that when Congress broadly displaces state laws aimed at remedying negligence (as it did with ERISA), it would put in place meaningful enforcement provisions in the federal law. Yet the remedies available under ERISA are dramatically more limited than those available under state law. Under ERISA, employees and their beneficiaries are effectively limited to suing to prospectively force a plan administrator to grant a covered benefit, to recover payment retrospectively when a covered benefit was improperly denied, and to enforce a plan administrator's fiduciary responsibilities.[30] The upshot of these rights is that they allow an employee injured by an action or decision of his benefit plan to recover *nothing beyond the actual cost of the benefit due in any event.*

Furthermore, in *Pilot Life Insurance Co. v. Dedeaux*,[31] the U.S. Supreme Court held that ERISA's enforcement provision constituted not merely *a* remedy for negligent administration of an employee benefit plan, but rather the *exclusive* remedy.

This means that all other state remedies generally available to individuals to remedy corporate negligence are preempted (and thus not available) to employees whose health benefits are provided through an ERISA-covered plan.

ERISA Preemption

In order to ensure the uniform regulation and administration of employee pension plans (and, as it turned out, other employee benefits) across the nation, Congress included in ERISA one of the most sweeping preemption provisions ever enacted under federal law. The uniqueness of the scope of ERISA's preemptive force is underscored by the fact that the states in America's governmental structure maintain broad authority to regulate many fields (including the fields of health care and health insurance) as they see fit, and federal law generally supplements, but does not replace, state law.

Furthermore, ERISA actually implicates two different types of preemption. The first, known as "conflict preemption," occurs when specific provisions of state law clearly conflict with federal law, in which case the state law is superseded. The second form of preemption triggered by ERISA is "field preemption," which the courts employ when they interpret federal law to occupy an entire field of law (e.g., employee benefit law), irrespective of whether there are any conflicting state law provisions (this is the type of preemption at work in ERISA's remedial provisions, described earlier). The practical import of this second type of preemption is that a wide range of state laws are preempted by ERISA even though they do not directly conflict with it. All in all, it is little wonder that ERISA is considered to function as a "regulatory vacuum."

The length of ERISA's conflict preemption provision belies its preemptive scope, and its wording belies the enormous amount of litigation it has engendered. The substantive entirety of the preemption clause reads: "[ERISA] shall supersede any and all State laws insofar as they may now or hereafter relate to any employee benefit plan."[32] Courts have grappled with the meaning of this language for decades. For example, the term "relate to" has been interpreted by the U.S. Supreme Court to include any state law that has "a connection with or reference to" an employee benefit plan,[33] but not those that only have a "remote and tenuous" relationship to benefit plans.[34] Thus, the former types of state laws are preempted, while the latter are not. The Supreme Court has also weighed in on the meaning of "employee benefit plan."[35]

In addition to the preemption clause itself, however, there are two additional pieces to the ERISA conflict preemption puzzle that only add to the law's complexity. The second piece is referred to as the "insurance savings" clause, which says that the preemption clause shall not "be construed to exempt or relieve any person from any law of any State which regulates insurance . . . ."[36] This essentially means that even where a state law relates to an employee benefit plan, it is saved from preemption if it regulates insurance.[37] The Supreme Court has interpreted this provision to mean a state law is saved from preemption if it is specifically directed toward entities engaged in insurance and substantially affects the risk pooling arrangement between an insurer and its beneficiaries.[38] The practical effect of the savings clause, then, is to narrow the reach of the preemption clause, because state laws that meet the "regulates insurance" test fall outside the scope of ERISA preemption.

The final element of ERISA conflict preemption is the "deemer" clause, which addresses the distinction between fully-insured and self-insured employee health benefit plans. A fully-insured health plan (sometimes referred to simply as an insured plan) is one in which an employer purchases health insurance coverage (i.e., pays premiums) to a conventional insurance company or MCO, and in return the insurance company or MCO accepts the financial risk of paying claims for covered benefits. A self-insured health plan (also called a self-funded plan) exists when an employer retains some or all of the financial risk for its employees' claims for covered benefits. Nearly one-half of all U.S. employers self-insure their health benefit plans.

ERISA's deemer clause reads in pertinent part: "[A]n employee benefit plan shall [not] be deemed to be an insurance company or other insurer, . . . or to be engaged in the business of insurance . . . for purposes of any law of any State purporting to regulate insurance companies."[39] The purpose of this clause is to prohibit states from deeming employee benefit plans as the functional equivalent of health insurers, and its practical effect is critical for the tens of millions of employees who receive their health benefits under self-insured plans: The deemer clause prevents state laws that meet the "regulates insurance" test from applying to self-insured employee health benefit plans.[40] In other words, even state laws "saved" from preemption do not apply to self-insured plans because under ERISA these types of plans are "deemed" not to be insurance companies. The ultimate result of the deemer clause's application is to *exempt completely* self-funded employee benefit plans from state insurance law. This allows sponsors of self-funded plans enormous discretion to design the plans as they choose.

The Intersection of ERISA Preemption and Managed Care Professional Medical Liability

The final matter to discuss in the context of ERISA preemption has been one of the most unstable over the past several

years: the extent to which ERISA preempts state tort law claims by individuals against managed care companies for negligent coverage decisions and substandard provision of care. This issue has played out over a series of federal court decisions attempting to define with some precision ERISA's application in the context of employer-sponsored managed care plans.

In the 1992 case of *Corcoran v. United HealthCare, Inc.*,[41] the Fifth Circuit Court of Appeals ruled that Florence Corcoran's state law claim against United HealthCare for the wrongful death of her fetus had to be dismissed under ERISA, regardless of any medical negligence on the part of the MCO. The court held that even if the company improperly denied coverage of preterm labor management services for Mrs. Corcoran, her state lawsuit seeking damages for a negligent coverage decision was preempted because the company's determination was, in the language of ERISA, sufficiently "related to" Mrs. Corcoran's employee benefit plan.

Three years later, the Third Circuit Court of Appeals ruled in *Dukes v. U.S. Healthcare, Inc.*[42] that although individuals in ERISA-covered health benefit plans may not be able to sue under state law for an MCO's negligent coverage denial (i.e., for a company's decision as to the *quantity* of care covered under the plan), they can seek state law damages where a managed care company's negligence is connected to the *quality* of care actually provided. The Third Circuit essentially ruled that Congress did not intend in passing ERISA to supersede state laws aimed at the regulation of healthcare quality, historically a subject area under the states' purview. Instead, according to the court, federal policymakers enacted ERISA to alleviate national companies' concerns over abiding by many different state pension and employee benefit laws and to instead subject them to a uniform set of funding and administration rules. Whatever Congress meant by a "state law that relates to an employee benefit plan," the *Dukes* court did not interpret ERISA's preemption provision to sweep in laws pertaining to the quality of medical care provided to beneficiaries of employer-sponsored health benefit plans.

In the five years after *Dukes* was decided, federal court decisions applying ERISA to managed care plans more or less subscribed to this quantity/quality distinction. However, the Supreme Court stepped into the fray in 2000 in the case of *Pegram v. Herdrich*,[43] seemingly altering the approach lower courts had been taking when analyzing ERISA preemption of state law negligence claims against MCOs. The main issue in *Pegram* was whether physician incentive arrangements were violative of the fiduciary responsibility rules contained in ERISA (incidentally, the Court ruled they were not). However, the Court included several paragraphs in its decision about the role of the treating physician in the case, who also happened to be one of the owners of the managed care company being sued for negligently failing to order a diagnostic test. In so doing, the Court described two different kinds of decisions made by MCOs:

> What we will call pure "eligibility decisions" turn on the plan's coverage of a particular condition or medical procedure for its treatment. "Treatment decisions," by contrast, are choices about how to go about diagnosing and treating a patient's condition: given a patient's constellation of symptoms, what is the appropriate medical response? *These decisions are often practically inextricable from one another . . . .* This is so not merely because . . . treatment and eligibility decisions are made by the same person, the treating physician. It is so because a great many *and possibly most* coverage questions are not simple yes-or-no questions, like whether appendicitis is a covered condition (when there is no dispute that a patient has appendicitis), or whether acupuncture is a covered procedure for pain relief (when the claim of pain is unchallenged). The more common coverage question is a when-and-how question. Although coverage for many conditions will be clear and various treatment options will be indisputably compensable, physicians still must decide what to do in particular cases . . . . In practical terms, these eligibility decisions cannot be untangled from physicians' judgments about reasonable medical treatment.[44]

Importantly, the Court went on to suggest that these intertwined decisions fall beyond ERISA's reach and that state laws implicated when these decisions are negligently made are not preempted, though the Court provided no clear guidance as to when managed care decisions tipped sufficiently toward coverage or care to pull them out of the realm of being "mixed." Following the decision, many federal courts faced with ERISA's application to claims by managed care beneficiaries adopted *Pegram*'s approach over the one developed in *Dukes*. Courts favored *Pegram*'s approach because it opened the door to state law remedies for individuals (like Florence Corcoran) who were injured as a result of managed care negligence but who otherwise had no way to recover for their loss.

In the 2004 case of *Aetna Health, Inc. v. Davila*,[45] however, the Supreme Court appeared to close the door it seemed to open in *Pegram*, suggesting that lawsuits premised on the intertwined or "mixed" decisions made daily by MCOs escape ERISA's preemptive force only when the decisions include actual treatment by an MCO medical employee. The *Davila* decision actually represented a pair of cases (the other one originally called *Cigna v. Calad*) consolidated by the Court due to the similarity of the respective plaintiffs' claims. Both Juan Davila and Ruby Calad were members of ERISA-covered employee health benefit plans. Davila was injured when Aetna chose to substitute a less expensive medication for the one he normally took to control his arthritis pain; Calad suffered complications after being prematurely discharged from the hospital subsequent to Cigna's decision to cover just one day of hospitalization post-surgery. Rather than filing appeals directly with their insurance companies, Davila and Calad sued under a state law called the Texas Health Care Liability Act. They argued that their respective insurer's decision breached a duty under the Texas law to exercise reasonable care in healthcare decision making, and that the breach caused their injuries.

In rejecting both plaintiffs' claims, the Supreme Court ruled that ERISA preempts lawsuits for damages against ERISA-covered plans for negligent healthcare coverage decisions, even when the coverage decision was predicated on flawed medical judgment. Thus, *Davila* makes clear that when an individual covered by an ERISA plan complains only of negligent coverage decision making (including the wrongful denial of a benefit) on the part of an MCO, ERISA shields the MCO from liability beyond the actual value of the benefit itself.[f] However, the Supreme Court in *Davila* also explained that notwithstanding ERISA, MCOs remain liable under state tort laws for negligence when acting in their capacity as providers or arrangers of health care. Although this ruling sustains the general distinction made by the federal court of appeals in the *Dukes* decision, its effect on the legal remedies

BOX 11-5 Discussion Questions

The critical intersection between health care and health insurance as exemplified by the *Davila* decision leads to an important question: Is it reasonable to treat a healthcare coverage decision as having nothing to do with health care itself? Put another way, given the expense of health care today, do you believe that individuals and families can afford necessary health care if there is no third party responsible for covering at least some of the cost?

available to injured patients is likely to be limited, given that policymakers and courts still view coverage decision making, rather than the provision of health care, as the primary aim of MCOs.

MEASURING AND INCENTIVIZING HEALTHCARE QUALITY[g]

We turn now to the final topics in this chapter: what exactly is meant by healthcare "quality," how is it measured, and how should policy be designed in order to encourage and reward it? Given the explosive growth in healthcare costs in the United States over the past few decades, combined with evidence from leading researchers and experts[h] that collectively points to the disconnect between high spending and healthcare quality and to serious deficiencies in healthcare quality overall, these are important questions.

To analyze these questions, focusing on the Medicare program is particularly instructive. As the single largest payer (in terms of dollars spent) in the U.S. health system, Medicare is a major national driver of policy in other markets (both public and private). Therefore, how the Medicare program addresses issues pertaining to quality is not only important to Medicare beneficiaries and providers, but also to other purchasers/insurers whose policies and procedures are often driven by Medicare policy. The remainder of this section will focus on how the Medicare program, as authorized by federal legislation (including the Affordable Care Act), is improving the quality and lowering the cost of healthcare delivery.

Traditionally, the Medicare program has paid for health care services on a fee-for-service (FFS) basis, with the exception of inpatient hospital services, which are paid based on Diagnosis Related Groups (DRGs) under the prospective payment system (PPS), and the Medicare Advantage and Prescription Drug plans, which are paid on a capitated basis. All payment systems (public and private) tend to incentivize something; in the case of FFS, it is indiscriminant increases in the volume of treatments and services, while in case-based or capitation systems, it is indiscriminant reductions in volume. Whatever the payment arrangement, the challenge is to promote both quality and value while also apportioning financial risk appropriately. However, because Medicare lacks a program-wide and deliberate approach to promoting quality and value, and because it has relied principally on a FFS approach to payment for physician and other services, the program has experienced incredible growth in the volume of services for which it pays.

Over the years, Congress has passed a series of laws designed to move the Medicare program from a passive purchaser of volume-based health care to an active purchaser of high-quality, high-value health care based in large part on successful Medicare demonstration projects. For example, as authorized under the Medicare Prescription Drug and Modernization Act of 2003 (MMA) and extended by the Deficit Reduction Act of 2005 (DRA), hospitals that report on specific quality measures receive the full annual payment update, while failure to participate results in a 2% decrease in the annual payment update. Similarly, as authorized by the Tax Relief and Health Care Act of 2006 (TRHCA) and extended by the Medicare, Medicaid and SCHIP Extension Act of 2007 (MMSEA) and Medicare Improvements for Patients and Providers Act of 2008 (MIPPA), physicians who report on specific quality measures are eligible for a bonus payment. More recently, the American Recovery and Reinvestment Act of 2009 (ARRA) provided significant financial incentives to Medicare (and Medicaid) providers that "meaningfully use" electronic health records (EHRs) to improve the quality of care delivery.

Incentives to improve the quality of Medicare-covered care were also a focus of the 2010 Patient Protection and Affordable Care Act. The ACA set forth a broad vision for quality measurement, reporting, and financial incentives in Medicare, including quality measure development; quality measurement (including payment incentives); public reporting; and value-based purchasing. In short, the ACA greatly expands the existing efforts noted above while introducing new tools for the Medicare program to identify, measure, and pay for high-quality care. The ACA also moves the country toward implementing a "national quality strategy" that would work to align quality improvement and value-based purchasing initiatives among and across payers, both public and private.

Quality Measure Development

The ACA defines a "quality measure" as a "standard for measuring the performance and improvement of population health or of health plans, providers of services, and other clinicians in the delivery of healthcare services."[46] The U.S. Department of Health and Human Services (HHS) Secretary, acting through its Centers for Medicare and Medicaid Services, is required to identify gaps where no quality measures exist and also existing quality measures that need improvement, updating, or expansion for use in federal healthcare programs (including Medicare, Medicaid, and CHIP). Identified gaps must be reported on a publicly-available website and the HHS Secretary must make awards to develop, update, or expand quality measures. In developing new measures, priorities must include measures that assess outcomes, functional status, coordination of care across episodes, shared decision-making, use of health information technology, efficiency, safety, timeliness, equity, and patient experience. The Secretary also is required to develop (and update) outcome measures for acute and chronic diseases and primary and preventative care for hospitals and physicians. Finally, the ACA requires an entity selected by the Secretary (currently the National Quality Forum) to convene multi-stakeholder groups to provide input on the selection of quality measures and national priorities for existing and new Medicare (as well as Medicaid and CHIP) quality reporting and payment programs.

Quality Measurement

The ACA reauthorizes and develops new quality measurement programs for multiple types of providers. For example, the ACA reauthorizes incentive payments under the Physician Quality Reporting Program through 2014 (maximum 1% of estimated allowed charges) and institutes a penalty for failure to report beginning in 2015 (maximum 2%). The ACA also requires the HHS Secretary to provide feedback to eligible professionals on their performance on reported quality measures and to develop a plan to integrate reporting on quality measures with reporting on the meaningful use of EHRs. Selected quality measures must include measures related to process, structure, outcome, patients' perspective on care, efficiency, and costs of care. Existing and newly developed quality measures also will be used to determine whether participating providers are "meaningfully using" EHRs to improve the quality of care delivered and qualify for incentive payments.

Public Reporting

A good amount of quality and cost of care information is currently published on CMS's suite of *Compare* websites (e.g., Hospital Compare[i]). The ACA expands required public reporting to physicians and several other provider types including long-term care hospitals, inpatient rehabilitation hospitals, psychiatric hospitals, hospice programs, and non-PPS cancer hospitals. Information reported must include the quality measures as well as assessments of patient health outcomes, risk-adjusted resource use, efficiency, patient experience, and other relevant information deemed appropriate by the HHS Secretary.

Value-Based Purchasing

The voluntary quality improvement programs described above have focused on developing provider-specific quality measures and incentivizing providers to report specific quality information. Typically, the programs have begun with providers collecting and reporting information to CMS and then transitioned to linking incentive payments to the reporting. While these "pay for reporting" programs have been successful in encouraging providers to assess the quality of care they are delivering through the reporting mechanisms, they do not take into account individual patient outcomes or population health outcomes (i.e., they do not "pay for *performance*"). However, CMS is currently in the process of implementing an End Stage Renal Disease (ESRD) facility Quality Incentive Program (QIP) that will reduce payments to facilities that do not meet or exceed certain performance benchmarks. In addition, as authorized by the DRA, CMS has implemented a similar type of payment program that does not pay hospitals a higher rate associated with treatment of specific conditions if the conditions were acquired in the hospital (termed "hospital-acquired conditions" or HACs), rather than present on admission. It is worth noting that these programs are not unique to the Medicare program; many state Medicaid programs and private payers are also developing and implementing similar programs.[j]

Until passage of the ACA, CMS was not able to move beyond "pay for reporting" programs or the hospital HAC program because it did not have the necessary legal authority to vary payments based on actual provider performance. Specifically, the ACA requires the implementation of Medicare value-based purchasing programs for hospitals (other than psychiatric hospitals, rehabilitation hospitals, children's hospitals, long-term care hospitals, and certain cancer treatment and research facilities) and physicians (through a payment modifier) and the development of plans to implement value-based purchasing programs for skilled nursing facilities, home health agencies, and ambulatory surgical centers. These newly authorized programs require the Medicare program to financially reward and penalize providers (or develop plans to do so) based on their performance on specified quality measures and other indicators, such as rates of re-admission and hospital acquired conditions. For example, through the hospital value-based purchasing program, eligible hospitals will receive incentive payments for discharges after October 1, 2012 that meet certain performance standards. Selected measures on which the hospital performance will be evaluated include patient experience measures, quality measures addressing acute myocardial infarctions, heart failure, pneumonia, surgeries as measured by the Surgical Care Improvement Project, and healthcare-associated infections. Information regarding the performance of individual hospitals under the program will be made available online through the Hospital Compare website, as well as aggregate information on the program. Similarly, the ACA authorizes a physician and physician practice group value-based purchasing program that will provide differential payments to physicians and physician practice groups under the fee schedule based on the quality of care furnished compared to cost.

National Quality Strategy

In order to better align quality improvement initiatives across payers, the ACA also requires the development of a national quality strategy to improve the delivery of healthcare services, patient health outcomes, and population health. HHS released its initial report to Congress, titled "National Strategy for Quality Improvement in Health Care," in March of 2011 describing plans for implementation. What follows is a summary of the released strategy:

- National Aims: The National Quality Strategy will pursue three broad aims that will be used to guide and assess local, state, and national efforts to improve healthcare quality. These aims include:
  - Better Care: represents efforts to improve the overall quality of health care by making care more patient-centered, reliable, accessible, and safe.
  - Healthy People/Healthy Communities: encompasses efforts to improve the health of the population by supporting interventions that address behavioral, social, and environmental determinants of health.
  - Affordable Care: seeks to reduce the cost of quality health care for individuals, families, employers, and government.
- Setting Priorities: To advance these three aims, the Strategy focuses on six priorities. These include:
  - Making care safer by reducing harm caused in the delivery of care.
  - Ensuring that each person and family is engaged as partners in their care.
  - Promoting effective communication and coordination of care.
  - Promoting the most effective prevention and treatment practices for the leading causes of mortality, starting with cardiovascular disease.
  - Working with communities to promote wide use of best practices to enable healthy living.
  - Making quality care more affordable for individuals, families, employers, and governments by developing and spreading new healthcare delivery models.
- Setting Core Sets of Principles: In addition to the aims and priorities, the national quality strategy is guided by a core set of principles. These principles are to be used when designing specific initiatives to achieve the strategy's three broad aims. The initial strategy includes ten principles:
  - Payment: Payment arrangements should offer incentives to foster better health and promote quality improvement, greater value, and innovation.

- Public Reporting: Public reporting initiatives offer consumers and payers an opportunity to compare costs, review treatment outcomes, assess patient satisfaction, and hold providers accountable.
- Quality Improvement/Technical Assistance: Provider organizations, clinical specialty groups, and quality improvement organizations should work cooperatively with physicians, hospitals, and others to disseminate research evidence to the point of care, share best practices, and provide technical assistance.
- Certification, Accreditation, and Regulation: Through their regulatory authority, state and federal agencies overseeing provider organizations and facilities should continue to monitor providers, ensure feedback and accountability, and strengthen patient safety and quality improvement.
- Consumer Incentives and Benefit Designs: Consumer incentives are designed to turn good intentions into action, and may include financial assistance for tobacco cessation, incentives to adhere to recommended medications, and value-based insurance models.
- Measurement of Care Processes and Outcomes: Ensuring valid, reliable measures is the cornerstone of monitoring quality improvement efforts. Data on care delivery and outcomes should be measured using consistent, nationally endorsed measures in order to provide information that is timely, actionable, and meaningful to both providers and patients.
- Health Information Technology: Increased adoption of electronic health records has the power to cut healthcare costs, reduce paperwork, improve outcomes, and give patients more control over their health care, while maintaining full protections for the privacy of individual health information.
- Evaluation and Feedback: Clinicians and other providers need timely and actionable feedback in order to improve their quality of care. Similarly, new innovations in delivery and payment need robust and rapid evaluation to support potential widespread implementation.
- Training, Professional Certification, and Workforce and Capacity Development: Healthcare professionals should be encouraged to maximize their training and skills through life-long learning that includes the application of quality improvement principles and patient safety systems concepts.
- Promoting Innovation and Rapid-Cycle Learning: Innovations in care, collaboration, and communication

lead to major strides in the detection and treatment of diseases and care delivery.

- Next Steps: The national quality strategy is designed to adapt to the evolving needs of the nation's population, and will be shaped by recommendations, feedback, and discussions with private entities and states. Additionally, a federal Interagency Working Group on Health Care Quality began its work in 2011, with a mission to collaborate, cooperate, and consult with the departments and agencies that develop and disseminate the strategies, goals, models, and timetables needed to advance the national quality strategy's priorities.

CONCLUSION

This chapter introduced the concept of healthcare quality generally, briefly described the concepts of licensure and accreditation, discussed the specific quality concern of medical errors, detailed the topic of legal liability for substandard healthcare provision and decision making, and covered measurement of healthcare quality. While the majority of the chapter was dedicated to legal accountability for negligence in healthcare delivery, this is of course just one method used to promote high-quality care. Policymakers, health services researchers, the health professions themselves, and others have proposed or implemented several additional strategies (e.g., related to the healthcare system's organizational structure, or to evidence-based medicine, or to information technology) aimed at remedying existing quality concerns and improving the quality of care going forward, some of which are reflected in the ACA. Many of these strategies have yet to take hold on a national scale, however, and finding effective ways to mesh them with existing legal rules—and navigating the legal system's responses to them—are issues with which the country will continue to grapple.

REFERENCES

1. Kohn LT, Corrigan JM, Donaldson MS, eds. *To Err Is Human: Building a Safer Health System*. Washington, DC: National Academy Press; 2000.

2. Committee on Quality of Health Care in America. *Crossing the Quality Chasm: A New Health System for the 21st Century*. Washington, DC: National Academy Press; 2001.

3. Furrow BR, Greaney TL, Johnson SH, Jost TS, Schwartz RL. *Health Law: Cases, Materials and Problems*. St. Paul, MN: West Group; 2001.

4. 59 N.E. 1058 (Ind. 1901).

5. Rosenbaum S. et al. *Law and the American Health Care System*. 2nd ed. manuscript (2011), to be published by The Foundation Press, Westbury, CT; Ch. 18.

6. Ibid.

7. Ibid.

8. See http://www.nursingworld.org/search.aspx?SearchMode=1&SearchPhrase=scope+of+practice&SearchWithin=2. Accessed August 18, 2011.

9. See http://www.aapa.org/advocacy-and-practice-resources/state-government-and-licensing/scope-of-practice. Accessed August 18, 2011.

10. Teitelbaum J. "Nursing Workforce," Health Reform GPS Implementation Brief, available at http://www.healthreformgps.org/resources/nursing-workforce/. Accessed August 18, 2011.

11. Kaufman M. Medication errors harming millions, report says. *Washington Post*, July 21, 2006;A08.

12. Nordenberg T. Make no mistake: medical errors can be deadly serious. Available at http://www.fda.gov/fdac/features/2000/500_err.html. Accessed August 1, 2006.

13. P.L. 109-41 (July 29, 2005).

14. Rosenbaum S. et al. *Law and the American Health Care System*. 2nd ed. manuscript (2011), to be published by The Foundation Press, Westbury, CT; Ch. 13.

15. Small v. Howard, 128 Mass. 131, 132 (1880).

16. 519 P.2d 981 (Wash. 1974).

17. 60 F.2d 737 (2d Cir. 1932).

18. Ibid., 740 (italics added).

19. *Shilkret v. Annapolis Emergency Hospital Association*, 349 A. 2d 245, 253 (Md. 1975).

20. 466 So.2d 856 (Miss. 1985).

21. *Mehlman v. Powell*, 378 A. 2d 1121 (Md. 1977).

22. *Jackson v. Power*, 743 P. 2d 1376 (Alaska, 1987).

23. 211 N.E.2d 253 (Ill. 1965).

24. For example, see *Van Vector v. Blue Cross Association*, 365 N.E. 2d 638 (Ill. App. Ct., 1977).

25. For example, see *Gruenberg v. Aetna Insurance Co.*, 510 P. 2d 1032 (Cal., 1973).

26. Rosenbaum S, Frankford D, Moore B, Borzi P. Who should determine when health care is medically necessary? *New Engl J Med*. 1999;340(3):229–233.

27. 547 A. 2d 1229 (Pa. Super., 1988).

28. 730 N.E. 2d 1119 (2000).

29. Rosenbaum S. et al. *Law and the American Health Care System*. 2nd ed. manuscript (2011), to be published by The Foundation Press, Westbury, CT; Ch. 8.

30. 29 U.S.C. § 1132.

31. 481 U.S. 41 (1987).

32. 29 U.S.C. § 1144(a).

33. *Shaw v. Delta Air Lines, Inc.*, 463 U.S. 85 (1983).

34. *New York State Conference of Blue Cross & Blue Shield Plans v. Travelers Insurance Co.*, 514 U.S. 645 (1995).

35. *Fort Halifax Packing Co. v. Coyne*, 482 U.S. 1 (1987).

36. 29 U.S.C. § 1144(b)(2)(A).

37. *Metropolitan Life Insurance Co. v. Massachusetts*, 471 U.S. 724 (1985).

38. *Kentucky Association of Health Plans, Inc. v. Miller*, 538 U.S. 329 (2003).

39. 29 U.S.C. § 1144(b)(2)(B).

40. *Metropolitan Life Insurance Co. v. Massachusetts*, 471 U.S. 724 (1985).

41. 965 F.2d 1321 (5th Cir. 1992).

42. 57 F. 3d 350 (3d Cir. 1995).

43. 530 U.S. 211 (2000).

44. Ibid., 228-29 (italics added).

45. 542 U.S. 200 (2004).

46. Patient Protection and Affordable Care Act (Pub. L. 111-148) § 3013 (2010), adding Public Health Service Act § 931.

ENDNOTES

a. For example, in the lawsuit stemming from the facts described at the outset of this chapter, the parents of the infant who died alleged that their MCO's decision to precertify only 24 hours of hospital care coverage did not meet the requisite standard of care in several healthcare quality respects: it was not medically appropriate and was motivated by financial profit, not Michelina's health and well-being; it forced Michelina's premature discharge from the hospital; it was made despite the MCO's knowledge that newborns are particularly at risk for developing illnesses; and it discouraged physicians participating in the MCO's provider network from re-admitting infants to the hospital when problems arose after discharge.

b. Because the law's evolving view of the standard of care closely mirrors its view of the medical profession more generally, it is worth pausing for a moment to reflect on the health policy and law conceptual framework that is focused on historical, social, political, and economic views. This framework includes three perspectives: professional autonomy, social contract, and free market. The first perspective, dominant from about 1880–1960, argues that physicians' scientific and medical expertise leaves them in the best position to determine whether care rendered to patients is of adequate quality, and thus that legal oversight of the medical profession should be driven by the profession itself. The second perspective guided policymaking and legal principles for roughly 20 years beginning around 1960, and maintains that healthcare delivery and financing should be governed by enforcement of a "social contract" that generally elevates patient rights and societal values over physician autonomy and control. The free market perspective—dominant since the 1990s—contends that healthcare services are most efficiently delivered in a deregulated marketplace controlled by commercial competition. Bear in mind the first two perspectives specifically as you read this section.

c. One of the most commonly cited English cases for this rule is *Slater v. Baker and Stapleton*, in which the court ruled that the appropriate legal standard for determining a surgeon's liability was "the usage and law of surgeons . . . the rule of the profession" as testified to by practicing surgeons. 95 Eng. Rep. 860, 862 (King's Bench 1767).

d. An example of this shift can be seen in the case of *Canterbury v. Spence*, 464 F.2d 772 (D.C. Cir. 1972), which is often discussed in the context of a patient's right to make informed healthcare decisions. The *Canterbury* court ruled that a professional-oriented standard for measuring the legality of a physician's disclosure of information to a patient should be replaced by an objective standard predicated on what a reasonable patient would need to be told to effectuate the aforementioned right.

e. Even citations to ERISA are complicated, because the law's section numbers in the U.S. Code (where much of ERISA can be found under Title 29) do not always correspond to the section numbering in the original act as written by Congress. For a helpful website effectively decoding where ERISA provisions are located in the U.S. Code, go to http://benefitslink. com/erisa/crossreference.html.

f. Note how this outcome can reasonably be viewed as incentivizing ERISA plans to arbitrarily deny patients' claims for healthcare coverage, because even in the event that plans are found to have acted negligently, they are only responsible for paying the cost of the denied benefit, but nothing more.

g. We are deeply grateful to Professor Jane Thorpe, our friend and colleague in the George Washington University Department of Health Policy and a former Deputy Director of the Office of Policy in the federal Centers for Medicare and Medicaid Services, for the drafting of this section.

h. There is extensive literature on this topic. See, for example, Fisher E. et al. "Health Care Spending, Quality and Outcomes: More Isn't Always Better," Dartmouth Atlas Project Topics Brief, February 27, 2009; Fisher E. et al. "The Implications of Regional Variations in Medicare Spending. Part 1: The Content, Quality, and Accessibility of Care," *Annals Intern Med.* 2003;138:273–287; McGlynn E. et al. "The Quality of Health Care Delivered to Adults in the United States," *New Eng J Med.* 2003;348:2635–2645; Wennberg J. et al. "Geography and the Debate Over Medicare Reform," *Health Affairs Web Exclusive*, February 13, 2002. Wennberg J. et al.; "The Dartmouth Atlas of Health Care in the United States 1996," American Hospital Publishing, Inc.

i. Go to http://www.hospitalcompare.hhs.gov/ to see the hospital comparisons, and to http://www.medicare.gov/ to access other compare websites.

j. See, e.g., Integrated Healthcare Association's Pay for Performance Programs (http://www.iha.org/pay_performance.html); Kuhmerker K. Hartman T, *Pay-for-Performance in State Medicaid Programs: A Survey of State Medicaid Directors and Programs*, The Commonwealth Fund (April 2007).

CHAPTER 12

Public Health Preparedness Policy

LEARNING OBJECTIVES

By the end of this chapter, you will be able to:

- Describe what public health preparedness is and the role of the public health community in preparing for and responding to emergencies
- Understand the breadth of public health emergencies and the types of communities public health must work with to prepare for and respond to specific events
- Understand the threats from and history of use of weapons of mass destruction
- Define public health threats from biological agents and naturally occurring diseases
- Discuss the federal, state, and local policies and laws that support public health preparedness and the infrastructure that has been built to support preparedness activities at the federal, state, and local levels

INTRODUCTION

The last decade has seen many changes in terms of how the United States views homeland security and the role of the public health community in maintaining that security. There is an ever-evolving threat of the terrorist use of weapons of mass destruction—particularly in the case of biological weapons—against the U.S. population. Infectious diseases continue to emerge and re-emerge around the world, and the globalization of our food supply and the speed and volume of international travel make us all vulnerable to the emergence of a new agent anywhere in the world. Media reports include constant reminders of the devastating effects of natural disasters, such as hurricanes, fires, and earthquakes.

All of these factors—and mounting evidence that large-scale catastrophes and epidemics can dramatically affect the economic, social, and security foundations of a nation—have led to the rapid emergence at the federal, state, and local levels of a new sub-discipline within public health: public health preparedness. Public health preparedness refers to the ways in which nations, states, and communities identify, prepare for, respond to, contain, and recover from emergencies. It is imperative that public health students and professionals develop an awareness of these activities, and that they be able to identify and work with other sectors with relevant responsibilities.

The goal of this chapter is to introduce readers to the field of public health preparedness by providing an overview of the complex issues that must be considered by public health professionals in designing preparedness and response plans, policies, and laws. This chapter begins by defining public health preparedness and examines the types of threats that can lead to public health emergencies. It then describes possible policy responses to public health threats and emergencies, including a discussion of preparedness infrastructure, engagement, guidance documents, and legislation. The chapter closes by explaining the multitude of actors—from local to international—involved in public health preparedness.

DEFINING PUBLIC HEALTH PREPAREDNESS

Public health preparedness is a term that represents concerns and actions that have occurred throughout history. The term itself, however, and the field devoted to thinking about, preparing for, and mobilizing resources to respond to public health emergencies is relatively new—new enough that the field is still struggling to define itself and to establish core competencies for professionals working in the area.

The Association of Schools of Public Health defines public health preparedness as "a combination of comprehensive planning, infrastructure building, capacity building, communication, training, and evaluation that increase public health response effectiveness and efficiency in response to infectious disease outbreaks, bioterrorism, and emerging health threats."[1(p5)] A group at the RAND Corporation, however, proposed a definition in 2007 that offers a slightly broader characterization of the field:

> "[P]ublic health emergency preparedness . . . is the capability of the public health and health care systems, communities, and individuals, to prevent, protect against, quickly respond to, and recover from health emergencies, particularly those whose scale, timing, or unpredictability threatens to overwhelm routine capabilities. Preparedness involves a coordinated and continuous process of planning and implementation that relies on measuring performance and taking corrective action."[2(pS9)]

This definition raises the question: what exactly is a public health emergency? According to the RAND definition, it is an event "whose scale, timing, or unpredictability threatens to overwhelm routine capabilities." These types of events fit into four basic categories:

1. the intentional or accidental release of a chemical, biological, radiological, or nuclear (CBRN) agent;
2. natural epidemics or pandemics, which may involve a novel, emerging infectious disease, a re-emerging agent, or a previously controlled disease;
3. natural disasters such as hurricanes, earthquakes, floods, or fires; and
4. man-made environmental disasters such as oil spills.

For any of these categories of events to be classified as a public health emergency, it is not just enough for the event to occur: it also must pose a high probability of large-scale morbidity, mortality, or a risk of future harm.[3(p11)]

There is yet another category of public health emergency, as defined by the World Health Organization's International Health Regulations (2005). This international agreement defines a public health emergency of international concern (PHEIC) as, "[A]n extraordinary event which is determined . . . to constitute a public health risk to other States through the international spread of disease and to potentially require a coordinated international response."[4] Such an emergency can involve any of the above four types of public health events, as long as it has the potential to cross borders.

Some public health concerns that have been called "emergencies" do not meet the criteria of any of the previous definitions. Public health preparedness refers to planning for and responding to acute events, as opposed to chronic conditions that evolve over time. The prevalence of breast cancer,[5(pp2282–2283)] for example, may be a "public heath crisis," but it is not considered an emergency within the purview of public health preparedness.

Effective public health preparedness spans a wide range of activities. This chapter focuses primarily on the policy and legal actions to support preparedness, but a "prepared community" also entails the ability to:

- perform health risk assessments;
- establish an incident command system;
- actively engage the public;
- have functional epidemiologic and laboratory capacity to perform surveillance, detect emerging events, appropriately diagnose patients, and investigate emergencies;
- develop, stockpile, and distribute medical countermeasures (drugs and vaccines);
- have "surge capacity" within the medical system to provide care for large populations during an emergency; and
- maintain an appropriate workforce, financial resources, communication systems, and logistics to detect and respond to events.[2(pS10)]

The responsibility of the public health community to prepare for and address acute health emergencies is thus extensive and can be a challenge, particularly in environments where the public health system is under-resourced.

Threats to Public Health

As mentioned previously, there are four main categories of threats the public health community must be prepared to address. The first is the intentional or accidental release of a CBRN agent, followed by naturally occurring infectious diseases, natural disasters, and finally man-made environmental

BOX 12-1 Discussion Questions

What is public health preparedness? How do you define it? What is the role of the public health professional in detecting, responding to, and recovering from a public health emergency?

disasters with serious public health consequences. This section provides a brief overview of these threats.

Chemical, Biological, Radiological, and Nuclear Agents

The release of chemical, biological, radiological, or nuclear agents into a population center can have devastating consequences to the public's health. These agents may be released intentionally through an act of warfare or terrorism designed to cause large scale morbidity and mortality, or unintentionally through human or mechanical error. For example, an explosion at a nuclear plant may not be intended, yet it obviously can still expose nearby populations to radiation.[6] An improperly disposed piece of medical equipment may be found by children, passed around a neighborhood, and result in multiple deaths from radiation sickness.[7] A train carrying industrial chemical agents may derail, subjecting local communities to lethal doses of agents.[8] A worker at a biological weapons plant may forget to change a filter and through negligence expose a whole town to a deadly infectious disease.[9] What leads a CBRN agent to be let loose into a population varies greatly, but the consequences of fear, disruption, sickness, and death result regardless. Public health plays an essential role in mitigating the consequences of CBRN events.

Chemical Agents   There is a wide variety of chemical agents and toxins capable of causing injury or death to humans, ranging from chemicals found in cleaning supplies purchased at a local drug store, to carefully developed weapons designed to incapacitate and kill. (Toxins are nonliving poisons produced by living entities, such as plants, fungi, insects, and animals. Because they are chemical byproducts of biological agents, they occupy a conceptual grey area between chemical and biological weapons. The Biological Weapons Convention covers toxins, as does the Chemical Weapons Convention—or at least some toxins. Countries do not always agree on how toxins should be categorized for the purposes of arms control and legal international obligations.) Chemical agents may be highly toxic, and can enter the body through inhalation or through the skin. Adding to the complexity of treatment of a chemical agent injury is the fact that illness or death can come within minutes of exposure, or take as long as several hours.[10]

There are four main categories of chemical warfare agents: blister (e.g., mustard gas), blood (e.g., cyanide), choking (e.g., chlorine), and nerve (e.g., sarin). In addition, there is a class termed Riot Control Agents, which produce temporary, usually non-fatal irritation of the skin, eyes, and respiratory tract. Riot Control agents, often known as "tear gas," include

---

BOX 12-2   Types of Chemical Agents

- **Blister agents (or Vesicants):** primarily cause irritation of the skin and mucous membranes. Examples of this category include mustard gas and arsenical Lewisite.
- **Blood agents:** primarily cause seizures and respiratory and cardiac failure in high doses. Examples include hydrogen cyanide and cyanogen cyanide.
- **Choking agents or Pulmonary Toxicants:** primarily cause damage to the lungs, including pulmonary edema and hemorrhage. Examples include phosgene, diphosgene, and chlorine.
- **Nerve agents:** primarily act on the nervous system, causing seizures and death. Examples of this category include sarin, VX, tabun, and soman. This category also includes Fourth Generation Chemical Weapons, known as Novichok agents, which are thought to be much more lethal than VX.

---

chloroacetophenone (CN), chlorobenzylidenemalononitrile (CS), and chloropicrin (PS). Preparedness and response to a chemical agent event involves the development of medical countermeasures and antidotes, appropriate delivery mechanisms for these countermeasures, medical treatment and environmental decontamination following an event.

Biological Agents   Biological Warfare (BW) is the military use of a biological agent to cause death or harm to humans, animals, or plants. In warfare, the targets of biological agents are typically governments, armed forces, or resources that might affect the ability of a nation to attack an enemy or defend itself. Similarly, bioterrorism (BT) is the threat or use of a biological agent to harm or kill humans, plants, or animals; unlike BW, though, the target of BT is typically the civilian population or resources that might affect the civilian economy. Agroterrorism refers to the knowing or malicious use of biological agents to affect an agricultural industry or food supply.[11]

Not all biological agents are suitable for offensive use. For a biological agent to be an effective weapon, it should (from the perpetrator's perspective) have high toxicity; be fast acting; be predictable in its impact; have a capacity for survival outside the host for a long enough period of time to infect a victim; be relatively indestructible by air, water, or food purification;

potential use of these agents. Examples include smallpox and anthrax.

- **Enhanced:** Enhanced agents are traditional biological agents that have been altered to circumvent medical countermeasures. This group includes agents that are resistant to antibiotics.

- **Emerging:** This category includes any naturally occurring, emerging organism or emerging infectious disease. Examples include Severe Acute Respiratory Syndrome (SARS), H5N1, and novel H1N1.

- **Advanced:** The final category on the spectrum of biological threats encompasses novel pathogens and other artificial agents that are engineered in laboratories. It is virtually impossible to plan for the specific threats posed by this category of agents, thus forcing policy makers to look at biological threats with a much broader strategic approach.

The second classification method for biological threat agents is the Category A, B, and C list. This categorization originated with a 1999 Centers for Disease Control and Prevention (CDC) Strategic Planning Workgroup, which considered the public health impacts of biological agents, the potential of those agents to be effective weapons, public perception and fear, and preparedness requirements.[15] The resulting lists begins with Category A, which includes the highest priority/highest threat pathogens. These can cause large-scale morbidity and mortality and often require specific preparedness plans on the part of the public health community. Category B includes the second highest threat group. Most of the agents in this category are waterborne or foodborne agents. Many of them have either been used intentionally in the past, or were part of offensive research programs. The morbidity and mortality from these agents are not as significant as from Category A agents, but are still considerable, and they often

and be susceptible to medical countermeasures available to the attacker, but not to the intended victim(s). Of the many biological agents that exist in nature (including parasites, fungi and yeasts, bacteria, rickettsia and Chlamydia, viruses, prions, and toxins), most offensive development efforts are/were directed at a small group of bacteria, viruses, and toxins as the primary source of potential biological weapons.

Two major characterizations are used to classify biological agents. The first, used mostly by policy planners at the federal level, looks at the spectrum of agents and defines them as:

- **Traditional:** These are naturally occurring microorganisms or toxins that have long been connected with bioterrorism or biological warfare, either because they have been used in the past or they have been studied for use. There are a finite number of agents that are relatively well understood. The policy and public health community has devised specific plans to address the

BOX 12-5 Category A, B, and C Biological Threat Agents

Category A
- *Bacillus anthracis* (anthrax)
- *Clostridium botulinum*
- *Yersinia pestis* (plague)
- *Variola major* (smallpox) and other pox viruses
- *Francisella tularensis* (tularemia)
- Viral hemorrhagic fevers
  - Arenaviruses
    - LCM, Junin virus, Machupo virus, Guanarito virus
    - Lassa Fever
  - Bunyaviruses
    - Hantaviruses
    - Rift Valley Fever
  - Flaviviruses
    - Dengue
  - Filoviruses
    - Ebola
    - Marburg

Category B
- *Burkholderia pseudomallei*
- *Coxiella burnetii* (Q fever)
- *Brucella species* (brucellosis)
- *Burkholderia mallei* (glanders)
- Ricin toxin (from *Ricinus communis*)
- Epsilon toxin of *Clostridium perfringens*
- *Staphylococcus* enterotoxin B
- Typhus fever (*Rickettsia prowazekii*)
- Food and Waterborne Pathogens
  - Bacteria
    - Diarrheagenic E.coli
    - Pathogenic Vibrios
    - *Shigella* species
    - *Salmonella*

- *Listeria* monocytogenes
- *Campylobacter jejuni*
- *Yersinia enterocolitica*
- Viruses (Caliciviruses, Hepatitis A)
- Protozoa
  - *Cryptosporidium parvum*
  - *Cyclospora cayatanensis*
  - *Giardia lamblia*
  - *Entamoeba histolytica*
  - *Toxoplasma*
  - *Microsporidia*
- Additional viral encephalitides
  - West Nile Virus
  - LaCrosse
  - California encephalitis
  - Venezuelan equine encephalitis (VEE)
  - Eastern equine encephalitis (EEE)
  - Western equine encephalitis (WEE)
  - Japanese Encephalitis Virus
  - Kyasanur Forest Virus

Category C
- Emerging Infectious Diseases (including Nipah)
- Tickborne hemorrhagic fever viruses
  - Crimean-Congo Hemorrhagic fever virus
- Tickborne encephalitis viruses
- Yellow fever
- Multi-drug resistant tuberculosis (TB)
- Influenza
- Other *Rickettsias*
- Rabies
- Severe acute respiratory syndrome-associated coronavirus (SARS-CoV)
  - Antimicrobial resistance disease (excluding sexually transmitted diseases)

require the public health community to enhance surveillance and diagnostic capacity. The last group is Category C, which encompasses emerging pathogens or agents that have become resistant to medical countermeasures. These agents may cause high morbidity and mortality, and may be easily produced and transmitted.[16]

Biological weapons have been identified as a priority threat to national security, and potentially more likely than a nuclear attack.[17] There is a long history of the intentional use of biological agents. One regularly cited example derives from the 1346–1347 siege by Mongols of the city of Kaffa (now Feodosija), Ukraine. The Mongols reportedly catapulted corpses contaminated with plague over the walls of the city, causing an outbreak of *Yersinia pestis*.[18] Another history example comes from 1767, when British troops gave smallpox-infested blankets to Native Americans, causing a massive outbreak of smallpox among this as yet unexposed population.

The most well-known bioterrorism event in the United States occurred in the fall of 2001, just weeks after the World Trade Center attacks. That event, eventually named "Amerithrax" by the Federal Bureau of Investigation (FBI), targeted political figures and media outlets through the use of finely milled anthrax that was sent through the mail. Twenty-two people became ill, and five died. Thousands of post office workers, congressional staff, and other potentially exposed individuals received prophylactic antibiotics and were offered vaccines. The public fear resulting from these attacks, however, was far more significant, and the event led to a massive effort by the federal government to build up national biodefense capabilities.

Public health preparedness against biological weapons threats spans a wide range of activities. These include pre-event surveillance and detection, research and development of medical countermeasures, preparedness planning, and community engagement. Post-event, the public health community's responsibilities include mitigating the consequences of the event through containment of the agent (using pharmaceutical and non-pharmaceutical interventions), timely delivery of medical countermeasures, mass casualty care, environmental decontamination, public messaging, and ensuring community resilience.

Radiological and Nuclear Agents   A nuclear weapon that involves fission (the splitting of atoms), like the bombs that the United States dropped on Hiroshima and Nagasaki, Japan near the end of World War II, or the devastating weapons created and stockpiled by a small number of nations since that war, is so destructive as to leave in its aftermath a limited

role for the public health community. Nuclear weapons, once released, would instantly destroy people, buildings, and most everything else in the vicinity of the blast. There would be little need for a public health response because the chances of human survival would be minimal. Furthermore, the explosion would leave behind large amounts of radioactivity, threatening nearby regions and creating a challenge for future inhabitation of the area. Indeed, large doses of radiation can lead to acute radiation syndrome (ARS), and the higher the dose of radiation, the less likely it is that the infected person will survive. Those that do survive may take several weeks to two years to recover, and survivors may suffer from leukemia or other cancers.[21]

A radiologic event is an explosion or other release of radioactivity. Such an event might be caused by any of the following: a simple, non-explosive radiological device, an improvised nuclear device with a large blast radius (such as a "suitcase bomb") designed to release large amounts of radiation, a dispersal device that combines explosive materials and radioactive material (such as a "dirty bomb"), or sabotage or other damage to a nuclear reactor that results in the release of radiation.[22] The International Atomic Energy Agency (IAEA) receives, on average, a report every two days of an incident of illicit trafficking of nuclear or radiological material,[23] and in April 2010, President Obama called the danger of nuclear terrorism one of the greatest threats to global security.[24]

When the public is exposed to radiologic materials but the event that caused the exposure is something less than a catastrophic explosion, the public health response is critical. In addition to its usual functions, the public health community is responsible for:

- participating in shelter-in-place or evacuation decisions;
- identifying exposed populations through surveillance activities;
- conducting or assisting with environmental decontamination;
- determining safety requirements for working in or near the site of the incident; and
- conducting near and long-term follow up with exposed populations.[25]

Naturally-Occurring Disease Threats

Naturally occurring diseases can have both direct and indirect impacts on national security and require the same attention in terms of public health preparedness as CBRN agents. Directly, infectious diseases can affect armed forces, impacting force readiness and the ability of a nation to defend itself

---

BOX 12-6 Anthrax Event in Sverdlovsk

In 1979, in the Siberian town of Sverdlovsk in the Soviet Union (now Yekaterinburg), at least 77 people became ill with anthrax, resulting in 66 fatalities. Originally, the Soviet Union claimed that the cause of the outbreak was bad meat, and the route of infection gastrointestinal. In reality, the cause of the outbreak was human error: a worker forgot to replace a filter at a military installation that was producing anthrax for offensive purposes. The anthrax escaped into the air and those who became ill fell within the wind plume leading directly from the military compound. In 1992, Boris Yeltsin (the first president of the Russian Federation after the dissolution of the Soviet Union) admitted to the international community that the source of the anthrax in this outbreak came from the offensive military production site, and not from consumption of infected meat.[19,20(p163)]

BOX 12-7 Chernobyl Nuclear Power Plant Accident

The most serious radiation accidents have been associated with nuclear power plants. Sixty-three accidents have occurred at nuclear power plants, with the most serious occurring in Chernobyl, Ukraine. On April 26, 1986, at 1:23 in the morning, Reactor 4 of the Chernobyl Nuclear Power Plant exploded, instantly killing three and sending a plume of radioactive fallout into the air, which eventually drifted over parts of the Soviet Union, Eastern Europe, Western Europe, Northern Europe, and Eastern North America. Approximately 350,000 individuals had to be evacuated and resettled. Fifty-six people died as a direct result of the accident, and another 4,000 have died from cancers linked to radiation exposure.[26] The public health community's immediate and long-term responsibility in response to the Chernobyl disaster was significant, including assessing the safety of the environment for human habitation, addressing the psychological impact of the disaster on affected populations, monitoring the long-term health and well-being of exposed populations, and planning for the treatment of untold numbers of current and future cancer patients.[26,27]

mies, government stability, and military readiness in strategic countries and regions.[33]

The burden of infectious diseases, and of emerging infectious diseases in particular, tends to affect regions and countries least able to address the threat.[7] The World Health Organization, analyzing verified events of potential international public health concern between September 2003 and September 2006, found that the vast majority of events (288) occurred in Africa. The Western Pacific region was the second most affected with 108 events, followed by Eastern Mediterranean (89), Southeast Asia (81), Europe (78), and, finally, the Americas (41).[7(p63)] The regions where public health emergencies are most likely to emerge are the same regions experiencing critical shortages of healthcare personnel, and tend to have the least developed healthcare infrastructure.[7,34] In addition, many of the current and developing megacities (10 million or more inhabitants) can be found in the same regions that have relatively poor healthcare infrastructure, an understaffed healthcare workforce, and the most public health

BOX 12-8 National Security Strategy: The Threat of Naturally Occurring Disease

According to the 2010 National Security Strategy: "The threat of contagious disease transcends political boundaries, and the ability to prevent, quickly detect, and contain outbreaks with pandemic potential has never been so important. An epidemic that begins in a single community can quickly evolve into a multinational health crisis that causes millions to suffer, as well as spark major disruptions to travel and trade. Addressing these transnational risks requires advance preparation, extensive collaboration with the global community, and the development of a resilient population at home.

Recognizing that the health of the world's population has never been more interdependent, we are improving our public health and medical capabilities on the front lines, including domestic and international disease surveillance, situational awareness, rapid and reliable development of medical countermeasures to respond to public health threats, preparedness education and training, and surge capacity of the domestic health care system to respond to an influx of patients due to a disaster or emergency. These capabilities include our ability to work with international partners to mitigate and contain disease when necessary."[14(p48-49)]

militarily and engage in armed battles around the world. In fact, until World War II, more soldiers died from infectious diseases than from direct combat injuries.[28] Even today, troop exposure to diseases affects morbidity and mortality and readiness, and disease has periodically affected the balance of power among states. Hospital admissions from disease continue to outnumber injuries and wounds and, as a result, the military has invested significant resources in infectious disease research, building diagnostic laboratory capacity around the world, disease surveillance infrastructure, and vaccine development.[29,30,31,32]

Indirectly, disease affects security because it can create large-scale morbidity and mortality, leading to massive loss of life and affecting all sectors of society. Such morbidity and mortality could result in economic loss and even long-term deterioration of economic viability. Even fear of disease can lead to societal disruption, which can lead to civil disorder, political unrest, and, ultimately, destabilization. Also indirectly, chronic diseases, now the leading cause of morbidity and mortality around the world, can negatively affect econo-

emergencies.[34] This means that it is probable that a public health emergency will emerge in a place that is understaffed, under-resourced, and overpopulated—all conditions that may contribute to the spread of disease. Furthermore, given the speed with which and the quantity of people and goods that move around the world, it is very possible for diseases to emerge in one part of the world and spread rapidly to other populations. As President Obama explained in May 2009, "[a]n outbreak in Indonesia can reach Indiana within days, and public health crises abroad can cause widespread suffering, conflict, and economic contraction."[35]

Public health preparedness for naturally occurring diseases must focus on basic scientific research to better understand the threats and work to design effective drugs, vaccines, and other therapeutics, and ensure the existence of sufficient production capacity for these tools. Effective, comprehensive, global surveillance systems are essential for early detection of disease to enable rapid response and containment efforts. Medical, community, and public sector coordination are necessary for distribution of countermeasures, surge capacity for mass care, mortuary services when necessary, and non-pharmaceutical interventions including isolation and quarantine. Public health officials are also responsible for ensuring

that a sufficient workforce is available to detect, report on, and respond to emergencies, and help bring about a recovery as quickly as possible.

Natural Disasters

It is an absolute certainty that natural disasters will occur all over the world: hurricanes will form, earthquakes will occur near fault lines, active volcanoes will erupt, tornadoes will sweep through regions, snow will fall, fire will spread, and low-lying regions will flood. Public health emergency preparedness is as much about planning for and responding to these types of disasters as it is about responding to terrorist events. In fact, the public health community is much more likely to engage in a response to a natural disaster than to an intentional or accidental one.

Natural disasters have the potential to impact very large populations. They can lead to morbidity and mortality, disrupt basic services, pose environmental challenges, and completely unhinge a community. Table 12-1 illustrates the magnitude, as measured in mortality, of major natural disasters.

Public health professionals have long been engaged in disaster response; as long as there have been emergencies, there have been medical personnel attending to the needs of populations. CDC started responding officially to disasters in the 1960s, when an Epidemic Intelligence Service (EIS) team traveled to Nigeria to help maintain public health programs in the midst of a civil war. Over the decades, CDC has developed public health and epidemiologic tools to address the realities of disaster situations and displaced populations. The public health community enters a disaster situation and establishes prevention and control measures, collects critical data to support response, and works to meet the short- and

---

BOX 12-9 Discussion Question

How can a naturally occurring disease event lead to a public health emergency? Explain how disease can impact national, regional, or international security.

TABLE 12-1 Major Natural Disasters, 1900 to Present*[36(p5),37,38,39,40]

Date	Event	Location	Approximate Death Toll
January 12, 2010	Earthquake	Port-au-Prince, Haiti	230,000
December 26, 2004	Tsunami (Indian Ocean)	Indonesia, Thailand, Sri Lanka, India, and more	220,000 (+)
July 28, 1976	Earthquake	Tangshan, China	242,000–655,000
November 13, 1970	Cyclone	Bangladesh	500,000
May–August 1931	Yellow River and Yangtze River floods	China	1–3.7 million
May 22, 1927	Earthquake	Xining, China	200,000
September 1, 1923	Earthquake and Fires	Tokyo, Japan	143,000
December 16, 1920	Earthquake	Haiyuan, China	200,000

long-term needs of the population.[36,41] Often, the most experienced public health and medical professionals on the ground during an emergency come from the Nongovernmental Organization (NGO) community, which has decades of experience responding to and helping populations recover from disasters. In fact, the American Red Cross, an NGO, has a federal charter to engage in disaster relief, and has specific responsibilities outlined in the National Response Framework based on its recognized expertise in this area.[42] In addition, military assets are utilized during emergencies to get qualified personnel to the event site quickly and, most importantly, provide logistical support, since some disasters require resources only the militaries of the world possess (e.g., the ability to reach isolated populations, bring supplies to remote regions, and establish care and living centers in harsh environments).[43,44]

Manmade Environmental Disasters

The fourth category of public health emergencies is manmade environmental disasters. These are events where human intervention, accident, or other engagement leads to an environmental disaster with direct implications for population health. Long term, human conduct that degrades the environment could conceivably fall into this category, but for purposes of studying public health preparedness, the more important concern is with acute events, such as the oil spill disaster in the Gulf Coast resulting from an explosion on an oil rig in April

BOX 12-10 Hurricane Katrina and the Public Health Response

On August 29, 2005, Hurricane Katrina landed on the Gulf Coast of the United States, reaching Mississippi, Louisiana, and Alabama. It came ashore with 115–130 mph winds and brought with it a water surge that in some locations rose as high as 27 feet. The surge pushed 6–12 miles inland and flooded approximately 80% of the city of New Orleans. Some 93,000 square miles were affected, resulting in 1,300 fatalities, 2 million displaced persons, 300,000 destroyed homes, and almost $100 billion in property damage.[(45)(pp 5–9)]

Katrina was the worst domestic natural disaster in recent history, but the consequences of the event were made worse by a faltering levee system designed by the U.S. Army Corps of Engineers and a failure of government at all levels to properly prepare for and respond to the disaster. First, long-term warnings went unheeded. It was clear that a hurricane of this type would eventually hit the region, yet local and state officials, even after running exercises based on such a scenario, failed to properly prepare. Local and state officials were unable to evacuate all of the citizens, struggled with logistics, and did not make proper preparations for dealing with vulnerable populations, including nursing home residents. The federal government failed to adequately anticipate the needs of the state and local authorities, and the insufficient coordination resulted in a lack of resources and a too-slow response.

The public health and medical response coordinated by the federal government followed the traditional response to a flood or hurricane: focus on sanitation and hygiene, water safety, surveillance and infection control, environmental health, and access to care.[46,47] Katrina, though, also presented unique challenges, such as the inability of displaced persons to manage chronic disease conditions and access medications, death and illness from dehydration, and mental health problems, all associated with the widespread devastation among those affected.

Almost all offices and branches of the federal Department of Health and Human Services (of which CDC is a part) eventually became involved in the response to Katrina. CDC sent staff to the affected areas, deployed the Strategic National Stockpile (SNS) to provide drugs and medical supplies, and developed public health and occupational health guidance. The Food and Drug Administration issued recommendations for handling drugs that might have been affected by the flood. The National Institutes of Health set up a phone-based medical consultation service for providers in the region. The Substance Abuse and Mental Health Services Administration set up crises counseling assistance and provided emergency response grants.[47]

In addition, the National Disaster Medical System deployed 50 Disaster Medical Assistance Teams to try to accommodate and treat hurricane victims. Disaster Mortuary Operational Response Teams also deployed to help process bodies. The Department of Defense set up field hospitals at the New Orleans International Airport and aboard naval vessels. The Department of Veterans Affairs evacuated both of its local hospitals—one prior to the storm, one afterwards.[47]

2010. This and similar disasters required the public health community to team with a variety of sectors at the local, state, and federal levels, understand the consequences to human health, and take actions to mitigate the consequences and address the health concerns of the community.

PUBLIC HEALTH PREPAREDNESS POLICY

While government officials have long been aware of public health emergencies and the need for coordinated action to detect, report, and respond appropriately, the U.S. preparedness infrastructure did not truly take shape until after the attacks on U.S. soil on September 11, 2001. Almost immediately after the World Trade Center and subsequent anthrax letter attacks, the United States embarked on a series of changes that resulted in the most massive reorganization of the federal government since World War II. The first significant organizational change was announced on October 8, 2001, when Executive Order 12338 established both the federal Office of Homeland Security and the Homeland Security Council within the White House. This was followed by the Homeland Security Act of 2002, which created the Department of Homeland Security (DHS) by reorganizing multiple existing agencies under a single department and creating new responsibilities around homeland security and preparedness.

Within DHS, the main office created to address public health preparedness is the Office of Health Affairs. This office has four main branches. The Weapons of Mass Destruction and Biodefense Office oversees biodefense activities, including Project Bioshield and bio-aerosol environmental monitoring systems. The Medical Readiness Office works with the first responder community, provides for health and medical security issues during emergencies, and oversees health components of contingency planning for CBRN. The Component Services Office focuses on occupational health and safety, workforce health protection, and medical services for DHS. Lastly, the International Affairs and Global Health Security office provides expertise on health security and emergency planning and coordinates information sharing with global and private sector partners.[48] In addition, the Science and Technology

Directorate houses the Chemical and Biological Division, which works on threat awareness, surveillance and detection, and countermeasures. This directorate also is home to the Office of National Laboratories, which includes a series of major research laboratories that support biodefense, microbial forensics, and basic understandings of chemical, biological, and agricultural threats. Importantly, the Federal Emergency Management Agency (commonly known as FEMA), responsible for much of the emergency disaster response activities at the federal level, is now part of DHS.

In addition to the creation of the Department of Homeland Security, in the wake of the 9/11 attacks, many existing government departments and agencies established new offices, expanded existing ones, and redirected resources towards preparedness and homeland security. The following agencies and offices are most directly linked to public health preparedness policy at the federal level.

Department of Health and Human Services (HHS)

Office of the Assistant Secretary for Preparedness and Response

The Office of the Assistant Secretary for Preparedness and Response (ASPR) was created by the Pandemic and All Hazards Preparedness Act of 2006, and replaced the office previously known as the Office of Public Health Emergency Preparedness. ASPR is composed of multiple components, including the Biomedical Advanced Research and Development Authority (BARDA), the Office of Preparedness and Emergency Operations, and Policy and Planning. ASPR is responsible for "preventing, preparing for, and responding to adverse health effects of public health emergencies and disasters."[49] In addition to policy development, the office supports state and local capacity during emergencies, including deployment of clinicians through the National Disaster Medical System.

Centers for Disease Control and Prevention

The CDC has consolidated its preparedness activities under the Office of Public Health Preparedness and Response. This office coordinates and responds to public health threats through a multitude of programs, including an emergency operations division that constantly maintains situational awareness of potential threats; a division dedicated to supporting preparedness at the state, local, tribal, and territorial level through cooperative agreements providing approximately $7 billion to date; a division that hosts and manages the strategic national stockpile of medical countermeasures and supplies necessary to address large-scale public health emergencies; and a division devoted to regulating the select agent program.

National Institutes of Health

The National Institutes of Health (NIH) is engaged in public health preparedness through a variety of offices. The two primary ones are the Office of Science Policy, which houses the National Science Advisory Board for Biosecurity (NSABB), and the National Institute of Allergy and Infectious Diseases (NIAID), which hosts a robust research agenda, both intramural and in support of extramural programs, that supports the research and development of medical countermeasures against radiological, nuclear, and chemical threats and supports biodefense activities.[50]

The Food and Drug Administration

The Food and Drug Administration (FDA) has multiple offices that focus on emergency preparedness and response policy. These offices focus on regulatory oversight, monitoring infrastructure, and facilitating the delivery of appropriate countermeasures. Specifically, the Office of Crises Management coordinates emergency and crises response when FDA-regulated products are affected by public health emergencies. The Center for Biologics and Evaluation Research oversees safety and effectiveness of biologic products, including CBRN medical countermeasures. The Office of Counterterrorism and Emerging Threats works on policies, strategies, and interagency communications concerning counterterrorism, and also coordinates activities around Emergency Use Authorization for medical countermeasures.[51]

Department of Agriculture

The Animal and Plant Health Inspection Service (APHIS) at the Department of Agriculture (USDA) has a broad mission to protect and promote U.S. agricultural health. APHIS also works with DHS and FEMA to provide assistance and coordination during emergencies. This assistance ranges from disease containment in poultry, such as in cases of avian influenza, to protecting the health of livestock and crops from foreign disease.[52]

Department of Justice, Federal Bureau of Investigation

The FBI created a new Weapons of Mass Destruction (WMD) Directorate in 2006. This Directorate works in several areas, including countermeasures and preparedness, investigations and operations, and intelligence analysis. The investigative component directs the WMD threat credibility assessments and manages all WMD criminal investigations. On preparedness, the FBI works with field components as well as with other agencies. In particular, the FBI works closely with CDC on "Crim-Epi," the cooperation between law enforcement and epidemiologists in the investigation of potential WMD events in a way that enables the FBI to collect information that will lead to a prosecution, and that also enables epidemiologists to investigate, treat, and minimize morbidity and mortality.[53]

Department of Defense

The Department of Defense (DoD) has a massive infrastructure designed to address threats of any nature, including public health emergencies. The military is trained in emergency response and preparedness as critical components of an effective armed forces. While most DoD programs focus on protecting the war fighter, several also have implications for the broader civilian population. There is an active chemical and biological defense program that involves research, development, and testing defense systems and equipment, including medical countermeasures. The Threat Reduction Programs work to reduce the threat of WMD, while building global capacity for detection and response to biological threats. There is a large-scale laboratory network both in the United States and abroad engaged in basic scientific research on infectious diseases and appropriate epidemiologic responses to public health emergencies. For emergency response within the United States, the Northern Command has the lead within DoD, and is charged with coordinating DoD support to civilian authorities. There are also several DoD consequence management response teams, including those specifically trained to respond to WMD events.[54]

Preparedness Statutes, Regulations, and Policy Guidance

Statutes, regulations, and policy guidance documents form the foundation of public health preparedness. In the always-evolving, operations-based field of public health preparedness, the legal and regulatory framework creates the baseline from which all policymaking, planning, and action is taken. As this is a relatively new discipline, the statutes, regulations, and policy guidance are also relatively new, changing to meet an evolving threat, incorporating lessons from previous experiences, and adapting to feedback from those directly involved with implementing them. Below is a brief description of the key laws (both statutory and regulatory) and policy guidance documents that currently guide preparedness efforts.

Public Health Improvement Act of 2000 (Public Law 106-505)

The Public Health Improvement Act of 2000 has ten titles, or sections, nine of which address traditional public health interests such as sexually transmitted diseases, Alzheimer's research, organ donation, clinical research, and laboratory infrastructure. Title 1, however, addresses emerging threats to the public's health. This section authorizes the Secretary of HHS to take appropriate response actions during a public health emergency, including investigations, treatment, and prevention. The Act established the Public Health Emergency Fund to support response activities and directed the HHS Secretary to establish a working group to focus on the medical and public health effects of a bioterrorist attack.

USA PATRIOT Act of 2001 (Public Law 107-56)

The Uniting and Strengthening America by Providing Appropriate Tools Required to Intercept and Obstruct Terrorism (USA PATRIOT) Act was passed by Congress and signed into law by President George W. Bush in October 2001, immediately following the September 11, 2001 attacks and during the height of the anthrax-letters scare. This law includes a multitude of terrorism-related policies. Among them are provisions related to acquiring, handling, and transporting particularly dangerous pathogens; assistance to first responders; and funding for substantial new investments in bioterrorism preparedness and response.[55(§1013)]

Public Health Security and Bioterrorism Preparedness and Response Act of 2002 (Public Law 107-188)

Signed into law in June 2002, the Bioterrorism Act (as it is known) was the first major piece of legislation dedicated entirely to public health preparedness. The act has five titles:

1. *National Preparedness for Bioterrorism and Other Public Health Emergencies.* This section addresses national preparedness and response planning by calling for the development and maintenance of medical countermeasures, creation of a national disaster medical system, support for communications and surveillance among all levels of public health officials, creation of a core academic curriculum concerning bioweapons and other public health emergencies, improving hospital preparedness, and addressing workforce shortages for public health emergencies. Interestingly, this title also codifies what had already been established—a strategic national stockpile of medical countermeasures. Specifically, the law directs

HHS to ensure that there is enough smallpox vaccine in the stockpile to "meet the health security needs of the United States." It also specifically calls for the stockpile to have enough potassium iodide tablets to distribute to populations within 20 miles of a nuclear power plant.[56(TitleI,SubtitleB)]

2. *Enhancing Controls on Dangerous Biological Agents and Toxins.* This title addresses the control over select agents.

3. *Protecting Safety and Security of Food and Drug Supply.* Title III is focused on bioterrorist threats to the food supply, and what the FDA is permitted to do to address this threat. It also touches on the importance of ensuring the safety of drugs imported into the United States.

4. *Drinking Water Security and Safety.* This section of the law directs communities to do a full assessment of the vulnerabilities of the water supply to terrorist attacks.

5. *Additional Provisions.* The final section of the law includes miscellaneous provisions, including some focused on prescription drug user fees and Medicare plans.

Smallpox Emergency Personnel Protection Act of 2003 (Public Law 108-20)

In December 2002, the Bush Administration announced a program to vaccinate both military personnel and civilian emergency health workers against smallpox. The vaccine program for the military was obligatory, while the civilian vaccination program was voluntary. The Smallpox Emergency Personnel Protection Act, which became law nearly 3 months after the vaccination program started, focuses on compensation related to medical care, lost income, or death resulting from receipt of the smallpox vaccine.

The Project Bioshield Act of 2004 (Public Law 108-276)

While the Bioterrorism Act of 2002 codified into law the requirement for a Strategic National Stockpile, there remained in practice a problem: Because of the vast costs involved with producing and no guaranteed market in which to sell CBRN medical countermeasures (drugs and vaccines), pharmaceutical companies were reluctant to develop and bring to market these countermeasures. As a result, the National Stockpile remained underresourced. The Bioshield Act of 2004 aimed to create a guaranteed government-funded market for medical countermeasures, and included funding to purchase the products while they are still in the final stages of development. The Act also allowed HHS to expedite spending to procure products, hire experts, and award research grants pertaining to CBRN, and to allow for emergency use of countermeasures even if they lacked final FDA approval.

Public Readiness and Emergency Preparedness (PREP) Act of 2005 (Division C of the Department of Defense Emergency Supplemental Appropriations; Public Law 109-148)

Because the Project Bioshield Act allowed the Secretary of HHS to force the use of medical countermeasures for emergency purposes without final FDA approval, manufacturers, distributors, program administrators, prescribers, and dispensers expressed concern to policymakers that they could be held liable for any negative consequences associated with the use of unapproved countermeasures. In response, Congress and the Bush Administration passed the Public Readiness and Emergency Preparedness Act, which limits liability associated with public health countermeasures used on an emergency basis. The only exception is in the event of "willful misconduct."

Pandemic and All-Hazards Preparedness Act of 2006 (Public Law 109-417)

The Pandemic and All-Hazards Preparedness Act, known as PAHPA, reauthorized the Bioterrorism Act of 2002 and added broad provisions aimed at preparing for and responding to public health and medical emergencies, regardless of origin. PAHPA is organized into the following four main titles:

1. *National Preparedness and Response, Leadership, Organization, and Planning.* This title makes the HHS Secretary the lead person for all public health and medical responses to emergencies covered by the National Response Framework.[a] It also established the position of Assistant Secretary for Preparedness and Response at HHS and required HHS to create a National Health Security Strategy.
2. *Public Health Security Preparedness.* This section of the Act focuses on developing preparedness infrastructure, primarily at the state and local level, to include pandemic plans, interoperable networks for data sharing, and telehealth capabilities. It also addresses laboratory security and the need to ensure readiness of the Commissioned Corps of the Public Health Service to respond to public health emergencies.
3. *All-Hazards Medical Surge Capacity.* This title has several key provisions, including the transfer of the National Disaster Medical System (NDMS) back to HHS from DHS. HHS is responsible for evaluating capacity for a medical patient surge during a public health emergency, and is required to establish a Medical Reserve Corps of volunteers to assist during such emergencies. Title III also requires HHS to develop public health preparedness curricula and establish centers for preparedness at schools of public health.
4. *Pandemic and Biodefense Vaccine and Drug Development.* The final title of PAHPA builds on the Bioshield Act of 2004 by requiring the establishment of the Biomedical Advanced Research and Development Authority (BARDA) within HHS to coordinate countermeasure research and development. Although the Bioshield Act enticed manufacturers to develop countermeasures, it did not do enough to assist companies during the expensive years of product research and development. Through payment structure reform, Title IV permits BARDA to better enable countermeasure development and production.

Implementing Recommendations of the 9/11 Commission Act of 2007 (Public Law 110-53)

In August 2007, Congress passed the Implementing Recommendations of the 9/11 Commission Act, which, as the title suggests, focuses on implementing the recommendations from the 9/11 Commission Report. The Act includes numerous specific provisions pertaining to preparedness, such as preparedness grants to state and local entities, improving the incident command system, improving the sharing of intelligence information across the federal government, enhancing efforts to prevent terrorists from gaining entry into the United States, increasing the safety of transportation, and improving generally the preparedness infrastructure. It also includes sections on diplomatic engagement and advancing democratic values abroad. Specific to public health, Title XI of the Act addresses enhanced defenses against Weapons of Mass Destruction, particularly the need to maintain a National Biosurveillance Integration Center that reports to Congress on the "state of . . . biosurveillance efforts."[57]([§1102])

BOX 12-12   Discussion Question

The Pandemic and All-Hazards Preparedness Act of 2006 will be reauthorized at the end of 2011. What should be included in the new bill? What should not be? Compare your thoughts to the actual 2011 law.

Biodefense for the 21st Century: National Security Presidential Directive 33/Homeland Security Presidential Directive 10. April 2004

In 2004, the Bush Administration released Homeland Security Presidential Directive (HSPD) 10, which provided a strategic overview of the biological weapons threat and the Administration's approach to framing biodefense initiatives. The directive described four essential pillars of the national biodefense program: threat awareness, prevention and protection, surveillance and detection, and response and recovery. This document would remain the primary policy directive concerning biodefense until the National Strategy for Countering Biological Threats was released in late 2009.

Medical Countermeasures Against Weapons of Mass Destruction: Homeland Security Presidential Directive 18. February 2007

Following HSPD 10, the Bush Administration released a directive (HSPD 18) pertaining to the development of medical countermeasures to counter WMD. The directive defined the policies associated with medical countermeasures, from focused development of agent-specific countermeasures to a flexible capability for future countermeasures. HHS was directed to lead research, development, evaluation, and acquisition of public health emergency medical countermeasures, while DoD retained control over countermeasure development specific to the armed forces.

Public Health and Medical Preparedness: Homeland Security Presidential Directive 21. October 2007

Building upon HSPD 10, and in accordance with HSPD 18, HSPD 21 was released in the fall of 2007 and defines four critical components of public health and medical preparedness. The four components are a robust and integrated biosurveillance system, the ability to stockpile and distribute medical countermeasures, the capacity to engage in mass casualty care in emergency situations, and building resilient communities at the state and local level. The directive also mandates the creation of task forces, studies, and plans to meet public health and medical preparedness needs.

Establishing Federal Capability for the Timely Provision of Medical Countermeasures Following a Biological Attack, Executive Order 13527. December 2009

In the last days of 2009, President Obama released Executive Order 13527, establishing a policy of timely provision of medical countermeasures in the event of a biological attack and tasking the federal government with assisting state and local entities in this endeavor. The order also spells out the role of the U.S. Postal Service in the delivery of medical countermeasures and calls on HHS to develop continuity of operations plans in the event of a large-scale biological attack.

National Strategy for Countering Biological Threats, Presidential Policy Directive 2. November 2009

The National Strategy for Countering Biological Threats was released in time for Undersecretary of State Ellen Tauscher to share it with the international community at the December 2009 Meeting of States Parties of the Biological Weapons Convention.[58] The Strategy, the first major policy statement by the Obama Administration on the topic of biological threats, spells out seven major objectives:

Promote global health security;
Reinforce norms of safe and responsible conduct;
Obtain timely and accurate insight on current and emerging risks;
Take reasonable steps to reduce the potential for exploitation;
Expand our capability to prevent, attribute, and apprehend;
Communicate effectively with all stakeholders; and
Transform the international dialogue on biological threats.[59,60]

While many of the Bush Administration directives focused on policies for responding to a biological threat, the Obama Strategy directive placed more emphasis on prevention, with particular stress on the importance of working with international partners, reinforcing norms of responsible scientific conduct, and engaging scientists so that they can continue beneficial work in the life sciences.

National Preparedness Presidential Policy Directive 8. March 2011

In early 2011, the Obama Administration released Presidential Policy Directive (PPD) 8, replacing HSPD 8. The PPD required the development of a national preparedness goal (as did HSPD 8) and the creation of a National Preparedness System to integrate guidance, programs, and processes to build and sustain capabilities essential for preparedness. PPD 8 takes an "all-of-Nation" approach, identifying the importance of collaboration between governments at all levels and the private and not-for-profit sectors as well as the public in order to enhance resilience,[61] which the directive defines as "the ability to adapt to changing conditions and withstand and rapidly recover from disruption due to emergencies."[62]

In addition to domestic statutes, regulations, and formal policy guidance documents, there are a host of formal international agreements that attempt to coordinate global efforts to respond to the threats posed to populations by weapons of mass destruction and infectious diseases. These international agreements include a series of arms control treaties, including the Geneva Protocol, the Biological and Toxin Weapons Convention, the Chemical Weapons Convention, and the Nuclear Nonproliferation Treaty. In addition, United Nations (UN) Security Council Resolution 1540 obligates UN Member States (including the United States) to ensure they do not support non-state actors in their efforts to develop, acquire, possess, or use nuclear, chemical, or biological weapons.

In 2005, the World Health Assembly (WHA) of the World Health Organization (WHO) adopted the International Health Regulations. This agreement recognizes the threat of emerging infectious diseases, the globalization of society, and the need for improved surveillance, response, communication, and coordination to effectively detect and respond to public health threats. A primary purpose of the regulations is to improve global health security through international collaboration and communication by detecting and containing public health emergencies at the source.

The International Health Regulations obligate nations to build disease surveillance capacity, and report in a timely fashion to WHO any potential public health emergencies and any public health emergencies of international concern (PHEIC). PHEICs are defined through an algorithm in the regulations themselves (e.g., the emergencies should have the potential to cross borders, possibly requiring international coordination for response efforts) and may stem from naturally occurring disease, accidental releases of agents, or intentional events involving biological, chemical, or radiological agents.

Depending on the type of public health emergency, there are a range of global actors that become involved to aid, augment, or help govern national response efforts. These actors

range from Interpol, to the WHO and the Food and Agriculture Organization, to organizations connected to arms control efforts, such as the Organization for the Prohibition of Chemical Weapons and the International Association for Atomic Energy. In addition, there are networks of laboratories, regional cooperation organizations, and a vast conglomeration of nongovernmental organizations which may become involved in the detection, response, and recovery from global public health emergencies.

PUBLIC HEALTH PREPAREDNESS FEDERALISM

Public health preparedness requires cooperation among a variety of sectors at multiple levels of government. At the federal level, multiple agencies, including HHS; DHS; the Environmental Protection Agency; the Departments of State, Defense, Justice, Transportation, Commerce, Energy, and Treasury; and the intelligence community are all involved and are coordinated in the end by the National Security Staff of the White House.

While a strong federal policy and infrastructure is essential, public health professionals recognize that most public health activities occur at the local and state level. Clinical care is an essential component of public health, yet that care is not coordinated or delivered in Washington, DC. It is in every doctor's office, hospital, and clinic around the country. Disease surveillance is essential, but it starts with detection of an unusual event by an astute clinician and a capable laboratory, wherever the event emerges. Not only is this a reality in practice, it is codified by the 10th Amendment of the Constitution: "The powers not delegated to the United States by the Constitution, nor prohibited by it to the States, are reserved to the States respectively, or to the people."[63(amend.10)] This means that police powers, including the powers to regulate health and safety, are the responsibility of the states. The federal government supports public health preparedness domestically, as it must build relations globally to ensure an effective worldwide system for preparedness, information sharing, and collaboration in preventing, detecting, reporting, and responding to public health threats. It is the state and local entities, however, that are relied upon to implement policies, build infrastructure, and interface with local populations to promote health security. This is the case in the United States, as it is throughout the world.

States have the responsibility for developing their own emergency preparedness plans, and all have some level of planning and preparedness training in place. Preparedness efforts at the state level have strived to meet national preparedness objectives, yet at the same time focus on the unique threats, challenges, assets, and populations specific to particular jurisdictions. States that are subject to relatively more frequent hurricanes may have well-developed plans to address that particular hazard, while landlocked states far from oceans may have better-developed plans for disasters such as tornadoes. States will also take into account the particular demographics of their region when planning how to address vulnerable populations, nursing homes, and schools in emergencies. All states have more developed emergency plans then pre-9/11, but all continue to have some gaps, be it around medical surge capacity, school-based preparedness, or preparedness for radiation events.[64,65,66]

In carrying out their responsibilities, state and local public health professionals are supported by several professional associations, including the American Public Health Association (APHA), the Council of State and Territorial Epidemiologists (CSTE), the Association of Public Health Laboratories (APHL), the Association of State and Territorial Health Officers (ASTHO), and the National Association of County and City Health Officials (NACCHO). These associations play an active role in providing guidance, securing funding, and assisting the public health workforce in meeting the preparedness challenge.

CONCLUSION

The United States has made great strides in public health preparedness in the past decade. This success was due in no small part to a massive influx of funding to support federal, state, and local entities in building capacity, planning, and response efforts. Between 2003 and 2007, DHS alone awarded over $27 billion in preparedness grants to state and local governments, although this represents only a small fraction of total state and local preparedness expenditures.[67]

Recently, however, preparedness budgets have been reduced as the nation and its individual states grapple with debt, deficits, and reduced revenues. For example, approximately $107 million was cut from the CDC's preparedness funding for fiscal year 2011, an almost 13% drop from FY 2010.[68] Reduced funding means that policymakers and program managers have to make difficult decisions about how best to allocate and plan for preparedness activities in a resource-constrained environment.

Assuming sufficient funding, there are several areas of public health preparedness that should be targeted for further development. These include:

- Comprehensive disease surveillance: the development of a fully integrated, national disease surveillance system capable of early detection of events should be supported. This may involve integration of electronic

BOX 12-14 Discussion Question

What are the distinct roles of local, state, federal, and international governments and organizations in managing a public health emergency of international concern?

health records and exploration of other information and technology opportunities.
- Workforce: the public health workforce, particularly epidemiologists and laboratory workers, must be developed and sustained.
- Resilience and community planning: the public health community must continue to engage community members and work with local entities to develop recovery and resilience plans.
- Countermeasures: continued investment must be made in the basic research and development of medical countermeasures, as well as ways to store and disperse such countermeasures during a public health emergency.
- Chemical and radiological preparedness: public health professionals must continue to conduct research and better understand chemical and radiological threats to further develop plans to address such events.
- Public and private partnerships: local, state, and federal entities must continue to explore partnerships with the private sector to enhance preparedness efforts.

Finally, the public health community must continue to develop opportunities and curricula to train the next generation of public health professionals. Understanding threats; planning effectively to detect, respond to, and recover from emergencies; and appropriately engaging with counterparts across communities, governments, and nations are essential to future public health practice and policy.

REFERENCES

1. Association of Schools of Public Health Core Curricula Working Group. *Practical Implications, Approaches, Opportunities and Challenges of A Preparedness Core Curricula in Accredited Schools of Public Health*. Available at http://www.asph.org/UserFiles/finalcorecurriculawhitepaper1.pdf.
2. Nelson C, Lurie N, Wasserman J, Zakowski S. Conceptualizing and Defining Public Health Emergency Preparedness. *Am J Pub Health*. 2007;97:S9–S11.
3. The Center for Law and the Public's Health at Georgetown and Johns Hopkins Universities. *The Model State Emergency Health Powers Act*. December 21, 2001.
4. World Health Organization. *International Health Regulations (2005) Second Edition*. 2008: Article I. Available at http://whqlibdoc.who.int/publications/2008/9789241580410_eng.pdf.

5. Harford J, Azavedo E, Fischietto M. Guideline Implementation for Breast Healthcare in Low- and Middle-Income Countries: Breast Healthcare Program Resource Allocation. *Cancer.* 2008;S8:2282–2296.

6. World Health Organization, Western Pacific Region. *Japan earthquake and tsunami. Situation Report No 33.* s.l. Available at http://www.wpro.who.int/NR/rdonlyres/B614B476-46F1-4094-846D-F5B9D5BD0FB7/0/Sitrep3311May.pdf. Accessed May 18, 2011.

7. World Health Organization. *The World Health Report 2007: A Safer Future—Global Public Health Security in the 21st Century.* 2007.

8. Wenck MA, Van Sickle D, Drociuk D, Belflower A, Youngblood C, Whisnant D, Taylor R, Rudnick V, Gibson J. Rapid Assessment of Exposure to Cholorine Released from a Train Derailment and Resulting Health Impact. *Pub Health Reports.* 2007;6(122):784–792.

9. Handelman K, Alibek S. *Biohazard: The Chilling True Story of the Largest Covert Biological Weapons Program in the World—Told from Inside by the Man Who Ran It.* s.l.: New York: Delta, 2000.

10. Nuclear Threat Initiative. Introduction to BW Terrorism. *BW Terrorism Tutorial.* [Online] 2004. Available at http://www.nti.org/h_learnmore/bwtutorial/chapter01_03.html. Accessed June 26, 2010.

11. Monke J. *CRS Report for Congress: Agroterrorism: Threats.* Federation of American Scientists. [Online] August 13, 2004. Available at http://www.fas.org/irp/crs/RL32521.pdf. Accessed July 10, 2010.

12. Vale A. What lessons can we learn from the Japanese sarin attacks? *Przegląd lekarski.* 2005;6(62):528–532.

13. UN News Centre. Toxic wastes caused deaths, illnesses in Côte d'Ivoire—UN expert. *United Nations.* [Online] September 16, 2009. Available at http://www.un.org/apps/news/story.asp?NewsID=32072. Accessed July 8, 2010.

14. Polgreen L, Simons M. Global Sludge Ends in Tragedy for Ivory Coast. *The New York Times.* [Online] October 2, 2006. Available at http://www.nytimes.com/2006/10/02/world/africa/02ivory.html. Accessed July 8, 2010.

15. Elrod S. Category A–C Agents. In: Katz R, Zilinikas R, Eds. *Encyclopedia of Bioterrorism Defense.* 2nd Edition. s.l.: Hoboken, NJ: Wiley and Sons, 2011.

16. Centers for Disease Control and Prevention. Bioterrorism Agents/Diseases—By Category. *Emergency Preparedness and Response.* [Online] Available at http://www.bt.cdc.gov/agent/agentlist-category.asp. Accessed July 10, 2010.

17. Commission on the Prevention of Weapons of Mass Destruction, Proliferation and Terrorism. *World at Risk: The Report of the Commission on the Prevention of WMD Proliferation and Terrorism.* New York: First Vintage Books Edition, 2008.

18. Wheelis M. Biological Warfare at the 1346 Siege of Caffa. *Emerg Infect Dis.* 2002;8(9):971–975.

19. Meselson M, Guillemin J, Hugh-Jones M, Langmuir A, Popova I, Shelokov A, Yampolskaya O. The Sverdlovsk anthrax outbreak of 1979. *Science.* 1994;266(5188):1202–1208.

20. Guillemin J. *Anthrax: The Investigation of a Deadly Outbreak.* s.l.: Berkley: University of California Press, 2001.

21. Centers for Disease Control and Prevention. Acute Radiation Syndrome (ARS): A Fact Sheet for the Public. *Emergency Preparedness and Response.* [Online] May 10, 2006. Available at http://www.bt.cdc.gov/radiation/ars.asp. Accessed July 8, 2010.

22. Durham B. The Background and History of Manmade Disasters. *Topics Emerg Med.* 2002;24(2):1–14.

23. International Atomic Energy Agency (IAEA). Statement at Nuclear Security Summit by IAEA Director General Yukiya Amano. *Statements of the Director General.* [Online] April 13, 2010. Available at http://www.iaea.org/NewsCenter/Statements/2010/amsp2010n007.html. Accessed July 8, 2010.

24. The White House, Office of the Press Secretary. Remarks by the President at the Opening Plenary Session of the Nuclear Security Summit. *The White House.* [Online] April 13, 2010. Available at http://www.whitehouse.gov/the-press-office/remarks-president-opening-plenary-session-nuclear-security-summit. Accessed July 8, 2010.

25. The White House, Office of the Press Secretary. Radiation Emergencies—Information for Public Health Professionals. *Emergency Preparedness and Response.* [Online] March 31, 2010. Available at http://www.bt.cdc.gov/radiation/publichealth.asp. Accessed July 8, 2010.

26. The Chernobyl Forum: 2003–2005. Chernobyl's Legacy: Health, Environmental and Socio-Economic Impacts and Recommendations to the Governments of Belarus, the Russian Federation and Ukraine. *International Atomic Energy Agency (IAEA).* [Online] April 2006. Available at http://www.iaea.org/Publications/Booklets/Chernobyl/chernobyl.pdf. Accessed July 8, 2010.

27. Jargin SV. Overestimation of Thyroid Cancer Incidence after the Chernobyl Accident. *BMJ.* [Online] October 11, 2008. Available at http://www.bmj.com/cgi/eletters/316/7136/952#202977. Accessed July 8, 2010.

28. Medical Follow-Up Agency (MFUA); Institute of Medicine (IOM). Introduction and History—Naturally Occurring Infectious Diseases in the U.S. Military. In: Lemon SM, Thaul S, Fisseha S, O'Maonaigh HC. *Protecting Our Forces: Improving Vaccine Acquisition and Availability in the U.S. Military.* Washington, DC: The National Academies Press, 2002, p. 9. Available at http://www.nap.edu/openbook.php?record_id=10483&page=9.

29. Murry CK, Hinkle MK, Yun HC. History of Infections Associated With Combat-Related Injuries. *J Trauma.* 2008;64(3):S221–S231. Available at http://www.afids.org/Prevention%20and%20Management%20of%20CRI%20(4)%20-%20History.pdf.

30. Writer JV, DeFraites RF, Keep LW. Non-battle injury casualties during the Persian Gulf War and other deployments. *Am J Prevent Med.* 2000;18(3, Suppl. 1):64–70.

31. Global Emerging Infections Surveillance and Response Systems (GEIS) Operations. *Armed Forces Health Surveillance Center.* [Online] Available at http://www.afhsc.mil/geis. Accessed July 25, 2010.

32. Walter Reed Army Institute of Research. *U.S. Army Medical Research and Material Command.* [Online] Available at http://wrair-www.army.mil/. Accessed July 25, 2010.

33. U.S. Department of State. *Infectious and Chronic Disease.* [Online] Available at http://www.state.gov/g/oes/intlhealthbiodefense/id/index.htm. Accessed August 1, 2010.

34. National Intelligence Council. Strategic Implications of Global Health. *National Intelligence Council.* [Online] December 2008. Available at http://www.dni.gov/nic/PDF_GIF_otherprod/ICA_Global_Health_2008.pdf. Accessed July 25, 2010.

35. The White House, Office of the Press Secretary. Statement by the President on Global Health Initiative. *The White House.* [Online] May 5, 2009. Available at http://www.whitehouse.gov/the_press_office/Statement-by-the-President-on-Global-Health-Initiative/. Accessed August 1, 2010.

36. Noji EK. *The Public Health Consequences of Disasters.* s.l.: New York: Oxford University Press, 1997.

37. CBC News. The world's worst natural disasters: Calamities of the 20th and 21st centuries. *CBC News.* [Online] August 30, 2010. Available at http://www.cbc.ca/world/story/2008/05/08/f-natural-disasters-history.html?rdr=525. Accessed December 15, 2010.

38. U.S. Agency for International Development, Office of U.S. Foreign Disaster Assistance. Disaster History: Significant Data on Major Disasters Worldwide, 1900–Present. *U.S. Agency for International Development.* [Online] August 1993. Available at http://pdf.usaid.gov/pdf_docs/PNABP986.pdf. Accessed December 15, 2010.

39. Associated Press. Haiti raises earthquake toll to 230,000. *The Washington Post.* [Online] February 10, 2010. Available at http://www.washingtonpost.com/wp-dyn/content/article/2010/02/09/AR2010020904447.html. Accessed December 15, 2010.

40. U.S. Agency for International Development. USAID Disaster Assistance, Indian Ocean Tsunami. *U.S. Agency for International Development.*

[Online] May 30, 2007. Available at http://www.usaid.gov/our_work/humanitarian_assistance/disaster_assistance/countries/indian_ocean/template/index.html. Accessed December 15, 2010.

41. Gregg MB, ed. *The Public Health Consequences of Disasters. CDC Monograph*. Atlanta, GA: Centers for Disease Control and Prevention, 1989.

42. The American National Red Cross. The Federal Charter of the American Red Cross. *American Red Cross*. [Online] Available at http://www.redcross.org/portal/site/en/menuitem.d229a5f06620c6052b1ecfbf43181aa0/?vgnextoid=39c2a8f21931f110VgnVCM10000089f0870aRCRD&cpsextcurrchannel=1. Accessed December 15, 2010.

43. Wiharta S, Ahmad H, Haine J-Y, Löfgren J, Randall T. *The Effectiveness of Foreign Military Assets in Natural Disaster Response*. Solna, Sweden: Stockholm International Peace Research Institute, 2008.

44. VanYooyen M, Leaning J. After the Tsunami—Facing the Public Health Challenges. *The N Engl J Med*. 2005;352(5):435–438.

45. The White House. The Federal Response to Hurricane Katrina Lessons Learned. [Online] February 2006. Available at http://library.stmarytx.edu/acadlib/edocs/katrinawh.pdf. Accessed September 10, 2010.

46. Greenough PG, Kirsch TD. *Public Health Response—Assessing Needs*. Greenough P. Gregg and Kirsch, Thomas D. *N Engl J Med*. 2005;353(15):1544–1546.

47. Lister SA. CRS Report for Congress: Hurricane Katrina: The Public Health and Medical Response. *U.S. Department of State, Foreign Press Centers*. [Online] September 21, 2005. Available at http://fpc.state.gov/documents/organization/54255.pdf. Accessed November 5, 2010.

48. U.S. Department of Homeland Security. Office of Health Affairs. *U.S. Department of Homeland Security*. [Online] August 26, 2009. Available at http://www.dhs.gov/xabout/structure/editorial_0880.shtm. Accessed August 23, 2010.

49. U.S. Department of Health and Human Services. Office of the Assistant Secretary for Preparedness and Response (ASPR). *Public Health Emergency*. [Online] May 11, 2010. Available at http://www.phe.gov/about/aspr/pages/default.aspx. Accessed August 23, 2010.

50. U.S. Department of Health and Human Services. Office of the Assistant Secretary for Preparedness and Response (ASPR). Biodefense & Related Programs. *National Institute of Allergy and Infectious Diseases*. [Online] November 16, 2009. Available at http://www.niaid.nih.gov/topics/biodefenserelated/pages/default.aspx. Accessed August 23, 2010.

51. U.S. Department of Health and Human Services. Office of the Assistant Secretary for Preparedness and Response (ASPR). Emergency Preparedness and Response. *U.S. Food and Drug Administration*. [Online] Available at http://www.fda.gov/EmergencyPreparedness/default.htm. Accessed August 23, 2010.

52. U.S. Department of Agriculture. *Animal and Plant Health Inspection Service*. [Online] August 23, 2010. Available at http://www.aphis.usda.gov/. Accessed August 23, 2010.

53. U.S. Department of Justice. *Federal Bureau of Investigation*. [Online] Available at http://www.fbi.gov/homepage.htm. Accessed August 23, 2010.

54. Sandor K. Department of Defense. In: Katz R, Zilinikas R, Eds. *Encyclopedia of Bioterrorism Defense*. 2nd Edition. Hoboken, NJ: Wiley and Sons, 2011.

55. *Uniting and Strengthening America by Providing Appropriate Tools Required to Intercept and Obstruct Terrorism (USA PATRIOT) Act of 2001*; Public Law No. 107-56.

56. *Public Health Security and Bioterrorism Preparedness and Response Act of 2002*; Public Law No. 107-188.

57. *Implementing Recommendations of the 9/11 Commission Act of 2007*; Public Law No. 110-53.

58. Tauscher EO. Undersecretary of State Ellen Tauscher: Address to States Parties of the BWC. *United States Mission to the United Nations and Other International Organizations in Geneva*. [Online] December 9, 2009. Available at http://geneva.usmission.gov/2009/12/09/tauscher-bwc/. Accessed September 10, 2010.

59. National Security Council. National Strategy for Countering Biological Threats. *The White House*. [Online] November 2009. Available at http://www.whitehouse.gov/sites/default/files/National_Strategy_for_Countering_BioThreats.pdf. Accessed September 10, 2010.

60. Miller JE. National Strategy for Countering Biological Threats. In: Katz R, Zilinikas R, Eds. *Encyclopedia of Bioterrorism Defense*. 2nd Edition. Hoboken, NJ: Wiley and Sons, 2011.

61. Balboni M, Kaniewski D, Paulison RD. *Preparedness, Response and Resilience Task Force: Interim Task Force Report on Resilience*. Washington, DC: Homeland Security Policy Institute. Available at www.gwumc.edu/hspi/policy/report_Resilience1.pdf. Accessed May 20, 2011.

62. The White House. *Presidential Policy Directive 8, National Preparedness*. March 30, 2011.

63. Constitution of the United States of America. Tenth amendment.

64. Watkins WM, Perrotta D, Stanbury M, Heumann M, Anderson H, Simms E, Huang M. State-level emergency preparedness and response capabilities. *Disaster Medicine and Public Health Preparedness*. 2011;5:S134–S142.

65. Government Accountability Office. *Emergency Management: Most School Districts Have Developed Emergency Management Plans, but Would Benefit from Additional Federal Guidance*. Washington DC: GAO, 2007. GAO-07-609.

66. Government Accountability Office. *Emergency Preparedess: State efforts to plan for medical surge capacity could benefit from shared guidance for allocating scarce medical resources*. Washington DC: GAO, 2010. GAO-10-831T.

67. Local, State, Tribal and Federal Preparedness Task Force. *Perspective on Preparedness: Taking Stock Since 9/11*. 2010. Available at www.fema.gov/pdf.preparednesstaksforce/perspective_on_preparedness.pdf. Accessed May 19, 2011.

68. Schnirring L. Public health groups sound warning about preparedness cuts. *Center for Infectious Disease Research and Policy*. May 19, 2011. Available at http://www.cidrap.umn.edu/cidrap/content/bt/bioprep/news/may1911prepared-jw.html. Accessed December 1, 2011.

ENDNOTES

a. The Act actually refers to the National Response Plan, which was later updated and renamed the National Response Framework.

PART III

Basic Skills in Health Policy Analysis

Parts I and II covered fundamental concepts of health policy and law and engaged in a substantive discussion of essential issues in health policy. This analysis of the content of health policy and law is paired in Part III with a tutorial covering one of the most important skills in the field of health policy: writing a health policy analysis.

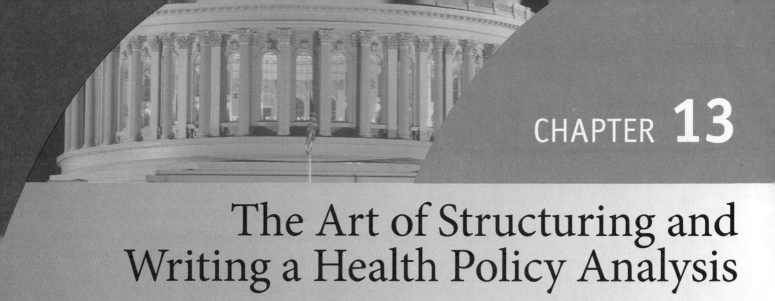

CHAPTER 13

The Art of Structuring and Writing a Health Policy Analysis

Defining Policy Analysis

We use the following definition to describe a policy analysis: *An analysis that provides informed advice to a client that relates to a public policy decision, includes a recommended course of action/inaction, and is framed by the client's powers and values.*

We briefly review each element of this definition below.

INTRODUCTION

Imagine you work for the governor of a state that recently received a large sum of federal money for anti-bioterrorism efforts and your boss asks you how it should be spent. How are you going to respond? Or, assume you are an assistant to the director of a state nutrition program for low-income children and the program's budget was slashed by the legislature. The program's director needs to reduce costs and turns to you for help; how will you approach this problem? Finally, pretend you work in the White House as a domestic policy advisor and the president is considering revising the administration's national stem cell research guidelines. What guidance will you offer? The substance of health policy and law has been discussed in detail elsewhere, and this chapter teaches you what policy

analysis is and how to address complex health policy questions through a written policy analysis that thoroughly analyzes the question with which you are grappling.

POLICY ANALYSIS OVERVIEW

In this section we define policy analysis and review the purposes for developing one. In the following section, we provide a step-by-step process detailing how to create a written health policy analysis.

Client-Oriented Advice

The "client" is the particular stakeholder that requests the policy analysis, and the analysis must be developed to suit the needs of the client. (The client could be a policymaker who hires you, a fictional policymaker in an exercise developed by your professor, an employer who asks you to analyze a problem, etc.) In general, a stakeholder refers to an individual or a group that has an interest in the issue at hand. There may be many stakeholders related to a particular policy issue. Of course, the client requesting an analysis is also a stakeholder because that person or entity has an interest in the issue. However, to avoid confusion, we refer to the person or group that requests the analysis as the client, and the other interested parties as stakeholders.

Informed Advice

Providing informed advice means the analysis is based on thorough and well-rounded information. The information included in the analysis must convey all sides of an issue, not just the facts and theories supporting a particular perspective. If a decision maker is only presented with evidence supporting one course of action or one side of a debate, it will be impossible for the client to make a well-informed decision. In addition, to be effective in persuading others to favor the recommended policy, your client must be able to understand and, when necessary, refute alternative solutions to the problem.

Public Policy Decision
Policy analyses involve public policy decisions. A public policy problem goes beyond the individual sphere and affects the greater community.

Providing Options and a Recommendation
A key component of any policy analysis is providing the client with several options to consider, analyzing those options, and settling on one recommendation. In other words, a policy analysis is not simply a background report that identifies a variety of issues relating to a particular problem; instead, it gives the client ideas about what steps to take to address the problem and concludes by recommending a specific course of action.

Your Client's Power and Values
Finally, the analysis should be framed by the client's power and values. The first requirement is fairly straightforward and uncontroversial: The options presented and the recommendation made must be within the power of the client to accomplish. On the other hand, the notion of framing an analysis according to the client's values is more controversial. In most conceptualizations of policy analysis, including the one discussed later in this chapter, the process is roughly the same: Define the problem and provide information about it, analyze a set of alternatives to solve the problem, and implement the best solution based on the analysis.[1(p3)] As new information is uncovered or the problem is reformulated, analysts may move back and forth among these steps in an iterative process.[2(p47)] However, although there is general agreement that politics and values play a role in policy analysis, there is disagreement over at which stage of the analysis they come into play.

To understand this controversy, it is necessary to discuss two models of policy analysis: the rational model and the political model. The rational model was developed in an attempt to base policy decisions on reason and science, rather than the vagaries of politics.[2(p7)] In the traditional rational model, the analyst does not consider politics and values. Instead, she should recommend the "rational, logical, and technically desirable policy."[2(p51)] According to the rational model, the

decision maker infuses the analysis with politics and values once the analyst's work is complete.

Professor John Kingdon and others have moved away from the rational model and toward a political model. Kingdon suggests that policy analysis occurs through the development of three streams: problems, policies, and politics.[3,a] The problem stream is where problems are defined and noticed by decision makers. The policy stream is where solutions are proposed. These proposals may be solutions to identified problems, but they are often favored projects of policymakers or advocates that exist separate from specific problems that have garnered attention. Finally, the political stream refers to the ever-changing political mood. As a general matter, these streams develop separately, only coming together at critical junctures when the problem reaches the top of the agenda, the solutions to that problem are viable, and the political atmosphere makes the time right for change.[4(p87)]

Kingdon's approach discusses occurrences the rational model does not, such as why some problems are addressed and others are not, why some solutions are favored even if they are not technically the best approach, and why action is taken at some junctures but not at others.[3] In addition, the rational model only refers to one cycle of problems. As Kingdon and others have noted, solutions to one problem often lead to unintended consequences that create other problems to be addressed, resulting in an ongoing policy analysis cycle instead of an event with a start and a finish.[4(p260)]

Professor Deborah Stone also focuses on the role of politics and values in analysis.[2(pp1–14)] She argues that the idea of the rational policy analysis model misses the point because "analysis itself is a creature of politics."[2(p8)] According to Stone, everything from defining a problem, to selecting analytic criteria, to choosing which options to evaluate, to making a recommendation is a political and value-laden choice. "[R]ational policy analysis can begin only after the relevant values have been identified and . . . these values change over time as a result of the policymaking process."[2(p32)] She contends that policy analysis should do the very things that the rational model does not permit—allow for changing objectives, permit contradictory goals, and turn apparent losses into political gains.[2(p9)] The goal of the rational model founders—to divorce analysis from the vagaries of politics—is simply not possible in Stone's view.

Having differentiated these models, we now return to our definition of policy analysis: *An analysis that provides informed advice to a client that relates to a public policy decision, includes a recommended course of action/inaction, and is framed by the client's powers and values.* You can see that this definition follows Stone's political model of policy analysis, requiring the analysis to be developed with a particular client's values in mind. After reviewing the numerous examples provided in the following section, it will be evident that client values permeate all aspects of a policy analysis. Only after you take into account your client's values, combine it with the information you have gathered, place it in the prevailing political context, and understand your client's powers, can you make an appropriate policy recommendation.

Multiple Purposes

The ultimate product of a policy analysis is a recommendation to a specific client about how to address a problem. However, a policy analysis has several other purposes as well. It provides general information necessary to understand the problem at hand and may be an important tool to inform stakeholders about a policy problem. In addition, the analysis may be a vehicle for widespread dissemination of ideas and arguments. Although your analysis is targeted to the client requesting advisement, it may also be used to inform and persuade other supporters, opponents, the media, the general public, and others. Finally, it will help you, the policy analyst, learn how to think through problems and develop solutions in an organized, concise, and useful way.

Policy analyses can take many forms—a memorandum, an oral briefing, a report, and so on—and, correspondingly, have varying degrees of formality. This chapter explains how to construct a *short, written* analysis because it is a commonly used, highly effective, and often practical way to provide a policy analysis to your client. Whether you are aiding a governor, the director of a state program, the CEO of a private business, or any other decision maker, you often will not have the opportunity to discuss issues in person or for a significant length of time. Furthermore, given time pressures, the demands on high-level policymakers, the need for rapid decision making, and the variety of issues most policymakers deal with, many clients will not read a lengthy analysis. That is why it is essential for anyone who wants to influence policy to be able to craft a clear and concise written analysis.

STRUCTURING A POLICY ANALYSIS

We now turn to a five-step method for writing a thorough yet concise policy analysis. Regardless of the subject matter, you can use this structure to analyze the question your client is considering. As you review each part of the analysis, notice the various disciplines and tools that may be part of writing an effective policy analysis. Analysts draw from a variety of disciplines—law, economics, political science, sociology, history, and others—and use a number of quantitative and qualitative tools when explaining issues, analyzing options, and making recommendations.

Although policy analyses come in various formats and use different terminology, they will all contain these essential elements:

Problem statement: Defines the problem addressed in the analysis

Background: Provides factual information needed to understand the problem

Landscape: Reviews the various stakeholders and their concerns

Options: Describes and analyzes several options to address the problem

Recommendation: Offers one option as the best action to pursue

The following sections discuss each of these elements in detail.

The Problem Statement

The first step in writing a policy analysis is to clearly define the problem you are analyzing. A problem statement should be succinct and written in the form of a question that identifies the problem addressed in the analysis. It usually consists of a single sentence, though it may be two sentences if you are analyzing a particularly complex issue. Although a problem statement is simple to define, it is often one of the most difficult parts of the analysis to do well. It is also one of the most important.

The problem statement is the key to your analysis because it frames the problem at hand. Indeed, some policy battles are won or lost simply by how the problem statement is crafted. For example, consider the different questions asked in these problem statements:

Problem Statement 1:

What type of tax credit, if any, should the president include in the next budget proposal?

Problem Statement 2:

What type and size of health insurance tax credit should the president include in the next budget proposal?

The first problem statement asks what type of tax credit, if any, should be considered. One possible answer to that question is that no tax credit of any kind should be considered. Another answer could involve a tax credit, but not one related to health insurance. The second problem statement suggests that the option of not proposing a health insurance tax credit is unacceptable. Instead, the second problem statement lends itself to an analysis of identifying the pros and cons of various health insurance tax credit options. In other words, one option that may be considered based on the first problem statement (no tax credit) is excluded based on the second problem statement.

Consider another example:

Problem Statement 1:

Should the governor's top priorities include initiating a new state program to reduce the number of obese residents?

Problem Statement 2:

Should the governor's priority of reducing the number of obese residents be accomplished by relying on currently existing programs?

Again, the first problem statement asks *whether* providing a new healthcare program relating to obesity should be at the top of the governor's agenda. It is possible that the answer is "No, other priorities such as education and transportation should take priority." The second problem statement starts with the governor committed to reducing the obesity rate and asks how to best accomplish that goal. These may sound like similar questions, but they lead to very different analyses and (most likely) different recommendations.

It is possible that your client's values will be evident from the way the problem statement is phrased. For instance, in the second example, the second policy statement clearly reflects the governor's desire to reduce the obesity rate. Consider another example. You have been asked to write a policy analysis about the merits of importing low-cost prescription drugs from Canada. How might the problem statement differ if your client is a pharmaceutical lobbying group, on the one hand, and an elder rights association on the other? Here are two possible problem statements.

Acceptable problem statement for the pharmaceutical lobbying firm:

How can this firm help improve medical care quality in the United States by reducing the importation of dangerous prescription drugs from Canada?

Acceptable problem statement for the elder rights association:

How can this association help seniors obtain low-priced prescription drugs from Canada?

The vast differences in these problem statements reflect differing viewpoints regarding the importation of prescription drugs. A pharmaceutical lobbying firm is more likely to be concerned about reduced profits for its drug company clients and therefore would want to deter or restrict importation, which could lead to more competition in the market. One way to accomplish that goal is to phrase the issue as a safety/quality of care concern. An elder rights association is more likely to be concerned with high-priced prescription drugs in the United States and would therefore want to promote drug importation. One way to accomplish that goal is to phrase the issue as one of cost reduction.

It is also possible to write solid, yet neutral problem statements. From the immediate example previously, analysts for both groups could use the following problem statement:

What action should [the client] take in response to recent congressional proposals relating to importing prescription drugs from Canada?

A neutral statement is not necessarily better or worse than a value-driven statement. The value-driven statement provides additional information about the direction of the policy analysis and clearly limits some of the options that might otherwise be considered. A neutral statement is often broader, leaving more options on the table at the outset. Yet, even if a neutral statement is used, the options the analyst considers and the recommendation the analyst makes will still be constrained by the client's values and needs.

Because it is possible to create numerous problem statements for any issue, how do you develop the best one? Follow these guidelines.

Make the Problem Statement Analytically Manageable

Acceptable problem statements can be broad or narrow. One is not better than the other; they suit different purposes. Policy analyses with broad problem statements may require more diverse information in terms of background and may consider a wider range of issues in the paper's landscape section. Also, the recommendations may promote "big picture" changes instead of specific and tailored ideas. Narrower problem statements may require less extensive background and landscape information, but they may not capture big picture, systemic concerns relating to the problem under consideration.

Reflect on the following examples. They both may be acceptable problem statements, depending on the needs of your client.

A broad problem statement:

What action should the U.S. Department of Health and Human Services take to avoid another flu vaccine shortage?

A narrow problem statement:

How can the U.S. Department of Health and Human Services create incentives for additional manufacturers to supply flu vaccine to the United States?

The first problem statement could result in a variety of recommendations, such as improving surveillance to lower the incidence of flu in the future, developing new vaccines that have longer-lasting immunity, finding ways to entice additional manufacturers to provide supplies to the United States, and others. It is a broad problem statement that will lead to an analysis that could recommend a wide variety of actions. The second problem statement focuses on one particular way to decrease a flu vaccine shortage—increasing the number of suppliers. Although the analysis will also provide a number of options, all of the options will address the specific issue of increasing suppliers. Again, there is no single right or wrong problem statement. Whether it is more useful to have a broad or narrow problem statement will depend on the needs and concerns of your client.

However, it is possible to make a problem statement so vague that it will be impossible to write a sound policy analysis. Unfortunately, there is no easy way to differentiate an acceptably broad problem statement from an unmanageably vague one when you begin your analysis. You will know your problem statement is too vague, however, if you find it impossible to write a *complete and concise* policy analysis. Your paper will require too much information in the background and landscape sections if you draft an overly vague problem statement. In addition, you will find that you cannot devise a coherent series of options addressing the problem because the problem statement is too broadly defined. Instead of a concise and useful policy analysis, you will end up with a lengthy and unfocused paper.

If you believe your problem statement may be so vague that it is analytically unmanageable, ask yourself if you are addressing one specific problem that may be countered with a few specific options. If you are having trouble narrowing your problem statement, you can try including limitations based on geography (e.g., refer to a particular state or city), time (e.g., focus on the next year or over the next five years), or numerical boundaries (e.g., use a goal of reducing a figure by a certain percentage or a budget by a specific dollar amount). Consider this example:

An unmanageably vague problem statement:

What is the best use of Centers for Disease Control and Prevention's resources to improve the health status of our citizens?

This problem statement is not analytically manageable. It is extremely broad and unfocused. Using this problem statement, your analysis could address any health issue, such as access to care problems, the need to improve vaccination rates, racial disparities in health care, or many others. The list is endless and your policy analysis will be as well.

A manageable problem statement:

What preventive health issue should be the top priority for the Centers for Disease Control and Prevention next year?

This problem statement is analytically manageable. It is focused on preventive measures specifically and is limited

to determining the top priority. In addition, the problem is focused on what can be done in the upcoming year. The second problem statement allows for a much more concise and directed policy analysis.

Do Not Include the Recommendation in Your Problem Statement

Another pitfall in writing problem statements is crafting a problem in a way that suggests a particular solution to the issue. A problem statement should define a specific problem; it should not indicate how that problem should be solved. If the answer is preordained, why bother with the analysis? When drafting your problem statement, ask yourself if you can imagine three, four, or five potentially viable options to address the problem. If you cannot, then you have not defined the problem well.

For example, assume you've been asked to address reducing medical malpractice insurance premiums. Here is a problem statement that leads the reader to one conclusion:

To what extent should jury awards be limited in malpractice cases in order to reduce malpractice premiums?

This problem statement leads to one very specific solution (limiting jury awards) as a way to counter a broad problem (reducing malpractice premiums). The only question presented by this problem statement is what the award limit should be. It does not provide a range of options for reducing malpractice premiums (one of which may be limiting jury awards) for your client to consider. (Of course, if you were specifically asked to address how to limit jury awards in malpractice cases, this would be an appropriate problem statement.) A better problem statement would be:

What action should be taken to stem the rise in malpractice premiums nationwide?

This problem statement lends itself to an analysis that considers several options. Possible alternatives include limiting jury awards, enacting regulations that limit the amount insurance companies can increase premiums each year, and a host of other options. The problem statement also narrows the focus of the analysis to national solutions.

Once you have written your concise and precise problem statement, you have set the framework for your analysis. Every other section of the analysis should relate directly to the problem statement. Remember that writing a policy analysis is an iterative process; you must review, revise, and tighten the information and arguments throughout the writing process. As you review the other components of your policy analysis, it may become evident that what you thought was the best problem statement can be further improved. There is nothing wrong with revising your problem statement as you craft your analysis, as long as you remain true to your client's values and power.

The Background Section

The first substantive information your analysis provides is in the background section. The background informs the reader why the particular problem has been chosen for analysis. This section should make clear why the issue is important and needs to be addressed now. In addition to providing general information about the topic, your background and landscape (discussed next) sections provide the information necessary to assess the options you lay out.

Much of the information in the background will be relevant regardless of who assigned the analysis. However, because the background provides information necessary to understand the problem, it is essential to understand the knowledge level of your client when constructing the background. For example, assume you are writing an analysis relating to state preparedness planning for smallpox vaccination in the event of a bioterror attack. Regardless of your client, your background would likely include information about why a smallpox attack is a threat, including (but not limited to):

- Reference to the September 11, 2001, attacks on the World Trade Center and subsequent events
- The belief that although smallpox has been eradicated as a natural disease, it is likely that samples of the virus still exist
- Reference to any information provided by the federal government or other sources relating to the possibility of a bioterror attack

If your client does not have knowledge relating to smallpox, you would also include details about smallpox transmission, the effects of the disease, the vaccination procedure, and the risks associated with vaccination.

In addition, your background should include whatever factual information is necessary to fully assess the options discussed. Remember, your client needs a complete picture, not just the information that supports the recommended action or your client's viewpoint. By the time the reader reaches your paper's options section, all of the information necessary to evaluate the options should have been presented in your background or landscape.

For example, assume one of your options for the smallpox vaccination state preparedness analysis is immediate compulsory vaccination of all first responders and establishment of a protocol for vaccinating the remaining population if there is a smallpox outbreak. In that case, your background (and possibly the landscape) should provide information regarding who first responders are, where they are located, how many there are, legal issues relating to compulsory vaccination, and so on.

Because the background section is an informational—not analytical—part of the analysis, the material provided in it should be mostly factual. The tone of the background is not partisan or argumentative. It should simply state the necessary information.

The Landscape Section

Together, the background and landscape sections frame the context of the analysis for your client. Whereas the background provides factual information to assist the client in understanding what the problem is and why it is being addressed, the landscape provides the overall context for the analysis by identifying key stakeholders and the factors that must be considered when analyzing the problem. In the following discussion, you will read about numerous types of people, groups, and issues that might be included in a landscape. These examples are meant to provide suggestions and provoke thought about what should be included in an analysis. It would be impossible to include everything discussed below in any single landscape section. It is the job of the policy analyst to choose among these options—to be able to identify whose views and which factors are the most salient ones in creating a complete landscape.

Identifying Key Stakeholders

Up to this point, the policy analysis discussion has focused on just one stakeholder: the client who asked for the policy analysis. The landscape brings in other stakeholders who have an interest in the issue. Although it is often impossible to include every possible stakeholder in a single analysis, it is necessary to identify the key stakeholders whose positions and concerns must be understood before a well-informed decision can be made.

How do you identify the key stakeholders particular to your issue? Unfortunately, there is no magic formula. The best approach is through research and thinking. Also, bear in mind that the stakeholders and issues discussed in the landscape must relate to your overall policy analysis. Your options must address the problem identified initially, and all of the information necessary to assess the options must be presented in the background and landscape. As you learn about the problem to be analyzed and think about options for addressing the problem, it should become apparent which stakeholders have a significant interest in the issue.

For example, assume your analysis relates to proposed legislation regulating pharmacists and pharmaceuticals. Who are possible key stakeholders regarding this issue? They may include:

- Democratic and Republican politicians (you might need to distinguish among those in Congress, state legislatures, and governors)
- Pharmaceutical industry
- Health insurance industry
- AARP and other elder rights groups
- Advocacy groups for the disabled
- Pharmacists' lobby
- Foreign pharmaceutical companies
- Internet-based pharmaceutical companies

Can you think of others?

Which of these stakeholders *must* be included in an analysis depends on the exact problem being analyzed. For example, assume you are writing an analysis about requirements relating to how pharmacists inform consumers about their medications. If your problem dealt with face-to-face encounters only, Internet-based pharmaceutical companies would not be a key stakeholder. Alternatively, if the problem definition dealt with purchasing limitations over the Internet, Internet-based pharmaceutical companies must be included in the analysis. If your client is a politician in Florida, elder rights groups should be included in the analysis because there is a large and influential elderly population in Florida. If your client is someone running for public office in a county where the health insurance industry is a major employer, the views of those companies would be essential to include. In other words, although it is possible to make a generic list of the types of individuals and groups that could be included, the specific list for any policy analysis will depend on the client for whom the analysis is being written and the specific problem being addressed.

Identifying Key Factors

Once you have settled on a list of key stakeholders, it is necessary to analyze their position on the issue at the center of the analysis. Earlier, we described the landscape as the portion of the analysis that provides the overall context of the issue. The "overall context" refers to the mix of factors that are relevant when any decision is being made. These factors are used to analyze stakeholder positions. Although there is not one comprehensive list of context factors and not all factors are relevant to all analyses, the list in Box 13-1 includes some common factors that could be discussed.

This list of factors is by no means exhaustive, but rather is intended to provide a sense of the types of questions that are often relevant to understanding the context of a problem. Just as it would be impossible to discuss every stakeholder who might be connected to the problem, it would be impossible to include in a concise analysis of all the issues raised by the five factors listed in Box 13-1. It is the policy analyst's job to be able to identify not only which key stakeholders must be included, but also which key factors must be discussed.

Consider again the example relating to limiting prescription drug purchases made over the Internet. Some key factors probably would include:

Political factor: Who supports or opposes the limitation and how influential are they?

Economic factor: Would it be costly to implement this limitation or costly to key constituents who may need more prescription drugs than allowed by the limit? Would it provide an economic benefit to some stakeholders?

Practical factor: Is it possible to implement and enforce a restricted purchasing system over the Internet?

Legal factor: Are there legal barriers to limiting Internet prescription drug purchases?

For each factor, the analysis should discuss relevant views of the stakeholders you included in your analysis. For example, when discussing economic factors, the analysis might explain that Internet-based pharmaceutical companies would experience a loss of revenue; some consumers would pay more for prescription drugs if they needed more than the limited amount; and storefront pharmaceutical companies would make money because consumers probably would have to fill more of their orders in person. Depending on the political situation, the analysis might explain that the client's most influential constituents are elderly people who use many prescription drugs and are likely to oppose any restriction, or that storefront pharmaceutical companies are large campaign contributors and would support a restriction.

Writing Structure

The landscape may be organized by stakeholder or by factor. In other words, it is acceptable to identify stakeholder #1 and then describe that stakeholder's views based on various concerns, and then identify stakeholder #2 and describe that stakeholder's views, and so on. Alternatively, the landscape could be structured based on the factors described in Table 13-1. Within that structure, the landscape would address one set of factors (e.g., economic), then another set (e.g., social), and so on. Some stakeholders may not have relevant views

BOX 13-1 Possible Factors to Include in a Landscape Section

Political Factors

What is the political salience of the issue?

Is this a front-burner issue?

Is this a controversial issue?

Do key constituents, opponents, interest groups, etc. have an opinion about the issue? Who is likely to support or oppose change?

Is there bipartisan support for the issue?

Is there a reason to act now?

Is there a reason to delay action?

Social Factors

Who is affected by this problem?

According to the client who assigned the analysis, are influential or valued people or groups affected by this problem?

Is there a fairness concern relating to this issue?

Economic Factors

What is the economic impact of addressing and of not addressing this problem?

Are various people or groups impacted differently?

Are there competing demands for resources that relate to this issue?

What is the economic situation of the state or nation? How does this affect the politics relating to this issue?

Practical Factors

Is it realistic to try to solve this problem?

Would it be more practical to solve this problem later?

Are other people in a better position to solve this problem?

What do we know about solutions that do or do not work?

If this problem cannot be solved, is it still necessary (politically, socially) to act in some way to address the problem?

Legal Factors

Are there legal restrictions affecting this problem?

Are there legal requirements that impact the analysis?

Is new legislative authority necessary to solve the problem?

Is there legal uncertainty relating to this problem?

Is future litigation a concern if action is taken?

TABLE 13-1 A Descriptive Side-by-Side Table

INCREASING ACCESS TO CARE FOR IMMIGRANTS—OPTIONS DESCRIPTION

	Public Education Campaign	Grants to States	Health Center Funding
General Description	Campaign on radio, television, and public areas	Federal government provides funds to states to increase access to care for immigrants	Federal government provides funding to health centers for services
Populations Affected	All will hear, focus on immigrants in community	Only immigrants in the state	All health center patients, including immigrants
Length of Option	1 year	5 years, subject to annual appropriations	2 years
Payer	Federal	Federal	Federal

for all of the factors, but each stakeholder must be addressed as often as necessary to convey their policy position. For example, the economic factors section would identify various stakeholders and their views based on economic concerns. It would include information such as "Canadian companies would oppose regulating Internet pharmacies because it would increase the cost of doing business with Americans, while U.S. storefront pharmacists would support regulating Internet pharmacies because it may increase prices for their competitors' products."

When you discuss a particular view, it is important to identify which stakeholders hold that view. At the same time, do not insert opinions unattached to individuals or groups. For example, it would not be helpful to write, "Some oppose legislation regulating Internet pharmacies." Such a statement does not identify *who* opposes the legislation or *why* they oppose the legislation. If your client is going to be able to assess the political, practical, and ethical feasibility of taking a particular action, she needs to understand where the various groups stand and why they hold those views. Thus, a more helpful sentence would be: "RxData, a large software company that assists Internet pharmacies and who is a major employer in your congressional district, opposes legislation regulating Internet pharmacies because it will add costs to its business and may result in future employee layoffs." That sentence tells your client who is opposed to the legislation, why they are opposed to it, and why they are a key stakeholder.

The tone of the landscape should be neutral and objective. The landscape is not an argumentative section to persuade the reader that one view is better than another. Its purpose is to identify all of the key stakeholders and their concerns so the decision maker is well-informed before assessing options.

The Options Section

Once your client finishes reading the background and landscape sections, he should have a thorough understanding of the policy problem and the overall context in which a decision will be made. The time has come for him to consider what action to take. This is where your paper's options section comes in, providing three to five alternatives for your client to consider. This section is more than a recitation of various choices; it provides an analysis of each option by stating the positive and negative aspects of pursuing each path.

Identifying Options

The first step to writing your options section is to identify the various options you could analyze. Although you may develop a new option not previously considered by others, it is likely that you will find numerous possibilities that others have

already suggested. Some places to find already-considered options include:

Media
Scholarly articles
Interest group recommendations
Think tanks/experts in the field
Congressional testimony
Legislation (passed or proposed)
Agency reports

Another approach to developing options is to consider several major actions that policymakers often take to deal with a policy problem. For example, look at the following list of possible actions that, depending on the circumstances, could be added, eliminated, or altered by a policymaker in response to a policy problem:

Taxes
Subsidies
Laws
Regulations
Programs
Government organizations
Information

Once you have compiled a list of options, how do you choose the best three to five options to include in the analysis? As always, the guiding principle underlying your decision is to base your decision on your client's values and powers. You should not suggest an option that clearly violates your client's values because your client will not seriously consider that option. For example, if your client has rejected spending new state money to solve a problem, you should not include an option that would cost the state money (or if you did, you would need to be clear about how these funds would be offset). Also, it is important to remember the extent of your client's power. For example, an analyst might recommend that a member of Congress introduce or sponsor a bill, or that an interest group submit a comment as part of the public notice and comment period before a regulation is finalized. On the other hand, an analyst should not recommend that a member of Congress force a state to pass a particular law because that action is not within Congress' power—the responsibility of passing state laws falls to state legislatures. Similarly, an interest group cannot issue an Executive Order or force an administrative agency to craft a regulation in a particular way. In other words, any option you include must be within the ability of your client to undertake.

In addition, you will probably want to include in your analysis any major proposals that are currently being considered. You may also choose to include proposals backed by key allies and constituents. Even if your client does not act on these proposals, it is important to be able to explain why "mainstream" options are being rejected. Also, it may be appropriate to consider the status quo (the "do nothing" approach) as an option. Even when considering the do nothing tactic, it is necessary to evaluate the pros and cons of this option. In addition, your options should be different enough from one another to give your client a real choice. One final rule to follow: Whichever alternative you ultimately recommend must be analyzed in the options section of your analysis.

All of the options included in the analysis must directly address the problem identified in your problem statement. For example, if your problem statement involved ways to reduce the number of uninsured individuals, an option that promotes increasing access to care for insured residents would be inappropriate because it does not directly address the problem. Indeed, everything in your analysis must flow from your problem statement, from what is included in the background and the issues discussed in your landscape, to the alternatives suggested in the options section, and (as discussed later) your final recommendation.

Assessing Your Options

Your options analysis must include a discussion of the pros (what is useful) as well as the cons (what is problematic) of each option. Although policymakers often seek a "silver bullet" that solves a problem without any negative effects, it is highly unlikely that such an option exists. As a result, an analysis must include the positive and negative aspects of an option. Also, all options must be analyzed equally. Do not provide more analysis for the option you decide to recommend even though it is your preferred option. Your client can make a fully informed decision only if you analyze what is both good and bad about each proposal.

In order to draft your pros and cons, you must identify the appropriate criteria for the analysis of the pros and cons and apply each criterion to all of the options. Many possible criteria could be used, so it is necessary to pick the ones that best fit your client's values and that address the key issues relating to the policy problem. Sometimes your client will provide you with criteria; other times you must deduce the correct criteria based on what you know about your client and the problem. Generally you should choose between three and five criteria for your analysis of the pros and cons. Typically, fewer than three will not allow for a full analysis, and more than five are difficult to assess in a relatively short analysis.

Your choice of criteria should reflect the concerns discussed in the landscape, where you identified the key factors relating to the problem. For example, if economic burden was an important aspect of the issue being considered, costs should be one of the criteria used to analyze the options. If the need for quick action was an important aspect of the issue, timeliness and administrative ease might be important criteria to consider. In general, cost and political feasibility are usually important criteria to include in your analysis. However, the specific criteria that are best for your analysis will depend on your client, the specific problem statement being addressed, and the landscape of the issue. Box 13-2 provides some criteria that could be considered when analyzing options. Can you think of others?

Writing Structure

When structuring your options section, you may find it helpful to use headings or bullets delineating each option. Your headings should clearly label each option. Also, it is generally useful to separate out the options by paragraph instead of having a continuous page or two assessing all of the options. The first sentence or two of each options paragraph should be a clear description of that option so the client understands what is being proposed; then assess the pros and cons of the option

BOX 13-2 Sample Options Criteria

Cost: How much does this option cost? (You may have to break this down: How much does it cost the federal government, state government, individuals, etc.?)

Cost–benefit: How much "bang for the buck" does this option provide?

Political feasibility: Is this option politically viable?

Legality: Is this option legal? If so, are there any restrictions?

Administrative ease: Does this option have steep implementation hurdles?

Fairness: Are people impacted by this option treated fairly/equally?

Timeliness: Can this option be implemented in an appropriate or useful amount of time?

Targeted impact: Does this option target the population/issue involved?

based on the criteria you identified. You should explicitly state the criteria prior to your options description.

For example, assume you are writing a policy analysis for the secretary of the Department of Health and Human Services about how to increase access to care for immigrants. After drafting the necessary background and landscape information, you decided to assess the following options: (1) creating a public education campaign, (2) providing grants to states, and (3) increasing funding to community health centers. You decide the best criteria to use are cost to the federal government, political feasibility, and increasing the number of immigrants who seek care. In your options section, you would have three different parts—one for each option—assessing the pros and cons based on the criteria you chose. Although the structure of the analysis may vary, you might have a paragraph looking something like this:

> **Option 1: Create a Public Education Campaign.** This option refers to the creation of a public education campaign to alert immigrants to the various ways they can access health care in their area. The campaign will be delivered in English and the most common immigrant language in the area, and will occur on television, over the radio, and in public (e.g., billboards). In these difficult economic times, this is a relatively low-cost option (although if immigrants access more care, the cost of providing care will increase). In addition, the political feasibility is somewhat high because this option does not call for any policy changes, but rather merely alerting individuals to policies that already exist. On the other hand, the political feasibility is tempered because the option focuses on helping immigrants, a group that has been under attack politically in recent times. The most significant disadvantage of this option is that it may not be very effective in increasing the number of immigrants who access care because it does not increase access points, reduce the cost of care, or address concerns in the immigrant community about being deported if they participate in public programs.

You would write a similar analysis for each of the options under consideration.

Side-by-Side Tables

You may choose to assess your options with the help of a side-by-side table. This table may be descriptive or analytic. A descriptive table would provide a description of each option but not provide any analysis. An analytic table would assess the options based on the criteria chosen. In either case, the table should be appropriately labeled and easy to read. As a general matter, a side-by-side table should supplement, not replace, your textual analysis because it is difficult to provide sufficient information within the space provided by a table. However, a table is a useful visual aid that may enhance the reader's understanding of your options and overall analysis. Tables 13-1 and 13-2 provide examples of side-by-sides.

As you can see from both tables, additional information is necessary for a complete analysis. In the text of your options section you would need to provide a more complete explanation of each option. It is difficult (but not impossible) to provide sufficient depth of analysis in a chart without creating a busy, difficult-to-read table.

Although the second table uses the terms low, medium, and high to assess the options, other terms or symbols (e.g., +, –) may be used. In addition, you may choose to include phrases instead of single words or symbols. Whatever choice you make, be sure that it is clear which assessment is positive and which is negative. When necessary, provide a legend explaining your terms. Also, some people prefer to use numerical assessments (e.g., 1 = low, 2 = medium, 3 = high). Although debates exist regarding the value of this type of quantitative

TABLE 13-2 An Analytic Side-by-Side Table

INCREASING ACCESS TO CARE FOR IMMIGRANTS—OPTIONS ASSESSMENT			
Options Criteria	**Public Education Campaign**	**Grants to States**	**Health Center Funding**
Cost to Federal Government	Low	Medium	High
Political Feasibility	Medium	Low	High
Increase in Access for Immigrants	Low	High	Medium

assessment in a side-by-side chart, we strongly discourage it. Policy analysis is both an art and a science, and using a numerically based table can obscure that balance. An attempt to use quantitative measures may lead readers to assume a simple summation will suffice—just add up the columns and choose the best one. Overall, reducing the analysis to numerical labels hides the value judgments that are part of every analysis, fails to address whether certain criteria should be weighted more than others, and makes the optimal solution appear more certain than it probably is.

The Recommendation Section

The time has finally arrived in your policy analysis to make a recommendation. You should choose *one* of your options as your recommendation. Although it is possible to make more than one recommendation or a hybrid recommendation of multiple options, we discourage those approaches. Making multiple recommendations might make it necessary for your client to conduct further analysis to choose among the options, and making a hybrid recommendation (a combination of two or more options) is not appropriate unless the hybrid

option was analyzed separately as a single option. In general, it is the analyst's job to organize and clarify the issues and place them in the context of the client's views and power. Ultimately, this should result in one path that you believe best suits your client.

The recommendation section should begin by clearly identifying which option is favored and why this option is preferred over the other ones. As mentioned in the options section, every alternative will have pros and cons. The recommendation section does not simply repeat the analysis in the options section. Instead, this portion of the analysis must explain why, despite the drawbacks, this is the best action to take based on your client's values and power. In addition, the recommendation section also identifies what, if any, actions may be taken to mitigate or overcome the negative aspects of your recommendation.

CONCLUSION

You now have a basic understanding of what policy analysis is and an introduction to the tools necessary to analyze a policy problem. Additionally, thinking through the process just described should train you to evaluate your options when

---

BOX 13-3 Checklist for Writing a Policy Analysis

1. Problem Statement

Is my problem statement one sentence in the form of a question?

Can I identify the focus of my problem statement?

Can I identify several options for solving the problem?

2. Background

Does my background include all necessary factual information?

Have I eliminated information that is not directly relevant to the analysis?

Is the tone of my background appropriate?

3. Landscape

Does the landscape identify all of the key stakeholders?

Are the stakeholders' views described clearly and accurately?

Is the structure of the landscape consistent and easy to follow?

Is the tone of the landscape appropriate?

Does the reader have all the information necessary to assess the options?

4. Options

Do my options directly address the issue identified in the problem statement?

Do I assess the pros and cons of each option?

Did I apply all of the criteria to each option's assessment?

Are the options sufficiently different from each other to give the client a real choice?

Are all of the options within the power of my client?

5. Recommendation

Is my recommendation one of the options assessed?

Did I recommend only one of my options?

Did I explain why this recommendation is the best option, despite its flaws?

you become the decision maker. The checklist in Box 13-3 provides examples of what should be included in each section of a written policy analysis.

REFERENCES

1. Patton CV, Sawicki DS. *Basic Methods of Policy Analysis and Planning.* 2nd ed. Englewood Cliffs, NJ: Prentice Hall; 1993.

2. Stone D. *Policy Paradox: The Art of Political Decision Making.* New York, NY: W.W. Norton; 2002.

3. Kingdon J. *Agendas, Alternatives, and Public Policies.* 2nd ed. New York, NY: Addison-Wesley Educational Publishers; 1995.

4. Weissert CS, Weissert WG. *Governing Health: The Politics of Health Policy.* 2nd ed. Baltimore, MD: Johns Hopkins University Press; 2002.

Glossary

Accountable Care Organization (ACO): A group of health-care providers that is collectively reimbursed for a single patient's care. This arrangement is meant to give providers an incentive to deliver high quality, cost-effective care.

Accreditation: A process applied to healthcare institutions to ensure that all necessary and required processes, standards, competencies, ethics, etc. are up to par.

Administrative Law: The body of law produced by executive (i.e., administrative) agencies of federal, state, and local governments.

Administrative Procedures Act: A federal law that governs the way in which administrative agencies of the federal government may propose and establish regulations.

Adverse Selection: Refers to the idea that individuals with a higher-than-average risk of needing health care are more likely to seek health insurance coverage.

Annual Aggregate Limit: A cap imposed by health insurance companies on the amount a policy will pay during a single year.

Bioterrorism: The threat or use of a biological agent, typically by a non-state actor, to cause death or harm to humans, animals, or plants and specifically targeting civilian populations or resources.

Block Grant: A large sum of money granted by the national government to a regional government with only general provisions as to the way the money is to be spent.

Bundling: Instead of compensating healthcare providers separately for every service performed, "bundling" is an arrangement by which providers are paid a predetermined amount for all services related to treating a specific condition. This arrangement is meant to give providers an incentive to deliver cost-effective care.

"Cadillac" Healthcare Plans: Refers to health insurance plans and other products whose value exceeds a stated annual dollar threshold.

Cafeteria Plans: Employer-sponsored health benefit plans under which employees may set aside wages to be used for medical expenses not otherwise covered by their basic health insurance. Also called Flexible Spending Accounts (FSAs).

Capitation: A method of payment for health services in which a fixed amount is paid for each person served without regard to the actual number or nature of services provided.

Catastrophic Coverage: A health insurance coverage option with limited benefits and a high deductible, intended to protect against medical bankruptcy due to an unforeseen illness or injury.

Centers for Disease Control and Prevention (CDC): The federal agency within the Department of Health and Human Services charged with disease prevention, education, and public health activities.

Centers for Medicare and Medicaid Services (CMS): The federal agency within the Department of Health and Human Services that administers the Medicare and Medicaid programs.

Children's Health Insurance Program (CHIP): A health insurance program targeted to low-income children, established in 1997 and reauthorized in 2009, which is administered by states and funded through a combination of federal and state payments.

COBRA: The nickname for a law, enacted as part of the Consolidated Omnibus Budget Reconciliation Act of 1985, that allows individuals to continue to purchase employee health benefits for a period of 18 to 36 months following a "qualifying event" such as unemployment, death of a wage earner, divorce, or termination of minor dependent coverage.

Coinsurance: Refers to a form of beneficiary cost-sharing for covered health insurance benefits and services, expressed as a percentage of the approved payment amount for the benefit or service (e.g., 20% of the payable amount).

Community Health Centers: A type of community clinic that provides a broad range of healthcare services and that charges on a sliding-scale fee basis. See also *Federally Qualified Health Center.*

Community Rating: Requires health insurance providers to offer health insurance policies within a given territory at the same price to all persons without medical underwriting, regardless of individual health status.

Comparative Effectiveness Research (CER): A type of health services research that compares different approaches to treating medical conditions in order to determine which methods are most likely to produce the best outcomes.

Coordination of Benefits: A process by which health services are paid for by more than one health insurance plan. For example, if a child is insured through both parents, one insurer is generally considered the primary policy, and the secondary policy reimburses for services not covered under the primary policy.

Copayments: Refers to a form of beneficiary cost-sharing for covered health insurance benefits and services, expressed as a flat dollar payment (e.g., $5.00 for a prescription drug).

Cost-sharing: A requirement that insured patients pay a portion of their medical costs, either as coinsurance or as a fixed copayment.

Culturally and Linguistically Appropriate Care: Refers to a federal standard designed to eliminate ethnic and racial disparities in health care.

Deductible: The amount patients must pay out of their own pocket before their health insurance policy begins contributing to the cost of their care.

Department of Health and Human Services: A federal agency that administers federal health and welfare programs and activities.

Dependent Coverage: Health insurance coverage of a spouse, child, or domestic partner of an insured individual.

Diagnostic Related Group (DRG): A system used to classify patients (particularly under Medicare) for the purpose of reimbursing hospitals. Hospitals are paid a fixed fee for each case in a given category, regardless of the actual costs of providing care.

Department of Defense (DoD): A federal agency that, among other things, administers healthcare programs for active military and their dependents through a publicly funded and privately administered health program called TriCare.

Department of Labor (DoL): A federal agency responsible for administration and enforcement of ERISA, a federal law that sets requirements for employer-provided health benefits that are not offered through state-licensed health insurance plans.

Discrimination in Health Care: Failure by providers to treat patients equitably for any of a number of reasons including race, gender, age, ability to pay for care, or severity of illness. Can also be used to describe the insurance company practice of medical underwriting and rating.

Doughnut Hole: A gap in prescription drug coverage under Medicare Part D, for which beneficiaries pay 100% of their prescription drug costs after their total drug spending exceeds an initial coverage limit until they qualify for catastrophic coverage. The coverage gap will be gradually phased out under the Affordable Care Act by 2020.

Electronic Medical Record (EMR): An individual medical record that is stored electronically.

Employee Retirement Income Security Act (ERISA): A 1974 federal law that establishes standards governing both pension plans and "welfare benefit plans" (such as health benefits, dependent care benefits, and other types of benefits and services) and applicable to non-federal employers, multi-employer arrangements, and union plans.

Employer Responsibility: Refers to a requirement that employers assist in covering workers and their dependents, either through the provision of a health plan or through a contribution toward coverage which may be expressed as payment of a flat dollar charge (e.g., $500 per worker), a percentage of payroll, a percentage of an annual insurance premium, or some other amount. Also referred to as an "employer mandate."

Employer-Sponsored Insurance (ESI): A health benefit plan offered by an employer to its employees (and often to employee dependents). Some employers purchase plans from a traditional insurance company, while other (primarily large) employers may choose to directly insure its employees through its own plan.

Entitlement Programs: Refers to a guarantee of access to benefits or services based on established rights or by legislation (e.g., the Medicaid program).

Epidemic: Refers to when new cases of a certain disease, in a given human population during a given period, substantially exceed what is expected based on recent experience.

Epidemiology: The study of patterns of health and illness and associated factors at the population level.

Essential Benefits: A list of core benefits established under the Affordable Care Act that must be included under any health insurance plan in order to meet minimum coverage requirements.

Exchange Eligible Employer: An employer that is permitted to enroll in a health insurance exchange in order to offer health benefits to its employees.

Exchange Eligible Individual: An individual who is permitted to obtain coverage through a health insurance exchange.

Exchange-participating Health Benefit Plans: Health insurance plans offered to individuals and small employers through health insurance exchanges. They must meet federal insurance market and benefit requirements.

Excise Tax: A tax on health insurance and health benefit plans whose annual dollar value exceeds a specified limit, as well as on the sale of specified healthcare items and services such as medical devices and equipment.

Exclusion: The practice by which an insurer or health benefit plan classifies certain otherwise-covered items and treatments as ineligible for coverage. Common exclusions include "experimental," "educational," and "cosmetic" treatments and services.

Executive Order: A presidential directive, with the authority of a law, that directs and governs actions by executive officials and agencies.

Fair Marketing: A term used to encompass a range of health insurance market reforms to protect consumers from medical underwriting and other practices designed to limit the amount an insurer pays for medical claims.

Federal Emergency Management Agency (FEMA): A federal agency responsible for responding to national emergencies, including natural disasters.

Federalism: Refers to a system of government in which sovereignty is constitutionally divided between a central governing authority and constituent political units (e.g., states), and in which the power to govern is shared between the national and state governments.

Federally Qualified Health Center (FQHC): A community health center that either receives funding under Section 440 of the Public Health Service Act, or a center that has been certified as meeting the same criteria.

Fee-for-Service: A method of paying for medical services under which doctors are paid for each service provided. Bills are paid by the patient, who then submits them to the insurance company for reimbursement.

Fraud and Abuse: Refers to a range of wasteful healthcare activities, including billing for services not performed, billing for more expensive services than performed ("up-coding"), and performing inappropriate or unnecessary care.

Gainsharing: A system in which the government passes on savings from providing more-efficient care to insurers and providers.

Guaranteed Issue and Renewal: A rule that bars health insurers from denying or dropping an individual's coverage for any reason other than fraud or nonpayment of health insurance premiums. This is especially important to prevent insurance companies from denying coverage based on individuals' health status.

Healthcare/Public Health Workforce: A term used to define a range of health professionals in private and public practice who provide medical care and public health services such as primary care, disease diagnosis, and public education.

Health Information Privacy and Security: Standards or procedures to ensure that personal health information is not compromised or disclosed in processing healthcare transactions.

Health Information Technology (HIT): Technology that allows the comprehensive management of health information and enables its exchange among health professionals, healthcare providers, healthcare payers, and public health agencies.

Health Insurance Exchange Subsidies: Federal subsidies made available on an income-related basis to exchange-eligible individuals for the purchase of health insurance coverage through health insurance exchanges.

Health Insurance Exchanges: Regulated marketplaces for the sale and purchase of health insurance established under federal law and operated in accordance with federal requirements.

Health Insurance Issuers: Entities that sell health insurance in the individual and employer-sponsored group markets.

Health Insurance Portability and Accountability Act (HIPAA): A federal law that regulates health insurers and health benefit plans in the group market, and provides privacy protections for health information.

Health Maintenance Organization (HMO): A type of health insurance plan that provides a coordinated array of preventive and treatment services for a fixed payment per month. Enrollees receive medically necessary services regardless of whether the cost of those services exceeds the premium paid on the enrollees' behalf.

Health Status: All aspects of physical and mental health and their manifestations in daily living, including impairment, disability, and handicap.

Health Threat: In the context of national or global security, an environmental, biological, chemical, radiological, or physical risk to public or community health.

High-risk Insurance Pool: Refers to an insurance option for patients with existing medical conditions that make them expensive to insure.

Homeland Defense: The protection of U.S. territory, populations, and infrastructure against external threats or aggression.

Incidence: The number of new cases of illness or disease during a specific period of time in a specific population.

Indian Health Care Improvement Act: A federal law creating programs to strengthen healthcare options in Native American communities.

Indian Health Service: A federal health program to provide health care to Native Americans and Alaska natives.

Individual Market: The insurance market for individuals who are purchasing insurance for themselves and their families and are not part of a group plan, such as one offered by an employer. Also known as the "non-group market."

Individual Responsibility: The requirement that all individuals must carry health insurance or pay a penalty. Also referred to as an "individual mandate."

Insurance Pool: A group of individuals whose premiums are used to pay all covered medical costs of its members. Insurance companies may charge higher premiums to a pool whose members are older or less-healthy than other pools in order to cover the risk that its members may submit more medical claims.

Interest Group: An organization that uses various forms of advocacy to influence public opinion and/or policy. Groups vary considerably in size, influence, and purpose. Also referred to as special interest groups, advocacy groups, or lobby groups.

International Health Regulations: A 2005 international treaty obligating all Member States of the World Health Organization to detect, report, and respond to potential public health emergencies of international concern. Aimed at improving global health security through international collaboration and communication.

Large Group Market: The market for health insurance or health benefit plans among employers whose employee numbers exceed a specified threshold size (e.g., 100 full-time workers).

Lifetime Aggregate Limits: Provisions included in health insurance contracts designed to limit the total amount the policy will pay out in claims and benefits over the lifetime of the policy.

Long-term Care: A set of healthcare, personal care, and social services provided to persons who have lost, or never acquired, some degree of functional capacity (e.g., the chronically ill, aged, or disabled) in an institution or at home, on a long-term basis.

Managed Care: Health insurance arrangements that integrate the financing and delivery of services to covered individuals.

Market Failure: Refers to a concept within economic theory in which the allocation of goods and services by a free market is not efficient.

Medicaid: A program established in 1965 to provide health insurance to low-income families and individuals with certain disabilities. It is administered by the states, and funded jointly with the federal government.

Medical Home: A clinic focused on primary care and preventative services that offers a range of coordinated treatment services.

Medical Underwriting: The insurance industry practice of assessing the medical condition of individuals at the time that insurance enrollment is sought in order to identify existing physical or mental health conditions that may affect an individual's or group's eligibility for enrollment, the application of pre-existing condition exclusions or waiting periods, or the price to be charged for coverage.

Medicare: A federal program enacted in 1965 that provides government-sponsored health insurance to individuals ages 65 and older and certain individuals under age 65 with disabilities that meet federal requirements.

Medicare Advantage: Optional private insurance plans in which Medicare beneficiaries may enroll to receive their federal benefits.

Medigap Coverage: Supplemental health insurance designed to cover all or most of the charges that are not covered by Medicare, including the 20% co-payment required for many outpatient services.

National Health Service Corps: A commissioned corps of public health professionals employed by the federal Department of Health and Human Services. Members are assigned to settings that include clinics in underserved areas, state and local health departments, and federal agencies such as the Centers for Disease Control and Prevention.

National Institutes of Health: A federal agency within the Department of Health and Human Services that is primarily responsible for conducting and supporting medical research.

Notifiable Disease: A disease that, once diagnosed, must be reported under the law to a public health authority.

Office of the Inspector General (OIG): Located within the federal Department of Health and Human Services, this office is charged with protecting the integrity of programs administered by the Department, protecting the health and welfare of program beneficiaries, and reporting problems to the Department Secretary and to Congress.

Pandemic: An infectious disease that spreads through human populations across a large region, over multiple continents.

Parity: A term generally used to require that large group insurers or plans pay equivalent benefits for different kinds of services. For example, federal law requires "mental health parity," which means that for health plans that include mental health benefits as well as medical ones, the services must be covered with the same financial requirements and treatment limitations.

Patient Protection and Affordable Care Act: Also known as the Affordable Care Act or ACA, a major federal health reform law enacted in March 2010.

Patient Protections: Laws establishing protections for patients, such as the right to health information, to choice of providers, to access to care, to file a grievance, or to appeal a denied health benefit claim.

Pay-for-Performance (P4P): A healthcare payment system in which providers receive incentives for meeting quality and cost benchmarks (or, in some cases, penalties for not meeting established benchmarks).

Performance Measurement: A set of recommendations, requirements, or data used to determine whether plans, providers, or programs meet or exceed a standard of care.

Policy Analysis: An analysis that provides informed advice to a client that relates to a public policy decision, includes a recommended course of action/inaction, and is framed by the client's powers and values.

Population Health: Health outcomes of a group of individuals, including the distribution of such outcomes within the group.

Pre-existing Conditions: Health conditions that exist prior to or at the time of enrollment into a health insurance or health benefit plan.

Preferred Provider Organization (PPO): A health insurance plan in which providers agree to provide care to covered individuals at a negotiated price. Covered individuals receive all medically necessary services regardless of whether the cost of the services exceeds the premium paid, although members do have cost-sharing obligations.

Premium: The amount a business or individual pays regularly to maintain health insurance coverage.

Premium Rating: An insurance industry practice determining health insurance premiums based on factors including age, health status, gender, industry, geography, or other factors.

Prevalence: The total number of cases of a disease or illness in the population at a given time.

Preventive Services: Measures taken to prevent the development of disease or to treat illnesses early so that they do not become more acute and expensive to treat. Examples include vaccination, weight loss programs, and mammograms.

Primary Care Providers (PCPs): Healthcare providers, such as physicians engaged in the practice of internal medicine, pediatric, or geriatric care, or nurse practitioners, who provide general medical care and coordinate treatment.

Public Health Emergency: An acute event capable of causing large-scale morbidity and mortality, either immediately or over time. These events have the ability to overwhelm normal public health and medical care capabilities.

Public Health Insurance: A health insurance plan that is administered by the government either directly or through the use of private contractors. Medicare, Medicaid, and CHIP all are considered forms of public health insurance.

Public Health Preparedness: The actions and policies associated with preventing, protecting against, responding to, and recovering from a major public health event.

Quarantine: The separation and restriction of movement of people or animals that may have been exposed to an infectious agent.

Reinsurance: Refers to the fact that when health insurers predict how much they will pay out each year in medical claims, they may underestimate and choose to protect themselves against losses by purchasing "reinsurance" from a separate company.

Rescission: A process by which an insurance company seeks to recover the amount paid out for covered services after discovering that information on a beneficiary's initial enrollment form was incomplete or incorrect.

Retiree Health Benefits: Health benefits provided by an employer to its retirees.

Risk Adjustment: A tool for evaluating the relative risk of enrollees within insurance plans and providing for a financial transfer from plans with low-risk enrollees to plans with higher risk enrollees.

Safety Net: The collection of healthcare providers who serve patients regardless of patients' ability to pay for care. Providers include community health centers, public hospitals, local health departments, school- and church-based health clinics, and private physicians and non-profit hospitals committed to serving uninsured and low-income, vulnerable patients.

Skimming: The insurance plan practice of enrolling predominantly healthy individuals in order to reduce the costs to the plan.

Small Group Market: The health insurance market for employers whose size is smaller than a specified threshold (e.g., 100 full-time workers).

Stare Decisis: A Latin term that refers to the legal principle that prior case law decisions should be accorded great deference and should not be frequently overturned.

Surge Capacity: The ability of clinical care facilities and laboratories to accommodate a sharp increase in patients and samples during a public health emergency.

Telehealth: Refers to the use of electronic information and telecommunications technologies to support long-distance clinical health care, patient and professional health-related education, public health, and health administration. Technologies may include videoconferencing, the Internet, store-and-forward imaging, streaming media, and terrestrial and wireless communications.

Uncompensated Care: Services provided by physicians and hospitals for which no payment is received from the patient or from third-party payers.

Underinsured: Those with insurance policies that do not cover all necessary healthcare services, resulting in out-of-pocket expenses that exceed the ability to pay.

Uninsured: Refers to individuals who lack public or private health insurance.

Universal Coverage: The provision of at least basic or medically necessary health insurance for an entire population.

Utilization Review: The examination, usually by an insurer or third-party-administrator (TPA), of the necessity and/or appropriateness of healthcare services provided to a patient.

Weapons of Mass Destruction (WMD): Weapons that cause large-scale destruction, generally including nuclear, radiological, chemical, or biological weapons.

Wellness Programs: Special services and benefits offered by employers to employees in addition to health benefit plans, including nutrition classes, smoking-cessation programs, or gym memberships.

World Health Organization (WHO): The directing and coordinating authority for health within the United Nations system.

The following sources were used, in part, in the compilation of this Glossary:

Health Reform GPS, "Health Reform Glossary," at http://www.healthreformgps.org/glossary/ accessed August 16, 2011.

The Health Policy Institute of Ohio, "Glossary of Health Policy Terms," at http://www.hpio.net/resources/other-resources/glossary.php accessed August 16, 2011.

Index